D0131979

College Mathematics I

Third Custom Edition

Robert Blitzer

Taken From:

Algebra and Trigonometry, Third Edition
by Robert Blitzer

Intermediate Algebra, Fifth Edition
by John Tobey and Jeffrey Slater

PEARSON Custom Publishing

PEARSON Prentice Hall

Cover Art: *Big Wheel,* by Barry Cronin.

Taken from:

Algebra and Trigonometry, Third Edition
by Robert Blitzer
Copyright (c) 2007, 2004, 2001 by Prentice-Hall, Inc.
A Pearson Education Company
Upper Saddle River, New Jersey 07458

Intermediate Algebra, Fifth Edition
by John Tobey and Jeffrey Slater
Copyright (c) 2006, 2002, 1998, 1995, 1991 by Pearson Education, Inc.
Published by Pearson Prentice Hall

All rights reserved. No part of this book may be reproduced, in any form or by any means, without permission in writing from the publisher.

This special edition published in cooperation with Pearson Custom Publishing.

Printed in the United States of America

10 9 8 7 6 5 4 3 2

ISBN 0-536-26102-4

2006360670

EM

Please visit our web site at *www.pearsoncustom.com*

PEARSON Custom Publishing

PEARSON CUSTOM PUBLISHING
75 Arlington Street, Suite 300, Boston, MA 02116
A Pearson Education Compnay

Contents

Taken from: Algebra and Trigonometry, Third Edition, by Robert Blitzer

Chapter P

Chapter 1

*Taken from: Intermediate Algebra, Fifth Edition by John Tobey and Jeffrey Slater

Preface

I've written **Algebra and Trigonometry, Third Edition** to help diverse students, with different backgrounds and future goals, to succeed. The book has three fundamental goals:

1. To help students acquire a solid foundation in algebra and trigonometry, preparing them for other courses such as calculus, business calculus, and finite mathematics.

2. To show students how algebra and trigonometry can model and solve authentic real-world problems.

3. To enable students to develop problem-solving skills, while fostering critical thinking, within an interesting setting.

One major obstacle in the way of achieving these goals is the fact that very few students actually read their textbook. This has been a regular source of frustration for me and for my colleagues in the classroom. Anectodal evidence gathered over years highlights two basic reasons that students do not take advantage of their textbook:

- "I'll never use this information."
- "I can't follow the explanations."

I've written every page of the Third Edition with the intent of eliminating these two objections. The ideas and tools I've used to do so are described for the student in "A Brief Guide to Getting the Most from This Book" which appears inside the front cover.

What's New in the Third Edition?

- **Practice Plus Exercises.** More challenging practice exercises that often require students to combine several skills or concepts have been added to the exercise sets. The Practice Plus Exercises in the Third Edition, averaging 10 of these exercises per exercise set, provide instructors with the option of creating assignments that take practice exercises to a more challenging level than in the previous edition.
- **Mid-Chapter Check Points.** At approximately the midway point in each chapter, an integrated set of review exercises allows students to review and assimilate the skills and concepts they learned separately over several sections. The exercises that make up the Mid-Chapter Check Points, averaging 30 exercises per check point, are of a mixed nature, requiring students to discriminate which concepts or skills to apply. The Mid-Chapter Check Points should help students bring together the different objectives covered in the first half of the chapter before they move on to the material in the remainder of the chapter.
- **New Applications and Real-World Data.** I researched hundreds of books, magazines, almanacs, and online data sites to prepare the Third Edition. The Third Edition contains more new, innovative, applications, supported by data that extend as far up to the present as possible, than any previous revisions of this book.
- **New Examples and Exercises.** In addition to the Practice Plus Exercises and the Mid-Chapter Check Points, the Third Edition contains more than new exercises that appear primarily in the practice and application categories of the exercise sets.

- **Integration of Technology Using Graphical and Numerical Approaches to Problems.** New side-by-side features in the technology boxes connect algebraic solutions to graphical and numerical approaches to problems. Although the use of graphing utilites is optional, students can use the explanatory voice balloons to understand different approaches to problems even if they are not using a graphing utility in the course.
- **Increased Study Tip Boxes.** The book's Study Tip boxes offer suggestions for problem solving, point out common errors to avoid, and provide informal hints and suggestions. These invaluable hints appear in greater abundance in the Third Edition.

What Content and Organizational Changes Have Been Made to the Third Edition?

- **Section P.1 (Algebraic Expressions and Real Numbers)** now includes an early discussion of mathematical modeling and mathematical models, central themes of the book. Mathematical models now appear throughout Chapter P. A new discussion of intersection and union of sets paves the way for this notation to be used throughout the book.
- **Section P.2 (Exponents and Scientific Notation)** includes negative numbers in scientific notation, as well as an expanded discussion of converting from decimal to scientific notation.
- **Section P.6 (Rational Expressions)** takes the discussion of simplifying complex rational expressions to a slightly higher level, including expressions such as

$$\frac{\frac{1}{x+h}-\frac{1}{x}}{h}.$$

- **Section 1.2 (Linear Equations and Rational Equations)** has more to say on solving rational equations, including examples that illustrate the solutions of equations such as

$$\frac{x+2}{4}-\frac{x-1}{3}=2 \quad\text{and}\quad \frac{3}{x+6}+\frac{1}{x-2}=\frac{4}{x^2+4x-12}.$$

- **Section 1.6 (Other Types of Equations) and Section 1.7 (Linear Inequalities and Absolute Value Inequalities)** take the discussion of absolute value to a slightly higher level, including solutions of equations and inequalities such as

$$5|1-4x|-15=0 \quad\text{and}\quad -2|3x+5|+7>-13.$$

  Section 1.7 contains a new discussion of intersections and unions of intervals.
- **Chapter 2 (Functions and Graphs)** has been reorganized around the book's central idea: functions. Functions are introduced in the first section. All subsequent topics are viewed from the perspective of functions and relations. New multipart exercises that require students to bring together their knowledge of functions appear throughout the chapter.
- **Section 2.1 (Basics of Functions and Their Graphs)** contains a more detailed discussion, including new graphics, of identifying domain and range from a function's graph.
- **Section 2.3 (Linear Functions and Slope) and Section 2.4 (More on Slope)** develop lines and slope from the perspective of functions. Section 2.3 contains

a new example on using intercepts to graph the general form of a line's equation. Section 2.4 contains a more thoroughly developed example on writing equations of a line perpendicular to a given line.

- **Section 2.5 (Transformations of Functions)** adds the graph of the cube root function, $f(x) = \sqrt[3]{x}$, to the table of common graphs, using this graph, as well as the other six graphs in the table, in the discussion of transformations. New graphics with clarifying voice balloons illustrate transformations. A new discussion of horizontally stretching and shrinking a graph is included among the transformations.

- **Section 4.1 (Angles and Radian Measure)** contains new examples that help students "think in radians" by drawing angles of known radian measure in standard position without converting to degrees. The theme of "thinking in radians" is extended to new examples involving finding positive angles less than 2π coterminal with angles in standard position measuring $\frac{17\pi}{6}, -\frac{\pi}{12}, \frac{22\pi}{3}$, and $-\frac{17\pi}{6}$.

- **Section 4.2 (Right Triangle Trigonometry)** contains more examples on radicals in fractions and rationalizing denominators, a problem area for some students.

- **Section 4.3 (Trigonometric Functions of Any Angle)** contains new examples and a reference sheet (in the form of a Study Tip) that combines concepts in the first three sections of the chapter, including finding coterminal angles and reference angles, locating special angles, determining the signs of the trigonometric functions in specific quadrants, and finding the trigonometric functions of special angles. Students are reminded that to be successful in trigonometry, it is frequently necessary to connect concepts.

- **Section 4.4 (Trigonometric Functions of Real Numbers; Periodic Functions)** contains new graphics and more developed discussions on using the unit circle to determine the domain and the range of the sine and cosine functions.

I hope that my love for learning, as well as my respect for the diversity of students I have taught and learned from over the years, is apparent throughout this new edition. By connecting algebra and trigonometry to the whole spectrum of learning, it is my intent to show students that their world is profoundly mathematical, and indeed, π is in the sky.

Robert Blitzer

STUDENT RESOURCES	INSTRUCTOR RESOURCES
Student Study Pack Everything a student needs to succeed in one place. It is available for purchase by qualified adopters. Study Pack contains: • ***Student Solutions Manual*** Fully worked solutions to odd-numbered exercises.	**Instructor Resource Distribution** All instructor resources can be downloaded from the web site, www.prenhall.com. Select "Browse our catalog," then, click on "Mathematics"; select your course and choose your text. Under "Resources," on the left side, select "instructor" and choose the supplement you need to download. You will be required to run through a one time registration before you can complete this process. • ***TestGen*** Easily create tests from textbook section objectives. Questions are algorithmically generated allowing for unlimited versions. Edit problems or create your own. • ***Test Item File*** A printed test bank derived from TestGen. • ***PowerPoint Lecture Slides*** Fully editable slides that follow the textbook. Project in class or post to a website in an online course. • ***Instructor Solutions Manual*** Fully worked solutions to all textbook exercises and chapter projects. **Instructor's Edition** Provides answers to *all* exercises in the back of the text.

MathXL®

MathXL® is a powerful online homework, tutorial, and assessment system that accompanies your textbook. Instructors can create edit, and assign online homework and tests using algorithmically generated exercises correlated at the objective level to the textbook. Student work is tracked in an online gradebook. Students can take chapter tests and receive personalized study plans based on their results. The study plan diagnoses weaknesses and links students to tutorial exercises for objectives they need to study. Students can also access video clips from selected exercises. MathXL® is available to qualified adopters. For more information, visit our website at *www.mathxl.con*, or contact your Prentice Hall sales representative for a demonstration.

MyMathLab

MyMathLab is a text-specific, customizable online course for your textbooks, MyMathLab is powered by CourseCompass™—Pearson Education's online teaching and learning environment—and by MathXL®—our online homework, tutorial, and assessment system. MyMathLab gives you the tools you need to deliver all or a portion of your course online, whether your students are in a lab setting or working from home.

MyMathLab provides a rich and flexible set of course materials, featuring free-response exercises that are algorithmically generated for unlimited practice. Students can use online tools such as video lectures and a multimedia textbook to improve their performance. Instructors can use MyMathLab's homework and test managers to select and assign online exercises correlated to the textbook, and can import TestGen tests for added flexibility. The only gradebook—designed specifically for mathematics—automatically tracks students' homework and test results and gives the instructor control over how to calculate final grades. MyMathLab is available to qualified adopters. For more information, visit our website at *www.mymathlab.com* or contact your Prentice Hall sales representative for a product demonstration.

Acknowledgments

I wish to express my appreciation to all the reviewers of my precalculus series for their helpful feedback, frequently transmitted with wit, humor, and intelligence. Every change to this edition is the result of their thoughtful comments and suggestions. In particular, I would like to thank the following people for reviewing **College Algebra**, **Algebra and Trigonometry**, and **Precalculus**.

Barnhill, Kayoko Yates, *Clark College*
Beaver, Timothy, *Isothermal Community College*
Best, Lloyd, *Pacific Union College*
Burgin, Bill, *Gaston College*
Chang, Jimmy, *St. Petersburg College*
Colt, Diana, *University of Minnesota-Duluth*
Densmore, Donna, *Bossier Parish Community College*
Enegren, Disa, *Rose State College*
Fisher, Nancy, *University of Alabama*
Glickman, Cynthia, *Community College of Southern Nevada*
Goel, Sudhir Kumar, *Valdosta State University*
Gordon, Donald, *Manatee Community College*
Gross, David L., *University of Connecticut*
Haack, Joelx K., *University of Northern Iowa*
Haefner, Jeremy, *University of Colorado*
Hague, Joyce, *University of Wisconsin at River Falls*
Hall, Mike, *Univeristy of Mississippi*
Hay-Jahans, Christopher N., *University of South Dakota*
Hernandez, Celeste, *Richland College*
Ihlow, Winfield A., *SUNY College at Oswego*
Johnson, Nancy Raye, *Manatee Community College*
Leesburg, Mary, *Manatee Community College*
Lehmann, Christine Heinecke, *Purdue University North Central*
Levichev, Alexander, *Boston University*
Lin, Zongzhu, *Kansas State University*
Marlin, Benjamin, *Northwestern Oklahoma State University*
Massey, Marilyn, *Collin County Community College*
McCarthy-Germain, Yvelyne, *University of New Orleans*
Miller, James, *West Virginia University*
Pharo, Debra A., *Northwestern Michigan College*
Phoenix, Gloria, *North Carolina Agricultural and Technical State University*
Platt, David, *Front Range Community College*
Pohjanpelto, Juha, *Oregon State University*
Rech, Janice, *University of Nebraska at Omaha*
Salmon, Judith, *Fitchburg State College*
Schultz, Cynthia, *Illinois Valley Community College*
Stump, Chris, *Bethel College*
Trim, Pamela, *Southwest Tennessee Community College*
Turner, Chris, *Arkansas State University*
Van Lommel, Richard E., *California State University-Sacramento*
Van Peursem, Dan, *University of South Dakota*
Van Veldhuizen, Philip, *University of Nevada at Reno*
White, David, *The Victoria College*
Wienckowski, Tracy, *Univesity of Buffalo*

Special thanks to Professor Phoebe Rousse at Louisiana State University for your detailed notebooks of suggestions, including examples and exercise descriptions, as well as actual problems, that helped increase the rigor of the text without affecting its tone or diversity of applications.

Additional acknowledgments are extended to Dan Miller, for the Herculean task of preparing the solutions manuals, Brad Davis, for preparing the answer section and serving as accuracy checker, the Preparè Inc. formatting and production team, including Frank Weihenig and Linda Martino, for the book's brilliant paging, as well as keeping this complex project moving through its many stages, Aaron Darnall at Scientific Illustrators, for superbly illustrating the book, Melinda Alexander, photo researcher, for obtaining the book's new photographs, Kirk Trigsted and Scott Satake, for preparing the videotape series, including the chapter test prep video CDs, and Bayani Mendoza de Leon, assistant managing editor, for orchestrating the entire production process.

I would like to thank my editor at Prentice Hall, Adam Jaworski, and Project Manager, Dawn Murrin, who guided and coordinated the book from manuscript through production. Thanks to Kenny Beck for the beautiful covers and interior design. Finally, thanks to Halee Dinsey and Patrice Jones, for your innovative marketing efforts, to Sally Yagan, for your continuing support, and to the entire Prentice Hall sales force, for your confidence and enthusiasm about the book.

Many thanks to Dr. Earl Mark and Dr. Xuan Ma of the Indianapolis, Indiana campus, ITT Technical Institute, for their editorial review and selection of this textbook.

The following chapters have been chosen specifically for this course by your Curriculum Manager. Sections have been selected from various sources and the publisher makes every attempt to ensure consistency throughout this custom textbook. We apologize for any internal references that do not match.

To the Student

I've written this book so that you can learn about the power of algebra and trigonometry and how they relate directly to your life outside the classroom. All concepts are carefully explained, important definitions and procedures are set off in boxes, and worked-out examples that present solutions in a step-by-step manner appear in every section. Each example is followed by a similar matched problem, called a Check Point, for you to try so that you can actively participate in the learning process as you read the book. (Answers to all Check Points appear in the back of the book.) Study Tips offer hints and suggestions and often point out common errors to avoid. A great deal of attention has been given to applying algebra and trigonometry to your life to make your learning experience both interesting and relevant.

As you begin your studies, I would like to offer some specific suggestions for using this book and for being successful in this course:

1. **Read the book.** Read each section with pen (or pencil) in hand. Move through the worked-out examples with great care. These examples provide a model for doing exercises in the exercise sets. As you proceed through the reading, do not give up if you do not understand every single word. Things will become clearer as you read on and see how various procedures are applied to specific worked-out examples.
2. **Work problems every day and check your answers.** The way to learn mathematics is by doing mathematics, which means working the Check Points and assigned exercises in the exercise sets. The more exercises you work, the better you will understand the material.
3. **Review for quizzes and tests.** After completing a chapter, study the chapter summary, work the exercises in the Chapter Review, and work the exercises in the Chapter Test. Answers to all these exercises are given in the back of the book.

The methods that I've used to help you read the book, work the problems, and review for tests are described in "A Brief Guide to Getting the Most from This Book," which appears inside the front cover. Spend a few minutes reviewing the guide to familiarize yourself with the book's features and their benefits.

4. **Use the resources available with this book.** Additional resources to aid your study are described following the guide to getting the most from your book. These resources include a Solutions Manual, an online homework, tutorial, and assessment system of the text, and tutorial support at no charge at the PH Tutor Center.
5. **Attend all lectures.** No book is intended to be a substitute for valuable insights and interactions that occur in the classroom. In addition to arriving for lecture on time and being prepared, you will find it useful to read a section before it is covered in lecture. This will give you a clear idea of the new material that will be discussed.

I wrote this book in Point Reyes National Seashore, 40 miles north of San Francisco. The park consists of 75,000 acres with miles of pristine surf-washed beaches, forested ridges, and bays bordered by white cliffs. It was my hope to convey the beauty and excitement of mathematics using nature's unspoiled beauty as a source of inspiration and creativity. Enjoy the pages that follow as you empower yourself with the algebra and trigonometry needed to succeed in college, your career, and in your life.

Regards,

Bob

Robert Blitzer

About the Author

Bob Blitzer is a native of Manhattan and received a Bachelor of Arts degree with dual majors in mathematics and psychology (minor: English literature) from the City College of New York. His unusual combination of academic interests led him toward a Master of Arts in mathematics from the University of Miami and a doctorate in behavioral sciences from Nova University. Bob is most energized by teaching mathematics and has taught a variety of mathematics courses at Miami Dade College for nearly 30 years. He has received numerous teaching awards, including Innovator of the Year from the League for Innovations in the Community College, and was among the first group of recipients at Miami Dade College for an endowed chair based on excellence in the classroom. In addition to *Algebra and Trigonometry*, Bob has written textbooks covering introductory algebra, intermediate algebra, college algebra, precalculus, and liberal arts mathematics, all published by Prentice Hall.

Applications Index

CHAPTER P

Prerequisites: Fundamental Concepts of Algebra

THIS CHAPTER REVIEWS fundamental concepts of algebra that are prerequisites for the study of college algebra. Algebra, like all of mathematics, provides the tools to help you recognize, classify, and explore the hidden patterns of your world, revealing its underlying structure. You will see how the special language of algebra describes phenomena as diverse as life expectancy, windchill, costs of reducing environmental pollution, the amount Americans spend on online dating, and, as described in the photo caption, your return to a world where the people you knew have long since departed. In many ways, algebra will provide you with a new way of looking at our world.

THE FUTURE IS NOW: YOU HAVE the opportunity to explore the cosmos in a starship traveling near the speed of light. The experience will enable you to understand the mysteries of the universe first hand, transporting you to unimagined levels of knowing and being. The down side: According to Einstein's theory of relativity, close to the speed of light, your aging rate relative to friends on Earth is nearly zero. You will return from your two-year journey to a futuristic world in which friends and loved ones are long dead. Do you explore space or stay here on Earth?

This discussion is developed algebraically in the essay on page 35 and in Exercise 120 in Exercise Set P. 3.

SECTION P.1 Algebraic Expressions and Real Numbers

Objectives

1. Evaluate algebraic expressions.
2. Use mathematical models.
3. Find the intersection of two sets.
4. Find the union of two sets.
5. Recognize subsets of the real numbers.
6. Use inequality symbols.
7. Evaluate absolute value.
8. Use absolute value to express distance.
9. Identify properties of the real numbers.
10. Simplify algebraic expressions.

Insatiable killer. That's the reputation the gray wolf acquired in the United States in the nineteenth and early twentieth centuries. Although the label was undeserved, an estimated 2 million wolves were shot, trapped, or poisoned. By 1960, the population was reduced to 800 wolves. In this section, you will learn how the special language of algebra describes your world, including the increasing wolf population in the continental United States following the Endangered Species Act of 1973.

Algebraic Expressions

Algebra uses letters, such as x and y, to represent numbers. If a letter is used to represent various numbers, it is called a **variable**. For example, imagine that you are basking in the sun on the beach. We can let x represent the number of minutes that you can stay in the sun without burning with no sunscreen. With a number 6 sunscreen, exposure time without burning is six times as long, or 6 times x. This can be written $6 \cdot x$, but it is usually expressed as $6x$. Placing a number and a letter next to one another indicates multiplication.

Notice that $6x$ combines the number 6 and the variable x using the operation of multiplication. A combination of variables and numbers using the operations of addition, subtraction, multiplication, or division, as well as powers or roots, is called an **algebraic expression**. Here are some examples of algebraic expressions:

$$x + 6, \quad x - 6, \quad 6x, \quad \frac{x}{6}, \quad 3x + 5, \quad x^2 - 3, \quad \sqrt{x} + 7.$$

Many algebraic expressions involve *exponents*. For example, the algebraic expression

$$0.72x^2 + 9.4x + 783$$

approximates the gray wolf population in the United States x years after 1960. The expression x^2 means $x \cdot x$, and is read "x to the second power" or "x squared." The exponent, 2, indicates that the base, x, appears as a factor two times.

Exponential Notation

If n is a counting number (1, 2, 3, and so on),

$$b^n = \underbrace{b \cdot b \cdot b \cdot \cdots \cdot b}_{b \text{ appears as a factor } n \text{ times.}}$$

(Exponent or Power: n; Base: b)

b^n is read "the nth power of b" or "b to the nth power." Thus, the nth power of b is defined as the product of n factors of b. The expression b^n is called an **exponential expression**. Furthermore, $b^1 = b$.

For example,

$$8^2 = 8 \cdot 8 = 64, \quad 5^3 = 5 \cdot 5 \cdot 5 = 125, \quad \text{and} \quad 2^4 = 2 \cdot 2 \cdot 2 \cdot 2 = 16.$$

1 Evaluate algebraic expressions.

Evaluating Algebraic Expressions

Evaluating an algebraic expression means to find the value of the expression for a given value of the variable. For example, we can evaluate $6x$ (from the sunscreen example) when $x = 15$. We substitute 15 for x. We obtain $6 \cdot 15$, or 90. This means that if you can stay in the sun for 15 minutes without burning when you don't put on any lotion, then with a number 6 lotion, you can "cook" for 90 minutes without burning.

Many algebraic expressions involve more than one operation. Evaluating an algebraic expression without a calculator involves carefully applying the following order of operations agreement:

The Order of Operations Agreement

1. Perform operations within the innermost parentheses and work outward. If the algebraic expression involves a fraction, treat the numerator and the denominator as if they were each enclosed in parentheses.
2. Evaluate all exponential expressions.
3. Perform multiplications and divisions as they occur, working from left to right.
4. Perform additions and subtractions as they occur, working from left to right.

EXAMPLE 1 Evaluating an Algebraic Expression

Evaluate $7 + 5(x - 4)^3$ for $x = 6$.

Solution

$$7 + 5(x - 4)^3 = 7 + 5(6 - 4)^3$$ Replace x with 6.

$$= 7 + 5(2)^3$$ First work inside parentheses: $6 - 4 = 2$.

$$= 7 + 5(8)$$ Evaluate the exponential expression: $2^3 = 2 \cdot 2 \cdot 2 = 8$.

$$= 7 + 40$$ Multiply: $5(8) = 40$.

$$= 47$$ Add.

Check Point 1 Evaluate $8 + 6(x - 3)^2$ for $x = 13$.

2 Use mathematical models.

Formulas and Mathematical Models

An **equation** is formed when an equal sign is placed between two algebraic expressions. One aim of algebra is to provide a compact, symbolic description of the world. These descriptions involve the use of *formulas*. A **formula** is an equation that uses letters to express a relationship between two or more variables. Here is an example of a formula:

$$C = \frac{5}{9}(F - 32).$$

Celsius temperature | is | $\frac{5}{9}$ of | the difference between Fahrenheit temperature and 32°.

The process of finding formulas to describe real-world phenomena is called **mathematical modeling**. Such formulas, together with the meaning assigned to the variables, are called **mathematical models**. We often say that these formulas model, or describe, the relationships among the variables.

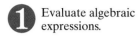

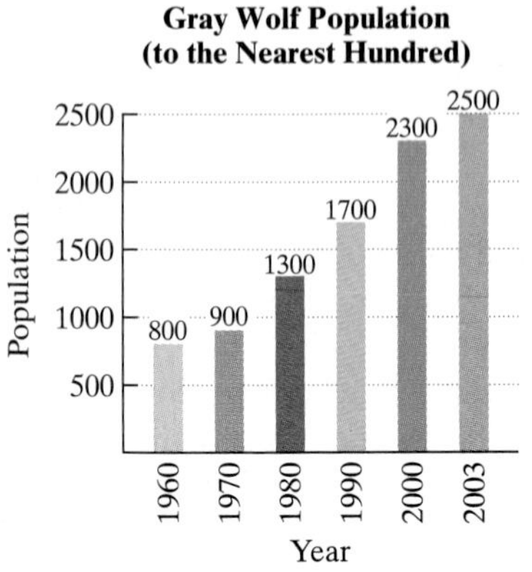

Figure P.1

Source: U.S. Department of the Interior

EXAMPLE 2 Modeling the Gray Wolf Population

The formula

$$P = 0.72x^2 + 9.4x + 783$$

models the gray wolf population, P, in the United States, x years after 1960. Use the formula to find the population in 1990. How well does the formula model the actual data shown in the bar graph in Figure P.1?

Solution Because 1990 is 30 years after 1960, we substitute 30 for x in the given formula. Then we use the order of operations to find P, the gray wolf population in 1990.

$$P = 0.72x^2 + 9.4x + 783$$ This is the given mathematical model.

$$P = 0.72(30)^2 + 9.4(30) + 783$$ Replace each occurrence of x with 30.

$$P = 0.72(900) + 9.4(30) + 783$$ Evaluate the exponential expression: $30^2 = 30 \cdot 30 = 900$.

$$P = 648 + 282 + 783$$ Multiply from left to right: $0.72(900) = 648$ and $9.4(30) = 282$.

$$P = 1713$$ Add.

The formula indicates that in 1990, the gray wolf population in the United States was 1713. The number given in Figure P.1 is 1700, so the formula models the data quite well.

Check Point 2 Use the formula in Example 2 to find the gray wolf population in 2000. How well does the formula model the data in Figure P.1?

Sometimes a mathematical model gives an estimate that is not a good approximation or is extended to include values of the variable that do not make sense. In these cases, we say that **model breakdown** has occurred.

Sets

Before we describe the set of real numbers, let's be sure you are familiar with some basic ideas about sets. A **set** is a collection of objects whose contents can be clearly determined. The objects in a set are called the **elements** of the set. For example, the set of numbers used for counting can be represented by

$$\{1, 2, 3, 4, 5, \dots\}.$$

The braces, { }, indicate that we are representing a set. This form of representation, called the **roster method**, uses commas to separate the elements of the set. The three dots after the 5, called an *ellipsis*, indicate that there is no final element and that the listing goes on forever.

A set can also be written in **set-builder notation**. In this notation, the elements of the set are described, but not listed. Here is an example:

$$\{x | x \text{ is a counting number less than } 6\}.$$

The set of all x | such that | x is a counting number less than 6.

The same set written using the roster method is

$$\{1, 2, 3, 4, 5\}.$$

Study Tip

Grouping symbols such as parentheses, ( ), and square brackets, [ ], are not used to represent sets. Only commas are used to separate the elements of a set. Separators such as colons or semicolons are not used.

3 Find the intersection of two sets.

If A and B are sets, we can form a new set consisting of all elements that are in both A and B. This set is called the *intersection* of the two sets.

Definition of the Intersection of Sets

The **intersection** of sets A and B, written $A \cap B$, is the set of elements common to both set A **and** set B. This definition can be expressed in set-builder notation as follows:

$$A \cap B = \{x | x \text{ is an element of } A \text{ AND } x \text{ is an element of } B\}.$$

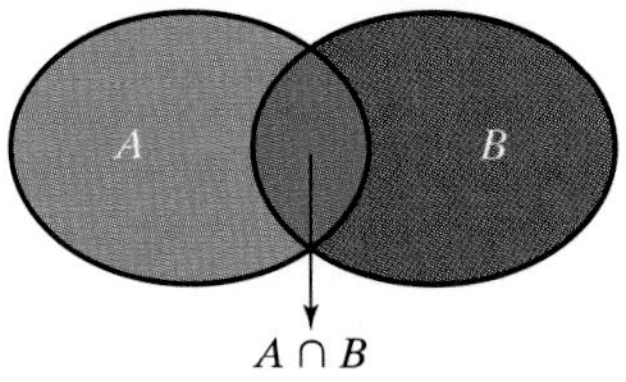

Figure P.2 Picturing the intersection of two sets

Figure P.2 shows a useful way of picturing the intersection of sets A and B. The figure indicates that $A \cap B$ contains those elements that belong to both A and B at the same time.

EXAMPLE 3 Finding the Intersection of Two Sets

Find the intersection: $\{7, 8, 9, 10, 11\} \cap \{6, 8, 10, 12\}$.

Solution The elements common to $\{7, 8, 9, 10, 11\}$ and $\{6, 8, 10, 12\}$ are 8 and 10. Thus,

$$\{7, 8, 9, 10, 11\} \cap \{6, 8, 10, 12\} = \{8, 10\}.$$

Check Point 3 Find the intersection: $\{3, 4, 5, 6, 7\} \cap \{3, 7, 8, 9\}$.

If a set has no elements, it is called the **empty set**, or the **null set**, and is represented by the symbol $\emptyset$ (the Greek letter phi). Here is an example that shows how the empty set can result when finding the intersection of two sets:

$$\{2, 4, 6\} \cap \{3, 5, 7\} = \emptyset.$$

These sets have no common elements.

Their intersection has no elements and is the empty set.

4 Find the union of two sets.

Another set that we can form from sets A and B consists of elements that are in A or B or in both sets. This set is called the *union* of the two sets.

Definition of the Union of Sets

The **union** of sets A and B, written $A \cup B$, is the set of elements that are members of set A **or** of set B or of both sets. This definition can be expressed in set-builder notation as follows:

$$A \cup B = \{x | x \text{ is an element of } A \text{ OR } x \text{ is an element of } B\}.$$

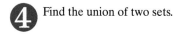

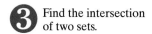

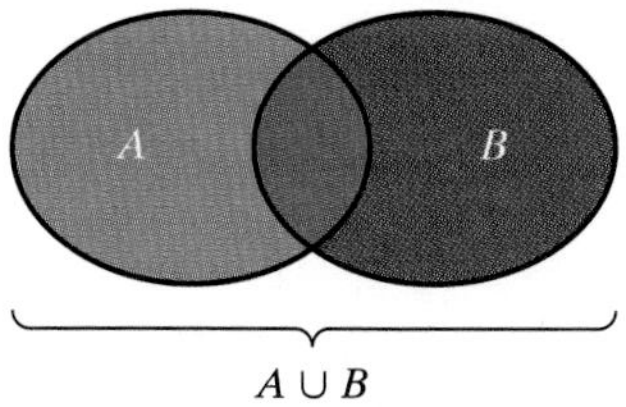

Figure P.3 Picturing the union of two sets

Figure P.3 shows a useful way of picturing the union of sets A and B. The figure indicates that $A \cup B$ is formed by joining the sets together.

We can find the union of set A and set B by listing the elements of set A. Then, we include any elements of set B that have not already been listed. Enclose all elements that are listed with braces. This shows that the union of two sets is also a set.

Study Tip

When finding the union of two sets, do not list twice any elements that appear in both sets.

EXAMPLE 4 Finding the Union of Two Sets

Find the union: $\{7, 8, 9, 10, 11\} \cup \{6, 8, 10, 12\}$.

Solution To find $\{7, 8, 9, 10, 11\} \cup \{6, 8, 10, 12\}$, start by listing all the elements from the first set, namely 7, 8, 9, 10, and 11. Now list all the elements from the second set that are not in the first set, namely 6 and 12. The union is the set consisting of all these elements. Thus,

$$\{7, 8, 9, 10, 11\} \cup \{6, 8, 10, 12\} = \{6, 7, 8, 9, 10, 11, 12\}.$$

Check Point 4 Find the union: $\{3, 4, 5, 6, 7\} \cup \{3, 7, 8, 9\}$.

5 Recognize subsets of the real numbers.

The Set of Real Numbers

The sets that make up the real numbers are summarized in Table P.1. We refer to these sets as **subsets** of the real numbers, meaning that all elements in each subset are also elements in the set of real numbers.

Notice the use of the symbol $\approx$ in the examples of irrational numbers. The symbol means "is approximately equal to." Thus,

$$\sqrt{2} \approx 1.414214.$$

We can verify that this is only an approximation by multiplying 1.414214 by itself. The product is very close to, but not exactly, 2:

$$1.414214 \times 1.414214 = 2.000001237796.$$

Technology

A calculator with a square root key gives a decimal approximation for $\sqrt{2}$, not the exact value.

Table P.1 Important Subsets of the Real Numbers

Name	Description	Examples
Natural numbers $\mathbb{N}$	$\{1, 2, 3, 4, 5, \ldots\}$ These are the numbers that we use for counting.	2, 3, 5, 17
Whole numbers $\mathbb{W}$	$\{0, 1, 2, 3, 4, 5, \ldots\}$ The set of whole numbers includes 0 and the natural numbers.	0, 2, 3, 5, 17
Integers $\mathbb{Z}$	$\{\ldots, -5, -4, -3, -2, -1, 0, 1, 2, 3, 4, 5, \ldots\}$ The set of integers includes the negatives of the natural numbers and the whole numbers.	−17, −5, −3, −2, 0, 2, 3, 5, 17
Rational numbers $\mathbb{Q}$	$\left\{\frac{a}{b} \mid a \text{ and } b \text{ are integers and } b \neq 0\right\}$ This means that b is not equal to zero. The set of rational numbers is the set of all numbers that can be expressed as a quotient of two integers, with the denominator not 0. Rational numbers can be expressed as terminating or repeating decimals.	$-17 = \frac{-17}{1}, -5 = \frac{-5}{1}, -3, -2,$ 0, 2, 3, 5, 17, $\frac{2}{5} = 0.4,$ $\frac{-2}{3} = -0.6666\ldots = -0.\overline{6}$
Irrational numbers $\mathbb{I}$	The set of irrational numbers is the set of all numbers whose decimal representations are neither terminating nor repeating. Irrational numbers cannot be expressed as a quotient of integers.	$\sqrt{2} \approx 1.414214$ $-\sqrt{3} \approx -1.73205$ $\pi \approx 3.142$ $-\frac{\pi}{2} \approx -1.571$

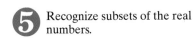

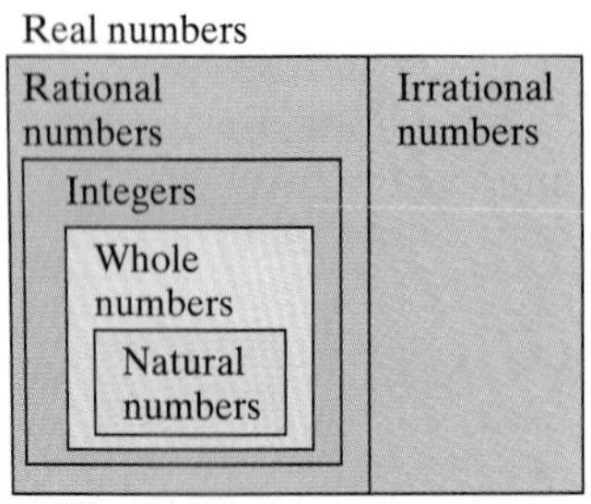

Figure P.4 Every real number is either rational or irrational.

Not all square roots are irrational. For example, $\sqrt{25} = 5$ because $5^2 = 5 \cdot 5 = 25$. Thus, $\sqrt{25}$ is a natural number, a whole number, an integer, and a rational number $\left(\sqrt{25} = \frac{5}{1}\right)$.

The set of *real numbers* is formed by taking the union of the sets of rational numbers and irrational numbers. Thus, every real number is either rational or irrational, as shown in Figure P.4.

Real Numbers

The set of **real numbers** is the set of numbers that are either rational or irrational:

$$\{x|x \text{ is rational or } x \text{ is irrational}\}.$$

The symbol $\mathbb{R}$ is used to represent the set of real numbers. Thus,

$$\mathbb{R} = \{x|x \text{ is rational}\} \cup \{x|x \text{ is irrational}\}.$$

EXAMPLE 5 Recognizing Subsets of the Real Numbers

Consider the following set of numbers:

$$\left\{-7, -\frac{3}{4}, 0, 0.\overline{6}, \sqrt{5}, \pi, 7.3, \sqrt{81}\right\}.$$

List the numbers in the set that are

a. natural numbers. **b.** whole numbers. **c.** integers.

d. rational numbers. **e.** irrational numbers. **f.** real numbers.

Solution

a. Natural numbers: The natural numbers are the numbers used for counting. The only natural number in the set is $\sqrt{81}$ because $\sqrt{81} = 9$. (9 multiplied by itself, or 9^2, is 81.)

b. Whole numbers: The whole numbers consist of the natural numbers and 0. The elements of the set that are whole numbers are 0 and $\sqrt{81}$.

c. Integers: The integers consist of the natural numbers, 0, and the negatives of the natural numbers. The elements of the set that are integers are $\sqrt{81}$, 0, and -7.

d. Rational numbers: All numbers in the set that can be expressed as the quotient of integers are rational numbers. These include $-7\left(-7 = \frac{-7}{1}\right)$, $-\frac{3}{4}$, $0\left(0 = \frac{0}{1}\right)$, and $\sqrt{81}\left(\sqrt{81} = \frac{9}{1}\right)$. Furthermore, all numbers in the set that are terminating or repeating decimals are also rational numbers. These include $0.\overline{6}$ and 7.3.

e. Irrational numbers: The irrational numbers in the set are $\sqrt{5}\left(\sqrt{5} \approx 2.236\right)$ and $\pi(\pi \approx 3.14)$. Both $\sqrt{5}$ and π are only approximately equal to 2.236 and 3.14, respectively. In decimal form, $\sqrt{5}$ and π neither terminate nor have blocks of repeating digits.

f. Real numbers: All the numbers in the given set are real numbers.

Check Point 5 Consider the following set of numbers:

$$\left\{-9, -1.3, 0, 0.\overline{3}, \frac{\pi}{2}, \sqrt{9}, \sqrt{10}\right\}.$$

List the numbers in the set that are

a. natural numbers. **b.** whole numbers.

c. integers. **d.** rational numbers.

e. irrational numbers. **f.** real numbers.

The Real Number Line

The **real number line** is a graph used to represent the set of real numbers. An arbitrary point, called the **origin**, is labeled 0. Select a point to the right of 0 and label it 1. The distance from 0 to 1 is called the **unit distance**. Numbers to the right of the origin are **positive** and numbers to the left of the origin are **negative**. The real number line is shown in Figure P.5.

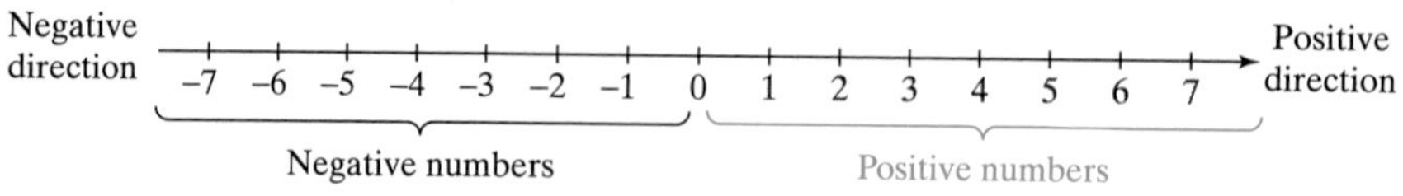

Figure P.5 The real number line

Real numbers are **graphed** on a number line by placing a dot at the correct location for each number. The integers are easiest to locate. In Figure P.6, we've graphed the integers −3, 0, and 4.

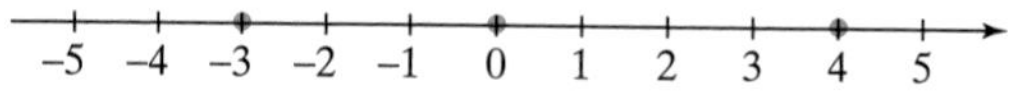

Figure P.6

Every real number corresponds to a point on the number line and every point on the number line corresponds to a real number. We say that there is a **one-to-one correspondence** between all the real numbers and all points on a real number line.

⑥ Use inequality symbols.

Ordering the Real Numbers

On the real number line, the real numbers increase from left to right. The lesser of two real numbers is the one farther to the left on a number line. The greater of two real numbers is the one farther to the right on a number line.

Look at the number line in Figure P.7. The integers −4 and −1 are graphed.

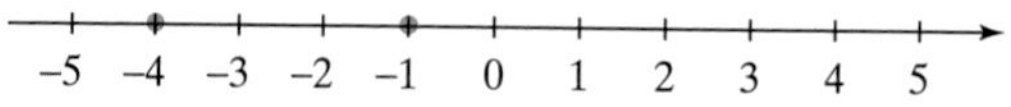

+——+——●——+——+——●——+——+——+——+——+——+——→
−5 −4 −3 −2 −1 0 1 2 3 4 5 **Figure P.7**

Observe that −4 is to the left of −1 on the number line. This means that −4 is less than −1.

$$-4 < -1$$ −4 is less than −1 because −4 is to the **left** of −1 on the number line.

In Figure P.7, we can also observe that −1 is to the right of −4 on the number line. This means that −1 is greater than −4.

$$-1 > -4$$ −1 is greater than −4 because −1 is to the **right** of −4 on the number line.

The symbols $<$ and $>$ are called **inequality symbols**. These symbols always point to the lesser of the two real numbers when the inequality statement is true.

−4 is less than −1. $-4 < -1$ The symbol points to − 4, the lesser number.

−1 is greater than −4. $-1 > -4$ The symbol still points to − 4, the lesser number.

The symbols $<$ and $>$ may be combined with an equal sign, as shown in the following table:

Symbols	Meaning	Examples	Explanation
$a \leq b$	a is less than or equal to b.	$2 \leq 9$ $9 \leq 9$	Because $2 < 9$ Because $9 = 9$
$b \geq a$	b is greater than or equal to a.	$9 \geq 2$ $2 \geq 2$	Because $9 > 2$ Because $2 = 2$

This inequality is true if either the < part or the = part is true.

This inequality is true if either the > part or the = part is true.

7 Evaluate absolute value.

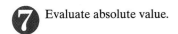

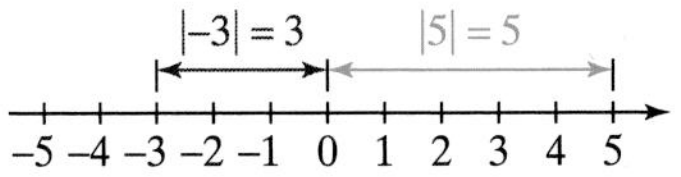

Figure P.8 Absolute value as the distance from 0

Absolute Value

The **absolute value** of a real number a, denoted by $|a|$, is the distance from 0 to a on the number line. This distance is always taken to be nonnegative. For example, the real number line in Figure P.8 shows that

$$|-3| = 3 \quad \text{and} \quad |5| = 5.$$

The absolute value of -3 is 3 because -3 is 3 units from 0 on the number line. The absolute value of 5 is 5 because 5 is 5 units from 0 on the number line. The absolute value of a positive real number or 0 is the number itself. The absolute value of a negative real number, such as -3, is the number without the negative sign.

We can define the absolute value of the real number x without referring to a number line. The algebraic definition of the absolute value of x is given as follows:

Definition of Absolute Value

$$|x| = \begin{cases} x & \text{if } x \geq 0 \\ -x & \text{if } x < 0 \end{cases}$$

If x is nonnegative (that is, $x \geq 0$), the absolute value of x is the number itself. For example,

$$|5| = 5 \qquad |\pi| = \pi \qquad \left|\frac{1}{3}\right| = \frac{1}{3} \qquad |0| = 0.$$

Zero is the only number whose absolute value is 0.

If x is a negative number (that is, $x < 0$), the absolute value of x is the opposite of x. This makes the absolute value positive. For example,

$$|-3| = -(-3) = 3 \qquad |-\pi| = -(-\pi) = \pi \qquad \left|-\frac{1}{3}\right| = -\left(-\frac{1}{3}\right) = \frac{1}{3}.$$

This middle step is usually omitted.

EXAMPLE 6 Evaluating Absolute Value

Rewrite each expression without absolute value bars:

a. $|\sqrt{3} - 1|$ **b.** $|2 - \pi|$ **c.** $\frac{|x|}{x}$ if $x < 0$.

Solution

a. Because $\sqrt{3} \approx 1.7$, the number inside the absolute value bars, $\sqrt{3} - 1$, is positive. The absolute value of a positive number is the number itself. Thus,

$$|\sqrt{3} - 1| = \sqrt{3} - 1.$$

b. Because $\pi \approx 3.14$, the number inside the absolute value bars, $2 - \pi$, is negative. The absolute value of x when $x < 0$ is $-x$. Thus,

$$|2 - \pi| = -(2 - \pi) = \pi - 2.$$

c. If $x < 0$, then $|x| = -x$. Thus,

$$\frac{|x|}{x} = \frac{-x}{x} = -1.$$

Check Point 6 Rewrite each expression without absolute value bars:

a. $|1 - \sqrt{2}|$ **b.** $|\pi - 3|$ **c.** $\frac{|x|}{x}$ if $x > 0$.

Discovery

Verify the triangle inequality if $a = 4$ and $b = 5$. Verify the triangle inequality if $a = 4$ and $b = -5$.

When does equality occur in the triangle inequality and when does inequality occur? Verify your observation with additional number pairs.

Listed below are several basic properties of absolute value. Each of these properties can be derived from the definition of absolute value.

Properties of Absolute Value

For all real numbers a and b,

1. $|a| \geq 0$ **2.** $|-a| = |a|$ **3.** $a \leq |a|$

4. $|ab| = |a||b|$ **5.** $\left|\frac{a}{b}\right| = \frac{|a|}{|b|}, \quad b \neq 0$

6. $|a + b| \leq |a| + |b|$ (called the triangle inequality)

8 Use absolute value to express distance.

Distance between Points on a Real Number Line

Absolute value is used to find the distance between two points on a real number line. If a and b are any real numbers, the **distance between *a* and *b*** is the absolute value of their difference. For example, the distance between 4 and 10 is 6. Using absolute value, we find this distance in one of two ways:

$$|10 - 4| = |6| = 6 \quad \text{or} \quad |4 - 10| = |-6| = 6.$$

The distance between 4 and 10 on the real number line is 6.

Notice that we obtain the same distance regardless of the order in which we subtract.

Distance between Two Points on the Real Number Line

If a and b are any two points on a real number line, then the distance between a and b is given by

$$|a - b| \quad \text{or} \quad |b - a|.$$

EXAMPLE 7 Distance between Two Points on a Number Line

Find the distance between -5 and 3 on the real number line.

Solution Because the distance between a and b is given by $|a - b|$, the distance between -5 and 3 is

$$|-5 - 3| = |-8| = 8.$$

$a = -5$ $b = 3$

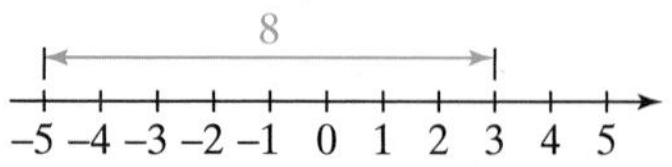

Figure P.9 The distance between -5 and 3 is 8.

Figure P.9 verifies that there are 8 units between -5 and 3 on the real number line. We obtain the same distance if we reverse the order of the subtraction:

$$|3 - (-5)| = |8| = 8.$$

Check Point 7 Find the distance between -4 and 5 on the real number line.

9 Identify properties of the real numbers.

Properties of Real Numbers and Algebraic Expressions

When you use your calculator to add two real numbers, you can enter them in any order. The fact that two real numbers can be added in any order is called the **commutative property of addition**. You probably use this property, as well as other properties of real numbers listed in Table P.2, without giving it much thought. The properties of the real numbers are especially useful when working with algebraic expressions. For each property listed in Table P.2, a, b, and c represent real numbers, variables, or algebraic expressions.

The Associative Property and the English Language

In the English language, phrases can take on different meanings depending on the way the words are associated with commas. Here are three examples.

- Woman, without her man, is nothing.
 Woman, without her, man is nothing.
- What's the latest dope?
 What's the latest, dope?
- Population of Amsterdam broken down by age and sex
 Population of Amsterdam, broken down by age and sex

Table P.2 Properties of the Real Numbers

Name	Meaning	Examples
Commutative Property of Addition	Changing order when adding does not affect the sum. $a + b = b + a$	• $13 + 7 = 7 + 13$ • $13x + 7 = 7 + 13x$
Commutative Property of Multiplication	Changing order when multiplying does not affect the product. $ab = ba$	• $\sqrt{2} \cdot \sqrt{5} = \sqrt{5} \cdot \sqrt{2}$ • $x \cdot 6 = 6x$
Associative Property of Addition	Changing grouping when adding does not affect the sum. $(a + b) + c = a + (b + c)$	• $3 + (8 + x) = (3 + 8) + x$ $\qquad\qquad\quad = 11 + x$
Associative Property of Multiplication	Changing grouping when multiplying does not affect the product. $(ab)c = a(bc)$	• $-2(3x) = (-2 \cdot 3)x = -6x$
Distributive Property of Multiplication over Addition	Multiplication distributes over addition. $a \cdot (b + c) = a \cdot b + a \cdot c$	• $7(4 + \sqrt{3}) = 7 \cdot 4 + 7 \cdot \sqrt{3}$ $\qquad\qquad\quad = 28 + 7\sqrt{3}$ • $5(3x + 7) = 5 \cdot 3x + 5 \cdot 7$ $\qquad\qquad\quad = 15x + 35$
Identity Property of Addition	Zero can be deleted from a sum. $a + 0 = a$ $0 + a = a$	• $\sqrt{3} + 0 = \sqrt{3}$ • $0 + 6x = 6x$
Identity Property of Multiplication	One can be deleted from a product. $a \cdot 1 = a$ $1 \cdot a = a$	• $1 \cdot \pi = \pi$ • $13x \cdot 1 = 13x$
Inverse Property of Addition	The sum of a real number and its additive inverse gives 0, the additive identity. $a + (-a) = 0$ $(-a) + a = 0$	• $\sqrt{5} + (-\sqrt{5}) = 0$ • $-\pi + \pi = 0$ • $6x + (-6x) = 0$ • $(-4y) + 4y = 0$
Inverse Property of Multiplication	The product of a nonzero real number and its multiplicative inverse gives 1, the multiplicative identity. $a \cdot \dfrac{1}{a} = 1, \quad a \neq 0$ $\dfrac{1}{a} \cdot a = 1, \quad a \neq 0$	• $7 \cdot \dfrac{1}{7} = 1$ • $\left(\dfrac{1}{x-3}\right)(x-3) = 1, \quad x \neq 3$

Commutative Words and Sentences

The commutative property states that a change in order produces no change in the answer. The words and sentences listed here suggest a characteristic of the commutative property; they read the same from left to right and from right to left!

- dad
- repaper
- never odd or even
- Go deliver a dare, vile dog!
- May a moody baby doom a yam?
- Madam, in Eden I'm Adam.
- Ma is a nun, as I am.
- A man, a plan, a canal: Panama
- Are we not drawn onward, we few, drawn onward to new era?

The properties of the real numbers in Table P.2 on page 11 apply to the operations of addition and multiplication. Subtraction and division are defined in terms of addition and multiplication.

Definitions of Subtraction and Division

Let a and b represent real numbers.

Subtraction: $a - b = a + (-b)$
We call $-b$ the **additive inverse** or **opposite** of b.

Division: $a \div b = a \cdot \frac{1}{b}$, where $b \neq 0$
We call $\frac{1}{b}$ the **multiplicative inverse** or **reciprocal** of b. The quotient of a and b, $a \div b$, can be written in the form $\frac{a}{b}$, where a is the **numerator** and b the **denominator** of the fraction.

Because subtraction is defined in terms of adding an inverse, the distributive property can be applied to subtraction:

$$a(b - c) = ab - ac$$

$$(b - c)a = ba - ca.$$

For example,

$$4(2x - 5) = 4 \cdot 2x - 4 \cdot 5 = 8x - 20.$$

10 Simplify algebraic expressions.

Simplifying Algebraic Expressions

The **terms** of an algebraic expression are those parts that are separated by addition. For example, consider the algebraic expression

$$7x - 9y + z - 3,$$

which can be expressed as

$$7x + (-9y) + z + (-3).$$

This expression contains four terms, namely $7x$, $-9y$, z, and -3.

The numerical part of a term is called its **coefficient**. In the term $7x$, the 7 is the coefficient. If a term containing one or more variables is written without a coefficient, the coefficient is understood to be 1. Thus, z means $1z$. If a term is a constant, its coefficient is that constant. Thus, the coefficient of the constant term -3 is -3.

$$7x + (-9y) + z + (-3)$$

Coefficient is 7.
Coefficient is −9.
Coefficient is 1; z means $1z$.
Coefficient is −3.

The parts of each term that are multiplied are called the **factors** of the term. The factors of the term $7x$ are 7 and x.

Like terms are terms that have exactly the same variable factors. For example, $3x$ and $7x$ are like terms. The distributive property in the form

$$ba + ca = (b + c)a$$

enables us to add or subtract like terms. For example,

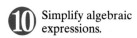

Study Tip

To combine like terms mentally, add or subtract the coefficients of the terms. Use this result as the coefficient of the terms' variable factor(s).

$$3x + 7x = (3 + 7)x = 10x$$

$$7y^2 - y^2 = 7y^2 - 1y^2 = (7 - 1)y^2 = 6y^2.$$

This process is called **combining like terms**.

An algebraic expression is **simplified** when parentheses have been removed and like terms have been combined.

EXAMPLE 8 Simplifying an Algebraic Expression

Simplify: $6(2x^2 + 4x) + 10(4x^2 + 3x)$.

Solution

$$6(2x^2 + 4x) + 10(4x^2 + 3x)$$

$= 6 \cdot 2x^2 + 6 \cdot 4x + 10 \cdot 4x^2 + 10 \cdot 3x$ — Use the distributive property to remove the parentheses.

$= 12x^2 + 24x + 40x^2 + 30x$ — Multiply.

$= (12x^2 + 40x^2) + (24x + 30x)$ — Group like terms.

$= 52x^2 + 54x$ — Combine like terms.

$52x^2$ and $54x$ are not like terms. They contain different variable factors, x^2 and x, and cannot be combined.

Check Point 8 Simplify: $7(4x^2 + 3x) + 2(5x^2 + x)$.

Properties of Negatives

The distributive property can be extended to cover more than two terms within parentheses. For example,

This sign represents subtraction. This sign tells us that the number is negative.

$$-3(4x - 2y + 6) = -3 \cdot 4x - (-3) \cdot 2y - 3 \cdot 6$$

$$= -12x - (-6y) - 18$$

$$= -12x + 6y - 18.$$

The voice balloons illustrate that negative signs can appear side by side. They can represent the operation of subtraction or the fact that a real number is negative. Here is a list of properties of negatives and how they are applied to algebraic expressions:

Properties of Negatives

Let a and b represent real numbers, variables, or algebraic expressions.

Property	Examples
1. $(-1)a = -a$	$(-1)4xy = -4xy$
2. $-(-a) = a$	$-(-6y) = 6y$
3. $(-a)b = -ab$	$(-7)4xy = -7 \cdot 4xy = -28xy$
4. $a(-b) = -ab$	$5x(-3y) = -5x \cdot 3y = -15xy$
5. $-(a + b) = -a - b$	$-(7x + 6y) = -7x - 6y$
6. $-(a - b) = -a + b$	$-(3x - 7y) = -3x + 7y$
$= b - a$	$= 7y - 3x$

It is not uncommon to see algebraic expressions with parentheses preceded by a negative sign or subtraction. Properties 5 and 6 in the box on the previous page, $-(a + b) = -a - b$ and $-(a - b) = -a + b$, are related to this situation. An expression of the form $-(a + b)$ can be simplified as follows:

$$-(a + b) = -1(a + b) = (-1)a + (-1)b = -a + (-b) = -a - b.$$

Do you see a fast way to obtain the simplified expression on the right? **If a negative sign or a subtraction symbol appears outside parentheses, drop the parentheses and change the sign of every term within the parentheses.** For example,

$$-(3x^2 - 7x - 4) = -3x^2 + 7x + 4.$$

EXAMPLE 9 Simplifying an Algebraic Expression

Simplify: $8x + 2[5 - (x - 3)]$.

Solution

$$8x + 2[5 - (x - 3)]$$

$= 8x + 2[5 - x + 3]$ Drop parentheses and change the sign of each term in parentheses: $-(x - 3) = -x + 3$.

$= 8x + 2[8 - x]$ Simplify inside brackets: $5 + 3 = 8$.

$= 8x + 16 - 2x$ Apply the distributive property: $2[8 - x] = 2 \cdot 8 - 2x = 16 - 2x$.

$= (8x - 2x) + 16$ Group like terms.

$= (8 - 2)x + 16$ Apply the distributive property.

$= 6x + 16$ Simplify.

Check Point 9 Simplify: $6 + 4[7 - (x - 2)]$.

EXERCISE SET P.1

Practice Exercises

In Exercises 1–16, evaluate each algebraic expression for the given value or values of the variable(s).

1. $7 + 5x$, for $x = 10$

2. $8 + 6x$, for $x = 5$

3. $6x - y$, for $x = 3$ and $y = 8$

4. $8x - y$, for $x = 3$ and $y = 4$

5. $x^2 + 3x$, for $x = 8$

6. $x^2 + 5x$, for $x = 6$

7. $x^2 - 6x + 3$, for $x = 7$

8. $x^2 - 7x + 4$, for $x = 8$

9. $4 + 5(x - 7)^3$, for $x = 9$

10. $6 + 5(x - 6)^3$, for $x = 8$

11. $x^2 - 3(x - y)$, for $x = 8$ and $y = 2$

12. $x^2 - 4(x - y)$, for $x = 8$ and $y = 3$

13. $\frac{5(x + 2)}{2x - 14}$, for $x = 10$

14. $\frac{7(x - 3)}{2x - 16}$, for $x = 9$

15. $\frac{2x + 3y}{x + 1}$, for $x = -2$ and $y = 4$

16. $\frac{2x + y}{xy - 2x}$, for $x = -2$ and $y = 4$

The formula

$$C = \frac{5}{9}(F - 32)$$

expresses the relationship between Fahrenheit temperature, F, and Celsius temperature, C. In Exercises 17–18, use the formula to convert the given Fahrenheit temperature to its equivalent temperature on the Celsius scale.

17. 50°F

18. 86°F

A football was kicked vertically upward from a height of 4 feet with an initial speed of 60 feet per second. The formula

$$h = 4 + 60t - 16t^2$$

describes the ball's height above the ground, h, in feet, t seconds after it was kicked. Use this formula to solve Exercises 19–20.

19. What was the ball's height 2 seconds after it was kicked?

20. What was the ball's height 3 seconds after it was kicked?

In Exercises 21–28, find the intersection of the sets.

21. $\{1, 2, 3, 4\} \cap \{2, 4, 5\}$

22. $\{1, 3, 7\} \cap \{2, 3, 8\}$

23. $\{s, e, t\} \cap \{t, e, s\}$

24. $\{r, e, a, l\} \cap \{l, e, a, r\}$

25. $\{1, 3, 5, 7\} \cap \{2, 4, 6, 8, 10\}$

26. $\{0, 1, 3, 5\} \cap \{-5, -3, -1\}$

27. $\{a, b, c, d\} \cap \varnothing$ **28.** $\{w, y, z\} \cap \varnothing$

In Exercises 29–34, find the union of the sets.

29. $\{1, 2, 3, 4\} \cup \{2, 4, 5\}$ **30.** $\{1, 3, 7, 8\} \cup \{2, 3, 8\}$

31. $\{1, 3, 5, 7\} \cup \{2, 4, 6, 8, 10\}$

32. $\{0, 1, 3, 5\} \cup \{2, 4, 6\}$ **33.** $\{a, e, i, o, u\} \cup \varnothing$

34. $\{e, m, p, t, y\} \cup \varnothing$

In Exercises 35–38, list all numbers from the given set that are **a.** *natural numbers,* **b.** *whole numbers,* **c.** *integers,* **d.** *rational numbers,* **e.** *irrational numbers,* **f.** *real numbers.*

35. $\left\{-9, -\frac{4}{5}, 0, 0.25, \sqrt{3}, 9.2, \sqrt{100}\right\}$

36. $\left\{-7, -0.\overline{6}, 0, \sqrt{49}, \sqrt{50}\right\}$

37. $\left\{-11, -\frac{5}{6}, 0, 0.75, \sqrt{5}, \pi, \sqrt{64}\right\}$

38. $\left\{-5, -0.\overline{3}, 0, \sqrt{2}, \sqrt{4}\right\}$

39. Give an example of a whole number that is not a natural number.

40. Give an example of a rational number that is not an integer.

41. Give an example of a number that is an integer, a whole number, and a natural number.

42. Give an example of a number that is a rational number, an integer, and a real number.

Determine whether each statement in Exercises 43–50 is true or false.

43. $-13 \le -2$ **44.** $-6 > 2$

45. $4 \ge -7$ **46.** $-13 < -5$

47. $-\pi \ge -\pi$ **48.** $-3 > -13$

49. $0 \ge -6$ **50.** $0 \ge -13$

In Exercises 51–60, rewrite each expression without absolute value bars.

51. $|300|$ **52.** $|-203|$

53. $|12 - \pi|$ **54.** $|7 - \pi|$

55. $|\sqrt{2} - 5|$ **56.** $|\sqrt{5} - 13|$

57. $\dfrac{-3}{|-3|}$ **58.** $\dfrac{-7}{|-7|}$

59. $||-3| - |-7||$ **60.** $||-5| - |-13||$

In Exercises 61–66, evaluate each algebraic expression for $x = 2$ and $y = -5$.

61. $|x + y|$ **62.** $|x - y|$

63. $|x| + |y|$ **64.** $|x| - |y|$

65. $\dfrac{y}{|y|}$ **66.** $\dfrac{|x|}{x} + \dfrac{|y|}{y}$

In Exercises 67–74, express the distance between the given numbers using absolute value. Then find the distance by evaluating the absolute value expression.

67. 2 and 17 **68.** 4 and 15

69. -2 and 5 **70.** -6 and 8

71. -19 and -4 **72.** -26 and -3

73. -3.6 and -1.4 **74.** -5.4 and -1.2

In Exercises 75–84, state the name of the property illustrated.

75. $6 + (-4) = (-4) + 6$

76. $11 \cdot (7 + 4) = 11 \cdot 7 + 11 \cdot 4$

77. $6 + (2 + 7) = (6 + 2) + 7$

78. $6 \cdot (2 \cdot 3) = 6 \cdot (3 \cdot 2)$

79. $(2 + 3) + (4 + 5) = (4 + 5) + (2 + 3)$

80. $7 \cdot (11 \cdot 8) = (11 \cdot 8) \cdot 7$

81. $2(-8 + 6) = -16 + 12$

82. $-8(3 + 11) = -24 + (-88)$

83. $\dfrac{1}{(x + 3)}(x + 3) = 1, x \ne -3$

84. $(x + 4) + [-(x + 4)] = 0$

In Exercises 85–96, simplify each algebraic expression.

85. $5(3x + 4) - 4$ **86.** $2(5x + 4) - 3$

87. $5(3x - 2) + 12x$ **88.** $2(5x - 1) + 14x$

89. $7(3y - 5) + 2(4y + 3)$ **90.** $4(2y - 6) + 3(5y + 10)$

91. $5(3y - 2) - (7y + 2)$ **92.** $4(5y - 3) - (6y + 3)$

93. $7 - 4[3 - (4y - 5)]$ **94.** $6 - 5[8 - (2y - 4)]$

95. $18x^2 + 4 - [6(x^2 - 2) + 5]$

96. $14x^2 + 5 - [7(x^2 - 2) + 4]$

In Exercises 97–102, write each algebraic expression without parentheses.

97. $-(-14x)$ **98.** $-(-17y)$

99. $-(2x - 3y - 6)$ **100.** $-(5x - 13y - 1)$

101. $\frac{1}{3}(3x) + [(4y) + (-4y)]$

102. $\frac{1}{2}(2y) + [(-7x) + 7x]$

Practice Plus

In Exercises 103–110, insert either $<$, $>$, or $=$ in the shaded area to make a true statement.

103. $|-6| \;\square\; |-3|$ **104.** $|-20| \;\square\; |-50|$

105. $\left|\dfrac{3}{5}\right| \;\square\; |-0.6|$ **106.** $\left|\dfrac{5}{2}\right| \;\square\; |-2.5|$

107. $\dfrac{30}{40} - \dfrac{3}{4} \;\square\; \dfrac{14}{15} \cdot \dfrac{15}{14}$ **108.** $\dfrac{17}{18} \cdot \dfrac{18}{17} \;\square\; \dfrac{50}{60} - \dfrac{5}{6}$

109. $\dfrac{8}{13} \div \dfrac{8}{13} \;\square\; |-1|$ **110.** $|-2| \;\square\; \dfrac{4}{17} \div \dfrac{4}{17}$

In Exercises 111–118, write each English phrase as an algebraic expression. Then simplify the expression. Let x represent the number.

111. A number decreased by the sum of the number and four

112. A number decreased by the difference between eight and the number

113. Six times the product of negative five and a number

114. Ten times the product of negative four and a number

115. The difference between the product of five and a number and twice the number

116. The difference between the product of six and a number and negative two times the number

117. The difference between eight times a number and six more than three times the number

118. Eight decreased by three times the sum of a number and six

Application Exercises

The bar graph shows the number of billionaires in the United States from 2000 through 2004.

A Growing Club: U.S. Billionaires

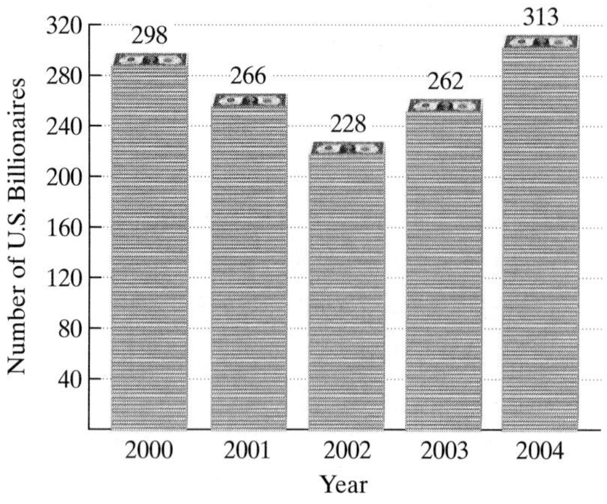

Source: Forbes magazine

The formula

$$N = 17x^2 - 65.4x + 302.2$$

models the number of billionaires, N, in the United States, x years after 2000. Use the formula to solve Exercises 119–122.

119. According to the formula, how many U.S. billionaires, to the nearest whole number, were there in 2004? How well does the formula model the actual data shown in the bar graph?

120. According to the formula, how many U.S. billionaires, to the nearest whole number, were there in 2003? How well does the formula model the actual data shown in the bar graph?

121. According to the formula, how many U.S. billionaires, to the nearest whole number, will there be in 2006?

122. According to the formula, how many U.S. billionaires, to the nearest whole number, will there be in 2007?

The bar graph shows that since her blockbuster debut, Britney Spears's album sales have slid downward.

Slipped Discs: Britney Spears's Album Sales

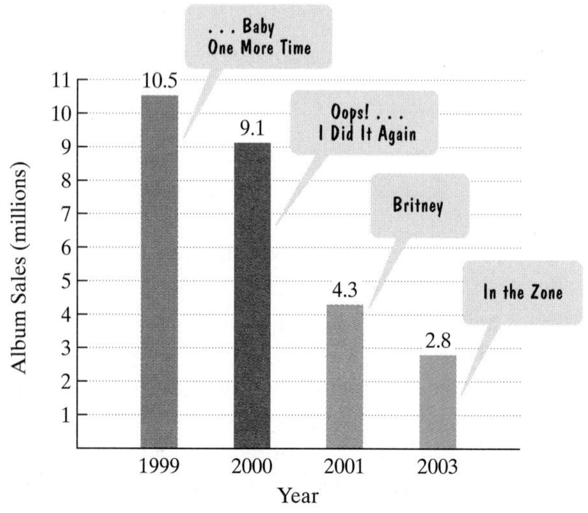

Source: Entertainment Weekly

Here are three mathematical models for the data shown in the graph. In each formula, N represents Britney Spears's album sales, in millions, x years after 1999.

Model 1 $N = -2.04x + 10.24$

Model 2 $N = 0.04x^2 - 3.6x + 11$

Model 3 $N = 0.76x^3 - 4x^2 + 1.8x + 10.5$

Use these models to solve Exercises 123–126.

123. Which of the three models best describes the actual number of album sales in 1999?

124. Which of the three models best describes the actual number of album sales in 2000?

125. Which of the three models best describes the actual number of album sales in 2003?

126. For which formula does model breakdown occur when describing the number of album sales in 2003?

127. You had \$10,000 to invest. You put x dollars in a safe, government-insured certificate of deposit paying 5% per year. You invested the remainder of the money in noninsured corporate bonds paying 12% per year. Your total interest earned at the end of the year is given by the algebraic expression

$$0.05x + 0.12(10{,}000 - x).$$

a. Simplify the algebraic expression.

b. Use each form of the algebraic expression to determine your total interest earned at the end of the year if you invested \$6000 in the safe, government-insured certificate of deposit.

128. It takes you 50 minutes to get to campus. You spend t minutes walking to the bus stop and the rest of the time riding the bus. Your walking rate is 0.06 miles per minute and the bus travels at a rate of 0.5 miles per minute. The total distance walking and traveling by bus is given by the algebraic expression

$$0.06t + 0.5(50 - t).$$

a. Simplify the algebraic expression.

b. Use each form of the algebraic expression to determine the total distance that you travel if you spend 20 minutes walking to the bus stop.

Writing in Mathematics

Writing about mathematics will help you learn mathematics. For all writing exercises in this book, use complete sentences to respond to the question. Some writing exercises can be answered in a sentence; others require a paragraph or two. You can decide how much you need to write as long as your writing clearly and directly answers the question in the exercise. Standard references such as a dictionary and a thesaurus should be helpful.

129. What is an algebraic expression? Give an example with your explanation.

130. If n is a natural number, what does b^n mean? Give an example with your explanation.

131. What does it mean when we say that a formula models real-world phenomena?

132. What is the intersection of sets A and B?

133. What is the union of sets A and B?

134. How do the whole numbers differ from the natural numbers?

135. Can a real number be both rational and irrational? Explain your answer.

136. If you are given two real numbers, explain how to determine which is the lesser.

137. How can $\frac{|x|}{x}$ be equal to 1 or -1?

138. Describe the difference between the commutative and the associative properties of addition.

139. Why is $3(x + 7) - 4x$ not simplified? What must be done to simplify the expression?

Critical Thinking Exercises

140. Which one of the following statements is true?

a. Every rational number is an integer.
b. Some whole numbers are not integers.
c. Some rational numbers are not positive.
d. Irrational numbers cannot be negative.

141. Which of the following is true?

a. The term x has no coefficient.
b. $5 + 3(x - 4) = 8(x - 4) = 8x - 32$
c. $-x - x = -x + (-x) = 0$
d. $x - 0.02(x + 200) = 0.98x - 4$

In Exercises 142–144, insert either $<$ or $>$ in the shaded area between the numbers to make the statement true.

142. $\sqrt{2}$ ▒ 1.5

143. $-\pi$ ▒ -3.5

144. $-\frac{3.14}{2}$ ▒ $-\frac{\pi}{2}$

145. A business that manufactures small alarm clocks has a weekly fixed cost of \$5000. The average cost per clock for the business to manufacture x clocks is described by

$$\frac{0.5x + 5000}{x}.$$

a. Find the average cost when $x = 100$, 1000, and 10,000.

b. Like all other businesses, the alarm clock manufacturer must make a profit. To do this, each clock must be sold for at least 50¢ more than what it costs to manufacture. Due to competition from a larger company, the clocks can be sold for \$1.50 each and no more. Our small manufacturer can only produce 2000 clocks weekly. Does this business have much of a future? Explain.

SECTION P.2 Exponents and Scientific Notation

Objectives

1. Use the product rule.
2. Use the quotient rule.
3. Use the zero-exponent rule.
4. Use the negative-exponent rule.
5. Use the power rule.
6. Find the power of a product.
7. Find the power of a quotient.
8. Simplify exponential expressions.
9. Use scientific notation.

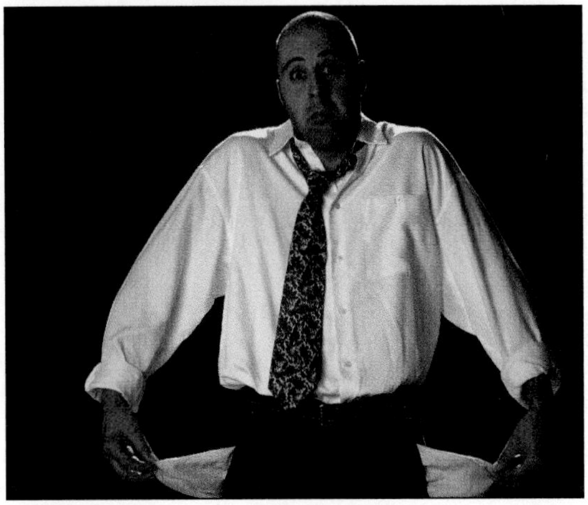

People who complain about paying their income tax can be divided into two types: men and women. Perhaps we can quantify the complaining by examining the data in Figure P.10. The bar graphs show the U.S. population, in millions, and the total amount we paid in federal taxes, in trillions of dollars, for six selected years.

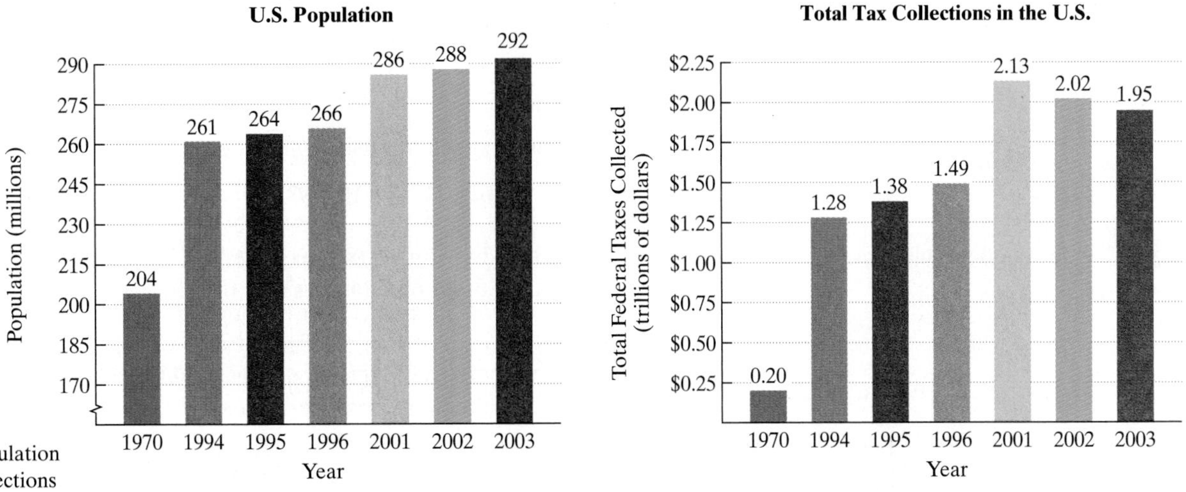

Figure P.10 Population and total tax collections in the U.S.

Source: U.S. Census Bureau

Source: Internal Revenue Service

The bar graph in Figure P.10 shows that in 2003, total tax collections were $1.95 trillion. How can we place this amount in the proper perspective? If the total tax collections were evenly divided among all Americans, how much would each citizen pay in taxes?

In this section, you will learn to use exponents to provide a way of putting large and small numbers in perspective. Using this skill, we will explore the per capita tax for some of the years shown in Figure P.10 on the previous page.

1 Use the product rule.

The Product and Quotient Rules

We have seen that exponents are used to indicate repeated multiplication. Now consider the multiplication of two exponential expressions, such as $b^4 \cdot b^3$. We are multiplying 4 factors of b and 3 factors of b. We have a total of 7 factors of b:

4 factors of b 3 factors of b

$$b^4 \cdot b^3 = (b \cdot b \cdot b \cdot b)(b \cdot b \cdot b) = b^7.$$

Total: 7 factors of b

The product is exactly the same if we add the exponents:

$$b^4 \cdot b^3 = b^{4+3} = b^7.$$

This suggests the following rule:

The Product Rule

$$b^m \cdot b^n = b^{m+n}$$

When multiplying exponential expressions with the same base, add the exponents. Use this sum as the exponent of the common base.

EXAMPLE 1 Using the Product Rule

Multiply each expression using the product rule:

 a. $2^2 \cdot 2^3$ **b.** $(6x^4y^3)(5x^2y^7).$

Solution

 a. $2^2 \cdot 2^3 = 2^{2+3} = 2^5$ or 32 $2^5 = 2 \cdot 2 \cdot 2 \cdot 2 \cdot 2 = 32$

 b. $(6x^4y^3)(5x^2y^7)$

$$= 6 \cdot 5 \cdot x^4 \cdot x^2 \cdot y^3 \cdot y^7 \quad \text{Use the associative and commutative properties. This step can be done mentally.}$$

$$= 30x^{4+2}y^{3+7}$$

$$= 30x^6y^{10}$$

Check Point 1 Multiply each expression using the product rule:

 a. $3^3 \cdot 3^2$ **b.** $(4x^3y^4)(10x^2y^6).$

2 Use the quotient rule.

Now, consider the division of two exponential expressions, such as the quotient of b^7 and b^3. We are dividing 7 factors of b by 3 factors of b.

$$\frac{b^7}{b^3} = \frac{b \cdot b \cdot b \cdot b \cdot b \cdot b \cdot b}{b \cdot b \cdot b} = \boxed{\frac{b \cdot b \cdot b}{b \cdot b \cdot b}} \cdot b \cdot b \cdot b \cdot b = 1 \cdot b \cdot b \cdot b \cdot b = b^4$$

This factor is equal to 1.

The quotient is exactly the same if we subtract the exponents:

$$\frac{b^7}{b^3} = b^{7-3} = b^4.$$

This suggests the following rule:

The Quotient Rule

$$\frac{b^m}{b^n} = b^{m-n}, \quad b \neq 0 \quad \checkmark$$

When dividing exponential expressions with the same nonzero base, subtract the exponent in the denominator from the exponent in the numerator. Use this difference as the exponent of the common base.

EXAMPLE 2

Divide each expression using the quotient rule:

a. $\dfrac{(-2)^7}{(-2)^4}$ b. $\dfrac{30x^{12}y^9}{5x^3y^7}$.

Solution

a. $\dfrac{(-2)^7}{(-2)^4} = (-2)^{7-4} = (-2)^3$ or -8 $\boxed{(-2)^3 = (-2)(-2)(-2) = -8}$

b. $\dfrac{30x^{12}y^9}{5x^3y^7} = \dfrac{30}{5} \cdot \dfrac{x^{12}}{x^3} \cdot \dfrac{y^9}{y^7} = 6x^{12-3}y^{9-7} = 6x^9y^2$

Check Point 2 Divide each expression using the quotient rule:

a. $\dfrac{(-3)^6}{(-3)^3}$ b. $\dfrac{27x^{14}y^8}{3x^3y^5}$.

❸ Use the zero-exponent rule.

Zero as an Exponent

A nonzero base can be raised to the 0 power. The quotient rule can be used to help determine what zero as an exponent should mean. Consider the quotient of b^4 and b^4, where b is not zero. We can determine this quotient in two ways.

$$\frac{b^4}{b^4} = 1 \qquad\qquad \frac{b^4}{b^4} = b^{4-4} = b^0$$

Any nonzero expression divided by itself is 1.

Use the quotient rule and subtract exponents.

This means that b^0 must equal 1.

The Zero-Exponent Rule

If b is any real number other than 0,

$$b^0 = 1.$$

Here are examples involving simplification using the zero-exponent rule:

$$8^0 = 1, \quad (-6)^0 = 1, \quad -6^0 = -1, \quad (5x)^0 = 1, \quad 5x^0 = 5.$$

Only 6 is raised to the 0 power:
$-6^0 = -(6^0) = -1.$

Only x is raised to the 0 power:
$5x^0 = 5 \cdot 1 = 5.$

4 Use the negative-exponent rule.

Negative Integers as Exponents

A nonzero base can be raised to a negative power. The quotient rule can be used to help determine what a negative integer as an exponent should mean. Consider the quotient of b^3 and b^5, where b is not zero. We can determine this quotient in two ways.

$$\frac{b^3}{b^5} = \frac{\cancel{b} \cdot \cancel{b} \cdot \cancel{b}}{\cancel{b} \cdot \cancel{b} \cdot \cancel{b} \cdot b \cdot b} = \frac{1}{b^2} \qquad \frac{b^3}{b^5} = b^{3-5} = b^{-2}$$

After dividing common factors, we have two factors of b in the denominator.

Use the quotient rule and subtract exponents.

Notice that $\frac{b^3}{b^5}$ equals both b^{-2} and $\frac{1}{b^2}$. This means that b^{-2} must equal $\frac{1}{b^2}$. This example is a special case of the **negative-exponent rule**.

The Negative-Exponent Rule

If b is any real number other than 0 and n is a natural number, then

$$b^{-n} = \frac{1}{b^n}.$$

EXAMPLE 3 Using the Negative-Exponent Rule

Use the negative-exponent rule to write each expression with a positive exponent. Simplify, if possible:

a. 9^{-2} **b.** $(-2)^{-5}$ **c.** $\frac{1}{6^{-2}}$ **d.** $7x^{-5}y^2$.

Solution

a. $9^{-2} = \frac{1}{9^2} = \frac{1}{81}$

b. $(-2)^{-5} = \frac{1}{(-2)^5} = \frac{1}{(-2)(-2)(-2)(-2)(-2)} = \frac{1}{-32} = -\frac{1}{32}$

Only the sign of the exponent, −5, changes. The base, −2, does not change sign.

c. $\frac{1}{6^{-2}} = \frac{1}{\frac{1}{6^2}} = 1 \cdot \frac{6^2}{1} = 6^2 = 36$

d. $7x^{-5}y^2 = 7 \cdot \frac{1}{x^5} \cdot y^2 = \frac{7y^2}{x^5}$

Check Point 3 Use the negative-exponent rule to write each expression with a positive exponent. Simplify, if possible:

a. 5^{-2} **b.** $(-3)^{-3}$ **c.** $\frac{1}{4^{-2}}$ **d.** $3x^{-6}y^4$.

In Example 3 and Check Point 3, did you notice that

$$\frac{1}{6^{-2}} = 6^2 \quad \text{and} \quad \frac{1}{4^{-2}} = 4^2?$$

In general, if a negative exponent appears in a denominator, an expression can be written with a positive exponent using

$$\frac{1}{b^{-n}} = b^n.$$

Negative Exponents in Numerators and Denominators

If b is any real number other than 0 and n is a natural number, then

$$b^{-n} = \frac{1}{b^n} \quad \text{and} \quad \frac{1}{b^{-n}} = b^n.$$

When a negative number appears as an exponent, switch the position of the base (from numerator to denominator or from denominator to numerator) and make the exponent positive. The sign of the base does not change.

5 Use the power rule.

The Power Rule for Exponents (Powers to Powers)

The next property of exponents applies when an exponential expression is raised to a power. Here is an example:

$$(b^2)^4.$$

The exponential expression b^2 is raised to the fourth power.

There are 4 factors of b^2. Thus,

$$(b^2)^4 = b^2 \cdot b^2 \cdot b^2 \cdot b^2 = b^{2+2+2+2} = b^8.$$

Add exponents when multiplying with the same base.

We can obtain the answer, b^8, by multiplying the exponents:

$$(b^2)^4 = b^{2 \cdot 4} = b^8.$$

This suggests the following rule:

The Power Rule (Powers to Powers)

$$(b^m)^n = b^{mn}$$

When an exponential expression is raised to a power, multiply the exponents. Place the product of the exponents on the base and remove the parentheses.

EXAMPLE 4 Using the Power Rule (Powers to Powers)

Simplify each expression using the power rule:

a. $(2^2)^3$ **b.** $(y^5)^{-3}$ **c.** $(b^{-4})^{-2}$.

Solution

a. $(2^2)^3 = 2^{2 \cdot 3} = 2^6$ or 64 **b.** $(y^5)^{-3} = y^{5(-3)} = y^{-15} = \frac{1}{y^{15}}$

c. $(b^{-4})^{-2} = b^{(-4)(-2)} = b^8$

Check Point 4 Simplify each expression using the power rule:

a. $(3^3)^2$ **b.** $(y^7)^{-2}$ **c.** $(b^{-3})^{-4}$.

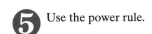

6 Find the power of a product.

The Products-to-Powers Rule for Exponents

The next property of exponents applies when we are raising a product to a power. Here is an example:

$$(2x)^4.$$

The product $2x$ is raised to the fourth power.

There are four factors of $2x$. Thus,

$$(2x)^4 = 2x \cdot 2x \cdot 2x \cdot 2x = 2 \cdot 2 \cdot 2 \cdot 2 \cdot x \cdot x \cdot x \cdot x = 2^4 x^4.$$

We can obtain the answer, 2^4x^4, by raising each factor within the parentheses to the fourth power:

$$(2x)^4 = 2^4x^4.$$

This suggests the following rule:

Products to Powers

$$(ab)^n = a^n b^n$$

When a product is raised to a power, raise each factor to that power.

EXAMPLE 5 Raising a Product to a Power

Simplify: $(-2y^2)^4$.

Solution

$$(-2y^2)^4 = (-2)^4(y^2)^4 \quad \text{Raise each factor to the fourth power.}$$

$$= (-2)^4 y^{2\cdot 4} \quad \text{To raise an exponential expression to a power, multiply exponents: } (b^m)^n = b^{mn}.$$

$$= 16y^8 \quad \text{Simplify: } (-2)^4 = (-2)(-2)(-2)(-2) = 16.$$

Check Point 5 Simplify: $(-4x)^3$.

The rule for raising a product to a power can be extended to cover three or more factors. For example,

$$(-2xy)^3 = (-2)^3x^3y^3 = -8x^3y^3.$$

7 Find the power of a quotient.

The Quotients-to-Powers Rule for Exponents

The following rule is used to raise a quotient to a power:

Quotients to Powers

If b is a nonzero real number, then

$$\left(\frac{a}{b}\right)^n = \frac{a^n}{b^n}.$$

When a quotient is raised to a power, raise the numerator to that power and divide by the denominator to that power.

EXAMPLE 6 Raising Quotients to Powers

Simplify by raising each quotient to the given power:

a. $\left(-\frac{3}{x}\right)^4$ **b.** $\left(\frac{x^2}{4}\right)^3$.

Solution

a. $\left(-\frac{3}{x}\right)^4 = \frac{(-3)^4}{x^4} = \frac{(-3)(-3)(-3)(-3)}{x^4} = \frac{81}{x^4}$

b. $\left(\frac{x^2}{4}\right)^3 = \frac{(x^2)^3}{4^3} = \frac{x^{2\cdot 3}}{4\cdot 4\cdot 4} = \frac{x^6}{64}$

Check Point 6 Simplify:

a. $\left(-\frac{2}{y}\right)^5$ **b.** $\left(\frac{x^5}{3}\right)^3$.

8 Simplify exponential expressions.

Simplifying Exponential Expressions

Properties of exponents are used to simplify exponential expressions. An exponential expression is **simplified** when

- No parentheses appear.
- No powers are raised to powers.
- Each base occurs only once.
- No negative or zero exponents appear.

Simplifying Exponential Expressions

	Example
1. If necessary, remove parentheses by using $(ab)^n = a^nb^n$ or $\left(\frac{a}{b}\right)^n = \frac{a^n}{b^n}$.	$(xy)^3 = x^3y^3$
2. If necessary, simplify powers to powers by using $(b^m)^n = b^{mn}$.	$(x^4)^3 = x^{4\cdot 3} = x^{12}$
3. If necessary, be sure that each base appears only once by using $b^m \cdot b^n = b^{m+n}$ or $\frac{b^m}{b^n} = b^{m-n}$.	$x^4 \cdot x^3 = x^{4+3} = x^7$
4. If necessary, rewrite exponential expressions with zero powers as 1 ($b^0 = 1$). Furthermore, write the answer with positive exponents by using $b^{-n} = \frac{1}{b^n}$ or $\frac{1}{b^{-n}} = b^n$.	$\frac{x^5}{x^8} = x^{5-8} = x^{-3} = \frac{1}{x^3}$

The following example shows how to simplify exponential expressions. Throughout the example, assume that no variable in a denominator is equal to zero.

EXAMPLE 7 Simplifying Exponential Expressions

Simplify:

a. $(-3x^4y^5)^3$ **b.** $(-7xy^4)(-2x^5y^6)$ **c.** $\frac{-35x^2y^4}{5x^6y^{-8}}$ **d.** $\left(\frac{4x^2}{y}\right)^{-3}$.

Solution

a. $(-3x^4y^5)^3 = (-3)^3(x^4)^3(y^5)^3$ Raise each factor inside the parentheses to the third power.

$= (-3)^3x^{4\cdot 3}y^{5\cdot 3}$ Multiply the exponents when raising powers to powers.

$= -27x^{12}y^{15}$ $(-3)^3 = (-3)(-3)(-3) = -27$

b. $(-7xy^4)(-2x^5y^6) = (-7)(-2)xx^5y^4y^6$ Group factors with the same base.

$= 14x^{1+5}y^{4+6}$ When multiplying expressions with the same base, add the exponents.

$= 14x^6y^{10}$ Simplify.

c. $\dfrac{-35x^2y^4}{5x^6y^{-8}} = \left(\dfrac{-35}{5}\right)\left(\dfrac{x^2}{x^6}\right)\left(\dfrac{y^4}{y^{-8}}\right)$ Group factors with the same base.

$= -7x^{2-6}y^{4-(-8)}$ When dividing expressions with the same base, subtract the exponents.

$= -7x^{-4}y^{12}$ Simplify. Notice that $4 - (-8) = 4 + 8 = 12$.

$= \dfrac{-7y^{12}}{x^4}$ Move the base with the negative exponent, x^{-4}, to the other side of the fraction bar and make the negative exponent positive.

d. $\left(\dfrac{4x^2}{y}\right)^{-3} = \dfrac{(4x^2)^{-3}}{y^{-3}}$ Raise the numerator and the denominator to the -3 power.

$= \dfrac{4^{-3}(x^2)^{-3}}{y^{-3}}$ Raise each factor in the numerator to the -3 power.

$= \dfrac{4^{-3}x^{-6}}{y^{-3}}$ Multiply the exponents when raising a power to a power: $(x^2)^{-3} = x^{2(-3)} = x^{-6}$.

$= \dfrac{y^3}{4^3x^6}$ Move each base with a negative exponent to the other side of the fraction bar and make each negative exponent positive.

$= \dfrac{y^3}{64x^6}$ $4^3 = 4 \cdot 4 \cdot 4 = 64$

Check Point 7 Simplify:

a. $(2x^3y^6)^4$ **b.** $(-6x^2y^5)(3xy^3)$ **c.** $\dfrac{100x^{12}y^2}{20x^{16}y^{-4}}$ **d.** $\left(\dfrac{5x}{y^4}\right)^{-2}$.

Study Tip

Try to avoid the following common errors that can occur when simplifying exponential expressions.

Correct	Incorrect	Description of Error
$b^3 \cdot b^4 = b^7$	~~$b^3 \cdot b^4 = b^{12}$~~	The exponents should be added, not multiplied.
$3^2 \cdot 3^4 = 3^6$	~~$3^2 \cdot 3^4 = 9^6$~~	The common base should be retained, not multiplied.
$\dfrac{5^{16}}{5^4} = 5^{12}$	~~$\dfrac{5^{16}}{5^4} = 5^4$~~	The exponents should be subtracted, not divided.
$(4a)^3 = 64a^3$	~~$(4a)^3 = 4a^3$~~	Both factors should be cubed.
$b^{-n} = \dfrac{1}{b^n}$	~~$b^{-n} = -\dfrac{1}{b^n}$~~	Only the exponent should change sign.
$(a+b)^{-1} = \dfrac{1}{a+b}$	~~$(a+b)^{-1} = \dfrac{1}{a} + \dfrac{1}{b}$~~	The exponent applies to the entire expression $a + b$.

9 Use scientific notation.

Scientific Notation

We have seen that in 2003, total tax collections were \$1.95 trillion. Because a trillion is 10^{12} (see Table P.3), this amount can be expressed as

$$1.95 \times 10^{12}.$$

The number 1.95×10^{12} is written in a form called *scientific notation.*

Table P.3 Names of Large Numbers

10^2	hundred
10^3	thousand
10^6	million
10^9	billion
10^{12}	trillion
10^{15}	quadrillion
10^{18}	quintillion
10^{21}	sextillion
10^{24}	septillion
10^{27}	octillion
10^{30}	nonillion
10^{100}	googol

Scientific Notation

A number is written in **scientific notation** when it is expressed in the form

$$a \times 10^n,$$

where the absolute value of a is greater than or equal to 1 and less than 10 $(1 \leq |a| < 10)$, and n is an integer.

It is customary to use the multiplication symbol, $\times$, rather than a dot, when writing a number in scientific notation.

Converting from Scientific to Decimal Notation

Here are two examples of numbers in scientific notation:

$$6.4 \times 10^5 \text{ means } 640{,}000.$$

$$2.17 \times 10^{-3} \text{ means } 0.00217.$$

Do you see that the number with the positive exponent is relatively large and the number with the negative exponent is relatively small?

We can use n, the exponent on the 10 in $a \times 10^n$, to change a number in scientific notation to decimal notation. If n is **positive**, move the decimal point in a to the **right** n places. If n is **negative**, move the decimal point in a to the **left** $|n|$ places.

EXAMPLE 8 Converting from Scientific to Decimal Notation

Write each number in decimal notation:

a. 6.2×10^7 **b.** -6.2×10^7 **c.** 2.019×10^{-3} **d.** -2.019×10^{-3}.

Solution In each case, we use the exponent on the 10 to move the decimal point. In parts (a) and (b), the exponent is positive, so we move the decimal point to the right. In parts (c) and (d), the exponent is negative, so we move the decimal point to the left.

a. $6.2 \times 10^7 = 62{,}000{,}000$

$n = 7$ — Move the decimal point 7 places to the right.

b. $-6.2 \times 10^7 = -62{,}000{,}000$

$n = 7$ — Move the decimal point 7 places to the right.

c. $2.019 \times 10^{-3} = 0.002019$

$n = -3$ — Move the decimal point $|-3|$ places, or 3 places, to the left.

d. $-2.019 \times 10^{-3} = -0.002019$

$n = -3$ — Move the decimal point $|-3|$ places, or 3 places, to the left.

Check Point 8 Write each number in decimal notation:

a. -2.6×10^9 **b.** 3.017×10^{-6}.

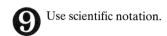

Converting from Decimal to Scientific Notation

To convert from decimal notation to scientific notation, we reverse the procedure of Example 8.

Converting from Decimal to Scientific Notation

Write the number in the form $a \times 10^n$.

- Determine a, the numerical factor. Move the decimal point in the given number to obtain a number whose absolute value is between 1 and 10, including 1.
- Determine n, the exponent on 10^n. The absolute value of n is the number of places the decimal point was moved. The exponent n is positive if the decimal point was moved to the left, negative if the decimal point was moved to the right, and 0 if the decimal point was not moved.

EXAMPLE 9 Converting from Decimal Notation to Scientific Notation

Write each number in scientific notation:

a. 34,970,000,000,000 **b.** −34,970,000,000,000
b. 0.0000000000802 **d.** −0.0000000000802.

Solution

a. $34{,}970{,}000{,}000{,}000 = 3.497 \times 10^{13}$

Move the decimal point to get a number whose absolute value is between 1 and 10.

The decimal point was moved 13 places to the left, so $n = 13$.

b. $-34{,}970{,}000{,}000{,}000 = -3.497 \times 10^{13}$

c. $0.0000000000802 = 8.02 \times 10^{-11}$

Move the decimal point to get a number whose absolute value is between 1 and 10.

The decimal point was moved 11 places to the right, so $n = -11$.

d. $-0.0000000000802 = -8.02 \times 10^{-11}$

Technology

You can use your calculator's [EE] (enter exponent) or [EXP] key to convert from decimal to scientific notation. Here is how it's done for 0.0000000000802.

Many Scientific Calculators

Keystrokes

.0000000000802 [EE] [=]

Display

8.02 − 11

Many Graphing Calculators

Use the mode setting for scientific notation.

Keystrokes

.0000000000802 [ENTER]

Display

8.02E −11

Study Tip

If the absolute value of a number is greater than 10, it will have a positive exponent in scientific notation. If the absolute value of a number is less than 1, it will have a negative exponent in scientific notation.

Check Point 9 Write each number in scientific notation:

a. 5,210,000,000 **b.** −0.00000006893.

EXAMPLE 10 Expressing the U.S. Population in Scientific Notation

In 2003, the population of the United States was approximately 292 million. Express the population in scientific notation.

Solution Because one million is 10^6 (see Table P.3 on page 25), the 2003 population can be expressed as

$$292 \times 10^6.$$

This factor is not between 1 and 10, so the number is not in scientific notation.

The voice balloon indicates that we need to convert 292 to scientific notation.

$$292 \times 10^6 = (2.92 \times 10^2) \times 10^6 = 2.92 \times 10^{2+6} = 2.92 \times 10^8$$

$$292 = 2.92 \times 10^2$$

In scientific notation, the population is 2.92×10^8.

Check Point 10 Express 410×10^7 in scientific notation.

Computations with Scientific Notation

Properties of exponents are used to perform computations with numbers that are expressed in scientific notation.

Technology

$$(6.1 \times 10^5)(4 \times 10^{-9})$$
On a Calculator:

Many Scientific Calculators

6.1 $\boxed{\text{EE}}$ 5 $\boxed{\times}$ 4 $\boxed{\text{EE}}$ 9 $\boxed{+/-}$ $\boxed{=}$

Display

$$2.44 - 03$$

Many Graphing Calculators

6.1 $\boxed{\text{EE}}$ 5 $\boxed{\times}$ 4 $\boxed{\text{EE}}$ $\boxed{(-)}$ 9 $\boxed{\text{ENTER}}$

Display (in scientific notation mode)

$$2.44\text{E} - 3$$

EXAMPLE 11 Computations with Scientific Notation

Perform the indicated computations, writing the answers in scientific notation:

a. $(6.1 \times 10^5)(4 \times 10^{-9})$ **b.** $\dfrac{1.8 \times 10^4}{3 \times 10^{-2}}$.

Solution

a. $(6.1 \times 10^5)(4 \times 10^{-9})$

$= (6.1 \times 4) \times (10^5 \times 10^{-9})$ *Regroup factors.*

$= 24.4 \times 10^{5+(-9)}$ *Add the exponents on 10 and multiply the other parts.*

$= 24.4 \times 10^{-4}$ *Simplify.*

$= (2.44 \times 10^1) \times 10^{-4}$ *Convert 24.4 to scientific notation: $24.4 = 2.44 \times 10^1$.*

$= 2.44 \times 10^{-3}$ *$10^1 \times 10^{-4} = 10^{1+(-4)} = 10^{-3}$*

b. $\dfrac{1.8 \times 10^4}{3 \times 10^{-2}} = \left(\dfrac{1.8}{3}\right) \times \left(\dfrac{10^4}{10^{-2}}\right)$ *Regroup factors.*

$= 0.6 \times 10^{4-(-2)}$ *Subtract the exponents on 10 and divide the other parts.*

$= 0.6 \times 10^6$ *Simplify: $4 - (-2) = 4 + 2 = 6$.*

$= (6 \times 10^{-1}) \times 10^6$ *Convert 0.6 to scientific notation: $0.6 = 6 \times 10^{-1}$.*

$= 6 \times 10^5$ *$10^{-1} \times 10^6 = 10^{-1+6} = 10^5$*

Check Point 11 Perform the indicated computations, writing the answers in scientific notation:

a. $(7.1 \times 10^5)(5 \times 10^{-7})$ **b.** $\dfrac{1.2 \times 10^6}{3 \times 10^{-3}}$.

Applications: Putting Numbers in Perspective

We have seen that in 2003, the U.S. government collected $1.95 trillion in taxes. Example 12 shows how we can use scientific notation to comprehend the meaning of a number such as 1.95 trillion.

EXAMPLE 12 Tax per Capita

In 2003, the U.S. government collected 1.95×10^{12} dollars in taxes. At that time, the U.S. population was approximately 292 million, or 2.92×10^{8}. If the total tax collections were evenly divided among all Americans, how much would each citizen pay? Express the answer in decimal notation, rounded to the nearest dollar.

Solution The amount that we would each pay, or the tax per capita, is the total amount collected, 1.95×10^{12}, divided by the number of Americans, 2.92×10^{8}.

$$\frac{1.95 \times 10^{12}}{2.92 \times 10^{8}} = \left(\frac{1.95}{2.92}\right) \times \left(\frac{10^{12}}{10^{8}}\right) \approx 0.6678 \times 10^{12-8} = 0.6678 \times 10^{4} = 6678$$

To obtain an answer in decimal notation, it is not necessary to express this number in scientific notation.

Move the decimal point 4 places to the right.

If total tax collections were evenly divided, we would each pay approximately \$6678 in taxes.

Check Point 12 In 2002, the U.S. government collected 2.02×10^{12} dollars in taxes. At that time, the U.S. population was approximately 288 million, or 2.88×10^{8}. Find the per capita tax, rounded to the nearest dollar, in 2002.

EXERCISE SET P.2

Practice Exercises

Evaluate each exponential expression in Exercises 1–22.

1. $5^2 \cdot 2$
2. $6^2 \cdot 2$
3. $(-2)^6$
4. $(-2)^4$
5. -2^6
6. -2^4
7. $(-3)^0$
8. $(-9)^0$
9. -3^0
10. -9^0
11. 4^{-3}
12. 2^{-6}
13. $2^2 \cdot 2^3$
14. $3^3 \cdot 3^2$
15. $(2^2)^3$
16. $(3^3)^2$
17. $\frac{2^8}{2^4}$
18. $\frac{3^8}{3^4}$
19. $3^{-3} \cdot 3$
20. $2^{-3} \cdot 2$
21. $\frac{2^3}{2^7}$
22. $\frac{3^4}{3^7}$

Simplify each exponential expression in Exercises 23–64.

23. $x^{-2}y$
24. xy^{-3}
25. x^0y^5
26. x^7y^0
27. $x^3 \cdot x^7$
28. $x^{11} \cdot x^5$
29. $x^{-5} \cdot x^{10}$
30. $x^{-6} \cdot x^{12}$
31. $(x^3)^7$
32. $(x^{11})^5$
33. $(x^{-5})^3$
34. $(x^{-6})^4$
35. $\frac{x^{14}}{x^7}$
36. $\frac{x^{30}}{x^{10}}$
37. $\frac{x^{14}}{x^{-7}}$
38. $\frac{x^{30}}{x^{-10}}$
39. $(8x^3)^2$
40. $(6x^4)^2$
41. $\left(-\frac{4}{x}\right)^3$
42. $\left(-\frac{6}{y}\right)^3$
43. $(-3x^2y^5)^2$
44. $(-3x^4y^6)^3$
45. $(3x^4)(2x^7)$
46. $(11x^5)(9x^{12})$
47. $(-9x^3y)(-2x^6y^4)$
48. $(-5x^4y)(-6x^7y^{11})$
49. $\frac{8x^{20}}{2x^4}$
50. $\frac{20x^{24}}{10x^6}$
51. $\frac{25a^{13}b^4}{-5a^2b^3}$
52. $\frac{35a^{14}b^6}{-7a^7b^3}$
53. $\frac{14b^7}{7b^{14}}$
54. $\frac{20b^{10}}{10b^{20}}$
55. $(4x^3)^{-2}$
56. $(10x^2)^{-3}$
57. $\frac{24x^3y^5}{32x^7y^{-9}}$
58. $\frac{10x^4y^9}{30x^{12}y^{-3}}$
59. $\left(\frac{5x^3}{y}\right)^{-2}$
60. $\left(\frac{3x^4}{y}\right)^{-3}$
61. $\left(\frac{-15a^4b^2}{5a^{10}b^{-3}}\right)^3$
62. $\left(\frac{-30a^{14}b^8}{10a^{17}b^{-2}}\right)^3$
63. $\left(\frac{3a^{-5}b^2}{12a^3b^{-4}}\right)^0$
64. $\left(\frac{4a^{-5}b^3}{12a^3b^{-5}}\right)^0$

In Exercises 65–76, write each number in decimal notation without the use of exponents.

65. 3.8×10^2 **66.** 9.2×10^2
67. 6×10^{-4} **68.** 7×10^{-5}
69. -7.16×10^6 **70.** -8.17×10^6
71. 7.9×10^{-1} **72.** 6.8×10^{-1}
73. -4.15×10^{-3} **74.** -3.14×10^{-3}
75. -6.00001×10^{10} **76.** -7.00001×10^{10}

In Exercises 77–86, write each number in scientific notation.

77. 32,000 **78.** 64,000
79. 638,000,000,000,000,000 **80.** 579,000,000,000,000,000
81. -5716 **82.** -3829
83. 0.0027 **84.** 0.0083
85. -0.00000000504 **86.** -0.00000000405

In Exercises 87–106, perform the indicated computations. Write the answers in scientific notation. If necessary, round the decimal factor in your scientific notation answer to two decimal places.

87. $(3 \times 10^4)(2.1 \times 10^3)$ **88.** $(2 \times 10^4)(4.1 \times 10^3)$

89. $(1.6 \times 10^{15})(4 \times 10^{-11})$ **90.** $(1.4 \times 10^{15})(3 \times 10^{-11})$

91. $(6.1 \times 10^{-8})(2 \times 10^{-4})$ **92.** $(5.1 \times 10^{-8})(3 \times 10^{-4})$

93. $(4.3 \times 10^8)(6.2 \times 10^4)$ **94.** $(8.2 \times 10^8)(4.6 \times 10^4)$

95. $\dfrac{8.4 \times 10^8}{4 \times 10^5}$ **96.** $\dfrac{6.9 \times 10^8}{3 \times 10^5}$

97. $\dfrac{3.6 \times 10^4}{9 \times 10^{-2}}$ **98.** $\dfrac{1.2 \times 10^4}{2 \times 10^{-2}}$

99. $\dfrac{4.8 \times 10^{-2}}{2.4 \times 10^6}$ **100.** $\dfrac{7.5 \times 10^{-2}}{2.5 \times 10^6}$

101. $\dfrac{2.4 \times 10^{-2}}{4.8 \times 10^{-6}}$ **102.** $\dfrac{1.5 \times 10^{-2}}{3 \times 10^{-6}}$

103. $\dfrac{480{,}000{,}000{,}000}{0.00012}$ **104.** $\dfrac{282{,}000{,}000{,}000}{0.00141}$

105. $\dfrac{0.00072 \times 0.003}{0.00024}$ **106.** $\dfrac{66{,}000 \times 0.001}{0.003 \times 0.002}$

Practice Plus

In Exercises 107–114, simplify each exponential expression. Assume that variables represent nonzero real numbers.

107. $\dfrac{(x^{-2}y)^{-3}}{(x^2y^{-1})^3}$ **108.** $\dfrac{(xy^{-2})^{-2}}{(x^{-2}y)^{-3}}$

109. $(2x^{-3}yz^{-6})(2x)^{-5}$ **110.** $(3x^{-4}yz^{-7})(3x)^{-3}$

111. $\left(\dfrac{x^3y^4z^5}{x^{-3}y^{-4}z^{-5}}\right)^{-2}$ **112.** $\left(\dfrac{x^4y^5z^6}{x^{-4}y^{-5}z^{-6}}\right)^{-4}$

113. $\dfrac{(2^{-1}x^{-2}y^{-1})^{-2}(2x^{-4}y^3)^{-2}(16x^{-3}y^3)^0}{(2x^{-3}y^{-5})^2}$

114. $\dfrac{(2^{-1}x^{-3}y^{-1})^{-2}(2x^{-6}y^4)^{-2}(9x^3y^{-3})^0}{(2x^{-4}y^{-6})^2}$

Application Exercises

The graph shows the number of people in the United States ages 65 and over for the year 2000 and projections beyond. Use 10^6 for one million and the figures shown to solve Exercises 115–118. Express all answers in scientific notation.

U.S. Population, Ages 65 and Over

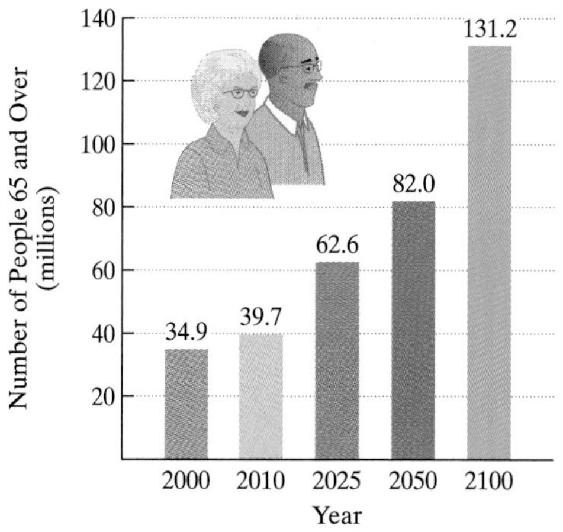

Source: U.S. Bureau of the Census

115. How many people 65 and over will there be in 2025?
116. How many people 65 and over will there be in 2050?
117. How many more people 65 and over will there be in 2100 than in 2000?
118. How many more people 65 and over will there be in 2050 than in 2000?

Our ancient ancestors hunted for their meat and expended a great deal of energy chasing it down. Today, our animal protein is raised in cages and on feedlots, delivered in great abundance nearly to our door. Use the numbers shown below to solve Exercises 119–122. Use 10^6 for one million and 10^9 for one billion.

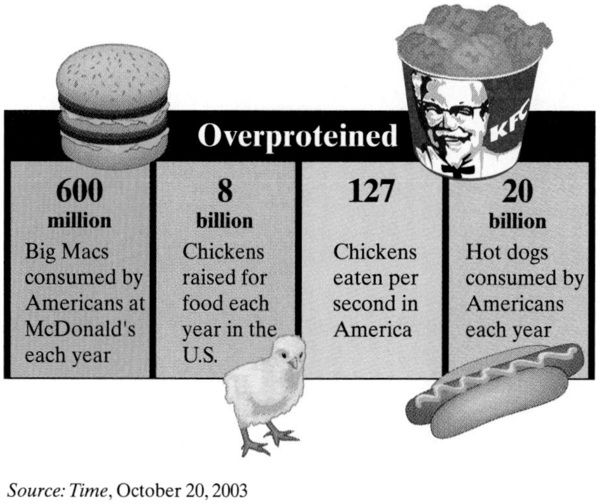

Overproteined
600 million
Big Macs consumed by Americans at McDonald's each year
8 billion
Chickens raised for food each year in the U.S.
127
Chickens eaten per second in America
20 billion
Hot dogs consumed by Americans each year
KFC

Source: Time, October 20, 2003

In Exercises 119–120, use 292 million, or 2.92×10^8, for the U.S. population. Express answers in decimal notation, rounded to the nearest whole number.

119. Find the number of hot dogs consumed by each American in a year.
120. If the consumption of Big Macs was divided evenly among all Americans, how many Big Macs would we each consume in a year?

In Exercises 121–122, use the Overproteined table on the previous page and the fact that there are approximately 3.2×10^7 seconds in a year.

121. How many chickens are raised for food each second in the United States? Express the answer in scientific and decimal notations.

122. How many chickens are eaten per year in the United States? Express the answer in scientific notation.

123. Due to tax cuts and spending increases, the United States began accumulating large deficits in the 1980s. The graph shows the national debt increasing over time.

The National Debt

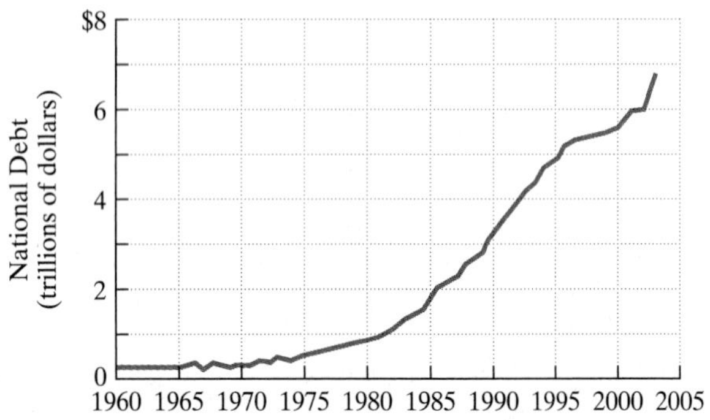

As of November 2003, to finance the deficit, the government had borrowed \$6.8 trillion and the national debt was \$6.8 trillion, or 6.8×10^{12} dollars. At that time, the U.S. population was approximately 290,000,000 (290 million), or 2.9×10^8. If the national debt was evenly divided among every individual in the United States, how much would each citizen have to pay?

124. In Exercises 121–122, we used 3.2×10^7 as an approximation for the number of seconds in a year. Convert 365 days (one year) to hours, to minutes, and, finally, to seconds, to determine precisely how many seconds there are in a year. Express the answer in scientific notation.

Writing in Mathematics

125. Describe what it means to raise a number to a power. In your description, include a discussion of the difference between -5^2 and $(-5)^2$.

126. Explain the product rule for exponents. Use $2^3 \cdot 2^5$ in your explanation.

127. Explain the power rule for exponents. Use $(3^2)^4$ in your explanation.

128. Explain the quotient rule for exponents. Use $\frac{5^8}{5^2}$ in your explanation.

129. Why is $(-3x^2)(2x^{-5})$ not simplified? What must be done to simplify the expression?

130. How do you know if a number is written in scientific notation?

131. Explain how to convert from scientific to decimal notation and give an example.

132. Explain how to convert from decimal to scientific notation and give an example.

Critical Thinking Exercises

133. Which one of the following is true?

a. $4^{-2} < 4^{-3}$ **b.** $5^{-2} > 2^{-5}$
c. $(-2)^4 = 2^{-4}$ **d.** $5^2 \cdot 5^{-2} > 2^5 \cdot 2^{-5}$

134. The mad Dr. Frankenstein has gathered enough bits and pieces (so to speak) for $2^{-1} + 2^{-2}$ of his creature-to-be. Write a fraction that represents the amount of his creature that must still be obtained.

135. If $b^A = MN$, $b^C = M$, and $b^D = N$, what is the relationship among A, C, and D?

136. Our hearts beat approximately 70 times per minute. Express in scientific notation how many times the heart beats over a lifetime of 80 years. Round the decimal factor in your scientific notation answer to two decimal places.

Group Exercise

137. Putting Numbers into Perspective. A large number can be put into perspective by comparing it with another number. For example, we put the \$1.95 trillion the government collected in taxes (Example 12) and the \$6.8 trillion national debt (Exercise 123) by comparing these numbers to the number of U.S. citizens.

For this project, each group member should consult an almanac, a newspaper, or the World Wide Web to find a number greater than one million. Explain to other members of the group the context in which the large number is used. Express the number in scientific notation. Then put the number into perspective by comparing it with another number.

SECTION P.3 Radicals and Rational Exponents

Objectives

1. Evaluate square roots.
2. Simplify expressions of the form $\sqrt{a^2}$.
3. Use the product rule to simplify square roots.
4. Use the quotient rule to simplify square roots.
5. Add and subtract square roots.
6. Rationalize denominators.
7. Evaluate and perform operations with higher roots.
8. Understand and use rational exponents.

What is the maximum speed at which a racing cyclist can turn a corner without tipping over? The answer, in miles per hour, is given by the algebraic expression $4\sqrt{x}$, where x is the radius of the corner, in feet. Algebraic expressions containing roots describe phenomena as diverse as the distance we can see to the horizon, how we perceive the temperature on a cold day, and Albert Einstein's bizarre concept of how an astronaut moving close to the speed of light would barely age relative to friends watching from Earth. No description of your world can be complete without roots and radicals. In this section, we review the basics of radical expressions and the use of rational exponents to indicate radicals.

1 Evaluate square roots.

Square Roots

From our earlier work with exponents, we are aware that the square of both 5 and −5 is 25:

$$5^2 = 25 \quad \text{and} \quad (-5)^2 = 25.$$

The reverse operation of squaring a number is finding the *square root* of the number. For example,

- One square root of 25 is 5 because $5^2 = 25$.
- Another square root of 25 is −5 because $(-5)^2 = 25$.

In general, **if $b^2 = a$, then b is a square root of a.**

The symbol $\sqrt{}$ is used to denote the *positive* or *principal square root* of a number. For example,

- $\sqrt{25} = 5$ because $5^2 = 25$ and 5 is positive.
- $\sqrt{100} = 10$ because $10^2 = 100$ and 10 is positive.

The symbol $\sqrt{}$ that we use to denote the principal square root is called a **radical sign**. The number under the radical sign is called the **radicand**. Together we refer to the radical sign and its radicand as a **radical expression**.

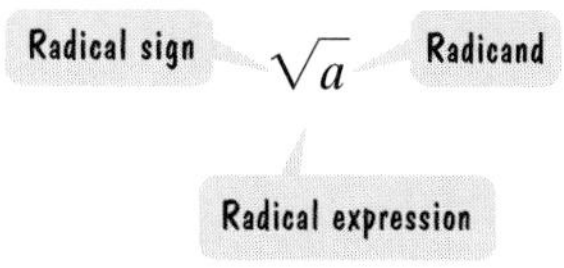

Definition of the Principal Square Root

If a is a nonnegative real number, the nonnegative number b such that $b^2 = a$, denoted by $b = \sqrt{a}$, is the **principal square root** of a.

The symbol $-\sqrt{}$ is used to denote the negative square root of a number. For example,

- $-\sqrt{25} = -5$ because $(-5)^2 = 25$ and -5 is negative.
- $-\sqrt{100} = -10$ because $(-10)^2 = 100$ and -10 is negative.

EXAMPLE 1 Evaluating Square Roots

Evaluate:

a. $\sqrt{64}$ **b.** $-\sqrt{49}$ **c.** $\sqrt{\frac{1}{4}}$ **d.** $\sqrt{9+16}$ **e.** $\sqrt{9}+\sqrt{16}$.

Solution

a. $\sqrt{64} = 8$ — The principal square root of 64 is 8. Check: $8^2 = 64$.

b. $-\sqrt{49} = -7$ — The negative square root of 49 is -7. Check: $(-7)^2 = 49$.

c. $\sqrt{\frac{1}{4}} = \frac{1}{2}$ — The principal square root of $\frac{1}{4}$ is $\frac{1}{2}$. Check: $\left(\frac{1}{2}\right)^2 = \frac{1}{4}$.

d. $\sqrt{9+16} = \sqrt{25}$ — First simplify the expression under the radical sign.
$= 5$ — Then take the principal square root of 25, which is 5.

e. $\sqrt{9}+\sqrt{16} = 3+4$
$= 7$ — $\sqrt{9} = 3$ because $3^2 = 9$. $\sqrt{16} = 4$ because $4^2 = 16$.

Study Tip

In Example 1, parts (d) and (e), observe that $\sqrt{9+16}$ is not equal to $\sqrt{9}+\sqrt{16}$. In general,

$$\sqrt{a+b} \neq \sqrt{a}+\sqrt{b}$$

and

$$\sqrt{a-b} \neq \sqrt{a}-\sqrt{b}.$$

Check Point 1 Evaluate:

a. $\sqrt{81}$ **b.** $-\sqrt{9}$ **c.** $\sqrt{\frac{1}{25}}$

d. $\sqrt{36+64}$ **e.** $\sqrt{36}+\sqrt{64}$.

A number that is the square of a rational number is called a **perfect square**. All the radicands in Example 1 and Check Point 1 are perfect squares.

- 64 is a perfect square because $64 = 8^2$. Thus, $\sqrt{64} = 8$.
- $\frac{1}{4}$ is a perfect square because $\frac{1}{4} = \left(\frac{1}{2}\right)^2$. Thus, $\sqrt{\frac{1}{4}} = \frac{1}{2}$.

Let's see what happens to the radical expression $\sqrt{x}$ if x is a negative number. Is the square root of a negative number a real number? For example, consider $\sqrt{-25}$. Is there a real number whose square is -25? No. Thus, $\sqrt{-25}$ is not a real number. In general, **a square root of a negative number is not a real number.**

If a number is nonnegative ($a \geq 0$), then $(\sqrt{a})^2 = a$. For example,

$$(\sqrt{2})^2 = 2,\quad (\sqrt{3})^2 = 3,\quad (\sqrt{4})^2 = 4,\quad \text{and}\quad (\sqrt{5})^2 = 5.$$

2 Simplify expressions of the form $\sqrt{a^2}$.

Simplifying Expressions of the Form $\sqrt{a^2}$

You may think that $\sqrt{a^2} = a$. However, this is not necessarily true. Consider the following examples:

$$\sqrt{4^2} = \sqrt{16} = 4$$
$$\sqrt{(-4)^2} = \sqrt{16} = 4.$$

The result is not -4, but rather the absolute value of -4, or 4.

Here is a rule for simplifying expressions of the form $\sqrt{a^2}$:

Simplifying $\sqrt{a^2}$

For any real number a,

$$\sqrt{a^2} = |a|.$$

In words, the principal square root of a^2 is the absolute value of a.

For example, $\sqrt{6^2} = |6| = 6$ and $\sqrt{(-6)^2} = |-6| = 6$.

3 Use the product rule to simplify square roots.

The Product Rule for Square Roots

A rule for multiplying square roots can be generalized by comparing $\sqrt{25} \cdot \sqrt{4}$ and $\sqrt{25 \cdot 4}$. Notice that

$$\sqrt{25} \cdot \sqrt{4} = 5 \cdot 2 = 10 \quad \text{and} \quad \sqrt{25 \cdot 4} = \sqrt{100} = 10.$$

Because we obtain 10 in both situations, the original radical expressions must be equal. That is,

$$\sqrt{25} \cdot \sqrt{4} = \sqrt{25 \cdot 4}.$$

This result is a special case of the **product rule for square roots** that can be generalized as follows:

The Product Rule for Square Roots

If a and b represent nonnegative real numbers, then

$$\sqrt{ab} = \sqrt{a} \cdot \sqrt{b} \quad \text{and} \quad \sqrt{a} \cdot \sqrt{b} = \sqrt{ab}.$$

The square root of a product is the product of the square roots.

A square root is **simplified** when its radicand has no factors other than 1 that are perfect squares. For example, $\sqrt{500}$ is not simplified because it can be expressed as $\sqrt{100 \cdot 5}$ and 100 is a perfect square. Example 2 shows how the product rule is used to remove from the square root any perfect squares that occur as factors.

EXAMPLE 2 Using the Product Rule to Simplify Square Roots

Simplify: **a.** $\sqrt{500}$ **b.** $\sqrt{6x} \cdot \sqrt{3x}$.

Solution

a.

$\sqrt{500} = \sqrt{100 \cdot 5}$ Factor 500. 100 is the greatest perfect square factor.

$= \sqrt{100}\sqrt{5}$ Use the product rule: $\sqrt{ab} = \sqrt{a}\sqrt{b}$.

$= 10\sqrt{5}$ Write $\sqrt{100}$ as 10. We read $10\sqrt{5}$ as "ten times the square root of 5."

b. We can simplify $\sqrt{6x} \cdot \sqrt{3x}$ using the product rule only if $6x$ and $3x$ represent nonnegative real numbers. Thus, $x \geq 0$.

$\sqrt{6x} \cdot \sqrt{3x} = \sqrt{6x \cdot 3x}$ Use the product rule: $\sqrt{a}\sqrt{b} = \sqrt{ab}$.

$= \sqrt{18x^2}$ Multiply in the radicand.

$= \sqrt{9x^2 \cdot 2}$ Factor 18. 9 is the greatest perfect square factor.

$= \sqrt{9x^2}\sqrt{2}$ Use the product rule: $\sqrt{ab} = \sqrt{a}\sqrt{b}$.

$= \sqrt{9}\sqrt{x^2}\sqrt{2}$ Use the product rule to write $\sqrt{9x^2}$ as the product of two square roots.

$= 3x\sqrt{2}$ $\sqrt{x^2} = |x| = x$ because $x \geq 0$.

Study Tip

When simplifying square roots, always look for the *greatest* perfect square factor possible. The following factorization will lead to further simplification:

$$\sqrt{500} = \sqrt{25 \cdot 20} = \sqrt{25}\sqrt{20} = 5\sqrt{20}.$$

25 is a perfect square factor of 500, but not the greatest perfect square factor.

Because 20 contains a perfect square factor, 4, the simplification is not complete.

$$5\sqrt{20} = 5\sqrt{4 \cdot 5} = 5\sqrt{4}\sqrt{5} = 5 \cdot 2\sqrt{5} = 10\sqrt{5}$$

Although the result checks with our simplification using $\sqrt{500} = \sqrt{100 \cdot 5}$, more work is required when the greatest perfect square factor is not used.

Check Point 2 Simplify:

a. $\sqrt{75}$ **b.** $\sqrt{5x} \cdot \sqrt{10x}$.

4 Use the quotient rule to simplify square roots.

The Quotient Rule for Square Roots

Another property for square roots involves division.

The Quotient Rule for Square Roots

If a and b represent nonnegative real numbers and $b \neq 0$, then

$$\sqrt{\frac{a}{b}} = \frac{\sqrt{a}}{\sqrt{b}} \quad \text{and} \quad \frac{\sqrt{a}}{\sqrt{b}} = \sqrt{\frac{a}{b}}.$$

The square root of a quotient is the quotient of the square roots.

EXAMPLE 3 Using the Quotient Rule to Simplify Square Roots

Simplify: **a.** $\sqrt{\dfrac{100}{9}}$ **b.** $\dfrac{\sqrt{48x^3}}{\sqrt{6x}}$.

Solution

a. $\sqrt{\dfrac{100}{9}} = \dfrac{\sqrt{100}}{\sqrt{9}} = \dfrac{10}{3}$

b. We can simplify the quotient of $\sqrt{48x^3}$ and $\sqrt{6x}$ using the quotient rule only if $48x^3$ and $6x$ represent nonnegative real numbers and $6x \neq 0$. Thus, $x > 0$.

$$\frac{\sqrt{48x^3}}{\sqrt{6x}} = \sqrt{\frac{48x^3}{6x}} = \sqrt{8x^2} = \sqrt{4x^2}\sqrt{2} = \sqrt{4}\sqrt{x^2}\sqrt{2} = 2x\sqrt{2}$$

$\sqrt{x^2} = |x| = x$ because $x > 0$.

Check Point 3 Simplify: **a.** $\sqrt{\dfrac{25}{16}}$ **b.** $\dfrac{\sqrt{150x^3}}{\sqrt{2x}}$.

5 Add and subtract square roots.

Adding and Subtracting Square Roots

Two or more square roots can be combined using the distributive property provided that they have the same radicand. Such radicals are called **like radicals**. For example,

$$7\sqrt{11} + 6\sqrt{11} = (7 + 6)\sqrt{11} = 13\sqrt{11}.$$

7 square roots of 11 plus 6 square roots of 11 result in 13 square roots of 11.

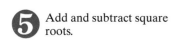

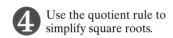

A Radical Idea: Time Is Relative

What does travel in space have to do with radicals? Imagine that in the future we will be able to travel at velocities approaching the speed of light (approximately 186,000 miles per second). According to Einstein's theory of relativity, time would pass more quickly on Earth than it would in the moving spaceship. The radical expression

$$R_f\sqrt{1-\left(\frac{v}{c}\right)^2}$$

gives the aging rate of an astronaut relative to the aging rate of a friend on Earth, R_f. In the expression, v is the astronaut's speed and c is the speed of light. As the astronaut's speed approaches the speed of light, we can substitute c for v:

$$R_f\sqrt{1-\left(\frac{v}{c}\right)^2} \quad \text{Let } v = c.$$
$$= R_f\sqrt{1-\left(\frac{c}{c}\right)^2}$$
$$= R_f\sqrt{1-1^2}$$
$$= R_f\sqrt{0} = 0$$

Close to the speed of light, the astronaut's aging rate relative to a friend on Earth is nearly 0. What does this mean? As we age here on Earth, the space traveler would barely get older. The space traveler would return to a futuristic world in which friends and loved ones would be long dead.

EXAMPLE 4 Adding and Subtracting Like Radicals

Add or subtract as indicated:

a. $7\sqrt{2} + 5\sqrt{2}$ **b.** $\sqrt{5x} - 7\sqrt{5x}$.

Solution

a. $7\sqrt{2} + 5\sqrt{2} = (7+5)\sqrt{2}$ Apply the distributive property.

$= 12\sqrt{2}$ Simplify.

b. $\sqrt{5x} - 7\sqrt{5x} = 1\sqrt{5x} - 7\sqrt{5x}$ Write $\sqrt{5x}$ as $1\sqrt{5x}$.

$= (1-7)\sqrt{5x}$ Apply the distributive property.

$= -6\sqrt{5x}$ Simplify.

Check Point 4 Add or subtract as indicated:

a. $8\sqrt{13} + 9\sqrt{13}$ **b.** $\sqrt{17x} - 20\sqrt{17x}$.

In some cases, radicals can be combined once they have been simplified. For example, to add $\sqrt{2}$ and $\sqrt{8}$, we can write $\sqrt{8}$ as $\sqrt{4\cdot 2}$ because 4 is a perfect square factor of 8.

$$\sqrt{2} + \sqrt{8} = \sqrt{2} + \sqrt{4\cdot 2} = 1\sqrt{2} + 2\sqrt{2} = (1+2)\sqrt{2} = 3\sqrt{2}$$

EXAMPLE 5 Combining Radicals That First Require Simplification

Add or subtract as indicated:

a. $7\sqrt{3} + \sqrt{12}$ **b.** $4\sqrt{50x} - 6\sqrt{32x}$.

Solution

a. $7\sqrt{3} + \sqrt{12}$

$= 7\sqrt{3} + \sqrt{4\cdot 3}$ Split 12 into two factors such that one is a perfect square.

$= 7\sqrt{3} + 2\sqrt{3}$ $\sqrt{4\cdot 3} = \sqrt{4}\sqrt{3} = 2\sqrt{3}$

$= (7+2)\sqrt{3}$ Apply the distributive property. You will find that this step is usually done mentally.

$= 9\sqrt{3}$ Simplify.

b. $4\sqrt{50x} - 6\sqrt{32x}$

$= 4\sqrt{25\cdot 2x} - 6\sqrt{16\cdot 2x}$ 25 is the greatest perfect square factor of 50x and 16 is the greatest perfect square factor of 32x.

$= 4\cdot 5\sqrt{2x} - 6\cdot 4\sqrt{2x}$ $\sqrt{25\cdot 2x} = \sqrt{25}\sqrt{2x} = 5\sqrt{2x}$ and $\sqrt{16\cdot 2x} = \sqrt{16}\sqrt{2x} = 4\sqrt{2x}$.

$= 20\sqrt{2x} - 24\sqrt{2x}$ Multiply: $4\cdot 5 = 20$ and $6\cdot 4 = 24$.

$= (20-24)\sqrt{2x}$ Apply the distributive property.

$= -4\sqrt{2x}$ Simplify.

Check Point 5 Add or subtract as indicated:

a. $5\sqrt{27} + \sqrt{12}$ **b.** $6\sqrt{18x} - 4\sqrt{8x}$.

6 Rationalize denominators.

Rationalizing Denominators

You can use a calculator to compare the approximate values for $\frac{1}{\sqrt{3}}$ and $\frac{\sqrt{3}}{3}$. The two approximations are the same. This is not a coincidence:

$$\frac{1}{\sqrt{3}} = \frac{1}{\sqrt{3}} \cdot \boxed{\frac{\sqrt{3}}{\sqrt{3}}} = \frac{\sqrt{3}}{\sqrt{9}} = \frac{\sqrt{3}}{3}.$$

Any number divided by itself is 1. Multiplication by 1 does not change the value of $\frac{1}{\sqrt{3}}$.

This process involves rewriting a radical expression as an equivalent expression in which the denominator no longer contains any radicals. The process is called **rationalizing the denominator**. If the denominator contains the square root of a natural number that is not a perfect square, **multiply the numerator and the denominator by the smallest number that produces the square root of a perfect square in the denominator.**

EXAMPLE 6 Rationalizing Denominators

Rationalize the denominator: **a.** $\frac{15}{\sqrt{6}}$ **b.** $\frac{12}{\sqrt{8}}$.

Solution

a. If we multiply the numerator and the denominator of $\frac{15}{\sqrt{6}}$ by $\sqrt{6}$, the denominator becomes $\sqrt{6} \cdot \sqrt{6} = \sqrt{36} = 6$. Therefore, we multiply by 1, choosing $\frac{\sqrt{6}}{\sqrt{6}}$ for 1.

$$\frac{15}{\sqrt{6}} = \frac{15}{\sqrt{6}} \cdot \frac{\sqrt{6}}{\sqrt{6}} = \frac{15\sqrt{6}}{\sqrt{36}} = \frac{15\sqrt{6}}{6} = \frac{5\sqrt{6}}{2}$$

Multiply by 1.

Simplify: $\frac{15}{6} = \frac{15 \div 3}{6 \div 3} = \frac{5}{2}$.

b. The *smallest* number that will produce a perfect square in the denominator of $\frac{12}{\sqrt{8}}$ is $\sqrt{2}$, because $\sqrt{8} \cdot \sqrt{2} = \sqrt{16} = 4$. We multiply by 1, choosing $\frac{\sqrt{2}}{\sqrt{2}}$ for 1.

$$\frac{12}{\sqrt{8}} = \frac{12}{\sqrt{8}} \cdot \frac{\sqrt{2}}{\sqrt{2}} = \frac{12\sqrt{2}}{\sqrt{16}} = \frac{12\sqrt{2}}{4} = 3\sqrt{2}$$

Check Point 6 Rationalize the denominator: **a.** $\frac{5}{\sqrt{3}}$ **b.** $\frac{6}{\sqrt{12}}$.

Radical expressions that involve the sum and difference of the same two terms are called **conjugates**. Thus,

$$\sqrt{a} + \sqrt{b} \quad \text{and} \quad \sqrt{a} - \sqrt{b}$$

are conjugates. Conjugates are used to rationalize denominators because the product of such pairs contains no radicals:

Multiply each term of $\sqrt{a} - \sqrt{b}$
by each term of $\sqrt{a} + \sqrt{b}$.

$$(\sqrt{a} + \sqrt{b})(\sqrt{a} - \sqrt{b})$$
$$= \sqrt{a}(\sqrt{a} - \sqrt{b}) + \sqrt{b}(\sqrt{a} - \sqrt{b})$$

Distribute $\sqrt{a}$ Distribute $\sqrt{b}$
over $\sqrt{a} - \sqrt{b}$. over $\sqrt{a} - \sqrt{b}$.

$$= \sqrt{a} \cdot \sqrt{a} - \sqrt{a} \cdot \sqrt{b} + \sqrt{b} \cdot \sqrt{a} - \sqrt{b} \cdot \sqrt{b}$$
$$= (\sqrt{a})^2 - \sqrt{ab} + \sqrt{ab} - (\sqrt{b})^2$$

$-\sqrt{ab} + \sqrt{ab} = 0$

$$= (\sqrt{a})^2 - (\sqrt{b})^2$$
$$= a - b.$$

Multiplying Conjugates

$$\left(\sqrt{a} + \sqrt{b}\right)\left(\sqrt{a} - \sqrt{b}\right) = (\sqrt{a})^2 - (\sqrt{b})^2 = a - b$$

How can we rationalize a denominator if the denominator contains two terms with one or more square roots? **Multiply the numerator and the denominator by the conjugate of the denominator.** Here are three examples of such expressions:

$$\bullet \quad \frac{7}{5 + \sqrt{3}} \qquad \bullet \quad \frac{8}{3\sqrt{2} - 4} \qquad \bullet \quad \frac{h}{\sqrt{x + h} - \sqrt{x}}$$

The conjugate of the The conjugate of the The conjugate of the
denominator is $5 - \sqrt{3}$. denominator is $3\sqrt{2} + 4$. denominator is $\sqrt{x+h} + \sqrt{x}$.

The product of the denominator and its conjugate is found using the formula

$$\left(\sqrt{a} + \sqrt{b}\right)\left(\sqrt{a} - \sqrt{b}\right) = (\sqrt{a})^2 - (\sqrt{b})^2 = a - b.$$

The simplified product will not contain a radical.

EXAMPLE 7 Rationalizing a Denominator Containing Two Terms

Rationalize the denominator: $\dfrac{7}{5 + \sqrt{3}}$.

Solution The conjugate of the denominator is $5 - \sqrt{3}$. If we multiply the numerator and denominator by $5 - \sqrt{3}$, the simplified denominator will not contain a radical. Therefore, we multiply by 1, choosing $\dfrac{5 - \sqrt{3}}{5 - \sqrt{3}}$ for 1.

$$\frac{7}{5 + \sqrt{3}} = \frac{7}{5 + \sqrt{3}} \cdot \frac{5 - \sqrt{3}}{5 - \sqrt{3}} = \frac{7(5 - \sqrt{3})}{5^2 - (\sqrt{3})^2} = \frac{7(5 - \sqrt{3})}{25 - 3}$$

Multiply by 1. $(\sqrt{a} + \sqrt{b})(\sqrt{a} - \sqrt{b})$
$= (\sqrt{a})^2 - (\sqrt{b})^2$

$$= \frac{7(5 - \sqrt{3})}{22} \quad \text{or} \quad \frac{35 - 7\sqrt{3}}{22}$$

In either form of the answer, there
is no radical in the denominator.

Check Point 7 Rationalize the denominator: $\dfrac{8}{4 + \sqrt{5}}$.

⑦ Evaluate and perform operations with higher roots.

Other Kinds of Roots

We define the **principal nth root** of a real number a, symbolized by $\sqrt[n]{a}$, as follows:

Study Tip

Some higher even and odd roots occur so frequently that you might want to memorize them.

Cube Roots	
$\sqrt[3]{1} = 1$	$\sqrt[3]{125} = 5$
$\sqrt[3]{8} = 2$	$\sqrt[3]{216} = 6$
$\sqrt[3]{27} = 3$	$\sqrt[3]{1000} = 10$
$\sqrt[3]{64} = 4$	

Fourth Roots	**Fifth Roots**
$\sqrt[4]{1} = 1$	$\sqrt[5]{1} = 1$
$\sqrt[4]{16} = 2$	$\sqrt[5]{32} = 2$
$\sqrt[4]{81} = 3$	$\sqrt[5]{243} = 3$
$\sqrt[4]{256} = 4$	
$\sqrt[4]{625} = 5$	

> **Definition of the Principal nth Root of a Real Number**
> $$\sqrt[n]{a} = b \text{ means that } b^n = a.$$
> If n, the **index**, is even, then a is nonnegative ($a \geq 0$) and b is also nonnegative ($b \geq 0$). If n is odd, a and b can be any real numbers.

For example,
$$\sqrt[3]{64} = 4 \text{ because } 4^3 = 64 \quad \text{and} \quad \sqrt[5]{-32} = -2 \text{ because } (-2)^5 = -32.$$

The same vocabulary that we learned for square roots applies to nth roots. The symbol $\sqrt[n]{a}$ is called a **radical** and a is called the **radicand**.

A number that is the nth power of a rational number is called a **perfect nth power**. For example, 8 is a perfect third power, or perfect cube, because $8 = 2^3$. Thus, $\sqrt[3]{8} = \sqrt[3]{2^3} = 2$. In general, one of the following rules can be used to find nth roots of perfect nth powers:

> **Finding nth Roots of Perfect nth Powers**
> If n is odd, $\sqrt[n]{a^n} = a$.
> If n is even, $\sqrt[n]{a^n} = |a|$.

For example,
$$\sqrt[3]{(-2)^3} = -2 \qquad \text{and} \qquad \sqrt[4]{(-2)^4} = |-2| = 2.$$

Absolute value is not needed with odd roots, but is necessary with even roots.

The Product and Quotient Rules for Other Roots

The product and quotient rules apply to cube roots, fourth roots, and all higher roots.

> **The Product and Quotient Rules for nth Roots**
> For all real numbers, where the indicated roots represent real numbers,
> $$\sqrt[n]{ab} = \sqrt[n]{a} \cdot \sqrt[n]{b} \quad \text{and} \quad \sqrt[n]{\dfrac{a}{b}} = \dfrac{\sqrt[n]{a}}{\sqrt[n]{b}}, \quad b \neq 0.$$

EXAMPLE 8 Simplifying, Multiplying, and Dividing Higher Roots

Simplify: **a.** $\sqrt[3]{24}$ **b.** $\sqrt[4]{8} \cdot \sqrt[4]{4}$ **c.** $\sqrt[4]{\dfrac{81}{16}}$.

Solution

a. $\sqrt[3]{24} = \sqrt[3]{8 \cdot 3}$ Find the greatest perfect cube that is a factor of 24. $2^3 = 8$, so 8 is a perfect cube and is the greatest perfect cube factor of 24.

$= \sqrt[3]{8} \cdot \sqrt[3]{3}$ $\sqrt[n]{ab} = \sqrt[n]{a} \sqrt[n]{b}$

$= 2\sqrt[3]{3}$ $\sqrt[3]{8} = 2$

b. $\sqrt[4]{8} \cdot \sqrt[4]{4} = \sqrt[4]{8 \cdot 4}$ — $\sqrt[n]{a} \cdot \sqrt[n]{b} = \sqrt[n]{ab}$

$= \sqrt[4]{32}$ — Find the greatest perfect fourth power that is a factor of 32.

$= \sqrt[4]{16 \cdot 2}$ — $2^4 = 16$, so 16 is a perfect fourth power and is the greatest perfect fourth power that is a factor of 32.

$= \sqrt[4]{16} \cdot \sqrt[4]{2}$ — $\sqrt[n]{ab} = \sqrt[n]{a} \cdot \sqrt[n]{b}$

$= 2\sqrt[4]{2}$ — $\sqrt[4]{16} = 2$

c. $\sqrt[4]{\frac{81}{16}} = \frac{\sqrt[4]{81}}{\sqrt[4]{16}}$ — $\sqrt[n]{\frac{a}{b}} = \frac{\sqrt[n]{a}}{\sqrt[n]{b}}$

$= \frac{3}{2}$ — $\sqrt[4]{81} = 3$ because $3^4 = 81$ and $\sqrt[4]{16} = 2$ because $2^4 = 16$.

Check Point 8 Simplify: **a.** $\sqrt[3]{40}$ **b.** $\sqrt[5]{8} \cdot \sqrt[5]{8}$ **c.** $\sqrt[3]{\frac{125}{27}}$.

We have seen that adding and subtracting square roots often involves simplifying terms. The same idea applies to adding and subtracting *n*th roots.

EXAMPLE 9 Combining Cube Roots

Subtract: $5\sqrt[3]{16} - 11\sqrt[3]{2}$.

Solution

$5\sqrt[3]{16} - 11\sqrt[3]{2}$

$= 5\sqrt[3]{8 \cdot 2} - 11\sqrt[3]{2}$ — Factor 16. 8 is the greatest perfect cube factor: $2^3 = 8$ and $\sqrt[3]{8} = 2$.

$= 5 \cdot 2\sqrt[3]{2} - 11\sqrt[3]{2}$ — $\sqrt[3]{8 \cdot 2} = \sqrt[3]{8}\sqrt[3]{2} = 2\sqrt[3]{2}$

$= 10\sqrt[3]{2} - 11\sqrt[3]{2}$ — Multiply: $5 \cdot 2 = 10$.

$= (10 - 11)\sqrt[3]{2}$ — Apply the distributive property.

$= -1\sqrt[3]{2}$ or $-\sqrt[3]{2}$ — Simplify.

Check Point 9 Subtract: $3\sqrt[3]{81} - 4\sqrt[3]{3}$.

8 Understand and use rational exponents.

Rational Exponents

We define rational exponents so that their properties are the same as the properties for integer exponents. For example, we know that exponents are multiplied when an exponential expression is raised to a power. For this to be true,

$$\left(7^{\frac{1}{2}}\right)^2 = 7^{\frac{1}{2}\cdot 2} = 7^1 = 7.$$

We also know that

$$(\sqrt{7})^2 = \sqrt{7} \cdot \sqrt{7} = \sqrt{49} = 7.$$

Can you see that the square of both $7^{\frac{1}{2}}$ and $\sqrt{7}$ is 7? It is reasonable to conclude that

$$7^{\frac{1}{2}} \text{ means } \sqrt{7}.$$

We can generalize the fact that $7^{\frac{1}{2}}$ means $\sqrt{7}$ with the following definition:

The Definition of $a^{\frac{1}{n}}$

If $\sqrt[n]{a}$ represents a real number and $n \geq 2$ is an integer, then

$$a^{\frac{1}{n}} = \sqrt[n]{a}.$$

The denominator of the rational exponent is the radical's index.

Furthermore,

$$a^{-\frac{1}{n}} = \frac{1}{a^{\frac{1}{n}}} = \frac{1}{\sqrt[n]{a}}, \quad a \neq 0.$$

EXAMPLE 10 Using the Definition of $a^{\frac{1}{n}}$

Simplify:

a. $64^{\frac{1}{2}}$ **b.** $125^{\frac{1}{3}}$ **c.** $-16^{\frac{1}{4}}$ **d.** $(-27)^{\frac{1}{3}}$ **e.** $64^{-\frac{1}{3}}$.

Solution

a. $64^{\frac{1}{2}} = \sqrt{64} = 8$

b. $125^{\frac{1}{3}} = \sqrt[3]{125} = 5$

The denominator is the index.

c. $-16^{\frac{1}{4}} = -(\sqrt[4]{16}) = -2$

The base is 16 and the negative sign is not affected by the exponent.

d. $(-27)^{\frac{1}{3}} = \sqrt[3]{-27} = -3$

Parentheses show that the base is −27 and that the negative sign is affected by the exponent.

e. $64^{-\frac{1}{3}} = \frac{1}{64^{\frac{1}{3}}} = \frac{1}{\sqrt[3]{64}} = \frac{1}{4}$

Check Point 10 Simplify:

a. $25^{\frac{1}{2}}$ **b.** $8^{\frac{1}{3}}$ **c.** $-81^{\frac{1}{4}}$ **d.** $(-8)^{\frac{1}{3}}$ **e.** $27^{-\frac{1}{3}}$

In Example 10 and Check Point 10, each rational exponent had a numerator of 1. If the numerator is some other integer, we still want to multiply exponents when raising a power to a power. For this reason,

$$a^{\frac{2}{3}} = (a^{\frac{1}{3}})^2 \text{ and } a^{\frac{2}{3}} = (a^2)^{\frac{1}{3}}.$$

This means $(\sqrt[3]{a})^2$. This means $\sqrt[3]{a^2}$.

Thus,

$$a^{\frac{2}{3}} = (\sqrt[3]{a})^2 = \sqrt[3]{a^2}.$$

Do you see that the denominator, 3, of the rational exponent is the same as the index of the radical? The numerator, 2, of the rational exponent serves as an exponent in each of the two radical forms. We generalize these ideas with the following definition:

The Definition of $a^{\frac{m}{n}}$

If $\sqrt[n]{a}$ represents a real number and $\frac{m}{n}$ is a positive rational number, $n \geq 2$, then

$$a^{\frac{m}{n}} = (\sqrt[n]{a})^m.$$

Also,

$$a^{\frac{m}{n}} = \sqrt[n]{a^m}.$$

Furthermore, if $a^{-\frac{m}{n}}$ is a nonzero real number, then

$$a^{-\frac{m}{n}} = \frac{1}{a^{\frac{m}{n}}}.$$

The first form of the definition of $a^{\frac{m}{n}}$, shown again below, involves taking the root first. This form is often preferable because smaller numbers are involved. Notice that the rational exponent consists of two parts, indicated by the following voice balloons:

The numerator is the exponent.

$$a^{\frac{m}{n}} = (\sqrt[n]{a})^m.$$

The denominator is the radical's index.

EXAMPLE 11 Using the Definition of $a^{\frac{m}{n}}$

Simplify:

a. $27^{\frac{2}{3}}$ **b.** $9^{\frac{3}{2}}$ **c.** $81^{-\frac{3}{4}}$.

Technology

Here are the calculator keystroke sequences for $81^{-\frac{3}{4}}$:

Many Scientific Calculators

81 [y^x] [(] 3 [+/−] [÷] 4 [)] [=]

Many Graphing Calculators

81 [∧] [(] [(−)] 3 [÷] 4 [)] [ENTER].

Solution

a. $27^{\frac{2}{3}} = \left(\sqrt[3]{27}\right)^2 = 3^2 = 9$

b. $9^{\frac{3}{2}} = \left(\sqrt{9}\right)^3 = 3^3 = 27$

c. $81^{-\frac{3}{4}} = \frac{1}{81^{\frac{3}{4}}} = \frac{1}{\left(\sqrt[4]{81}\right)^3} = \frac{1}{3^3} = \frac{1}{27}$

Check Point 11 Simplify: **a.** $27^{\frac{4}{3}}$ **b.** $4^{\frac{3}{2}}$ **c.** $32^{-\frac{2}{5}}$

Properties of exponents can be applied to expressions containing rational exponents.

EXAMPLE 12 Simplifying Expressions with Rational Exponents

Simplify using properties of exponents:

a. $\left(5x^{\frac{1}{2}}\right)\left(7x^{\frac{3}{4}}\right)$ **b.** $\frac{32x^{\frac{5}{3}}}{16x^{\frac{3}{4}}}$.

Solution

a. $\left(5x^{\frac{1}{2}}\right)\left(7x^{\frac{3}{4}}\right) = 5 \cdot 7x^{\frac{1}{2}} \cdot x^{\frac{3}{4}}$ Group factors with the same base.

$= 35x^{\frac{1}{2}+\frac{3}{4}}$ When multiplying expressions with the same base, add the exponents.

$= 35x^{\frac{5}{4}}$ $\frac{1}{2} + \frac{3}{4} = \frac{2}{4} + \frac{3}{4} = \frac{5}{4}$

b. $\dfrac{32x^{\frac{5}{3}}}{16x^{\frac{3}{4}}} = \left(\dfrac{32}{16}\right)\left(\dfrac{x^{\frac{5}{3}}}{x^{\frac{3}{4}}}\right)$ Group factors with the same base.

$= 2x^{\frac{5}{3}-\frac{3}{4}}$ When dividing expressions with the same base, subtract the exponents.

$= 2x^{\frac{11}{12}}$ $\frac{5}{3} - \frac{3}{4} = \frac{20}{12} - \frac{9}{12} = \frac{11}{12}$

Check Point 12 Simplify: **a.** $\left(2x^{\frac{4}{3}}\right)\left(5x^{\frac{8}{3}}\right)$ **b.** $\dfrac{20x^4}{5x^{\frac{3}{2}}}$.

Rational exponents are sometimes useful for simplifying radicals by reducing their index.

EXAMPLE 13 Reducing the Index of a Radical

Simplify: $\sqrt[9]{x^3}$.

Solution $\sqrt[9]{x^3} = x^{\frac{3}{9}} = x^{\frac{1}{3}} = \sqrt[3]{x}$

Check Point 13 Simplify: $\sqrt[6]{x^3}$.

EXERCISE SET P.3

Practice Exercises

Evaluate each expression in Exercises 1–12, or indicate that the root is not a real number.

1. $\sqrt{36}$
2. $\sqrt{25}$
3. $-\sqrt{36}$
4. $-\sqrt{25}$
5. $\sqrt{-36}$
6. $\sqrt{-25}$
7. $\sqrt{25 - 16}$
8. $\sqrt{144 + 25}$
9. $\sqrt{25} - \sqrt{16}$
10. $\sqrt{144} + \sqrt{25}$
11. $\sqrt{(-13)^2}$
12. $\sqrt{(-17)^2}$

Use the product rule to simplify the expressions in Exercises 13–22. In Exercises 17–22, assume that variables represent nonnegative real numbers.

13. $\sqrt{50}$
14. $\sqrt{27}$
15. $\sqrt{45x^2}$
16. $\sqrt{125x^2}$
17. $\sqrt{2x} \cdot \sqrt{6x}$
18. $\sqrt{10x} \cdot \sqrt{8x}$
19. $\sqrt{x^3}$
20. $\sqrt{y^3}$
21. $\sqrt{2x^2} \cdot \sqrt{6x}$
22. $\sqrt{6x} \cdot \sqrt{3x^2}$

Use the quotient rule to simplify the expressions in Exercises 23–32. Assume that $x > 0$.

23. $\sqrt{\dfrac{1}{81}}$
24. $\sqrt{\dfrac{1}{49}}$
25. $\sqrt{\dfrac{49}{16}}$
26. $\sqrt{\dfrac{121}{9}}$
27. $\dfrac{\sqrt{48x^3}}{\sqrt{3x}}$
28. $\dfrac{\sqrt{72x^3}}{\sqrt{8x}}$
29. $\dfrac{\sqrt{150x^4}}{\sqrt{3x}}$
30. $\dfrac{\sqrt{24x^4}}{\sqrt{3x}}$
31. $\dfrac{\sqrt{200x^3}}{\sqrt{10x^{-1}}}$
32. $\dfrac{\sqrt{500x^3}}{\sqrt{10x^{-1}}}$

In Exercises 33–44, add or subtract terms whenever possible.

33. $7\sqrt{3} + 6\sqrt{3}$
34. $8\sqrt{5} + 11\sqrt{5}$
35. $6\sqrt{17x} - 8\sqrt{17x}$
36. $4\sqrt{13x} - 6\sqrt{13x}$
37. $\sqrt{8} + 3\sqrt{2}$
38. $\sqrt{20} + 6\sqrt{5}$
39. $\sqrt{50x} - \sqrt{8x}$
40. $\sqrt{63x} - \sqrt{28x}$
41. $3\sqrt{18} + 5\sqrt{50}$
42. $4\sqrt{12} - 2\sqrt{75}$
43. $3\sqrt{8} - \sqrt{32} + 3\sqrt{72} - \sqrt{75}$
44. $3\sqrt{54} - 2\sqrt{24} - \sqrt{96} + 4\sqrt{63}$

In Exercises 45–54, rationalize the denominator.

45. $\dfrac{1}{\sqrt{7}}$
46. $\dfrac{2}{\sqrt{10}}$
47. $\dfrac{\sqrt{2}}{\sqrt{5}}$
48. $\dfrac{\sqrt{7}}{\sqrt{3}}$
49. $\dfrac{13}{3 + \sqrt{11}}$
50. $\dfrac{3}{3 + \sqrt{7}}$
51. $\dfrac{7}{\sqrt{5} - 2}$
52. $\dfrac{5}{\sqrt{3} - 1}$
53. $\dfrac{6}{\sqrt{5} + \sqrt{3}}$
54. $\dfrac{11}{\sqrt{7} - \sqrt{3}}$

Evaluate each expression in Exercises 55–66, or indicate that the root is not a real number.

55. $\sqrt[3]{125}$
56. $\sqrt[3]{8}$
57. $\sqrt[3]{-8}$
58. $\sqrt[3]{-125}$

59. $\sqrt[4]{-16}$ **60.** $\sqrt[4]{-81}$

61. $\sqrt[4]{(-3)^4}$ **62.** $\sqrt[4]{(-2)^4}$

63. $\sqrt[5]{(-3)^5}$ **64.** $\sqrt[5]{(-2)^5}$

65. $\sqrt[5]{-\frac{1}{32}}$ **66.** $\sqrt[6]{\frac{1}{64}}$

Simplify the radical expressions in Exercises 67–74.

67. $\sqrt[3]{32}$ **68.** $\sqrt[3]{150}$

69. $\sqrt[3]{x^4}$ **70.** $\sqrt[3]{x^5}$

71. $\sqrt[3]{9} \cdot \sqrt[3]{6}$ **72.** $\sqrt[3]{12} \cdot \sqrt[3]{4}$

73. $\dfrac{\sqrt[5]{64x^6}}{\sqrt[5]{2x}}$ **74.** $\dfrac{\sqrt[4]{162x^5}}{\sqrt[4]{2x}}$

In Exercises 75–82, add or subtract terms whenever possible.

75. $4\sqrt[5]{2} + 3\sqrt[5]{2}$ **76.** $6\sqrt[5]{3} + 2\sqrt[5]{3}$

77. $5\sqrt[3]{16} + \sqrt[3]{54}$ **78.** $3\sqrt[3]{24} + \sqrt[3]{81}$

79. $\sqrt[3]{54xy^3} - y\sqrt[3]{128x}$ **80.** $\sqrt[3]{24xy^3} - y\sqrt[3]{81x}$

81. $\sqrt{2} + \sqrt[3]{8}$ **82.** $\sqrt{3} + \sqrt[3]{15}$

In Exercises 83–90, evaluate each expression without using a calculator.

83. $36^{\frac{1}{2}}$ **84.** $121^{\frac{1}{2}}$

85. $8^{\frac{1}{3}}$ **86.** $27^{\frac{1}{3}}$

87. $125^{\frac{2}{3}}$ **88.** $8^{\frac{2}{3}}$

89. $32^{-\frac{4}{5}}$ **90.** $16^{-\frac{5}{2}}$

In Exercises 91–100, simplify using properties of exponents.

91. $\left(7x^{\frac{1}{3}}\right)\left(2x^{\frac{1}{4}}\right)$ **92.** $\left(3x^{\frac{2}{3}}\right)\left(4x^{\frac{3}{4}}\right)$

93. $\dfrac{20x^{\frac{1}{2}}}{5x^{\frac{1}{4}}}$ **94.** $\dfrac{72x^{\frac{3}{4}}}{9x^{\frac{1}{3}}}$

95. $\left(x^{\frac{2}{3}}\right)^3$ **96.** $\left(x^{\frac{4}{5}}\right)^5$

97. $(25x^4y^6)^{\frac{1}{2}}$ **98.** $(125x^9y^6)^{\frac{1}{3}}$

99. $\dfrac{\left(3y^{\frac{1}{4}}\right)^3}{y^{\frac{1}{12}}}$ **100.** $\dfrac{\left(2y^{\frac{1}{5}}\right)^4}{y^{\frac{3}{10}}}$

In Exercises 101–108, simplify by reducing the index of the radical.

101. $\sqrt[4]{5^2}$ **102.** $\sqrt[4]{7^2}$

103. $\sqrt[3]{x^6}$ **104.** $\sqrt[4]{x^{12}}$

105. $\sqrt[6]{x^4}$ **106.** $\sqrt[9]{x^6}$

107. $\sqrt[9]{x^6y^3}$ **108.** $\sqrt[12]{x^4y^8}$

Practice Plus

In Exercises 109–110, evaluate each expression.

109. $\sqrt[3]{\sqrt[4]{16} + \sqrt{625}}$

110. $\sqrt[3]{\sqrt{\sqrt{169} + \sqrt{9}} + \sqrt{\sqrt[3]{1000} + \sqrt[3]{216}}}$

In Exercises 111–114, simplify each expression. Assume that all variables represent positive numbers.

111. $(49x^{-2}y^4)^{-\frac{1}{2}}\left(xy^{\frac{1}{2}}\right)$ **112.** $(8x^{-6}y^3)^{\frac{1}{3}}\left(x^{\frac{5}{6}}y^{-\frac{1}{3}}\right)^6$

113. $\left(\dfrac{x^{-\frac{5}{4}}y^{\frac{1}{3}}}{x^{-\frac{3}{4}}}\right)^{-6}$ **114.** $\left(\dfrac{x^{\frac{1}{2}}y^{-\frac{7}{4}}}{y^{-\frac{5}{4}}}\right)^{-4}$

Application Exercises

The formula

$$d = \sqrt{\frac{3h}{2}}$$

models the distance, d, in miles, that a person h feet high can see to the horizon. Use this formula to solve Exercises 115–116.

115. The pool deck on a cruise ship is 72 feet above the water. How far can passengers on the pool deck see? Write the answer in simplified radical form. Then use the simplified radical form and a calculator to express the answer to the nearest tenth of a mile.

116. The captain of a cruise ship is on the star deck, which is 120 feet above the water. How far can the captain see? Write the answer in simplified radical form. Then use the simplified radical form and a calculator to express the answer to the nearest tenth of a mile.

Police use the formula $v = 2\sqrt{5L}$ to estimate the speed of a car, v, in miles per hour, based on the length, L, in feet, of its skid marks upon sudden braking on a dry asphalt road. Use the formula to solve Exercises 117–118.

117. A motorist is involved in an accident. A police officer measures the car's skid marks to be 245 feet long. Estimate the speed at which the motorist was traveling before braking. If the posted speed limit is 50 miles per hour and the motorist tells the officer he was not speeding, should the officer believe him? Explain.

118. A motorist is involved in an accident. A police officer measures the car's skid marks to be 45 feet long. Estimate the speed at which the motorist was traveling before braking. If the posted speed limit is 35 miles per hour and the motorist tells the officer she was not speeding, should the officer believe her? Explain.

119. In the Peanuts cartoon shown below, Woodstock appears to be working steps mentally. Fill in the missing steps that show how to go from $\dfrac{7\sqrt{2 \cdot 2 \cdot 3}}{6}$ to $\dfrac{7}{3}\sqrt{3}$.

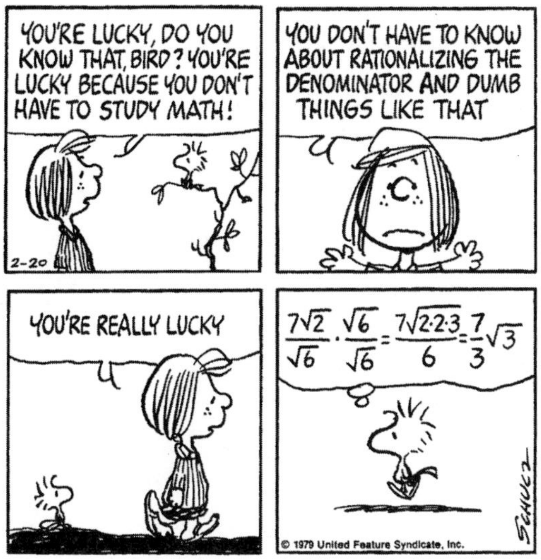

PEANUTS reprinted by permission of United Feature Syndicate, Inc.

120. According to Einstein's theory of relativity, traveling in starships at velocities approaching the speed of light (approximately 186,000 miles per second), time would pass more quickly on Earth than it would in the moving starship. The radical expression

$$R_f\frac{\sqrt{c^2 - v^2}}{\sqrt{c^2}}$$

gives the aging rate of an astronaut relative to the aging rate of a friend, R_f, on Earth. In the expression, v is the astronaut's velocity and c is the speed of light. Use the expression to solve this exercise. Imagine that you are the astronaut on the starship.

a. Use the quotient rule and simplify the expression that shows your aging rate relative to a friend on Earth. Working step-by-step, express your aging rate as

$$R_f\sqrt{1 - \left(\frac{v}{c}\right)^2}.$$

b. You are moving at 90% of the speed of light. Substitute $0.9c$ for v, your velocity, in the simplified expression from part (a). What is your aging rate, correct to two decimal places, relative to a friend on Earth? If you are gone for 44 weeks, approximately how many weeks have passed for your friend?

The way that we perceive the temperature on a cold day depends on both air temperature and wind speed. The windchill is what the air temperature would have to be with no wind to achieve the same chilling effect on the skin. In 2002, the National Weather Service issued new windchill temperatures, shown in the table below. (One reason for this new windchill index is that the wind speed is now calculated at 5 feet, the average height of the human body's face, rather than 33 feet, the height of the standard anemometer, an instrument that calculates wind speed.)

New Windchill Temperature Index

Wind Speed (miles per hour) \ Air Temperature (°F)	30	25	20	15	10	5	0	−5	−10	−15	−20	−25
5	25	19	13	7	1	−5	−11	−16	−22	−28	−34	−40
10	21	15	9	3	−4	−10	−16	−22	−28	−35	−41	−47
15	19	13	6	0	−7	−13	−19	−26	−32	−39	−45	−51
20	17	11	4	−2	−9	−15	−22	−29	−35	−42	−48	−55
25	16	9	3	−4	−11	−17	−24	−31	−37	−44	−51	−58
30	15	8	1	−5	−12	−19	−26	−33	−39	−46	−53	−60
35	14	7	0	−7	−14	−21	−27	−34	−41	−48	−55	−62
40	13	6	−1	−8	−15	−22	−29	−36	−43	−50	−57	−64
45	12	5	−2	−9	−16	−23	−30	−37	−44	−51	−58	−65
50	12	4	−3	−10	−17	−24	−31	−38	−45	−52	−60	−67
55	11	4	−3	−11	−18	−25	−32	−39	−46	−54	−61	−68
60	10	3	−4	−11	−19	−26	−33	−40	−48	−55	−62	−69

(shaded) Frostbite occurs in 15 minutes or less.

Source: National Weather Service

The windchill temperatures shown in the table can be calculated using

$$C = 35.74 + 0.6215t - 35.74\sqrt[25]{v^4} + 0.4275t\sqrt[25]{v^4},$$

in which C is the windchill, in degrees Fahrenheit, t is the air temperature, in degrees Fahrenheit, and v is the wind speed, in miles per hour. Use the formula to solve Exercises 121–122.

121. a. Rewrite the equation for calculating windchill temperatures using rational exponents.

b. Use the form of the equation in part (a) and a calculator to find the windchill temperature, to the nearest degree, when the air temperature is 25°F and the wind speed is 30 miles per hour.

122. a. Rewrite the equation for calculating windchill temperatures using rational exponents.

b. Use the form of the equation in part (a) and a calculator to find the windchill temperature, to the nearest degree, when the air temperature is 35°F and the wind speed is 15 miles per hour.

In Exercises 123–124, find the perimeter and area of each rectangle. Express answers in simplified radical form.

123.

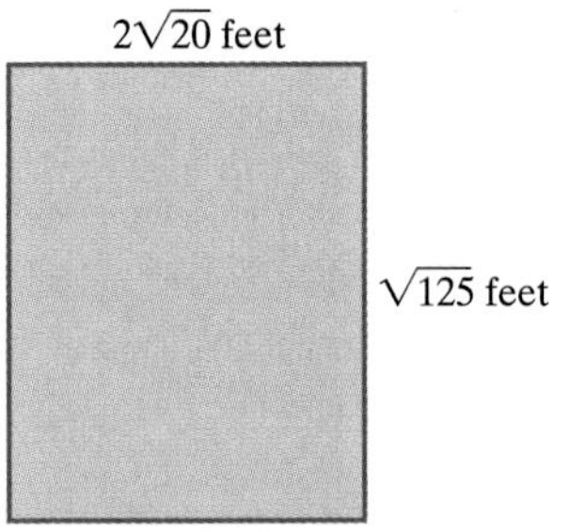

124.

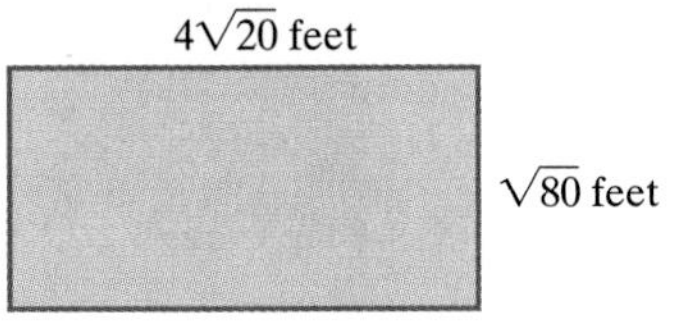

Writing in Mathematics

125. Explain how to simplify $\sqrt{10} \cdot \sqrt{5}$.

126. Explain how to add $\sqrt{3} + \sqrt{12}$.

127. Describe what it means to rationalize a denominator. Use both $\frac{1}{\sqrt{5}}$ and $\frac{1}{5 + \sqrt{5}}$ in your explanation.

128. What difference is there in simplifying $\sqrt[3]{(-5)^3}$ and $\sqrt[4]{(-5)^4}$?

129. What does $a^{\frac{m}{n}}$ mean?

130. Describe the kinds of numbers that have rational fifth roots.

131. Why must a and b represent nonnegative numbers when we write $\sqrt{a} \cdot \sqrt{b} = \sqrt{ab}$? Is it necessary to use this restriction in the case of $\sqrt[3]{a} \cdot \sqrt[3]{b} = \sqrt[3]{ab}$? Explain.

132. Answer the question posed in the chapter opener on page 1. What will you do: explore space or stay here on Earth? What are the reasons for your choice?

Critical Thinking Exercises

133. Which one of the following is true?

a. Neither $(-8)^{\frac{1}{2}}$ nor $(-8)^{\frac{1}{3}}$ represents real numbers.

b. $\sqrt{x^2 + y^2} = x + y$

c. $8^{-\frac{1}{3}} = -2$

d. $2^{\frac{1}{2}} \cdot 2^{\frac{1}{2}} = 2$

In Exercises 134–135, fill in each box to make the statement true.

134. $(5 + \sqrt{\square})(5 - \sqrt{\square}) = 22$

135. $\sqrt{\square x^{\square}} = 5x^7$

136. Find exact value of $\sqrt{13 + \sqrt{2} + \dfrac{7}{3 + \sqrt{2}}}$ without the use of a calculator.

137. Place the correct symbol, > or <, in the shaded area between each of the given numbers. *Do not use a calculator.* Then check your result with a calculator.

a. $3^{\frac{1}{2}} \;\square\; 3^{\frac{1}{3}}$ **b.** $\sqrt{7} + \sqrt{18} \;\square\; \sqrt{7 + 18}$

138. a. A mathematics professor recently purchased a birthday cake for her son with the inscription

$$\text{Happy}\left(2^{\frac{5}{2}} \cdot 2^{\frac{3}{4}} \div 2^{\frac{1}{4}}\right)\text{th Birthday.}$$

How old is the son?

b. The birthday boy, excited by the inscription on the cake, tried to wolf down the whole thing. Professor Mom, concerned about the possible metamorphosis of her son into a blimp, exclaimed, "Hold on! It is your birthday, so why not take $\dfrac{8^{-\frac{4}{3}} + 2^{-2}}{16^{-\frac{3}{4}} + 2^{-1}}$ of the cake? I'll eat half of what's left over." How much of the cake did the professor eat?

SECTION P.4 Polynomials

Objectives

1. Understand the vocabulary of polynomials.
2. Add and subtract polynomials.
3. Multiply polynomials.
4. Use FOIL in polynomial multiplication.
5. Use special products in polynomial multiplication.
6. Perform operations with polynomials in several variables.

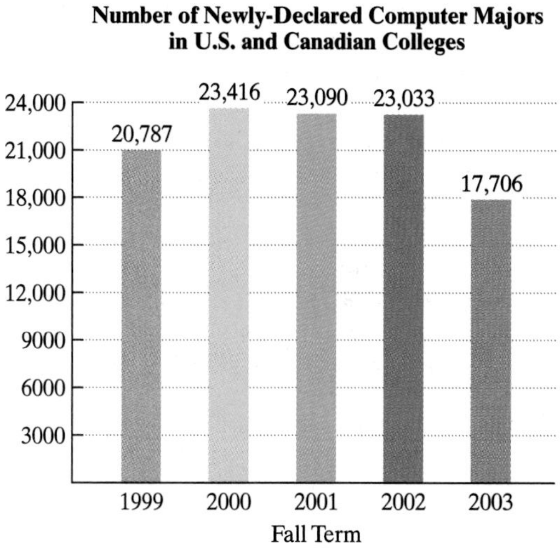

Figure P.11

Source: Computing Research Association

Tech firms might be rebounding from the dot-com bust, but enrollment in college computer programs keeps falling. In the past, a computer degree meant "instant riches, or at least a well-paying, secure job," says San Jose computer science chair David Hayes. "Now, the perception is jobs are going overseas and people are being laid off."

The bar graph in Figure P.11 shows the number of newly-declared computer science and computer engineering majors for the fall term in U.S. and Canadian colleges from 1999 through 2003. The data can be modeled by the formula

$$N = -365x^4 + 2728x^3 - 7106x^2 + 7372x + 20{,}787,$$

where N is the number of newly-declared computer majors for the fall term x years after 1999.

The algebraic expression on the right side of the equation,

$$-365x^4 + 2728x^3 - 7106x^2 + 7372x + 20{,}787,$$

is an example of a *polynomial.* A **polynomial** is a single term or the sum of two or more terms containing variables in the numerator with whole-number exponents. This particular polynomial contains five terms. Equations containing polynomials are used in such diverse areas as science, business, medicine, psychology, and sociology. In this section, we review basic ideas about polynomials and their operations.

1 Understand the vocabulary of polynomials.

How We Describe Polynomials

Consider the polynomial

$$7x^3 - 9x^2 + 13x - 6.$$

We can express this polynomial as

$$7x^3 + (-9x^2) + 13x + (-6).$$

The polynomial contains four terms. It is customary to write the terms in the order of descending powers of the variable. This is the **standard form** of a polynomial.

Some polynomials contain only one variable. Each term of such a polynomial in x is of the form ax^n. If $a \neq 0$, the **degree** of ax^n is n. For example, the degree of the term $7x^3$ is 3.

Study Tip

We can express 0 in many ways, including $0x$, $0x^2$, and $0x^3$. It is impossible to assign a single exponent on the variable. This is why 0 has no defined degree.

The Degree of ax^n

If $a \neq 0$, the degree of ax^n is n. The degree of a nonzero constant is 0. The constant 0 has no defined degree.

Here is an example of a polynomial and the degree of each of its four terms:

$$6x^4 - 3x^3 + 2x - 5.$$

degree 4 | degree 3 | degree 1 | degree of nonzero constant: 0

Notice that the exponent on x for the term $2x$ is understood to be $1: 2x^1$. For this reason, the degree of $2x$ is 1. You can think of -5 as $-5x^0$; thus, its degree is 0.

A polynomial which when simplified has exactly one term is called a **monomial**. A **binomial** is a polynomial that has two terms, each with a different exponent. A **trinomial** is a polynomial with three terms, each with a different exponent. Simplified polynomials with four or more terms have no special names.

The **degree of a polynomial** is the greatest of the degrees of all its terms. For example, $4x^2 + 3x$ is a binomial of degree 2 because the degree of the first term is 2, and the degree of the other term is less than 2. Also, $7x^5 - 2x^2 + 4$ is a trinomial of degree 5 because the degree of the first term is 5, and the degrees of the other terms are less than 5.

Up to now, we have used x to represent the variable in a polynomial. However, any letter can be used. For example,

- $7x^5 - 3x^3 + 8$ is a polynomial (in x) of degree 5. Because there are three terms, the polynomial is a trinomial.
- $6y^3 + 4y^2 - y + 3$ is a polynomial (in y) of degree 3. Because there are four terms, the polynomial has no special name.
- $z^7 + \sqrt{2}$ is a polynomial (in z) of degree 7. Because there are two terms, the polynomial is a binomial.

Not every algebraic expression is a polynomial. Algebraic expressions whose variables do not contain whole number exponents in numerators such as

$$3x^{-2} + 7 \quad \text{and} \quad 5x^{\frac{3}{2}} + 9x^{\frac{1}{2}} + 2$$

are not polynomials. Furthermore, a quotient of polynomials such as

$$\frac{x^2 + 2x + 5}{x^3 - 7x^2 + 9x - 3}$$

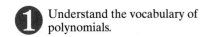

is not a polynomial because the form of a polynomial involves only addition and subtraction of terms, not division.

We can tie together the threads of our discussion with the formal definition of a polynomial in one variable. In this definition, the coefficients of the terms are represented by a_n (read "a sub n"), a_{n-1} (read "a sub n minus 1"), a_{n-2}, and so on. The small letters to the lower right of each a are called **subscripts** and are *not exponents*. Subscripts are used to distinguish one constant from another when a large and undetermined number of such constants are needed.

Definition of a Polynomial in x

A **polynomial in x** is an algebraic expression of the form

$$a_n x^n + a_{n-1}x^{n-1} + a_{n-2}x^{n-2} + \cdots + a_1 x + a_0,$$

where $a_n, a_{n-1}, a_{n-2}, \ldots, a_1$, and a_0 are real numbers, $a_n \neq 0$, and n is a non-negative integer. The polynomial is of **degree n**, a_n is the **leading coefficient**, and a_0 is the **constant term**.

2 Add and subtract polynomials.

Adding and Subtracting Polynomials

Polynomials are added and subtracted by combining like terms. For example, we can combine the monomials $-9x^3$ and $13x^3$ using addition as follows:

$$-9x^3 + 13x^3 = (-9 + 13)x^3 = 4x^3.$$

These like terms both contain x to the third power.

Add coefficients and keep the same variable factor, x^3.

EXAMPLE 1 Adding and Subtracting Polynomials

Perform the indicated operations and simplify:

a. $(-9x^3 + 7x^2 - 5x + 3) + (13x^3 + 2x^2 - 8x - 6)$

b. $(7x^3 - 8x^2 + 9x - 6) - (2x^3 - 6x^2 - 3x + 9)$.

Solution

a. $(-9x^3 + 7x^2 - 5x + 3) + (13x^3 + 2x^2 - 8x - 6)$

$= (-9x^3 + 13x^3) + (7x^2 + 2x^2) + (-5x - 8x) + (3 - 6)$ Group like terms.

$= 4x^3 + 9x^2 + (-13x) + (-3)$ Combine like terms.

$= 4x^3 + 9x^2 - 13x - 3$ Simplify.

b. $(7x^3 - 8x^2 + 9x - 6) - (2x^3 - 6x^2 - 3x + 9)$

Change the sign of each coefficient.

$= (7x^3 - 8x^2 + 9x - 6) + (-2x^3 + 6x^2 + 3x - 9)$ Rewrite subtraction as addition of the additive inverse.

$= (7x^3 - 2x^3) + (-8x^2 + 6x^2)$
$+ (9x + 3x) + (-6 - 9)$ Group like terms.

$= 5x^3 + (-2x^2) + 12x + (-15)$ Combine like terms.

$= 5x^3 - 2x^2 + 12x - 15$ Simplify.

Study Tip

You can also arrange like terms in columns and combine vertically:

$$\begin{array}{r} 7x^3 - 8x^2 + \ \ 9x - \ \ 6 \\ -2x^3 + 6x^2 + \ \ 3x - \ \ 9 \\ \hline 5x^3 - 2x^2 + 12x - 15 \end{array}$$

The like terms can be combined by adding their coefficients and keeping the same variable factor.

Check Point 1 Perform the indicated operations and simplify:

a. $(-17x^3 + 4x^2 - 11x - 5) + (16x^3 - 3x^2 + 3x - 15)$

b. $(13x^3 - 9x^2 - 7x + 1) - (-7x^3 + 2x^2 - 5x + 9)$.

③ Multiply polynomials.

Study Tip

Don't confuse adding and multiplying monomials.

Addition:
$$5x^4 + 6x^4 = 11x^4$$

Multiplication:
$$(5x^4)(6x^4) = (5 \cdot 6)(x^4 \cdot x^4)$$
$$= 30x^{4+4}$$
$$= 30x^8$$

Only like terms can be added or subtracted, but unlike terms may be multiplied.

Addition:
$5x^4 + 3x^2$ cannot be simplified.

Multiplication:
$$(5x^4)(3x^2) = (5 \cdot 3)(x^4 \cdot x^2)$$
$$= 15x^{4+2}$$
$$= 15x^6$$

Multiplying Polynomials

The product of two monomials is obtained by using properties of exponents. For example,

$$(-8x^6)(5x^3) = -8 \cdot 5x^{6+3} = -40x^9.$$

Multiply coefficients and add exponents.

Furthermore, we can use the distributive property to multiply a monomial and a polynomial that is not a monomial. For example,

$$3x^4(2x^3 - 7x + 3) = 3x^4 \cdot 2x^3 - 3x^4 \cdot 7x + 3x^4 \cdot 3 = 6x^7 - 21x^5 + 9x^4.$$

Monomial Trinomial

How do we multiply two polynomials if neither is a monomial? For example, consider

$$(2x + 3)(x^2 + 4x + 5).$$

Binomial Trinomial

One way to perform this multiplication is to distribute $2x$ throughout the trinomial

$$2x(x^2 + 4x + 5)$$

and 3 throughout the trinomial

$$3(x^2 + 4x + 5).$$

Then combine the like terms that result.

Multiplying Polynomials When Neither Is a Monomial

Multiply each term of one polynomial by each term of the other polynomial. Then combine like terms.

EXAMPLE 2 Multiplying a Binomial and a Trinomial

Multiply: $(2x + 3)(x^2 + 4x + 5)$.

Solution

$(2x + 3)(x^2 + 4x + 5)$

$= 2x(x^2 + 4x + 5) + 3(x^2 + 4x + 5)$ Multiply the trinomial by each term of the binomial.

$= 2x \cdot x^2 + 2x \cdot 4x + 2x \cdot 5 + 3x^2 + 3 \cdot 4x + 3 \cdot 5$ Use the distributive property.

$= 2x^3 + 8x^2 + 10x + 3x^2 + 12x + 15$ Multiply monomials: Multiply coefficients and add exponents.

$= 2x^3 + 11x^2 + 22x + 15$ Combine like terms: $8x^2 + 3x^2 = 11x^2$ and $10x + 12x = 22x.$

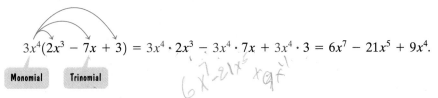

Another method for solving Example 2 is to use a vertical format similar to that used for multiplying whole numbers.

$$x^2 + 4x + 5$$
$$2x + 3$$
$$\overline{3x^2 + 12x + 15}$$ $3(x^2 + 4x + 5)$

Write like terms in $2x^3 + 8x^2 + 10x$ $2x(x^2 + 4x + 5)$
the same column. $\overline{2x^3 + 11x^2 + 22x + 15}$ *Combine like terms.*

Check Point 2 Multiply: $(5x - 2)(3x^2 - 5x + 4)$.

④ Use FOIL in polynomial multiplication.

The Product of Two Binomials: FOIL

Frequently, we need to find the product of two binomials. One way to perform this multiplication is to distribute each term in the first binomial through the second binomial. For example, we can find the product of the binomials $3x + 2$ and $4x + 5$ as follows:

$$(3x + 2)(4x + 5) = 3x(4x + 5) + 2(4x + 5)$$

Distribute $3x$ Distribute 2 $= 3x(4x) + 3x(5) + 2(4x) + 2(5)$
over $4x + 5$. over $4x + 5$.
 $= 12x^2 + 15x + 8x + 10.$

We can also find the product of $3x + 2$ and $4x + 5$ using a method called FOIL, which is based on our work shown above. Any two binomials can be quickly multiplied by using the FOIL method, in which **F** represents the product of the **first** terms in each binomial, **O** represents the product of the **outside** terms, **I** represents the product of the **inside** terms, and **L** represents the product of the **last**, or second, terms in each binomial. For example, we can use the FOIL method to find the product of the binomials $3x + 2$ and $4x + 5$ as follows:

$$= 12x^2 + 23x + 10$$ *Combine like terms.*

In general, here's how to use the FOIL method to find the product of $ax + b$ and $cx + d$:

Using the FOIL Method to Multiply Binomials

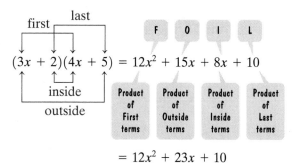

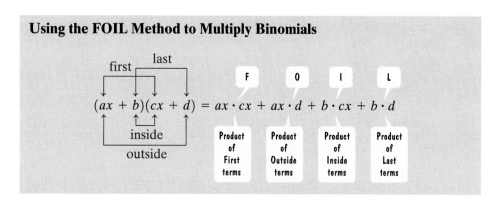

EXAMPLE 3 Using the FOIL Method

Multiply: $(3x + 4)(5x - 3)$.

Solution

first, last, inside, outside

F O I L

$$(3x + 4)(5x - 3) = 3x \cdot 5x + 3x(-3) + 4 \cdot 5x + 4(-3)$$
$$= 15x^2 - 9x + 20x - 12$$
$$= 15x^2 + 11x - 12 \quad \text{Combine like terms.}$$

Check Point 3 Multiply: $(7x - 5)(4x - 3)$.

5 Use special products in polynomial multiplication.

Multiplying the Sum and Difference of Two Terms

We can use the FOIL method to multiply $A + B$ and $A - B$ as follows:

F O I L

$$(A + B)(A - B) = A^2 - AB + AB - B^2 = A^2 - B^2.$$

Notice that the outside and inside products have a sum of 0 and the terms cancel. The FOIL multiplication provides us with a quick rule for multiplying the sum and difference of two terms, referred to as a special-product formula.

The Product of the Sum and Difference of Two Terms

$$(A + B)(A - B) = A^2 - B^2$$

The product of the sum and the difference of the same two terms is the square of the first term minus the square of the second term.

EXAMPLE 4 Finding the Product of the Sum and Difference of Two Terms

Find each product:

a. $(4y + 3)(4y - 3)$ **b.** $(5a^4 + 6)(5a^4 - 6)$.

Solution Use the special-product formula shown.

$$(A + B)(A - B) = A^2 - B^2$$

	First term squared	−	Second term squared	=	Product
a. $(4y + 3)(4y - 3)$ =	$(4y)^2$	−	3^2	=	$16y^2 - 9$
b. $(5a^4 + 6)(5a^4 - 6)$ =	$(5a^4)^2$	−	6^2	=	$25a^8 - 36$

Check Point 4 Find each product:

a. $(7x + 8)(7x - 8)$ **b.** $(2y^3 - 5)(2y^3 + 5)$.

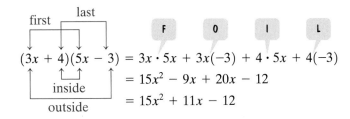

The Square of a Binomial

Let us find $(A + B)^2$, the square of a binomial sum. To do so, we begin with the FOIL method and look for a general rule.

F O I L

$$(A + B)^2 = (A + B)(A + B) = A \cdot A + A \cdot B + A \cdot B + B \cdot B$$
$$= A^2 + 2AB + B^2$$

This result implies the following rule, which is another example of a special-product formula:

The Square of a Binomial Sum

$$(A + B)^2 = A^2 + 2AB + B^2$$

The square of a binomial sum is first term squared plus 2 times the product of the terms plus last term squared.

Study Tip

Caution! The square of a sum is *not* the sum of the squares.

$(A + B)^2 \neq A^2 + B^2$

The middle term $2AB$ is missing.

$(x + 3)^2 \neq x^2 + 9$

Incorrect!

Show that $(x + 3)^2$ and $x^2 + 9$ are not equal by substituting 5 for x in each expression and simplifying.

EXAMPLE 5 Finding the Square of a Binomial Sum

Square each binomial:

a. $(x + 3)^2$ **b.** $(3x + 7)^2$.

Solution Use the special-product formula shown.

$$(A + B)^2 = A^2 + 2AB + B^2$$

	(First Term)^2	+	2 · Product of the Terms	+	(Last Term)^2	= Product
a. $(x + 3)^2 =$	x^2	+	$2 \cdot x \cdot 3$	+	3^2	$= x^2 + 6x + 9$
b. $(3x + 7)^2 =$	$(3x)^2$	+	$2(3x)(7)$	+	7^2	$= 9x^2 + 42x + 49$

Check Point 5 Square each binomial:

a. $(x + 10)^2$ **b.** $(5x + 4)^2$.

Using the FOIL method on $(A - B)^2$, the square of a binomial difference, we obtain the following rule:

The Square of a Binomial Difference

$$(A - B)^2 = A^2 - 2AB + B^2$$

The square of a binomial difference is first term squared minus 2 times the product of the terms plus last term squared.

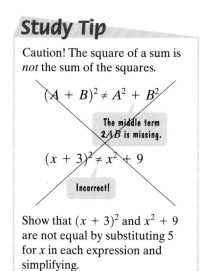

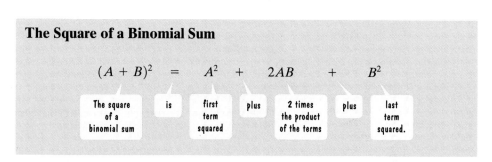

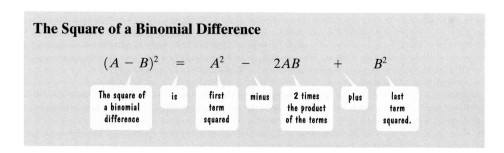

EXAMPLE 6 Finding the Square of a Binomial Difference

Square each binomial using the preceding rule:

a. $(x - 4)^2$ **b.** $(5y - 6)^2$.

Solution Use the special-product formula shown.

$$(A - B)^2 = A^2 - 2AB + B^2$$

	(First Term)^2	−	2 · Product of the Terms	+	(Last Term)^2	= Product
a. $(x - 4)^2 =$	x^2	−	$2 \cdot x \cdot 4$	+	4^2	$= x^2 - 8x + 16$
b. $(5y - 6)^2 =$	$(5y)^2$	−	$2(5y)(6)$	+	6^2	$= 25y^2 - 60y + 36$

Check Point 6 Square each binomial:

a. $(x - 9)^2$ **b.** $(7x - 3)^2$.

Special Products

There are several products that occur so frequently that it's convenient to memorize the form, or pattern, of these formulas.

Special Products

Let A and B represent real numbers, variables, or algebraic expressions.

Special Product	**Example**
Sum and Difference of Two Terms	
$(A + B)(A - B) = A^2 - B^2$	$(2x + 3)(2x - 3) = (2x)^2 - 3^2$ $= 4x^2 - 9$
Squaring a Binomial	
$(A + B)^2 = A^2 + 2AB + B^2$	$(y + 5)^2 = y^2 + 2 \cdot y \cdot 5 + 5^2$ $= y^2 + 10y + 25$
$(A - B)^2 = A^2 - 2AB + B^2$	$(3x - 4)^4$ $= (3x)^2 - 2 \cdot 3x \cdot 4 + 4^2$ $= 9x^2 - 24x + 16$
Cubing a Binomial	
$(A + B)^3 = A^3 + 3A^2B + 3AB^2 + B^3$	$(x + 4)^3$ $= x^3 + 3x^2(4) + 3x(4)^2 + 4^3$ $= x^3 + 12x^2 + 48x + 64$
$(A - B)^3 = A^3 - 3A^2B + 3AB^2 - B^3$	$(x - 2)^3$ $= x^3 - 3x^2(2) + 3x(2)^2 - 2^3$ $= x^3 - 6x^2 + 12x - 8$

Study Tip

Although it's convenient to memorize these forms, the FOIL method can be used on all five examples in the box. To cube $x + 4$, you can first square $x + 4$ using FOIL and then multiply this result by $x + 4$. In short, you do not necessarily have to utilize these special formulas. What is the advantage of knowing and using these forms?

6 Perform operations with polynomials in several variables.

Polynomials in Several Variables

The next time you visit the lumber yard and go rummaging through piles of wood, think *polynomials*, although polynomials a bit different from those we have encountered so far. The forestry industry uses a polynomial in two variables to determine the number of board feet that can be manufactured from a tree with a diameter of x inches and a length of y feet. This polynomial is

$$\tfrac{1}{4}x^2y - 2xy + 4y.$$

In general, a **polynomial in two variables**, x and y, contains the sum of one or more monomials in the form ax^ny^m. The constant, a, is the **coefficient**. The exponents, n and m, represent whole numbers. The **degree** of the monomial ax^ny^m is $n + m$. We'll use the polynomial from the forestry industry to illustrate these ideas.

The coefficients are $\frac{1}{4}$, -2, and 4.

$$\frac{1}{4}x^2y \quad - 2xy \quad + 4y$$

Degree of monomial: $2 + 1 = 3$

Degree of monomial: $1 + 1 = 2$

Degree of monomial $(4x^0y^1)$: $0 + 1 = 1$

The **degree of a polynomial in two variables** is the highest degree of all its terms. For the preceding polynomial, the degree is 3.

Polynomials containing two or more variables can be added, subtracted, and multiplied just like polynomials that contain only one variable. For example, we can add the monomials $-7xy^2$ and $13xy^2$ as follows:

$$-7xy^2 + 13xy^2 = (-7 + 13)xy^2 = 6xy^2.$$

These like terms both contain the variable factors x and y^2.

Add coefficients and keep the same variable factors, xy^2.

EXAMPLE 7 Subtracting Polynomials in Two Variables

Subtract:

$$(5x^3 - 9x^2y + 3xy^2 - 4) - (3x^3 - 6x^2y - 2xy^2 + 3).$$

Solution

$$(5x^3 - 9x^2y + 3xy^2 - 4) - (3x^3 - 6x^2y - 2xy^2 + 3)$$

Change the sign of each coefficient.

$$= (5x^3 - 9x^2y + 3xy^2 - 4) + (-3x^3 + 6x^2y + 2xy^2 - 3)$$

Add the opposite of the polynomial being subtracted.

$$= (5x^3 - 3x^3) + (-9x^2y + 6x^2y) + (3xy^2 + 2xy^2) + (-4 - 3)$$

Group like terms.

$$= 2x^3 - 3x^2y + 5xy^2 - 7$$

Combine like terms by adding coefficients and keeping the same variable factors.

Check Point 7 Subtract: $(x^3 - 4x^2y + 5xy^2 - y^3) - (x^3 - 6x^2y + y^3)$.

EXAMPLE 8 Multiplying Polynomials in Two Variables

Multiply: **a.** $(x + 4y)(3x - 5y)$ **b.** $(5x + 3y)^2$.

Solution We will perform the multiplication in part (a) using the FOIL method. We will multiply in part (b) using the formula for the square of a binomial sum, $(A + B)^2$.

a. $(x + 4y)(3x - 5y)$ *Multiply these binomials using the FOIL method.*

F O I L

$= (x)(3x) + (x)(-5y) + (4y)(3x) + (4y)(-5y)$
$= 3x^2 - 5xy + 12xy - 20y^2$
$= 3x^2 + 7xy - 20y^2$ *Combine like terms.*

$(A + B)^2 = A^2 + 2 \cdot A \cdot B + B^2$

b. $(5x + 3y)^2 = (5x)^2 + 2(5x)(3y) + (3y)^2$
$= 25x^2 + 30xy + 9y^2$

Check Point 8 Multiply:
a. $(7x - 6y)(3x - y)$ **b.** $(2x + 4y)^2$.

EXERCISE SET P.4

Practice Exercises

In Exercises 1–4, is the algebraic expression a polynomial? If it is, write the polynomial in standard form.

1. $2x + 3x^2 - 5$ **2.** $2x + 3x^{-1} - 5$
3. $\frac{2x + 3}{x}$ **4.** $x^2 - x^3 + x^4 - 5$

In Exercises 5–8, find the degree of the polynomial.

5. $3x^2 - 5x + 4$ **6.** $-4x^3 + 7x^2 - 11$
7. $x^2 - 4x^3 + 9x - 12x^4 + 63$
8. $x^2 - 8x^3 + 15x^4 + 91$

In Exercises 9–14, perform the indicated operations. Write the resulting polynomial in standard form and indicate its degree.

9. $(-6x^3 + 5x^2 - 8x + 9) + (17x^3 + 2x^2 - 4x - 13)$
10. $(-7x^3 + 6x^2 - 11x + 13) + (19x^3 - 11x^2 + 7x - 17)$
11. $(17x^3 - 5x^2 + 4x - 3) - (5x^3 - 9x^2 - 8x + 11)$
12. $(18x^4 - 2x^3 - 7x + 8) - (9x^4 - 6x^3 - 5x + 7)$
13. $(5x^2 - 7x - 8) + (2x^2 - 3x + 7) - (x^2 - 4x - 3)$
14. $(8x^2 + 7x - 5) - (3x^2 - 4x) - (-6x^3 - 5x^2 + 3)$

In Exercises 15–58, find each product.

15. $(x + 1)(x^2 - x + 1)$ **16.** $(x + 5)(x^2 - 5x + 25)$
17. $(2x - 3)(x^2 - 3x + 5)$ **18.** $(2x - 1)(x^2 - 4x + 3)$
19. $(x + 7)(x + 3)$ **20.** $(x + 8)(x + 5)$
21. $(x - 5)(x + 3)$ **22.** $(x - 1)(x + 2)$
23. $(3x + 5)(2x + 1)$ **24.** $(7x + 4)(3x + 1)$
25. $(2x - 3)(5x + 3)$ **26.** $(2x - 5)(7x + 2)$
27. $(5x^2 - 4)(3x^2 - 7)$ **28.** $(7x^2 - 2)(3x^2 - 5)$
29. $(8x^3 + 3)(x^2 - 5)$ **30.** $(7x^3 + 5)(x^2 - 2)$
31. $(x + 3)(x - 3)$ **32.** $(x + 5)(x - 5)$
33. $(3x + 2)(3x - 2)$ **34.** $(2x + 5)(2x - 5)$
35. $(5 - 7x)(5 + 7x)$ **36.** $(4 - 3x)(4 + 3x)$
37. $(4x^2 + 5x)(4x^2 - 5x)$ **38.** $(3x^2 + 4x)(3x^2 - 4x)$
39. $(1 - y^5)(1 + y^5)$ **40.** $(2 - y^5)(2 + y^5)$
41. $(x + 2)^2$ **42.** $(x + 5)^2$
43. $(2x + 3)^2$ **44.** $(3x + 2)^2$
45. $(x - 3)^2$ **46.** $(x - 4)^2$
47. $(4x^2 - 1)^2$ **48.** $(5x^2 - 3)^2$
49. $(7 - 2x)^2$ **50.** $(9 - 5x)^2$
51. $(x + 1)^3$ **52.** $(x + 2)^3$
53. $(2x + 3)^3$ **54.** $(3x + 4)^3$
55. $(x - 3)^3$ **56.** $(x - 1)^3$
57. $(3x - 4)^3$ **58.** $(2x - 3)^3$

In Exercises 59–66, perform the indicated operations. Indicate the degree of the resulting polynomial.

59. $(5x^2y - 3xy) + (2x^2y - xy)$
60. $(-2x^2y + xy) + (4x^2y + 7xy)$
61. $(4x^2y + 8xy + 11) + (-2x^2y + 5xy + 2)$
62. $(7x^4y^2 - 5x^2y^2 + 3xy) + (-18x^4y^2 - 6x^2y^2 - xy)$
63. $(x^3 + 7xy - 5y^2) - (6x^3 - xy + 4y^2)$
64. $(x^4 - 7xy - 5y^3) - (6x^4 - 3xy + 4y^3)$
65. $(3x^4y^2 + 5x^3y - 3y) - (2x^4y^2 - 3x^3y - 4y + 6x)$
66. $(5x^4y^2 + 6x^3y - 7y) - (3x^4y^2 - 5x^3y - 6y + 8x)$

In Exercises 67–82, find each product.

67. $(x + 5y)(7x + 3y)$ **68.** $(x + 9y)(6x + 7y)$
69. $(x - 3y)(2x + 7y)$ **70.** $(3x - y)(2x + 5y)$
71. $(3xy - 1)(5xy + 2)$ **72.** $(7x^2y + 1)(2x^2y - 3)$
73. $(7x + 5y)^2$ **74.** $(9x + 7y)^2$
75. $(x^2y^2 - 3)^2$ **76.** $(x^2y^2 - 5)^2$
77. $(x - y)(x^2 + xy + y^2)$ **78.** $(x + y)(x^2 - xy + y^2)$
79. $(3x + 5y)(3x - 5y)$ **80.** $(7x + 3y)(7x - 3y)$
81. $(7xy^2 - 10y)(7xy^2 + 10y)$
82. $(3xy^2 - 4y)(3xy^2 + 4y)$

Practice Plus

In Exercises 83–90, perform the indicated operation or operations.

83. $(3x + 4y)^2 - (3x - 4y)^2$

84. $(5x + 2y)^2 - (5x - 2y)^2$

85. $(5x - 7)(3x - 2) - (4x - 5)(6x - 1)$

86. $(3x + 5)(2x - 9) - (7x - 2)(x - 1)$

87. $(2x + 5)(2x - 5)(4x^2 + 25)$

88. $(3x + 4)(3x - 4)(9x^2 + 16)$

89. $\dfrac{(2x - 7)^5}{(2x - 7)^3}$ **90.** $\dfrac{(5x - 3)^6}{(5x - 3)^4}$

Application Exercises

The bar graph shows the number of people in the United States, in millions, who do yoga.

Yoga Stretch: Number of U.S. Yoga Practitioners

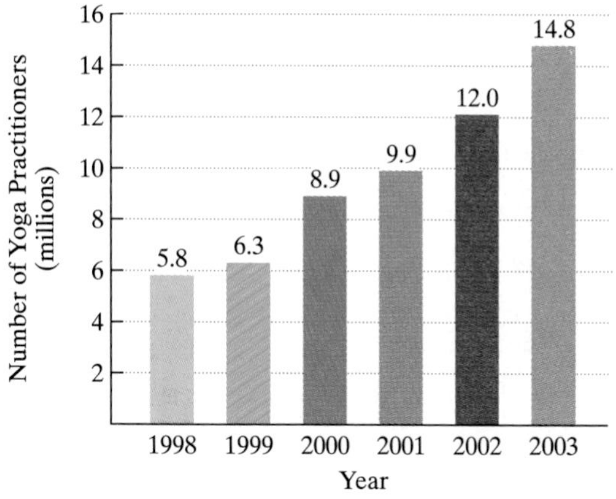

Source: Yoga Journal

Here are four mathematical models for the data shown in the graph. In each formula, N represents the number of U.S. yoga practitioners, in millions, x years after 1998.

Model 1 $N = 1.8x + 5.1$

Model 2 $N = 5.6(1.2)^x$

Model 3 $N = 0.17x^2 + 0.95x + 5.68$

Model 4 $N = 0.09x^2 + 0.01x^3 + 1.1x + 5.64$

Use these models to solve Exercises 91–96.

91. Which model uses a polynomial that is not in standard form? Rewrite the model in standard form.

92. If x is any real number from 0 to 5, inclusive, which model does not use a polynomial?

93. Which model best describes the data for 2000?

94. Which model best describes the data for 1998?

95. How well does the model of degree 2 describe the data for 2003?

96. How well does the polynomial model that is not in standard form describe the data for 2002?

In Exercises 97–98, write a polynomial in standard form that models, or represents, the volume of the open box.

97.

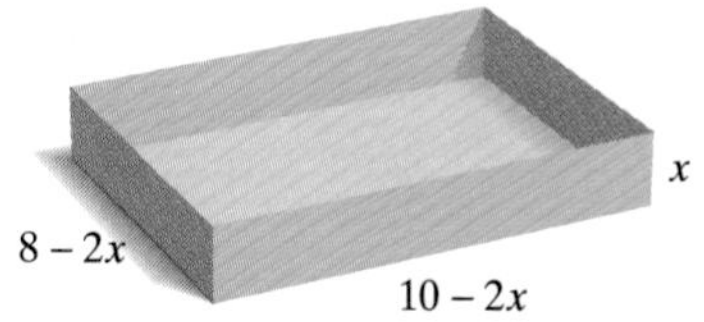

98.

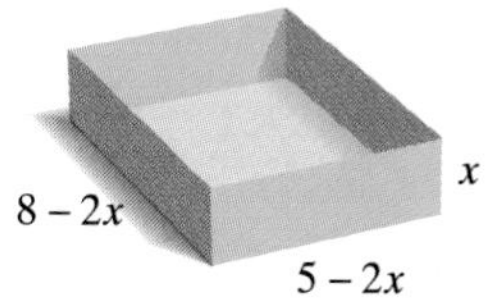

In Exercises 99–100, write a polynomial in standard form that models, or represents, the area of the shaded region.

99.

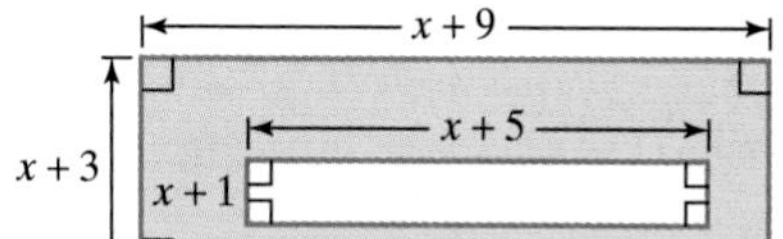

100.

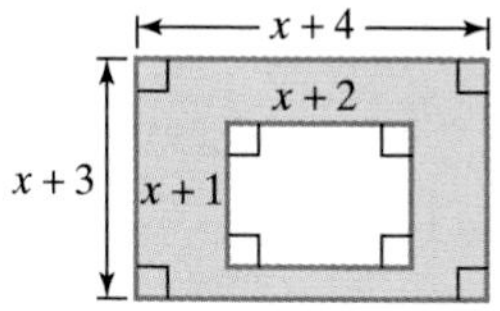

Writing in Mathematics

101. What is a polynomial in x?

102. Explain how to subtract polynomials.

103. Explain how to multiply two binomials using the FOIL method. Give an example with your explanation.

104. Explain how to find the product of the sum and difference of two terms. Give an example with your explanation.

105. Explain how to square a binomial difference. Give an example with your explanation.

106. Explain how to find the degree of a polynomial in two variables.

107. In the section opener, we used the mathematical model

$$N = -365x^4 + 2728x^3 - 7106x^2 + 7372x + 20{,}787$$

to describe the number of newly-declared computer majors, N, for the fall term x years after 1999. Use a calculator to determine these numbers from 1999 through 2003. Compare your results with the data shown in Figure P.11 on page 45. Describe what you observe.

Critical Thinking Exercises

108. Which one of the following is true?

a. $(3x^3 + 2)(3x^3 - 2) = 9x^9 - 4$

b. $(x - 5)^2 = x^2 - 5x + 25$

c. $(x + 1)^2 = x^2 + 1$

d. Suppose a square garden has an area represented by $9x^2$ square feet. If one side is made 7 feet longer and the other side is made 2 feet shorter, then the trinomial that represents the area of the larger garden is $9x^2 + 15x - 14$ square feet.

In Exercises 109–111, perform the indicated operations.

109. $[(7x + 5) + 4y][(7x + 5) - 4y]$

110. $[(3x + y) + 1]^2$

111. $(x^n + 2)(x^n - 2) - (x^n - 3)^2$

112. Express the area of the plane figure shown as a polynomial in standard form.

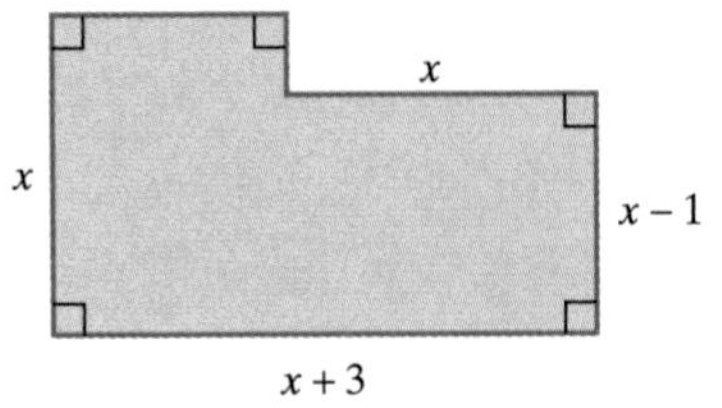

CHAPTER P MID-CHAPTER CHECK POINT

What You Know: We defined the real numbers $[\{x|x \text{ is rational}\} \cup \{x|x \text{ is irrational}\}]$ and graphed them as points on a number line. We reviewed the basic rules of algebra, using these properties to simplify algebraic expressions. We expanded our knowledge of exponents to include exponents other than natural numbers:

$$b^0 = 1;\quad b^{-n} = \frac{1}{b^n};\quad \frac{1}{b^{-n}} = b^n;\quad b^{\frac{1}{n}} = \sqrt[n]{b};$$

$$b^{\frac{m}{n}} = \left(\sqrt[n]{b}\right)^m = \sqrt[n]{b^m};\quad b^{-\frac{m}{n}} = \frac{1}{b^{\frac{m}{n}}}.$$

We used properties of exponents to simplify exponential expressions and properties of radicals to simplify radical expressions. Finally, we performed operations with polynomials. We used a number of fast methods for finding products of polynomials, including the FOIL method for multiplying binomials, a special-product formula for the product of the sum and difference of two terms $[(A + B)(A - B) = A^2 - B^2]$, and special-product formulas for squaring binomials $[(A + B)^2 = A^2 + 2AB = B^2;$ $(A - B)^2 = A^2 - 2AB + B^2]$.

In Exercises 1–25, simplify the given expression or perform the indicated operation (and simplify, if possible), whichever is appropriate.

1. $(3x + 5)(4x - 7)$

2. $(3x + 5) - (4x - 7)$

3. $\sqrt{6} + 9\sqrt{6}$

4. $3\sqrt{12} - \sqrt{27}$

5. $7x + 3[9 - (2x - 6)]$

6. $(8x - 3)^2$

7. $\left(x^{\frac{1}{3}}y^{-\frac{1}{2}}\right)^6$

8. $\left(\frac{2}{7}\right)^0 - 32^{-\frac{2}{5}}$

9. $(2x - 5) - (x^2 - 3x + 1)$

10. $(2x - 5)(x^2 - 3x + 1)$

11. $x^3 + x^3 - x^3 \cdot x^3$

12. $(9a - 10b)(2a + b)$

13. $\{a, c, d, e\} \cup \{c, d, f, h\}$

14. $\{a, c, d, e\} \cap \{c, d, f, h\}$

15. $(3x^2y^3 - xy + 4y^2) - (-2x^2y^3 - 3xy + 5y^2)$

16. $\dfrac{24x^2y^{13}}{-2x^5y^{-2}}$

17. $\left(\frac{1}{3}x^{-5}y^4\right)(18x^{-2}y^{-1})$

18. $\sqrt[12]{x^4}$

19. $\dfrac{24 \times 10^3}{2 \times 10^6}$ (Express the answer in scientific notation.)

20. $\dfrac{\sqrt[3]{32}}{\sqrt[3]{2}}$

21. $(x^3 + 2)(x^3 - 2)$

22. $(x^2 + 2)^2$

23. $\sqrt{50} \cdot \sqrt{6}$

24. $\dfrac{11}{7 - \sqrt{3}}$

25. $\dfrac{11}{\sqrt{3}}$

26. List all the rational numbers in this set:

$$\left\{-11, -\frac{3}{7}, 0, 0.45, \sqrt{23}, \sqrt{25}\right\}.$$

In Exercises 27–28, rewrite each expression without absolute value bars.

27. $|2 - \sqrt{13}|$

28. $x^2|x|$ if $x < 0$

29. If the population of the United States is 2.9×10^8 and each person spends about \$120 per year on ice cream, express the total annual spending on ice cream in scientific notation.

30. A human brain contains 3×10^{10} neurons and a gorilla brain contains 7.5×10^9 neurons. How many times as many neurons are in the brain of a human as in the brain of a gorilla?

31. In 2003, 28.5 million U.S. adults browsed Internet personals and 17.4 million posted online personal ads. The bar graph shows the amount spent in the United States, in millions of dollars, on online dating.

Shopping for a Date: Millions of Dollars Spent in the U.S. on Online Dating

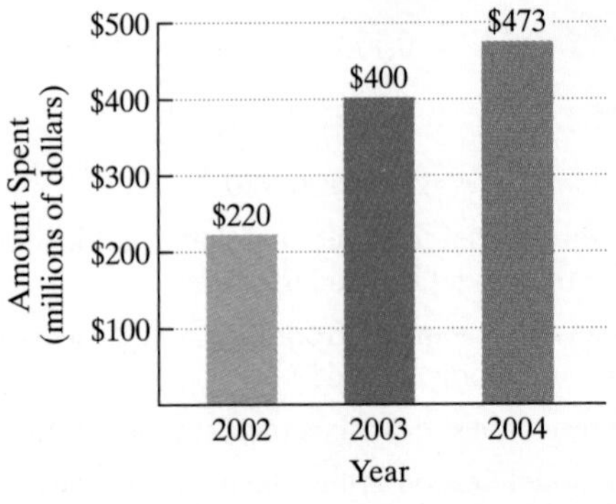

Source: Jupiter Research

Here are three mathematical models for the data shown in the graph. In each formula, D represents the amount spent on online dating, in millions of dollars, x years after 2002.

Model 1 $D = 236(1.5)^x$

Model 2 $D = 127x + 239$

Model 3 $D = -54x^2 + 234x + 220$

a. Which model best describes the data for 2004?

b. According to the polynomial model of degree 1, how much will Americans spend on online dating in 2008?

SECTION P.5 *Factoring Polynomials*

Objectives

1. Factor out the greatest common factor of a polynomial.
2. Factor by grouping.
3. Factor trinomials.
4. Factor the difference of squares.
5. Factor perfect square trinomials.
6. Factor the sum and difference of two cubes.
7. Use a general strategy for factoring polynomials.
8. Factor algebraic expressions containing fractional and negative exponents.

A two-year-old boy is asked, "Do you have a brother?" He answers, "Yes." "What is your brother's name?" "Tom." Asked if Tom has a brother, the two-year-old replies, "No." The child can go in the direction from self to brother, but he cannot reverse this direction and move from brother back to self.

As our intellects develop, we learn to reverse the direction of our thinking. Reversibility of thought is found throughout algebra. For example, we can multiply polynomials and show that

$$5x(2x + 3) = 10x^2 + 15x.$$

We can also reverse this process and express the resulting polynomial as

$$10x^2 + 15x = 5x(2x + 3).$$

Factoring a polynomial containing the sum of monomials means finding an equivalent expression that is a product.

Factoring $10x^2 + 15x$

Sum of monomials

Equivalent expression that is a product

$$10x^2 + 15x = 5x(2x + 3)$$

The factors of $10x^2 + 15x$ are $5x$ and $2x + 3$.

In this section, we will be **factoring over the set of integers**, meaning that the coefficients in the factors are integers. Polynomials that cannot be factored using integer coefficients are called **irreducible over the integers**, or **prime**.

The goal in factoring a polynomial is to use one or more factoring techniques until each of the polynomial's factors, except possibly for a monomial factor, is prime or irreducible. In this situation, the polynomial is said to be **factored completely**.

We will now discuss basic techniques for factoring polynomials.

Factor out the greatest common factor of a polynomial.

Common Factors

In any factoring problem, the first step is to look for the *greatest common factor*. The **greatest common factor**, abbreviated GCF, is an expression of the highest degree that divides each term of the polynomial. The distributive property in the reverse direction

$$ab + ac = a(b + c)$$

can be used to factor out the greatest common factor.

EXAMPLE 1 Factoring out the Greatest Common Factor

Factor: **a.** $18x^3 + 27x^2$ **b.** $x^2(x + 3) + 5(x + 3)$.

Solution

a. First, determine the greatest common factor.

> 9 is the greatest integer that divides 18 and 27.

$$18x^3 + 27x^2$$

> x^2 is the greatest expression that divides x^3 and x^2.

The GCF of the two terms of the polynomial is $9x^2$.

$$18x^3 + 27x^2$$
$$= 9x^2(2x) + 9x^2(3) \quad \text{Express each term as the product of the GCF and its other factor.}$$
$$= 9x^2(2x + 3) \quad \text{Factor out the GCF.}$$

b. In this situation, the greatest common factor is the common binomial factor $(x + 3)$. We factor out this common factor as follows:

$$x^2(x + 3) + 5(x + 3) = (x + 3)(x^2 + 5). \quad \text{Factor out the common binomial factor.}$$

Check Point 1 Factor: **a.** $10x^3 - 4x^2$ **b.** $2x(x - 7) + 3(x - 7)$.

 Factor by grouping.

Factoring by Grouping

Some polynomials have only a greatest common factor of 1. However, by a suitable grouping of the terms, it still may be possible to factor. This process, called **factoring by grouping**, is illustrated in Example 2.

EXAMPLE 2 Factoring by Grouping

Factor: $x^3 + 4x^2 + 3x + 12$.

Solution There is no factor other than 1 common to all terms. However, we can group terms that have a common factor:

$$\boxed{x^3 + 4x^2} \quad + \quad \boxed{3x + 12}.$$

> Common factor is x^2.

> Common factor is 3.

We now factor the given polynomial as follows:

$$x^3 + 4x^2 + 3x + 12$$
$$= (x^3 + 4x^2) + (3x + 12) \quad \text{Group terms with common factors.}$$
$$= x^2(x + 4) + 3(x + 4) \quad \text{Factor out the greatest common factor from the grouped terms. The remaining two terms have } x + 4 \text{ as a common binomial factor.}$$
$$= (x + 4)(x^2 + 3). \quad \text{Factor out the GCF, } x + 4.$$

Study Tip

The variable part of the greatest common factor always contains the *smallest* power of a variable or algebraic expression that appears in all terms of the polynomial.

Discovery

In Example 2, group the terms as follows:

$$(x^3 + 3x) + (4x^2 + 12).$$

Factor out the greatest common factor from each group and complete the factoring process. Describe what happens. What can you conclude?

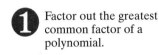

Thus, $x^3 + 4x^2 + 3x + 12 = (x + 4)(x^2 + 3)$. Check the factorization by multiplying the right side of the equation using the FOIL method. Because the factorization is correct, you should obtain the original polynomial.

Check Point 2 Factor: $x^3 + 5x^2 - 2x - 10$.

3 Factor trinomials.

Factoring Trinomials

To factor a trinomial of the form $ax^2 + bx + c$, a little trial and error may be necessary.

A Strategy for Factoring $ax^2 + bx + c$

Assume, for the moment, that there is no greatest common factor.

1. Find two First terms whose product is ax^2:

$$(\square x + \quad)(\square x + \quad) = ax^2 + bx + c.$$

2. Find two Last terms whose product is c:

$$(x + \square)(x + \square) = ax^2 + bx + c.$$

3. By trial and error, perform steps 1 and 2 until the sum of the Outside product and the Inside product is bx:

$$(\square x + \square)(\square x + \square) = ax^2 + bx + c.$$

I

O

Sum of O + I

If no such combination exists, the polynomial is prime.

Study Tip

The *error* part of the factoring strategy plays an important role in the process. If you do not get the correct factorization the first time, this is not a bad thing. This error is often helpful in leading you to the correct factorization.

EXAMPLE 3 Factoring Trinomials Whose Leading Coefficients Are 1

Factor: **a.** $x^2 + 6x + 8$ **b.** $x^2 + 3x - 18$.

Solution

a. The factors of the first term are x and x:

$$x^2 + 6x + 8 = (x \quad)(x \quad).$$

To find the second term of each factor, we must find two integers whose product is 8 and whose sum is 6. From the table in the margin, we see that 4 and 2 are the required integers. Thus,

$$x^2 + 6x + 8 = (x + 4)(x + 2) \text{ or } (x + 2)(x + 4).$$

Factors of 8	8, 1	4, 2	−8, −1	−4, −2
Sum of Factors	9	6	−9	−6

This is the desired sum.

Factors of −18	18, −1	−18, 1	9, −2	−9, 2	6, −3	−6, 3
Sum of Factors	17	−17	7	−7	3	−3

This is the desired sum.

b. We begin with

$$x^2 + 3x - 18 = (x \quad)(x \quad).$$

To find the second term of each factor, we must find two integers whose product is −18 and whose sum is 3. From the table in the margin, we see that 6 and −3 are the required integers. Thus,

$$x^2 + 3x - 18 = (x + 6)(x - 3) \quad \text{or} \quad (x - 3)(x + 6).$$

Check Point 3 Factor:

a. $x^2 + 13x + 40$ **b.** $x^2 - 5x - 14$.

EXAMPLE 4 Factoring a Trinomial Whose Leading Coefficient Is Not 1

Factor: $8x^2 - 10x - 3$.

Solution

Step 1 Find two First terms whose product is $8x^2$.

$$8x^2 - 10x - 3 \stackrel{?}{=} (8x \quad)(x \quad)$$

$$8x^2 - 10x - 3 \stackrel{?}{=} (4x \quad)(2x \quad)$$

Step 2 Find two Last terms whose product is −3. The possible factorizations are $1(-3)$ and $-1(3)$.

Step 3 Try various combinations of these factors. The correct factorization of $8x^2 - 10x - 3$ is the one in which the sum of the Outside and Inside products is equal to $-10x$. Here is a list of the possible factorizations:

Possible Factorizations of $8x^2 - 10x - 3$	Sum of Outside and Inside Products (Should Equal $-10x$)
$(8x + 1)(x - 3)$	$-24x + x = -23x$
$(8x - 3)(x + 1)$	$8x - 3x = 5x$
$(8x - 1)(x + 3)$	$24x - x = 23x$
$(8x + 3)(x - 1)$	$-8x + 3x = -5x$
$(4x + 1)(2x - 3)$	$-12x + 2x = -10x$
$(4x - 3)(2x + 1)$	$4x - 6x = -2x$
$(4x - 1)(2x + 3)$	$12x - 2x = 10x$
$(4x + 3)(2x - 1)$	$-4x + 6x = 2x$

This is the required middle term.

Thus,

$$8x^2 - 10x - 3 = (4x + 1)(2x - 3) \quad \text{or} \quad (2x - 3)(4x + 1).$$

Show that either of these factorizations is correct by multiplying the factors using the FOIL method. You should obtain the original trinomial.

Check Point 4 Factor: $6x^2 + 19x - 7$.

Study Tip

Here are some suggestions for reducing the list of possible factorizations for $ax^2 + bx + c$:

1. If b is relatively small, avoid the larger factors of a.

2. If c is positive, the signs in both binomial factors must match the sign of b.

3. If the trinomial has no common factor, no binomial factor can have a common factor.

4. Reversing the signs in the binomial factors reverses the sign of bx, the middle term.

EXAMPLE 5 Factoring a Trinomial in Two Variables

Factor: $2x^2 - 7xy + 3y^2$.

Solution

Step 1 Find two First terms whose product is $2x^2$.

$$2x^2 - 7xy + 3y^2 = (2x \quad)(x \quad)$$

Step 2 Find two Last terms whose product is $3y^2$. The possible factorizations are $(y)(3y)$ and $(-y)(-3y)$.

Step 3 Try various combinations of these factors. The correct factorization of $2x^2 - 7xy + 3y^2$ is the one in which the sum of the Outside and Inside products is equal to $-7xy$. Here is a list of possible factorizations:

Possible Factorizations of $2x^2 - 7xy + 3y^2$	Sum of Outside and Inside Products (Should Equal $-7xy$)
$(2x + 3y)(x + y)$	$2xy + 3xy = 5xy$
$(2x + y)(x + 3y)$	$6xy + xy = 7xy$
$(2x - 3y)(x - y)$	$-2xy - 3xy = -5xy$
$(2x - y)(x - 3y)$	$-6xy - xy = -7xy$

This is the required middle term.

Thus,

$$2x^2 - 7xy + 3y^2 = (2x - y)(x - 3y) \quad \text{or} \quad (x - 3y)(2x - y).$$

Use FOIL multiplication to check either of these factorizations.

Check Point 5 Factor: $3x^2 - 13xy + 4y^2$.

④ Factor the difference of squares.

Factoring the Difference of Two Squares

A method for factoring the difference of two squares is obtained by reversing the special product for the sum and difference of two terms.

> **The Difference of Two Squares**
>
> If A and B are real numbers, variables, or algebraic expressions, then
> $$A^2 - B^2 = (A + B)(A - B).$$
> In words: The difference of the squares of two terms factors as the product of a sum and a difference of those terms.

EXAMPLE 6 Factoring the Difference of Two Squares

Factor: **a.** $x^2 - 4$ **b.** $81x^2 - 49$.

Solution We must express each term as the square of some monomial. Then we use the formula for factoring $A^2 - B^2$.

a. $x^2 - 4 = x^2 - 2^2 = (x + 2)(x - 2)$

$A^2 - B^2 = (A + B)(A - B)$

b. $81x^2 - 49 = (9x)^2 - 7^2 = (9x + 7)(9x - 7)$

Check Point 6 Factor: **a.** $x^2 - 81$ **b.** $36x^2 - 25$.

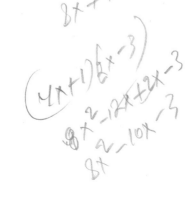

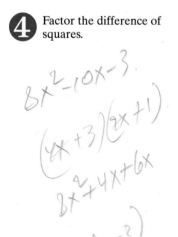

We have seen that a polynomial is factored completely when it is written as the product of prime polynomials. To be sure that you have factored completely, check to see whether any factors with more than one term in the factored polynomial can be factored further. If so, continue factoring.

EXAMPLE 7 A Repeated Factorization

Factor completely: $x^4 - 81$.

Solution

Study Tip

Factoring $x^4 - 81$ as
$$(x^2 + 9)(x^2 - 9)$$
is not a complete factorization. The second factor, $x^2 - 9$, is itself a difference of two squares and can be factored.

$$
\begin{aligned}
x^4 - 81 &= (x^2)^2 - 9^2 && \text{Express as the difference of two squares.} \\
&= (x^2 + 9)(x^2 - 9) && \text{The factors are the sum and the difference of the expressions being squared.} \\
&= (x^2 + 9)(x^2 - 3^2) && \text{The factor } x^2 - 9 \text{ is the difference of two squares and can be factored.} \\
&= (x^2 + 9)(x + 3)(x - 3) && \text{The factors of } x^2 - 9 \text{ are the sum and the difference of the expressions being squared.}
\end{aligned}
$$

Are you tempted to further factor $x^2 + 9$, the sum of two squares, in Example 7? Resist the temptation! **The sum of two squares, $A^2 + B^2$, with no common factor other than 1 is a prime polynomial over the integers**.

Check Point 7 Factor completely: $81x^4 - 16$.

Factoring Perfect Square Trinomials

⑤ Factor perfect square trinomials.

Our next factoring technique is obtained by reversing the special products for squaring binomials. The trinomials that are factored using this technique are called **perfect square trinomials**.

> **Factoring Perfect Square Trinomials**
>
> Let A and B be real numbers, variables, or algebraic expressions.
>
> **1.** $A^2 + 2AB + B^2 = (A + B)^2$
>
> Same sign
>
> **2.** $A^2 - 2AB + B^2 = (A - B)^2$
>
> Same sign

The two items in the box show that perfect square trinomials come in two forms: one in which the coefficient of the middle term is positive and one in which the coefficient of the middle term is negative. Here's how to recognize a perfect square trinomial:

1. The first and last terms are squares of monomials or integers.
2. The middle term is twice the product of the expressions being squared in the first and last terms.

EXAMPLE 8 Factoring Perfect Square Trinomials

Factor: **a.** $x^2 + 6x + 9$ **b.** $25x^2 - 60x + 36$.

Solution

a. $x^2 + 6x + 9 = x^2 + 2 \cdot x \cdot 3 + 3^2 = (x + 3)^2$ The middle term has a positive sign.

$$
\underbrace{A^2}\ +\ \underbrace{2AB}\ +\ \underbrace{B^2}\ =\ \underbrace{(A + B)^2}
$$

b. We suspect that $25x^2 - 60x + 36$ is a perfect square trinomial because $25x^2 = (5x)^2$ and $36 = 6^2$. The middle term can be expressed as twice the product of $5x$ and 6.

$$25x^2 - 60x + 36 = (5x^2) - 2 \cdot 5x \cdot 6 + 6^2 = (5x - 6)^2$$

$$A^2 \quad - \quad 2AB \quad + \quad B^2 \quad = \quad (A - B)^2$$

Check Point 8 Factor: **a.** $x^2 + 14x + 49$ **b.** $16x^2 - 56x + 49$.

6 Factor the sum and difference of two cubes.

Factoring the Sum and Difference of Two Cubes

We can use the following formulas to factor the sum or the difference of two cubes:

Factoring the Sum and Difference of Two Cubes

1. Factoring the Sum of Two Cubes

$$A^3 + B^3 = (A + B)(A^2 - AB + B^2)$$

Same signs Opposite signs

2. Factoring the Difference of Two Cubes

$$A^3 - B^3 = (A - B)(A^2 + AB + B^2)$$

Same signs Opposite signs

EXAMPLE 9 Factoring Sums and Differences of Two Cubes

Factor: **a.** $x^3 + 8$ **b.** $64x^3 - 125$.

Solution

a. To factor $x^3 + 8$, we must express each term as the cube of some monomial. Then we use the formula for factoring $A^3 + B^3$.

$$x^3 + 8 = x^3 + 2^3 = (x + 2)(x^2 - x \cdot 2 + 2^2) = (x + 2)(x^2 - 2x + 4)$$

$$A^3 \quad + \quad B^3 \quad = \quad (A + B)\;(A^2 \quad - \quad AB \quad + \quad B^2)$$

b. To factor $64x^3 - 125$, we must express each term as the cube of some monomial. Then use the formula for factoring $A^3 - B^3$.

$$64x^3 - 125 = (4x)^3 - 5^3 = (4x - 5)[(4x)^2 + (4x)(5) + 5^2]$$

$$A^3 \quad - \quad B^3 \quad = \quad (A - B)\;(A^2 \quad + \quad AB \quad + \quad B^2)$$

$$= (4x - 5)(16x^2 + 20x + 25)$$

Check Point 9 Factor: **a.** $x^3 + 1$ **b.** $125x^3 - 8$.

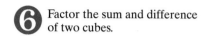

7 Use a general strategy for factoring polynomials.

A Strategy for Factoring Polynomials

It is important to practice factoring a wide variety of polynomials so that you can quickly select the appropriate technique. The polynomial is factored completely when all its polynomial factors, except possibly for monomial factors, are prime. Because of the commutative property, the order of the factors does not matter.

A Strategy for Factoring a Polynomial

1. If there is a common factor, factor out the GCF.
2. Determine the number of terms in the polynomial and try factoring as follows:
   a. If there are two terms, can the binomial be factored by one of the following special forms?

      Difference of two squares: $A^2 - B^2 = (A + B)(A - B)$

      Sum of two cubes: $A^3 + B^3 = (A + B)(A^2 - AB + B^2)$

      Difference of two cubes: $A^3 - B^3 = (A - B)(A^2 + AB + B^2)$

   b. If there are three terms, is the trinomial a perfect square trinomial? If so, factor by one of the following special forms:

      $$A^2 + 2AB + B^2 = (A + B)^2$$
      $$A^2 - 2AB + B^2 = (A - B)^2$$

      If the trinomial is not a perfect square trinomial, try factoring by trial and error.

   c. If there are four or more terms, try factoring by grouping.
3. Check to see if any factors with more than one term in the factored polynomial can be factored further. If so, factor completely.

EXAMPLE 10 Factoring a Polynomial

Factor: $2x^3 + 8x^2 + 8x$.

Solution

Step 1 If there is a common factor, factor out the GCF. Because $2x$ is common to all terms, we factor it out.

$$2x^3 + 8x^2 + 8x = 2x(x^2 + 4x + 4) \quad \text{Factor out the GCF.}$$

Step 2 Determine the number of terms and factor accordingly. The factor $x^2 + 4x + 4$ has three terms and is a perfect square trinomial. We factor using $A^2 + 2AB + B^2 = (A + B)^2$.

$$\begin{aligned} 2x^3 + 8x^2 + 8x &= 2x(x^2 + 4x + 4) \\ &= 2x(\underbrace{x^2}_{A^2} + \underbrace{2 \cdot x \cdot 2}_{2AB} + \underbrace{2^2}_{B^2}) \\ &= 2x(x + 2)^2 \qquad A^2 + 2AB + B^2 = (A + B)^2 \end{aligned}$$

Step 3 Check to see if factors can be factored further. In this problem, they cannot. Thus,

$$2x^3 + 8x^2 + 8x = 2x(x + 2)^2.$$

Check Point 10 Factor: $3x^3 - 30x^2 + 75x$.

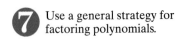

EXAMPLE 11 Factoring a Polynomial

Factor: $x^2 - 25a^2 + 8x + 16$.

Solution

Step 1 If there is a common factor, factor out the GCF. Other than 1 or -1, there is no common factor.

Step 2 Determine the number of terms and factor accordingly. There are four terms. We try factoring by grouping. Grouping into two groups of two terms does not result in a common binomial factor. Let's try grouping as a difference of squares.

$$x^2 - 25a^2 + 8x + 16$$

$$= (x^2 + 8x + 16) - 25a^2$$ Rearrange terms and group as a perfect square trinomial minus $25a^2$ to obtain a difference of squares.

$$= (x + 4)^2 - (5a)^2$$ Factor the perfect square trinomial.

$$= (x + 4 + 5a)(x + 4 - 5a)$$ Factor the difference of squares. The factors are the sum and difference of the expressions being squared.

Step 3 Check to see if factors can be factored further. In this case, they cannot, so we have factored completely.

Check Point 11 Factor: $x^2 - 36a^2 + 20x + 100$.

8 Factor algebraic expressions containing fractional and negative exponents.

Factoring Algebraic Expressions Containing Fractional and Negative Exponents

Although expressions containing fractional and negative exponents are not polynomials, they can be simplified using factoring techniques.

EXAMPLE 12 Factoring Involving Fractional and Negative Exponents

Factor and simplify: $x(x + 1)^{-\frac{3}{4}} + (x + 1)^{\frac{1}{4}}$.

Solution The greatest common factor is $x + 1$ with the *smallest exponent* in the two terms. Thus, the greatest common factor is $(x + 1)^{-\frac{3}{4}}$.

$$x(x + 1)^{-\frac{3}{4}} + (x + 1)^{\frac{1}{4}}$$

$$= (x + 1)^{-\frac{3}{4}}x + (x + 1)^{-\frac{3}{4}}(x + 1)$$ Express each term as the product of the greatest common factor and its other factor.

$$= (x + 1)^{-\frac{3}{4}}[x + (x + 1)]$$ Factor out the greatest common factor.

$$= \frac{2x + 1}{(x + 1)^{\frac{3}{4}}}$$ $b^{-n} = \frac{1}{b^n}$

Check Point 12 Factor and simplify: $x(x - 1)^{-\frac{1}{2}} + (x - 1)^{\frac{1}{2}}$.

EXERCISE SET P.5

Practice Exercises

In Exercises 1–10, factor out the greatest common factor.

1. $18x + 27$ **2.** $16x - 24$
3. $3x^2 + 6x$ **4.** $4x^2 - 8x$
5. $9x^4 - 18x^3 + 27x^2$ **6.** $6x^4 - 18x^3 + 12x^2$
7. $x(x + 5) + 3(x + 5)$ **8.** $x(2x + 1) + 4(2x + 1)$
9. $x^2(x - 3) + 12(x - 3)$ **10.** $x^2(2x + 5) + 17(2x + 5)$

In Exercises 11–16, factor by grouping.

11. $x^3 - 2x^2 + 5x - 10$ **12.** $x^3 - 3x^2 + 4x - 12$
13. $x^3 - x^2 + 2x - 2$ **14.** $x^3 + 6x^2 - 2x - 12$
15. $3x^3 - 2x^2 - 6x + 4$ **16.** $x^3 - x^2 - 5x + 5$

In Exercises 17–38, factor each trinomial, or state that the trinomial is prime.

17. $x^2 + 5x + 6$ **18.** $x^2 + 8x + 15$
19. $x^2 - 2x - 15$ **20.** $x^2 - 4x - 5$
21. $x^2 - 8x + 15$ **22.** $x^2 - 14x + 45$
23. $3x^2 - x - 2$ **24.** $2x^2 + 5x - 3$
25. $3x^2 - 25x - 28$ **26.** $3x^2 - 2x - 5$
27. $6x^2 - 11x + 4$ **28.** $6x^2 - 17x + 12$
29. $4x^2 + 16x + 15$ **30.** $8x^2 + 33x + 4$
31. $9x^2 - 9x + 2$ **32.** $9x^2 + 5x - 4$
33. $20x^2 + 27x - 8$ **34.** $15x^2 - 19x + 6$
35. $2x^2 + 3xy + y^2$ **36.** $3x^2 + 4xy + y^2$
37. $6x^2 - 5xy - 6y^2$ **38.** $6x^2 - 7xy - 5y^2$

In Exercises 39–48, factor the difference of two squares.

39. $x^2 - 100$ **40.** $x^2 - 144$
41. $36x^2 - 49$ **42.** $64x^2 - 81$
43. $9x^2 - 25y^2$ **44.** $36x^2 - 49y^2$
45. $x^4 - 16$ **46.** $x^4 - 1$
47. $16x^4 - 81$ **48.** $81x^4 - 1$

In Exercises 49–56, factor each perfect square trinomial.

49. $x^2 + 2x + 1$ **50.** $x^2 + 4x + 4$
51. $x^2 - 14x + 49$ **52.** $x^2 - 10x + 25$
53. $4x^2 + 4x + 1$ **54.** $25x^2 + 10x + 1$
55. $9x^2 - 6x + 1$ **56.** $64x^2 - 16x + 1$

In Exercises 57–64, factor using the formula for the sum or difference of two cubes.

57. $x^3 + 27$ **58.** $x^3 + 64$
59. $x^3 - 64$ **60.** $x^3 - 27$
61. $8x^3 - 1$ **62.** $27x^3 - 1$
63. $64x^3 + 27$ **64.** $8x^3 + 125$

In Exercises 65–92, factor completely, or state that the polynomial is prime.

65. $3x^3 - 3x$ **66.** $5x^3 - 45x$
67. $4x^2 - 4x - 24$ **68.** $6x^2 - 18x - 60$
69. $2x^4 - 162$ **70.** $7x^4 - 7$
71. $x^3 + 2x^2 - 9x - 18$ **72.** $x^3 + 3x^2 - 25x - 75$
73. $2x^2 - 2x - 112$ **74.** $6x^2 - 6x - 12$
75. $x^3 - 4x$ **76.** $9x^3 - 9x$
77. $x^2 + 64$ **78.** $x^2 + 36$
79. $x^3 + 2x^2 - 4x - 8$ **80.** $x^3 + 2x^2 - x - 2$
81. $y^5 - 81y$ **82.** $y^5 - 16y$
83. $20y^4 - 45y^2$ **84.** $48y^4 - 3y^2$
85. $x^2 - 12x + 36 - 49y^2$ **86.** $x^2 - 10x + 25 - 36y^2$
87. $9b^2x - 16y - 16x + 9b^2y$
88. $16a^2x - 25y - 25x + 16a^2y$
89. $x^2y - 16y + 32 - 2x^2$ **90.** $12x^2y - 27y - 4x^2 + 9$
91. $2x^3 - 8a^2x + 24x^2 + 72x$
92. $2x^3 - 98a^2x + 28x^2 + 98x$

In Exercises 93–102, factor and simplify each algebraic expression.

93. $x^{\frac{3}{2}} - x^{\frac{1}{2}}$ **94.** $x^{\frac{3}{4}} - x^{\frac{1}{4}}$
95. $4x^{-\frac{2}{3}} + 8x^{\frac{1}{3}}$ **96.** $12x^{-\frac{3}{4}} + 6x^{\frac{1}{4}}$
97. $(x + 3)^{\frac{1}{2}} - (x + 3)^{\frac{3}{2}}$ **98.** $(x^2 + 4)^{\frac{3}{2}} + (x^2 + 4)^{\frac{7}{2}}$
99. $(x + 5)^{-\frac{1}{2}} - (x + 5)^{-\frac{3}{2}}$
100. $(x^2 + 3)^{-\frac{2}{3}} + (x^2 + 3)^{-\frac{5}{3}}$
101. $(4x - 1)^{\frac{1}{2}} - \frac{1}{3}(4x - 1)^{\frac{3}{2}}$
102. $-8(4x + 3)^{-2} + 10(5x + 1)(4x + 3)^{-1}$

Practice Plus

In Exercises 103–114, factor completely.

103. $10x^2(x + 1) - 7x(x + 1) - 6(x + 1)$
104. $12x^2(x - 1) - 4x(x - 1) - 5(x - 1)$
105. $6x^4 + 35x^2 - 6$ **106.** $7x^4 + 34x^2 - 5$
107. $y^7 + y$ **108.** $(y + 1)^3 + 1$
109. $x^4 - 5x^2y^2 + 4y^4$ **110.** $x^4 - 10x^2y^2 + 9y^4$
111. $(x - y)^4 - 4(x - y)^2$ **112.** $(x + y)^4 - 100(x + y)^2$
113. $2x^2 - 7xy^2 + 3y^4$ **114.** $3x^2 + 5xy^2 + 2y^4$

Application Exercises

115. Your computer store is having an incredible sale. The price on one model is reduced by 40%. Then the sale price is reduced by another 40%. If x is the computer's original price, the sale price can be represented by

$$(x - 0.4x) - 0.4(x - 0.4x).$$

a. Factor out $(x - 0.4x)$ from each term. Then simplify the resulting expression.

b. Use the simplified expression from part (a) to answer these questions. With a 40% reduction followed by a 40% reduction, is the computer selling at 20% of its original price? If not, at what percentage of the original price is it selling?

116. Your local electronics store is having an end-of-the-year sale. The price on a large-screen television had been reduced by 30%. Now the sale price is reduced by another 30%. If x is the television's original price, the sale price can be represented by

$$(x - 0.3x) - 0.3(x - 0.3x).$$

a. Factor out $(x - 0.3x)$ from each term. Then simplify the resulting expression.

b. Use the simplified expression from part (a) to answer these questions. With a 30% reduction followed by a 30% reduction, is the television selling at 40% of its original price? If not, at what percentage of the original price is it selling?

In Exercises 117–120,

a. *Write an expression for the area of the shaded region.*

b. *Write the expression in factored form.*

117.

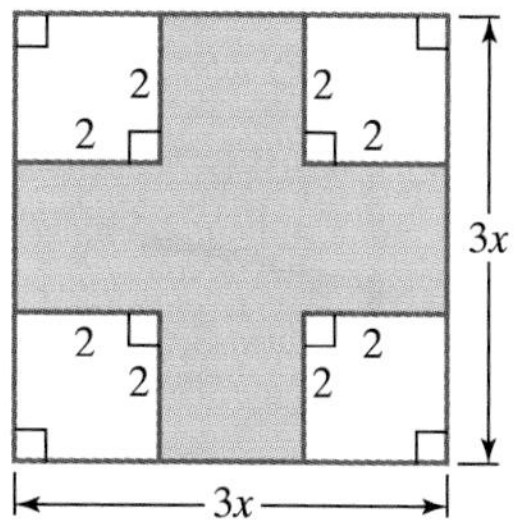

118.

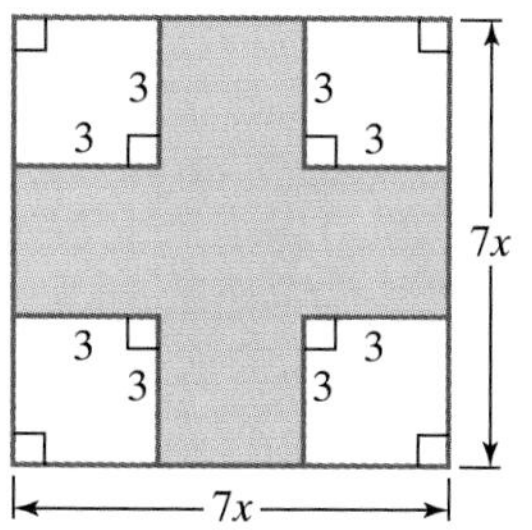

119.

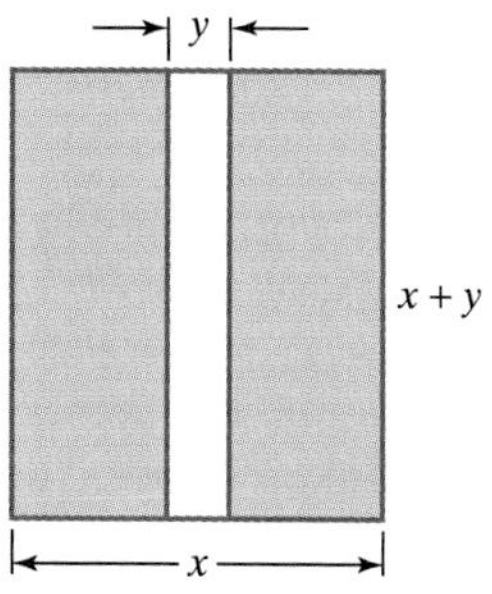

120.

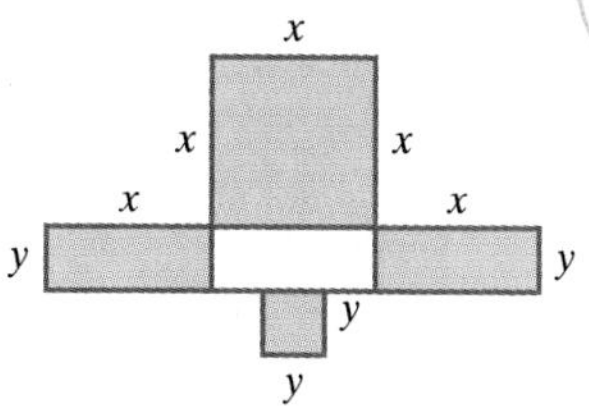

In Exercises 121–122, find the formula for the volume of the region outside the smaller rectangular solid and inside the larger rectangular solid. Then express the volume in factored form.

121.

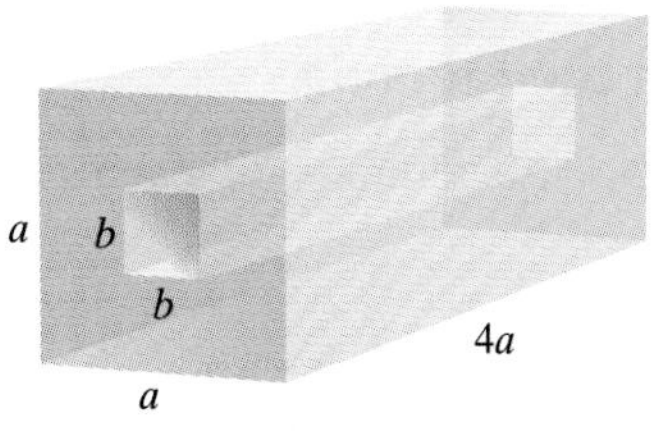

122.

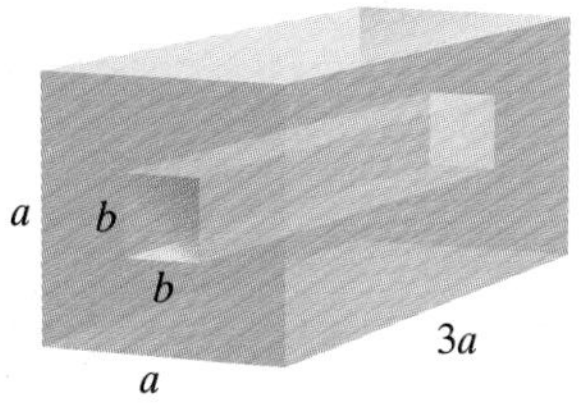

Writing in Mathematics

123. Using an example, explain how to factor out the greatest common factor of a polynomial.

124. Suppose that a polynomial contains four terms. Explain how to use factoring by grouping to factor the polynomial.

125. Explain how to factor $3x^2 + 10x + 8$.

126. Explain how to factor the difference of two squares. Provide an example with your explanation.

127. What is a perfect square trinomial and how is it factored?

128. Explain how to factor $x^3 + 1$.

129. What does it mean to factor completely?

Critical Thinking Exercises

130. Which one of the following is true?

a. Because $x^2 + 1$ is irreducible over the integers, it follows that $x^3 + 1$ is also irreducible.

b. One correct factored form for $x^2 - 4x + 3$ is $x(x - 4) + 3$.

c. $x^3 - 64 = (x - 4)^3$

d. None of the above is true.

In Exercises 131–134, factor completely.

131. $x^{2n} + 6x^n + 8$ **132.** $-x^2 - 4x + 5$

133. $x^4 - y^4 - 2x^3y + 2xy^3$

134. $(x - 5)^{-\frac{1}{2}}(x + 5)^{-\frac{1}{2}} - (x + 5)^{\frac{1}{2}}(x - 5)^{-\frac{3}{2}}$

In Exercises 135–136, find all integers b so that the trinomial can be factored.

135. $x^2 + bx + 15$ **136.** $x^2 + 4x + b$

Group Exercise

137. Divide the group in half. Without looking at any factoring problems in the book, each group should create five factoring problems. Make sure that some of your problems require at least two factoring strategies. Next, exchange problems with the other half of the group. Work to factor the five problems. After completing the factorizations, evaluate the factoring problems that you were given. Are they too easy? Too difficult? Can the polynomials really be factored? Share your responses with the half of the group that wrote the problems. Finally, grade each other's work in factoring the polynomials. Each factoring problem is worth 20 points. You may award partial credit. If you take off points, explain why points are deducted and how you decided to take off a particular number of points for the error(s) that you found.

SECTION P.6 Rational Expressions

Objectives

1. Specify numbers that must be excluded from the domain of a rational expression.
2. Simplify rational expressions.
3. Multiply rational expressions.
4. Divide rational expressions.
5. Add and subtract rational expressions.
6. Simplify complex rational expressions.

How can we describe the costs of reducing environmental pollution? We often use algebraic expressions involving quotients of polynomials. For example, the algebraic expression

$$\frac{250x}{100 - x}$$

describes the cost, in millions of dollars, to remove x percent of the pollutants that are discharged into a river. Removing a modest percentage of pollutants, say 40%, is far less costly than removing a substantially greater percentage, such as 95%. We see this by evaluating the algebraic expression for $x = 40$ and $x = 95$.

$$\text{Evaluating } \frac{250x}{100 - x} \text{ for}$$

$x = 40$: Cost is $\frac{250(40)}{100 - 40} \approx 167.$

$x = 95$: Cost is $\frac{250(95)}{100 - 95} = 4750.$

Discovery

What happens if you try substituting 100 for x in

$$\frac{250x}{100 - x}?$$

What does this tell you about the cost of cleaning up all of the river's pollutants?

The cost increases from approximately \$167 million to a possibly prohibitive \$4750 million, or \$4.75 billion. Costs spiral upward as the percentage of removed pollutants increases.

Many algebraic expressions that describe costs of environmental projects are examples of *rational expressions*. First we will define rational expressions. Then we will review how to perform operations with such expressions.

1 Specify numbers that must be excluded from the domain of a rational expression.

Rational Expressions

A **rational expression** is the quotient of two polynomials. Some examples are

$$\frac{x - 2}{4}, \quad \frac{4}{x - 2}, \quad \frac{x}{x^2 - 1}, \quad \text{and} \quad \frac{x^2 + 1}{x^2 + 2x - 3}.$$

The set of real numbers for which an algebraic expression is defined is the **domain** of the expression. Because rational expressions indicate division and division by zero is undefined, we must exclude numbers from a rational expression's domain that make the denominator zero.

EXAMPLE 1 Excluding Numbers from the Domain

Find all the numbers that must be excluded from the domain of each rational expression:

a. $\frac{4}{x - 2}$ **b.** $\frac{x}{x^2 - 1}$.

Solution To determine the numbers that must be excluded from each domain, examine the denominators.

a. $\dfrac{4}{x-2}$ **b.** $\dfrac{x}{x^2-1} = \dfrac{x}{(x+1)(x-1)}$

This denominator would equal zero if $x = 2$. This factor would equal zero if $x = -1$. This factor would equal zero if $x = 1$.

For the rational expression in part (a), we must exclude 2 from the domain. For the rational expression in part (b), we must exclude both -1 and 1 from the domain. These excluded numbers are often written to the right of a rational expression.

$$\frac{4}{x-2}, x \neq 2 \qquad \frac{x}{x^2-1}, x \neq -1, x \neq 1$$

Check Point 1 Find all the numbers that must be excluded from the domain of each rational expression:

a. $\dfrac{7}{x+5}$ **b.** $\dfrac{x}{x^2-36}$.

2 Simplify rational expressions.

Simplifying Rational Expressions

A rational expression is **simplified** if its numerator and denominator have no common factors other than 1 or -1. The following procedure can be used to simplify rational expressions:

Simplifying Rational Expressions

1. Factor the numerator and the denominator completely.
2. Divide both the numerator and the denominator by any common factors.

EXAMPLE 2 Simplifying Rational Expressions

Simplify: **a.** $\dfrac{x^3+x^2}{x+1}$ **b.** $\dfrac{x^2+6x+5}{x^2-25}$.

Solution

a. $\dfrac{x^3+x^2}{x+1} = \dfrac{x^2(x+1)}{x+1}$ Factor the numerator. Because the denominator is $x+1$, $x \neq -1$.

$= \dfrac{x^2\cancel{(x+1)}^{1}}{\cancel{x+1}_{1}}$ Divide out the common factor, $x+1$.

$= x^2, x \neq -1$ Denominators of 1 need not be written because $\frac{a}{1} = a$.

b. $\dfrac{x^2+6x+5}{x^2-25} = \dfrac{(x+5)(x+1)}{(x+5)(x-5)}$ Factor the numerator and denominator. Because the denominator is $(x+5)(x-5)$, $x \neq -5$ and $x \neq 5$.

$= \dfrac{\cancel{(x+5)}^{1}(x+1)}{\cancel{(x+5)}_{1}(x-5)}$ Divide out the common factor, $x+5$.

$= \dfrac{x+1}{x-5}, \quad x \neq -5, \quad x \neq 5$

Check Point 2 Simplify: **a.** $\dfrac{x^3+3x^2}{x+3}$ **b.** $\dfrac{x^2-1}{x^2+2x+1}$.

3 Multiply rational expressions.

Multiplying Rational Expressions

The product of two rational expressions is the product of their numerators divided by the product of their denominators. Here is a step-by-step procedure for multiplying rational expressions:

Multiplying Rational Expressions

1. Factor all numerators and denominators completely.
2. Divide numerators and denominators by common factors.
3. Multiply the remaining factors in the numerators and multiply the remaining factors in the denominators.

EXAMPLE 3 Multiplying Rational Expressions

Multiply and simplify:

$$\frac{x-7}{x-1} \cdot \frac{x^2-1}{3x-21}.$$

Solution

$$\frac{x-7}{x-1} \cdot \frac{x^2-1}{3x-21}$$

This is the given multiplication problem.

$$= \frac{x-7}{x-1} \cdot \frac{(x+1)(x-1)}{3(x-7)}$$

Factor as many numerators and denominators as possible. Because the denominator has factors of $x - 1$ and $x - 7$, $x \neq 1$ and $x \neq 7$.

$$= \frac{\overset{1}{\cancel{x-7}}}{\underset{1}{\cancel{x-1}}} \cdot \frac{(x+1)\overset{1}{\cancel{(x-1)}}}{3\underset{1}{\cancel{(x-7)}}}$$

Divide numerators and denominators by common factors.

$$= \frac{x+1}{3}, x \neq 1, x \neq 7$$

Multiply the remaining factors in the numerators and denominators.

These excluded numbers from the domain must also be excluded from the simplified expression's domain.

Check Point 3 Multiply and simplify:

$$\frac{x+3}{x^2-4} \cdot \frac{x^2-x-6}{x^2+6x+9}.$$

4 Divide rational expressions.

Dividing Rational Expressions

The quotient of two rational expressions is the product of the first expression and the multiplicative inverse, or reciprocal, of the second expression. The reciprocal is found by interchanging the numerator and the denominator. Thus, **we find the quotient of two rational expressions by inverting the divisor and multiplying.**

EXAMPLE 4 Dividing Rational Expressions

Divide and simplify:

$$\frac{x^2-2x-8}{x^2-9} \div \frac{x-4}{x+3}.$$

Solution

$$\frac{x^2 - 2x - 8}{x^2 - 9} \div \frac{x - 4}{x + 3}$$ This is the given division problem.

$$= \frac{x^2 - 2x - 8}{x^2 - 9} \cdot \frac{x + 3}{x - 4}$$ Invert the divisor and multiply.

$$= \frac{(x - 4)(x + 2)}{(x + 3)(x - 3)} \cdot \frac{x + 3}{x - 4}$$ Factor as many numerators and denominators as possible. For nonzero denominators, $x \neq -3$, $x \neq 3$, and $x \neq 4$.

$$= \frac{\overset{1}{\cancel{(x - 4)}}(x + 2)}{\underset{1}{\cancel{(x + 3)}}(x - 3)} \cdot \frac{\overset{1}{\cancel{(x + 3)}}}{\underset{1}{\cancel{(x - 4)}}}$$ Divide numerators and denominators by common factors.

$$= \frac{x + 2}{x - 3}, x \neq -3, x \neq 3, x \neq 4$$ Multiply the remaining factors in the numerators and the denominators.

Check Point 4 Divide and simplify:

$$\frac{x^2 - 2x + 1}{x^3 + x} \div \frac{x^2 + x - 2}{3x^2 + 3}.$$

5 Add and subtract rational expressions.

Adding and Subtracting Rational Expressions with the Same Denominator

We add or subtract rational expressions with the same denominator by (1) adding or subtracting the numerators, (2) placing this result over the common denominator, and (3) simplifying, if possible.

EXAMPLE 5 Subtracting Rational Expressions with the Same Denominator

Subtract: $\frac{5x + 1}{x^2 - 9} - \frac{4x - 2}{x^2 - 9}$.

Study Tip

Example 5 shows that when a numerator is being subtracted, we must subtract every term in that expression.

Solution

$$\frac{5x + 1}{x^2 - 9} - \frac{4x - 2}{x^2 - 9} = \frac{5x + 1 - (4x - 2)}{x^2 - 9}$$ Subtract numerators and include parentheses to indicate that both terms are subtracted. Place this difference over the common denominator.

$$= \frac{5x + 1 - 4x + 2}{x^2 - 9}$$ Remove parentheses and then change the sign of each term.

$$= \frac{x + 3}{x^2 - 9}$$ Combine like terms.

$$= \frac{\overset{1}{\cancel{x + 3}}}{\underset{1}{\cancel{(x + 3)}}(x - 3)}$$ Factor and simplify ($x \neq -3$ and $x \neq 3$).

$$= \frac{1}{x - 3}, x \neq -3, x \neq 3$$

Check Point 5 Subtract: $\frac{x}{x + 1} - \frac{3x + 2}{x + 1}$.

Adding and Subtracting Rational Expressions with Different Denominators

Rational expressions that have no common factors in their denominators can be added or subtracted using one of the following properties:

$$\frac{a}{b} + \frac{c}{d} = \frac{ad + bc}{bd} \qquad \frac{a}{b} - \frac{c}{d} = \frac{ad - bc}{bd}, b \neq 0, d \neq 0.$$

The denominator, bd, is the product of the factors in the two denominators. Because we are looking at rational expressions that have no common factors in their denominators, the product bd gives the least common denominator.

EXAMPLE 6 Subtracting Rational Expressions Having No Common Factors in Their Denominators

Subtract: $\frac{x+2}{2x-3} - \frac{4}{x+3}$.

Solution We need to find the least common denominator. This is the product of the distinct factors in each denominator, namely $(2x - 3)(x + 3)$. We can therefore use the subtraction property given previously as follows:

$$\frac{a}{b} - \frac{c}{d} = \frac{ad - bc}{bd}$$

$$\frac{x+2}{2x-3} - \frac{4}{x+3} = \frac{(x+2)(x+3) - (2x-3)4}{(2x-3)(x+3)}$$

Observe that $a = x + 2$, $b = 2x - 3$, $c = 4$, and $d = x + 3$.

$$= \frac{x^2 + 5x + 6 - (8x - 12)}{(2x-3)(x+3)}$$

Multiply.

$$= \frac{x^2 + 5x + 6 - 8x + 12}{(2x-3)(x+3)}$$

Remove parentheses and then change the sign of each term.

$$= \frac{x^2 - 3x + 18}{(2x-3)(x+3)}, x \neq \frac{3}{2}, x \neq -3$$

Combine like terms in the numerator.

Check Point 6 Add: $\frac{3}{x+1} + \frac{5}{x-1}$.

The **least common denominator**, or LCD, of several rational expressions is a polynomial consisting of the product of all prime factors in the denominators, with each factor raised to the greatest power of its occurrence in any denominator. When adding and subtracting rational expressions that have different denominators with one or more common factors in the denominators, it is efficient to find the least common denominator first.

Finding the Least Common Denominator

1. Factor each denominator completely.
2. List the factors of the first denominator.
3. Add to the list in step 2 any factors of the second denominator that do not appear in the list.
4. Form the product of each different factor from the list in step 3. This product is the least common denominator.

EXAMPLE 7 Finding the Least Common Denominator

Find the least common denominator of

$$\frac{7}{5x^2 + 15x} \quad \text{and} \quad \frac{9}{x^2 + 6x + 9}.$$

Solution

Step 1 Factor each denominator completely.

$$5x^2 + 15x = 5x(x + 3)$$
$$x^2 + 6x + 9 = (x + 3)^2$$

Step 2 List the factors of the first denominator.

$$5, x, (x + 3)$$

Step 3 Add any unlisted factors from the second denominator. The second denominator is $(x + 3)^2$ or $(x + 3)(x + 3)$. One factor of $x + 3$ is already in our list, but the other factor is not. We add a second factor of $x + 3$ to the list. We have

$$5, x, (x + 3), (x + 3).$$

Step 4 The least common denominator is the product of all factors in the final list. Thus,

$$5x(x + 3)(x + 3), \quad \text{or} \quad 5x(x + 3)^2$$

is the least common denominator.

Check Point 7 Find the least common denominator of

$$\frac{3}{x^2 - 6x + 9} \quad \text{and} \quad \frac{7}{x^2 - 9}.$$

Finding the least common denominator for two (or more) rational expressions is the first step needed to add or subtract the expressions.

Adding and Subtracting Rational Expressions That Have Different Denominators

1. Find the LCD of the rational expressions.
2. Rewrite each rational expression as an equivalent expression whose denominator is the LCD. To do so, multiply the numerator and the denominator of each rational expression by any factor(s) needed to convert the denominator into the LCD.
3. Add or subtract numerators, placing the resulting expression over the LCD.
4. If possible, simplify the resulting rational expression.

EXAMPLE 8 Adding Rational Expressions with Different Denominators

Add: $\dfrac{x+3}{x^2+x-2}+\dfrac{2}{x^2-1}$.

Solution

Step 1 Find the least common denominator. Start by factoring the denominators.

$$x^2+x-2=(x+2)(x-1)$$
$$x^2-1=(x+1)(x-1)$$

The factors of the first denominator are $x+2$ and $x-1$. The only factor from the second denominator that is not listed is $x+1$. Thus, the least common denominator is

$$(x+2)(x-1)(x+1).$$

Step 2 Write equivalent expressions with the LCD as denominators. We must rewrite each rational expression with a denominator of $(x+2)(x-1)(x+1)$. We do so by multiplying both the numerator and the denominator of each rational expression by any factor(s) needed to convert the expression's denominator into the LCD.

$$\frac{x+3}{(x+2)(x-1)}\cdot\frac{x+1}{x+1}=\frac{(x+3)(x+1)}{(x+2)(x-1)(x+1)}\qquad\frac{2}{(x+1)(x-1)}\cdot\frac{x+2}{x+2}=\frac{2(x+2)}{(x+2)(x+1)(x-1)}$$

Multiply the numerator and denominator by $x+1$ to get $(x+2)(x-1)(x+1)$, the LCD.

Multiply the numerator and denominator by $x+2$ to get $(x+2)(x+1)(x-1)$, the LCD.

Because $\dfrac{x+1}{x+1}=1$ and $\dfrac{x+2}{x+2}=1$, we are not changing the value of either rational expression, only its appearance.

Now we are ready to perform the indicated addition.

$$\frac{x+3}{x^2+x-2}+\frac{2}{x^2-1}$$

This is the given problem.

$$=\frac{x+3}{(x+2)(x-1)}+\frac{2}{(x+1)(x-1)}$$

Factor the denominators. The LCD is $(x+2)(x+1)(x-1)$.

$$=\frac{(x+3)(x+1)}{(x+2)(x-1)(x+1)}+\frac{2(x+2)}{(x+2)(x-1)(x+1)}$$

Rewrite equivalent expressions with the LCD.

Step 3 Add numerators, putting this sum over the LCD.

$$=\frac{(x+3)(x+1)+2(x+2)}{(x+2)(x-1)(x+1)}$$

$$=\frac{x^2+4x+3+2x+4}{(x+2)(x-1)(x+1)}$$

Perform the multiplications in the numerator.

$$=\frac{x^2+6x+7}{(x+2)(x-1)(x+1)},\ x\neq-2,\ x\neq1,\ x\neq-1$$

Combine like terms in the numerator: $4x+2x=6x$ and $3+4=7$.

Step 4 If necessary, simplify. Because the numerator is prime, no further simplification is possible.

Check Point 8 Subtract: $\dfrac{x}{x^2-10x+25}-\dfrac{x-4}{2x-10}$.

6 Simplify complex rational expressions.

Complex Rational Expressions

Complex rational expressions, also called **complex fractions**, have numerators or denominators containing one or more rational expressions. Here are two examples of such expressions:

$$\frac{1+\frac{1}{x}}{1-\frac{1}{x}}$$

Separate rational expressions occur in the numerator and the denominator.

$$\frac{\frac{1}{x+h}-\frac{1}{x}}{h}.$$

Separate rational expressions occur in the numerator.

One method for simplifying a complex rational expression is to combine its numerator into a single expression and combine its denominator into a single expression. Then perform the division by inverting the denominator and multiplying.

EXAMPLE 9 Simplifying a Complex Rational Expression

Simplify: $\dfrac{1+\frac{1}{x}}{1-\frac{1}{x}}$.

Solution

Step 1 Add to get a single rational expression in the numerator.

$$1+\frac{1}{x}=\frac{1}{1}+\frac{1}{x}=\frac{1\cdot x}{1\cdot x}+\frac{1}{x}=\frac{x}{x}+\frac{1}{x}=\frac{x+1}{x}$$

The LCD is $1 \cdot x$, or x.

Step 2 Subtract to get a single rational expression in the denominator.

$$1-\frac{1}{x}=\frac{1}{1}-\frac{1}{x}=\frac{1\cdot x}{1\cdot x}-\frac{1}{x}=\frac{x}{x}-\frac{1}{x}=\frac{x-1}{x}$$

The LCD is $1 \cdot x$, or x.

Step 3 Perform the division indicated by the main fraction bar: Invert and multiply. If possible, simplify.

$$\frac{1+\frac{1}{x}}{1-\frac{1}{x}}=\frac{\frac{x+1}{x}}{\frac{x-1}{x}}=\frac{x+1}{x}\cdot\frac{x}{x-1}=\frac{x+1}{\cancel{x}_1}\cdot\frac{\cancel{x}^1}{x-1}=\frac{x+1}{x-1}$$

Invert and multiply.

Check Point 9 Simplify: $\dfrac{\frac{1}{x}-\frac{3}{2}}{\frac{1}{x}+\frac{3}{4}}$.

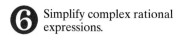

A second method for simplifying a complex rational expression is to find the least common denominator of all the rational expressions in its numerator and denominator. Then multiply each term in its numerator and denominator by this least common denominator. Because we are multiplying by a form of 1, we will obtain an equivalent expression that does not contain fractions in its numerator or denominator. Here we use this method to simplify the complex rational expression in Example 9.

$$\frac{1+\frac{1}{x}}{1-\frac{1}{x}} = \frac{\left(1+\frac{1}{x}\right)}{\left(1-\frac{1}{x}\right)} \cdot \frac{x}{x}$$

The least common denominator of all the rational expressions is x. Multiply the numerator and denominator by x. Because $\frac{x}{x} = 1$, we are not changing the complex fraction ($x \neq 0$).

$$= \frac{1 \cdot x + \frac{1}{x} \cdot x}{1 \cdot x - \frac{1}{x} \cdot x}$$

Use the distributive property. Be sure to distribute x to every term.

$$= \frac{x+1}{x-1}, x \neq 0, x \neq 1$$

Multiply. The complex rational expression is now simplified.

EXAMPLE 10 Simplifying a Complex Rational Expression

Simplify: $\dfrac{\frac{1}{x+h} - \frac{1}{x}}{h}$.

Solution We will use the method of multiplying each of the three terms, $\frac{1}{x+h}$, $\frac{1}{x}$, and h by the least common denominator. The least common denominator is $x(x+h)$.

$$\frac{\frac{1}{x+h} - \frac{1}{x}}{h}$$

$$= \frac{\left(\frac{1}{x+h} - \frac{1}{x}\right)x(x+h)}{hx(x+h)}$$

Multiply the numerator and denominator by $x(x+h)$, $h \neq 0, x \neq 0, x \neq -h$.

$$= \frac{\frac{1}{x+h} \cdot x(x+h) - \frac{1}{x} \cdot x(x+h)}{hx(x+h)}$$

Use the distributive property in the numerator.

$$= \frac{x-(x+h)}{hx(x+h)}$$

Simplify: $\frac{1}{\cancel{x+h}} \cdot x(\cancel{x+h}) = x$ and $\frac{1}{\cancel{x}} \cdot \cancel{x}(x+h) = x+h$.

$$= \frac{x-x-h}{hx(x+h)}$$

Subtract in the numerator.

$$= \frac{-\overset{1}{\cancel{h}}}{\underset{1}{\cancel{h}}x(x+h)}$$

Simplify: $x - x - h = -h$.

$$= -\frac{1}{x(x+h)}, h \neq 0, x \neq 0, x \neq -h$$

Divide the numerator and denominator by h.

Check Point 10 Simplify: $\dfrac{\frac{1}{x+7} - \frac{1}{x}}{7}$.

EXERCISE SET P.6

Practice Exercises

In Exercises 1–6, find all numbers that must be excluded from the domain of each rational expression.

1. $\frac{7}{x-3}$ **2.** $\frac{13}{x+9}$

3. $\frac{x+5}{x^2-25}$ **4.** $\frac{x+7}{x^2-49}$

5. $\frac{x-1}{x^2+11x+10}$ **6.** $\frac{x-3}{x^2+4x-45}$

In Exercises 7–14, simplify each rational expression. Find all numbers that must be excluded from the domain of the simplified rational expression.

7. $\frac{3x-9}{x^2-6x+9}$ **8.** $\frac{4x-8}{x^2-4x+4}$

9. $\frac{x^2-12x+36}{4x-24}$ **10.** $\frac{x^2-8x+16}{3x-12}$

11. $\frac{y^2+7y-18}{y^2-3y+2}$ **12.** $\frac{y^2-4y-5}{y^2+5y+4}$

13. $\frac{x^2+12x+36}{x^2-36}$ **14.** $\frac{x^2-14x+49}{x^2-49}$

In Exercises 15–32, multiply or divide as indicated.

15. $\frac{x-2}{3x+9}\cdot\frac{2x+6}{2x-4}$ **16.** $\frac{6x+9}{3x-15}\cdot\frac{x-5}{4x+6}$

17. $\frac{x^2-9}{x^2}\cdot\frac{x^2-3x}{x^2+x-12}$ **18.** $\frac{x^2-4}{x^2-4x+4}\cdot\frac{2x-4}{x+2}$

19. $\frac{x^2-5x+6}{x^2-2x-3}\cdot\frac{x^2-1}{x^2-4}$ **20.** $\frac{x^2+5x+6}{x^2+x-6}\cdot\frac{x^2-9}{x^2-x-6}$

21. $\frac{x^3-8}{x^2-4}\cdot\frac{x+2}{3x}$ **22.** $\frac{x^2+6x+9}{x^3+27}\cdot\frac{1}{x+3}$

23. $\frac{x+1}{3}\div\frac{3x+3}{7}$ **24.** $\frac{x+5}{7}\div\frac{4x+20}{9}$

25. $\frac{x^2-4}{x}\div\frac{x+2}{x-2}$ **26.** $\frac{x^2-4}{x-2}\div\frac{x+2}{4x-8}$

27. $\frac{4x^2+10}{x-3}\div\frac{6x^2+15}{x^2-9}$ **28.** $\frac{x^2+x}{x^2-4}\div\frac{x^2-1}{x^2+5x+6}$

29. $\frac{x^2-25}{2x-2}\div\frac{x^2+10x+25}{x^2+4x-5}$

30. $\frac{x^2-4}{x^2+3x-10}\div\frac{x^2+5x+6}{x^2+8x+15}$

31. $\frac{x^2+x-12}{x^2+x-30}\cdot\frac{x^2+5x+6}{x^2-2x-3}\div\frac{x+3}{x^2+7x+6}$

32. $\frac{x^3-25x}{4x^2}\cdot\frac{2x^2-2}{x^2-6x+5}\div\frac{x^2+5x}{7x+7}$

In Exercises 33–54, add or subtract as indicated.

33. $\frac{4x+1}{6x+5}+\frac{8x+9}{6x+5}$ **34.** $\frac{3x+2}{3x+4}+\frac{3x+6}{3x+4}$

35. $\frac{x^2-2x}{x^2+3x}+\frac{x^2+x}{x^2+3x}$ **36.** $\frac{x^2-4x}{x^2-x-6}+\frac{4x-4}{x^2-x-6}$

37. $\frac{4x-10}{x-2}-\frac{x-4}{x-2}$ **38.** $\frac{2x+3}{3x-6}-\frac{3-x}{3x-6}$

39. $\frac{x^2+3x}{x^2+x-12}-\frac{x^2-12}{x^2+x-12}$

40. $\frac{x^2-4x}{x^2-x-6}-\frac{x-6}{x^2-x-6}$

41. $\frac{3}{x+4}+\frac{6}{x+5}$ **42.** $\frac{8}{x-2}+\frac{2}{x-3}$

43. $\frac{3}{x+1}-\frac{3}{x}$ **44.** $\frac{4}{x}-\frac{3}{x+3}$

45. $\frac{2x}{x+2}+\frac{x+2}{x-2}$ **46.** $\frac{3x}{x-3}-\frac{x+4}{x+2}$

47. $\frac{x+5}{x-5}+\frac{x-5}{x+5}$ **48.** $\frac{x+3}{x-3}+\frac{x-3}{x+3}$

49. $\frac{4}{x^2+6x+9}+\frac{4}{x+3}$ **50.** $\frac{3}{5x+2}+\frac{5x}{25x^2-4}$

51. $\frac{3x}{x^2+3x-10}-\frac{2x}{x^2+x-6}$

52. $\frac{x}{x^2-2x-24}-\frac{x}{x^2-7x+6}$

53. $\frac{4x^2+x-6}{x^2+3x+2}-\frac{3x}{x+1}+\frac{5}{x+2}$

54. $\frac{6x^2+17x-40}{x^2+x-20}+\frac{3}{x-4}-\frac{5x}{x+5}$

In Exercises 55–68, simplify each complex rational expression.

55. $\frac{\frac{x}{3}-1}{x-3}$ **56.** $\frac{\frac{x}{4}-1}{x-4}$

57. $\frac{1+\frac{1}{x}}{3-\frac{1}{x}}$ **58.** $\frac{8+\frac{1}{x}}{4-\frac{1}{x}}$

59. $\frac{\frac{1}{x}+\frac{1}{y}}{x+y}$ **60.** $\frac{1-\frac{1}{x}}{xy}$

61. $\frac{x-\frac{x}{x+3}}{x+2}$ **62.** $\frac{x-3}{x-\frac{3}{x-2}}$

63. $\frac{\frac{3}{x-2}-\frac{4}{x+2}}{\frac{7}{x^2-4}}$ **64.** $\frac{\frac{x}{x-2}+1}{\frac{3}{x^2-4}+1}$

65. $\dfrac{\dfrac{1}{x+1}}{\dfrac{1}{x^2-2x-3}+\dfrac{1}{x-3}}$

66. $\dfrac{\dfrac{6}{x^2+2x-15}-\dfrac{1}{x-3}}{\dfrac{1}{x+5}+1}$

67. $\dfrac{\dfrac{1}{(x+h)^2}-\dfrac{1}{x^2}}{h}$

68. $\dfrac{\dfrac{x+h}{x+h+1}-\dfrac{x}{x+1}}{h}$

Practice Plus

In Exercises 69–76, perform the indicated operations. Simplify the result, if possible.

69. $\left(\dfrac{2x+3}{x+1}\cdot\dfrac{x^2+4x-5}{2x^2+x-3}\right)-\dfrac{2}{x+2}$

70. $\dfrac{1}{x^2-2x-8}\div\left(\dfrac{1}{x-4}-\dfrac{1}{x+2}\right)$

71. $\left(2-\dfrac{6}{x+1}\right)\left(1+\dfrac{3}{x-2}\right)$

72. $\left(4-\dfrac{3}{x+2}\right)\left(1+\dfrac{5}{x-1}\right)$

73. $\dfrac{y^{-1}-(y+5)^{-1}}{5}$

74. $\dfrac{y^{-1}-(y+2)^{-1}}{2}$

75. $\left(\dfrac{1}{a^3-b^3}\cdot\dfrac{ac+ad-bc-bd}{1}\right)-\dfrac{c-d}{a^2+ab+b^2}$

76. $\dfrac{ab}{a^2+ab+b^2}+\left(\dfrac{ac-ad-bc+bd}{ac-ad+bc-bd}\div\dfrac{a^3-b^3}{a^3+b^3}\right)$

Application Exercises

77. The rational expression

$$\frac{130x}{100-x}$$

describes the cost, in millions of dollars, to inoculate x percent of the population against a particular strain of flu.

a. Evaluate the expression for $x = 40$, $x = 80$, and $x = 90$. Describe the meaning of each evaluation in terms of percentage inoculated and cost.

b. For what value of x is the expression undefined?

c. What happens to the cost as x approaches 100%? How can you interpret this observation?

78. Doctors use the rational expression

$$\frac{DA}{A+12}$$

to determine the dosage of a drug prescribed for children. In this expression, A = child's age and D = adult dosage. What is the difference in the child's dosage for a 7-year-old child and a 3-year-old child? Express the answer as a single rational expression in terms of D. Then describe what your answer means in terms of the variables in the rational expression.

79. The bar graph shows the total number of crimes in the United States, in millions, from 1995 through 2002.

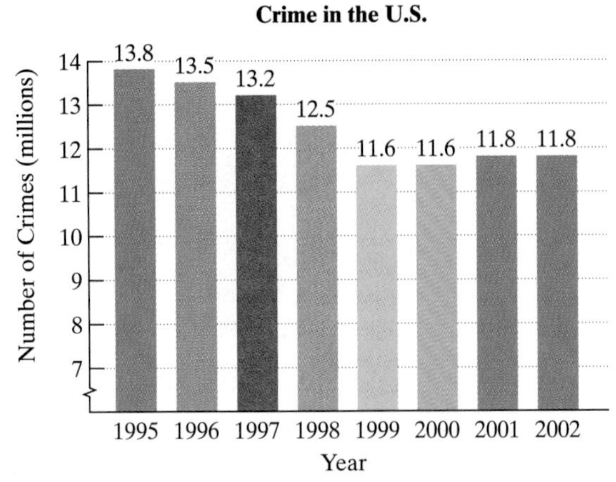

Source: FBI

The polynomial $3.6t + 260$ describes the U.S. population, in millions, t years after 1994. The polynomial $-0.3t + 14$ describes the number of crimes in the United States, in millions, t years after 1994.

a. Write a rational expression that describes the crime rate in the United States t years after 1994.

b. According to the rational expression in part (a), what was the crime rate in 2002? Round to two decimal places. How many crimes does this indicate per 100,000 inhabitants?

c. According to the FBI, there were 4119 crimes per 100,000 U.S. inhabitants in 2002. How well does the rational expression that you evaluated in part (b) model this number?

80. The average rate on a round-trip commute having a one-way distance d is given by the complex rational expression

$$\frac{2d}{\dfrac{d}{r_1}+\dfrac{d}{r_2}},$$

in which r_1 and r_2 are the average rates on the outgoing and return trips, respectively. Simplify the expression. Then find your average rate if you drive to campus averaging 40 miles per hour and return home on the same route averaging 30 miles per hour. Explain why the answer is not 25 miles per hour.

In Exercises 81–82, express the perimeter of each rectangle as a single rational expression.

81.

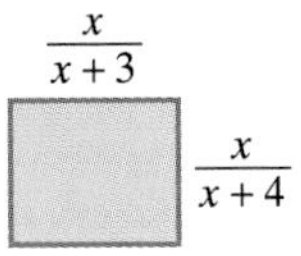

82.

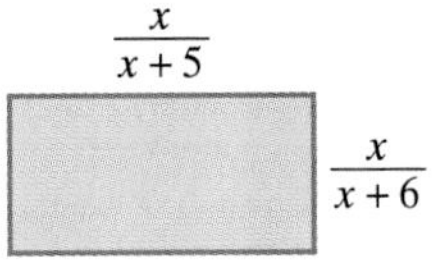

Writing in Mathematics

83. What is a rational expression?

84. Explain how to determine which numbers must be excluded from the domain of a rational expression.

85. Explain how to simplify a rational expression.

86. Explain how to multiply rational expressions.

87. Explain how to divide rational expressions.

88. Explain how to add or subtract rational expressions with the same denominators.

89. Explain how to add rational expressions having no common factors in their denominators. Use $\frac{3}{x+5} + \frac{7}{x+2}$ in your explanation.

90. Explain how to find the least common denominator for denominators of $x^2 - 100$ and $x^2 - 20x + 100$.

91. Describe two ways to simplify $\dfrac{\frac{3}{x} + \frac{2}{x^2}}{\frac{1}{x^2} + \frac{2}{x}}$.

Explain the error in Exercises 92–94. Then rewrite the right side of the equation to correct the error that now exists.

92. $\frac{1}{a} + \frac{1}{b} = \frac{1}{a+b}$

93. $\frac{1}{x} + 7 = \frac{1}{x+7}$

94. $\frac{a}{x} + \frac{a}{b} = \frac{a}{x+b}$

95. A politician claims that each year the crime rate in the United States is decreasing. Explain how to use the polynomials in Exercise 79 to verify this claim.

Critical Thinking Exercises

96. Which one of the following is true?

a. $\frac{a}{b} + \frac{a}{c} = \frac{a}{b+c}$ **b.** $6 + \frac{1}{x} = \frac{7}{x}$

c. $\frac{1}{x+3} + \frac{x+3}{2} = \frac{1}{\cancel{(x+3)}} + \frac{\cancel{(x+3)}}{2} = 1 + \frac{1}{2} = \frac{3}{2}$

d. $\frac{x^2 - 25}{x - 5} = x - 5$ **e.** None of the above is true.

In Exercises 97–99, perform the indicated operations.

97. $\frac{1}{x^n - 1} - \frac{1}{x^n + 1} - \frac{1}{x^{2n} - 1}$

98. $\left(1 - \frac{1}{x}\right)\left(1 - \frac{1}{x+1}\right)\left(1 - \frac{1}{x+2}\right)\left(1 - \frac{1}{x+3}\right)$

99. $(x - y)^{-1} + (x - y)^{-2}$

100. In one short sentence, five words or less, explain what

$$\frac{\frac{1}{x} + \frac{1}{x^2} + \frac{1}{x^3}}{\frac{1}{x^4} + \frac{1}{x^5} + \frac{1}{x^6}}$$

does to each number x.

Chapter P
Summary, Review, and Test

Summary: Basic Formulas

Definition of Absolute Value

$$|x| = \begin{cases} x & \text{if } x \ge 0 \\ -x & \text{if } x < 0 \end{cases}$$

Distance between Points a and b on a Number Line

$$|a - b| \quad \text{or} \quad |b - a|$$

Properties of Algebra

Commutative	$a + b = b + a$ $ab = ba$
Associative	$(a + b) + c = a + (b + c)$ $(ab)c = a(bc)$
Distributive	$a(b + c) = ab + ac$
Identity	$a + 0 = a$ $a \cdot 1 = a$
Inverse	$a + (-a) = 0$ $a \cdot \frac{1}{a} = 1, a \neq 0$

Properties of Exponents

$$b^{-n} = \frac{1}{b^n}, \quad b^0 = 1, \quad b^m \cdot b^n = b^{m+n},$$

$$(b^m)^n = b^{mn}, \quad \frac{b^m}{b^n} = b^{m-n}, \quad (ab)^n = a^n b^n, \quad \left(\frac{a}{b}\right)^n = \frac{a^n}{b^n}$$

Product and Quotient Rules for nth Roots

$$\sqrt[n]{ab} = \sqrt[n]{a} \cdot \sqrt[n]{b}, \quad \sqrt[n]{\frac{a}{b}} = \frac{\sqrt[n]{a}}{\sqrt[n]{b}}$$

Rational Exponents

$$a^{\frac{1}{n}} = \sqrt[n]{a}, \quad a^{-\frac{1}{n}} = \frac{1}{a^{\frac{1}{n}}} = \frac{1}{\sqrt[n]{a}},$$

$$a^{\frac{m}{n}} = (\sqrt[n]{a})^m = \sqrt[n]{a^m}, \quad a^{-\frac{m}{n}} = \frac{1}{a^{\frac{m}{n}}}$$

Special Products

$$(A + B)(A - B) = A^2 - B^2$$
$$(A + B)^2 = A^2 + 2AB + B^2$$
$$(A - B)^2 = A^2 - 2AB + B^2$$
$$(A + B)^3 = A^3 + 3A^2B + 3AB^2 + B^3$$
$$(A - B)^3 = A^3 - 3A^2B + 3AB^2 - B^3$$

Factoring Formulas

$$A^2 - B^2 = (A + B)(A - B)$$
$$A^2 + 2AB + B^2 = (A + B)^2$$
$$A^2 - 2AB + B^2 = (A - B)^2$$
$$A^3 + B^3 = (A + B)(A^2 - AB + B^2)$$
$$A^3 - B^3 = (A - B)(A^2 + AB + B^2)$$

Review Exercises

You can use these review exercises, like the review exercises at the end of each chapter, to test your understanding of the chapter's topics. However, you can also use these exercises as a prerequisite test to check your mastery of the fundamental algebra skills needed in this book.

P.1

In Exercises 1–2, evaluate each algebraic expression for the given value or values of the variable(s).

1. $3 + 6(x - 2)^3$ for $x = 4$

2. $x^2 - 5(x - y)$ for $x = 6$ and $y = 2$

3. You are riding along an expressway traveling x miles per hour. The formula

$$S = 0.015x^2 + x + 10$$

models the recommended safe distance, S, in feet, between your car and other cars on the expressway. What is the recommended safe distance when your speed is 60 miles per hour?

In Exercises 4–7, let $A = \{a, b, c\}$, $B = \{a, c, d, e\}$, and $C = \{a, d, f, g\}$. Find the indicated set.

4. $A \cap B$ **5.** $A \cup B$

6. $A \cup C$ **7.** $C \cap A$

8. Consider the set:

$$\left\{-17, -\tfrac{9}{13}, 0, 0.75, \sqrt{2}, \pi, \sqrt{81}\right\}.$$

List all numbers from the set that are **a.** natural numbers, **b.** whole numbers, **c.** integers, **d.** rational numbers, **e.** irrational numbers, **f.** real numbers.

In Exercises 9–11, rewrite each expression without absolute value bars.

9. $|-103|$ **10.** $|\sqrt{2} - 1|$

11. $|3 - \sqrt{17}|$

12. Express the distance between the numbers -17 and 4 using absolute value. Then evaluate the absolute value.

In Exercises 13–18, state the name of the property illustrated.

13. $3 + 17 = 17 + 3$

14. $(6 \cdot 3) \cdot 9 = 6 \cdot (3 \cdot 9)$

15. $\sqrt{3}(\sqrt{5} + \sqrt{3}) = \sqrt{15} + 3$

16. $(6 \cdot 9) \cdot 2 = 2 \cdot (6 \cdot 9)$

17. $\sqrt{3}(\sqrt{5} + \sqrt{3}) = (\sqrt{5} + \sqrt{3})\sqrt{3}$

18. $(3 \cdot 7) + (4 \cdot 7) = (4 \cdot 7) + (3 \cdot 7)$

In Exercises 19–22, simplify each algebraic expression.

19. $5(2x - 3) + 7x$

20. $\frac{1}{5}(5x) + [(3y) + (-3y)] - (-x)$

21. $3(4y - 5) - (7y + 2)$ **22.** $8 - 2[3 - (5x - 1)]$

23. The bar graph shows the number of endangered animal species in the United States for six selected years. The data can be modeled by the formulas $E = 10x + 166$ and $E = 0.04x^2 + 9.2x + 169$, in which E represents the number of endangered species x years after 1980. Which formula best describes the actual number of endangered animal species in 2000?

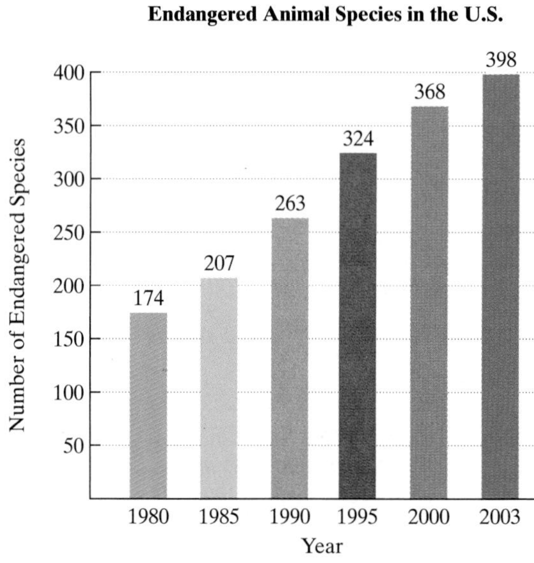

Source: U.S. Fish and Wildlife Service

P.2

Evaluate each exponential expression in Exercises 24–27.

24. $(-3)^3(-2)^2$ **25.** $2^{-4} + 4^{-1}$

26. $5^{-3} \cdot 5$ **27.** $\frac{3^3}{3^6}$

Simplify each exponential expression in Exercises 28–31.

28. $(-2x^4y^3)^3$ **29.** $(-5x^3y^2)(-2x^{-11}y^{-2})$

30. $(2x^3)^{-4}$ **31.** $\frac{7x^5y^6}{28x^{15}y^{-2}}$

In Exercises 32–33, write each number in decimal notation.

32. 3.74×10^4 **33.** 7.45×10^{-5}

In Exercises 34–35, write each number in scientific notation.

34. 3,590,000 **35.** 0.00725

In Exercises 36–37, perform the indicated operation and write the answer in decimal notation.

36. $(3 \times 10^3)(1.3 \times 10^2)$ **37.** $\frac{6.9 \times 10^3}{3 \times 10^5}$

38. If you earned \$1 million per year (\$$10^6$), how long would it take to accumulate \$1 billion (\$$10^9$)?

39. If the population of the United States is 2.9×10^8 and each person spends about \$150 per year going to the movies (or renting movies), express the total annual spending on movies in scientific notation.

P.3

Use the product rule to simplify the expressions in Exercises 40–43. In Exercises 42–43, assume that variables represent nonnegative real numbers.

40. $\sqrt{300}$
41. $\sqrt{12x^2}$
42. $\sqrt{10x} \cdot \sqrt{2x}$
43. $\sqrt{r^3}$

Use the quotient rule to simplify the expressions in Exercises 44–45.

44. $\sqrt{\frac{121}{4}}$
45. $\frac{\sqrt{96x^3}}{\sqrt{2x}}$ (Assume that $x > 0$.)

In Exercises 46–48, add or subtract terms whenever possible.

46. $7\sqrt{5} + 13\sqrt{5}$
47. $2\sqrt{50} + 3\sqrt{8}$
48. $4\sqrt{72} - 2\sqrt{48}$

In Exercises 49–52, rationalize the denominator.

49. $\frac{30}{\sqrt{5}}$
50. $\frac{\sqrt{2}}{\sqrt{3}}$
51. $\frac{5}{6 + \sqrt{3}}$
52. $\frac{14}{\sqrt{7} - \sqrt{5}}$

Evaluate each expression in Exercises 53–56 or indicate that the root is not a real number.

53. $\sqrt[3]{125}$
54. $\sqrt[5]{-32}$
55. $\sqrt[4]{-125}$
56. $\sqrt[4]{(-5)^4}$

Simplify the radical expressions in Exercises 57–61.

57. $\sqrt[3]{81}$
58. $\sqrt[3]{y^5}$
59. $\sqrt[3]{8} \cdot \sqrt[3]{10}$
60. $4\sqrt[3]{16} + 5\sqrt[3]{2}$
61. $\frac{\sqrt[4]{32x^5}}{\sqrt[4]{16x}}$ (Assume that $x > 0$.)

In Exercises 62–67, evaluate each expression.

62. $16^{\frac{1}{2}}$
63. $25^{-\frac{1}{2}}$
64. $125^{\frac{1}{3}}$
65. $27^{-\frac{1}{3}}$
66. $64^{\frac{2}{3}}$
67. $27^{-\frac{4}{3}}$

In Exercises 68–70, simplify using properties of exponents.

68. $\left(5x^{\frac{2}{3}}\right)\left(4x^{\frac{1}{4}}\right)$
69. $\frac{15x^{\frac{3}{4}}}{5x^{\frac{1}{2}}}$
70. $(125x^6)^{\frac{2}{3}}$

71. Simplify by reducing the index of the radical: $\sqrt[6]{y^3}$.

P.4

In Exercises 72–73, perform the indicated operations. Write the resulting polynomial in standard form and indicate its degree.

72. $(-6x^3 + 7x^2 - 9x + 3) + (14x^3 + 3x^2 - 11x - 7)$
73. $(13x^4 - 8x^3 + 2x^2) - (5x^4 - 3x^3 + 2x^2 - 6)$

In Exercises 74–80, find each product.

74. $(3x - 2)(4x^2 + 3x - 5)$
75. $(3x - 5)(2x + 1)$
76. $(4x + 5)(4x - 5)$
77. $(2x + 5)^2$
78. $(3x - 4)^2$
79. $(2x + 1)^3$
80. $(5x - 2)^3$

In Exercises 81–82, perform the indicated operations. Indicate the degree of the resulting polynomial.

81. $(7x^2 - 8xy + y^2) + (-8x^2 - 9xy - 4y^2)$
82. $(13x^3y^2 - 5x^2y - 9x^2) - (-11x^3y^2 - 6x^2y + 3x^2 - 4)$

In Exercises 83–87, find each product.

83. $(x + 7y)(3x - 5y)$
84. $(3x - 5y)^2$
85. $(3x^2 + 2y)^2$
86. $(7x + 4y)(7x - 4y)$
87. $(a - b)(a^2 + ab + b^2)$

P.5

In Exercises 88–104, factor completely, or state that the polynomial is prime.

88. $15x^3 + 3x^2$
89. $x^2 - 11x + 28$
90. $15x^2 - x - 2$
91. $64 - x^2$
92. $x^2 + 16$
93. $3x^4 - 9x^3 - 30x^2$
94. $20x^7 - 36x^3$
95. $x^3 - 3x^2 - 9x + 27$
96. $16x^2 - 40x + 25$
97. $x^4 - 16$
98. $y^3 - 8$
99. $x^3 + 64$
100. $3x^4 - 12x^2$
101. $27x^3 - 125$
102. $x^5 - x$
103. $x^3 + 5x^2 - 2x - 10$
104. $x^2 + 18x + 81 - y^2$

In Exercises 105–107, factor and simplify each algebraic expression.

105. $16x^{-\frac{3}{4}} + 32x^{\frac{1}{4}}$
106. $(x^2 - 4)(x^2 + 3)^{\frac{1}{2}} - (x^2 - 4)^2(x^2 + 3)^{\frac{3}{2}}$
107. $12x^{-\frac{1}{2}} + 6x^{-\frac{3}{2}}$

P.6

In Exercises 108–110, simplify each rational expression. Also, list all numbers that must be excluded from the domain.

108. $\frac{x^3 + 2x^2}{x + 2}$
109. $\frac{x^2 + 3x - 18}{x^2 - 36}$
110. $\frac{x^2 + 2x}{x^2 + 4x + 4}$

In Exercises 111–113, multiply or divide as indicated.

111. $\frac{x^2 + 6x + 9}{x^2 - 4} \cdot \frac{x + 3}{x - 2}$
112. $\frac{6x + 2}{x^2 - 1} \div \frac{3x^2 + x}{x - 1}$
113. $\frac{x^2 - 5x - 24}{x^2 - x - 12} \div \frac{x^2 - 10x + 16}{x^2 + x - 6}$

In Exercises 114–117, add or subtract as indicated.

114. $\frac{2x - 7}{x^2 - 9} - \frac{x - 10}{x^2 - 9}$
115. $\frac{3x}{x + 2} + \frac{x}{x - 2}$
116. $\frac{x}{x^2 - 9} + \frac{x - 1}{x^2 - 5x + 6}$
117. $\frac{4x - 1}{2x^2 + 5x - 3} - \frac{x + 3}{6x^2 + x - 2}$

In Exercises 118–120, simplify each complex rational expression.

118. $\frac{\frac{1}{x} - \frac{1}{2}}{\frac{1}{3} - \frac{x}{6}}$
119. $\frac{3 + \frac{12}{x}}{1 - \frac{16}{x^2}}$
120. $\frac{3 - \frac{1}{x + 3}}{3 + \frac{1}{x + 3}}$

Chapter P Test

In Exercises 1–18, simplify the given expression or perform the indicated operation (and simplify, if possible), whichever is appropriate.

1. $5(2x^2 - 6x) - (4x^2 - 3x)$

2. $7 + 2[3(x + 1) - 2(3x - 1)]$

3. $\{1, 2, 5\} \cap \{5, a\}$ **4.** $\{1, 2, 5\} \cup \{5, a\}$

5. $(2x^2y^3 - xy + y^2) - (-4x^2y^3 - 5xy - y^2)$

6. $\dfrac{30x^3y^4}{6x^9y^{-4}}$

7. $\sqrt{6r}\sqrt{3r}$ (Assume that $r \geq 0$.)

8. $4\sqrt{50} - 3\sqrt{18}$

9. $\dfrac{3}{5 + \sqrt{2}}$ **10.** $\sqrt[3]{16x^4}$

11. $\dfrac{x^2 + 2x - 3}{x^2 - 3x + 2}$

12. $\dfrac{5 \times 10^{-6}}{20 \times 10^{-8}}$ (Express the answer in scientific notation.)

13. $(2x - 5)(x^2 - 4x + 3)$ **14.** $(5x + 3y)^2$

15. $\dfrac{2x + 8}{x - 3} \div \dfrac{x^2 + 5x + 4}{x^2 - 9}$ **16.** $\dfrac{x}{x + 3} + \dfrac{5}{x - 3}$

17. $\dfrac{2x + 3}{x^2 - 7x + 12} - \dfrac{2}{x - 3}$ **18.** $\dfrac{\frac{1}{x} - \frac{1}{3}}{\frac{1}{x}}$

In Exercises 19–24, factor completely, or state that the polynomial is prime.

19. $x^2 - 9x + 18$ **20.** $x^3 + 2x^2 + 3x + 6$

21. $25x^2 - 9$ **22.** $36x^2 - 84x + 49$

23. $y^3 - 125$ **24.** $x^2 + 10x + 25 - 9y^2$

25. Factor and simplify:

$$x(x + 3)^{-\frac{3}{5}} + (x + 3)^{\frac{2}{5}}.$$

26. List all the rational numbers in this set:

$$\left\{-7, -\tfrac{4}{5}, 0, 0.25, \sqrt{3}, \sqrt{4}, \tfrac{22}{7}, \pi\right\}.$$

In Exercises 27–28, state the name of the property illustrated.

27. $3(2 + 5) = 3(5 + 2)$ **28.** $6(7 + 4) = 6 \cdot 7 + 6 \cdot 4$

29. Express in scientific notation: 0.00076.

30. Evaluate: $27^{-\frac{5}{3}}$.

31. In 2003, world population was approximately 6.3×10^9. By some projections, world population will double by 2040. Express the population at that time in scientific notation.

32. Your life expectancy is related to the year when you were born. The bar graph shows life expectancy in the United States by year of birth.

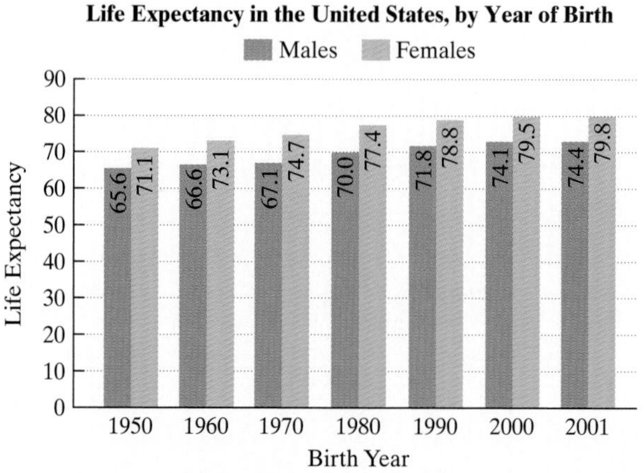

Source: U.S. Bureau of the Census

Here are two mathematical models for the data shown in the graph. In each formula, E represents life expectancy for Americans born t years after 1950.

Model 1 $E = 0.17t + 71$

Model 2 $E = 0.18t + 65$

a. Which model describes the data for the men and which model describes the data for the women?

b. According to the model that describes the data for the men, what is the life expectancy for U.S. men born in 2000? How well does the model describe the life expectancy shown in the graph?

CHAPTER 1

Equations and Inequalities

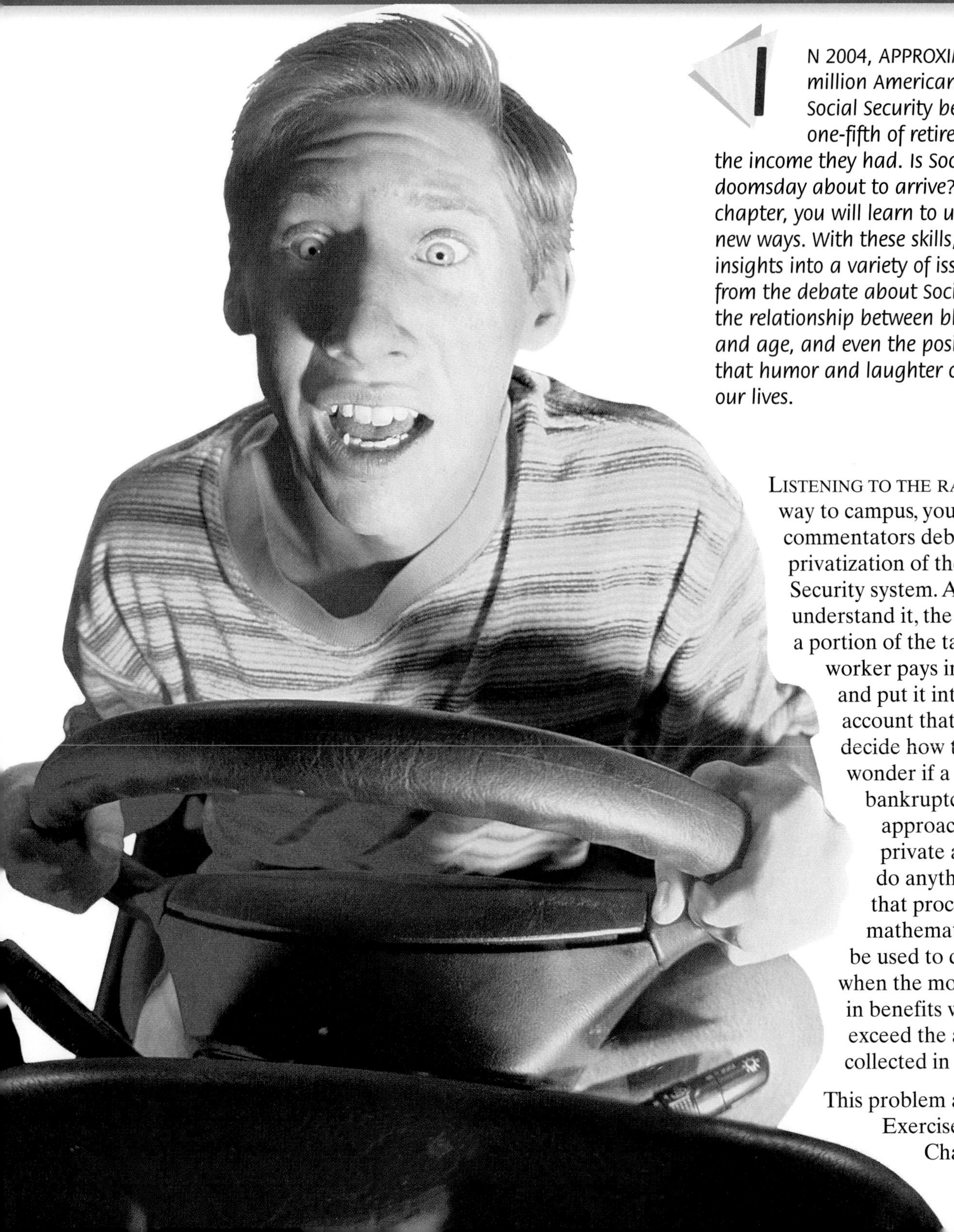

IN 2004, APPROXIMATELY 48 million Americans received Social Security benefits. For one-fifth of retirees, this was all the income they had. Is Social Security doomsday about to arrive? In this chapter, you will learn to use formulas in new ways. With these skills, you will gain insights into a variety of issues, ranging from the debate about Social Security to the relationship between blood pressure and age, and even the positive benefits that humor and laughter can have on our lives.

LISTENING TO THE RADIO ON THE way to campus, you hear political commentators debating the privatization of the Social Security system. As you understand it, the idea is to take a portion of the tax every worker pays into the system and put it into a savings account that workers can decide how to invest. You wonder if a crisis and bankruptcy are fast approaching, and if private accounts will do anything to slow that process. How can mathematical models be used to determine when the money paid out in benefits will begin to exceed the amount collected in taxes?

This problem appears as Exercises 35–37 in the Chapter 1 Test.

SECTION 1.1 Graphs and Graphing Utilities

Objectives

1. Plot points in the rectangular coordinate system.
2. Graph equations in the rectangular coordinate system.
3. Interpret information about a graphing utility's viewing rectangle or table.
4. Use a graph to determine intercepts.
5. Interpret information given by graphs.

The beginning of the seventeenth century was a time of innovative ideas and enormous intellectual progress in Europe. English theatergoers enjoyed a succession of exciting new plays by Shakespeare. William Harvey proposed the radical notion that the heart was a pump for blood rather than the center of emotion. Galileo, with his new-fangled invention called the telescope, supported the theory of Polish astronomer Copernicus that the sun, not the Earth, was the center of the solar system. Monteverdi was writing the world's first grand operas. French mathematicians Pascal and Fermat invented a new field of mathematics called probability theory.

Into this arena of intellectual electricity stepped French aristocrat René Descartes (1596–1650). Descartes (pronounced "day cart"), propelled by the creativity surrounding him, developed a new branch of mathematics that brought together algebra and geometry in a unified way—a way that visualized numbers as points on a graph, equations as geometric figures, and geometric figures as equations. This new branch of mathematics, called *analytic geometry*, established Descartes as one of the founders of modern thought and among the most original mathematicians and philosophers of any age. We begin this section by looking at Descartes's deceptively simple idea, called the **rectangular coordinate system** or (in his honor) the **Cartesian coordinate system**.

1 Plot points in the rectangular coordinate system.

Points and Ordered Pairs

Descartes used two number lines that intersect at right angles at their zero points, as shown in Figure 1.1. The horizontal number line is the ***x*-axis**. The vertical number line is the ***y*-axis**. The point of intersection of these axes is their zero points, called the **origin**. Positive numbers are shown to the right and above the origin. Negative numbers are shown to the left and below the origin. The axes divide the plane into four quarters, called **quadrants**. The points located on the axes are not in any quadrant.

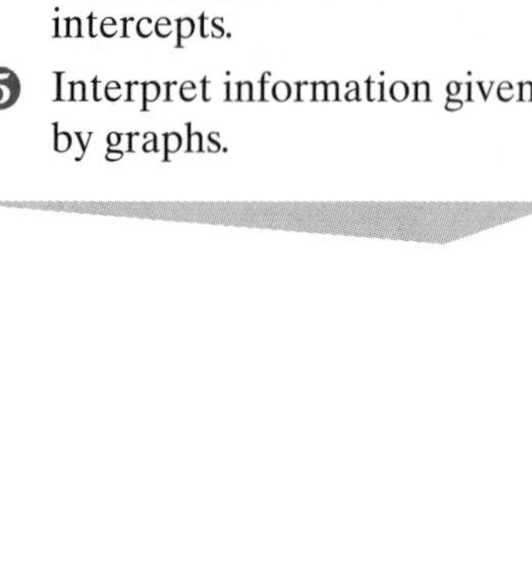

Figure 1.1 The rectangular coordinate system

Each point in the rectangular coordinate system corresponds to an **ordered pair** of real numbers, (x, y). Examples of such pairs are $(-5, 3)$ and $(3, -5)$. The first number in each pair, called the ***x*-coordinate**, denotes the distance and direction from the origin along the x-axis. The second number in each pair, called the ***y*-coordinate**, denotes vertical distance and direction along a line parallel to the y-axis or along the y-axis itself.

Figure 1.2 shows how we **plot**, or locate, the points corresponding to the ordered pairs $(-5, 3)$ and $(3, -5)$. We plot $(-5, 3)$ by going 5 units from 0 to the left along the x-axis. Then we go 3 units up parallel to the y-axis. We plot $(3, -5)$ by going 3 units from 0 to the right along the x-axis and 5 units down parallel to the y-axis. The phrase "the points corresponding to the ordered pairs $(-5, 3)$ and $(3, -5)$" is often abbreviated as "the points $(-5, 3)$ and $(3, -5)$."

Study Tip

The phrase *ordered pair* is used because order is important. The order in which coordinates appear makes a difference in a point's location. This is illustrated in Figure 1.2.

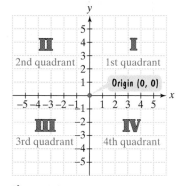

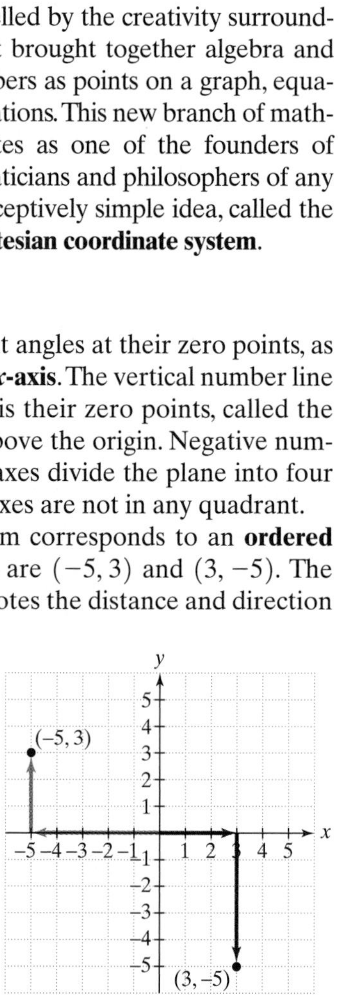

Figure 1.2 Plotting $(-5, 3)$ and $(3, -5)$

EXAMPLE 1 Plotting Points in the Rectangular Coordinate System

Plot the points: $A(-3, 5)$, $B(2, -4)$, $C(5, 0)$, $D(-5, -3)$, $E(0, 4)$ and $F(0, 0)$.

Solution See Figure 1.3. We move from the origin and plot the points in the following way:

$A(-3, 5)$:	3 units left, 5 units up
$B(2, -4)$:	2 units right, 4 units down
$C(5, 0)$:	5 units right, 0 units up or down
$D(-5, -3)$:	5 units left, 3 units down
$E(0, 4)$:	0 units right or left, 4 units up
$F(0, 0)$:	0 units right or left, 0 units up or down

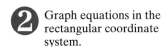

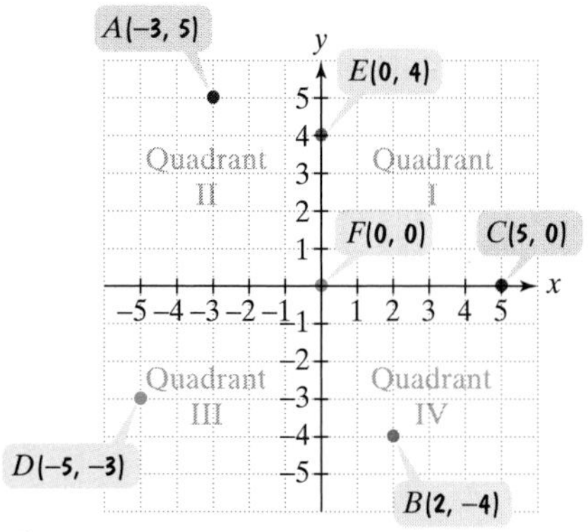

Figure 1.3 Plotting points

Reminder: Answers to all Check Point exercises are given in the answer section. Check your answer before continuing your reading to verify that you understand the concept.

Check Point 1 Plot the points: $A(-2, 4)$, $B(4, -2)$, $C(-3, 0)$, and $D(0, -3)$.

2 Graph equations in the rectangular coordinate system.

Graphs of Equations

A relationship between two quantities can be expressed as an **equation in two variables**, such as

$$y = 4 - x^2.$$

A **solution of an equation in two variables**, x and y, is an ordered pair of real numbers with the following property: When the x-coordinate is substituted for x and the y-coordinate is substituted for y in the equation, we obtain a true statement. For example, consider the equation $y = 4 - x^2$ and the ordered pair $(3, -5)$. When 3 is substituted for x and -5 is substituted for y, we obtain the statement $-5 = 4 - 3^2$, or $-5 = 4 - 9$, or $-5 = -5$. Because this statement is true, the ordered pair $(3, -5)$ is a solution of the equation $y = 4 - x^2$. We also say that $(3, -5)$ **satisfies** the equation.

We can generate as many ordered-pair solutions as desired to $y = 4 - x^2$ by substituting numbers for x and then finding the corresponding values for y. For example, suppose we let $x = 3$:

Start with x. Compute y. Form the ordered pair (x, y).

x	$y = 4 - x^2$	Ordered Pair (x, y)
3	$y = 4 - 3^2 = 4 - 9 = -5$	$(3, -5)$

Let $x = 3$. $(3, -5)$ is a solution of $y = 4 - x^2$.

The **graph of an equation in two variables** is the set of all points whose coordinates satisfy the equation. One method for graphing such equations is the **point-plotting method**. First, we find several ordered pairs that are solutions of the equation. Next, we plot these ordered pairs as points in the rectangular coordinate system. Finally, we connect the points with a smooth curve or line. This often gives us a picture of all ordered pairs that satisfy the equation.

EXAMPLE 2 Graphing an Equation Using the Point-Plotting Method

Graph $y = 4 - x^2$. Select integers for x, starting with -3 and ending with 3.

Solution For each value of x, we find the corresponding value for y.

Start with x. Compute y. Form the ordered pair (x, y).

We selected integers from -3 to 3, inclusive, to include three negative numbers, 0, and three positive numbers. We also wanted to keep the resulting computations for y relatively simple.

x	$y = 4 - x^2$	Ordered Pair (x, y)
-3	$y = 4-(-3)^2 = 4 - 9 = -5$	$(-3, -5)$
-2	$y = 4-(-2)^2 = 4 - 4 = 0$	$(-2, 0)$
-1	$y = 4-(-1)^2 = 4 - 1 = 3$	$(-1, 3)$
0	$y = 4 - 0^2 = 4 - 0 = 4$	$(0, 4)$
1	$y = 4 - 1^2 = 4 - 1 = 3$	$(1, 3)$
2	$y = 4 - 2^2 = 4 - 4 = 0$	$(2, 0)$
3	$y = 4 - 3^2 = 4 - 9 = -5$	$(3, -5)$

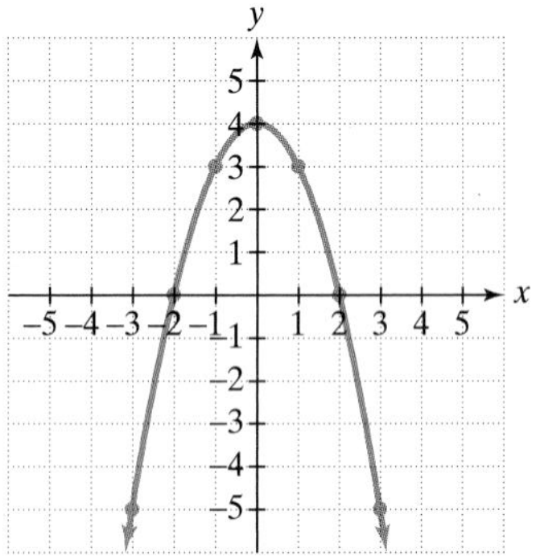

Figure 1.4 The graph of $y = 4 - x^2$

Now we plot the seven points and join them with a smooth curve, as shown in Figure 1.4. The graph of $y = 4 - x^2$ is a curve where the part of the graph to the right of the y-axis is a reflection of the part to the left of it and vice versa. The arrows on the left and the right of the curve indicate that it extends indefinitely in both directions.

Check Point 2 Graph $y = 4 - x$. Select integers for x, starting with -3 and ending with 3.

Study Tip

In Chapters 2 and 3, we will be studying graphs of equations in two variables in which

$$y = \text{a polynomial in } x.$$

Do not be concerned that we have not yet learned techniques, other than plotting points, for graphing such equations. As you solve some of the equations in this chapter, we will display graphs simply to enhance your visual understanding of your work. For now, think of graphs of first-degree polynomials as lines and graphs of second-degree polynomials as symmetric U-shaped cups that open upward or downward.

EXAMPLE 3 Graphing an Equation Using the Point-Plotting Method

Graph $y = |x|$. Select integers for x, starting with -3 and ending with 3.

Solution For each value of x, we find the corresponding value for y.

x	$y = \lvert x\rvert$	Ordered Pair (x, y)
-3	$y = \lvert -3\rvert = 3$	$(-3, 3)$
-2	$y = \lvert -2\rvert = 2$	$(-2, 2)$
-1	$y = \lvert -1\rvert = 1$	$(-1, 1)$
0	$y = \lvert 0\rvert = 0$	$(0, 0)$
1	$y = \lvert 1\rvert = 1$	$(1, 1)$
2	$y = \lvert 2\rvert = 2$	$(2, 2)$
3	$y = \lvert 3\rvert = 3$	$(3, 3)$

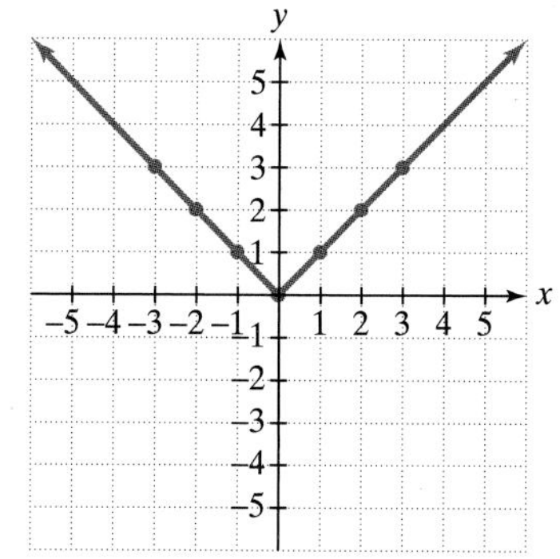

Figure 1.5 The graph of $y = |x|$

We plot the points and connect them, resulting in the graph shown in Figure 1.5. The graph is V-shaped and centered at the origin. For every point (x, y) on the graph, the point $(-x, y)$ is also on the graph. This shows that the absolute value of a positive number is the same as the absolute value of its opposite.

Check Point 3 Graph $y = |x + 1|$. Select integers for x, starting with -4 and ending with 2.

3 Interpret information about a graphing utility's viewing rectangle or table.

Graphing Equations and Creating Tables Using a Graphing Utility

Graphing calculators or graphing software packages for computers are referred to as **graphing utilities** or graphers. A graphing utility is a powerful tool that quickly generates the graph of an equation in two variables. Figures 1.6(a) and 1.6(b) show two such graphs for the equations in Examples 2 and 3.

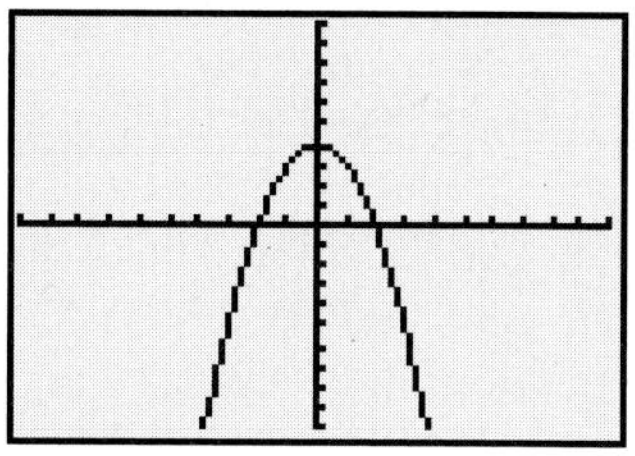

Figure 1.6(a) The graph of $y = 4 - x^2$

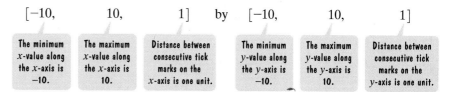

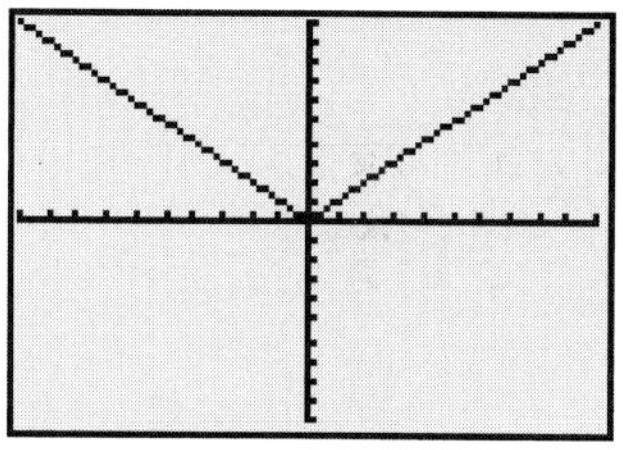

Figure 1.6(b) The graph of $y = |x|$

What differences do you notice between these graphs and the graphs that we drew by hand? They do seem a bit "jittery." Arrows do not appear on the left and right ends of the graphs. Furthermore, numbers are not given along the axes. For both graphs in Figure 1.6, the x-axis extends from -10 to 10 and the y-axis also extends from -10 to 10. The distance represented by each consecutive tick mark is one unit. We say that the **viewing rectangle**, or the **viewing window**, is $[-10, 10, 1]$ by $[-10, 10, 1]$.

Study Tip

Even if you are not using a graphing utility in the course, read this part of the section. Knowing about viewing rectangles will enable you to understand the graphs that we display in the technology boxes throughout the book.

$[-10,$ 10, $1]$ by $[-10,$ 10, $1]$

- $[-10,$ — The minimum x-value along the x-axis is -10.
- 10, — The maximum x-value along the x-axis is 10.
- $1]$ — Distance between consecutive tick marks on the x-axis is one unit.
- $[-10,$ — The minimum y-value along the y-axis is -10.
- 10, — The maximum y-value along the y-axis is 10.
- $1]$ — Distance between consecutive tick marks on the y-axis is one unit.

To graph an equation in x and y using a graphing utility, enter the equation and specify the size of the viewing rectangle. The size of the viewing rectangle sets minimum and maximum values for both the x- and y-axes. Enter these values, as well as the values between consecutive tick marks, on the respective axes. The $[-10, 10, 1]$ by $[-10, 10, 1]$ viewing rectangle used in Figure 1.6 is called the **standard viewing rectangle.**

EXAMPLE 4 Understanding the Viewing Rectangle

What is the meaning of a $[-2, 3, 0.5]$ by $[-10, 20, 5]$ viewing rectangle?

Solution We begin with $[-2, 3, 0.5]$, which describes the x-axis. The minimum x-value is -2 and the maximum x-value is 3. The distance between consecutive tick marks is 0.5.

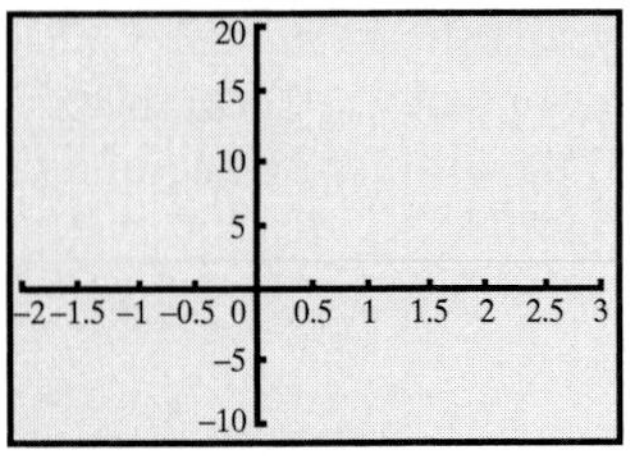

Figure 1.7 A $[-2, 3, 0.5]$ by $[-10, 20, 5]$ viewing rectangle

Next, consider $[-10, 20, 5]$, which describes the y-axis. The minimum y-value is -10 and the maximum y-value is 20. The distance between consecutive tick marks is 5.

Figure 1.7 illustrates a $[-2, 3, 0.5]$ by $[-10, 20, 5]$ viewing rectangle. To make things clearer, we've placed numbers by each tick mark. These numbers do not appear on the axes when you use a graphing utility to graph an equation.

Check Point 4 What is the meaning of a $[-100, 100, 50]$ by $[-100, 100, 10]$ viewing rectangle? Create a figure like the one in Figure 1.7 that illustrates this viewing rectangle.

On most graphing utilities, the display screen is two-thirds as high as it is wide. By using a square setting, you can equally space the x and y tick marks. (This does not occur in the standard viewing rectangle.) Graphing utilities can also *zoom in* and *zoom out.* When you zoom in, you see a smaller portion of the graph, but you do so in greater detail. When you zoom out, you see a larger portion of the graph. Thus, zooming out may help you to develop a better understanding of the overall character of the graph. With practice, you will become more comfortable with graphing equations in two variables using your graphing utility. You will also develop a better sense of the size of the viewing rectangle that will reveal needed information about a particular graph.

Graphing utilities can also be used to create tables showing solutions of equations in two variables. Use the Table Setup function to choose the starting value of x and to input the increment, or change, between the consecutive x-values. The corresponding y-values are calculated based on the equation(s) in two variables in the Y= screen. In Figure 1.8, we used a TI-83 Plus to create a table for $y = 4 - x^2$ and $y = |x|$, the equations in Examples 2 and 3.

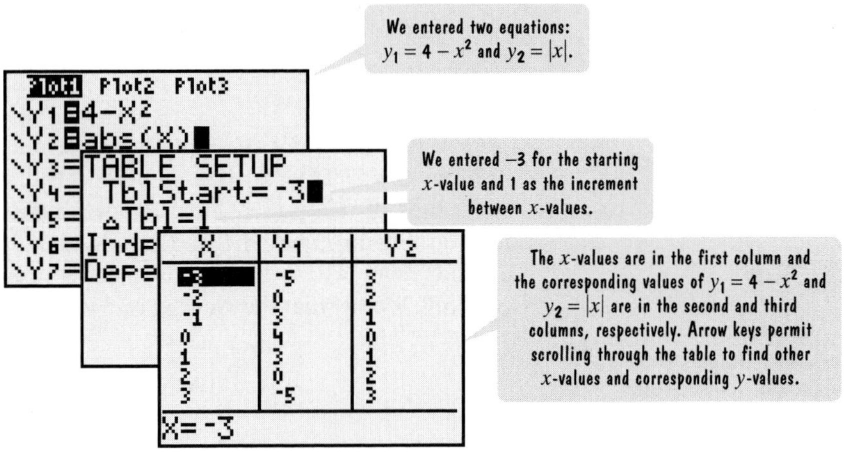
We entered two equations: $y_1 = 4 - x^2$ and $y_2 = |x|$.
Plot1 Plot2 Plot3
\Y1=4-X²
\Y2=abs(X)
\Y3=
\Y4=
\Y5=
\Y6=
\Y7=
TABLE SETUP
TblStart=-3
ΔTbl=1
Indpnt
Depend
We entered −3 for the starting x-value and 1 as the increment between x-values.
X Y1 Y2
-3 -5 3
-2 0 2
-1 3 1
0 4 0
1 3 1
2 0 2
3 -5 3
X=-3
The x-values are in the first column and the corresponding values of $y_1 = 4 - x^2$ and $y_2 = |x|$ are in the second and third columns, respectively. Arrow keys permit scrolling through the table to find other x-values and corresponding y-values.

Figure 1.8 Creating a table for $y_1 = 4 - x^2$ and $y_2 = |x|$

4 Use a graph to determine intercepts.

Intercepts

An ***x*-intercept** of a graph is the x-coordinate of a point where the graph intersects the x-axis. For example, look at the graph of $y = 4 - x^2$ in Figure 1.9. The graph crosses the x-axis at $(-2, 0)$ and $(2, 0)$. Thus, the x-intercepts are -2 and 2. **The *y*-coordinate corresponding to an *x*-intercept is always zero.**

A ***y*-intercept** of a graph is the y-coordinate of a point where the graph intersects the y-axis. The graph of $y = 4 - x^2$ in Figure 1.9 shows that the graph crosses the y-axis at $(0, 4)$. Thus, the y-intercept is 4. **The *x*-coordinate corresponding to a *y*-intercept is always zero.**

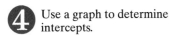

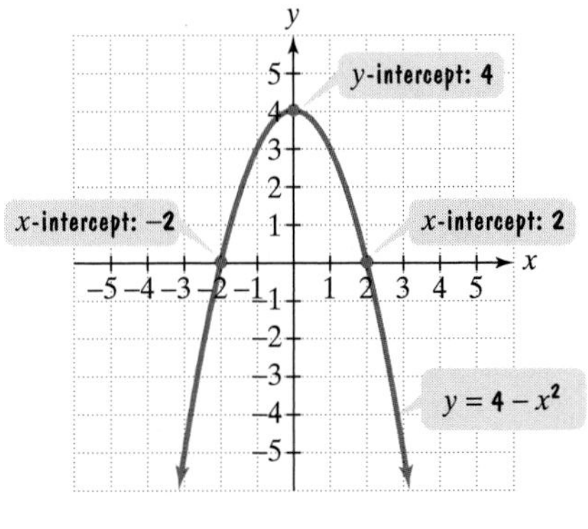

Figure 1.9 Intercepts of $y = 4 - x^2$

Study Tip

Mathematicians tend to use two ways to describe intercepts. Did you notice that we are using single numbers? If a is an x-intercept of a graph, then the graph passes through the point $(a, 0)$. If b is a y-intercept of a graph, then the graph passes through the point $(0, b)$.

Some books state that the x-intercept is the *point* $(a, 0)$ and the x-intercept is *at a* on the x-axis. Similarly, the y-intercept is the *point* $(0, b)$ and the y-intercept is *at b* on the y-axis. In these descriptions, the intercepts are the actual points where the graph intersects the axes.

Although we'll describe intercepts as single numbers, we'll immediately state the point on the x- or y-axis that the graph passes through. Here's the important thing to keep in mind:

x-intercept: The corresponding value of y is 0.

y-intercept: The corresponding value of x is 0.

EXAMPLE 5 Identifying Intercepts

Identify the x- and y-intercepts.

a. b. c.

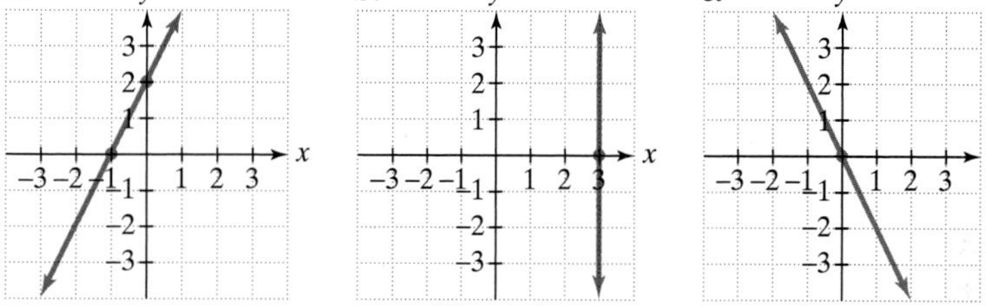

Solution

a. The graph crosses the x-axis at $(-1, 0)$. Thus, the x-intercept is -1. The graph crosses the y-axis at $(0, 2)$. Thus, the y-intercept is 2.

b. The graph crosses the x-axis at $(3, 0)$, so the x-intercept is 3. This vertical line does not cross the y-axis. Thus, there is no y-intercept.

c. This graph crosses the x- and y-axes at the same point, the origin. Because the graph crosses both axes at $(0, 0)$, the x-intercept is 0 and the y-intercept is 0.

Check Point 5 Identify the x- and y-intercepts.

a. b. c.

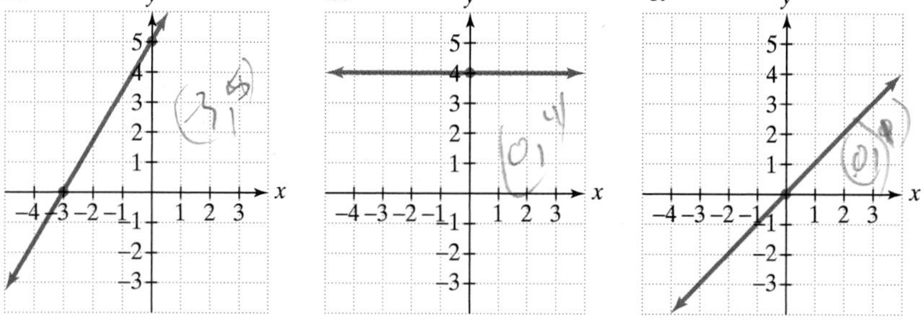

Figure 1.10 illustrates that a graph may have no intercepts or several intercepts.

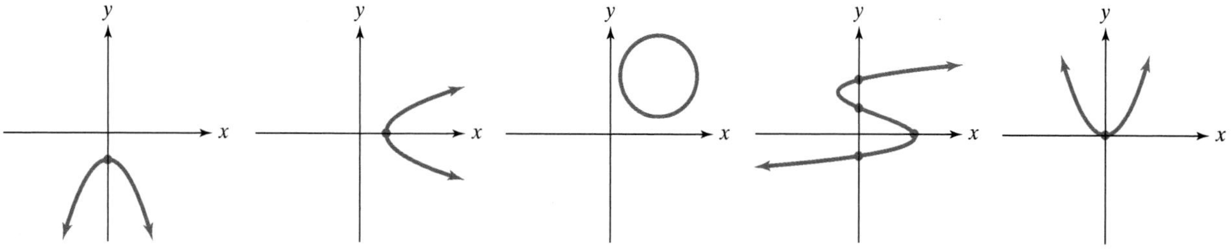

Figure 1.10

No x-intercept One y-intercept | One x-intercept No y-intercept | No intercepts | One x-intercept Three y-intercepts | The same x-intercept and y-intercept

5 Interpret information given by graphs.

Interpreting Information Given by Graphs

Line graphs are often used to illustrate trends over time. Some measure of time, such as months or years, frequently appears on the horizontal axis. Amounts are generally listed on the vertical axis. Points are drawn to represent the given information. The graph is formed by connecting the points with line segments.

Figure 1.11 is an example of a typical line graph. The graph shows the average age at which women in the United States married for the first time from 1890 through 2003. The years are listed on the horizontal axis and the ages are listed on the vertical axis. The symbol ⸗ on the vertical axis shows that there is a break in values between 0 and 20. Thus, the first tick mark on the vertical axis represents an average age of 20.

Figure 1.11

Source: U.S. Census Bureau

A line graph displays information in the first quadrant of a rectangular coordinate system. By identifying points on line graphs and their coordinates, you can interpret specific information given by the graph.

For example, the red lines in Figure 1.11 show how to find the average age at which women married for the first time in 1980.

Step 1 Locate 1980 on the horizontal axis.

Step 2 Locate the point on the line graph above 1980.

Step 3 Read across to the corresponding age on the vertical axis.

The age appears to be exactly at 22. Thus, in 1980, women in the United States married for the first time at an average age of 22.

EXAMPLE 6 Interpreting Information Given by a Graph

The line graph in Figure 1.12 shows the percentage of federal prisoners in the United States sentenced for drug offenses from 1970 through 2003.

a. For the period shown, estimate the maximum percentage of federal prisoners sentenced for drug offenses. When did this occur?

b. Table 1.1 shows the number, in thousands, of federal prisoners in the United States for four selected years. Estimate the number of federal prisoners sentenced for drug offenses for the year in part (a).

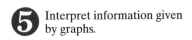

Figure 1.12

Source: Frank Schmalleger, *Criminal Justice Today,* 7th Edition, Prentice Hall, 2003.

Table 1.1 Number of U.S. Federal Prisoners

Year	Federal Prisoners
1990	58,838
1995	89,538
2000	133,921
2003	159,275

Source: Bureau of Justice Statistics

Solution

a. The maximum fraction of federal prisoners sentenced for drug offenses can be found by locating the highest point on the graph. This point lies above 1995 on the horizontal axis. Read across to the corresponding percent on the vertical axis. The number falls below 60% by approximately one unit. It appears that 59% is a reasonable estimate. Thus, the maximum fraction of federal prisoners sentenced for drug offenses is approximately 59%. This occurred in 1995.

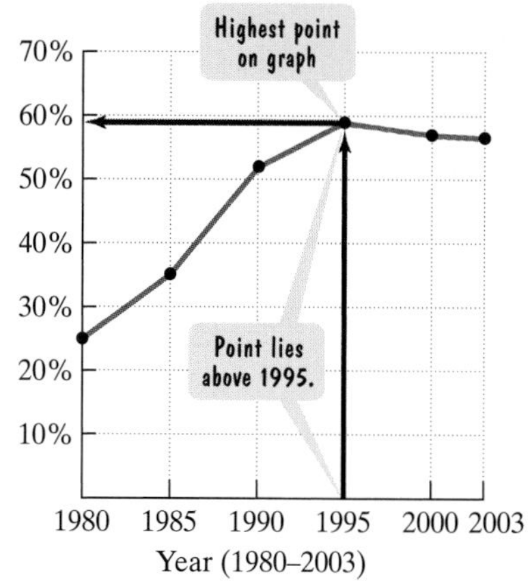

b. Table 1.1 shows that there were 89,538 federal prisoners in 1995. The number sentenced for drug offenses can be determined as follows:

$$\text{Number sentenced for drug offenses} = 0.59 \times 89{,}538.$$

To estimate the number sentenced for drug offenses, we round the percent to 60% and the total federal prison population to 90,000.

$$\text{Number sentenced for drug offenses} \approx 60\% \text{ of } 90{,}000$$
$$= 0.6 \times 90{,}000$$
$$= 54{,}000$$

In 1995, approximately 54,000 federal prisoners were sentenced for drug offenses.

Check Point 6 Use Figure 1.12 and Table 1.1 to estimate the number of federal prisoners sentenced for drug offenses in 2003.

EXERCISE SET 1.1

Practice Exercises

In Exercises 1–12, plot the given point in a rectangular coordinate system.

1. $(1, 4)$	**2.** $(2, 5)$	**3.** $(-2, 3)$
4. $(-1, 4)$	**5.** $(-3, -5)$	**6.** $(-4, -2)$
7. $(4, -1)$	**8.** $(3, -2)$	**9.** $(-4, 0)$
10. $(0, -3)$	**11.** $\left(\frac{7}{2}, -\frac{3}{2}\right)$	**12.** $\left(-\frac{5}{2}, \frac{3}{2}\right)$

Graph each equation in Exercises 13–28. Let $x = -3, -2, -1, 0, 1, 2,$ and 3.

13. $y = x^2 - 2$	**14.** $y = x^2 + 2$	**15.** $y = x - 2$						
16. $y = x + 2$	**17.** $y = 2x + 1$	**18.** $y = 2x - 4$						
19. $y = -\frac{1}{2}x$	**20.** $y = -\frac{1}{2}x + 2$	**21.** $y = 2	x	$				
22. $y = -2	x	$	**23.** $y =	x	+ 1$	**24.** $y =	x	- 1$
25. $y = 9 - x^2$	**26.** $y = -x^2$	**27.** $y = x^3$						
28. $y = x^3 - 1$								

In Exercises 29–32, match the viewing rectangle with the correct figure. Then label the tick marks in the figure to illustrate this viewing rectangle.

29. $[-5, 5, 1]$ by $[-5, 5, 1]$ **30.** $[-10, 10, 2]$ by $[-4, 4, 2]$

31. $[-20, 80, 10]$ by $[-30, 70, 10]$

32. $[-40, 40, 20]$ by $[-1000, 1000, 100]$

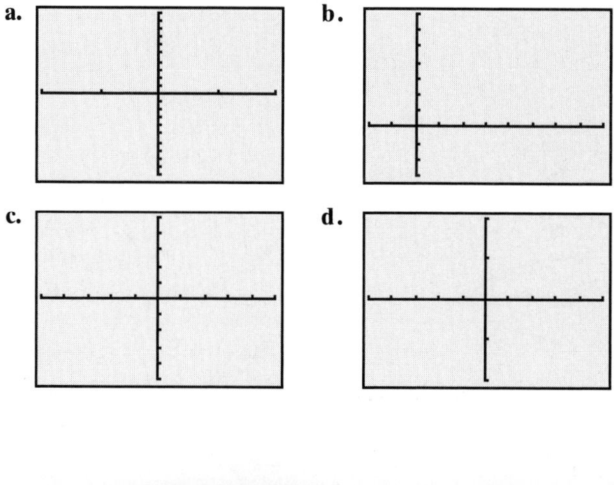

The table of values was generated by a graphing utility with a TABLE feature. Use the table to solve Exercises 33–40.

33. Which equation corresponds to Y_2 in the table?

 a. $y_2 = x + 8$ **b.** $y_2 = x - 2$

 c. $y_2 = 2 - x$ **d.** $y_2 = 1 - 2x$

34. Which equation corresponds to Y_1 in the table?

 a. $y_1 = -3x$ **b.** $y_1 = x^2$

 c. $y_1 = -x^2$ **d.** $y_1 = 2 - x$

35. Does the graph of Y_2 pass through the origin?

36. Does the graph of Y_1 pass through the origin?

37. At which point does the graph of Y_2 cross the x-axis?

38. At which point does the graph of Y_2 cross the y-axis?

39. At which points do the graphs of Y_1 and Y_2 intersect?

40. For which values of x is $Y_1 = Y_2$?

*In Exercises 41–46, use the graph to **a.** determine the x-intercepts, if any; **b.** determine the y-intercepts, if any. For each graph, tick marks along the axes represent one unit each.*

41.

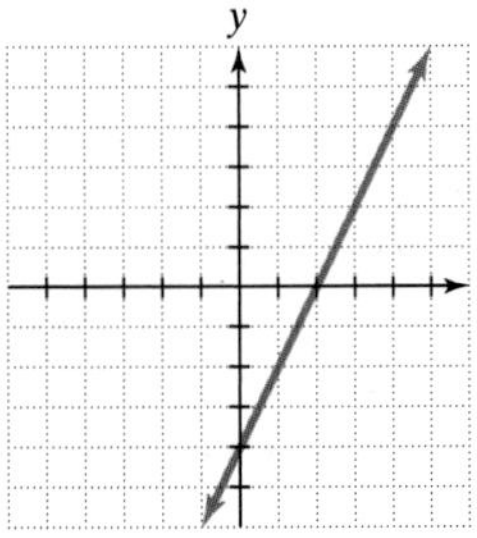

42.

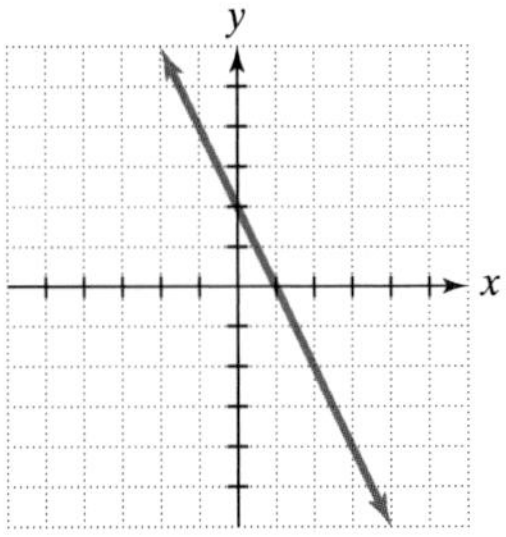

43.

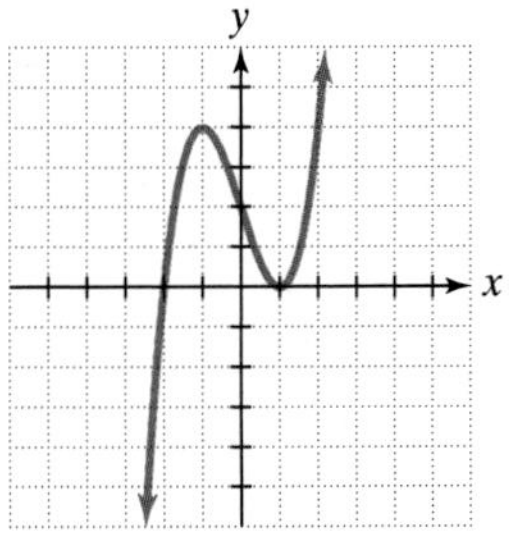

44.

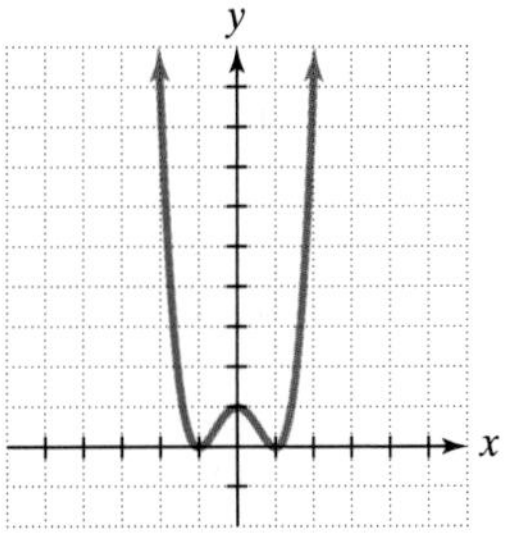

45.

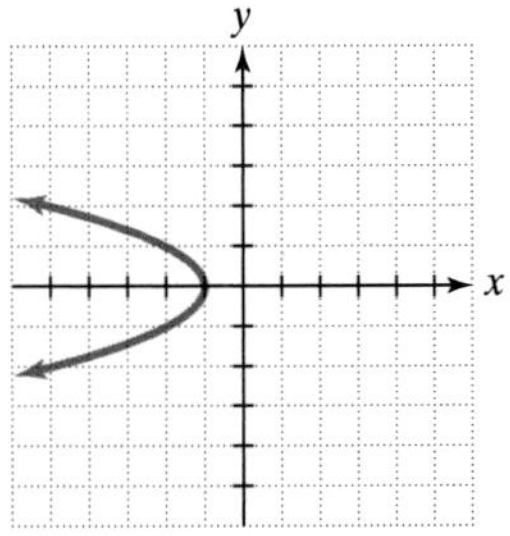

46.

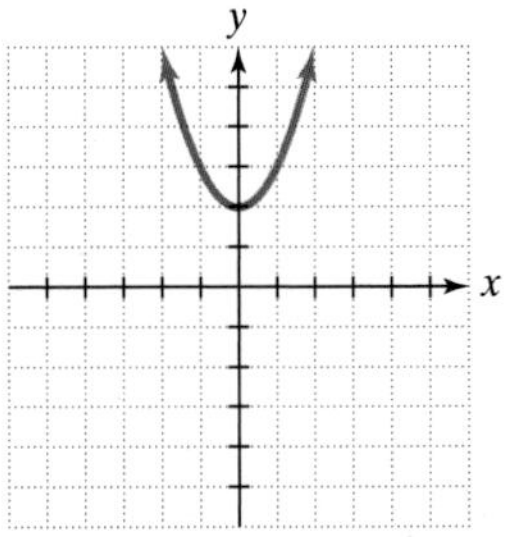

Practice Plus

In Exercises 47–50, write each English sentence as an equation in two variables. Then graph the equation.

47. The y-value is four more than twice the x-value.

48. The y-value is the difference between four and twice the x-value.

49. The y-value is three decreased by the square of the x-value.

50. The y-value is two more than the square of the x-value.

In Exercises 51–54, graph each equation.

51. $y = 5$ (Let $x = -3, -2, -1, 0, 1, 2,$ and 3.)

52. $y = -1$ (Let $x = -3, -2, -1, 0, 1, 2,$ and 3.)

53. $y = \dfrac{1}{x}$ (Let $x = -2, -1, -\dfrac{1}{2}, -\dfrac{1}{3}, \dfrac{1}{3}, \dfrac{1}{2}, 1,$ and 2.)

54. $y = -\dfrac{1}{x}$ (Let $x = -2, -1, -\dfrac{1}{2}, -\dfrac{1}{3}, \dfrac{1}{3}, \dfrac{1}{2}, 1,$ and 2.)

Application Exercises

We live in an era of democratic aspiration. The number of democracies worldwide is on the rise. The line graph shows the number of democracies worldwide, in four-year periods, from 1973 through 2001, including 2002. Use the graph to solve Exercises 55–60.

Tracking Democracy: Number of Democracies Worldwide

[Line graph with vertical axis "Number of Democracies" ranging from 40 to 130, and horizontal axis "Year" ranging from 1973 to 2005.]

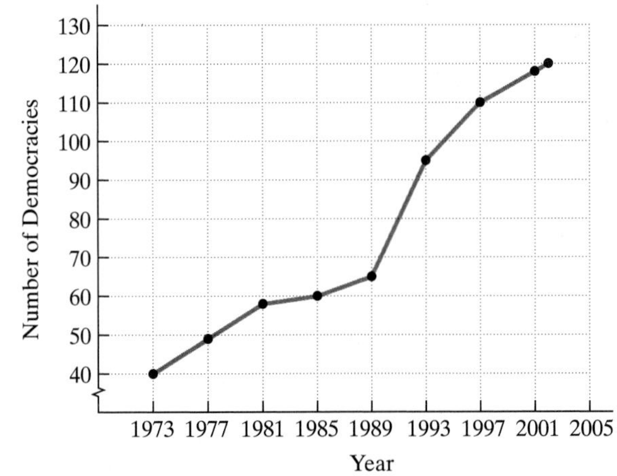

Source: The Freedom House

55. Find an estimate for the number of democracies in 1989.

56. How many more democracies were there in 2002 than in 1973?

57. In which four-year period did the number of democracies increase at the greatest rate?

58. In which four-year period did the number of democracies increase at the slowest rate?

59. In which year were there 49 democracies?

60. In which year were there 110 democracies?

Medical researchers have found that the desirable heart rate, R, in beats per minute, for beneficial exercise is approximated by the mathematical models

$$R = 165 - 0.75A \quad \text{for men}$$
$$R = 143 - 0.65A \quad \text{for women}$$

where A is the person's age. Use these mathematical models to solve Exercises 61–62.

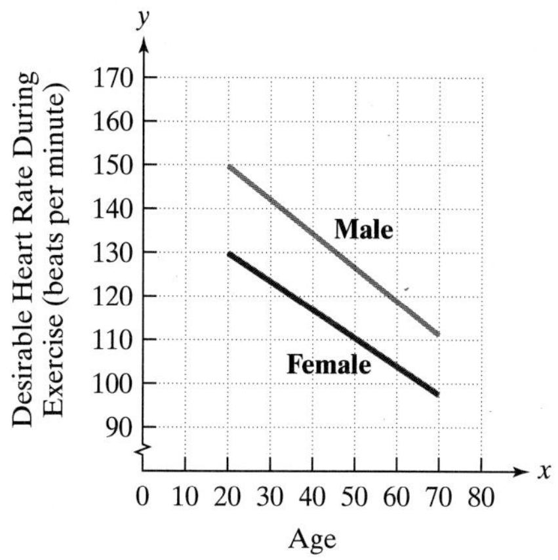

61. What is the desirable heart rate during exercise for a 40-year-old man? Identify your computation as an appropriate point on the blue graph.

62. What is the desirable heart rate during exercise for a 40-year-old woman? Identify your computation as an appropriate point on the red graph.

Autism is a neurological disorder that impedes language and derails social and emotional development. New findings suggest that the condition is not a sudden calamity that strikes children at the age of 2 or 3, but a developmental problem linked to abnormally rapid brain growth during infancy. The graphs show that the heads of severely autistic children start out smaller than average and then go through a period of explosive growth. Exercises 63–64 involve mathematical models for the data shown by the graphs.

Developmental Differences between Healthy Children and Severe Autistics

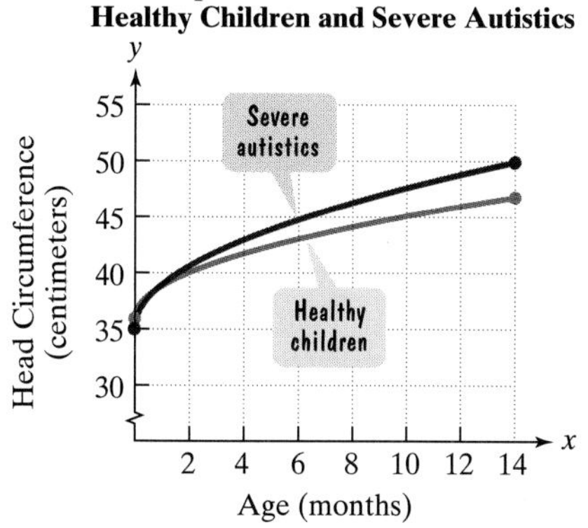

Source: The Journal of the American Medical Association

63. The data for one of the two groups shown by the graphs can be modeled by

$$y = 2.9\sqrt{x} + 36,$$

where y is the head circumference, in centimeters, at age x months, $0 \le x \le 14$.

a. According to the model, what is the head circumference at birth?

b. According to the model, what is the head circumference at 9 months?

c. According to the model, what is the head circumference at 14 months? Use a calculator and round to the nearest tenth of a centimeter.

d. Use the values that you obtained in parts (a) through (c) and the graphs shown above to determine whether the given model describes healthy children or severe autistics.

64. The data for one of the two groups shown by the graphs can be modeled by

$$y = 4\sqrt{x} + 35,$$

where y is the head circumference, in centimeters, at age x months, $0 \le x \le 14$.

a. According to the model, what is the head circumference at birth?

b. According to the model, what is the head circumference at 9 months?

c. According to the model, what is the head circumference at 14 months? Use a calculator and round to the nearest centimeter.

d. Use the values that you obtained in parts (a) through (c) and the graphs shown in the previous column to determine whether the given model describes healthy children or severe autistics.

Writing in Mathematics

65. What is the rectangular coordinate system?

66. Explain how to plot a point in the rectangular coordinate system. Give an example with your explanation.

67. Explain why $(5, -2)$ and $(-2, 5)$ do not represent the same point.

68. Explain how to graph an equation in the rectangular coordinate system.

69. What does a $[-20, 2, 1]$ by $[-4, 5, 0.5]$ viewing rectangle mean?

Technology Exercises

70. Use a graphing utility to verify each of your hand-drawn graphs in Exercises 13–28. Experiment with the size of the viewing rectangle to make the graph displayed by the graphing utility resemble your hand-drawn graph as much as possible.

71. The stated intent of the 1994 "don't ask, don't tell" policy was to reduce the number of discharges of gay men and lesbians from the military. The equation

$$y = 45.48x^2 - 334.35x + 1237.9$$

describes the number of service members, y, discharged from the military for homosexuality x years after 1990. Graph the equation in a $[0, 10, 1]$ by $[0, 2200, 100]$ viewing rectangle. Then describe something about the relationship between x and y that is revealed by looking at the graph that is not obvious from the equation. What does the graph reveal about the success or lack of success of "don't ask, don't tell"?

Critical Thinking Exercises

72. Which one of the following is true?

a. If the coordinates of a point satisfy the inequality $xy > 0$, then (x, y) must be in quadrant I.

b. The ordered pair $(2, 5)$ satisfies $3y - 2x = -4$.

c. If a point is on the x-axis, it is neither up nor down, so $x = 0$.

d. None of the above is true.

In Exercises 73–76, match the story with the correct figure. The figures are labeled (a), (b), (c), and (d).

73. As the blizzard got worse, the snow fell harder and harder.

74. The snow fell more and more softly.

75. It snowed hard, but then it stopped. After a short time, the snow started falling softly.

76. It snowed softly, and then it stopped. After a short time, the snow started falling hard.

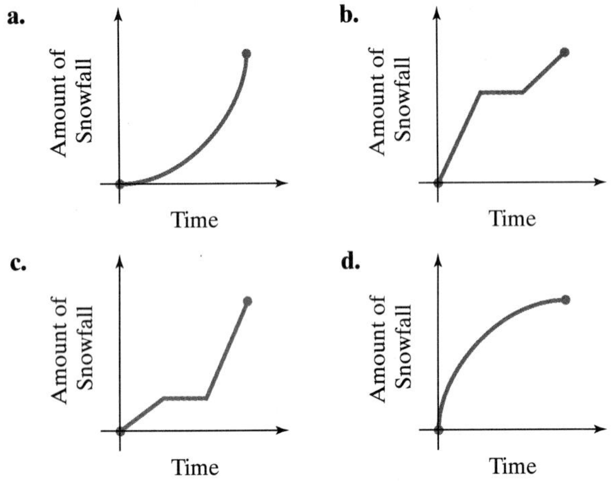

In Exercises 77–78, select the graph that best illustrates each story.

77. An airplane flew from Miami to San Francisco.

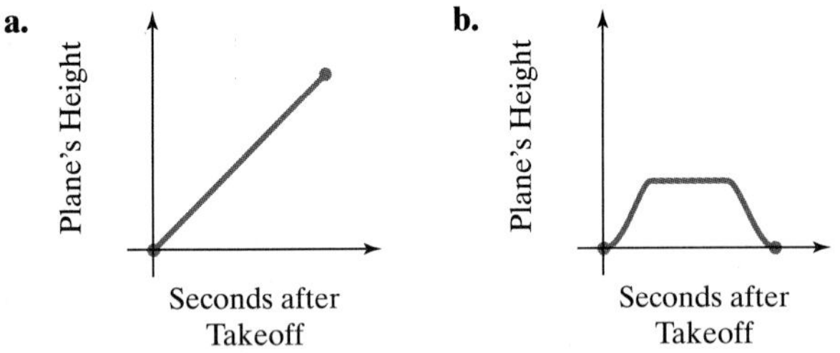

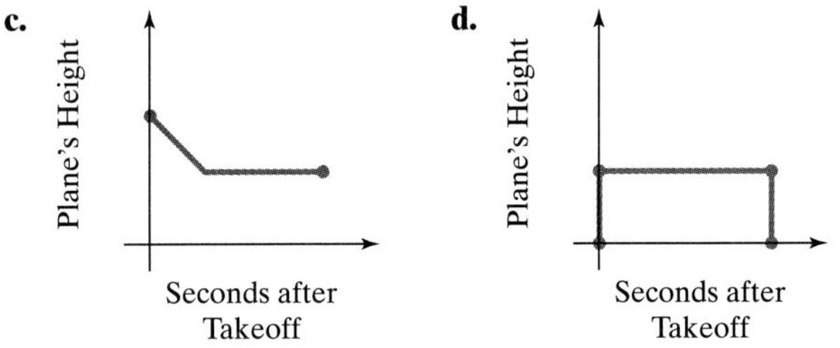

78. At noon, you begin to breathe in.

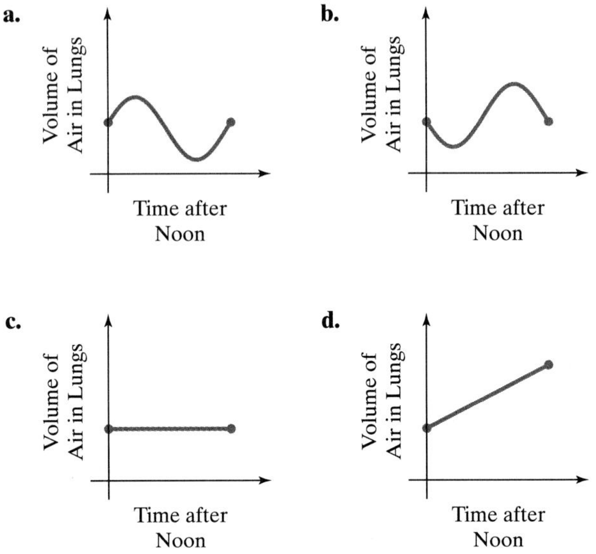

SECTION 1.2 Linear Equations and Rational Equations

Objectives

1. Solve linear equations in one variable.
2. Solve linear equations containing fractions.
3. Solve rational equations with variables in the denominators.
4. Recognize identities, conditional equations, and inconsistent equations.

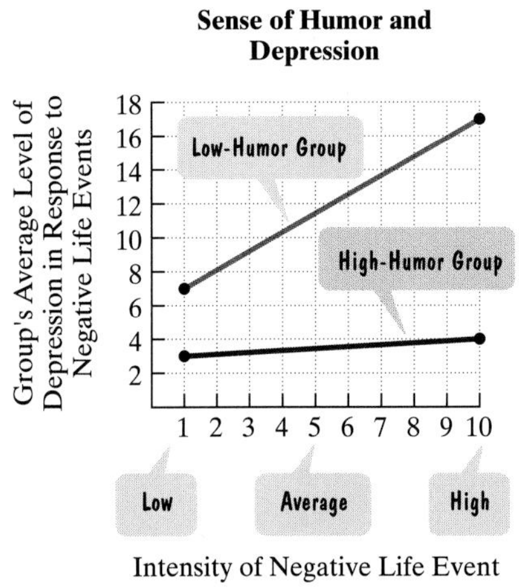

Figure 1.13
Source: Steven Davis and Joseph Palladino, *Psychology*, 3rd Edition, Prentice Hall, 2003.

The belief that humor and laughter can have positive benefits on our lives is not new. The graphs in Figure 1.13 indicate that persons with a low sense of humor have higher levels of depression in response to negative life events than those with a high sense of humor. These graphs can be modeled by the following formulas:

Low-Humor Group High-Humor Group

$$D = \frac{10}{9}x + \frac{53}{9} \qquad D = \frac{1}{9}x + \frac{26}{9}.$$

In each formula, x represents the intensity of a negative life event (from 1, low, to 10, high) and D is the level of depression in response to that event.

Suppose that the low-humor group averages a level of depression of 10 in response to a negative life event. We can determine the intensity of that event by substituting 10 for D in the low-humor model:

$$10 = \frac{10}{9}x + \frac{53}{9}.$$

The two sides of an equation can be reversed. So, we can also express this equation as

$$\frac{10}{9}x + \frac{53}{9} = 10.$$

Notice that the highest exponent on the variable is 1. Such an equation is called a *linear equation in one variable*. In this section, we will study how to solve linear equations.

Solving Linear Equations in One Variable

We begin with a general definition of a linear equation in one variable.

① Solve linear equations in one variable.

> **Definition of a Linear Equation**
> A **linear equation in one variable** x is an equation that can be written in the form
> $$ax + b = 0,$$
> where a and b are real numbers, and $a \neq 0$.

An example of a linear equation in one variable is

$$4x + 12 = 0.$$

Solving an equation in x involves determining all values of x that result in a true statement when substituted into the equation. Such values are **solutions**, or **roots**, of the equation. For example, substitute -3 for x in $4x + 12 = 0$. We obtain

$$4(-3) + 12 = 0, \quad \text{or} \quad -12 + 12 = 0.$$

This simplifies to the true statement $0 = 0$. Thus, -3 is a solution of the equation $4x + 12 = 0$. We also say that -3 **satisfies** the equation $4x + 12 = 0$, because when we substitute -3 for x, a true statement results. The set of all such solutions is called the equation's **solution set**. For example, the solution set of the equation $4x + 12 = 0$ is $\{-3\}$.

Two or more equations that have the same solution set are called **equivalent equations**. For example, the equations

$$4x + 12 = 0 \quad \text{and} \quad 4x = -12 \quad \text{and} \quad x = -3$$

are equivalent equations because the solution set for each is $\{-3\}$. To solve a linear equation in x, we transform the equation into an equivalent equation one or more times. Our final equivalent equation should be of the form

$$x = \text{a number.}$$

The solution set of this equation is the set consisting of the number.

To generate equivalent equations, we will use the following principles:

Generating Equivalent Equations

An equation can be transformed into an equivalent equation by one or more of the following operations:

	Example
1. Simplify an expression by removing grouping symbols and combining like terms.	$3(x-6)=6x-x$ $3x-18=5x$
2. Add (or subtract) the same real number or variable expression on *both* sides of the equation.	$3x-18=5x$ $3x-18-3x=5x-3x$ (Subtract $3x$ from both sides of the equation.) $-18=2x$
3. Multiply (or divide) on *both* sides of the equation by the same *nonzero* quantity.	$-18=2x$ $\frac{-18}{2}=\frac{2x}{2}$ (Divide both sides of the equation by 2.) $-9=x$
4. Interchange the two sides of the equation.	$-9=x$ $x=-9$

If you look closely at the equations in the box, you will notice that we have solved the equation $3(x-6)=6x-x$. The final equation, $x=-9$, with x isolated by itself on the left side, shows that $\{-9\}$ is the solution set. The idea in solving a linear equation is to get the variable by itself on one side of the equal sign and a number by itself on the other side.

EXAMPLE 1 Solving a Linear Equation

Solve and check: $2x+3=17$.

Solution Our goal is to obtain an equivalent equation with x isolated on one side and a number on the other side.

$$2x+3=17 \quad \text{This is the given equation.}$$
$$2x+3-3=17-3 \quad \text{Subtract 3 from both sides.}$$
$$2x=14 \quad \text{Simplify.}$$
$$\frac{2x}{2}=\frac{14}{2} \quad \text{Divide both sides by 2.}$$
$$x=7 \quad \text{Simplify.}$$

Now we check the proposed solution, 7, by replacing x with 7 in the original equation.

$$2x+3=17 \quad \text{This is the original equation.}$$
$$2\cdot 7+3\stackrel{?}{=}17 \quad \text{Substitute 7 for x. The question mark indicates that we do not yet know if the two sides are equal.}$$
$$14+3\stackrel{?}{=}17 \quad \text{Multiply: } 2\cdot 7=14.$$

This statement is true.

$$17=17 \quad \text{Add: } 14+3=17.$$

Because the check results in a true statement, we conclude that the solution set of the given equation is $\{7\}$.

Check Point 1 Solve and check: $4x + 5 = 29$.

Study Tip

We simplify algebraic expressions. We solve algebraic equations. Notice the differences between the procedures:

Simplifying an Algebraic Expression

Simplify: $3(x - 7) - (5x - 11)$.

This is not an equation. There is no equal sign.

Solution

$$3(x - 7) - (5x - 11)$$
$$= 3x - 21 - 5x + 11$$
$$= (3x - 5x) + (-21 + 11)$$
$$= -2x + (-10)$$
$$= -2x - 10$$

Stop! Further simplification is not possible. Avoid the common error of setting $-2x - 10$ equal to 0.

Solving an Algebraic Equation

Solve: $3(x - 7) - (5x - 11) = 14$.

This is an equation. There is an equal sign.

Solution

$$3(x - 7) - (5x - 11) = 14$$
$$3x - 21 - 5x + 11 = 14$$
$$-2x - 10 = 14$$

Add 10 to both sides.

$$-2x - 10 + 10 = 14 + 10$$
$$-2x = 24$$

Divide both sides by -2.

$$\frac{-2x}{-2} = \frac{24}{-2}$$
$$x = -12$$

The solution set is $\{-12\}$.

Here is a step-by-step procedure for solving a linear equation in one variable. Not all of these steps are necessary to solve every equation.

Solving a Linear Equation

1. Simplify the algebraic expression on each side by removing grouping symbols and combining like terms.
2. Collect all the variable terms on one side and all the numbers, or constant terms, on the other side.
3. Isolate the variable and solve.
4. Check the proposed solution in the original equation.

EXAMPLE 2 Solving a Linear Equation

Solve and check: $2(x - 3) - 17 = 13 - 3(x + 2)$.

Solution

Step 1 Simplify the algebraic expression on each side.

Do not begin with $13 - 3$. Multiplication (the distributive property) is applied before subtraction.

$2(x - 3) - 17 = 13 - 3(x + 2)$	This is the given equation.
$2x - 6 - 17 = 13 - 3x - 6$	Use the distributive property.
$2x - 23 = -3x + 7$	Combine like terms.

Step 2 Collect variable terms on one side and constant terms on the other side. We will collect variable terms on the left by adding $3x$ to both sides. We will collect the numbers on the right by adding 23 to both sides.

$2x - 23 + 3x = -3x + 7 + 3x$	Add $3x$ to both sides.
$5x - 23 = 7$	Simplify: $2x + 3x = 5x$.
$5x - 23 + 23 = 7 + 23$	Add 23 to both sides.
$5x = 30$	Simplify.

Step 3 Isolate the variable and solve. We isolate the variable, x, by dividing both sides of $5x = 30$ by 5.

$$\frac{5x}{5} = \frac{30}{5} \qquad \text{Divide both sides by 5.}$$

$$x = 6 \qquad \text{Simplify.}$$

Step 4 Check the proposed solution in the original equation. Substitute 6 for x in the original equation.

$$2(x - 3) - 17 = 13 - 3(x + 2) \qquad \text{This is the original equation.}$$

$$2(6 - 3) - 17 \stackrel{?}{=} 13 - 3(6 + 2) \qquad \text{Substitute 6 for x.}$$

$$2(3) - 17 \stackrel{?}{=} 13 - 3(8) \qquad \text{Simplify inside parentheses.}$$

$$6 - 17 \stackrel{?}{=} 13 - 24 \qquad \text{Multiply.}$$

$$-11 = -11 \qquad \text{Subtract.}$$

The true statement $-11 = -11$ verifies that the solution set is $\{6\}$.

Discovery

Solve the equation in Example 2 by collecting terms with the variable on the right and numerical terms on the left. What do you observe?

Technology

You can use a graphing utility to check the solution of a linear equation. Enter each side of the equation separately under y_1 and y_2. Then use the table or the graphs to locate the x-value for which the y-values are the same. This x-value is the solution.

Let's verify our work in Example 2 and show that 6 is the solution of

$$2(x - 3) - 17 = 13 - 3(x + 2).$$

Enter $y_1 = 2(x - 3) - 17$ in the $\boxed{y=}$ screen.

Enter $y_2 = 13 - 3(x + 2)$ in the $\boxed{y=}$ screen.

Numeric Check

Display a table for y_1 and y_2.

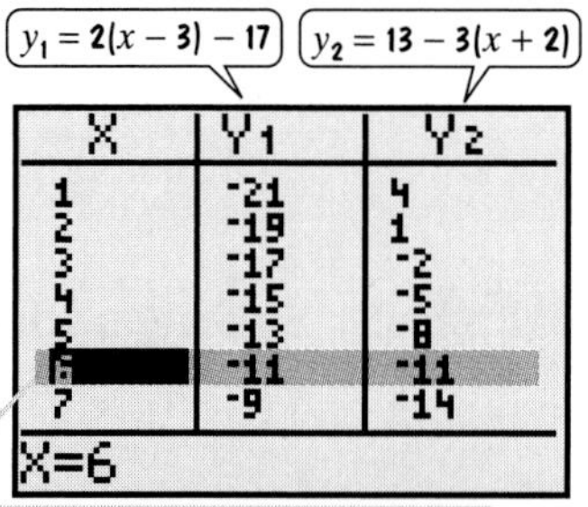

When $x = 6$, y_1 and y_2 have the same value, namely -11. This verifies that 6 is the solution of $2(x - 3) - 17 = 13 - 3(x + 2)$.

Graphic Check

Display graphs for y_1 and y_2 and use the intersection feature. The solution is the x-coordinate of the intersection point.

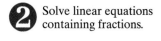

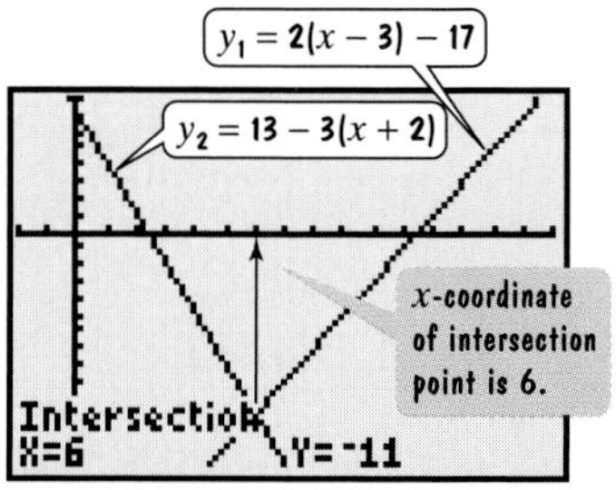

$[-2, 16, 1]$ by $[-14, 8, 1]$

Choose a large enough viewing rectangle so that you can see the intersection point.

Check Point 2 Solve and check: $4(2x + 1) = 29 + 3(2x - 5)$.

2 Solve linear equations containing fractions.

Linear Equations with Fractions

Equations are easier to solve when they do not contain fractions. How do we remove fractions from an equation? We begin by multiplying both sides of the equation by the least common denominator of any fractions in the equation. The least common denominator is the smallest number that all denominators will divide into. Multiplying every term on both sides of the equation by the least common denominator will eliminate the fractions in the equation. Example 3 shows how we "clear an equation of fractions."

EXAMPLE 3 Solving a Linear Equation Involving Fractions

Solve and check: $\frac{x+2}{4} - \frac{x-1}{3} = 2$.

Solution The fractional terms have denominators of 4 and 3. The smallest number that is divisible by 4 and 3 is 12. We begin by multiplying both sides of the equation by 12, the least common denominator.

$$\frac{x+2}{4} - \frac{x-1}{3} = 2 \quad \text{This is the given equation.}$$

$$12\left(\frac{x+2}{4} - \frac{x-1}{3}\right) = 12 \cdot 2 \quad \text{Multiply both sides by 12.}$$

$$12\left(\frac{x+2}{4}\right) - 12\left(\frac{x-1}{3}\right) = 24 \quad \text{Use the distributive property and multiply each term on the left by 12.}$$

$$\overset{3}{\cancel{12}}\left(\frac{x+2}{\underset{1}{\cancel{4}}}\right) - \overset{4}{\cancel{12}}\left(\frac{x-1}{\underset{1}{\cancel{3}}}\right) = 24 \quad \text{Divide out common factors in each multiplication on the left.}$$

$$3(x+2) - 4(x-1) = 24 \quad \text{The fractions are now cleared.}$$

$$3x + 6 - 4x + 4 = 24 \quad \text{Use the distributive property.}$$

$$-x + 10 = 24 \quad \text{Combine like terms: } 3x - 4x = -x \text{ and } 6 + 4 = 10.$$

$$-x + 10 - 10 = 24 - 10 \quad \text{Subtract 10 from both sides.}$$

$$-x = 14 \quad \text{Simplify.}$$

We're not finished. A negative sign should not precede the variable.

Isolate x by multiplying or dividing both sides of this equation by -1.

$$\frac{-x}{-1} = \frac{14}{-1} \quad \text{Divide both sides by } -1.$$

$$x = -14 \quad \text{Simplify.}$$

Check the proposed solution. Substitute –14 for x in the original equation. You should obtain $2 = 2$. This true statement verifies that the solution set is $\{-14\}$.

Check Point 3 Solve and check: $\frac{x-3}{4} = \frac{5}{14} - \frac{x+5}{7}$.

3 Solve rational equations with variables in the denominators.

Rational Equations

A **rational equation** is an equation containing one or more rational expressions. In Example 3, we solved a rational equation with constants in the denominators. This rational equation was a linear equation. Now, let's consider a rational equation such as

$$\frac{1}{x} = \frac{1}{5} + \frac{3}{2x}.$$

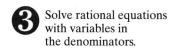

Can you see how this rational equation differs from the rational equation that we solved earlier? The variable, x, appears in two of the denominators. Although this rational equation is not a linear equation, the solution procedure still involves multiplying each side by the least common denominator. However, we must avoid any values of the variable that make a denominator zero. For example, examine the denominators in the equation

$$\frac{1}{x} = \frac{1}{5} + \frac{3}{2x}.$$

This denominator would equal zero if $x = 0$. This denominator would equal zero if $x = 0$.

We see that x cannot equal zero. With this in mind, let's solve the equation.

EXAMPLE 4 Solving a Rational Equation

Solve: $\frac{1}{x} = \frac{1}{5} + \frac{3}{2x}$.

Solution The denominators are x, 5, and $2x$. The least common denominator is $10x$. We begin by multiplying both sides of the equation by $10x$. We will also write the restriction that x cannot equal zero to the right of the equation.

$$\frac{1}{x} = \frac{1}{5} + \frac{3}{2x}, \quad x \neq 0$$ This is the given equation.

$$10x \cdot \frac{1}{x} = 10x\left(\frac{1}{5} + \frac{3}{2x}\right)$$ Multiply both sides by 10x.

$$10x \cdot \frac{1}{x} = 10x \cdot \frac{1}{5} + 10x \cdot \frac{3}{2x}$$ Use the distributive property. Be sure to multiply each term by 10x.

$$\cancel{10x} \cdot \frac{1}{\cancel{x}} = \overset{2}{\cancel{10}}x \cdot \frac{1}{\underset{1}{\cancel{5}}} + \overset{5}{\cancel{10}}\cancel{x} \cdot \frac{3}{\underset{1}{\cancel{2}}\cancel{x}}$$ Divide out common factors in the multiplications.

$$10 = 2x + 15$$ Complete the multiplications.

Observe that the resulting equation,

$$10 = 2x + 15,$$

is now cleared of fractions. With the variable term, $2x$, already on the right, we will collect constant terms on the left by subtracting 15 from both sides.

$$10 - 15 = 2x + 15 - 15$$ Subtract 15 from both sides.

$$-5 = 2x$$ Simplify.

Finally, we isolate the variable, x, in $-5 = 2x$ by dividing both sides by 2.

$$\frac{-5}{2} = \frac{2x}{2}$$ Divide both sides by 2.

$$-\frac{5}{2} = x$$ Simplify.

We check our solution by substituting $-\frac{5}{2}$ into the original equation or by using a calculator. With a calculator, evaluate each side of the equation for $x = -\frac{5}{2}$, or for $x = -2.5$. Note that the original restriction that $x \neq 0$ is met. The solution set is $\left\{-\frac{5}{2}\right\}$.

Check Point 4 Solve: $\frac{5}{2x} = \frac{17}{18} - \frac{1}{3x}$.

EXAMPLE 5 Solving a Rational Equation

Solve: $\frac{x}{x-3} = \frac{3}{x-3} + 9.$

Solution We must avoid any values of the variable x that make a denominator zero.

$$\frac{x}{x-3} = \frac{3}{x-3} + 9$$

These denominators are zero if $x = 3$.

We see that x cannot equal 3. With denominators of $x - 3$, $x - 3$, and 1, the least common denominator is $x - 3$. We multiply both sides of the equation by $x - 3$. We also write the restriction that x cannot equal 3 to the right of the equation.

$$\frac{x}{x-3} = \frac{3}{x-3} + 9, \quad x \neq 3$$ This is the given equation.

$$(x-3)\cdot\frac{x}{x-3} = (x-3)\left(\frac{3}{x-3} + 9\right)$$ Multiply both sides by $x - 3$.

$$(x-3)\cdot\frac{x}{x-3} = (x-3)\cdot\frac{3}{x-3} + (x-3)\cdot 9$$ Use the distributive property.

$$\cancel{(x-3)}\cdot\frac{x}{\cancel{x-3}} = \cancel{(x-3)}\cdot\frac{3}{\cancel{x-3}} + 9(x-3)$$ Divide out common factors in two of the multiplications.

$$x = 3 + 9(x-3)$$ Simplify.

The resulting equation is cleared of fractions. We now solve for x.

$$x = 3 + 9x - 27$$ Use the distributive property.

$$x = 9x - 24$$ Combine numerical terms.

$$x - 9x = 9x - 24 - 9x$$ Subtract $9x$ from both sides.

$$-8x = -24$$ Simplify.

$$\frac{-8x}{-8} = \frac{-24}{-8}$$ Divide both sides by -8.

$$x = 3$$ Simplify.

The proposed solution, 3, is *not* a solution because of the restriction that $x \neq 3$. There is *no solution to this equation.* The solution set for this equation contains no elements. The solution set is $\varnothing$, the empty set.

Study Tip

Reject any proposed solution that causes any denominator in an equation to equal 0.

Check Point 5 Solve: $\frac{x}{x-2} = \frac{2}{x-2} - \frac{2}{3}.$

EXAMPLE 6 Solving a Rational Equation to Determine When Two Equations Are Equal

Consider the equations

$$y_1 = \frac{3}{x+6} + \frac{1}{x-2} \quad \text{and} \quad y_2 = \frac{4}{x^2 + 4x - 12}.$$

Find all values of x for which $y_1 = y_2$.

Solution Because we are interested in one or more values of x that cause y_1 and y_2 to be equal, we set the expressions that define y_1 and y_2 equal to each other:

$$\frac{3}{x+6} + \frac{1}{x-2} = \frac{4}{x^2 + 4x - 12}.$$

To identify values of x that make denominators zero, let's factor $x^2 + 4x - 12$, the denominator on the right. This factorization is also necessary in identifying the least common denominator.

$$\frac{3}{x+6} + \frac{1}{x-2} = \frac{4}{(x+6)(x-2)}$$

This denominator is zero if $x = -6$. This denominator is zero if $x = 2$. This denominator is zero if $x = -6$ or $x = 2$.

We see that x cannot equal -6 or 2. The least common denominator is $(x + 6)(x - 2)$.

$$\frac{3}{x+6} + \frac{1}{x-2} = \frac{4}{(x+6)(x-2)}, \quad x \neq -6, \quad x \neq 2$$

This is the given equation with a denominator factored.

$$(x+6)(x-2)\left(\frac{3}{x+6} + \frac{1}{x-2}\right) = (x+6)(x-2) \cdot \frac{4}{(x+6)(x-2)}$$

Multiply both sides by $(x + 6)(x - 2)$, the LCD.

$$\cancel{(x+6)}(x-2) \cdot \frac{3}{\cancel{x+6}} + (x+6)\cancel{(x-2)} \cdot \frac{1}{\cancel{x-2}} = \cancel{(x+6)}\cancel{(x-2)} \cdot \frac{4}{\cancel{(x+6)}\cancel{(x-2)}}$$

Use the distributive property and divide out common factors.

$$3(x-2) + 1(x+6) = 4$$

Simplify. This equation is cleared of fractions.

$$3x - 6 + x + 6 = 4$$

Use the distributive property.

$$4x = 4$$

Combine like terms.

$$\frac{4x}{4} = \frac{4}{4}$$

Divide both sides by 4.

$$x = 1$$

Simplify. This is not part of the restriction that $x \neq -6$ and $x \neq 2$.

The value of x for which $y_1 = y_2$ is 1.

Check

Is $y_1 = y_2$ when $x = 1$? We use the given equations

$$y_1 = \frac{3}{x+6} + \frac{1}{x-2} \quad \text{and} \quad y_2 = \frac{4}{x^2 + 4x - 12}$$

to answer the question.

Checking by Hand

Substitute 1 for x in y_1 and y_2.

$$y_1 = \frac{3}{1+6} + \frac{1}{1-2} = \frac{3}{7} + \frac{1}{-1}$$
$$= \frac{3}{7} - 1 = \frac{3}{7} - \frac{7}{7} = -\frac{4}{7}$$
$$y_2 = \frac{4}{1^2 + 4 \cdot 1 - 12} = \frac{4}{1 + 4 - 12}$$
$$= \frac{4}{-7} = -\frac{4}{7}$$

When $x = 1$, y_1 and y_2 have the same value, namely, $-\frac{4}{7}$.

Checking with a Graphing Utility

Display a table showing values for y_1 and y_2. Enter the equations as y_1 and y_2, and be careful with parentheses.

$y_1 = 3 \div (x + 6) + 1 \div (x - 2)$ $y_2 = 4 \div (x^2 + 4x - 12)$

X	Y1	Y2
-3	.8	-.2667
-2	.5	-.25
-1	.26667	-.2667
0	0	-.3333
1	-.5714	-.5714
2	ERROR	ERROR
3	1.3333	.44444

X=1

No matter how far up or down you scroll, $y_1 = y_2$ only when $x = 1$.

Check Point 6 Consider the equations

$$y_1 = \frac{1}{x+4} + \frac{1}{x-4} \quad \text{and} \quad y_2 = \frac{22}{x^2-16}.$$

Find all values of x for which $y_1 = y_2$ and check.

4 Recognize identities, conditional equations, and inconsistent equations.

Types of Equations

We tend to place things in categories, allowing us to order and structure the world. For example, you can categorize yourself by your age group, your ethnicity, your academic major, or your gender. Equations can be placed into categories that depend on their solution sets.

An equation that is true for all real numbers for which both sides are defined is called an **identity**. An example of an identity is

$$x + 3 = x + 2 + 1.$$

Every number plus 3 is equal to that number plus 2 plus 1. Therefore, the solution set to this equation is the set of all real numbers, expressed as $\{x|x \text{ is a real number}\}$.

Another example of an identity is

$$\frac{2x}{x} = 2.$$

Because division by 0 is undefined, this equation is true for all real number values of x except 0. The solution set is the set of nonzero real numbers, expressed as $\{x|x \text{ is a real number and } x \neq 0\}$.

An equation that is not an identity, but that is true for at least one real number, is called a **conditional equation**. The equation $2x + 3 = 17$ is an example of a conditional equation. The equation is not an identity and is true only if x is 7.

An **inconsistent equation** is an equation that is not true for even one real number. An example of an inconsistent equation is

$$x = x + 7.$$

There is no number that is equal to itself plus 7. The equation's solution set is $\varnothing$, the empty set. Some inconsistent equations are less obvious than this. Consider the equation in Example 5,

$$\frac{x}{x-3} = \frac{3}{x-3} + 9.$$

This equation is not true for any real number and has no solution. Thus, it is inconsistent.

Study Tip

If you are concerned by the vocabulary of equation types, keep in mind that there are three possible situations. We can state these situations informally as follows:

1. x = a real number
   conditional equation
2. x = all real numbers
   identity
3. x = no real numbers.
   inconsistent equation

EXAMPLE 7 Categorizing an Equation

Solve and determine whether the equation

$$2(x + 1) = 2x + 3$$

is an identity, a conditional equation, or an inconsistent equation.

Solution Begin by applying the distributive property on the left side. We obtain

$$2x + 2 = 2x + 3$$

Does something look strange? Can doubling a number and increasing the product by 2 give the same result as doubling the same number and increasing the product by 3? No. Let's continue solving the equation by subtracting $2x$ from both sides.

$$2x - 2x + 2 = 2x - 2x + 3$$

$$2 = 3$$

Keep reading. $2 = 3$ is not the solution.

The original equation, $2(x + 1) = 2x + 3$, is equivalent to the statement $2 = 3$, which is false for every value of x. The equation is inconsistent and has no solution. The solution set is $\varnothing$, the empty set.

Technology

Consider the graphs of $y_1 = 2(x + 1) = 2x + 2$ and $y_2 = 2x + 3$. The graphs appear to be parallel lines with no intersection point. This verifies that the equation

$$2(x + 1) = 2x + 3$$

has no solution and is inconsistent.

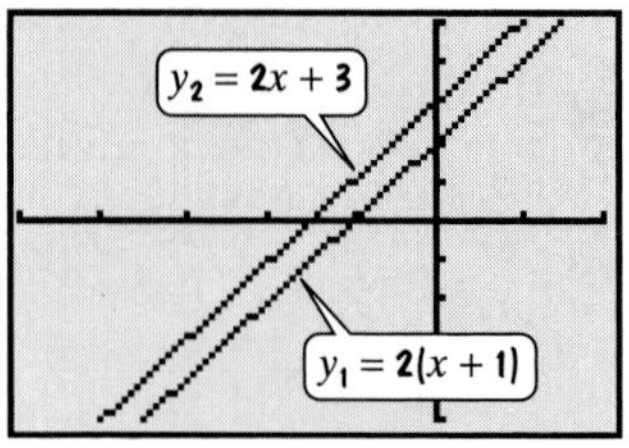

[−5, 2, 1] by [−5, 5, 1]

Check Point 7 Solve and determine whether the equation

$$4x - 7 = 4(x - 1) + 3$$

is an identity, a conditional equation, or an inconsistent equation.

EXERCISE SET 1.2

Practice Exercises

In Exercises 1–16, solve and check each linear equation.

1. $7x - 5 = 72$
2. $6x - 3 = 63$
3. $11x - (6x - 5) = 40$
4. $5x - (2x - 10) = 35$
5. $2x - 7 = 6 + x$
6. $3x + 5 = 2x + 13$
7. $7x + 4 = x + 16$
8. $13x + 14 = 12x - 5$
9. $3(x - 2) + 7 = 2(x + 5)$
10. $2(x - 1) + 3 = x - 3(x + 1)$
11. $3(x - 4) - 4(x - 3) = x + 3 - (x - 2)$
12. $2 - (7x + 5) = 13 - 3x$
13. $16 = 3(x - 1) - (x - 7)$
14. $5x - (2x + 2) = x + (3x - 5)$
15. $25 - [2 + 5y - 3(y + 2)] = -3(2y - 5) - [5(y - 1) - 3y + 3]$
16. $45 - [4 - 2y - 4(y + 7)] = -4(1 + 3y) - [4 - 3(y + 2) - 2(2y - 5)]$

Exercises 17–30 contain linear equations with constants in denominators. Solve each equation.

17. $\frac{x}{3} = \frac{x}{2} - 2$
18. $\frac{x}{5} = \frac{x}{6} + 1$
19. $20 - \frac{x}{3} = \frac{x}{2}$
20. $\frac{x}{5} - \frac{1}{2} = \frac{x}{6}$
21. $\frac{3x}{5} = \frac{2x}{3} + 1$
22. $\frac{x}{2} = \frac{3x}{4} + 5$
23. $\frac{3x}{5} - x = \frac{x}{10} - \frac{5}{2}$
24. $2x - \frac{2x}{7} = \frac{x}{2} + \frac{17}{2}$
25. $\frac{x + 3}{6} = \frac{3}{8} + \frac{x - 5}{4}$
26. $\frac{x + 1}{4} = \frac{1}{6} + \frac{2 - x}{3}$
27. $\frac{x}{4} = 2 + \frac{x - 3}{3}$
28. $5 + \frac{x - 2}{3} = \frac{x + 3}{8}$
29. $\frac{x + 1}{3} = 5 - \frac{x + 2}{7}$
30. $\frac{3x}{5} - \frac{x - 3}{2} = \frac{x + 2}{3}$

Exercises 31–50 contain rational equations with variables in denominators. For each equation, **a.** *Write the value or values of the variable that make a denominator zero. These are the restrictions on the variable.* **b.** *Keeping the restrictions in mind, solve the equation.*

31. $\frac{4}{x} = \frac{5}{2x} + 3$
32. $\frac{5}{x} = \frac{10}{3x} + 4$
33. $\frac{2}{x} + 3 = \frac{5}{2x} + \frac{13}{4}$
34. $\frac{7}{2x} - \frac{5}{3x} = \frac{22}{3}$
35. $\frac{2}{3x} + \frac{1}{4} = \frac{11}{6x} - \frac{1}{3}$
36. $\frac{5}{2x} - \frac{8}{9} = \frac{1}{18} - \frac{1}{3x}$
37. $\frac{x - 2}{2x} + 1 = \frac{x + 1}{x}$
38. $\frac{4}{x} = \frac{9}{5} - \frac{7x - 4}{5x}$
39. $\frac{1}{x - 1} + 5 = \frac{11}{x - 1}$
40. $\frac{3}{x + 4} - 7 = \frac{-4}{x + 4}$
41. $\frac{8x}{x + 1} = 4 - \frac{8}{x + 1}$
42. $\frac{2}{x - 2} = \frac{x}{x - 2} - 2$
43. $\frac{3}{2x - 2} + \frac{1}{2} = \frac{2}{x - 1}$
44. $\frac{3}{x + 3} = \frac{5}{2x + 6} + \frac{1}{x - 2}$
45. $\frac{3}{x + 2} + \frac{2}{x - 2} = \frac{8}{(x + 2)(x - 2)}$

46. $\dfrac{5}{x+2} + \dfrac{3}{x-2} = \dfrac{12}{(x+2)(x-2)}$

47. $\dfrac{2}{x+1} - \dfrac{1}{x-1} = \dfrac{2x}{x^2-1}$

48. $\dfrac{4}{x+5} + \dfrac{2}{x-5} = \dfrac{32}{x^2-25}$

49. $\dfrac{1}{x-4} - \dfrac{5}{x+2} = \dfrac{6}{x^2-2x-8}$

50. $\dfrac{6}{x+3} - \dfrac{5}{x-2} = \dfrac{-20}{x^2+x-6}$

In Exercises 51–56, find all values of x satisfying the given conditions.

51. $y_1 = 5(2x-8) - 2$, $y_2 = 5(x-3) + 3$, and $y_1 = y_2$.

52. $y_1 = 7(3x-2) + 5$, $y_2 = 6(2x-1) + 24$, and $y_1 = y_2$.

53. $y_1 = \dfrac{x-3}{5}$, $y_2 = \dfrac{x-5}{4}$, and $y_1 - y_2 = 1$.

54. $y_1 = \dfrac{x+1}{4}$, $y_2 = \dfrac{x-2}{3}$, and $y_1 - y_2 = -4$.

55. $y_1 = \dfrac{5}{x+4}$, $y_2 = \dfrac{3}{x+3}$, $y_3 = \dfrac{12x+19}{x^2+7x+12}$, and $y_1 + y_2 = y_3$.

56. $y_1 = \dfrac{2x-1}{x^2+2x-8}$, $y_2 = \dfrac{2}{x+4}$, $y_3 = \dfrac{1}{x-2}$, and $y_1 + y_2 = y_3$.

In Exercises 57–60, find all values of x such that $y = 0$.

57. $y = 4[x - (3-x)] - 7(x+1)$

58. $y = 2[3x - (4x-6)] - 5(x-6)$

59. $y = \dfrac{x+6}{3x-12} - \dfrac{5}{x-4} - \dfrac{2}{3}$

60. $y = \dfrac{1}{5x+5} - \dfrac{3}{x+1} + \dfrac{7}{5}$

In Exercises 61–68, determine whether each equation is an identity, a conditional equation, or an inconsistent equation.

61. $4(x-7) = 4x - 28$

62. $4(x-7) = 4x + 28$

63. $2x + 3 = 2x - 3$

64. $\dfrac{7x}{x} = 7$

65. $4x + 5x = 8x$

66. $8x + 2x = 9x$

67. $\dfrac{2x}{x-3} = \dfrac{6}{x-3} + 4$

68. $\dfrac{3}{x-3} = \dfrac{x}{x-3} + 3$

The equations in Exercises 69–80 combine the types of equations we have discussed in this section. Solve each equation. Then state whether the equation is an identity, a conditional equation, or an inconsistent equation.

69. $\dfrac{x+5}{2} - 4 = \dfrac{2x-1}{3}$

70. $\dfrac{x+2}{7} = 5 - \dfrac{x+1}{3}$

71. $\dfrac{2}{x-2} = 3 + \dfrac{x}{x-2}$

72. $\dfrac{6}{x+3} + 2 = \dfrac{-2x}{x+3}$

73. $8x - (3x+2) + 10 = 3x$

74. $2(x+2) + 2x = 4(x+1)$

75. $\dfrac{2}{x} + \dfrac{1}{2} = \dfrac{3}{4}$

76. $\dfrac{3}{x} - \dfrac{1}{6} = \dfrac{1}{3}$

77. $\dfrac{4}{x-2} + \dfrac{3}{x+5} = \dfrac{7}{(x+5)(x-2)}$

78. $\dfrac{1}{x-1} = \dfrac{1}{(2x+3)(x-1)} + \dfrac{4}{2x+3}$

79. $\dfrac{4x}{x+3} - \dfrac{12}{x-3} = \dfrac{4x^2+36}{x^2-9}$

80. $\dfrac{4}{x^2+3x-10} - \dfrac{1}{x^2+x-6} = \dfrac{3}{x^2-x-12}$

In Exercises 81–84, use the [Y=] *screen to write the equation being solved. Then use the table to solve the equation.*

81.

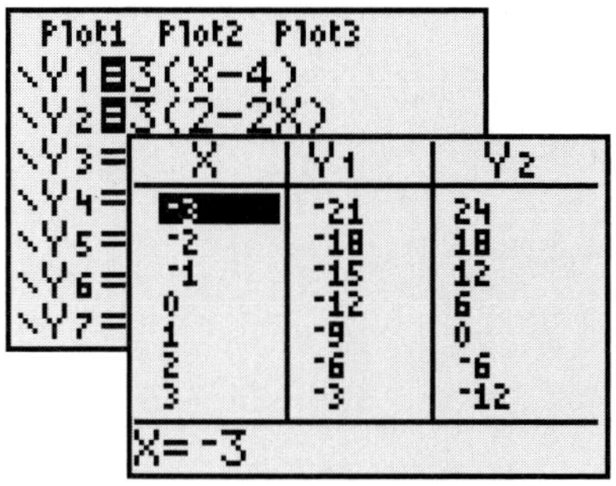

82.

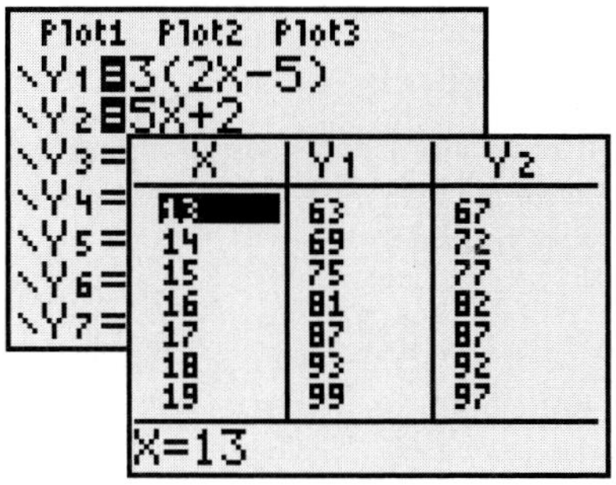

83.

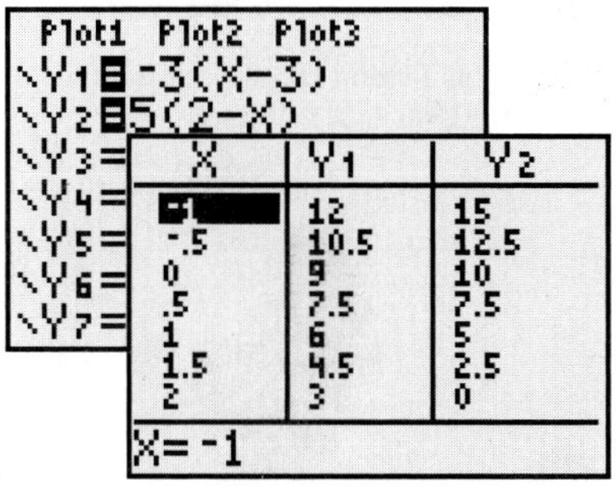

84.

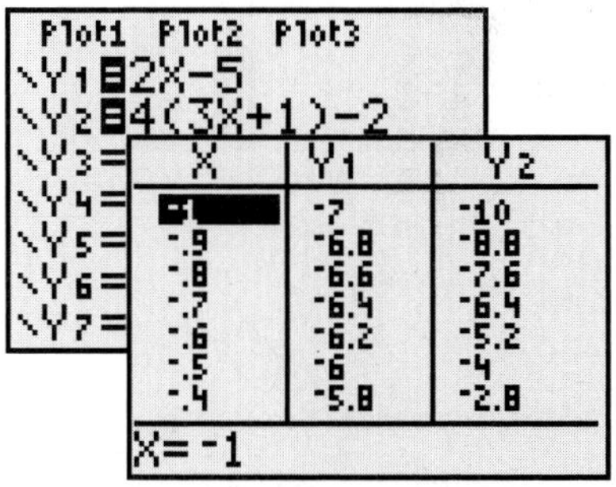

Practice Plus

85. Evaluate $x^2 - x$ for the value of x satisfying
$4(x - 2) + 2 = 4x - 2(2 - x)$.

86. Evaluate $x^2 - x$ for the value of x satisfying
$2(x - 6) = 3x + 2(2x - 1)$.

87. Evaluate $x^2 - (xy - y)$ for x satisfying $\dfrac{3(x + 3)}{5} = 2x + 6$
and y satisfying $-2y - 10 = 5y + 18$.

88. Evaluate $x^2 - (xy - y)$ for x satisfying $\dfrac{13x - 6}{4} = 5x + 2$
and y satisfying $5 - y = 7(y + 4) + 1$.

In Exercises 89–96, solve each equation.

89. $[(3 + 6)^2 \div 3] \cdot 4 = -54x$

90. $2^3 - [4(5 - 3)^3] = -8x$

91. $5 - 12x = 8 - 7x - [6 \div 3(2 + 5^3) + 5x]$

92. $2(5x + 58) = 10x + 4(21 \div 3.5 - 11)$

93. $0.7x + 0.4(20) = 0.5(x + 20)$

94. $0.5(x + 2) = 0.1 + 3(0.1x + 0.3)$

95. $4x + 13 - \{2x - [4(x - 3) - 5]\} = 2(x - 6)$

96. $-2\{7 - [4 - 2(1 - x) + 3]\} = 10 - [4x - 2(x - 3)]$

Application Exercises

The bar graph shows the average cost of tuition and fees at public four-year colleges in the United States. The data can be modeled by the formula

$$T = 165x + 2771,$$

where T represents the average cost of tuition and fees for the school year ending x years after 1996. Use the formula to solve Exercises 97–98.

Average Cost of Tuition and Fees at Public Four-Year U.S. Colleges

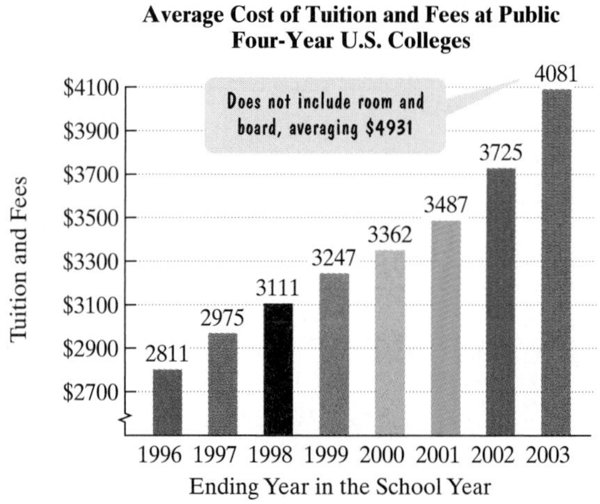

Source: The College Board

97. When will tuition and fees at public U.S. colleges average $4421?

98. When will tuition and fees at public U.S. colleges average $4751?

In the section opener, we used two formulas to model the level of depression, D, in response to the intensity of a negative life event, x, from 1, low, to 10, high:

Use these formulas to solve Exercises 99–100.

99. If the high-humor group averages a level of depression of 3.5, or $\dfrac{7}{2}$, in response to a negative life event, what is the intensity of that event? How is the solution shown on the line graph in Figure 1.13 on page 94?

100. If the low-humor group averages a level of depression of 10 in response to a negative life event, what is the intensity of that event? How is the solution shown on the line graph in Figure 1.13 on page 94?

Two formulas that approximate the dosage of a drug prescribed for children are

$$\text{Young's rule: } C = \frac{DA}{A + 12}$$

$$\text{and Cowling's rule: } C = \frac{D(A + 1)}{24}.$$

In each formula, A = the child's age, in years, D = an adult dosage, and C = the proper child's dosage. The formulas apply for ages 2 through 13, inclusive. Use the formulas to solve Exercises 101–102.

101. When the adult dosage is 1000 milligrams, a child is given 500 milligrams. Using Young's rule, what is that child's age?

102. When the adult dosage is 1000 milligrams, a child is given 300 milligrams. Using Young's rule, what is that child's age? Round to the nearest year.

The graphs illustrate Young's rule and Cowling's rule when the dosage of a drug prescribed for an adult is 1000 milligrams. Use the graphs to solve Exercises 103–106.

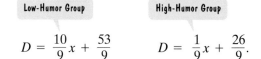

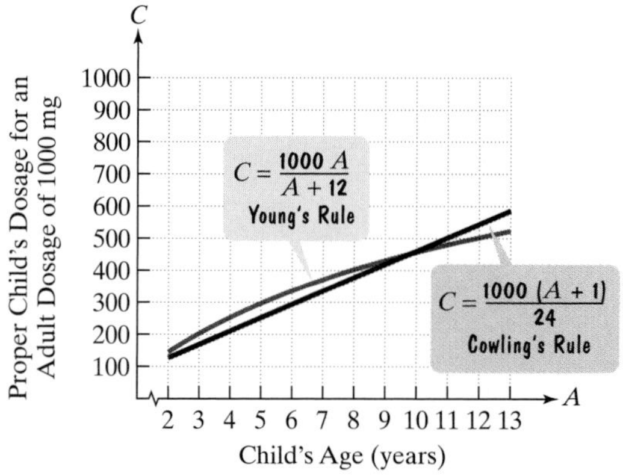

103. Identify your solution to Exercise 101 as a point on the appropriate graph.

104. Identify your solution to Exercise 102 as a point on the appropriate graph.

105. Does either formula consistently give a smaller dosage than the other? If so, which one?

106. Is there an age at which the dosage given by one formula becomes greater than the dosage given by the other? If so, what is a reasonable estimate of that age?

Formulas with rational expressions are often used to model learning. Many of these formulas model the proportion of correct responses in terms of the number of trials of a particular task. One such model, called a learning curve, is

$$P = \frac{0.9x - 0.4}{0.9x + 0.1},$$

where P is the proportion of correct responses after x trials. If P = 0, there are no correct responses. If P = 1, all responses are correct. The graph of the rational formula is shown. Use the formula to solve Exercises 107–108.

A Learning Curve

$P = \dfrac{0.9x - 0.4}{0.9x + 0.1}$

Proportion of Correct Responses

Number of Learning Trials

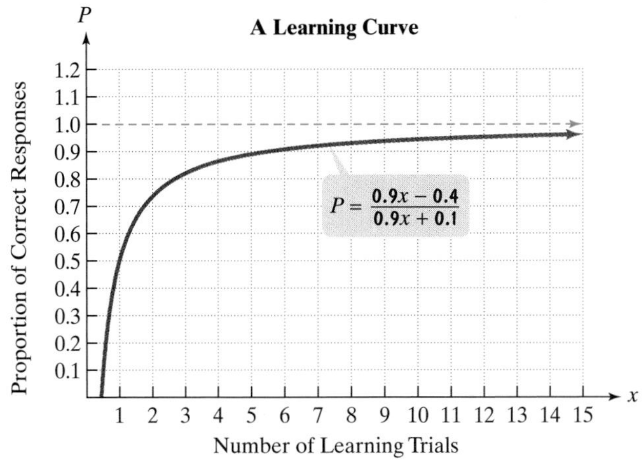

107. How many learning trials are necessary for 0.95 of the responses to be correct? Identify your solution as a point on the graph.

108. How many learning trials are necessary for 0.5 of the responses to be correct? Identify your solution as a point on the graph.

109. A company wants to increase the 10% peroxide content of its product by adding pure peroxide (100% peroxide). If x liters of pure peroxide are added to 500 liters of its 10% solution, the concentration, C, of the new mixture is given by

$$C = \frac{x + 0.1(500)}{x + 500}.$$

How many liters of pure peroxide should be added to produce a new product that is 28% peroxide?

110. Suppose that x liters of pure acid are added to 200 liters of a 35% acid solution.

a. Write a formula that gives the concentration, C, of the new mixture. (*Hint*: See Exercise 109.)

b. How many liters of pure acid should be added to produce a new mixture that is 74% acid?

Writing in Mathematics

111. What is a linear equation in one variable? Give an example of this type of equation.

112. Suppose that you solve $\dfrac{x}{5} - \dfrac{x}{2} = 1$ by multiplying both sides by 20, rather than the least common denominator of 5 and 2 (namely, 10). Describe what happens. If you get the correct solution, why do you think we clear the equation of fractions by multiplying by the *least* common denominator?

113. Suppose you are an algebra teacher grading the following solution on an examination:

$$-3(x - 6) = 2 - x$$
$$-3x - 18 = 2 - x$$
$$-2x - 18 = 2$$
$$-2x = -16$$
$$x = 8.$$

You should note that 8 checks, and the solution set is {8}. The student who worked the problem therefore wants full credit. Can you find any errors in the solution? If full credit is 10 points, how many points should you give the student? Justify your position.

114. Explain how to find restrictions on the variable in a rational equation.

115. Why should restrictions on the variable in a rational equation be listed before you begin solving the equation?

116. What is an identity? Give an example.

117. What is a conditional equation? Give an example.

118. What is an inconsistent equation? Give an example.

119. Describe the trend shown by the graph in Exercises 107–108 in terms of learning new tasks. What happens initially and what happens as time increases?

Technology Exercises

In Exercises 120–123, use your graphing utility to enter each side of the equation separately under y_1 and y_2. Then use the utility's TABLE *or* GRAPH *feature to solve the equation.*

120. $5x + 2(x - 1) = 3x + 10$

121. $2x + 3(x - 4) = 4x - 7$

122. $\dfrac{x - 3}{5} - 1 = \dfrac{x - 5}{4}$

123. $\dfrac{2x - 1}{3} - \dfrac{x - 5}{6} = \dfrac{x - 3}{4}$

Critical Thinking Exercises

124. Which one of the following is true?

a. The equation $-7x = x$ has no solution.

b. The equations $\dfrac{x}{x - 4} = \dfrac{4}{x - 4}$ and $x = 4$ are equivalent.

c. The equations $3y - 1 = 11$ and $3y - 7 = 5$ are equivalent.

d. If a and b are any real numbers, then $ax + b = 0$ always has one number in its solution set.

125. If x represents a number, write an English sentence about the number that results in an inconsistent equation.

126. Find b such that $\dfrac{7x + 4}{b} + 13 = x$ has a solution set given by $\{-6\}$.

127. Find b such that $\dfrac{4x - b}{x - 5} = 3$ has a solution set given by Ø.

SECTION 1.3 Models and Applications

Objectives

1. Use linear equations to solve problems.
2. Solve a formula for a variable.

The human race is undeniably becoming a faster race. Since the beginning of the past century, track-and-field records have fallen in everything from sprints to miles to marathons. The performance arc is clearly rising, but no one knows how much higher it can climb. At some point, even the best-trained body simply has to up and quit. The question is, just where is that point, and is it possible for athletes, trainers, and genetic engineers to push it higher? In this section, you will learn a problem-solving strategy that uses linear equations to determine if anyone will ever run a 3-minute mile.

1 Use linear equations to solve problems.

Problem Solving with Linear Equations

We have seen that a model is a mathematical representation of a real-world situation. In this section, we will be solving problems that are presented in English. This means that we must obtain models by translating from the ordinary language of English into the language of algebraic equations. To translate, however, we must understand the English prose and be familiar with the forms of algebraic language. Here are some general steps we will follow in solving word problems:

Study Tip

When solving word problems, particularly problems involving geometric figures, drawing a picture of the situation is often helpful. Label x on your drawing and, where appropriate, label other parts of the drawing in terms of x.

Strategy for Solving Word Problems

Step 1 Read the problem carefully. Attempt to state the problem in your own words and state what the problem is looking for. Let x (or any variable) represent one of the quantities in the problem.

Step 2 If necessary, write expressions for any other unknown quantities in the problem in terms of x.

Step 3 Write an equation in x that models the verbal conditions of the problem.

Step 4 Solve the equation and answer the problem's question.

Step 5 Check the solution *in the original wording* of the problem, not in the equation obtained from the words.

EXAMPLE 1 Walk It Off

Experts concerned with fitness and health suggest that we should walk 10,000 steps per day, about 5 miles. Depending on stride length, each mile ranges between 2000 and 2500 steps. The graph in Figure 1.14 at the top of the next page shows the number of steps it takes to burn off various foods. (The data are based on a body weight of 150 to 165 pounds.)

The number of steps needed to burn off a cheeseburger exceeds the number needed to burn off a 12-ounce soda by 4140. The number needed to burn off a doughnut exceeds the number needed to burn off a 12-ounce soda by 2300. If you chow down a cheeseburger, doughnut, and 12-ounce soda, a 16,790-step walk is needed to burn off the calories (and perhaps alleviate the guilt). Determine the number of steps it takes to burn off a cheeseburger, a doughnut, and a 12-ounce soda.

Number of Steps It Takes to Burn Off Various Foods

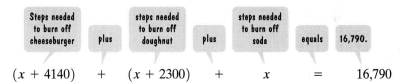

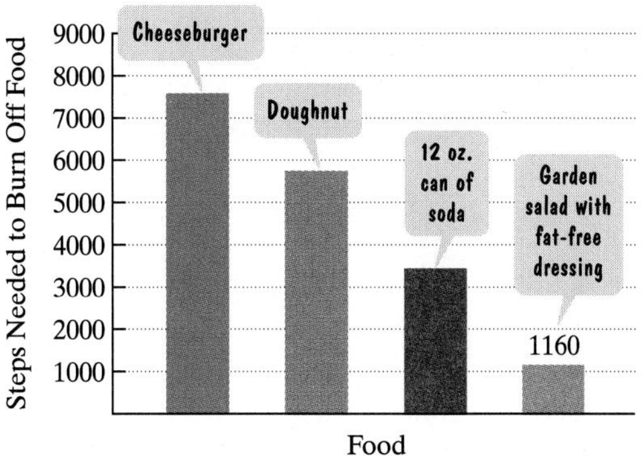

Figure 1.14
Source: The Step Diet Book

Solution

Step 1 Let x represent one of the quantities. We know something about the number of steps needed to burn off a cheeseburger and a doughnut: The numbers exceed that of a 12-ounce soda by 4140 and 2300, respectively. We will let

$x =$ the number of steps needed to burn off a 12-ounce soda.

Step 2 Represent other quantities in terms of x. Because the number of steps needed to burn off a cheeseburger exceeds the number needed to burn off a 12-ounce soda by 4140, let

$x + 4140 =$ the number of steps needed to burn off a cheeseburger.

Because the number of steps needed to burn off a doughnut exceeds the number needed to burn off a 12-ounce soda by 2300, let

$x + 2300 =$ the number of steps needed to burn off a doughnut.

Step 3 Write an equation in x that models the conditions. A 16,790-step walk is needed to burn off a "meal" consisting of a cheeseburger, a doughnut, and a 12-ounce soda.

Steps needed to burn off cheeseburger	plus	steps needed to burn off doughnut	plus	steps needed to burn off soda	equals	16,790.
$(x + 4140)$	$+$	$(x + 2300)$	$+$	x	$=$	16,790

Step 4 Solve the equation and answer the question.

$$(x + 4140) + (x + 2300) + x = 16{,}790$$ This is the equation that models the problem's conditions.

$$3x + 6440 = 16{,}790$$ Remove parentheses, regroup, and combine like terms.

$$3x = 10{,}350$$ Subtract 6440 from both sides.

$$x = 3450$$ Divide both sides by 3.

Thus,

the number of steps needed to burn off a 12-ounce soda $= x = 3450$.

the number of steps needed to burn off a cheeseburger
$= x + 4140 = 3450 + 4140 = 7590$.

the number of steps needed to burn off a doughnut
$= x + 2300 = 3450 + 2300 = 5750$.

It takes 7590 steps to burn off a cheeseburger, 5750 steps to burn off a doughnut, and 3450 steps to burn off a 12-ounce soda.

Step 5 Check the proposed solution in the original wording of the problem. The problem states that a 16,790-step walk is needed to burn off the calories in the three foods combined. By adding 7590, 5750, and 3450, the numbers that we found for each of the foods, we obtain

$$7590 + 5750 + 3450 = 16{,}790,$$

as specified by the problem's conditions.

Study Tip

Modeling with the word "exceeds" can be a bit tricky. It's helpful to identify the smaller quantity. Then add to this quantity to represent the larger quantity. For example, suppose that Tim's height exceeds Tom's height by a inches. Tom is the shorter person. If Tom's height is represented by x, then Tim's height is represented by $x + a$.

Check Point 1 Basketball, bicycle riding, and football are the three sports and recreational activities in the United States with the greatest number of medically treated injuries. In 2004, the number of injuries from basketball exceeded those from football by 0.6 million. The number of injuries from bicycling exceeded those from football by 0.3 million. Combined, basketball, bicycling, and football accounted for 3.9 million injuries. Determine the number of medically treated injuries from each of these recreational activities in 2004.

(*Source:* U.S. Consumer Product Safety Commission)

EXAMPLE 2 Will Anyone Ever Run a Three-Minute Mile?

Mile Records			
1886	4:12.3	1958	3:54.5
1923	4:10.4	1966	3:51.3
1933	4:07.6	1979	3:48.9
1945	4:01.3	1985	3:46.3
1954	3:59.4	1999	3:43.1

Source: U.S.A. Track and Field

One yardstick for measuring how steadily—if slowly—athletic performance has improved is the mile run. In 1923, the record for the mile was a comparatively sleepy 4 minutes, 10.4 seconds. In 1954, Roger Bannister of Britain cracked the 4-minute mark, coming in at 3 minutes, 59.4 seconds. In the half-century since, about 0.3 second per year has been shaved off Bannister's record. If this trend continues, by which year will someone run a 3-minute mile?

Solution In solving this problem, we will express time for the mile run in seconds. Our interest is in a time of 3 minutes, or 180 seconds.

Step 1 Let x represent one of the quantities. Here is the critical information in the problem:

- In 1954, the record was 3 minutes, 59.4 seconds, or 239.4 seconds.
- The record has decreased by 0.3 second per year since then.

We are interested in when the record will be 180 seconds. Let

x = the number of years after 1954 when someone will run a 3-minute mile.

Step 2 Represent other quantities in terms of x. There are no other unknown quantities to find, so we can skip this step.

Step 3 Write an equation in x that models the conditions.

The 1954 record time	decreased by	0.3 second per year for x years	equals	the 3-minute, or 180-second, mile.
239.4	$-$	$0.3x$	$=$	180

A Poky Species

For a species that prides itself on its athletic prowess, human beings are a pretty poky group. Lions can sprint at up to 50 miles per hour; cheetahs move even faster, flooring it to a sizzling 70 miles per hour. But most humans—with our willowy spines and awkward, upright gait—would have trouble cracking 20 miles per hour with a tail wind, a flat track, and a good pair of running shoes.

Step 4 Solve the equation and answer the question.

$$239.4 - 0.3x = 180$$ This is the equation that models the problem's conditions.

$$239.4 - 239.4 - 0.3x = 180 - 239.4$$ Subtract 239.4 from both sides.

$$-0.3x = -59.4$$ Simplify.

$$\frac{-0.3x}{-0.3} = \frac{-59.4}{-0.3}$$ Divide both sides by -0.3.

$$x = 198$$ Simplify.

Using current trends, by 198 years (gasp!) after 1954, or in 2152, someone will run a 3-minute mile.

Step 5 Check the proposed solution in the original wording of the problem. The problem states that the record time should be 180 seconds. Do we obtain 180 seconds if we decrease the 1954 record time, 239.4 seconds, by 0.3 second per year for 198 years, our proposed solution?

$$239.4 - 0.3(198) = 239.4 - 59.4 = 180$$

This verifies that, using current trends, the 3-minute mile will be run 198 years after 1954.

Check Point 2 Got organic milk? Although organic milk accounts for only 1.2% of the market, consumption is increasing. In 2004, Americans purchased 40.7 million gallons of organic milk, increasing at a rate of 5.6 million gallons per year. If this trend continues, when will Americans purchase 79.9 million gallons of organic milk?

(*Source*: National Dairy Council)

EXAMPLE 3 Selecting a Long-Distance Carrier

You are choosing between two long-distance telephone plans. Plan A has a monthly fee of \$20 with a charge of \$0.05 per minute for all long-distance calls. Plan B has a monthly fee of \$5 with a charge of \$0.10 per minute for all long-distance calls. For how many minutes of long-distance calls will the costs for the two plans be the same?

Solution

Step 1 Let x represent one of the quantities. Let

x = the number of minutes of long-distance calls for which the two plans cost the same.

Step 2 Represent other quantities in terms of x. There are no other unknown quantities, so we can skip this step.

Step 3 Write an equation in x that models the conditions. The monthly cost for plan A is the monthly fee, \$20, plus the per minute charge, \$0.05, times the number of minutes of long-distance calls, x. The monthly cost for plan B is the monthly fee, \$5, plus the per-minute charge, \$0.10, times the number of minutes of long-distance calls, x.

The monthly cost for plan A | must equal | the monthly cost for plan B.

$$20 + 0.05x = 5 + 0.10x$$

Step 4 Solve the equation and answer the question.

$$20 + 0.05x = 5 + 0.10x$$ This is the equation that models the problem's conditions.

$$20 = 5 + 0.05x$$ Subtract 0.05x from both sides.

$$15 = 0.05x$$ Subtract 5 from both sides.

$$\frac{15}{0.05} = \frac{0.05x}{0.05}$$ Divide both sides by 0.05.

$$300 = x$$ Simplify.

Because x represents the number of minutes of long-distance calls for which the two plans cost the same, the costs will be the same for 300 minutes of long-distance calls.

Step 5 Check the proposed solution in the original wording of the problem. The problem states that the costs for the two plans should be the same. Let's see if they are the same with 300 minutes of long-distance calls:

$$\text{Cost for plan A} = \$20 + \$0.05(300) = \$20 + \$15 = \$35$$

Monthly fee | Per-minute charge

$$\text{Cost for plan B} = \$5 + \$0.10(300) = \$5 + \$30 = \$35.$$

With 300 minutes, or 5 hours, of long-distance chatting, both plans cost $35 for the month. Thus, the proposed solution, 300 minutes, satisfies the problem's conditions.

Technology

We can use a graphing utility to numerically or graphically verify our work in Example 3.

The monthly cost for plan A | must equal | the monthly cost for plan B.

$$20 + 0.05x \quad = \quad 5 + 0.10x$$

Enter $y_1 = 20 + .05x$. Enter $y_2 = 5 + .10x$.

Numeric Check

Display a table for y_1 and y_2.

X	Y1	Y2
100	25	15
150	27.5	20
200	30	25
250	32.5	30
300	35	35
350	37.5	40
400	40	45

X=300

When $x = 300$, y_1 and y_2 have the same value, 35. With 300 minutes of calls, costs are the same, $35, for both plans.

Graphic Check

Display graphs for y_1 and y_2. Use the intersection feature.

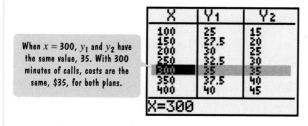

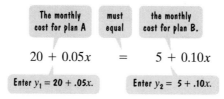

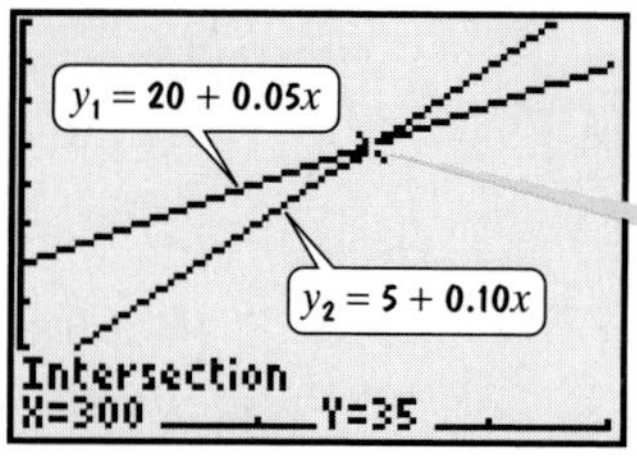

Graphs intersect at (300, 35). With 300 minutes of calls, costs are the same, $35, for both plans.

[0, 500, 100] by [0, 50, 5]

Check Point 3 You are choosing between two long-distance telephone plans. Plan A has a monthly fee of $15 with a charge of $0.08 per minute for all long-distance calls. Plan B has a monthly fee of $3 with a charge of $0.12 per minute for all long-distance calls. For how many minutes of long-distance calls will the costs for the two plans be the same?

EXAMPLE 4 Education Pays Off

The graph in Figure 1.15 shows that for the period from 1982 through 2002, those with the most education had the fastest growth in wages. In 2002, the median annual income for people with a college degree was \$52,000. This is a 160% increase over the median income in 1982. What were people with a college degree earning in 1982?

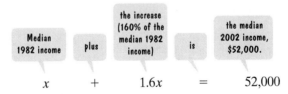

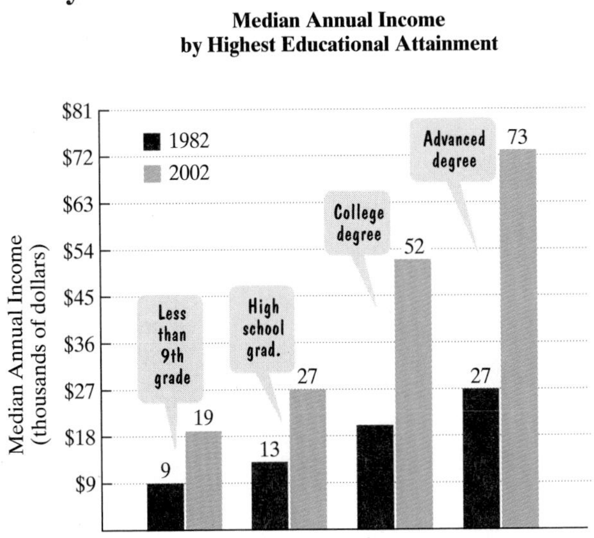

Figure 1.15

Source: U.S. Census Bureau

Solution

Step 1 Let x represent one of the quantities. We will let

x = the median income of people with a college degree in 1982.

Step 2 Represent other quantities in terms of x. There are no other unknown quantities to find, so we can skip this step.

Step 3 Write an equation in x that models the conditions. The median income in 1982 plus the 160% increase is the median income in 2002, \$52,000.

Median 1982 income	plus	the increase (160% of the median 1982 income)	is	the median 2002 income, \$52,000.
x	$+$	$1.6x$	$=$	$52{,}000$

> **Study Tip**
>
> Observe that the 1982 income, x, increased by 160% is $x + 1.6x$ and *not* $x + 1.6$ or $x + 160$.

Step 4 Solve the equation and answer the question.

$$x + 1.6x = 52{,}000$$ This is the equation that models the problem's conditions.

$$2.6x = 52{,}000$$ Combine like terms: $x + 1.6x = 1x + 1.6x = 2.6x$.

$$\frac{2.6x}{2.6} = \frac{52{,}000}{2.6}$$ Divide both sides by 2.6.

$$x = 20{,}000$$

In 1982, people with a college degree were earning \$20,000.

Step 5 Check the proposed solution in the original wording of the problem. The 1982 income, \$20,000, plus the 160% increase should equal the 2002 income given in the original wording, \$52,000:

$$20{,}000 + 160\% \text{ of } 20{,}000 = 20{,}000 + 1.6(20{,}000) = 20{,}000 + 32{,}000 = 52{,}000.$$

This verifies that in 1982, college graduates were earning \$20,000.

Check Point 4 After a 30% price reduction, you purchase a new computer for \$840. What was the computer's price before the reduction?

Our next example is about simple interest. Simple interest involves interest calculated only on the amount of money that we invest, called the **principal**. The formula $I = Pr$ is used to find the simple interest, I, earned for one year when the principal, P, is invested at an annual interest rate, r. Dual investment problems involve different amounts of money in two or more investments, each paying a different rate.

EXAMPLE 5 Solving a Dual Investment Problem

Your grandmother needs your help. She has $50,000 to invest. Part of this money is to be invested in noninsured bonds paying 15% annual interest. The rest of this money is to be invested in a government-insured certificate of deposit paying 7% annual interest. She told you that she requires $6000 per year in extra income from both of these investments. How much money should be placed in each investment?

Solution

Step 1 Let x represent one of the quantities. We will let

x = the amount invested in the noninsured bonds at 15%.

Step 2 Represent other quantities in terms of x. The other quantity that we seek is the amount invested at 7% in the certificate of deposit. Because the total amount Grandma has to invest is $50,000 and we already used up x,

$50{,}000 - x$ = the amount invested in the certificate of deposit at 7%.

Step 3 Write an equation in x that models the conditions. Because Grandma requires $6000 in total interest, the interest for the two investments combined must be $6000. Interest is Pr or rP for each investment.

Interest from the 15% investment	plus	interest from the 7% investment	is	$6000.
$0.15x$	$+$	$0.07(50{,}000 - x)$	$=$	6000
rate times principal		rate times principal		

Step 4 Solve the equation and answer the question.

$0.15x + 0.07(50{,}000 - x) = 6000$	This is the equation that models the problem's conditions.
$0.15x + 3500 - 0.07x = 6000$	Use the distributive property.
$0.08x + 3500 = 6000$	Combine like terms.
$0.08x = 2500$	Subtract 3500 from both sides.
$\frac{0.08x}{0.08} = \frac{2500}{0.08}$	Divide both sides by 0.08.
$x = 31{,}250$	Simplify.

Thus,

the amount invested at 15% $= x = 31{,}250$.

the amount invested at 7% $= 50{,}000 - 31{,}250 = 18{,}750$.

Grandma should invest $31,250 at 15% and $18,750 at 7%.

Step 5 Check the proposed solution in the original wording of the problem. The problem states that the total interest from the dual investments should be $6000. Can Grandma count on $6000 interest? The interest earned on $31,250 at 15% is ($31,250) (0.15), or $4687.50. The interest earned on $18,750 at 7% is ($18,750) (0.07), or \$1312.50. The total interest is \$4687.50 + \$1312.50, or \$6000, exactly as it should be. You've made your grandmother happy. (Now if you would just visit her more often ...)

Check Point 5 You inherited \$5000 with the stipulation that for the first year the money had to be invested in two funds paying 9% and 11% annual interest. How much did you invest at each rate if the total interest earned for the year was \$487?

Solving geometry problems usually requires a knowledge of basic geometric ideas and formulas. Formulas for area, perimeter, and volume are given in Table 1.2.

Table 1.2 Common Formulas for Area, Perimeter, and Volume

Square	Rectangle	Circle	Triangle	Trapezoid
$A = s^2$ $P = 4s$	$A = lw$ $P = 2l + 2w$	$A = \pi r^2$ $C = 2\pi r$	$A = \frac{1}{2}bh$	$A = \frac{1}{2}h(a + b)$

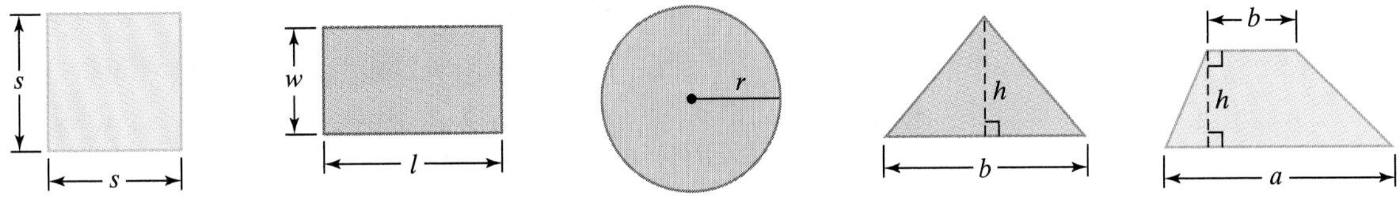

Cube	Rectangular Solid	Circular Cylinder	Sphere	Cone
$V = s^3$	$V = lwh$	$V = \pi r^2 h$	$V = \frac{4}{3}\pi r^3$	$V = \frac{1}{3}\pi r^2 h$

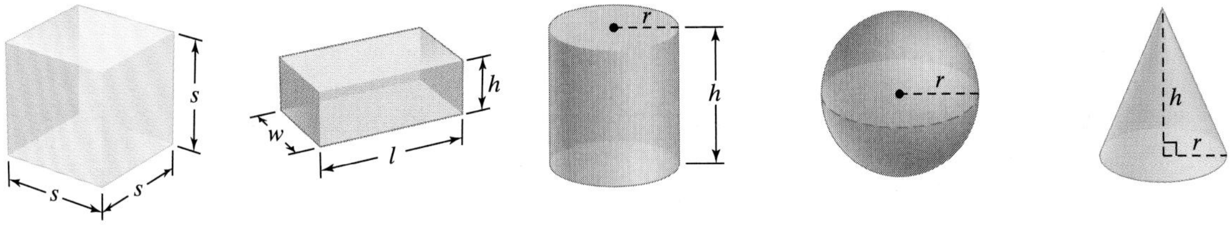

We will be using the formula for the perimeter of a rectangle, $P = 2l + 2w$, in our next example. The formula states that a rectangle's perimeter is the sum of twice its length and twice its width.

EXAMPLE 6 Finding the Dimensions of an American Football Field

The length of an American football field is 200 feet more than the width. If the perimeter of the field is 1040 feet, what are its dimensions?

Solution

Step 1 Let x represent one of the quantities. We know something about the length; the length is 200 feet more than the width. We will let

$$x = \text{the width.}$$

Step 2 Represent other quantities in terms of x. Because the length is 200 feet more than the width, we add 200 to the width to represent the length. Thus,

$$x + 200 = \text{the length.}$$

Figure 1.16 illustrates an American football field and its dimensions.

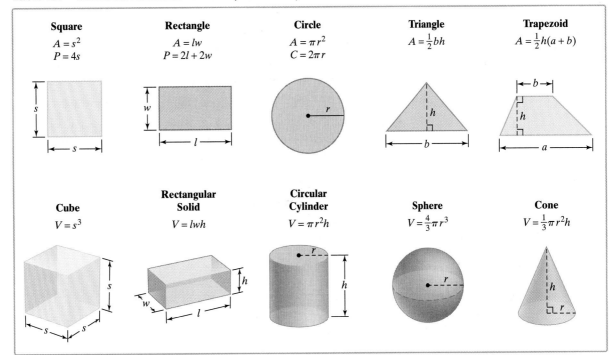

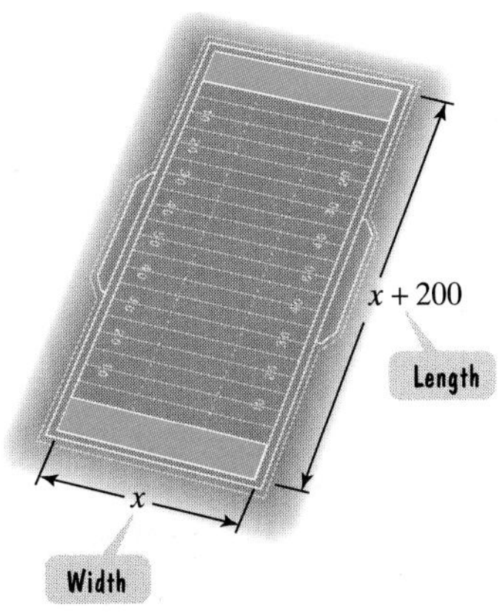

Figure 1.16 An American football field

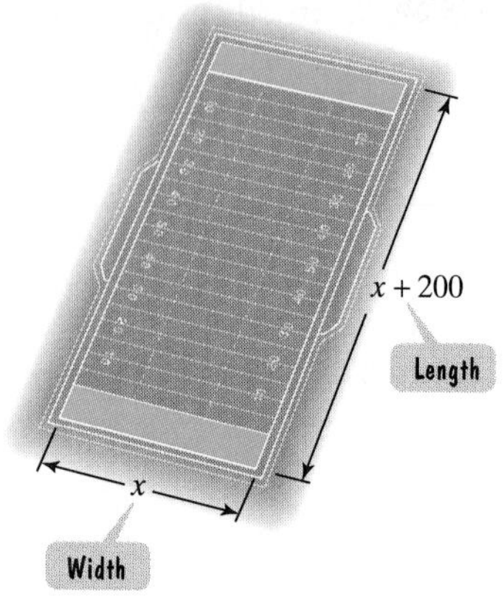

Figure 1.16 (repeated)

Step 3 Write an equation in x that models the conditions. Because the perimeter of the field is 1040 feet,

Twice the length	plus	twice the width	is	the perimeter.
$2(x + 200)$	$+$	$2x$	$=$	$1040.$

Step 4 Solve the equation and answer the question.

$$2(x + 200) + 2x = 1040$$ This is the equation that models the problem's conditions.

$$2x + 400 + 2x = 1040$$ Apply the distributive property.

$$4x + 400 = 1040$$ Combine like terms: $2x + 2x = 4x$.

$$4x = 640$$ Subtract 400 from both sides.

$$x = 160$$ Divide both sides by 4.

Thus,

$$\text{width} = x = 160.$$
$$\text{length} = x + 200 = 160 + 200 = 360.$$

The dimensions of an American football field are 160 feet by 360 feet. (The 360-foot length is usually described as 120 yards.)

Step 5 Check the proposed solution in the original wording of the problem. The perimeter of the football field using the dimensions that we found is

$$2(160 \text{ feet}) + 2(360 \text{ feet}) = 320 \text{ feet} + 720 \text{ feet} = 1040 \text{ feet}.$$

Because the problem's wording tells us that the perimeter is 1040 feet, our dimensions are correct.

Check Point 6 The length of a rectangular basketball court is 44 feet more than the width. If the perimeter of the basketball court is 288 feet, what are its dimensions?

2 Solve a formula for a variable.

Solving a Formula for One of Its Variables

We know that solving an equation is the process of finding the number (or numbers) that make the equation a true statement. All of the equations we have solved contained only one letter, x.

By contrast, formulas contain two or more letters, representing two or more variables. An example is the formula for the perimeter of a rectangle:

$$2l + 2w = P.$$

We say that this formula is solved for the variable P because P is alone on one side of the equation and the other side does not contain a P.

Solving a formula for a variable means rewriting the formula so that the variable is isolated on one side of the equation. It does not mean obtaining a numerical value for that variable.

To solve a formula for one of its variables, treat that variable as if it were the only variable in the equation. Think of the other variables as if they were numbers. Isolate all terms with the specified variable on one side of the equation and all terms without the specified variable on the other side. Then divide both sides by the same nonzero quantity to get the specified variable alone. The next example shows how to do this.

EXAMPLE 7 Solving a Formula for a Variable

Solve the formula $2l + 2w = P$ for l.

Solution First, isolate $2l$ on the left by subtracting $2w$ from both sides. Then solve for l by dividing both sides by 2.

> We need to isolate l.

$$2l + 2w = P \qquad \text{This is the given formula.}$$

$$2l + 2w - 2w = P - 2w \qquad \begin{array}{l}\text{Isolate 2l by subtracting 2w from}\\ \text{both sides.}\end{array}$$

$$2l = P - 2w \qquad \text{Simplify.}$$

$$\frac{2l}{2} = \frac{P - 2w}{2} \qquad \text{Solve for l by dividing both sides by 2.}$$

$$l = \frac{P - 2w}{2} \qquad \text{Simplify.}$$

Check Point 7 Solve the formula $2l + 2w = P$ for w.

EXAMPLE 8 Solving a Formula for a Variable That Occurs Twice

The formula

$$A = P + Prt$$

describes the amount, A, that a principal of P dollars is worth after t years when invested at a simple annual interest rate, r. Solve this formula for P.

Solution Notice that all the terms with P already occur on the right side of the formula.

> We need to isolate P.

$$A = P + Prt$$

Study Tip

You cannot solve $A = P + Prt$ for P by subtracting Prt from both sides and writing

$$A - Prt = P.$$

When a formula is solved for a specified variable, that variable must be isolated on one side. The variable P occurs on both sides of

$$A - Prt = P.$$

We can factor P from the two terms on the right to convert the two occurrences of P into one.

$$A = P + Prt \qquad \text{This is the given formula.}$$

$$A = P(1 + rt) \qquad \begin{array}{l}\text{Factor out P on the right side of}\\ \text{the equation.}\end{array}$$

$$\frac{A}{1 + rt} = \frac{P(1 + rt)}{1 + rt} \qquad \text{Divide both sides by } 1 + rt.$$

$$\frac{A}{1 + rt} = P \qquad \text{Simplify: } \frac{P\cancel{(1 + rt)}}{1\cancel{(1 + rt)}} = \frac{P}{1} = P.$$

Equivalently,

$$P = \frac{A}{1 + rt}.$$

Check Point 8 Solve the formula $P = C + MC$ for C.

EXERCISE SET 1.3

Practice Exercises

Use the five-step strategy for solving word problems to find the number or numbers described in Exercises 1–10.

1. When five times a number is decreased by 4, the result is 26. What is the number?
2. When two times a number is decreased by 3, the result is 11. What is the number?
3. When a number is decreased by 20% of itself, the result is 20. What is the number?
4. When a number is decreased by 30% of itself, the result is 28. What is the number?
5. When 60% of a number is added to the number, the result is 192. What is the number?
6. When 80% of a number is added to the number, the result is 252. What is the number?
7. 70% of what number is 224?
8. 70% of what number is 252?
9. One number exceeds another by 26. The sum of the numbers is 64. What are the numbers?
10. One number exceeds another by 24. The sum of the numbers is 58. What are the numbers?

Practice Plus

In Exercises 11–18, find all values of x satisfying the given conditions.

11. $y_1 = 13x - 4$, $y_2 = 5x + 10$, and y_1 exceeds y_2 by 2.
12. $y_1 = 10x + 6$, $y_2 = 12x - 7$, and y_1 exceeds y_2 by 3.
13. $y_1 = 10(2x - 1)$, $y_2 = 2x + 1$, and y_1 is 14 more than 8 times y_2.
14. $y_1 = 9(3x - 5)$, $y_2 = 3x - 1$, and y_1 is 51 less than 12 times y_2.
15. $y_1 = 2x + 6$, $y_2 = x + 8$, $y_3 = x$, and the difference between 3 times y_1 and 5 times y_2 is 22 less than y_3.
16. $y_1 = 2.5$, $y_2 = 2x + 1$, $y_3 = x$, and the difference between 2 times y_1 and 3 times y_2 is 8 less than 4 times y_3.
17. $y_1 = \frac{1}{x}$, $y_2 = \frac{1}{2x}$, $y_3 = \frac{1}{x-1}$, and the sum of 3 times y_1 and 4 times y_2 is the product of 4 and y_3.
18. $y_1 = \frac{1}{x}$, $y_2 = \frac{1}{x^2 - x}$, $y_3 = \frac{1}{x-1}$, and the difference between 6 times y_1 and 3 times y_2 is the product of 7 and y_3.

Application Exercises

19. Each day, the number of births in the world exceeds the number of deaths by 229 thousand. The combined number of births and deaths is 521 thousand. Determine the number of births and the number of deaths per day.

Daily Growth of World Population

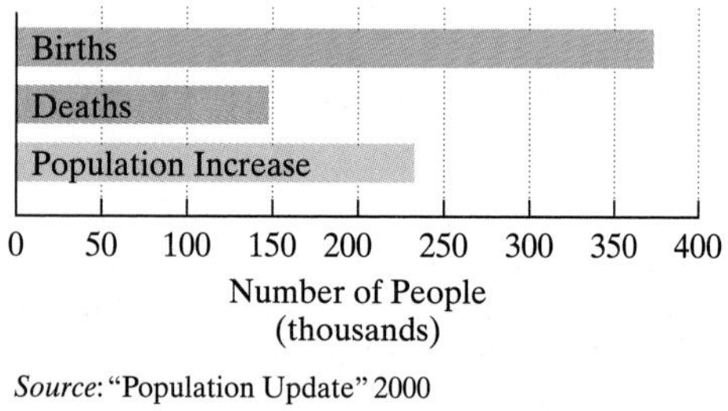

Source: "Population Update" 2000

20. Americans say keep the penny. A survey asked a random sample of U.S. adults if they favored abolishing the penny. The circle graph shows the results.

Do You Favor Abolishing the Penny?

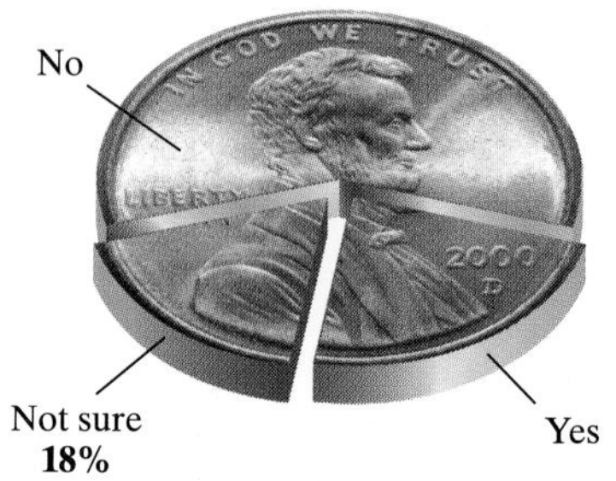

Source: Harris poll of 2136 adults

A total of 82% of those polled responded yes or no. The no responses (keep the penny) exceeded the yes responses (abolish the penny) by 36%. Determine the percentage who responded yes and the percentage who responded no.

21. The bar graph shows the number of Internet users, in millions, for the countries with the most users. The number of Internet users in Japan exceeds China by 10 million and the number of Internet users in the United States exceeds China by 123 million. There are a total of 271 million Internet users in the United States, Japan, and China. Determine the number of users, in millions, in each country.

Countries with the Most Internet Users

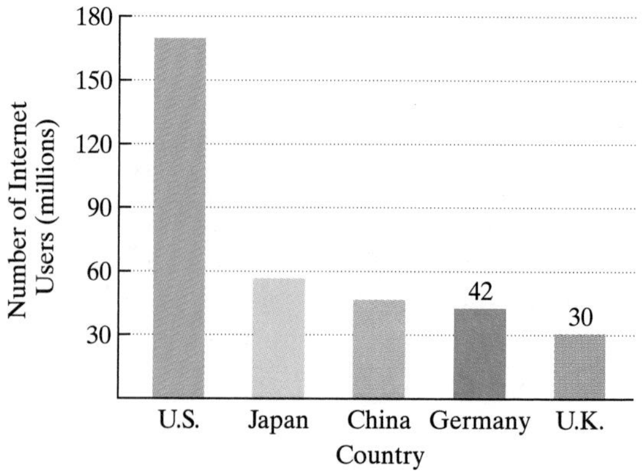

Source: CyberAtlas

22. The bar graph at the top of the next page shows the percentage of global energy used by the countries consuming the most energy. The percentage of global energy used by China exceeds Russia by 6% and the percentage of global energy used by the United States exceeds Russia by 16.4%. Combined, the United States, China, and Russia consume 40.4% of the world's energy. Determine the percentage of global energy used by each country.

Countries Using the Most Energy

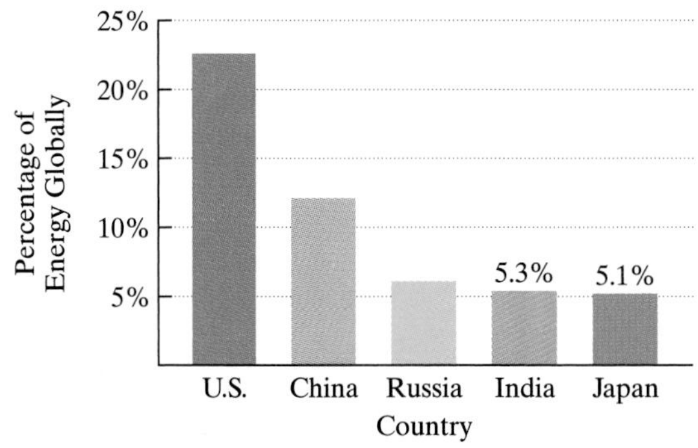

Source: World Bank Group

23. The circle graph shows the political ideology of U.S. college freshmen. The percentage of liberals exceeds twice that of conservatives by 4.4%. Find the percentage of liberals and the percentage of conservatives. (*Hint*: You'll need to use the percents displayed on the graph to determine the combined percentage of liberals and conservatives.)

Political Ideology of U.S. College Freshmen

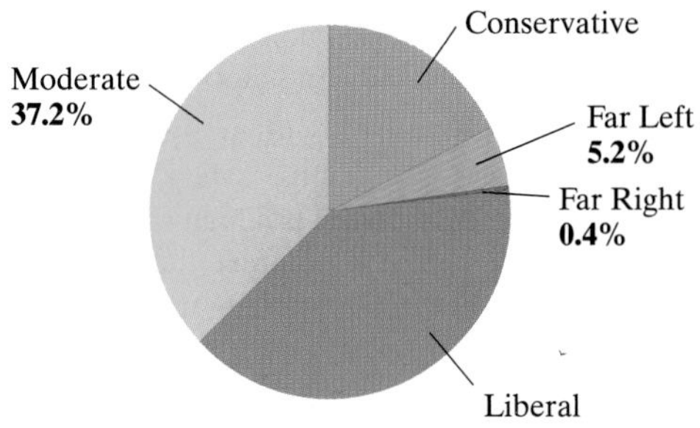

Source: *The Chronicle of Higher Education*

24. The bar graph shows the breakdown of the 7485 hate crimes reported in the United States in 2004. The number of hate crimes based on race exceeded three times the number based on sexual orientation by 127. Find the number of hate crimes reported in the United States in 2004 based on race and based on sexual orientation.

Hate Crimes in the U.S.

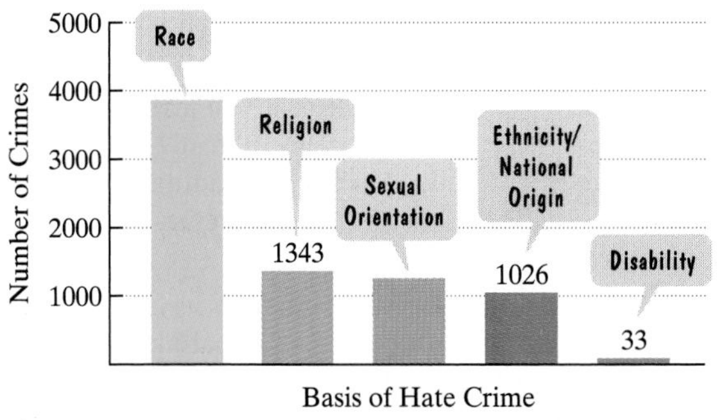

Source: F.B.I.

According to one mathematical model, the average life expectancy for American men born in 1900 was 55 years. Life expectancy has increased by about 0.2 year for each birth year after 1900. Use this information to solve Exercises 25–26.

25. If this trend continues, for which birth year will the average life expectancy be 85 years?

26. If this trend continues, for which birth year will the average life expectancy be 91 years?

The graph shows the number of Americans without health insurance from 2000 through 2003.

Number of Americans without Health Insurance

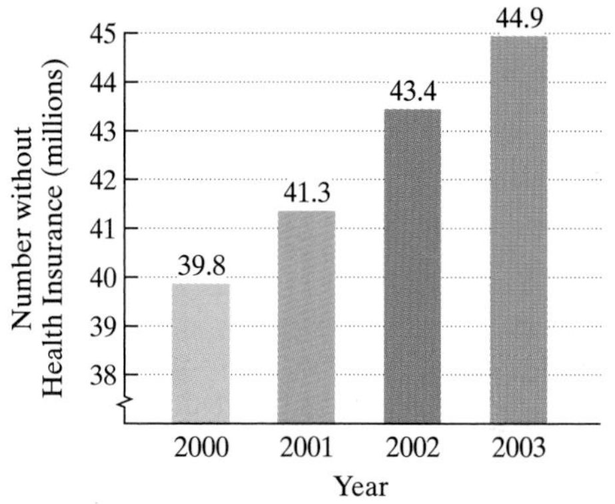

Source: U.S. Census Bureau

In 2000, there were 39.8 million Americans without health insurance. This number has increased at an average rate of 1.7 million people per year. Use this description to solve Exercises 27–28.

27. a. Write a formula that models the number of Americans without health insurance, y, x years after 2000.

b. Use the formula in part (a) to determine when the number of Americans without health insurance will exceed the number in 2003 by 8.5 million.

c. Graph the formula in part (a) and show the solution to part (b) on the graph.

28. a. Write a formula that models the number of Americans without health insurance, y, x years after 2000.

b. Use the formula in part (a) to determine when the number of Americans without health insurance will exceed the number in 2003 by 10.2 million.

c. Graph the formula in part (a) and show the solution to part (b) on the graph.

In 2003, the price of a BMW 7 Series was approximately $80,500 with a depreciation of $8705 per year. Use this information to solve Exercises 29–30.

29. After how many years will the car's value be $19,565?

30. After how many years will the car's value be $36,975?

31. You are choosing between two health clubs. Club A offers membership for a fee of $40 plus a monthly fee of $25. Club B offers membership for a fee of $15 plus a monthly fee of $30. After how many months will the total cost at each health club be the same? What will be the total cost for each club?

32. Video Store A charges $9 to rent a video game for one week. Although only members can rent from the store, membership is free. Video Store B charges only $4 to rent a video game for one week. Only members can rent from the store and membership is $50 per year. After how many video-game rentals will the total amount spent at each store be the same? What will be the total amount spent at each store?

33. The bus fare in a city is $1.25. People who use the bus have the option of purchasing a monthly coupon book for $15.00. With the coupon book, the fare is reduced to $0.75. Determine the number of times in a month the bus must be used so that the total monthly cost without the coupon book is the same as the total monthly cost with the coupon book.

34. A coupon book for a bridge costs $30 per month. The toll for the bridge is normally $5.00, but it is reduced to $3.50 for people who have purchased the coupon book. Determine the number of times in a month the bridge must be crossed so that the total monthly cost without the coupon book is the same as the total monthly cost with the coupon book.

35. In 2005, there were 13,300 students at college A, with a projected enrollment increase of 1000 students per year. In the same year, there were 26,800 students at college B, with a projected enrollment decline of 500 students per year.

a. According to these projections, when will the colleges have the same enrollment? What will be the enrollment in each college at that time?

b. Use the following table to numerically check your work in part (a). What equations were entered for Y_1 and Y_2 to obtain this table?

X	Y_1	Y_2
7	20300	23300
8	21300	22800
9	22300	22300
10	23300	21800
11	24300	21300
12	25300	20800
13	26300	20300

X=7

36. In 2000, the population of Greece was 10,600,000, with projections of a population decrease of 28,000 people per year. In the same year, the population of Belgium was 10,200,000, with projections of a population decrease of 12,000 people per year. (*Source*: United Nations) According to these projections, when will the two countries have the same population? What will be the population at that time?

37. After a 20% reduction, you purchase a television for $336. What was the television's price before the reduction?

38. After a 30% reduction, you purchase a dictionary for $30.80. What was the dictionary's price before the reduction?

39. Including 8% sales tax, an inn charges $162 per night. Find the inn's nightly cost before the tax is added.

40. Including 5% sales tax, an inn charges $252 per night. Find the inn's nightly cost before the tax is added.

The graph shows average yearly earnings in the United States by highest educational attainment. Use the relevant information shown in the graph to solve Exercises 41–42.

Average Earnings of Full-Time Workers in the U.S., by Highest Educational Attainment

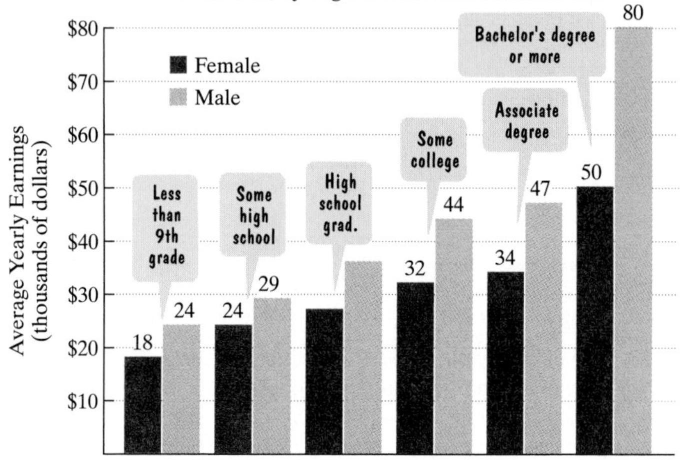

Source: U.S. Census Bureau

41. The annual salary for men with some college is an increase of 22% over the annual salary for men whose highest educational attainment is a high school degree. What is the annual salary, to the nearest thousand dollars, for men whose highest educational attainment is a high school degree?

42. The annual salary for women with an associate degree is an increase of 26% over the annual salary for women whose highest educational attainment is a high school degree. What is the annual salary, to the nearest thousand dollars, for women whose highest educational attainment is a high school degree?

Exercises 43–44 involve markup, the amount added to the dealer's cost of an item to arrive at the selling price of that item.

43. The selling price of a refrigerator is $584. If the markup is 25% of the dealer's cost, what is the dealer's cost of the refrigerator?

44. The selling price of a scientific calculator is $15. If the markup is 25% of the dealer's cost, what is the dealer's cost of the calculator?

45. You invested $7000 in two accounts paying 6% and 8% annual interest, respectively. If the total interest earned for the year was $520, how much was invested at each rate?

46. You invested $11,000 in stocks and bonds, paying 5% and 8% annual interest, respectively. If the total interest earned for the year was $730, how much was invested in stocks and how much was invested in bonds?

47. Things did not go quite as planned. You invested $8000, part of it in stock that paid 12% annual interest. However, the rest of the money suffered a 5% loss. If the total annual income from both investments was $620, how much was invested at each rate?

48. Things did not go quite as planned. You invested $12,000, part of it in stock that paid 14% annual interest. However, the rest of the money suffered a 6% loss. If the total annual income from both investments was $680, how much was invested at each rate?

49. A rectangular soccer field is twice as long as it is wide. If the perimeter of the soccer field is 300 yards, what are its dimensions?

50. A rectangular swimming pool is three times as long as it is wide. If the perimeter of the pool is 320 feet, what are its dimensions?

51. The length of the rectangular tennis court at Wimbledon is 6 feet longer than twice the width. If the court's perimeter is 228 feet, what are the court's dimensions?

52. The length of a rectangular pool is 6 meters less than twice the width. If the pool's perimeter is 126 meters, what are its dimensions?

53. The rectangular painting in the figure shown measures 12 inches by 16 inches and contains a frame of uniform width around the four edges. The perimeter of the rectangle formed by the painting and its frame is 72 inches. Determine the width of the frame.

54. The rectangular swimming pool in the figure shown measures 40 feet by 60 feet and contains a path of uniform width around the four edges. The perimeter of the rectangle formed by the pool and the surrounding path is 248 feet. Determine the width of the path.

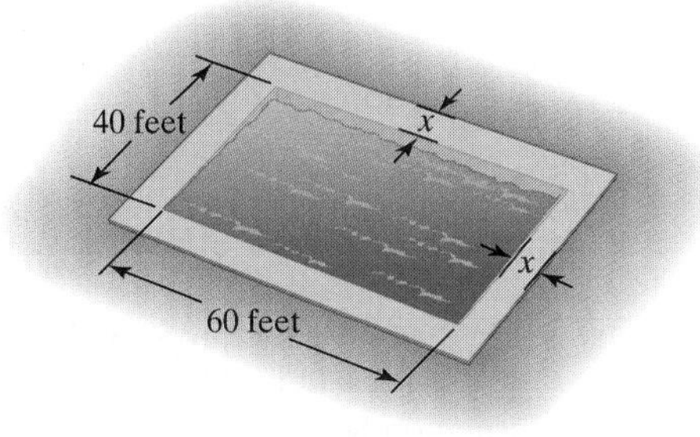

55. An automobile repair shop charged a customer \$448, listing \$63 for parts and the remainder for labor. If the cost of labor is \$35 per hour, how many hours of labor did it take to repair the car?

56. A repair bill on a sailboat came to \$1603, including \$532 for parts and the remainder for labor. If the cost of labor is \$63 per hour, how many hours of labor did it take to repair the sailboat?

57. An HMO pamphlet contains the following recommended weight for women: "Give yourself 100 pounds for the first 5 feet plus 5 pounds for every inch over 5 feet tall." Using this description, what height corresponds to a recommended weight of 135 pounds?

58. A job pays an annual salary of \$33,150, which includes a holiday bonus of \$750. If paychecks are issued twice a month, what is the gross amount for each paycheck?

59. Answer the question in the following *Peanuts* cartoon strip. (*Note:* You may not use the answer given in the cartoon!)

PEANUTS reprinted by permission of United Features Syndicate, Inc.

60. For a long-distance person-to-person telephone call, a telephone company charges \$0.43 for the first minute, \$0.32 for each additional minute, and a \$2.10 service charge. If the cost of a call is \$5.73, how long did the person talk?

In Exercises 61–80, solve each formula for the specified variable. Do you recognize the formula? If so, what does it describe?

61. $A = lw$ for w

62. $D = RT$ for R

63. $A = \frac{1}{2}bh$ for b

64. $V = \frac{1}{3}Bh$ for B

65. $I = Prt$ for P

66. $C = 2\pi r$ for r

67. $E = mc^2$ for m

68. $V = \pi r^2 h$ for h

69. $T = D + pm$ for p

70. $P = C + MC$ for M

71. $A = \frac{1}{2}h(a + b)$ for a

72. $A = \frac{1}{2}h(a + b)$ for b

73. $S = P + Prt$ for r

74. $S = P + Prt$ for t

75. $B = \dfrac{F}{S - V}$ for S

76. $S = \dfrac{C}{1 - r}$ for r

77. $IR + Ir = E$ for I

78. $A = 2lw + 2lh + 2wh$ for h

79. $\dfrac{1}{p} + \dfrac{1}{q} = \dfrac{1}{f}$ for f

80. $\dfrac{1}{R} = \dfrac{1}{R_1} + \dfrac{1}{R_2}$ for R_1

Writing in Mathematics

81. In your own words, describe a step-by-step approach for solving algebraic word problems.

82. Write an original word problem that can be solved using a linear equation. Then solve the problem.

83. Explain what it means to solve a formula for a variable.

84. Did you have difficulties solving some of the problems that were assigned in this exercise set? Discuss what you did if this happened to you. Did your course of action enhance your ability to solve algebraic word problems?

85. The mile records in Example 2 on page 110 are a yardstick for measuring how athletes are getting better and better. Do you think that there is a limit to human performance? Explain your answer. If so, when might we reach it?

86. The bar graph in Exercises 41–42 shows average earnings of U.S. men and women, by highest educational attainment. Describe the trend shown by the graph. Discuss any aspects of the data that surprised you.

Technology Exercises

87. Use a graphing utility to numerically or graphically verify your work in any one exercise from Exercises 31–34. For assistance on how to do this, refer to the Technology box on page 112.

88. The formula $y = 0.2x + 55$ models the average life expectancy, y, of American men born x years after 1900. Graph the formula in a $[0, 200, 20]$ by $[0, 100, 10]$ viewing rectangle. Then use the TRACE or ZOOM feature to verify your answer in Exercise 25 or 26.

89. A tennis club offers two payment options. Members can pay a monthly fee of $30 plus $5 per hour for court rental time. The second option has no monthly fee, but court time costs $7.50 per hour.

a. Write a mathematical model representing total monthly costs for each option for x hours of court rental time.

b. Use a graphing utility to graph the two models in a $[0, 15, 1]$ by $[0, 120, 20]$ viewing rectangle.

c. Use your utility's trace or intersection feature to determine where the two graphs intersect. Describe what the coordinates of this intersection point represent in practical terms.

d. Verify part (c) using an algebraic approach by setting the two models equal to one another and determining how many hours one has to rent the court so that the two plans result in identical monthly costs.

Critical Thinking Exercises

90. At the north campus of a performing arts school, 10% of the students are music majors. At the south campus, 90% of the students are music majors. The campuses are merged into one east campus. If 42% of the 1000 students at the east campus are music majors, how many students did the north and south campuses have before the merger?

91. The price of a dress is reduced by 40%. When the dress still does not sell, it is reduced by 40% of the reduced price. If the price of the dress after both reductions is $72, what was the original price?

92. In a film, the actor Charles Coburn plays an elderly "uncle" character criticized for marrying a woman when he is 3 times her age. He wittily replies, "Ah, but in 20 years time I shall only be twice her age." How old is the "uncle" and the woman?

93. Suppose that we agree to pay you 8¢ for every problem in this chapter that you solve correctly and fine you 5¢ for every problem done incorrectly. If at the end of 26 problems we do not owe each other any money, how many problems did you solve correctly?

94. It was wartime when the Ricardos found out Mrs. Ricardo was pregnant. Ricky Ricardo was drafted and made out a will, deciding that $14,000 in a savings account was to be divided between his wife and his child-to-be. Rather strangely, and certainly with gender bias, Ricky stipulated that if the child were a boy, he would get twice the amount of the mother's portion. If it were a girl, the mother would get twice the amount the girl was to receive. We'll never know what Ricky was thinking of, for (as fate would have it) he did not return from war. Mrs. Ricardo gave birth to twins—a boy and a girl. How was the money divided?

95. A thief steals a number of rare plants from a nursery. On the way out, the thief meets three security guards, one after another. To each security guard, the thief is forced to give one-half the plants that he still has, plus 2 more. Finally, the thief leaves the nursery with 1 lone palm. How many plants were originally stolen?

96. Solve for C: $V = C - \dfrac{C - S}{L}N.$

Group Exercise

97. One of the best ways to learn how to *solve* a word problem in algebra is to *design* word problems of your own. Creating a word problem makes you very aware of precisely how much information is needed to solve the problem. You must also focus on the best way to present information to a reader and on how much information to give. As you write your problem, you gain skills that will help you solve problems created by others.

The group should design five different word problems that can be solved using linear equations. All of the problems should be on different topics. For example, the group should not have more than one problem on simple interest. The group should turn in both the problems and their algebraic solutions.

SECTION 1.4 Complex Numbers

Objectives

1. Add and subtract complex numbers.
2. Multiply complex numbers.
3. Divide complex numbers.
4. Perform operations with square roots of negative numbers.

© 2005 Roz Chast from Cartoonbank.com. All rights reserved.

Who is this kid warning us about our eyeballs turning black if we attempt to find the square root of -9? Don't believe what you hear on the street. Although square roots of negative numbers are not real numbers, they do play a significant role in algebra. In this section, we move beyond the real numbers and discuss square roots with negative radicands.

The Imaginary Unit i

In the next section, we will study equations whose solutions may involve the square roots of negative numbers. Because the square of a real number is never negative, there is no real number x such that $x^2 = -1$. To provide a setting in which such equations have solutions, mathematicians invented an expanded system of numbers, the complex numbers. The *imaginary number i*, defined to be a solution of the equation $x^2 = -1$, is the basis of this new set.

The Imaginary Unit i

The **imaginary unit i** is defined as

$$i = \sqrt{-1}, \text{ where } i^2 = -1.$$

Using the imaginary unit i, we can express the square root of any negative number as a real multiple of i. For example,

$$\sqrt{-25} = \sqrt{-1}\sqrt{25} = i\sqrt{25} = 5i.$$

We can check this result by squaring $5i$ and obtaining -25.

$$(5i)^2 = 5^2 i^2 = 25(-1) = -25$$

A new system of numbers, called *complex numbers*, is based on adding multiples of i, such as $5i$, to the real numbers.

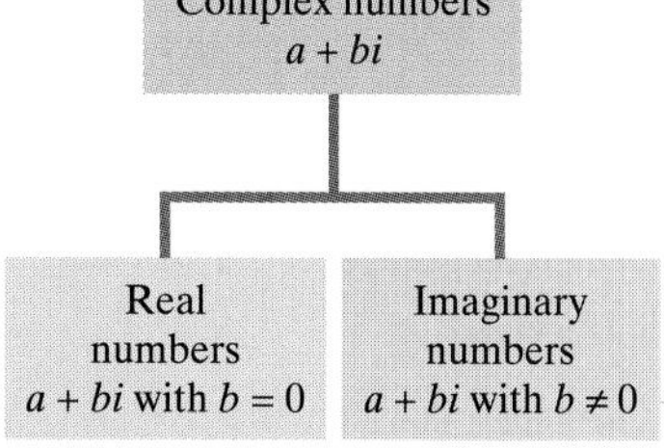

Figure 1.17 The complex number system

Complex Numbers and Imaginary Numbers

The set of all numbers in the form

$$a + bi$$

with real numbers a and b, and i, the imaginary unit, is called the set of **complex numbers**. The real number a is called the **real part** and the real number b is called the **imaginary part** of the complex number $a + bi$. If $b \neq 0$, then the complex number is called an **imaginary number** (Figure 1.17). An imaginary number in the form bi is called a **pure imaginary number**.

Here are some examples of complex numbers. Each number can be written in the form $a + bi$.

$-4 + 6i$		$2i = 0 + 2i$		$3 = 3 + 0i$	
a, the real part, is -4.	b, the imaginary part, is 6.	a, the real part, is 0.	b, the imaginary part, is 2.	a, the real part, is 3.	b, the imaginary part, is 0.

Can you see that b, the imaginary part, is not zero in the first two complex numbers? Because $b \neq 0$, these complex numbers are imaginary numbers. Furthermore, the imaginary number $2i$ is a pure imaginary number. By contrast, the imaginary part of the complex number on the right is zero. This complex number is not an imaginary number. The number 3, or $3 + 0i$, is a real number.

A complex number is said to be **simplified** if it is expressed in the **standard form** $a + bi$. If b is a radical, we usually write i before b. For example, we write $7 + i\sqrt{5}$ rather than $7 + \sqrt{5}i$, which could easily be confused with $7 + \sqrt{5i}$.

Expressed in standard form, two complex numbers are equal if and only if their real parts are equal and their imaginary parts are equal.

Equality of Complex Numbers

$a + bi = c + di$ if and only if $a = c$ and $b = d$.

1 Add and subtract complex numbers.

Operations with Complex Numbers

The form of a complex number $a + bi$ is like the binomial $a + bx$. Consequently, we can add, subtract, and multiply complex numbers using the same methods we used for binomials, remembering that $i^2 = -1$.

Adding and Subtracting Complex Numbers

1. $(a + bi) + (c + di) = (a + c) + (b + d)i$
   In words, this says that you add complex numbers by adding their real parts, adding their imaginary parts, and expressing the sum as a complex number.
2. $(a + bi) - (c + di) = (a - c) + (b - d)i$
   In words, this says that you subtract complex numbers by subtracting their real parts, subtracting their imaginary parts, and expressing the difference as a complex number.

EXAMPLE 1 Adding and Subtracting Complex Numbers

Perform the indicated operations, writing the result in standard form:

a. $(5 - 11i) + (7 + 4i)$ **b.** $(-5 + i) - (-11 - 6i)$.

Solution

a. $(5 - 11i) + (7 + 4i)$

$= 5 - 11i + 7 + 4i$ Remove the parentheses.

$= 5 + 7 - 11i + 4i$ Group real and imaginary terms.

$= (5 + 7) + (-11 + 4)i$ Add real parts and add imaginary parts.

$= 12 - 7i$ Simplify.

b. $(-5 + i) - (-11 - 6i)$

$= -5 + i + 11 + 6i$ Remove the parentheses. Change signs of real and imaginary parts in the complex number being subtracted.

$= -5 + 11 + i + 6i$ Group real and imaginary terms.

$= (-5 + 11) + (1 + 6)i$ Add real parts and add imaginary parts.

$= 6 + 7i$ Simplify.

Study Tip

The following examples, using the same integers as in Example 1, show how operations with complex numbers are just like operations with polynomials.

a. $(5 - 11x) + (7 + 4x)$
$= 12 - 7x$

b. $(-5 + x) - (-11 - 6x)$
$= -5 + x + 11 + 6x$
$= 6 + 7x$

Check Point 1 Add or subtract as indicated:

a. $(5 - 2i) + (3 + 3i)$ **b.** $(2 + 6i) - (12 - i)$.

Multiplication of complex numbers is performed the same way as multiplication of polynomials, using the distributive property and the FOIL method. After completing the multiplication, we replace any occurrences of i^2 with -1. This idea is illustrated in the next example.

2 Multiply complex numbers.

EXAMPLE 2 Multiplying Complex Numbers

Find the products:

a. $4i(3 - 5i)$ **b.** $(7 - 3i)(-2 - 5i)$.

Solution

a. $4i(3 - 5i)$

$= 4i \cdot 3 - 4i \cdot 5i$	Distribute $4i$ throughout the parentheses.
$= 12i - 20i^2$	Multiply.
$= 12i - 20(-1)$	Replace i^2 with -1.
$= 20 + 12i$	Simplify to $12i + 20$ and write in standard form.

b. $(7 - 3i)(-2 - 5i)$

F O I L

$= -14 - 35i + 6i + 15i^2$	Use the FOIL method.
$= -14 - 35i + 6i + 15(-1)$	$i^2 = -1$
$= -14 - 15 - 35i + 6i$	Group real and imaginary terms.
$= -29 - 29i$	Combine real and imaginary terms.

Check Point 2 Find the products:

a. $7i(2 - 9i)$ **b.** $(5 + 4i)(6 - 7i)$.

3 Divide complex numbers.

Complex Conjugates and Division

It is possible to multiply complex numbers and obtain a real number. This occurs when we multiply $a + bi$ and $a - bi$.

F O I L

$(a + bi)(a - bi) = a^2 - abi + abi - b^2i^2$	Use the FOIL method.
$= a^2 - b^2(-1)$	$i^2 = -1$
$= a^2 + b^2$	Notice that this product eliminates i.

For the complex number $a + bi$, we define its *complex conjugate* to be $a - bi$. The multiplication of complex conjugates results in a real number.

Conjugate of a Complex Number

The **complex conjugate** of the number $a + bi$ is $a - bi$, and the complex conjugate of $a - bi$ is $a + bi$. The multiplication of complex conjugates gives a real number.

$$(a + bi)(a - bi) = a^2 + b^2$$
$$(a - bi)(a + bi) = a^2 + b^2$$

Complex conjugates are used to divide complex numbers. By multiplying the numerator and the denominator of the division by the complex conjugate of the denominator, you will obtain a real number in the denominator.

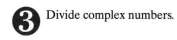

EXAMPLE 3 Using Complex Conjugates to Divide Complex Numbers

Divide and express the result in standard form: $\frac{7+4i}{2-5i}$.

Solution The complex conjugate of the denominator, $2-5i$, is $2+5i$. Multiplication of both the numerator and the denominator by $2+5i$ will eliminate i from the denominator.

$$\frac{7+4i}{2-5i} = \frac{(7+4i)}{(2-5i)} \cdot \frac{(2+5i)}{(2+5i)}$$

Multiply the numerator and the denominator by the complex conjugate of the denominator.

F O I L

$$= \frac{14+35i+8i+20i^2}{2^2+5^2}$$

Use the FOIL method in the numerator and $(a-bi)(a+bi)=a^2+b^2$ in the denominator.

$$= \frac{14+43i+20(-1)}{29}$$

Combine imaginary terms and replace i^2 with -1.

$$= \frac{-6+43i}{29}$$

Combine real terms in the numerator: $14+20(-1)=14-20=-6$.

$$= -\frac{6}{29}+\frac{43}{29}i$$

Express the answer in standard form.

Observe that the quotient is expressed in the standard form $a+bi$, with $a=-\frac{6}{29}$ and $b=\frac{43}{29}$.

Check Point 3 Divide and express the result in standard form: $\frac{5+4i}{4-i}$.

4 Perform operations with square roots of negative numbers.

Roots of Negative Numbers

The square of $4i$ and the square of $-4i$ both result in -16:

$$(4i)^2 = 16i^2 = 16(-1) = -16 \qquad (-4i)^2 = 16i^2 = 16(-1) = -16.$$

Consequently, in the complex number system -16 has two square roots, namely, $4i$ and $-4i$. We call $4i$ the **principal square root** of -16.

> **Principal Square Root of a Negative Number**
>
> For any positive real number b, the **principal square root** of the negative number $-b$ is defined by
>
> $$\sqrt{-b} = i\sqrt{b}.$$

Consider the multiplication problem

$$5i \cdot 2i = 10i^2 = 10(-1) = -10.$$

This problem can also be given in terms of principal square roots of negative numbers:

$$\sqrt{-25} \cdot \sqrt{-4}.$$

Because the product rule for radicals only applies to real numbers, multiplying radicands is incorrect. **When performing operations with square roots of negative numbers, begin by expressing all square roots in terms of i.** Then perform the indicated operation.

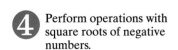

Correct:

$$\sqrt{-25}\cdot\sqrt{-4} = i\sqrt{25}\cdot i\sqrt{4} = 5i\cdot 2i = 10i^2 = 10(-1) = -10$$

Incorrect:

$$\sqrt{-25}\cdot\sqrt{-4} = \sqrt{(-25)(-4)} = \sqrt{100} = 10$$

EXAMPLE 4 Operations Involving Square Roots of Negative Numbers

Perform the indicated operations and write the result in standard form:

a. $\sqrt{-18} - \sqrt{-8}$ **b.** $\left(-1 + \sqrt{-5}\right)^2$ **c.** $\dfrac{-25 + \sqrt{-50}}{15}$.

Solution Begin by expressing all square roots of negative numbers in terms of i.

a. $\sqrt{-18} - \sqrt{-8} = i\sqrt{18} - i\sqrt{8} = i\sqrt{9\cdot 2} - i\sqrt{4\cdot 2}$
$= 3i\sqrt{2} - 2i\sqrt{2} = i\sqrt{2}$

$(A + B)^2 = A^2 + 2AB + B^2$

b. $(-1 + \sqrt{-5})^2 = (-1 + i\sqrt{5})^2 = (-1)^2 + 2(-1)(i\sqrt{5}) + (i\sqrt{5})^2$
$= 1 - 2i\sqrt{5} + 5i^2$
$= 1 - 2i\sqrt{5} + 5(-1)$
$= -4 - 2i\sqrt{5}$

c. $\dfrac{-25 + \sqrt{-50}}{15}$

$= \dfrac{-25 + i\sqrt{50}}{15}$ $\sqrt{-b} = i\sqrt{b}$

$= \dfrac{-25 + 5i\sqrt{2}}{15}$ $\sqrt{50} = \sqrt{25\cdot 2} = 5\sqrt{2}$

$= \dfrac{-25}{15} + \dfrac{5i\sqrt{2}}{15}$ Write the complex number in standard form.

$= -\dfrac{5}{3} + i\dfrac{\sqrt{2}}{3}$ Simplify.

Complex Numbers on a Postage Stamp

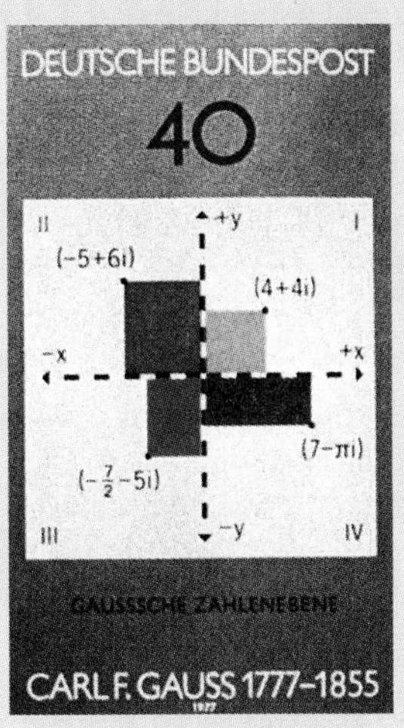

This stamp honors the work done by the German mathematician Carl Friedrich Gauss (1777–1855) with complex numbers. Gauss represented complex numbers as points in the plane.

Check Point 4 Perform the indicated operations and write the result in standard form:

a. $\sqrt{-27} + \sqrt{-48}$ **b.** $\left(-2 + \sqrt{-3}\right)^2$ **c.** $\dfrac{-14 + \sqrt{-12}}{2}$.

EXERCISE SET 1.4

Practice Exercises

In Exercises 1–8, add or subtract as indicated and write the result in standard form.

1. $(7 + 2i) + (1 - 4i)$
2. $(-2 + 6i) + (4 - i)$
3. $(3 + 2i) - (5 - 7i)$
4. $(-7 + 5i) - (-9 - 11i)$
5. $6 - (-5 + 4i) - (-13 - i)$
6. $7 - (-9 + 2i) - (-17 - i)$
7. $8i - (14 - 9i)$
8. $15i - (12 - 11i)$

In Exercises 9–20, find each product and write the result in standard form.

9. $-3i(7i - 5)$
10. $-8i(2i - 7)$
11. $(-5 + 4i)(3 + i)$
12. $(-4 - 8i)(3 + i)$
13. $(7 - 5i)(-2 - 3i)$
14. $(8 - 4i)(-3 + 9i)$
15. $(3 + 5i)(3 - 5i)$
16. $(2 + 7i)(2 - 7i)$
17. $(-5 + i)(-5 - i)$
18. $(-7 - i)(-7 + i)$
19. $(2 + 3i)^2$
20. $(5 - 2i)^2$

In Exercises 21–28, divide and express the result in standard form.

21. $\dfrac{2}{3-i}$ **22.** $\dfrac{3}{4+i}$

23. $\dfrac{2i}{1+i}$ **24.** $\dfrac{5i}{2-i}$

25. $\dfrac{8i}{4-3i}$ **26.** $\dfrac{-6i}{3+2i}$

27. $\dfrac{2+3i}{2+i}$ **28.** $\dfrac{3-4i}{4+3i}$

In Exercises 29–44, perform the indicated operations and write the result in standard form.

29. $\sqrt{-64}-\sqrt{-25}$ **30.** $\sqrt{-81}-\sqrt{-144}$

31. $5\sqrt{-16}+3\sqrt{-81}$ **32.** $5\sqrt{-8}+3\sqrt{-18}$

33. $\left(-2+\sqrt{-4}\right)^2$ **34.** $\left(-5-\sqrt{-9}\right)^2$

35. $\left(-3-\sqrt{-7}\right)^2$ **36.** $\left(-2+\sqrt{-11}\right)^2$

37. $\dfrac{-8+\sqrt{-32}}{24}$ **38.** $\dfrac{-12+\sqrt{-28}}{32}$

39. $\dfrac{-6-\sqrt{-12}}{48}$ **40.** $\dfrac{-15-\sqrt{-18}}{33}$

41. $\sqrt{-8}\left(\sqrt{-3}-\sqrt{5}\right)$ **42.** $\sqrt{-12}\left(\sqrt{-4}-\sqrt{2}\right)$

43. $\left(3\sqrt{-5}\right)\left(-4\sqrt{-12}\right)$ **44.** $\left(3\sqrt{-7}\right)\left(2\sqrt{-8}\right)$

Practice Plus

In Exercises 45–50, perform the indicated operation(s) and write the result in standard form.

45. $(2-3i)(1-i)-(3-i)(3+i)$

46. $(8+9i)(2-i)-(1-i)(1+i)$

47. $(2+i)^2-(3-i)^2$

48. $(4-i)^2-(1+2i)^2$

49. $5\sqrt{-16}+3\sqrt{-81}$

50. $5\sqrt{-8}+3\sqrt{-18}$

51. Evaluate x^2-2x+2 for $x=1+i$.

52. Evaluate x^2-2x+5 for $x=1-2i$.

53. Evaluate $\dfrac{x^2+19}{2-x}$ for $x=3i$.

54. Evaluate $\dfrac{x^2+11}{3-x}$ for $x=4i$.

Application Exercises

Complex numbers are used in electronics to describe the current in an electric circuit. Ohm's law relates the current in a circuit, I, in amperes, the voltage of the circuit, E, in volts, and the resistance of the circuit, R, in ohms, by the formula $E=IR$. Use this formula to solve Exercises 55–56.

55. Find E, the voltage of a circuit, if $I=(4-5i)$ amperes and $R=(3+7i)$ ohms.

56. Find E, the voltage of a circuit, if $I=(2-3i)$ amperes and $R=(3+5i)$ ohms.

57. The mathematician Girolamo Cardano is credited with the first use (in 1545) of negative square roots in solving the now-famous problem, "Find two numbers whose sum is 10 and whose product is 40." Show that the complex numbers $5+i\sqrt{15}$ and $5-i\sqrt{15}$ satisfy the conditions of the problem. (Cardano did not use the symbolism $i\sqrt{15}$ or even $\sqrt{-15}$. He wrote R.m 15 for $\sqrt{-15}$, meaning "radix minus 15." He regarded the numbers 5 + R.m 15 and 5 − R.m 15 as "fictitious" or "ghost numbers," and considered the problem "manifestly impossible." But in a mathematically adventurous spirit, he exclaimed, "Nevertheless, we will operate.")

Writing in Mathematics

58. What is i?

59. Explain how to add complex numbers. Provide an example with your explanation.

60. Explain how to multiply complex numbers and give an example.

61. What is the complex conjugate of $2+3i$? What happens when you multiply this complex number by its complex conjugate?

62. Explain how to divide complex numbers. Provide an example with your explanation.

63. Explain each of the three jokes in the cartoon on page 123.

64. A stand-up comedian uses algebra in some jokes, including one about a telephone recording that announces "You have just reached an imaginary number. Please multiply by i and dial again." Explain the joke.

Explain the error in Exercises 65–66.

65. $\sqrt{-9}+\sqrt{-16}=\sqrt{-25}=i\sqrt{25}=5i$

66. $\left(\sqrt{-9}\right)^2=\sqrt{-9}\cdot\sqrt{-9}=\sqrt{81}=9$

Critical Thinking Exercises

67. Which one of the following is true?

a. Some irrational numbers are not complex numbers.

b. $(3+7i)(3-7i)$ is an imaginary number.

c. $\dfrac{7+3i}{5+3i}=\dfrac{7}{5}$

d. In the complex number system, x^2+y^2 (the sum of two squares) can be factored as $(x+yi)(x-yi)$.

In Exercises 68–70, perform the indicated operations and write the result in standard form.

68. $\dfrac{4}{(2+i)(3-i)}$

69. $\dfrac{1+i}{1+2i}+\dfrac{1-i}{1-2i}$

70. $\dfrac{8}{1+\dfrac{2}{i}}$

SECTION 1.5 Quadratic Equations

Objectives

1. Solve quadratic equations by factoring.
2. Solve quadratic equations by the square root property.
3. Solve quadratic equations by completing the square.
4. Solve quadratic equations using the quadratic formula.
5. Use the discriminant to determine the number and type of solutions.
6. Determine the most efficient method to use when solving a quadratic equation.
7. Solve problems modeled by quadratic equations.

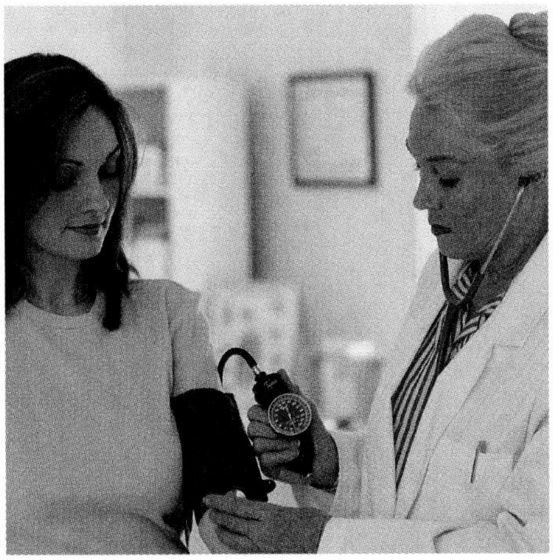

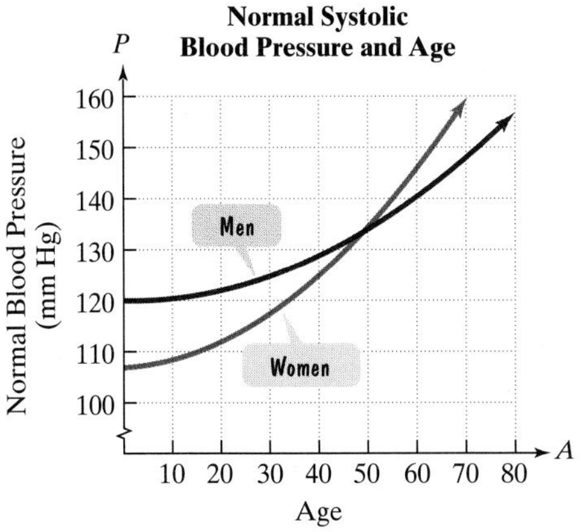

Figure 1.18

Until fairly recently, many doctors believed that your blood pressure was theirs to know and yours to worry about. Today, however, people are encouraged to find out their blood pressure. That pumped-up cuff that squeezes against your upper arm measures blood pressure in millimeters (mm) of mercury (Hg). Blood pressure is given in two numbers: systolic pressure over diastolic pressure, such as 120 over 80. Systolic pressure is the pressure of blood against the artery walls when the heart contracts. Diastolic pressure is the pressure of blood against the artery walls when the heart is at rest.

The graphs in Figure 1.18 illustrate how systolic pressure increases with age as the arteries become less elastic. The blue graph representing women's normal systolic blood pressure is narrower than the red graph representing men's normal systolic blood pressure. Up to approximately age 50, women's normal systolic blood pressure is lower than men's, although it is increasing at a faster rate. After age 50, women's normal systolic blood pressure is higher than men's.

Normal systolic blood pressure is modeled by the following formulas:

Men: $P = 0.006A^2 - 0.02A + 120$

Women: $P = 0.01A^2 + 0.05A + 107.$

In each formula, P is the normal systolic blood pressure, in millimeters of mercury, at age A.

Suppose we are interested in the age of a man with a normal systolic blood pressure of 125 millimeters of mercury. We can use the red graph in Figure 1.19 to approximate the value of A for which $P = 125$. Locate 125 on the vertical axis and then move to the right to the red graph and locate the point for which 125 is the second coordinate. From this point, we look to the horizontal axis to find the corresponding first coordinate. A reasonable estimate is 31. Thus, $P = 125$ for $A \approx 31$. We see that 31 is the approximate age of a man whose normal systolic blood pressure is 125 mm Hg.

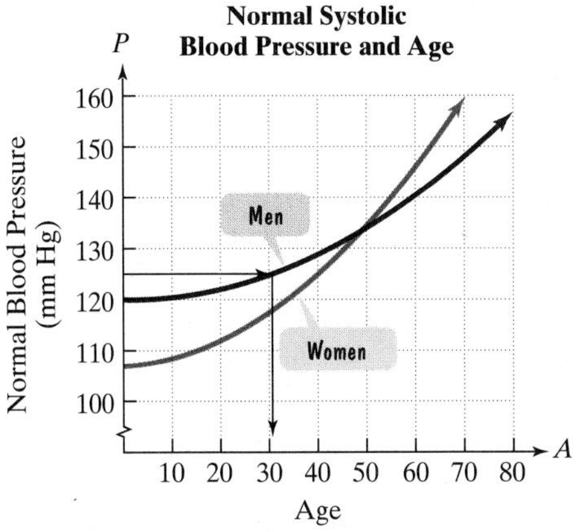

Figure 1.19

We can obtain this information algebraically by using the formula that models male blood pressure, $P = 0.006A^2 - 0.02A + 120$, and setting P equal to 125:

$$0.006A^2 - 0.02A + 120 = 125.$$

This equation is an example of a *quadratic equation*. By subtracting 125 from both sides, we can express the equation in *general form*:

$$0.006A^2 - 0.02A - 5 = 0.$$

Definition of a Quadratic Equation

A **quadratic equation** in x is an equation that can be written in the **general form**

$$ax^2 + bx + c = 0,$$

where a, b, and c are real numbers, with $a \neq 0$. A quadratic equation in x is also called a **second-degree polynomial equation** in x.

In this section, we study a number of methods for solving quadratic equations. We also look at applications of these equations, returning to the blood pressure application later in the section.

1 Solve quadratic equations by factoring.

Solving Quadratic Equations by Factoring

Here is an example of a quadratic equation in general form:

$$x^2 - 7x + 10 = 0.$$

$a = 1$ $b = -7$ $c = 10$

We can factor the left side of this equation. We obtain $(x - 5)(x - 2) = 0$. If a quadratic equation has zero on one side and a factored expression on the other side, it can be solved using the **zero-product principle**.

The Zero-Product Principle

If the product of two algebraic expressions is zero, then at least one of the factors is equal to zero.

If $AB = 0$, then $A = 0$ or $B = 0$.

For example, consider the equation $(x - 5)(x - 2) = 0$. According to the zero-product principle, this product can be zero only if at least one of the factors is zero. We set each individual factor equal to zero and solve each resulting equation for x.

$$(x - 5)(x - 2) = 0$$
$$x - 5 = 0 \quad \text{or} \quad x - 2 = 0$$
$$x = 5 \qquad\qquad x = 2$$

We can check each of these proposed solutions, 5 and 2, in the original quadratic equation, $x^2 - 7x + 10 = 0$. Substitute each one separately for x into the equation.

Check 5:

$$x^2 - 7x + 10 = 0$$
$$5^2 - 7 \cdot 5 + 10 \stackrel{?}{=} 0$$
$$25 - 35 + 10 \stackrel{?}{=} 0$$
$$0 = 0, \quad \text{true}$$

Check 2:

$$x^2 - 7x + 10 = 0$$
$$2^2 - 7 \cdot 2 + 10 \stackrel{?}{=} 0$$
$$4 - 14 + 10 \stackrel{?}{=} 0$$
$$0 = 0, \quad \text{true}$$

The resulting true statements indicate that the solutions are 2 and 5. The solution set is $\{2, 5\}$. Note that with a quadratic equation, we can have two solutions, compared to the conditional linear equation that had one.

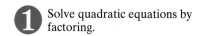

Solving a Quadratic Equation by Factoring

1. If necessary, rewrite the equation in the general form $ax^2 + bx + c = 0$, moving all terms to one side, thereby obtaining zero on the other side.
2. Factor completely.
3. Apply the zero-product principle, setting each factor containing a variable equal to zero.
4. Solve the equations in step 3.
5. Check the solutions in the original equation.

EXAMPLE 1 Solving Quadratic Equations by Factoring

Solve by factoring:

a. $4x^2 - 2x = 0$ **b.** $2x^2 + 7x = 4$.

Solution

a. We begin with $4x^2 - 2x = 0$.

Step 1 Move all terms to one side and obtain zero on the other side. All terms are already on the left and zero is on the other side, so we can skip this step.

Step 2 Factor. We factor out $2x$ from the two terms on the left side.

$$\begin{aligned} 4x^2 - 2x &= 0 && \text{This is the given equation.} \\ 2x(2x - 1) &= 0 && \text{Factor.} \end{aligned}$$

Steps 3 and 4 Set each factor equal to zero and solve the resulting equations.

$$\begin{aligned} 2x = 0 \quad &\text{or} \quad 2x - 1 = 0 \\ x = 0 \quad & \qquad\quad 2x = 1 \\ & \qquad\quad x = \tfrac{1}{2} \end{aligned}$$

Step 5 Check the solutions in the original equation.

Check 0:

$$\begin{aligned} 4x^2 - 2x &= 0 \\ 4 \cdot 0^2 - 2 \cdot 0 &\stackrel{?}{=} 0 \\ 0 - 0 &\stackrel{?}{=} 0 \\ 0 &= 0, \quad \text{true} \end{aligned}$$

Check $\frac{1}{2}$:

$$\begin{aligned} 4x^2 - 2x &= 0 \\ 4\left(\tfrac{1}{2}\right)^2 - 2\left(\tfrac{1}{2}\right) &\stackrel{?}{=} 0 \\ 4\left(\tfrac{1}{4}\right) - 2\left(\tfrac{1}{2}\right) &\stackrel{?}{=} 0 \\ 1 - 1 &\stackrel{?}{=} 0 \\ 0 &= 0, \quad \text{true} \end{aligned}$$

The solution set is $\left\{0, \frac{1}{2}\right\}$.

b. Next, we solve $2x^2 + 7x = 4$.

Step 1 Move all terms to one side and obtain zero on the other side. Subtract 4 from both sides and write the equation in general form.

$$\begin{aligned} 2x^2 + 7x &= 4 && \text{This is the given equation.} \\ 2x^2 + 7x - 4 &= 4 - 4 && \text{Subtract 4 from both sides.} \\ 2x^2 + 7x - 4 &= 0 && \text{Simplify.} \end{aligned}$$

Step 2 Factor.

$$\begin{aligned} 2x^2 + 7x - 4 &= 0 \\ (2x - 1)(x + 4) &= 0 \end{aligned}$$

Steps 3 and 4 Set each factor equal to zero and solve the resulting equations.

$$\begin{aligned} 2x - 1 = 0 \quad &\text{or} \quad x + 4 = 0 \\ 2x = 1 \quad & \qquad\quad x = -4 \\ x = \tfrac{1}{2} \quad & \end{aligned}$$

Step 5 **Check the solutions in the original equation.**

Check $\frac{1}{2}$:	**Check -4:**

$$\begin{array}{ll}
2x^2 + 7x = 4 & 2x^2 + 7x = 4 \\
2\left(\frac{1}{2}\right)^2 + 7\left(\frac{1}{2}\right) \stackrel{?}{=} 4 & 2(-4)^2 + 7(-4) \stackrel{?}{=} 4 \\
\frac{1}{2} + \frac{7}{2} \stackrel{?}{=} 4 & 32 + (-28) \stackrel{?}{=} 4 \\
4 = 4, \quad \text{true} & 4 = 4, \quad \text{true}
\end{array}$$

The solution set is $\left\{-4, \frac{1}{2}\right\}$.

Check Point 1 Solve by factoring:

a. $3x^2 - 9x = 0$ **b.** $2x^2 + x = 1$.

Technology

You can use a graphing utility to check the real solutions of a quadratic equation. **The real solutions of $ax^2 + bx + c = 0$ correspond to the x-intercepts of the graph of $y = ax^2 + bx + c$.** For example, to check the solutions of $2x^2 + 7x = 4$, or $2x^2 + 7x - 4 = 0$, graph $y = 2x^2 + 7x - 4$. The cuplike U-shaped graph is shown on the right. Note that it is important to have all nonzero terms on one side of the quadratic equation before entering it into the graphing utility. The x-intercepts are -4 and $\frac{1}{2}$, and the graph of $y = 2x^2 + 7x - 4$ passes through $(-4, 0)$ and $\left(\frac{1}{2}, 0\right)$. This verifies that $\left\{-4, \frac{1}{2}\right\}$ is the solution set of $2x^2 + 7x - 4 = 0$.

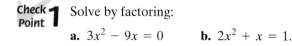

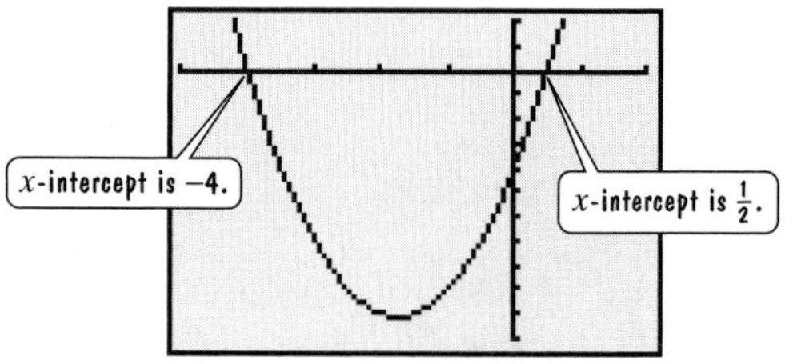

$[-5, 2, 1]$ by $[-11, 2, 1]$

❷ Solve quadratic equations by the square root property.

Solving Quadratic Equations by the Square Root Property

Quadratic equations of the form $u^2 = d$, where u is an algebraic expression, and d is a nonzero real number, can be solved by the *square root property*. First, isolate the squared expression u^2 on one side of the equation and the number d on the other side. Then take the square root of both sides. Remember, there are two numbers whose square is d. One number is $\sqrt{d}$ and one is $-\sqrt{d}$.

We can use factoring to verify that $u^2 = d$ has these two solutions.

$$\begin{array}{ll}
u^2 = d & \text{This is the given equation.} \\
u^2 - d = 0 & \text{Move all terms to one side and obtain zero} \\
& \text{on the other side.} \\
\left(u + \sqrt{d}\right)\left(u - \sqrt{d}\right) = 0 & \text{Factor.} \\
u + \sqrt{d} = 0 \quad \text{or} \quad u - \sqrt{d} = 0 & \text{Set each factor equal to zero.} \\
u = -\sqrt{d} \qquad\qquad u = \sqrt{d} & \text{Solve the resulting equations.}
\end{array}$$

Because the solutions differ only in sign, we can write them in abbreviated notation as $u = \pm\sqrt{d}$. We read this as "u equals positive or negative the square root of d" or "u equals plus or minus the square root of d."

Now that we have verified these solutions, we can solve $u^2 = d$ directly by taking square roots. This process is called the **square root property**.

> **The Square Root Property**
>
> If u is an algebraic expression and d is a nonzero real number, then $u^2 = d$ has exactly two solutions:
>
> $$\text{If } u^2 = d, \text{ then } u = \sqrt{d} \text{ or } u = -\sqrt{d}.$$
>
> Equivalently,
>
> $$\text{If } u^2 = d, \text{ then } u = \pm\sqrt{d}.$$

EXAMPLE 2 Solving Quadratic Equations by the Square Root Property

Solve by the square root property:

a. $3x^2 - 15 = 0$ **b.** $9x^2 + 25 = 0$ **c.** $(x - 2)^2 = 6.$

Solution To apply the square root property, we need a squared expression by itself on one side of the equation.

$3x^2 - 15 = 0$ (We want x^2 by itself.)

$9x^2 + 25 = 0$ (We want x^2 by itself.)

$(x - 2)^2 = 6$ (The squared expression is by itself.)

a.

$3x^2 - 15 = 0$ This is the original equation.

$3x^2 = 15$ Add 15 to both sides.

$x^2 = 5$ Divide both sides by 3.

$x = \sqrt{5}$ or $x = -\sqrt{5}$ Apply the square root property. Equivalently, $x = \pm\sqrt{5}$.

By checking both proposed solutions in the original equation, we can confirm that the solution set is $\{-\sqrt{5}, \sqrt{5}\}$ or $\{\pm\sqrt{5}\}$.

b.

$9x^2 + 25 = 0$ This is the original equation.

$9x^2 = -25$ Subtract 25 from both sides.

$x^2 = -\frac{25}{9}$ Divide both sides by 9.

$x = \pm\sqrt{-\frac{25}{9}}$ Apply the square root property.

$x = \pm i\sqrt{\frac{25}{9}} = \pm\frac{5}{3}i$ Express solutions in terms of i.

Because the equation has an x^2-term and no x-term, we can check both proposed solutions, $\pm\frac{5}{3}i$, at once.

Check $\frac{5}{3}i$ and $-\frac{5}{3}i$:

$$9x^2 + 25 = 0$$

$$9\left(\pm\frac{5}{3}i\right)^2 + 25 \stackrel{?}{=} 0$$

$$9\left(\frac{25}{9}i^2\right) + 25 \stackrel{?}{=} 0$$

$$25i^2 + 25 \stackrel{?}{=} 0$$

$i^2 = -1$

$$25(-1) + 25 \stackrel{?}{=} 0$$

$$0 = 0, \quad \text{true}$$

The solutions are $-\frac{5}{3}i$ and $\frac{5}{3}i$. The solution set is $\left\{-\frac{5}{3}i, \frac{5}{3}i\right\}$ or $\left\{\pm\frac{5}{3}i\right\}$.

c.

$(x - 2)^2 = 6$ This is the original equation.

$x - 2 = \pm\sqrt{6}$ Apply the square root property.

$x = 2 \pm \sqrt{6}$ Add 2 to both sides.

By checking both values in the original equation, we can confirm that the solution set is $\{2 + \sqrt{6}, 2 - \sqrt{6}\}$ or $\{2 \pm \sqrt{6}\}$.

Technology

The graph of

$$y = 9x^2 + 25$$

has no x-intercepts. This shows that

$$9x^2 + 25 = 0$$

has no real solutions. Example 2(b) on the previous page algebraically established that the solutions are imaginary numbers.

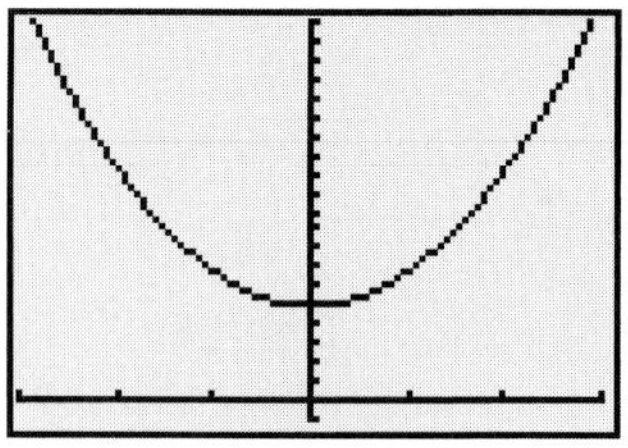

[−3, 3, 1] by [−5, 100, 5]

Check Point 2 Solve by the square root property:

a. $3x^2 - 21 = 0$ **b.** $5x^2 + 45 = 0$ **c.** $(x + 5)^2 = 11$.

3 Solve quadratic equations by completing the square.

Completing the Square

How do we solve an equation in the form $ax^2 + bx + c = 0$ if the trinomial $ax^2 + bx + c$ cannot be factored? We cannot use the zero-product principle in such a case. However, we can convert the equation into an equivalent equation that can be solved using the square root property. This is accomplished by **completing the square**.

Visualizing Completing the Square

This figure, with area $x^2 + 8x$, is not a complete square. The bottom-right corner is missing.

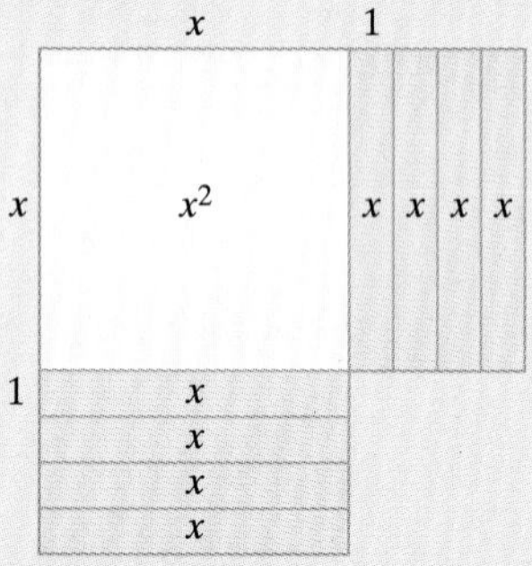

Area: $x^2 + 8x$

Add 16 square units to the missing portion and you, literally, complete the square.

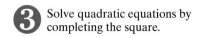

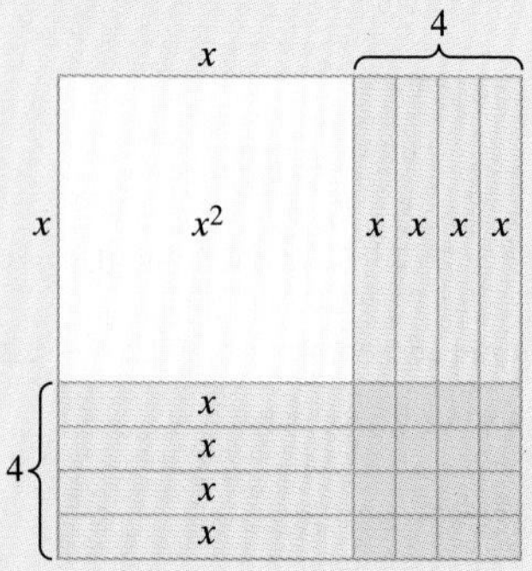

Area: $x^2 + 8x + 16 = (x + 4)^2$

Completing the Square

If $x^2 + bx$ is a binomial, then by adding $\left(\frac{b}{2}\right)^2$, which is the square of half the coefficient of x, a perfect square trinomial will result. That is,

$$x^2 + bx + \left(\frac{b}{2}\right)^2 = \left(x + \frac{b}{2}\right)^2$$

EXAMPLE 3 Completing the Square

What term should be added to each binomial so that it becomes a perfect square trinomial? Write and factor the trinomial.

a. $x^2 + 8x$ **b.** $x^2 - 7x$ **c.** $x^2 + \frac{3}{5}x$

Solution To complete the square, we must add a term to each binomial. The term that should be added is the square of half the coefficient of x.

$x^2 + 8x$	$x^2 - 7x$	$x^2 + \frac{3}{5}x$
Add $\left(\frac{8}{2}\right)^2 = 4^2$. Add 16 to complete the square.	Add $\left(\frac{-7}{2}\right)^2$, or $\frac{49}{4}$, to complete the square.	Add $\left(\frac{1}{2} \cdot \frac{3}{5}\right)^2 = \left(\frac{3}{10}\right)^2$. Add $\frac{9}{100}$ to complete the square.

a. The coefficient of the x-term in $x^2 + 8x$ is 8. Half of 8 is 4, and $4^2 = 16$. Add 16. The result is a perfect square trinomial.

$$x^2 + 8x + 16 = (x + 4)^2$$

b. The coefficient of the x-term in $x^2 - 7x$ is -7. Half of -7 is $-\frac{7}{2}$, and $\left(-\frac{7}{2}\right)^2 = \frac{49}{4}$. Add $\frac{49}{4}$. The result is a perfect square trinomial.

$$x^2 - 7x + \frac{49}{4} = \left(x - \frac{7}{2}\right)^2$$

c. The coefficient of the x-term in $x^2 + \frac{3}{5}x$ is $\frac{3}{5}$. Half of $\frac{3}{5}$ is $\frac{1}{2}\cdot\frac{3}{5}$, or $\frac{3}{10}$, and $\left(\frac{3}{10}\right)^2 = \frac{9}{100}$. Add $\frac{9}{100}$. The result is a perfect square trinomial.

$$x^2 + \frac{3}{5}x + \frac{9}{100} = \left(x + \frac{3}{10}\right)^2$$

Study Tip

You may not be accustomed to factoring perfect square trinomials in which fractions are involved. The constant in the factorization is always half the coefficient of x.

$$x^2 - 7x + \frac{49}{4} = \left(x - \frac{7}{2}\right)^2$$

Half the coefficient of x, -7, is $-\frac{7}{2}$.

$$x^2 + \frac{3}{5}x + \frac{9}{100} = \left(x + \frac{3}{10}\right)^2$$

Half the coefficient of x, $\frac{3}{5}$, is $\frac{3}{10}$.

Check Point 3 What term should be added to each binomial so that it becomes a perfect square trinomial? Write and factor the trinomial.

a. $x^2 + 6x$ **b.** $x^2 - 5x$ **c.** $x^2 + \frac{2}{3}x$

We can solve any quadratic equation by completing the square. If the coefficient of the x^2-term is one, we add the square of half the coefficient of x to both sides of the equation. **When you add a constant term to one side of the equation to complete the square, be certain to add the same constant to the other side of the equation.** These ideas are illustrated in Example 4.

EXAMPLE 4 Solving a Quadratic Equation by Completing the Square

Solve by completing the square: $x^2 - 6x + 4 = 0$.

Solution We begin by subtracting 4 from both sides. This is done to isolate the binomial $x^2 - 6x$, so that we can complete the square.

$x^2 - 6x + 4 = 0$ This is the original equation.

$x^2 - 6x = -4$ Subtract 4 from both sides.

Next, we work with $x^2 - 6x = -4$ and complete the square. Find half the coefficient of the x-term and square it. The coefficient of the x-term is -6. Half of -6 is -3 and $(-3)^2 = 9$. Thus, we add 9 to both sides of the equation.

$x^2 - 6x + 9 = -4 + 9$ Add 9 to both sides to complete the square.

$(x - 3)^2 = 5$ Factor and simplify.

$x - 3 = \sqrt{5}$ or $x - 3 = -\sqrt{5}$ Apply the square root property.

$x = 3 + \sqrt{5}$ $x = 3 - \sqrt{5}$ Add 3 to both sides in each equation.

The solutions are $3 \pm \sqrt{5}$, and the solution set is $\{3 + \sqrt{5}, 3 - \sqrt{5}\}$, or $\{3 \pm \sqrt{5}\}$.

Check Point 4 Solve by completing the square: $x^2 + 4x - 1 = 0$.

If the coefficient of the x^2-term in a quadratic equation is not 1, you must divide each side of the equation by this coefficient before completing the square. For example, to solve $9x^2 - 6x - 4 = 0$ by completing the square, first divide every term by 9:

$$\frac{9x^2}{9} - \frac{6x}{9} - \frac{4}{9} = \frac{0}{9}$$
$$x^2 - \frac{6}{9}x - \frac{4}{9} = 0$$
$$x^2 - \frac{2}{3}x - \frac{4}{9} = 0.$$

Now that the coefficient of the x^2-term is 1, we can solve by completing the square.

EXAMPLE 5 Solving a Quadratic Equation by Completing the Square

Solve by completing the square: $9x^2 - 6x - 4 = 0$.

Solution

$$9x^2 - 6x - 4 = 0$$ This is the original equation.

$$x^2 - \frac{2}{3}x - \frac{4}{9} = 0$$ Divide both sides by 9.

$$x^2 - \frac{2}{3}x = \frac{4}{9}$$ Add $\frac{4}{9}$ to both sides to isolate the binomial.

$$x^2 - \frac{2}{3}x + \frac{1}{9} = \frac{4}{9} + \frac{1}{9}$$ Complete the square: Half of $-\frac{2}{3}$ is $-\frac{2}{6}$, or $-\frac{1}{3}$, and $\left(-\frac{1}{3}\right)^2 = \frac{1}{9}$.

$$\left(x - \frac{1}{3}\right)^2 = \frac{5}{9}$$ Factor and simplify.

$$x - \frac{1}{3} = \sqrt{\frac{5}{9}} \quad \text{or} \quad x - \frac{1}{3} = -\sqrt{\frac{5}{9}}$$ Apply the square root property.

$$x - \frac{1}{3} = \frac{\sqrt{5}}{3} \qquad x - \frac{1}{3} = -\frac{\sqrt{5}}{3}$$ $\sqrt{\frac{5}{9}} = \frac{\sqrt{5}}{\sqrt{9}} = \frac{\sqrt{5}}{3}$

$$x = \frac{1}{3} + \frac{\sqrt{5}}{3} \qquad x = \frac{1}{3} - \frac{\sqrt{5}}{3}$$ Add $\frac{1}{3}$ to both sides and solve for x.

$$x = \frac{1 + \sqrt{5}}{3} \qquad x = \frac{1 - \sqrt{5}}{3}$$ Express solutions with a common denominator.

The solutions are $\frac{1 \pm \sqrt{5}}{3}$, and the solution set is $\left\{\frac{1 \pm \sqrt{5}}{3}\right\}$.

Technology

Obtain a decimal approximation for each solution of $9x^2 - 6x - 4 = 0$, the equation in Example 5.

$$\frac{1 + \sqrt{5}}{3} \approx 1.1$$
$$\frac{1 - \sqrt{5}}{3} \approx -0.4$$

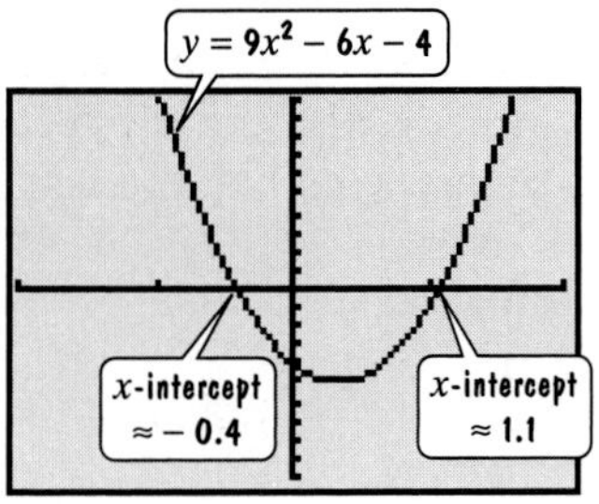

[−2, 2, 1] by [−10, 10, 1]

The x-intercepts of $y = 9x^2 - 6x - 4$ verify the solutions.

Check Point 5 Solve by completing the square: $2x^2 + 3x - 4 = 0$.

4 Solve quadratic equations using the quadratic formula.

Solving Quadratic Equations Using the Quadratic Formula

We can use the method of completing the square to derive a formula that can be used to solve all quadratic equations. The derivation given on the next page also shows a particular quadratic equation, $3x^2 - 2x - 4 = 0$, to specifically illustrate each of the steps.

Deriving the Quadratic Formula

General Form of a Quadratic Equation	Comment	A Specific Example
$ax^2 + bx + c = 0, a > 0$	This is the given equation.	$3x^2 - 2x - 4 = 0$
$x^2 + \frac{b}{a}x + \frac{c}{a} = 0$	Divide both sides by a so that the coefficient of x^2 is 1.	$x^2 - \frac{2}{3}x - \frac{4}{3} = 0$
$x^2 + \frac{b}{a}x = -\frac{c}{a}$	Isolate the binomial by adding $-\frac{c}{a}$ on both sides of the equation.	$x^2 - \frac{2}{3}x = \frac{4}{3}$
$x^2 + \frac{b}{a}x + \left(\frac{b}{2a}\right)^2 = -\frac{c}{a} + \left(\frac{b}{2a}\right)^2$ (half)^2 $x^2 + \frac{b}{a}x + \frac{b^2}{4a^2} = -\frac{c}{a} + \frac{b^2}{4a^2}$	Complete the square. Add the square of half the coefficient of x to both sides.	$x^2 - \frac{2}{3}x + \left(-\frac{1}{3}\right)^2 = \frac{4}{3} + \left(-\frac{1}{3}\right)^2$ (half)^2 $x^2 - \frac{2}{3}x + \frac{1}{9} = \frac{4}{3} + \frac{1}{9}$
$\left(x + \frac{b}{2a}\right)^2 = -\frac{c}{a} \cdot \frac{4a}{4a} + \frac{b^2}{4a^2}$	Factor on the left side and obtain a common denominator on the right side.	$\left(x - \frac{1}{3}\right)^2 = \frac{4}{3} \cdot \frac{3}{3} + \frac{1}{9}$
$\left(x + \frac{b}{2a}\right)^2 = \frac{-4ac + b^2}{4a^2}$ $\left(x + \frac{b}{2a}\right)^2 = \frac{b^2 - 4ac}{4a^2}$	Add fractions on the right side.	$\left(x - \frac{1}{3}\right)^2 = \frac{12 + 1}{9}$ $\left(x - \frac{1}{3}\right)^2 = \frac{13}{9}$
$x + \frac{b}{2a} = \pm\sqrt{\frac{b^2 - 4ac}{4a^2}}$	Apply the square root property.	$x - \frac{1}{3} = \pm\sqrt{\frac{13}{9}}$
$x + \frac{b}{2a} = \pm\frac{\sqrt{b^2 - 4ac}}{2a}$	Take the square root of the quotient, simplifying the denominator.	$x - \frac{1}{3} = \pm\frac{\sqrt{13}}{3}$
$x = \frac{-b}{2a} \pm \frac{\sqrt{b^2 - 4ac}}{2a}$	Solve for x by subtracting $\frac{b}{2a}$ from both sides.	$x = \frac{1}{3} \pm \frac{\sqrt{13}}{3}$
$x = \frac{-b \pm \sqrt{b^2 - 4ac}}{2a}$	Combine fractions on the right side.	$x = \frac{1 \pm \sqrt{13}}{3}$

The formula shown at the bottom of the left column is called the *quadratic formula.* A similar proof shows that the same formula can be used to solve quadratic equations if a, the coefficient of the x^2-term, is negative.

The Quadratic Formula

The solutions of a quadratic equation in general form $ax^2 + bx + c = 0$, with $a \neq 0$, are given by the **quadratic formula**

$$x = \frac{-b \pm \sqrt{b^2 - 4ac}}{2a}.$$

x equals negative b plus or minus the square root of $b^2 - 4ac$, all divided by $2a$.

To use the quadratic formula, write the quadratic equation in general form if necessary. Then determine the numerical values for a (the coefficient of the x^2-term), b (the coefficient of the x-term), and c (the constant term). Substitute the values of a, b, and c into the quadratic formula and evaluate the expression. The $\pm$ sign indicates that there are two solutions of the equation.

To Die at Twenty

Can the equations

$$7x^5 + 12x^3 - 9x + 4 = 0$$

and

$$8x^6 - 7x^5 + 4x^3 - 19 = 0$$

be solved using a formula similar to the quadratic formula? The first equation has five solutions and the second has six solutions, but they cannot be found using a formula. How do we know? In 1832, a 20-year-old Frenchman, Evariste Galois, wrote down a proof showing that there is no general formula to solve equations when the exponent on the variable is 5 or greater. Galois was jailed as a political activist several times while still a teenager. The day after his brilliant proof he fought a duel over a woman. The duel was a political setup. As he lay dying, Galois told his brother, Alfred, of the manuscript that contained his proof: "Mathematical manuscripts are in my room. On the table. Take care of my work. Make it known. Important. Don't cry, Alfred. I need all my courage—to die at twenty." (Our source is Leopold Infeld's biography of Galois, *Whom the Gods Love*. Some historians, however, dispute the story of Galois's ironic death the very day after his algebraic proof. Mathematical truths seem more reliable than historical ones!)

EXAMPLE 6 Solving a Quadratic Equation Using the Quadratic Formula

Solve using the quadratic formula: $2x^2 - 6x + 1 = 0$.

Solution The given equation is in general form. Begin by identifying the values for a, b, and c.

$$2x^2 - 6x + 1 = 0$$

$a = 2$ $b = -6$ $c = 1$

Substituting these values into the quadratic formula and simplifying gives the equation's solutions.

$$x = \frac{-b \pm \sqrt{b^2 - 4ac}}{2a}$$ Use the quadratic formula.

$$= \frac{-(-6) \pm \sqrt{(-6)^2 - 4(2)(1)}}{2 \cdot 2}$$ Substitute the values for a, b, and c: $a = 2$, $b = -6$, and $c = 1$.

$$= \frac{6 \pm \sqrt{36 - 8}}{4}$$ $-(-6) = 6$, $(-6)^2 = (-6)(-6) = 36$, and $4(2)(1) = 8$.

$$= \frac{6 \pm \sqrt{28}}{4}$$ Complete the subtraction under the radical.

$$= \frac{6 \pm 2\sqrt{7}}{4}$$ $\sqrt{28} = \sqrt{4 \cdot 7} = \sqrt{4}\sqrt{7} = 2\sqrt{7}$

$$= \frac{2(3 \pm \sqrt{7})}{4}$$ Factor out 2 from the numerator.

$$= \frac{3 \pm \sqrt{7}}{2}$$ Divide the numerator and denominator by 2.

The solution set is $\left\{\frac{3 + \sqrt{7}}{2}, \frac{3 - \sqrt{7}}{2}\right\}$ or $\left\{\frac{3 \pm \sqrt{7}}{2}\right\}$.

Technology

You can use a graphing utility to verify that the solutions of $2x^2 - 6x + 1 = 0$ are $\frac{3 \pm \sqrt{7}}{2}$. Begin by entering $y_1 = 2x^2 - 6x + 1$ in the [Y=] screen. Then evaluate this equation at each of the proposed solutions.

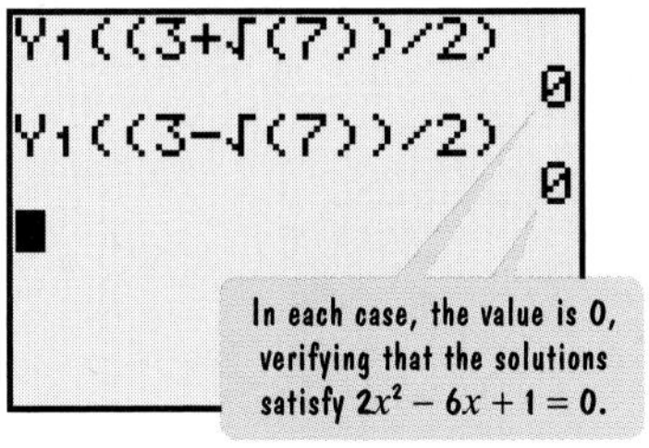
Y1((3+√(7))/2)
0
Y1((3−√(7))/2)
0
In each case, the value is 0, verifying that the solutions satisfy 2x² − 6x + 1 = 0.

Check Point 6 Solve using the quadratic formula:

$$2x^2 + 2x - 1 = 0.$$

EXAMPLE 7 Solving a Quadratic Equation Using the Quadratic Formula

Solve using the quadratic formula: $3x^2 - 2x + 4 = 0$.

Solution The given equation is in general form. Begin by identifying the values for *a*, *b*, and *c*.

$$3x^2 - 2x + 4 = 0$$

$a = 3$ $b = -2$ $c = 4$

$$x = \frac{-b \pm \sqrt{b^2 - 4ac}}{2a}$$ Use the quadratic formula.

$$= \frac{-(-2) \pm \sqrt{(-2)^2 - 4(3)(4)}}{2(3)}$$ Substitute the values for *a*, *b*, and *c*: $a = 3$, $b = -2$, and $c = 4$.

$$= \frac{2 \pm \sqrt{4 - 48}}{6}$$ $-(-2) = 2$ and $(-2)^2 = (-2)(-2) = 4$.

$$= \frac{2 \pm \sqrt{-44}}{6}$$ Subtract under the radical. Because the number under the radical sign is negative, the solutions will not be real numbers.

$$= \frac{2 \pm 2i\sqrt{11}}{6}$$ $\sqrt{-44} = \sqrt{4(11)(-1)} = 2i\sqrt{11}$

$$= \frac{2\left(1 \pm i\sqrt{11}\right)}{6}$$ Factor 2 from the numerator.

$$= \frac{1 \pm i\sqrt{11}}{3}$$ Divide numerator and denominator by 2.

$$= \frac{1}{3} \pm i\frac{\sqrt{11}}{3}$$ Write the complex numbers in standard form.

The solutions are complex conjugates, and the solution set is $\left\{\frac{1}{3} + i\frac{\sqrt{11}}{3}, \frac{1}{3} - i\frac{\sqrt{11}}{3}\right\}$ or $\left\{\frac{1}{3} \pm i\frac{\sqrt{11}}{3}\right\}$.

Study Tip

Checking irrational and imaginary solutions can be time-consuming. The solutions given by the quadratic formula are always correct, unless you have made a careless error. Checking for computational errors or errors in simplification is sufficient.

If $ax^2 + bx + c = 0$ has imaginary solutions, the graph of $y = ax^2 + bx + c$ will not have *x*-intercepts. This is illustrated by the imaginary solutions of $3x^2 - 2x + 4 = 0$ in Example 7 and the graph of $y = 3x^2 - 2x + 4$ in Figure 1.20.

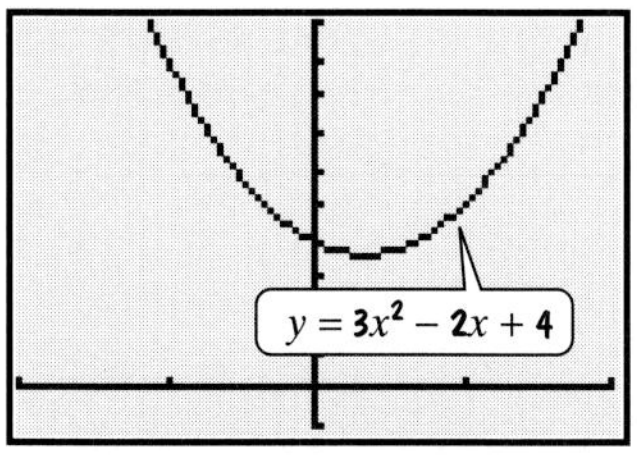

[−2, 2, 1] by [−1, 10, 1]

Figure 1.20 This graph has no *x*-intercepts

Check Point 7 Solve using the quadratic formula:

$$x^2 - 2x + 2 = 0.$$

5 Use the discriminant to determine the number and type of solutions.

The Discriminant

The quantity $b^2 - 4ac$, which appears under the radical sign in the quadratic formula, is called the **discriminant**. Table 1.3 on the next page shows how the discriminant of the quadratic equation $ax^2 + bx + c = 0$ determines the number and type of solutions.

Table 1.3 The Discriminant and the Kinds of Solutions to $ax^2 + bx + c = 0$

Discriminant $b^2 - 4ac$	Kinds of Solutions to $ax^2 + bx + c = 0$	Graph of $y = ax^2 + bx + c$
$b^2 - 4ac > 0$	**Two unequal real solutions;** If a, b, and c are rational numbers and the discriminant is a perfect square, the solutions are rational. If the discriminant is not a perfect square, the solutions are irrational.	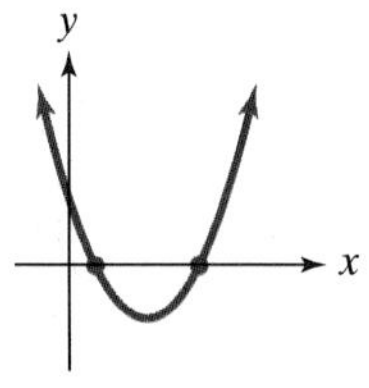 Two x-intercepts
$b^2 - 4ac = 0$	**One solution (a repeated solution) that is a real number;** If a, b, and c are rational numbers, the repeated solution is also a rational number.	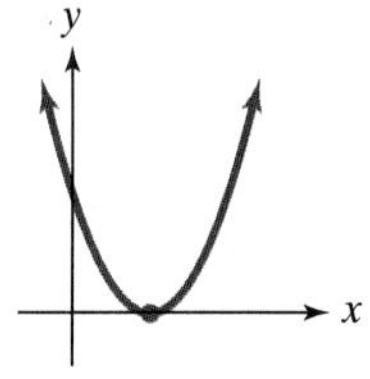 One x-intercept
$b^2 - 4ac < 0$	**No real solution; two imaginary solutions;** The solutions are complex conjugates.	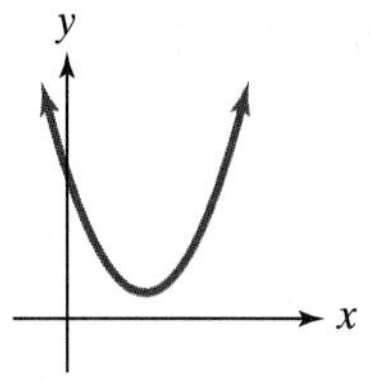 No x-intercepts

EXAMPLE 8 Using the Discriminant

For each equation, compute the discriminant. Then determine the number and type of solutions:

a. $3x^2 + 4x - 5 = 0$ **b.** $9x^2 - 6x + 1 = 0$ **c.** $3x^2 - 8x + 7 = 0.$

Solution Begin by identifying the values for a, b, and c in each equation. Then compute $b^2 - 4ac$, the discriminant.

a. $3x^2 + 4x - 5 = 0$

$a = 3$ $b = 4$ $c = -5$

Substitute and compute the discriminant:

$$b^2 - 4ac = 4^2 - 4 \cdot 3(-5) = 16 - (-60) = 16 + 60 = 76.$$

The discriminant, 76, is a positive number that is not a perfect square. Thus, there are two irrational solutions.

b. $9x^2 - 6x + 1 = 0$

$a = 9$ $b = -6$ $c = 1$

Substitute and compute the discriminant:

$$b^2 - 4ac = (-6)^2 - 4 \cdot 9 \cdot 1 = 36 - 36 = 0.$$

The discriminant, 0, shows that there is only one real solution. This real solution is a rational number.

c. $3x^2 - 8x + 7 = 0$

$a = 3$ $b = -8$ $c = 7$

$$b^2 - 4ac = (-8)^2 - 4 \cdot 3 \cdot 7 = 64 - 84 = -20$$

The negative discriminant, -20, shows that there are two imaginary solutions. (These solutions are complex conjugates of each other.)

Check Point 8 For each equation, compute the discriminant. Then determine the number and type of solutions:

a. $x^2 + 6x + 9 = 0$ **b.** $2x^2 - 7x - 4 = 0$ **c.** $3x^2 - 2x + 4 = 0$.

6 Determine the most efficient method to use when solving a quadratic equation.

Determining Which Method to Use

All quadratic equations can be solved by the quadratic formula. However, if an equation is in the form $u^2 = d$, such as $x^2 = 5$ or $(2x + 3)^2 = 8$, it is faster to use the square root property, taking the square root of both sides. If the equation is not in the form $u^2 = d$, write the quadratic equation in general form $(ax^2 + bx + c = 0)$. Try to solve the equation by factoring. If $ax^2 + bx + c$ cannot be factored, then solve the quadratic equation by the quadratic formula.

Because we used the method of completing the square to derive the quadratic formula, we no longer need it for solving quadratic equations. However, we will use completing the square later in the book to help graph circles and other kinds of equations.

Table 1.4 summarizes our observations about which technique to use when solving a quadratic equation.

Table 1.4 Determining the Most Efficient Technique to Use When Solving a Quadratic Equation

Description and Form of the Quadratic Equation	Most Efficient Solution Method	Example
$ax^2 + bx + c = 0$ and $ax^2 + bx + c$ can be factored easily.	Factor and use the zero-product principle.	$3x^2 + 5x - 2 = 0$ $(3x - 1)(x + 2) = 0$ $3x - 1 = 0$ or $x + 2 = 0$ $x = \frac{1}{3}$ $x = -2$
$ax^2 + bx = 0$ The quadratic equation has no constant term. $(c = 0)$	Factor and use the zero-product principle.	$6x^2 + 9x = 0$ $3x(2x + 3) = 0$ $3x = 0$ or $2x + 3 = 0$ $x = 0$ $2x = -3$ $x = -\frac{3}{2}$
$ax^2 + c = 0$ The quadratic equation has no x-term. $(b = 0)$	Solve for x^2 and apply the square root property.	$7x^2 - 4 = 0$ $7x^2 = 4$ $x^2 = \frac{4}{7}$ $x = \pm\frac{2}{\sqrt{7}} = \pm\frac{2}{\sqrt{7}} \cdot \frac{\sqrt{7}}{\sqrt{7}} = \pm\frac{2\sqrt{7}}{7}$
$u^2 = d$; u is a first-degree polynomial.	Use the square root property.	$(x + 4)^2 = 5$ $x + 4 = \pm\sqrt{5}$ $x = -4 \pm \sqrt{5}$
$ax^2 + bx + c = 0$ and $ax^2 + bx + c$ cannot be factored or the factoring is too difficult.	Use the quadratic formula: $x = \frac{-b \pm \sqrt{b^2 - 4ac}}{2a}$.	$x^2 - 2x - 6 = 0$ $a = 1$ $b = -2$ $c = -6$ $x = \frac{-(-2) \pm \sqrt{(-2)^2 - 4(1)(-6)}}{2}$ $= \frac{2 \pm \sqrt{4 - (-24)}}{2}$ $= \frac{2 \pm \sqrt{28}}{2} = \frac{2 \pm \sqrt{4}\sqrt{7}}{2}$ $= \frac{2 \pm 2\sqrt{7}}{2} = \frac{2(1 \pm \sqrt{7})}{2}$ $= 1 \pm \sqrt{7}$

7 Solve problems modeled by quadratic equations.

Applications

EXAMPLE 9 Blood Pressure and Age

We opened this section with graphs (Figure 1.18, repeated on the right) showing that a person's normal systolic pressure, measured in millimeters of mercury (mm Hg), depends on his or her age. The formula

$$P = 0.006A^2 - 0.02A + 120$$

models a man's normal systolic pressure, P, at age A. Find the age, to the nearest year, of a man whose normal systolic blood pressure is 125 mm Hg.

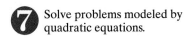

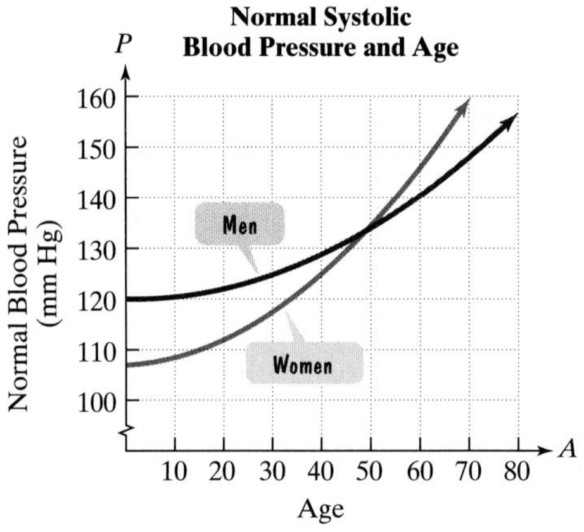

Figure 1.18 (repeated)

Solution We are interested in the age of a man with a normal systolic blood pressure of 125 millimeters of mercury. Thus, we substitute 125 for P in the given formula for men. Then we solve for A, the man's age.

$$P = 0.006A^2 - 0.02A + 120$$ This is the given formula for men.

$$125 = 0.006A^2 - 0.02A + 120$$ Substitute 125 for P.

$$0 = 0.006A^2 - 0.02A - 5$$ Subtract 125 from both sides and write the quadratic equation in general form.

$a = 0.006$ $\quad b = -0.02$ $\quad c = -5$

Because the trinomial on the right side of the equation is prime, we solve using the quadratic formula.

Notice that the variable is A, rather than the usual x.

$$A = \frac{-b \pm \sqrt{b^2 - 4ac}}{2a}$$ Use the quadratic formula.

$$= \frac{-(-0.02) \pm \sqrt{(-0.02)^2 - 4(0.006)(-5)}}{2(0.006)}$$ Substitute the values for a, b, and c: $a = 0.006$, $b = -0.02$, and $c = -5$.

$$= \frac{0.02 \pm \sqrt{0.1204}}{0.012}$$ Use a calculator to simplify the radicand.

$$\approx \frac{0.02 \pm 0.347}{0.012}$$ Use a calculator: $\sqrt{0.1204} \approx 0.347$.

$$A \approx \frac{0.02 + 0.347}{0.012} \quad \text{or} \quad A \approx \frac{0.02 - 0.347}{0.012}$$

$$A \approx 31 \qquad\qquad A \approx -27$$ Use a calculator and round to the nearest integer.

Reject this solution. Age cannot be negative.

The positive solution indicates that 31 is the approximate age of a man whose normal systolic blood pressure is 125 mm Hg. The solution can be visualized as the point (31, 125) on the red graph representing men in Figure 1.18. Take a moment to locate this point on the graph.

Technology

On most calculators, here is how to approximate

$$\frac{0.02 + \sqrt{0.1204}}{0.012}.$$

Many Scientific Calculators

(.02 [+] .1204 [√])

[÷] .012 [=]

Many Graphing Calculators

[(] .02 [+] [√] .1204 [)]

[÷] .012 [ENTER]

If your calculator displays an open parenthesis after √, you'll need to enter another closed parenthesis here.

Check Point 9 The formula $P = 0.01A^2 + 0.05A + 107$ models a woman's normal systolic blood pressure, P, at age A. Use this formula to find the age, to the nearest year, of a woman whose normal systolic blood pressure is 115 mm Hg. Use the blue graph in Figure 1.18 to verify your solution.

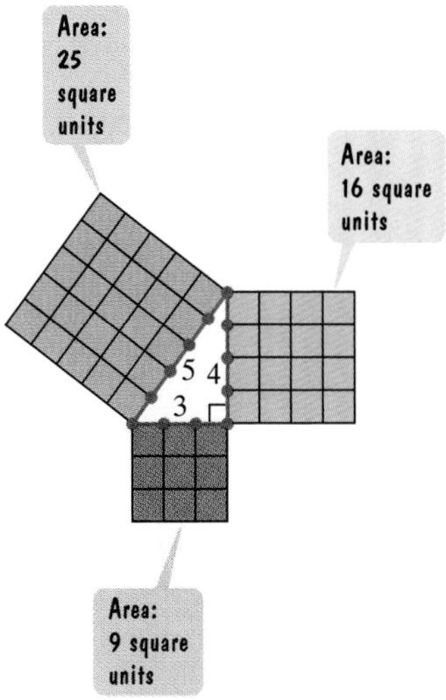

Figure 1.21 The area of the large square equals the sum of the areas of the smaller squares.

In our next example, we will be using the *Pythagorean Theorem* to obtain a verbal model. The ancient Greek philosopher and mathematician Pythagoras (approximately 582–500 B.C.) founded a school whose motto was "All is number." Pythagoras is best remembered for his work with the **right triangle**, a triangle with one angle measuring 90°. The side opposite the 90° angle is called the **hypotenuse**. The other sides are called **legs**. Pythagoras found that if he constructed squares on each of the legs, as well as a larger square on the hypotenuse, the sum of the areas of the smaller squares is equal to the area of the larger square. This is illustrated in Figure 1.21.

This relationship is usually stated in terms of the lengths of the three sides of a right triangle and is called the **Pythagorean Theorem**.

The Pythagorean Theorem

The sum of the squares of the lengths of the legs of a right triangle equals the square of the length of the hypotenuse.

If the legs have lengths a and b, and the hypotenuse has length c, then

$$a^2 + b^2 = c^2.$$

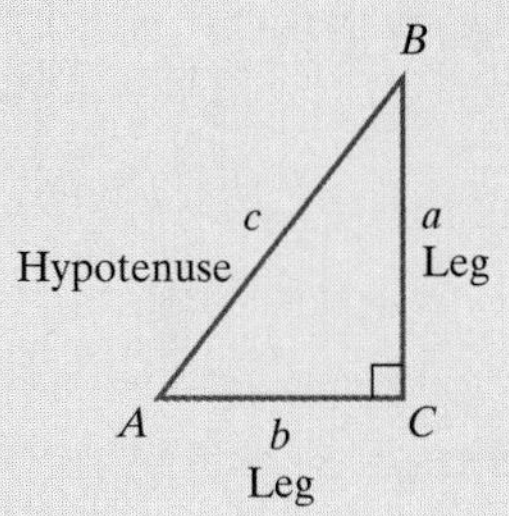

EXAMPLE 10 Using the Pythagorean Theorem

In a 25-inch television set, the length of the screen's diagonal is 25 inches. If the screen's height is 15 inches, what is its width?

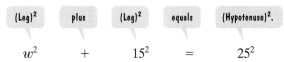

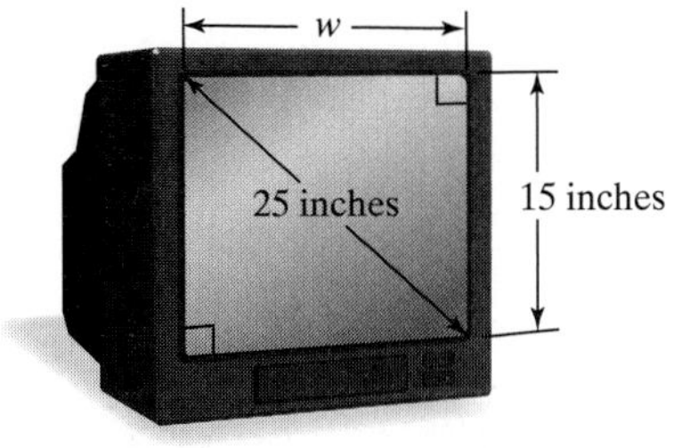

Figure 1.22 A right triangle is formed by the television's height, width, and diagonal.

Solution Figure 1.22 shows a right triangle that is formed by the height, width, and diagonal. We can find w, the screen's width, using the Pythagorean Theorem.

(Leg)^2	plus	(Leg)^2	equals	(Hypotenuse)^2.
w^2	$+$	15^2	$=$	25^2

The equation $w^2 + 15^2 = 25^2$ can be solved most efficiently by the square root property.

$$w^2 + 15^2 = 25^2$$ This is the equation resulting from the Pythagorean Theorem.

$$w^2 + 225 = 625$$ Square 15 and 25.

$$w^2 = 400$$ Isolate w^2 by subtracting 225 from both sides.

$$w = \sqrt{400} \quad \text{or} \quad w = -\sqrt{400}$$ Apply the square root property.

$$w = 20 \qquad w = -20$$ Simplify.

Because w represents the width of the television's screen, this dimension must be positive. We reject -20. Thus, the width of the television is 20 inches.

Check Point 10 What is the width of a 15-inch television set whose height is 9 inches?

EXERCISE SET 1.5

Practice Exercises

Solve each equation in Exercises 1–14 by factoring.

1. $x^2 - 3x - 10 = 0$ **2.** $x^2 - 13x + 36 = 0$

3. $x^2 = 8x - 15$ **4.** $x^2 = -11x - 10$

5. $6x^2 + 11x - 10 = 0$ **6.** $9x^2 + 9x + 2 = 0$

7. $3x^2 - 2x = 8$ **8.** $4x^2 - 13x = -3$

9. $3x^2 + 12x = 0$ **10.** $5x^2 - 20x = 0$

11. $2x(x - 3) = 5x^2 - 7x$ **12.** $16x(x - 2) = 8x - 25$

13. $7 - 7x = (3x + 2)(x - 1)$

14. $10x - 1 = (2x + 1)^2$

Solve each equation in Exercises 15–34 by the square root property.

15. $3x^2 = 27$ **16.** $5x^2 = 45$

17. $5x^2 + 1 = 51$ **18.** $3x^2 - 1 = 47$

19. $2x^2 - 5 = -55$ **20.** $2x^2 - 7 = -15$

21. $(x + 2)^2 = 25$ **22.** $(x - 3)^2 = 36$

23. $3(x - 4)^2 = 15$ **24.** $3(x + 4)^2 = 21$

25. $(x + 3)^2 = -16$ **26.** $(x - 1)^2 = -9$

27. $(x - 3)^2 = -5$ **28.** $(x + 2)^2 = -7$

29. $(3x + 2)^2 = 9$ **30.** $(4x - 1)^2 = 16$

31. $(5x - 1)^2 = 7$ **32.** $(8x - 3)^2 = 5$

33. $(3x - 4)^2 = 8$ **34.** $(2x + 8)^2 = 27$

In Exercises 35–46, determine the constant that should be added to the binomial so that it becomes a perfect square trinomial. Then write and factor the trinomial.

35. $x^2 + 12x$ **36.** $x^2 + 16x$

37. $x^2 - 10x$ **38.** $x^2 - 14x$

39. $x^2 + 3x$ **40.** $x^2 + 5x$

41. $x^2 - 7x$ **42.** $x^2 - 9x$

43. $x^2 - \frac{2}{3}x$ **44.** $x^2 + \frac{4}{5}x$

45. $x^2 - \frac{1}{3}x$ **46.** $x^2 - \frac{1}{4}x$

Solve each equation in Exercises 47–64 by completing the square.

47. $x^2 + 6x = 7$ **48.** $x^2 + 6x = -8$

49. $x^2 - 2x = 2$ **50.** $x^2 + 4x = 12$

51. $x^2 - 6x - 11 = 0$ **52.** $x^2 - 2x - 5 = 0$

53. $x^2 + 4x + 1 = 0$ **54.** $x^2 + 6x - 5 = 0$

55. $x^2 - 5x + 6 = 0$ **56.** $x^2 + 7x - 8 = 0$

57. $x^2 + 3x - 1 = 0$ **58.** $x^2 - 3x - 5 = 0$

59. $2x^2 - 7x + 3 = 0$ **60.** $2x^2 + 5x - 3 = 0$

61. $4x^2 - 4x - 1 = 0$ **62.** $2x^2 - 4x - 1 = 0$

63. $3x^2 - 2x - 2 = 0$ **64.** $3x^2 - 5x - 10 = 0$

Solve each equation in Exercises 65–74 using the quadratic formula.

65. $x^2 + 8x + 15 = 0$ **66.** $x^2 + 8x + 12 = 0$

67. $x^2 + 5x + 3 = 0$ **68.** $x^2 + 5x + 2 = 0$

69. $3x^2 - 3x - 4 = 0$ **70.** $5x^2 + x - 2 = 0$

71. $4x^2 = 2x + 7$ **72.** $3x^2 = 6x - 1$

73. $x^2 - 6x + 10 = 0$ **74.** $x^2 - 2x + 17 = 0$

In Exercises 75–82, compute the discriminant. Then determine the number and type of solutions for the given equation.

75. $x^2 - 4x - 5 = 0$ **76.** $4x^2 - 2x + 3 = 0$

77. $2x^2 - 11x + 3 = 0$ **78.** $2x^2 + 11x - 6 = 0$

79. $x^2 - 2x + 1 = 0$ **80.** $3x^2 = 2x - 1$

81. $x^2 - 3x - 7 = 0$ **82.** $3x^2 + 4x - 2 = 0$

Solve each equation in Exercises 83–108 by the method of your choice.

83. $2x^2 - x = 1$ **84.** $3x^2 - 4x = 4$

85. $5x^2 + 2 = 11x$ **86.** $5x^2 = 6 - 13x$

87. $3x^2 = 60$ **88.** $2x^2 = 250$

89. $x^2 - 2x = 1$ **90.** $2x^2 + 3x = 1$

91. $(2x + 3)(x + 4) = 1$ **92.** $(2x - 5)(x + 1) = 2$

93. $(3x - 4)^2 = 16$ **94.** $(2x + 7)^2 = 25$

95. $3x^2 - 12x + 12 = 0$ **96.** $9 - 6x + x^2 = 0$

97. $4x^2 - 16 = 0$ **98.** $3x^2 - 27 = 0$

99. $x^2 - 6x + 13 = 0$ **100.** $x^2 - 4x + 29 = 0$

101. $x^2 = 4x - 7$ **102.** $5x^2 = 2x - 3$

103. $2x^2 - 7x = 0$ **104.** $2x^2 + 5x = 3$

105. $\frac{1}{x} + \frac{1}{x + 2} = \frac{1}{3}$ **106.** $\frac{1}{x} + \frac{1}{x + 3} = \frac{1}{4}$

107. $\frac{2x}{x - 3} + \frac{6}{x + 3} = -\frac{28}{x^2 - 9}$

108. $\frac{3}{x - 3} + \frac{5}{x - 4} = \frac{x^2 - 20}{x^2 - 7x + 12}$

In Exercises 109–114, find the x-intercept(s) of the graph of each equation. Use the x-intercepts to match the equation with its graph. The graphs are shown in $[-10, 10, 1]$ by $[-10, 10, 1]$ viewing rectangles and labeled (a) through (f).

109. $y = x^2 - 4x - 5$ **110.** $y = x^2 - 6x + 7$

111. $y = -(x + 1)^2 + 4$ **112.** $y = -(x + 3)^2 + 1$

113. $y = x^2 - 2x + 2$ **114.** $y = x^2 + 6x + 9$

a.

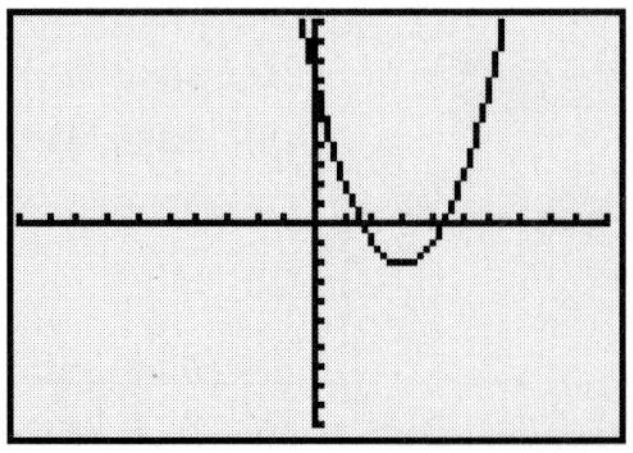

b.

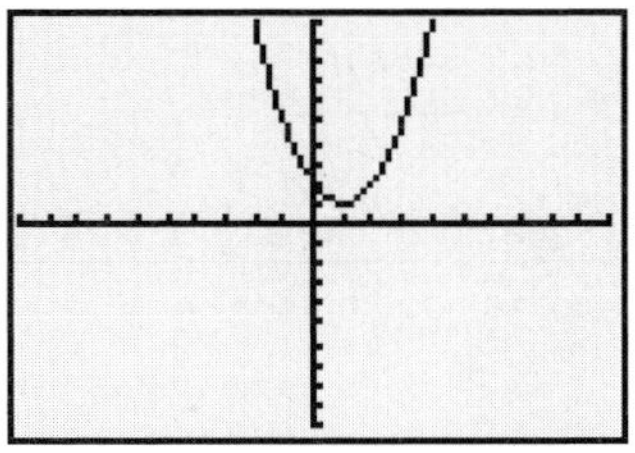

c.

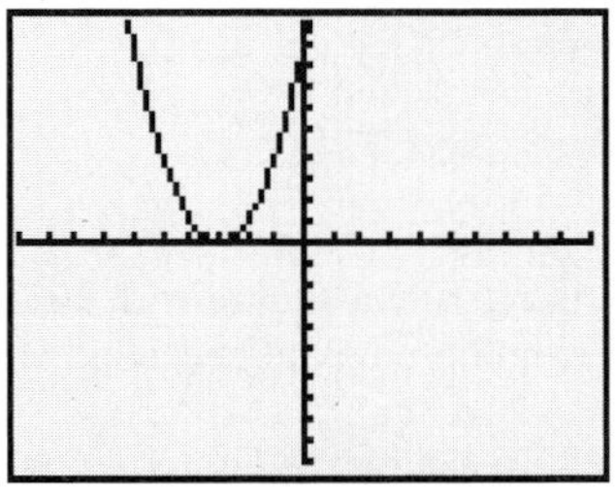

d.

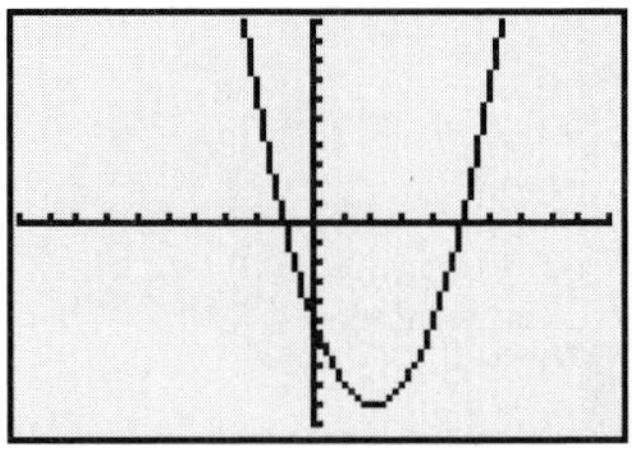

e.

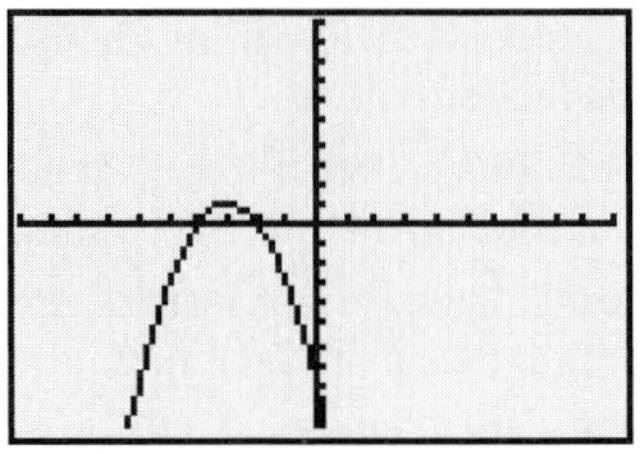

f.

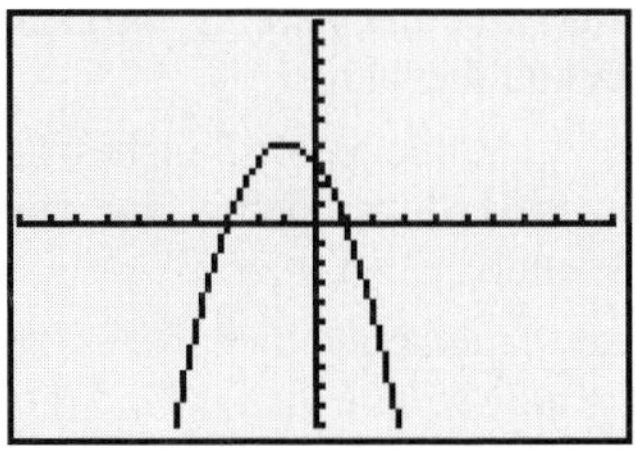

In Exercises 115–122, find all values of x satisfying the given conditions.

115. $y = 2x^2 - 3x$ and $y = 2$.

116. $y = 5x^2 + 3x$ and $y = 2$.

117. $y_1 = x - 1$, $y_2 = x + 4$, and $y_1 y_2 = 14$.

118. $y_1 = x - 3$, $y_2 = x + 8$, and $y_1 y_2 = -30$.

119. $y_1 = \dfrac{2x}{x + 2}$, $y_2 = \dfrac{3}{x + 4}$, and $y_1 + y_2 = 1$.

120. $y_1 = \dfrac{3}{x - 1}$, $y_2 = \dfrac{8}{x}$, and $y_1 + y_2 = 3$.

121. $y_1 = 2x^2 + 5x - 4$, $y_2 = -x^2 + 15x - 10$, and $y_1 - y_2 = 0$.

122. $y_1 = -x^2 + 4x - 2$, $y_2 = -3x^2 + x - 1$, and $y_1 - y_2 = 0$.

Practice Plus

In Exercises 123–124, list all numbers that must be excluded from the domain of each rational expression.

123. $\dfrac{3}{2x^2 + 4x - 9}$ **124.** $\dfrac{7}{2x^2 - 8x + 5}$

125. When the sum of 6 and twice a positive number is subtracted from the square of the number, 0 results. Find the number.

126. When the sum of 1 and twice a negative number is subtracted from twice the square of the number, 0 results. Find the number.

In Exercises 127–130, solve each equation by the method of your choice.

127. $\dfrac{1}{x^2 - 3x + 2} = \dfrac{1}{x + 2} + \dfrac{5}{x^2 - 4}$

128. $\dfrac{x - 1}{x - 2} + \dfrac{x}{x - 3} = \dfrac{1}{x^2 - 5x + 6}$

129. $\sqrt{2}x^2 + 3x - 2\sqrt{2} = 0$

130. $\sqrt{3}x^2 + 6x + 7\sqrt{3} = 0$

Application Exercises

A driver's age has something to do with his or her chance of getting into a fatal car crash. The bar graph shows the number of fatal vehicle crashes per 100 million miles driven for drivers of various age groups. For example, 25-year-old drivers are involved in 4.1 fatal crashes per 100 million miles driven. Thus, when a group of 25-year-old Americans have driven a total of 100 million miles, approximately 4 have been in accidents in which someone died.

Age of U.S. Drivers and Fatal Crashes

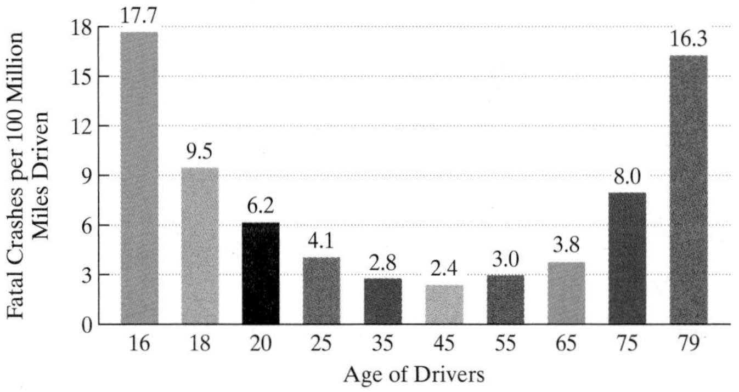

Source: Insurance Institute for Highway Safety

The number of fatal vehicle crashes per 100 million miles, y, for drivers of age x can be modeled by the formula

$$y = 0.013x^2 - 1.19x + 28.24.$$

Use the formula to solve Exercises 131–132.

131. What age groups are expected to be involved in 3 fatal crashes per 100 million miles driven? How well does the formula model the trend in the actual data shown in the bar graph?

132. What age groups are expected to be involved in 10 fatal crashes per 100 million miles driven? How well does the formula model the trend in the actual data shown in the bar graph ?

Throwing events in track and field include the shot put, the discus throw, the hammer throw, and the javelin throw. The distance that an athlete can achieve depends on the initial velocity of the object thrown and the angle above the horizontal at which the object leaves the hand.

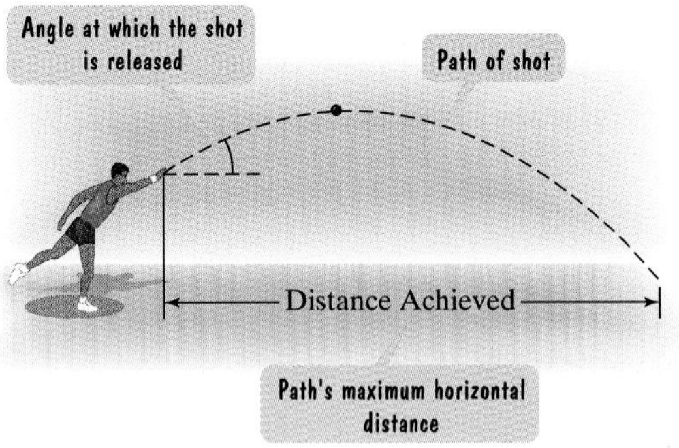

In Exercises 133–134, an athlete whose event is the shot put releases the shot with the same initial velocity, but at different angles.

133. When the shot is released at an angle of 35°, its path can be modeled by the formula

$$y = -0.01x^2 + 0.7x + 6.1,$$

in which x is the shot's horizontal distance, in feet, and y is its height, in feet. This formula is shown by one of the graphs, (a) or (b), in the figure. Use the formula to determine the shot's maximum distance. Use a calculator and round to the nearest tenth of a foot. Which graph, (a) or (b), shows the shot's path?

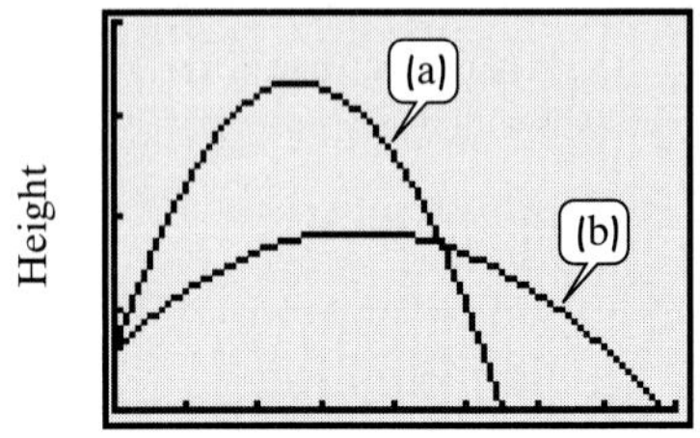

Horizontal Distance
[0, 80, 10] by [0, 40, 10]

134. When the shot is released at an angle of 65°, its path can be modeled by the formula

$$y = -0.04x^2 + 2.1x + 6.1,$$

in which x is the shot's horizontal distance, in feet, and y is its height, in feet. This formula is shown by one of the graphs, (a) or (b), in the figure in Exercise 133. Use the formula to determine the shot's maximum distance. Use a calculator and round to the nearest tenth of a foot. Which graph, (a) or (b), shows the shot's path?

Use the Pythagorean Theorem and the square root property to solve Exercises 135–138. Express answers in simplified radical form. Then find a decimal approximation to the nearest tenth.

135. The figure at the top of the next column shows that the doorway into a room is 4 feet wide and 8 feet high. What is the length of the longest rectangular panel that can be taken through this doorway diagonally?

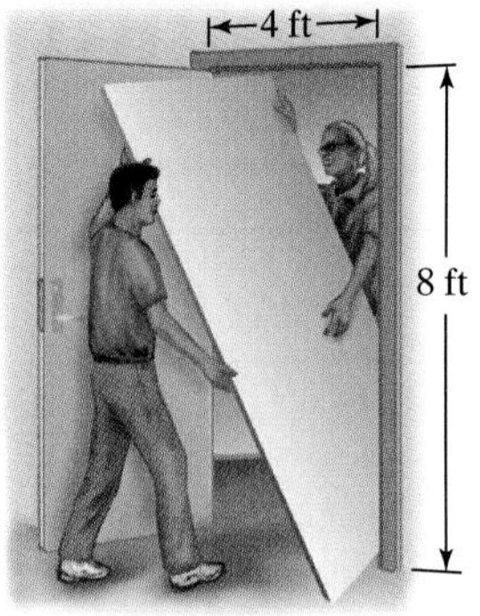

136. A baseball diamond is actually a square with 90-foot sides. What is the distance from home plate to second base?

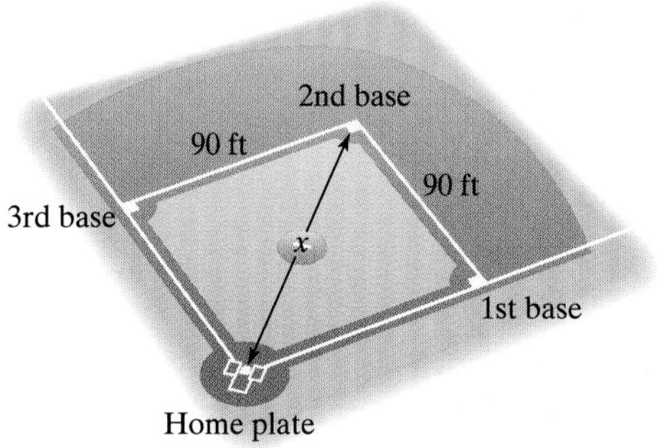

137. The base of a 20-foot ladder is 15 feet from a house. How far up the house does the ladder reach?

138. The base of a 30-foot ladder is 10 feet from a building. If the ladder reaches the flat roof, how tall is the building?

139. The length of a rectangular sign is 3 feet longer than the width. If the sign's area is 54 square feet, find its length and width.

140. A rectangular parking lot has a length that is 3 yards greater than the width. The area of the parking lot is 180 square yards. Find the length and the width.

141. Each side of a square is lengthened by 3 inches. The area of this new, larger square is 64 square inches. Find the length of a side of the original square.

142. Each side of a square is lengthened by 2 inches. The area of this new, larger square is 36 square inches. Find the length of a side of the original square.

143. A pool measuring 10 meters by 20 meters is surrounded by a path of uniform width, as shown in the figure. If the area of the pool and the path combined is 600 square meters, what is the width of the path?

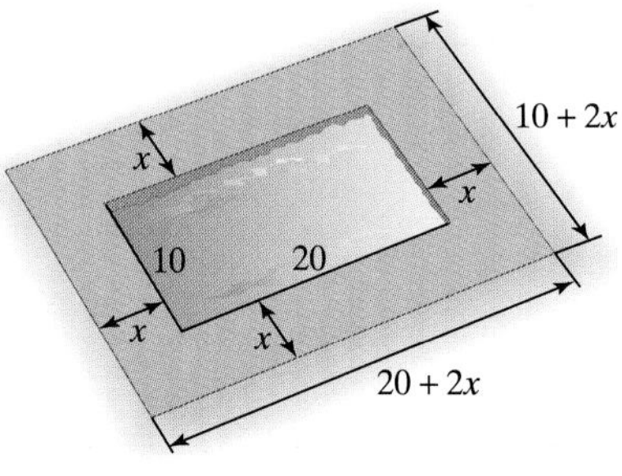

144. A vacant rectangular lot is being turned into a community vegetable garden measuring 15 meters by 12 meters. A path of uniform width is to surround the garden, as shown in the figure. If the area of the garden and path combined is 378 square meters, find the width of the path.

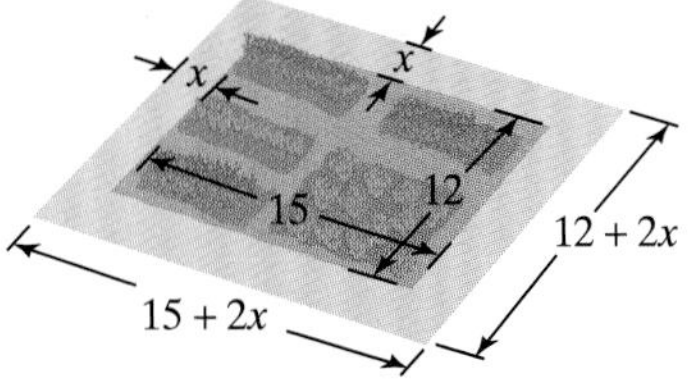

145. A machine produces open boxes using square sheets of metal. The figure illustrates that the machine cuts equal-sized squares measuring 2 inches on a side from the corners and then shapes the metal into an open box by turning up the sides. If each box must have a volume of 200 cubic inches, find the length and width of the open box.

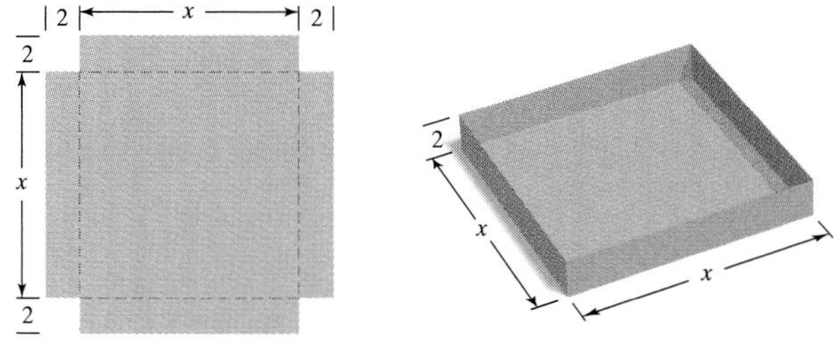

146. A machine produces open boxes using square sheets of metal. The machine cuts equal-sized squares measuring 3 inches on a side from the corners and then shapes the metal into an open box by turning up the sides. If each box must have a volume of 75 cubic inches, find the length and width of the open box.

147. A rain gutter is made from sheets of aluminum that are 20 inches wide. As shown in the figure, the edges are turned up to form right angles. Determine the depth of the gutter that will allow a cross-sectional area of 13 square inches. Show that there are two different solutions to the problem. Round to the nearest tenth of an inch.

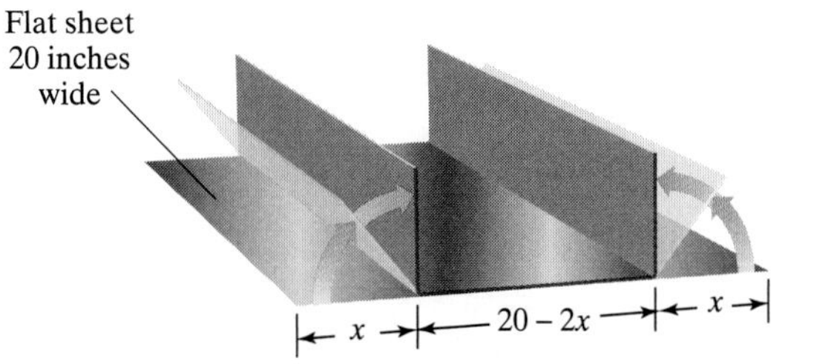

148. A piece of wire is 8 inches long. The wire is cut into two pieces and then each piece is bent into a square. Find the length of each piece if the sum of the areas of these squares is to be 2 square inches.

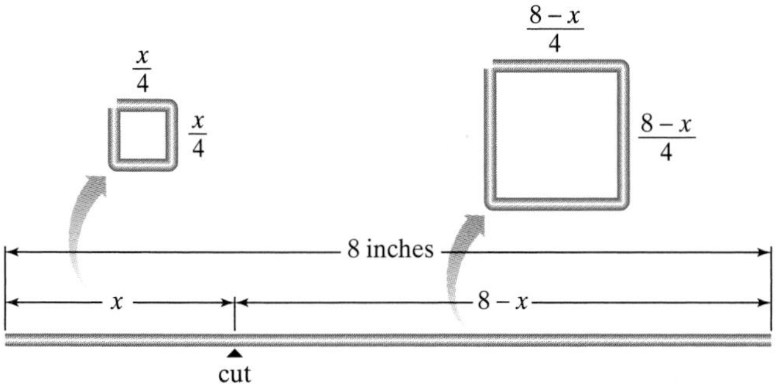

Writing in Mathematics

149. What is a quadratic equation?

150. Explain how to solve $x^2 + 6x + 8 = 0$ using factoring and the zero-product principle.

151. Explain how to solve $x^2 + 6x + 8 = 0$ by completing the square.

152. Explain how to solve $x^2 + 6x + 8 = 0$ using the quadratic formula.

153. How is the quadratic formula derived?

154. What is the discriminant and what information does it provide about a quadratic equation?

155. If you are given a quadratic equation, how do you determine which method to use to solve it?

156. Describe the relationship between the solutions of $ax^2 + bx + c = 0$ and the graph of $y = ax^2 + bx + c$.

157. If a quadratic equation $ax^2 + bx + c = 0$ has imaginary solutions, how is this shown on the graph of $y = ax^2 + bx + c$?

Technology Exercises

158. Use a graphing utility and x-intercepts to verify any of the real solutions that you obtained for three of the quadratic equations in Exercises 65–74.

159. Use a graphing utility to graph $y = ax^2 + bx + c$ related to any five of the quadratic equations, $ax^2 + bx + c = 0$, in Exercises 75–82. How does each graph illustrate what you determined algebraically using the discriminant?

Critical Thinking Exercises

160. Which one of the following is true?

a. The equation $(2x - 3)^2 = 25$ is equivalent to $2x - 3 = 5$.

b. Every quadratic equation has two distinct numbers in its solution set.

c. A quadratic equation whose coefficients are real numbers can never have a solution set containing one real number and one imaginary number.

d. The equation $ax^2 + c = 0$ cannot be solved by the quadratic formula.

161. Write a quadratic equation in general form whose solution set is $\{-3, 5\}$.

162. Solve for t: $s = -16t^2 + v_0 t$.

163. A rectangular swimming pool is 12 meters long and 8 meters wide. A tile border of uniform width is to be built around the pool using 120 square meters of tile. The tile is from a discontinued stock (so no additional materials are available) and all 120 square meters are to be used. How wide should the border be? Round to the nearest tenth of a meter. If zoning laws require at least a 2-meter-wide border around the pool, can this be done with the available tile?

CHAPTER 1
MID-CHAPTER CHECK POINT

What You Know: We used the rectangular coordinate system to represent ordered pairs of real numbers and to graph equations in two variables. We saw that linear equations can be written in the form $ax + b = 0$, $a \neq 0$, and quadratic equations can be written in the general form $ax^2 + bx + c = 0$, $a \neq 0$. We solved linear equations and saw that some linear equations have no solution, whereas others have all real numbers as solutions. We solved quadratic equations using factoring, the square root property, completing the square, and the quadratic formula. We saw that the discriminant of $ax^2 + bx + c = 0$, $b^2 - 4ac$, determines the number and type of solutions. We performed operations with complex numbers and used the imaginary unit i ($i = \sqrt{-1}$, where $i^2 = -1$) to represent solutions of quadratic equations with negative discriminants. Only real solutions correspond to x-intercepts. We also solved rational equations by multiplying both sides by the least common denominator and clearing fractions. We developed a strategy for solving a variety of applied problems, using equations to model verbal conditions.

In Exercises 1–12, solve each equation.

1. $-5 + 3(x + 5) = 2(3x - 4)$
2. $5x^2 - 2x = 7$
3. $\frac{x - 3}{5} - 1 = \frac{x - 5}{4}$
4. $3x^2 - 6x - 2 = 0$
5. $4x - 2(1 - x) = 3(2x + 1) - 5$
6. $5x^2 + 1 = 37$
7. $x(2x - 3) = -4$
8. $\frac{3x}{4} - \frac{x}{3} + 1 = \frac{4x}{5} - \frac{3}{20}$
9. $(x + 3)^2 = 24$
10. $\frac{1}{x^2} - \frac{4}{x} + 1 = 0$
11. $3x + 1 - (x - 5) = 2x - 4$
12. $\frac{2x}{x^2 + 6x + 8} = \frac{x}{x + 4} - \frac{2}{x + 2}$

In Exercises 13–17, find the x-intercepts of the graph of each equation.

13. $y = x^2 + 6x + 2$
14. $y = 4(x + 1) - 3x - (6 - x)$
15. $y = 2x^2 + 26$
16. $y = \frac{x^2}{3} + \frac{x}{2} - \frac{2}{3}$
17. $y = x^2 - 5x + 8$

In Exercises 18–19, find all values of x satisfying the given conditions.

18. $y_1 = 3(2x - 5) - 2(4x + 1)$, $y_2 = -5(x + 3) - 2$, and $y_1 = y_2$.
19. $y_1 = 2x + 3$, $y_2 = x + 2$, and $y_1 y_2 = 10$.
20. Solve by completing the square: $x^2 + 10x - 3 = 0$.

In Exercises 21–22, without solving the equation, determine the number and type of solutions.

21. $2x^2 + 5x + 4 = 0$
22. $10x(x + 4) = 15x - 15$

In Exercises 23–25, graph each equation in a rectangular coordinate system.

23. $y = 2x - 1$
24. $y = 1 - |x|$
25. $y = x^2 + 2$
26. Solve for n: $L = a + (n - 1)d$.
27. Solve for l: $A = 2lw + 2lh + 2wh$.
28. Solve for f_1: $f = \frac{f_1 f_2}{f_1 + f_2}$.
29. The bar graph shows the defense budget, in billions of dollars, for the countries with the largest defense budgets. The defense budget of Russia exceeds Japan's by \$4 billion, and the defense budget of the United States exceeds Japan's by \$251 billion. The combined defense budgets of the United States, Russia, and Japan are \$375 billion. Determine the defense budget, in billions of dollars, for each country.

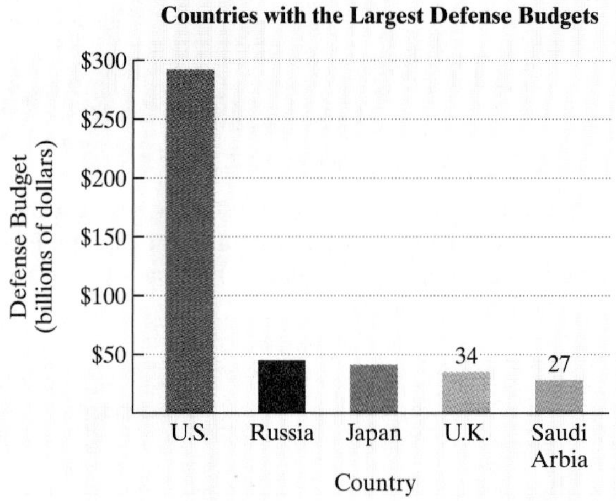

Source: Russell Ash, *The Top 10 of Everything 2004*

30. The average weight for female infants at birth is 7 pounds, with a monthly weight gain of 1.5 pounds. After how many months does a baby girl weigh 16 pounds?

31. You invested \$25,000 in two accounts paying 8% and 9% annual interest, respectively. At the end of the year, the total interest from these investments was \$2135. How much was invested at each rate?

32. Photo Shop A charges \$1.60 to develop a roll of film plus \$0.11 for each print. Photo Shop B charges \$1.20 to develop a roll of film plus \$0.13 per print. For how many prints will the amount spent at each photo shop be the same? What will be that amount?

33. In 2002, the average weight for an American woman aged 20 through 29 was 157 pounds. This is a 22% increase over the average weight in 1960. What was the average weight, to the nearest pound, for an American woman aged 20 through 29 in 1960? (*Source:* National Center for Health Statistics)

34. You invested \$4000. On part of this investment, you earned 4% interest. On the remainder of the investment, you lost 3%. Combining earnings and losses, the annual income from these investments was \$55. How much was invested at each rate?

In Exercises 35–36, find the dimensions of each rectangle.

35. The rectangle's length exceeds twice its width by 5 feet. The perimeter is 46 feet.

36. The rectangle's length is 1 foot shorter than twice its width. The area is 28 square feet.

37. A vertical pole is supported by three wires. Each wire is 13 yards long and is anchored in the ground 5 yards from the base of the pole. How far up the pole will the wires be attached?

38. The graph shows the rapid growth of multinational corporations from 1970 through 2001, including the starting dates of some notable corporations. The data can be modeled by the equation

$$N = 62.2x^2 + 7000,$$

where N represents the number of multinational corporations in the world x years after 1970. Use this model to determine in which year there were 46,000 multinational corporations. How well does the model describe the actual number of corporations for that year shown in the graph?

Number of Multinational Corporations in the World

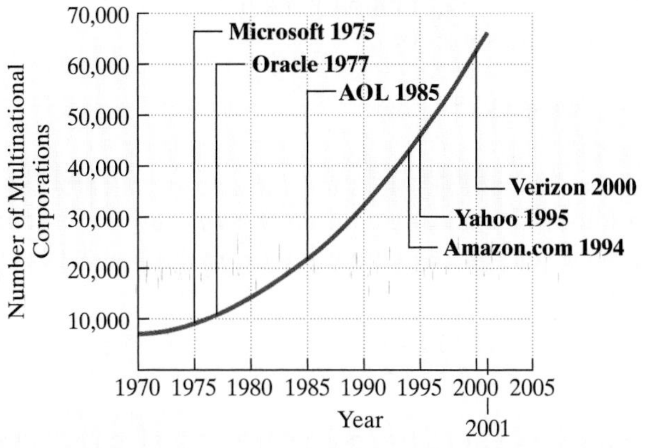

Source: Medard Gabel, *Global Inc.*, The New Press, 2003

39. The bar graph shows the percentage of foreign-born Americans from 1930 through 2003. The data can be modeled by the equation

$$P = 0.0049x^2 - 0.359x + 11.78,$$

where P is the percentage of the U.S. population that was foreign-born x years after 1930. If the trend shown by the data continues, in which year will 15% of the U.S. population be foreign-born?

Percentage of U.S. Population That Was Foreign-Born, 1930-2003

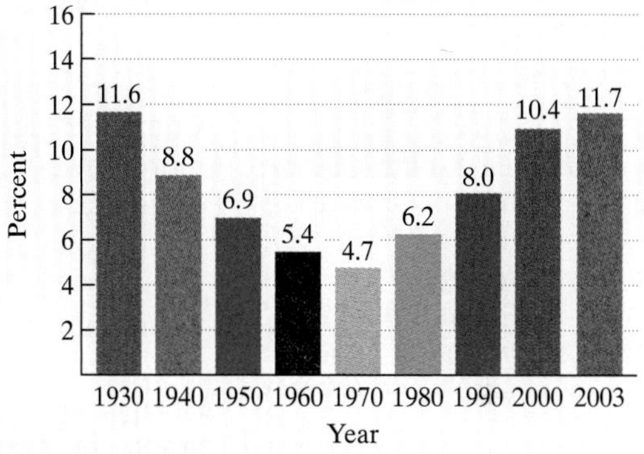

Source: U.S. Census Bureau

In Exercises 40–45, perform the indicated operations and write the result in standard form.

40. $(6 - 2i) - (7 - i)$

41. $3i(2 + i)$

42. $(1 + i)(4 - 3i)$

43. $\dfrac{1 + i}{1 - i}$

44. $\sqrt{-75} - \sqrt{-12}$

45. $(2 - \sqrt{-3})^2$

SECTION 1.6 Other Types of Equations

Objectives

1. Solve polynomial equations by factoring.
2. Solve radical equations.
3. Solve equations with rational exponents.
4. Solve equations that are quadratic in form.
5. Solve equations involving absolute value.

"A breakthrough is something that changes the behavior of hundreds of millions of people where, if you took it away from them, they'd say, 'You can't take that away from me.' Breakthroughs are critical for us."
Bill Gates

Computers have become faster and more powerful. Moore's Law, which states that every 18 months computer power doubles at no extra cost, is still going strong. But customers are not trading up for new models the way they used to, despite being lured by cheaper and cheaper prices. The bar graph in Figure 1.23 shows the number of personal computers sold in the United States each year from 1996 through 2002. Does the trend shown by the graph suggest a new idea afoot in the land, a philosophy of "good enough" when it comes to high tech? Or will a new wave of innovation reverse this trend?

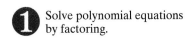

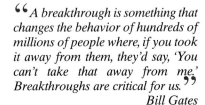

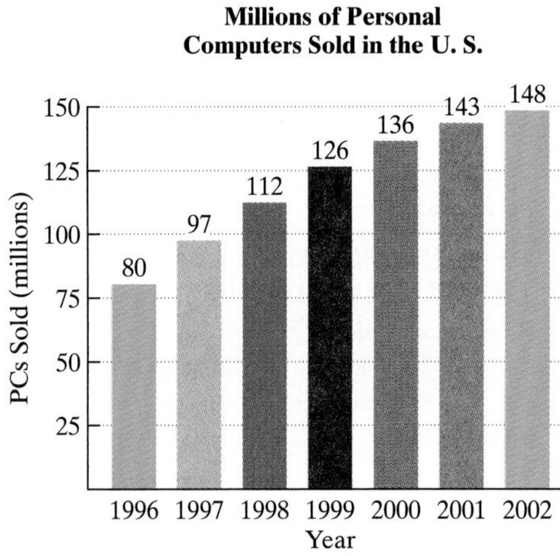

Figure 1.23
Source: Newsweek

The bar graph indicates that PC sales are increasing for the period shown. However, the rate of increase is slowing down. For this reason, a square-root formula is appropriate for modeling the data. The formula

$$P = 28\sqrt{t} + 80$$

models the number of personal computers sold in the United States, P, in millions, t years after 1996.

If trends from 1996 through 2002 continue and there are no new breakthroughs to spur sales, in what year will 192 million personal computers be sold? Substitute 192 for P in the formula and solve for t:

$$192 = 28\sqrt{t} + 80.$$

The resulting equation contains a variable in the radicand and is called a *radical equation*. In this section, in addition to radical equations, we will show you how to solve certain kinds of polynomial equations, equations involving rational exponents, and equations involving absolute value.

1 Solve polynomial equations by factoring.

Polynomial Equations

A **polynomial equation** is the result of setting two polynomials equal to each other. The equation is in **general form** if one side is 0 and the polynomial on the other side is in descending powers of the variable. The **degree of a polynomial equation** is the same as the highest degree of any term in the equation. Here are examples of three polynomial equations:

$$3x + 5 = 14 \qquad 2x^2 + 7x = 4 \qquad x^3 + x^2 = 4x + 4.$$

This equation is of degree 1 because 1 is the highest degree.

This equation is of degree 2 because 2 is the highest degree.

This equation is of degree 3 because 3 is the highest degree.

Notice that a polynomial equation of degree 1 is a linear equation. A polynomial equation of degree 2 is a quadratic equation.

Some polynomial equations of degree 3 or higher can be solved by moving all terms to one side, thereby obtaining 0 on the other side. Once the equation is in general form, factor and then set each factor equal to 0.

EXAMPLE 1 Solving a Polynomial Equation by Factoring

Solve by factoring: $3x^4 = 27x^2$.

Solution

Step 1 Move all terms to one side and obtain zero on the other side. Subtract $27x^2$ from both sides.

$$3x^4 = 27x^2 \quad \text{This is the given equation.}$$
$$3x^4 - 27x^2 = 27x^2 - 27x^2 \quad \text{Subtract } 27x^2 \text{ from both sides.}$$
$$3x^4 - 27x^2 = 0 \quad \text{Simplify.}$$

Step 2 Factor. We can factor $3x^2$ from each term.

$$3x^4 - 27x^2 = 0$$
$$3x^2(x^2 - 9) = 0$$

Steps 3 and 4 Set each factor equal to zero and solve the resulting equations.

$$3x^2 = 0 \quad \text{or} \quad x^2 - 9 = 0$$
$$x^2 = 0 \qquad x^2 = 9$$
$$x = \pm\sqrt{0} \qquad x = \pm\sqrt{9}$$
$$x = 0 \qquad x = \pm 3$$

Step 5 Check the solutions in the original equation. Check the three solutions, 0, –3, and 3, by substituting them into the original equation. Can you verify that the solution set is $\{-3, 0, 3\}$?

Study Tip

In solving $3x^4 = 27x^2$, be careful not to divide both sides by x^2. If you do, you'll lose 0 as a solution. In general, do not divide both sides of an equation by a variable because that variable might take on the value 0 and you cannot divide by 0.

Check Point 1 Solve by factoring: $4x^4 = 12x^2$.

EXAMPLE 2 Solving a Polynomial Equation by Factoring

Solve by factoring: $x^3 + x^2 = 4x + 4$.

Solution

Step 1 Move all terms to one side and obtain zero on the other side. Subtract $4x$ and subtract 4 from both sides.

$$x^3 + x^2 = 4x + 4 \quad \text{This is the given equation.}$$
$$x^3 + x^2 - 4x - 4 = 4x + 4 - 4x - 4 \quad \text{Subtract 4x and 4 from both sides.}$$
$$x^3 + x^2 - 4x - 4 = 0 \quad \text{Simplify.}$$

Technology

A graphing utility's $\boxed{\text{TABLE}}$ feature can be used to numerically verify that $\{-2, -1, 2\}$ is the solution set of

$$x^3 + x^2 = 4x + 4$$

Enter $y_1 = x^3 + x^2$. Enter $y_2 = 4x + 4$.

y_1 and y_2 are equal when $x = -2$, $x = -1$, and $x = 2$.

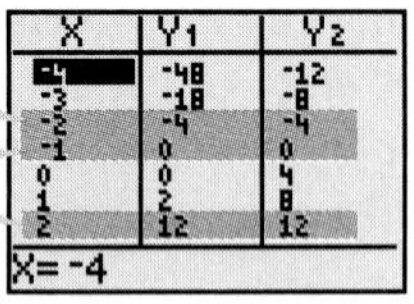

Step 2 Factor. Use factoring by grouping. Group terms that have a common factor.

$$\boxed{x^3 + x^2} + \boxed{-4x - 4} = 0$$

Common factor is x^2. Common factor is -4.

$$x^2(x + 1) - 4(x + 1) = 0 \qquad \text{Factor } x^2 \text{ from the first two terms and } -4 \text{ from the last two terms.}$$

$$(x + 1)(x^2 - 4) = 0 \qquad \text{Factor out the common binomial, } x + 1, \text{ from each term.}$$

Steps 3 and 4 Set each factor equal to zero and solve the resulting equations.

$$x + 1 = 0 \qquad \text{or} \qquad x^2 - 4 = 0$$
$$x = -1 \qquad\qquad\qquad x^2 = 4$$
$$x = \pm\sqrt{4} = \pm 2$$

Step 5 Check the solutions in the original equation. Check the three solutions, $-1, -2$ and 2, by substituting them into $x^3 + x^2 = 4x + 4$, the original equation. Can you verify that the solution set is $\{-2, -1, 2\}$?

Discovery

Suggest a method involving intersecting graphs that can be used with a graphing utility to verify that $\{-2, -1, 2\}$ is the solution set of

$$x^3 + x^2 = 4x + 4.$$

Apply this method to verify the solution set.

Technology

x-intercept: -1

x-intercept: -2 x-intercept: 2

$y = x^3 + x^2 - 4x - 4$

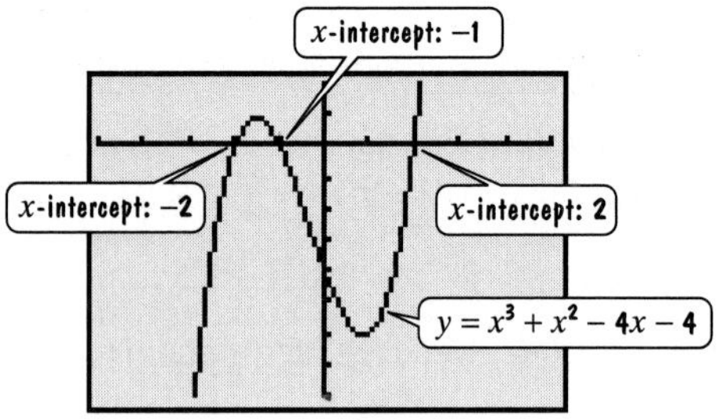

$[-5, 5, 1]$ by $[-8, 2, 1]$

You can use a graphing utility to check the solutions of $x^3 + x^2 - 4x - 4 = 0$. Graph $y = x^3 + x^2 - 4x - 4$, as shown on the left. The x-intercepts are $-2, -1$, and 2, corresponding to the equation's solutions.

Check Point 2 Solve by factoring: $2x^3 + 3x^2 = 8x + 12$.

2 Solve radical equations.

Radical Equations

A **radical equation** is an equation in which the variable occurs in a square root, cube root, or any higher root. An example of a radical equation is

$$\sqrt{x} = 9.$$

We solve the equation by squaring both sides:

Squaring both sides eliminates the square root. $\left(\sqrt{x}\right)^2 = 9^2$

$$x = 81.$$

The proposed solution, 81, can be checked in the original equation, $\sqrt{x} = 9$. Because $\sqrt{81} = 9$, the solution is 81 and the solution set is $\{81\}$.

In general, we solve radical equations with square roots by squaring both sides of the equation. We solve radical equations with nth roots by raising both sides of the equation to the nth power. Unfortunately, if n is even, all the solutions of the equation raised to the even power may not be solutions of the original equation. Consider, for example, the equation

$$x = 4.$$

If we square both sides, we obtain

$$x^2 = 16.$$
$$x = \pm\sqrt{16} = \pm 4$$

This new equation has two solutions, -4 and 4. By contrast, only 4 is a solution of the original equation, $x = 4$. For this reason, **when raising both sides of an equation to an even power, always check proposed solutions in the original equation.**

Here is a general method for solving radical equations with nth roots:

Solving Radical Equations Containing nth Roots

1. If necessary, arrange terms so that one radical is isolated on one side of the equation.
2. Raise both sides of the equation to the nth power to eliminate the nth root.
3. Solve the resulting equation. If this equation still contains radicals, repeat steps 1 and 2.
4. Check all proposed solutions in the original equation.

Extra solutions may be introduced when you raise both sides of a radical equation to an even power. Such solutions, which are not solutions of the given equation, are called **extraneous solutions** or **extraneous roots**.

EXAMPLE 3 Solving a Radical Equation

Solve: $\sqrt{2x - 1} + 2 = x$.

Solution

Step 1 Isolate a radical on one side. We isolate the radical, $\sqrt{2x - 1}$, by subtracting 2 from both sides.

$$\sqrt{2x - 1} + 2 = x \quad \text{This is the given equation.}$$
$$\sqrt{2x - 1} = x - 2 \quad \text{Subtract 2 from both sides.}$$

Step 2 Raise both sides to the nth power. Because n, the index, is 2, we square both sides.

$$\left(\sqrt{2x - 1}\right)^2 = (x - 2)^2$$
$$2x - 1 = x^2 - 4x + 4 \quad \text{Simplify. Use the formula } (A - B)^2 = A^2 - 2AB + B^2 \text{ on the right side.}$$

Study Tip

Be sure to square *both sides* of an equation. Do *not* square each term.

Correct:

$$\left(\sqrt{2x - 1}\right)^2 = (x - 2)^2$$

Incorrect!

$$\left(\sqrt{2x - 1}\right)^2 = x^2 - 2^2$$

Step 3 Solve the resulting equation. Because of the x^2-term, the resulting equation is a quadratic equation. We can obtain 0 on the left side by subtracting $2x$ and adding 1 on both sides.

$$2x - 1 = x^2 - 4x + 4 \quad \text{The resulting equation is quadratic.}$$
$$0 = x^2 - 6x + 5 \quad \text{Write in general form, subtracting } 2x \text{ and adding 1 on both sides.}$$
$$0 = (x - 1)(x - 5) \quad \text{Factor.}$$
$$x - 1 = 0 \quad \text{or} \quad x - 5 = 0 \quad \text{Set each factor equal to 0.}$$
$$x = 1 \qquad\qquad x = 5 \quad \text{Solve the resulting equations.}$$

Step 4 Check the proposed solutions in the original equation.

Check 1:

$$\sqrt{2x-1}+2=x$$
$$\sqrt{2\cdot 1-1}+2\stackrel{?}{=}1$$
$$\sqrt{1}+2\stackrel{?}{=}1$$
$$1+2\stackrel{?}{=}1$$
$$3=1,\quad \text{false}$$

Check 5:

$$\sqrt{2x-1}+2=x$$
$$\sqrt{2\cdot 5-1}+2\stackrel{?}{=}5$$
$$\sqrt{9}+2\stackrel{?}{=}5$$
$$3+2\stackrel{?}{=}5$$
$$5=5,\quad \text{true}$$

Thus, 1 is an extraneous solution. The only solution is 5, and the solution set is $\{5\}$.

Technology

A graphing utility's TABLE feature provides a numeric check that 1 is not a solution and 5 is a solution of $\sqrt{2x-1}+2=x$.

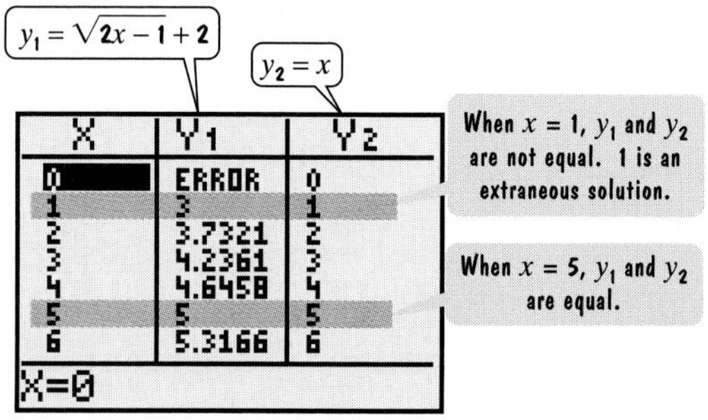

Check Point 3 Solve: $\sqrt{x+3}+3=x$.

The solution of radical equations with two or more square root expressions involves isolating a radical, squaring both sides, and then repeating this process. Let's consider an equation containing two square root expressions.

EXAMPLE 4 Solving an Equation That Has Two Radicals

Solve: $\sqrt{3x+1}-\sqrt{x+4}=1$.

Solution

Step 1 Isolate a radical on one side. We can isolate the radical $\sqrt{3x+1}$ by adding $\sqrt{x+4}$ to both sides. We obtain

$$\sqrt{3x+1}=\sqrt{x+4}+1.$$

Step 2 Square both sides.

$$\left(\sqrt{3x+1}\right)^2=\left(\sqrt{x+4}+1\right)^2$$

Squaring the expression on the right side of the equation can be a bit tricky. We have to use the formula

$$(A+B)^2=A^2+2AB+B^2.$$

Focusing on just the right side, here is how the squaring is done:

$$(A+B)^2 = A^2 + 2\cdot A\cdot B + B^2$$

$$\left(\sqrt{x+4}+1\right)^2=\left(\sqrt{x+4}\right)^2+2\cdot\sqrt{x+4}\cdot 1+1^2=x+4+2\sqrt{x+4}+1.$$

Now let's return to squaring both sides.

$$\left(\sqrt{3x+1}\right)^2 = \left(\sqrt{x+4}+1\right)^2$$ Square both sides of the equation with an isolated radical.

$$3x+1 = x+4+2\sqrt{x+4}+1$$ $\left(\sqrt{3x+1}\right)^2 = 3x+1$; square the right side using the formula for $(A+B)^2$.

$$3x+1 = x+5+2\sqrt{x+4}$$ Combine numerical terms on the right side: $4+1=5$.

Can you see that the resulting equation still contains a radical, namely $\sqrt{x+4}$? Thus, we need to repeat the first two steps.

Repeat Step 1 Isolate a radical on one side. We isolate $2\sqrt{x+4}$, the radical term, by subtracting $x+5$ from both sides. We obtain

$$3x+1 = x+5+2\sqrt{x+4}$$ This is the equation from our last step.

$$2x-4 = 2\sqrt{x+4}.$$ Subtract x and subtract 5 from both sides.

Although we can simplify the equation by dividing both sides by 2, this sort of simplification is not always helpful. Thus, we will work with the equation in this form.

Repeat Step 2 Square both sides.

Be careful in squaring both sides. Use $(A-B)^2 = A^2 - 2AB + B^2$ to square the left side. Use $(AB)^2 = A^2B^2$ to square the right side.

$$(2x-4)^2 = \left(2\sqrt{x+4}\right)^2$$ Square both sides.

$$4x^2-16x+16 = 4(x+4)$$ Square both 2 and $\sqrt{x+4}$ on the right side.

Step 3 Solve the resulting equation. We solve this quadratic equation by writing it in general form.

$$4x^2-16x+16 = 4x+16$$ Use the distributive property.

$$4x^2-20x = 0$$ Subtract $4x+16$ from both sides.

$$4x(x-5) = 0$$ Factor.

$$4x = 0 \quad \text{or} \quad x-5=0$$ Set each factor equal to zero.

$$x = 0 \qquad\qquad x = 5$$ Solve for x.

Step 4 Check the proposed solutions in the original equation.

Check 0:

$$\sqrt{3x+1} - \sqrt{x+4} = 1$$
$$\sqrt{3\cdot 0+1} - \sqrt{0+4} \stackrel{?}{=} 1$$
$$\sqrt{1} - \sqrt{4} \stackrel{?}{=} 1$$
$$1 - 2 \stackrel{?}{=} 1$$
$$-1 = 1, \text{ false}$$

Check 5:

$$\sqrt{3x+1} - \sqrt{x+4} = 1$$
$$\sqrt{3\cdot 5+1} - \sqrt{5+4} \stackrel{?}{=} 1$$
$$\sqrt{16} - \sqrt{9} \stackrel{?}{=} 1$$
$$4 - 3 \stackrel{?}{=} 1$$
$$1 = 1, \text{ true}$$

The check indicates that 0 is not a solution. It is an extraneous solution brought about by squaring each side of the equation. The only solution is 5, and the solution set is $\{5\}$.

Technology

The graph of

$$y = \sqrt{3x+1} - \sqrt{x+4} - 1$$

has only one x-intercept at 5. This verifies that the solution set of $\sqrt{3x+1} - \sqrt{x+4} = 1$ is $\{5\}$.

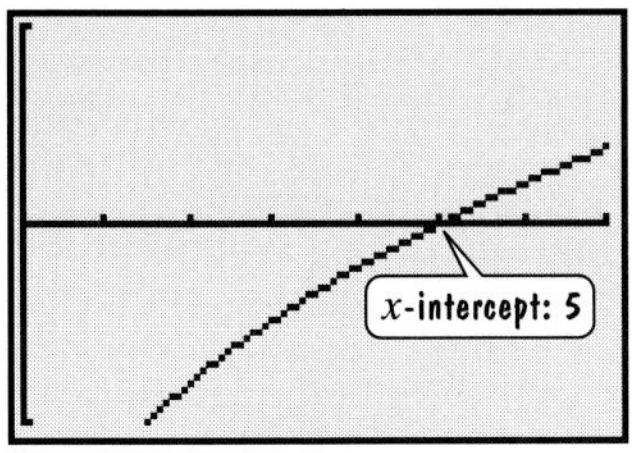

[0, 7, 1] by [−1, 1, 1]

Check Point 4 Solve: $\sqrt{x+5} - \sqrt{x-3} = 2$.

3 Solve equations with rational exponents.

Equations with Rational Exponents

We know that expressions with rational exponents represent radicals:

$$a^{\frac{m}{n}} = \left(\sqrt[n]{a}\right)^m = \sqrt[n]{a^m}.$$

For example, the radical equation $3\sqrt[4]{x^3} - 6 = 0$ can be expressed as $3x^{\frac{3}{4}} - 6 = 0$.

A radical equation with rational exponents can be solved by

1. isolating the expression with the rational exponent, and
2. raising both sides of the equation to a power that is the reciprocal of the rational exponent.

Solving Radical Equations of the Form $x^{\frac{m}{n}} = k$

Assume that m and n are positive integers, $\frac{m}{n}$ is in lowest terms, and k is a real number.

1. Isolate the expression with the rational exponent.
2. Raise both sides of the equation to the $\frac{n}{m}$ power.

If m is even:

$$x^{\frac{m}{n}} = k$$
$$\left(x^{\frac{m}{n}}\right)^{\frac{n}{m}} = \pm k^{\frac{n}{m}}$$
$$x = \pm k^{\frac{n}{m}}$$

If m is odd:

$$x^{\frac{m}{n}} = k$$
$$\left(x^{\frac{m}{n}}\right)^{\frac{n}{m}} = k^{\frac{n}{m}}$$
$$x = k^{\frac{n}{m}}$$

It is incorrect to insert the $\pm$ symbol when the numerator of the exponent is odd. An odd index has only one root.

3. Check all proposed solutions in the original equation to find out if they are actual solutions or extraneous solutions.

EXAMPLE 5 Solving Equations Involving Rational Exponents

Solve:

a. $3x^{\frac{3}{4}} - 6 = 0$ **b.** $x^{\frac{2}{3}} - \frac{3}{4} = -\frac{1}{2}$.

Solution

a. Our goal is to isolate $x^{\frac{3}{4}}$. Then we can raise both sides of the equation to the $\frac{4}{3}$ power because $\frac{4}{3}$ is the reciprocal of $\frac{3}{4}$.

$3x^{\frac{3}{4}} - 6 = 0$ This is the given equation; we will isolate $x^{\frac{3}{4}}$.

$3x^{\frac{3}{4}} = 6$ Add 6 to both sides.

$\frac{3x^{\frac{3}{4}}}{3} = \frac{6}{3}$ Divide both sides by 3.

$x^{\frac{3}{4}} = 2$ Simplify.

$\left(x^{\frac{3}{4}}\right)^{\frac{4}{3}} = 2^{\frac{4}{3}}$ Raise both sides to the $\frac{4}{3}$ power. Because $\frac{m}{n} = \frac{3}{4}$ and m is odd, we do not use the $\pm$ symbol.

$x = 2^{\frac{4}{3}}$ Simplify the left side: $\left(x^{\frac{3}{4}}\right)^{\frac{4}{3}} = x^{\frac{3\cdot4}{4\cdot3}} = x^{\frac{12}{12}} = x^1 = x$.

The proposed solution is $2^{\frac{4}{3}}$. Complete the solution process by checking this value in the given equation.

$3x^{\frac{3}{4}} - 6 = 0$ This is the original equation.

$3\left(2^{\frac{4}{3}}\right)^{\frac{3}{4}} - 6 \stackrel{?}{=} 0$ Substitute the proposed solution.

$3\cdot2 - 6 \stackrel{?}{=} 0$ $\left(2^{\frac{4}{3}}\right)^{\frac{3}{4}} = 2^{\frac{4\cdot3}{3\cdot4}} = 2^{\frac{12}{12}} = 2^1 = 2$

$0 = 0$, true $3\cdot2 - 6 = 6 - 6 = 0$

The solution is $2^{\frac{4}{3}} = \sqrt[3]{2^4} \approx 2.52$. The solution set is $\left\{2^{\frac{4}{3}}\right\}$.

b. To solve $x^{\frac{2}{3}} - \frac{3}{4} = -\frac{1}{2}$, our goal is to isolate $x^{\frac{2}{3}}$. Then we can raise both sides of the equation to the $\frac{3}{2}$ power because $\frac{3}{2}$ is the reciprocal of $\frac{2}{3}$.

$$x^{\frac{2}{3}} - \frac{3}{4} = -\frac{1}{2}$$ This is the given equation.

$$x^{\frac{2}{3}} = \frac{1}{4}$$ Add $\frac{3}{4}$ to both sides. $\frac{3}{4} - \frac{1}{2} = \frac{3}{4} - \frac{2}{4} = \frac{1}{4}$.

$$\left(x^{\frac{2}{3}}\right)^{\frac{3}{2}} = \pm\left(\frac{1}{4}\right)^{\frac{3}{2}}$$ Raise both sides to the $\frac{3}{2}$ power. Because $\frac{m}{n} = \frac{2}{3}$ and m is even, the $\pm$ symbol is necessary.

$$x = \pm\frac{1}{8}$$ $\left(\frac{1}{4}\right)^{\frac{3}{2}} = \left(\sqrt{\frac{1}{4}}\right)^3 = \left(\frac{1}{2}\right)^3 = \frac{1}{8}$

Take a moment to verify that the solution set is $\left\{-\frac{1}{8}, \frac{1}{8}\right\}$.

Check Point 5 Solve: **a.** $5x^{\frac{3}{2}} - 25 = 0$ **b.** $x^{\frac{2}{3}} - 8 = -4$.

4 Solve equations that are quadratic in form.

Equations That Are Quadratic in Form

Some equations that are not quadratic can be written as quadratic equations using an appropriate substitution. Here are some examples:

Given Equation	Substitution	New Equation
$x^4 - 8x^2 - 9 = 0$ or $(x^2)^2 - 8x^2 - 9 = 0$	$u = x^2$	$u^2 - 8u - 9 = 0$
$5x^{\frac{2}{3}} + 11x^{\frac{1}{3}} + 2 = 0$ or $5\left(x^{\frac{1}{3}}\right)^2 + 11x^{\frac{1}{3}} + 2 = 0$	$u = x^{\frac{1}{3}}$	$5u^2 + 11u + 2 = 0$

An equation that is **quadratic in form** is one that can be expressed as a quadratic equation using an appropriate substitution. Both of the preceding given equations are quadratic in form.

Equations that are quadratic in form contain an expression to a power, the same expression to that power squared, and a constant term. By letting u equal the expression to the power, a quadratic equation in u will result. Now it's easy. Solve this quadratic equation for u. Finally, use your substitution to find the values for the variable in the given equation. Example 6 shows how this is done.

EXAMPLE 6 Solving an Equation Quadratic in Form

Solve: $x^4 - 8x^2 - 9 = 0$.

Solution Notice that the equation contains an expression to a power, x^2, the same expression to that power squared, x^4 or $(x^2)^2$, and a constant term, -9. We let u equal the expression to the power. Thus,

$$\text{let } u = x^2.$$

Now we write the given equation as a quadratic equation in u and solve for u.

$$x^4 - 8x^2 - 9 = 0$$ This is the given equation.

$$(x^2)^2 - 8x^2 - 9 = 0$$ The given equation contains x^2 and x^2 squared.

$$u^2 - 8u - 9 = 0$$ Replace x^2 with u.

$$(u - 9)(u + 1) = 0$$ Factor.

$$u - 9 = 0 \quad \text{or} \quad u + 1 = 0$$ Apply the zero-product principle.

$$u = 9 \qquad\qquad u = -1$$ Solve for u.

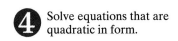

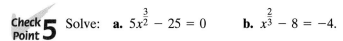

Technology

The graph of

$$y = x^4 - 8x^2 - 9$$

has x-intercepts at -3 and 3. This verifies that the real solutions of

$$x^4 - 8x^2 - 9 = 0$$

are -3 and 3. The imaginary solutions, $-i$ and i, are not shown as intercepts.

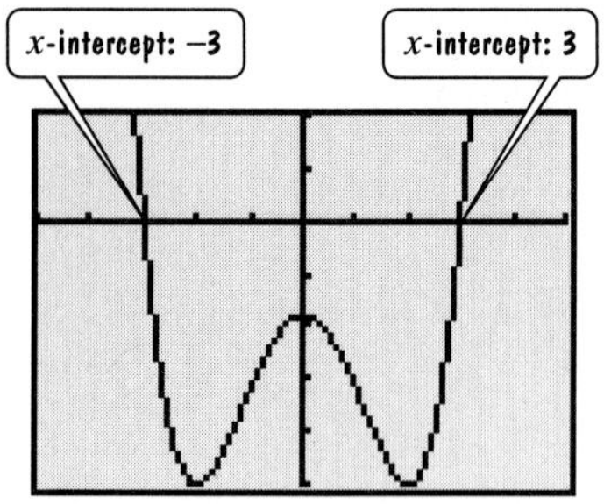

[−5, 5, 1] by [−25, 10, 5]

We're not done! Why not? We were asked to solve for x and we have values for u. We use the original substitution, $u = x^2$, to solve for x. Replace u with x^2 in each equation shown, namely $u = 9$ and $u = -1$.

$$x^2 = 9 \qquad x^2 = -1$$
$$x = \pm\sqrt{9} \qquad x = \pm\sqrt{-1}$$
$$x = \pm 3 \qquad x = \pm i$$

The solution set is $\{-3, 3, -i, i\}$. The graph in the technology box shows that only the real solutions, -3 and 3, appear as x-intercepts.

Check Point 6 Solve: $x^4 - 5x^2 + 6 = 0$.

EXAMPLE 7 Solving an Equation Quadratic in Form

Solve: $5x^{\frac{2}{3}} + 11x^{\frac{1}{3}} + 2 = 0$.

Solution Notice that the equation contains an expression to a power, $x^{\frac{1}{3}}$, the same expression to that power squared, $x^{\frac{2}{3}}$ or $\left(x^{\frac{1}{3}}\right)^2$, and a constant term, 2. We let u equal the expression to the power. Thus,

$$\text{let } u = x^{\frac{1}{3}}.$$

Now we write the given equation as a quadratic equation in u and solve for u.

$$5x^{\frac{2}{3}} + 11x^{\frac{1}{3}} + 2 = 0 \quad \text{This is the given equation.}$$

$$5\left(x^{\frac{1}{3}}\right)^2 + 11x^{\frac{1}{3}} + 2 = 0 \quad \text{The given equation contains } x^{\frac{1}{3}} \text{ and } x^{\frac{1}{3}} \text{ squared.}$$

$$5u^2 + 11u + 2 = 0 \quad \text{Replace } x^{\frac{1}{3}} \text{ with } u.$$

$$(5u + 1)(u + 2) = 0 \quad \text{Factor.}$$

$$5u + 1 = 0 \quad \text{or} \quad u + 2 = 0 \quad \text{Set each factor equal to 0.}$$

$$5u = -1 \qquad u = -2 \quad \text{Solve for } u.$$

$$u = -\frac{1}{5}$$

Use the original substitution, $u = x^{\frac{1}{3}}$, to solve for x. Replace u with $x^{\frac{1}{3}}$ in each of the preceding equations, namely $u = -\frac{1}{5}$ and $u = -2$.

$$x^{\frac{1}{3}} = -\frac{1}{5} \qquad x^{\frac{1}{3}} = -2 \quad \text{Replace } u \text{ with } x^{\frac{1}{3}}.$$

$$\left(x^{\frac{1}{3}}\right)^3 = \left(-\frac{1}{5}\right)^3 \qquad \left(x^{\frac{1}{3}}\right)^3 = (-2)^3 \quad \text{Solve for } x \text{ by cubing both sides of each equation.}$$

$$x = -\frac{1}{125} \qquad x = -8$$

Check these values to verify that the solution set is $\{-8, -\frac{1}{125}\}$.

Check Point 7 Solve: $3x^{\frac{2}{3}} - 11x^{\frac{1}{3}} - 4 = 0$.

5 Solve equations involving absolute value.

Equations Involving Absolute Value

We have seen that the absolute value of x, denoted $|x|$, describes the distance of x from zero on a number line. Now consider an **absolute value equation**, such as

$$|x| = 2.$$

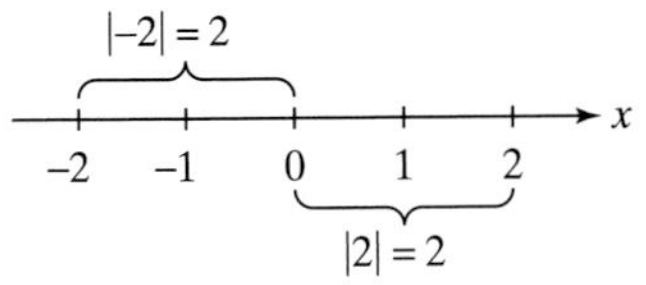

Figure 1.24

This means that we must determine real numbers whose distance from the origin on a number line is 2. Figure 1.24 shows that there are two numbers such that $|x| = 2$, namely, 2 and -2. We write $x = 2$ or $x = -2$. This observation can be generalized as follows:

> **Rewriting an Absolute Value Equation without Absolute Value Bars**
>
> If c is a positive real number and X represents any algebraic expression, then $|X| = c$ is equivalent to $X = c$ or $X = -c$.

Technology

You can use a graphing utility to verify the solution of an absolute value equation. Consider, for example,

$$|2x - 3| = 11$$

Graph $y_1 = |2x - 3|$ and $y_2 = 11$. The graphs are shown in a $[-10, 10, 1]$ by $[-1, 15, 1]$ viewing rectangle. The x-coordinates of the intersection points are -4 and 7, verifying that $\{-4, 7\}$ is the solution set.

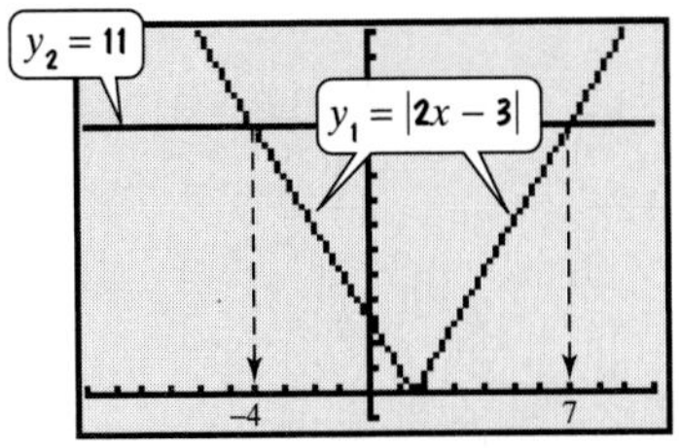

$[-10, 10, 1]$ by $[-1, 15, 1]$

EXAMPLE 8 Solving an Equation Involving Absolute Value

Solve: $|2x - 3| = 11$.

Solution

$	2x - 3	= 11$	This is the given equation.
$2x - 3 = 11$ or $2x - 3 = -11$	Rewrite the equation without absolute value bars.		
$2x = 14 \qquad\qquad 2x = -8$	Add 3 to both sides of each equation.		
$x = 7 \qquad\qquad\; x = -4$	Divide both sides of each equation by 2.		

Check 7:	**Check -4:**					
$	2x - 3	= 11$	$	2x - 3	= 11$	This is the original equation.
$	2(7) - 3	\stackrel{?}{=} 11$	$	2(-4) - 3	\stackrel{?}{=} 11$	Substitute the proposed solutions.
$	14 - 3	\stackrel{?}{=} 11$	$	-8 - 3	\stackrel{?}{=} 11$	Perform operations inside the absolute value bars.
$	11	\stackrel{?}{=} 11$	$	-11	\stackrel{?}{=} 11$	
$11 = 11$, true	$11 = 11$, true	These true statements indicate that 7 and -4 are solutions.				

The solution set is $\{-4, 7\}$.

Check Point 8 Solve: $|2x - 1| = 5$.

EXAMPLE 9 Solving an Equation Involving Absolute Value

Solve: $5|1 - 4x| - 15 = 0$.

Solution

$5	1 - 4x	- 15 = 0$	This is the given equation.

> We need to isolate $|1 - 4x|$, the absolute value expression.

$5	1 - 4x	= 15$	Add 15 to both sides.
$	1 - 4x	= 3$	Divide both sides by 5.
$1 - 4x = 3$ or $1 - 4x = -3$	Rewrite $	X	= c$ as $X = c$ or $X = -c$.
$-4x = 2 \qquad\qquad -4x = -4$	Subtract 1 from both sides of each equation.		
$x = -\frac{1}{2} \qquad\qquad\;\; x = 1$	Divide both sides of each equation by -4.		

Take a moment to check $-\frac{1}{2}$ and 1, the proposed solutions, in the original equation, $5|1 - 4x| - 15 = 0$. In each case, you should obtain the true statement $0 = 0$. The solution set is $\{-\frac{1}{2}, 1\}$. These solutions appear as x-intercepts for the graph of $y = 5|1 - 4x| - 15$, as shown in Figure 1.25.

x-intercept: $-\frac{1}{2}$

x-intercept: 1

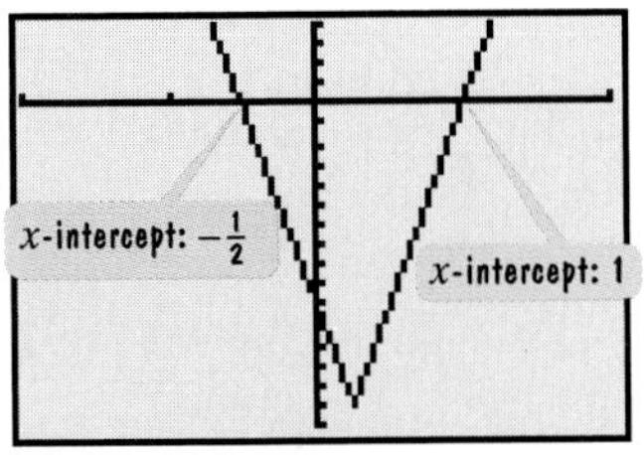

$[-2, 2, 1]$ by $[-16, 4, 1]$

Figure 1.25 The graph of $y = 5|1 - 4x| - 15$

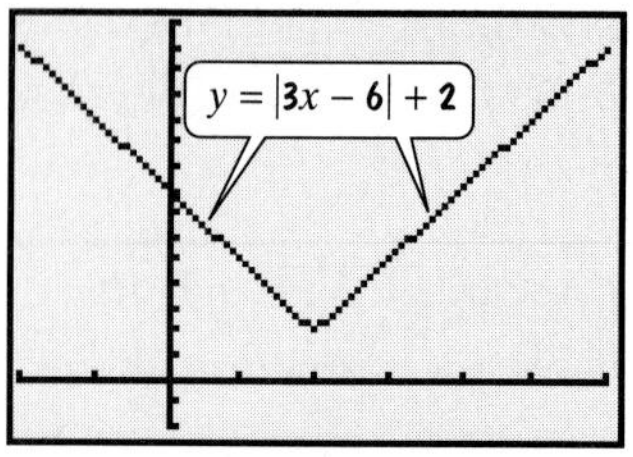

[−2, 6, 1] by [−2, 15, 1]

Figure 1.26 An absolute value equation whose graph has no x-intercepts

Check Point 9 Solve: $4|1 - 2x| - 20 = 0$.

The absolute value of a number is never negative. Thus, if X is an algebraic expression and c is a negative number, then $|X| = c$ has no solution. For example, the equation $|3x - 6| = -2$ has no solution because $|3x - 6|$ cannot be negative. The solution set is $\varnothing$, the empty set. The graph of $y = |3x - 6| + 2$, shown in Figure 1.26, lies above the x-axis and has no x-intercepts.

The absolute value of 0 is 0. Thus, if X is an algebraic expression and $|X| = 0$, the solution is found by solving $X = 0$. For example, the solution of $|x - 2| = 0$ is obtained by solving $x - 2 = 0$. The solution is 2 and the solution set is $\{2\}$.

EXERCISE SET 1.6

Practice Exercises

Solve each polynomial equation in Exercises 1–10 by factoring and then using the zero-product principle.

1. $3x^4 - 48x^2 = 0$
2. $5x^4 - 20x^2 = 0$
3. $3x^3 + 2x^2 = 12x + 8$
4. $4x^3 - 12x^2 = 9x - 27$
5. $2x - 3 = 8x^3 - 12x^2$
6. $x + 1 = 9x^3 + 9x^2$
7. $4y^3 - 2 = y - 8y^2$
8. $9y^3 + 8 = 4y + 18y^2$
9. $2x^4 = 16x$
10. $3x^4 = 81x$

Solve each radical equation in Exercises 11–30. Check all proposed solutions.

11. $\sqrt{3x + 18} = x$
12. $\sqrt{20 - 8x} = x$
13. $\sqrt{x + 3} = x - 3$
14. $\sqrt{x + 10} = x - 2$
15. $\sqrt{2x + 13} = x + 7$
16. $\sqrt{6x + 1} = x - 1$
17. $x - \sqrt{2x + 5} = 5$
18. $x - \sqrt{x + 11} = 1$
19. $\sqrt{2x + 19} - 8 = x$
20. $\sqrt{2x + 15} - 6 = x$
21. $\sqrt{3x} + 10 = x + 4$
22. $\sqrt{x} - 3 = x - 9$
23. $\sqrt{x + 8} - \sqrt{x - 4} = 2$
24. $\sqrt{x + 5} - \sqrt{x - 3} = 2$
25. $\sqrt{x - 5} - \sqrt{x - 8} = 3$
26. $\sqrt{2x - 3} - \sqrt{x - 2} = 1$
27. $\sqrt{2x + 3} + \sqrt{x - 2} = 2$
28. $\sqrt{x + 2} + \sqrt{3x + 7} = 1$
29. $\sqrt{3\sqrt{x + 1}} = \sqrt{3x - 5}$
30. $\sqrt{1 + 4\sqrt{x}} = 1 + \sqrt{x}$

Solve each equation with rational exponents in Exercises 31–40. Check all proposed solutions.

31. $x^{\frac{3}{2}} = 8$
32. $x^{\frac{3}{2}} = 27$
33. $(x - 4)^{\frac{3}{2}} = 27$
34. $(x + 5)^{\frac{3}{2}} = 8$
35. $6x^{\frac{5}{2}} - 12 = 0$
36. $8x^{\frac{5}{3}} - 24 = 0$
37. $(x - 4)^{\frac{2}{3}} = 16$
38. $(x + 5)^{\frac{2}{3}} = 4$
39. $(x^2 - x - 4)^{\frac{3}{4}} - 2 = 6$
40. $(x^2 - 3x + 3)^{\frac{3}{2}} - 1 = 0$

Solve each equation in Exercises 41–60 by making an appropriate substitution.

41. $x^4 - 5x^2 + 4 = 0$
42. $x^4 - 13x^2 + 36 = 0$
43. $9x^4 = 25x^2 - 16$
44. $4x^4 = 13x^2 - 9$
45. $x - 13\sqrt{x} + 40 = 0$
46. $2x - 7\sqrt{x} - 30 = 0$
47. $x^{-2} - x^{-1} - 20 = 0$
48. $x^{-2} - x^{-1} - 6 = 0$
49. $x^{\frac{2}{3}} - x^{\frac{1}{3}} - 6 = 0$
50. $2x^{\frac{2}{3}} + 7x^{\frac{1}{3}} - 15 = 0$
51. $x^{\frac{3}{2}} - 2x^{\frac{3}{4}} + 1 = 0$
52. $x^{\frac{2}{5}} + x^{\frac{1}{5}} - 6 = 0$
53. $2x - 3x^{\frac{1}{2}} + 1 = 0$
54. $x + 3x^{\frac{1}{2}} - 4 = 0$
55. $(x - 5)^2 - 4(x - 5) - 21 = 0$
56. $(x + 3)^2 + 7(x + 3) - 18 = 0$
57. $(x^2 - x)^2 - 14(x^2 - x) + 24 = 0$
58. $(x^2 - 2x)^2 - 11(x^2 - 2x) + 24 = 0$
59. $\left(y - \frac{8}{y}\right)^2 + 5\left(y - \frac{8}{y}\right) - 14 = 0$
60. $\left(y - \frac{10}{y}\right)^2 + 6\left(y - \frac{10}{y}\right) - 27 = 0$

In Exercises 61–78, solve each absolute value equation or indicate that the equation has no solution.

61. $|x| = 8$
62. $|x| = 6$
63. $|x - 2| = 7$
64. $|x + 1| = 5$
65. $|2x - 1| = 5$
66. $|2x - 3| = 11$
67. $2|3x - 2| = 14$
68. $3|2x - 1| = 21$
69. $7|5x| + 2 = 16$
70. $7|3x| + 2 = 16$
71. $2\left|4 - \frac{5}{2}x\right| + 6 = 18$
72. $4\left|1 - \frac{3}{4}x\right| + 7 = 10$
73. $|x + 1| + 5 = 3$
74. $|x + 1| + 6 = 2$
75. $|2x - 1| + 3 = 3$
76. $|3x - 2| + 4 = 4$

Hint for Exercises 77–78: Absolute value expressions are equal when the expressions inside the absolute value bars are equal to or opposites of each other.

77. $|3x - 1| = |x + 5|$
78. $|2x - 7| = |x + 3|$

In Exercises 79–84, find the x-intercepts of the graph of each equation. Then use the x-intercepts to match the equation with its graph. [The graphs are labeled (a) through (f).]

79. $y = \sqrt{x+2} + \sqrt{x-1} - 3$

80. $y = \sqrt{x-4} + \sqrt{x+4} - 4$

81. $y = x^{\frac{1}{3}} + 2x^{\frac{1}{6}} - 3$

82. $y = x^{-2} - x^{-1} - 6$

83. $y = (x+2)^2 - 9(x+2) + 20$

84. $y = 2(x+2)^2 + 5(x+2) - 3$

a.

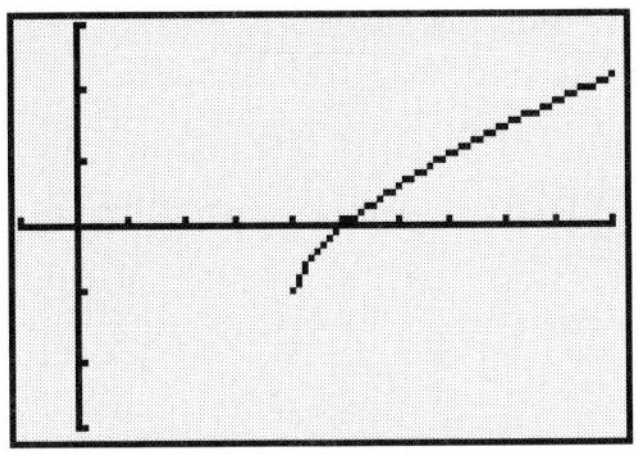

[−1, 10, 1] by [−3, 3, 1]

b.

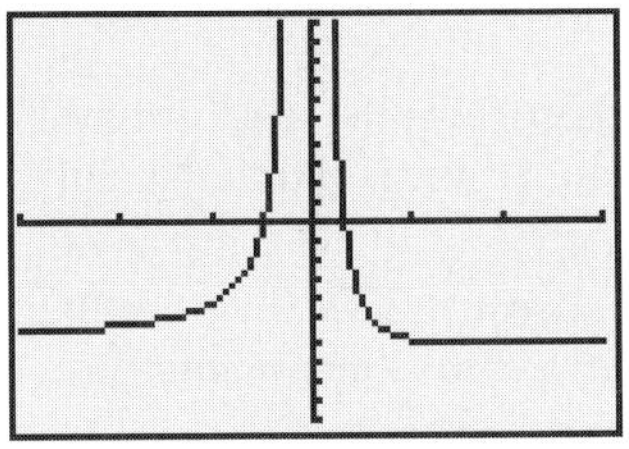

[−3, 3, 1] by [−10, 10, 1]

c.

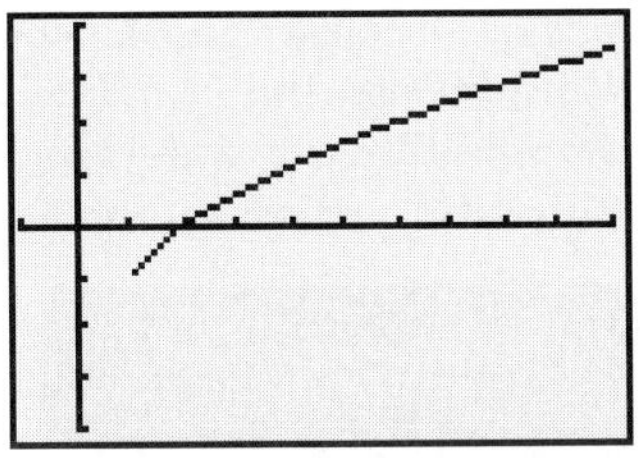

[−1, 10, 1] by [−4, 4, 1]

d.

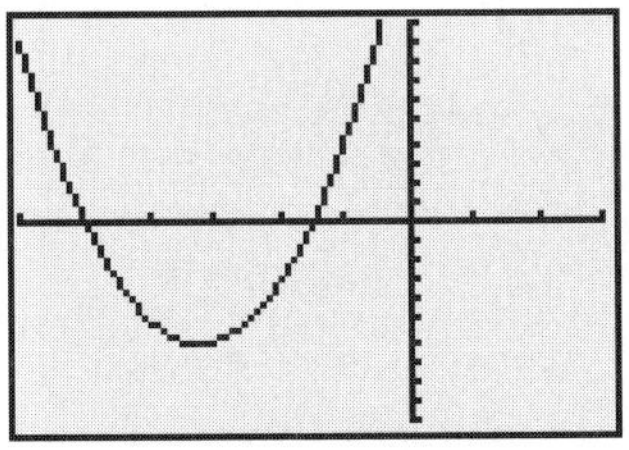

[−6, 3, 1] by [−10, 10, 1]

e.

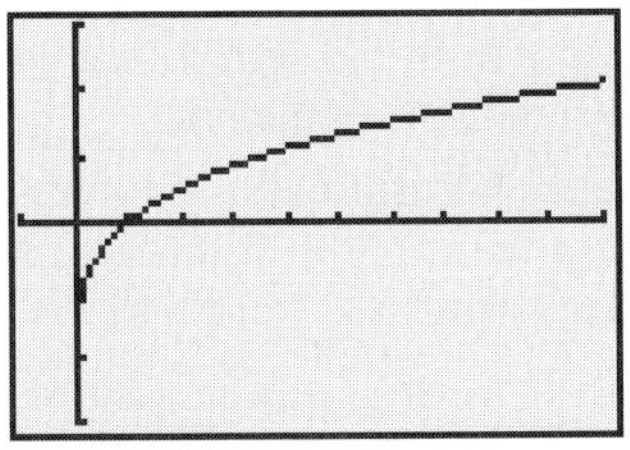

[−1, 10, 1] by [−3, 3, 1]

f.

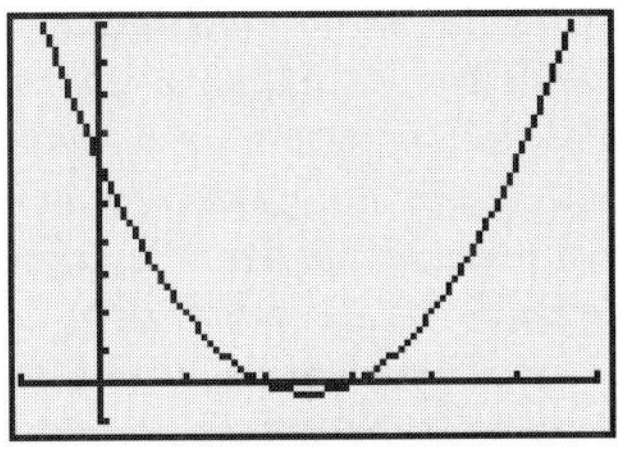

[−1, 6, 1] by [−1, 10, 1]

In Exercises 85–94, find all values of x satisfying the given conditions.

85. $y = |5 - 4x|$ and $y = 11$.

86. $y = |2 - 3x|$ and $y = 13$.

87. $y = x + \sqrt{x+5}$ and $y = 7$.

88. $y = x - \sqrt{x-2}$ and $y = 4$.

89. $y = 2x^3 + x^2 - 8x + 2$ and $y = 6$.

90. $y = x^3 + 4x^2 - x + 6$ and $y = 10$.

91. $y = (x+4)^{\frac{3}{2}}$ and $y = 8$.

92. $y = (x-5)^{\frac{3}{2}}$ and $y = 125$.

93. $y_1 = (x^2 - 1)^2$, $y_2 = 2(x^2 - 1)$, and y_1 exceeds y_2 by 3.

94. $y_1 = 6\left(\frac{2x}{x-3}\right)^2$, $y_2 = 5\left(\frac{2x}{x-3}\right)$, and y_1 exceeds y_2 by 6.

Practice Plus

In Exercises 95–98, solve each equation.

95. $|x^2 + 2x - 36| = 12$ **96.** $|x^2 + 6x + 1| = 8$

97. $x(x+1)^3 - 42(x+1)^2 = 0$

98. $x(x-2)^3 - 35(x-2)^2 = 0$

99. If 5 times a number is decreased by 4, the principal square root of this difference is 2 less than the number. Find the number(s).

100. If a number is decreased by 3, the principal square root of this difference is 5 less than the number. Find the number(s).

101. Solve for V: $r = \sqrt{\frac{3V}{\pi h}}$. **102.** Solve for A: $r = \sqrt{\frac{A}{4\pi}}$.

In Exercises 103–104, list all numbers that must be excluded from the domain of each expression.

103. $\frac{|x-1| - 3}{|x+2| - 14}$ **104.** $\frac{x^3 - 2x^2 - 9x + 18}{x^3 + 3x^2 - x - 3}$

Application Exercises

The formula

$$P = 28\sqrt{t} + 80$$

models the number of personal computers sold in the United States, P, in millions, t years after 1996. Use the model to solve Exercises 105–106.

105. If trends indicated by this model continue, in what year will 192 million personal computers be sold?

106. According to the model, in what year were 143 million personal computers sold? Round to the nearest year. How well does this describe the data shown for this year in Figure 1.23 on page 150?

In 2002, the average surface temperature on Earth was 57.9°F, approximately 1.4° higher than it was one hundred years ago. Worldwide temperatures have risen only 9°F since the end of the last ice age 12,000 years ago. Most climatologists are convinced that over the next one hundred years, global temperatures will continue to increase, possibly setting off a chain of devastating events beginning with a rise in sea levels worldwide and ending with the destruction of water supplies, forests, and agriculture in many parts of the world. The graph shows global annual average temperatures from 1880 through 2002, with projections from 2002 through 2100.

Global Annual Average Temperatures and Projections through 2100

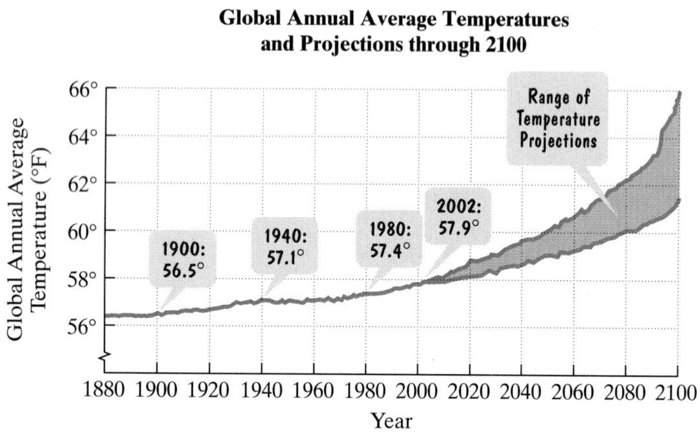

Source: National Oceanic and Atmospheric Administration

The temperature projections shown in the graph can be modeled by two equations:

$$H = 0.083x + 57.9$$

> Models temperatures at the high end of the range

$$L = 0.36\sqrt{x} + 57.9.$$

> Models temperatures at the low end of the range

In these equations, H and L describe projected global annual average temperatures, in degrees Fahrenheit, x years after 2002, where $0 \le x \le 98$. Use the models to solve Exercises 107–110.

107. Use H and L to determine the temperatures at the high and low end of the range of projected global average temperatures for 2100. Round to the nearest tenth of a degree.

108. Use H and L to determine the temperatures at the high and low end of the range of projected global average temperatures for 2080. Round to the nearest tenth of a degree.

109. Use H and L to determine by which year the projected global average temperature will exceed the 2002 average of 57.9° by one degree. Round to the nearest year.

110. Use H and L to determine by which year the projected global average temperature will exceed the 2002 average of 57.9° by two degrees.

Out of a group of 50,000 births, the number of people, y, surviving to age x is modeled by the equation

$$y = 5000\sqrt{100 - x}.$$

The graph of the equation is shown. Use the equation to solve Exercises 111–112.

Number of Survivors, by Age, from a Group of 50,000 Births

$$y = 5000\sqrt{100 - x}$$

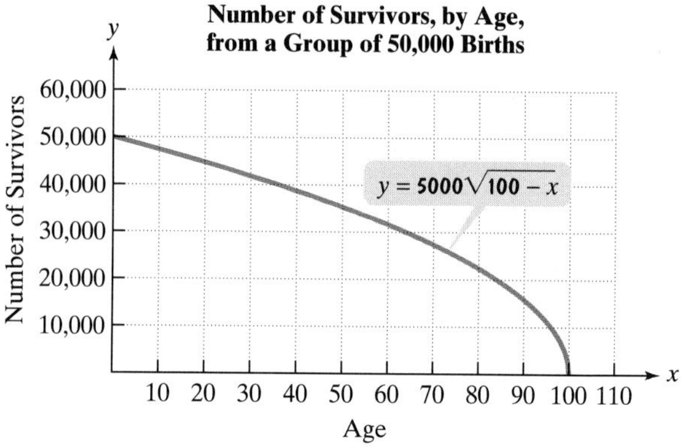

111. To what age will 40,000 people in the group survive? Identify the solution as a point on the graph of the equation.

112. To what age will 35,000 people in the group survive? Identify the solution as a point on the graph of the equation.

For each planet in our solar system, its year is the time it takes the planet to revolve once around the sun. The equation

$$E = 0.2x^{\frac{3}{2}}$$

models the number of Earth days in a planet's year, E, where x is the average distance of the planet from the sun, in millions of kilometers. Use the equation to solve Exercises 113–114.

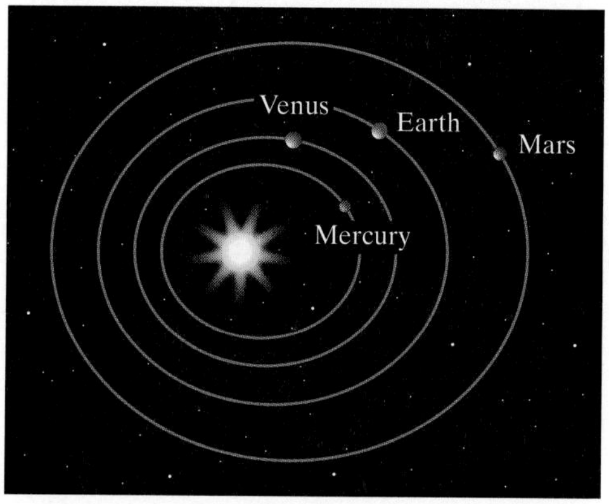

113. We, of course, have 365 Earth days in our year. What is the average distance of Earth from the sun? Use a calculator and round to the nearest million kilometers.

114. There are approximately 88 Earth days in the year of the planet Mercury. What is the average distance of Mercury from the sun? Use a calculator and round to the nearest million kilometers.

Use the Pythagorean Theorem to solve Exercises 115–116.

115. Two vertical poles of lengths 6 feet and 8 feet, respectively, stand 10 feet apart. A cable reaches from the top of one pole to some point on the ground between the poles and then to the top of the other pole. Where should this point be located to use 18 feet of cable?

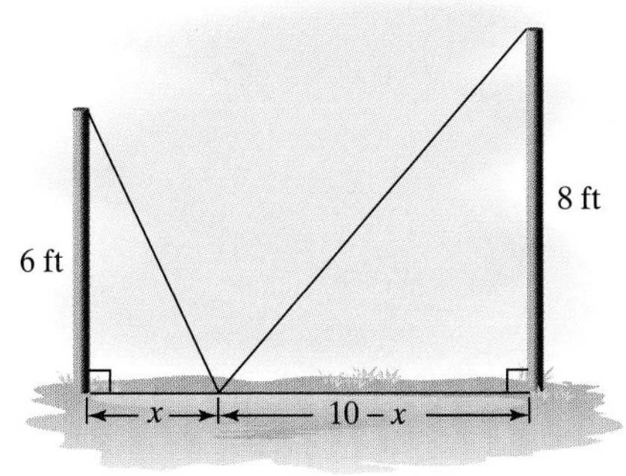

116. Towns A and B are located 6 miles and 3 miles, respectively, from a major expressway. The point on the expressway closest to town A is 12 miles from the point on the expressway closest to town B. Two new roads are to be built from A to the expressway and then to B.

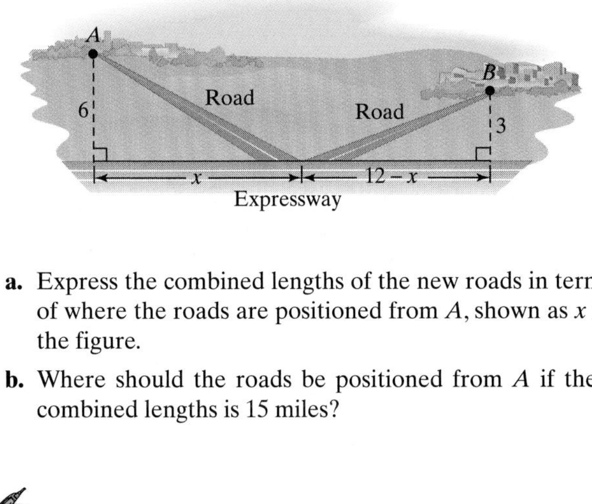

a. Express the combined lengths of the new roads in terms of where the roads are positioned from A, shown as x in the figure.

b. Where should the roads be positioned from A if their combined lengths is 15 miles?

Writing in Mathematics

117. Without actually solving the equation, give a general description of how to solve $x^3 - 5x^2 - x + 5 = 0$.

118. In solving $\sqrt{3x+4} - \sqrt{2x+4} = 2$, why is it a good idea to isolate a radical term? What if we don't do this and simply square each side? Describe what happens.

119. What is an extraneous solution to a radical equation?

120. Explain how to recognize an equation that is quadratic in form. Provide two original examples with your explanation.

121. Describe two methods for solving this equation: $x - 5\sqrt{x} + 4 = 0$.

122. Explain how to solve an equation involving absolute value.

123. Explain why the procedure that you explained in Exercise 122 does not apply to the equation $|x - 2| = -3$. What is the solution set for this equation?

124. Describe the trend shown by the graph in Exercises 111–112. When is the rate of decrease most rapid? What does this mean about survival rate by age?

Technology Exercises

In Exercises 125–127, use a graphing utility and the graph's x-intercepts to solve each equation. Check by direct substitution. A viewing rectangle is given.

125. $x^3 + 3x^2 - x - 3 = 0$

$[-6, 6, 1]$ by $[-6, 6, 1]$

126. $-x^4 + 4x^3 - 4x^2 = 0$

$[-6, 6, 1]$ by $[-9, 2, 1]$

127. $\sqrt{2x+13} - x - 5 = 0$

$[-5, 5, 1]$ by $[-5, 5, 1]$

128. Use a graphing utility to obtain the graph of the equation in Exercises 111–112. Then use the TRACE feature to trace along the curve until you reach the point that visually shows the solution to Exercise 111 or 112.

Critical Thinking Exercises

129. Which one of the following is true?

a. Squaring both sides of $\sqrt{y+4} + \sqrt{y-1} = 5$ leads to $y + 4 + y - 1 = 25$, an equation with no radicals.

b. The equation $(x^2 - 2x)^9 - 5(x^2 - 2x)^3 + 6 = 0$ is quadratic in form and can be solved by letting

$$u = (x^2 - 2x)^3.$$

c. If a radical equation has two proposed solutions and one of these values is not a solution, the other value is also not a solution.

d. None of these statements is true.

130. Solve: $\sqrt{6x-2} = \sqrt{2x+3} - \sqrt{4x-1}$.

131. Solve *without* squaring both sides:

$$5 - \frac{2}{x} = \sqrt{5 - \frac{2}{x}}.$$

132. Solve for x: $\sqrt[3]{x\sqrt{x}} = 9$.

133. Solve for x: $x^{\frac{5}{6}} + x^{\frac{2}{3}} - 2x^{\frac{1}{2}} = 0$.

SECTION 1.7 Linear Inequalities and Absolute Value Inequalities

Objectives

1. Use interval notation.
2. Find intersections and unions of intervals.
3. Solve linear inequalities.
4. Recognize inequalities with no solution or all real numbers as solutions.
5. Solve compound inequalities.
6. Solve absolute value inequalities.

Rent-a-Heap, a car rental company, charges \$125 per week plus \$0.20 per mile to rent one of their cars. Suppose you are limited by how much money you can spend for the week: You can spend at most \$335. If we let x represent the number of miles you drive the heap in a week, we can write an inequality that models the given conditions:

The weekly charge of \$125	plus	the charge of \$0.20 per mile for x miles	must be less than or equal to	\$335.
125	$+$	$0.20x$	$\leq$	335.

Placing an inequality symbol between a polynomial of degee 1 and a constant results in a *linear inequality in one variable*. In this section, we will study how to solve linear inequalities such as the one shown above. **Solving an inequality** is the process of finding the set of numbers that make the inequality a true statement. These numbers are called the **solutions** of the inequality and we say that they **satisfy** the inequality. The set of all solutions is called the **solution set** of the inequality. Set-builder notation and a new notation, called *interval notation*, are used to represent solution sets. We begin this section by looking at interval notation.

1 Use interval notation.

Interval Notation

Subsets of real numbers can be represented using **interval notation**. Suppose that a and b are two real numbers such that $a < b$.

Interval Notation	Graph
The **open interval** (a, b) represents the set of real numbers between, but not including, a and b. $(a, b) = \{x \mid a < x < b\}$ x is greater than a ($a < x$) and x is less than b ($x < b$).	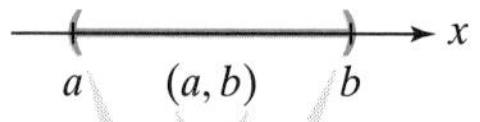 The parentheses in the graph and in interval notation indicate that a and b, the endpoints, are excluded from the interval.

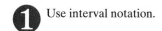

(continued)

Interval Notation	Graph
The **closed interval** $[a, b]$ represents the set of real numbers between, and including, a and b. $[a, b] = \{x \mid a \le x \le b\}$ x is greater than or equal to a $(a \le x)$ and x is less than or equal to b $(x \le b)$.	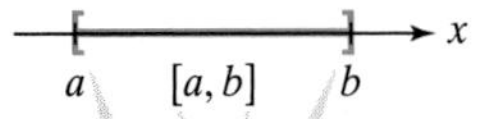 The square brackets in the graph and in interval notation indicate that a and b, the endpoints, are included in the interval.
The **infinite interval** (a, ∞) represents the set of real numbers that are greater than a. $(a, \infty) = \{x \mid x > a\}$ The infinity symbol does not represent a real number. It indicates that the interval extends indefinitely to the right.	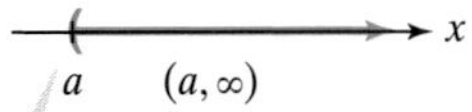 The parenthesis indicates that a is excluded from the interval.
The **infinite interval** $(-\infty, b]$ represents the set of real numbers that are less than or equal to b. $(-\infty, b] = \{x \mid x \le b\}$ The negative infinity symbol indicates that the interval extends indefinitely to the left.	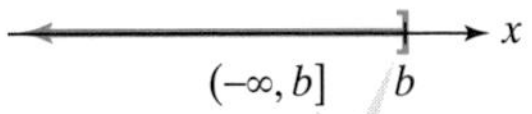 The square bracket indicates that b is included in the interval.

Parentheses and Brackets in Interval Notation

Parentheses indicate endpoints that are not included in an interval. Square brackets indicate endpoints that are included in an interval.

Table 1.5 lists nine possible types of intervals used to describe subsets of real numbers.

Table 1.5 Intervals on the Real Number Line

Let a and b be real numbers such that $a < b$.

Interval Notation	Set-Builder Notation	Graph
(a, b)	$\{x \mid a < x < b\}$	
$[a, b]$	$\{x \mid a \le x \le b\}$	
$[a, b)$	$\{x \mid a \le x < b\}$	
$(a, b]$	$\{x \mid a < x \le b\}$	
(a, ∞)	$\{x \mid x > a\}$	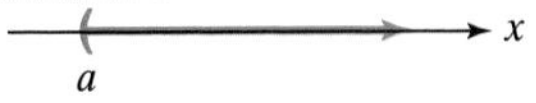
$[a, \infty)$	$\{x \mid x \ge a\}$	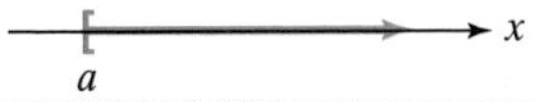
$(-\infty, b)$	$\{x \mid x < b\}$	
$(-\infty, b]$	$\{x \mid x \le b\}$	
$(-\infty, \infty)$	$\{x \mid x$ is a real number$\}$ or $\mathbb{R}$ (set of all real numbers)	

EXAMPLE 1 Using Interval Notation

Express each interval in set-builder notation and graph:

a. $(-1, 4]$ **b.** $[2.5, 4]$ **c.** $(-4, \infty)$.

Solution

a. $(-1, 4] = \{x \mid -1 < x \le 4\}$

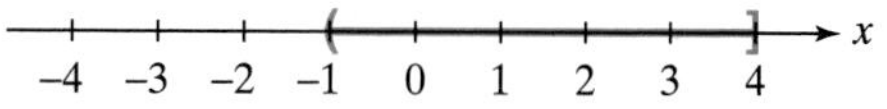

b. $[2.5, 4] = \{x \mid 2.5 \le x \le 4\}$

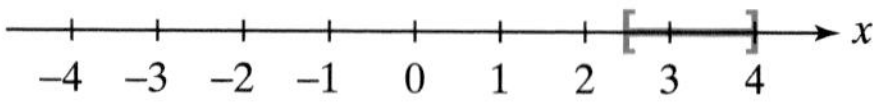

c. $(-4, \infty) = \{x \mid x > -4\}$

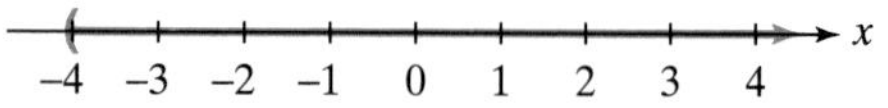

Check Point 1 Express each interval in set-builder notation and graph:

a. $[-2, 5)$ **b.** $[1, 3.5]$ **c.** $(-\infty, -1)$.

2 Find intersections and unions of intervals.

Intersections and Unions of Intervals

In Chapter P, we learned how to find intersections and unions of sets. Recall that $A \cap B$ (A intersection B) is the set of elements common to both set A and set B. By contrast, $A \cup B$ (A union B) is the set of elements in set A or in set B or in both sets.

Because intervals represent sets, it is possible to find their intersections and unions. Graphs are helpful in this process.

Finding Intersections and Unions of Intervals

1. Graph each interval on a number line.
2. **a.** To find the intersection, take the portion of the number line that the two graphs have in common.

   b. To find the union, take the portion of the number line representing the total collection of numbers in the two graphs.

EXAMPLE 2 Finding Intersections and Unions of Intervals

Use graphs to find each set:

a. $(1, 4) \cap [2, 8]$ **b.** $(1, 4) \cup [2, 8]$.

Solution

a. $(1, 4) \cap [2, 8]$, the intersection of the intervals $(1, 4)$ and $[2, 8]$, consists of the numbers that are in both intervals.

Graph $(1, 4)$:

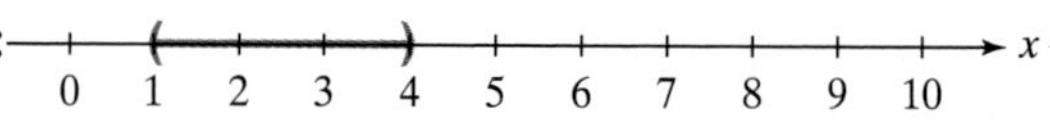

$\{x \mid 1 < x < 4\}$

Graph $[2, 8]$:

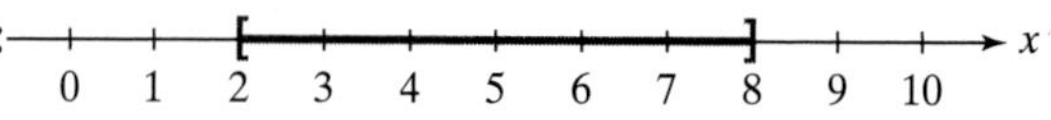

$\{x \mid 2 \le x \le 8\}$

To find $(1, 4) \cap [2, 8]$, take the portion of the number line that the two graphs have in common.

Numbers in both $(1, 4)$ and $[2, 8]$:

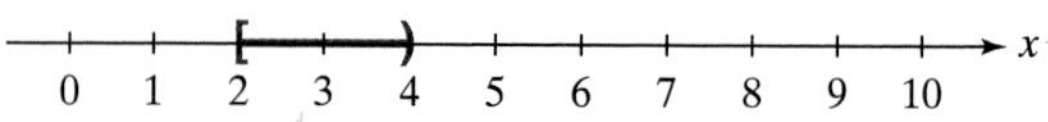

$\{x \mid 1 < x < 4$ and $2 \le x \le 8\}$

The numbers common to both intervals are those that are greater than or equal to 2 and less than 4: $[2, 4)$.

Thus, $(1, 4) \cap [2, 8] = [2, 4)$.

b. $(1, 4) \cup [2, 8]$, the union of the intervals $(1, 4)$ and $[2, 8]$, consists of the numbers that are in either one interval or the other (or both).

Graph $(1, 4)$:
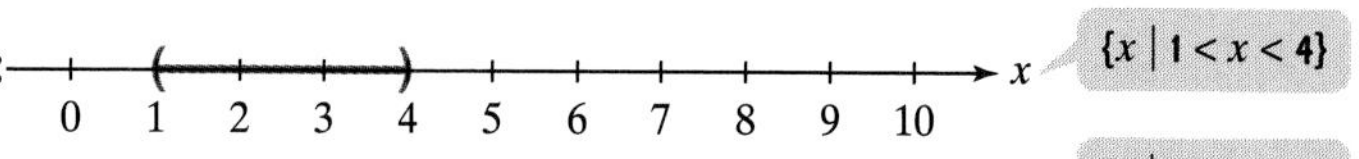

Graph $[2, 8]$:
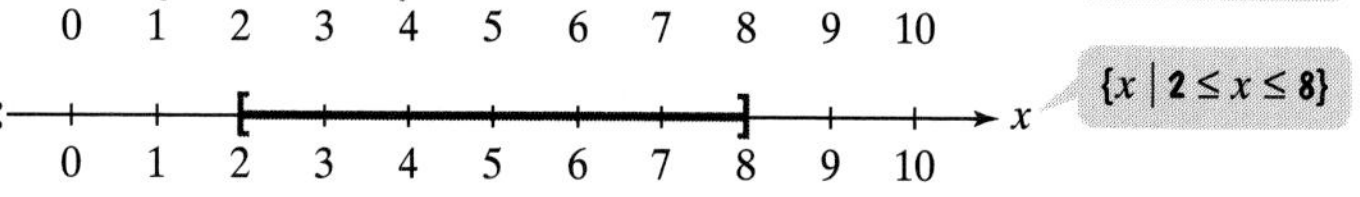

To find $(1, 4) \cup [2, 8]$, take the portion of the number line representing the total collection of numbers in the two graphs.

Numbers in either $(1, 4)$ or $[2, 8]$ or both:
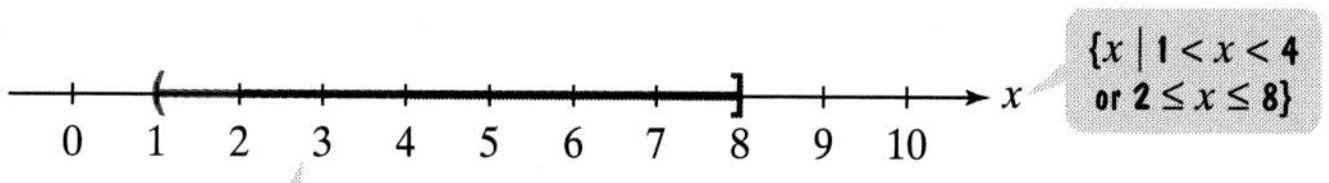

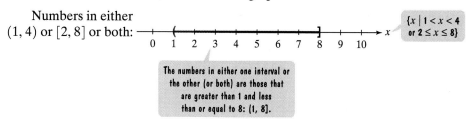

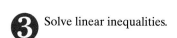

The numbers in either one interval or the other (or both) are those that are greater than 1 and less than or equal to 8: (1, 8].

Thus, $(1, 4) \cup [2, 8] = (1, 8]$.

Check Point 2 Use graphs to find each set:

a. $[1, 3] \cap (2, 6)$ **b.** $[1, 3] \cup (2, 6)$.

3 Solve linear inequalities.

Solving Linear Inequalities in One Variable

We know that a linear equation in x can be expressed as $ax + b = 0$. A **linear inequality in x** can be written in one of the following forms: $ax + b < 0$, $ax + b \leq 0$, $ax + b > 0$, $ax + b \geq 0$. In each form, $a \neq 0$. Back to our question that opened this section: How many miles can you drive your Rent-a-Heap car if you can spend at most \$335 per week? We answer the question by solving

$$0.20x + 125 \leq 335$$

for x. The solution procedure is nearly identical to that for solving

$$0.20x + 125 = 335.$$

Our goal is to get x by itself on the left side. We do this by subtracting 125 from both sides to isolate $0.20x$:

$$0.20x + 125 \leq 335 \quad \text{This is the given inequality.}$$
$$0.20x + 125 - 125 \leq 335 - 125 \quad \text{Subtract 125 from both sides.}$$
$$0.20x \leq 210. \quad \text{Simplify.}$$

Finally, we isolate x from $0.20x$ by dividing both sides of the inequality by 0.20:

$$\frac{0.20x}{0.20} \leq \frac{210}{0.20} \quad \text{Divide both sides by 0.20.}$$
$$x \leq 1050. \quad \text{Simplify.}$$

With at most \$335 per week to spend, you can travel at most 1050 miles.

We started with the inequality $0.20x + 125 \leq 335$ and obtained the inequality $x \leq 1050$ in the final step. Both of these inequalities have the same solution set, namely $\{x | x \leq 1050\}$. Inequalities such as these, with the same solution set, are said to be **equivalent**.

We isolated x from $0.20x$ by dividing both sides of $0.20x \leq 210$ by 0.20, a positive number. Let's see what happens if we divide both sides of an inequality by a negative number. Consider the inequality $10 < 14$. Divide 10 and 14 by -2:

$$\frac{10}{-2} = -5 \quad \text{and} \quad \frac{14}{-2} = -7.$$

Study Tip

English phrases such as "at least" and "at most" can be modeled by inequalities.

English Sentence	Inequality
x is at least 5.	$x \geq 5$
x is at most 5.	$x \leq 5$
x is between 5 and 7.	$5 < x < 7$
x is no more than 5.	$x \leq 5$
x is no less than 5.	$x \geq 5$

Because −5 lies to the right of −7 on the number line, −5 is greater than −7:

$$-5 > -7.$$

Notice that the direction of the inequality symbol is reversed:

$$10 < 14$$
$$\updownarrow$$
$$-5 > -7.$$

Dividing by −2 changes the direction of the inequality symbol.

In general, **when we multiply or divide both sides of an inequality by a negative number, the direction of the inequality symbol is reversed.** When we reverse the direction of the inequality symbol, we say that we change the *sense* of the inequality.

We can isolate a variable in a linear inequality the same way we can isolate a variable in a linear equation. The following properties are used to create equivalent inequalities:

Properties of Inequalities

Property	The Property in Words	Example
The Addition Property of Inequality If $a < b$, then $a + c < b + c$. If $a < b$, then $a - c < b - c$.	If the same quantity is added to or subtracted from both sides of an inequality, the resulting inequality is equivalent to the original one.	$2x + 3 < 7$ Subtract 3: $2x + 3 - 3 < 7 - 3.$ Simplify: $2x < 4.$
The Positive Multiplication Property of Inequality If $a < b$ and c is positive, then $ac < bc$. If $a < b$ and c is positive, then $\frac{a}{c} < \frac{b}{c}$.	If we multiply or divide both sides of an inequality by the same positive quantity, the resulting inequality is equivalent to the original one.	$2x < 4$ Divide by 2: $\frac{2x}{2} < \frac{4}{2}.$ Simplify: $x < 2.$
The Negative Multiplication Property of Inequality If $a < b$ and c is negative, then $ac > bc$. If $a < b$ and c is negative, $\frac{a}{c} > \frac{b}{c}$.	If we multiply or divide both sides of an inequality by the same negative quantity and reverse the direction of the inequality symbol, the resulting inequality is equivalent to the original one.	$-4x < 20$ Divide by −4 and reverse the sense of the inequality: $\frac{-4x}{-4} > \frac{20}{-4}.$ Simplify: $x > -5.$

EXAMPLE 3 Solving a Linear Inequality

Solve and graph the solution set on a number line:

$$3 - 2x \le 11.$$

Solution

$3 - 2x \le 11$	This is the given inequality.
$3 - 2x - 3 \le 11 - 3$	Subtract 3 from both sides.
$-2x \le 8$	Simplify.
$\frac{-2x}{-2} \ge \frac{8}{-2}$	Divide both sides by −2 and change the sense of the inequality.
$x \ge -4$	Simplify.

The solution set consists of all real numbers that are greater than or equal to −4, expressed as $\{x \mid x \ge -4\}$ in set-builder notation. The interval notation for this solution set is $[-4, \infty)$. The graph of the solution set is shown as follows:

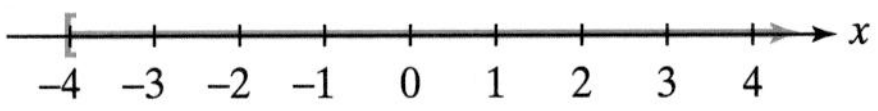

Discovery

As a partial check, select one number from the solution set for the inequality in Example 3. Substitute that number into the original inequality. Perform the resulting computations. You should obtain a true statement.

Is it possible to perform a partial check using a number that is not in the solution set? What should happen in this case? Try doing this.

Check Point 3 Solve and graph the solution set on a number line:

$$2 - 3x \le 5.$$

EXAMPLE 4 Solving a Linear Inequality

Solve and graph the solution set on a number line:

$$-2x - 4 > x + 5.$$

Solution

Step 1 Simplify each side. Because each side is already simplified, we can skip this step.

Step 2 Collect variable terms on one side and constant terms on the other side. We will collect variable terms on the left and constant terms on the right.

$-2x - 4 > x + 5$	This is the given inequality.
$-2x - 4 - x > x + 5 - x$	Subtract x from both sides.
$-3x - 4 > 5$	Simplify.
$-3x - 4 + 4 > 5 + 4$	Add 4 to both sides.
$-3x > 9$	Simplify.

Step 3 Isolate the variable and solve. We isolate the variable, x, by dividing both sides by -3. Because we are dividing by a negative number, we must reverse the inequality symbol.

$\frac{-3x}{-3} < \frac{9}{-3}$	Divide both sides by -3 and change the sense of the inequality.
$x < -3$	Simplify.

Step 4 Express the solution set in set-builder or interval notation and graph the set on a number line. The solution set consists of all real numbers that are less than -3, expressed in set-builder notation as $\{x|x < -3\}$. The interval notation for this solution set is $(-\infty, -3)$. The graph of the solution set is shown as follows:

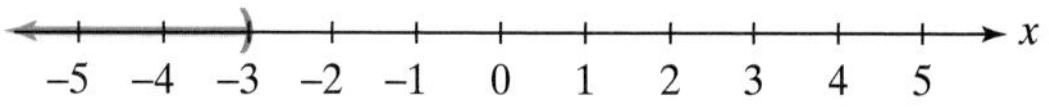

Study Tip

You can solve

$$-2x - 4 > x + 5$$

by isolating x on the right side. Add $2x$ to both sides.

$$-2x - 4 + 2x > x + 5 + 2x$$
$$-4 > 3x + 5$$

Now subtract 5 from both sides.

$$-4 - 5 > 3x + 5 - 5$$
$$-9 > 3x$$

Finally, divide both sides by 3.

$$\frac{-9}{3} > \frac{3x}{3}$$
$$-3 > x$$

This last inequality means the same thing as $x < -3$.

Technology

You can use a graphing utility to check the solution set of a linear inequality. Enter each side of the inequality separately under y_1 and y_2. Then use the table or the graphs. To use the table, first locate the x-value for which the y-values are the same. Then scroll up or down to locate x values for which y_1 is greater than y_2 or for which y_1 is less than y_2. To use the graphs, locate the intersection point and then find the x-values for which the graph of y_1 lies above the graph of $y_2 (y_1 > y_2)$ or for which the graph of y_1 lies below the graph of $y_2 (y_1 < y_2)$.

Let's verify our work in Example 4 and show that $(-\infty, -3)$ is the solution set of

$$-2x - 4 > x + 5.$$

Enter $y_1 = -2x - 4$ in the $\boxed{y=}$ screen.

Enter $y_2 = x + 5$ in the $\boxed{y=}$ screen.

We are looking for values of x for which y_1 is greater than y_2.

Numeric Check

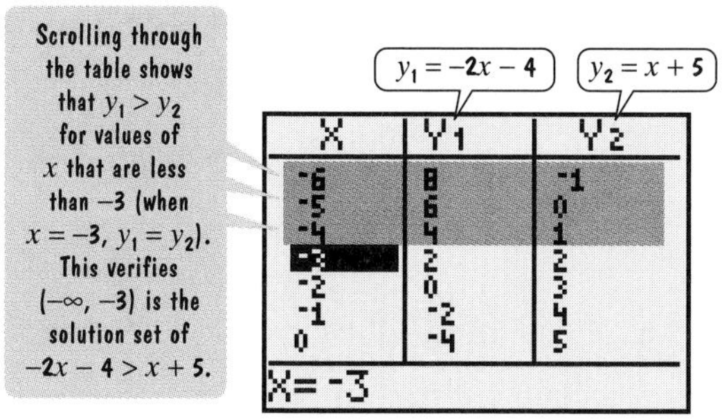

Scrolling through the table shows that $y_1 > y_2$ for values of x that are less than -3 (when $x = -3$, $y_1 = y_2$). This verifies $(-\infty, -3)$ is the solution set of $-2x - 4 > x + 5$.
$y_1 = -2x - 4$
$y_2 = x + 5$
X Y1 Y2
-6 8 -1
-5 6 0
-4 4 1
-3 2 2
-2 0 3
-1 -2 4
0 -4 5
X=-3

Graphic Check

Display the graphs for y_1 and y_2. Use the intersection feature. The solution set is the set of x-values for which the graph of y_1 lies above the graph of y_2.

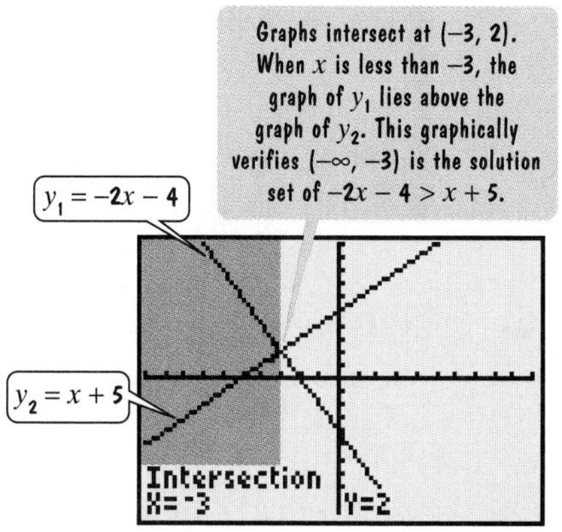

Graphs intersect at $(-3, 2)$. When x is less than -3, the graph of y_1 lies above the graph of y_2. This graphically verifies $(-\infty, -3)$ is the solution set of $-2x - 4 > x + 5$.
$y_1 = -2x - 4$
$y_2 = x + 5$
Intersection
X=-3
Y=2

[−10, 10, 1] by [−10, 10, 1]

Recognize inequalities with no solution or all real numbers as solutions.

 Solve compound inequalities.

Check Point **4** Solve and graph the solution set on a number line: $3x + 1 > 7x - 15$.

Inequalities with Unusual Solution Sets

We have seen that some equations have no solution. This is also true for some inequalities. An example of such an inequality is

$$x > x + 1.$$

There is no number that is greater than itself plus 1. This inequality has no solution and its solution set is $\emptyset$, the empty set.

By contrast, some inequalities are true for all real numbers. An example of such an inequality is

$$x < x + 1.$$

Every real number is less than itself plus 1. The solution set is $\{x \mid x \text{ is a real number}\}$ or $\mathbb{R}$. In interval notation, the solution set is $(-\infty, \infty)$.

If you attempt to solve an inequality that has no solution, you will eliminate the variable and obtain a false statement, such as $0 > 1$. If you attempt to solve an inequality that is true for all real numbers, you will eliminate the variable and obtain a true statement, such as $0 < 1$.

EXAMPLE 5 Solving Linear Inequalities

Solve each inequality:

a. $2(x + 4) > 2x + 3$ **b.** $x + 7 \leq x - 2$.

Solution

a.

$2(x + 4) > 2x + 3$	This is the given inequality.
$2x + 8 > 2x + 3$	Apply the distributive property.
$2x + 8 - 2x > 2x + 3 - 2x$	Subtract 2x from both sides.
$8 > 3$	Simplify. The statement $8 > 3$ is true.

The inequality $8 > 3$ is true for all values of x. Because this inequality is equivalent to the original inequality, the original inequality is true for all real numbers. The solution set is

$$\{x \mid x \text{ is a real number}\} \text{ or } \mathbb{R} \text{ or } (-\infty, \infty).$$

b.

$x + 7 \leq x - 2$	This is the given inequality.
$x + 7 - x \leq x - 2 - x$	Subtract x from both sides.
$7 \leq -2$	Simplify. The statement $7 \leq -2$ is false.

The inequality $7 \leq -2$ is false for all values of x. Because this inequality is equivalent to the original inequality, the original inequality has no solution. The solution set is $\emptyset$.

Check Point **5** Solve each inequality:

a. $3(x + 1) > 3x + 2$ **b.** $x + 1 \leq x - 1$.

Solving Compound Inequalities

We now consider two inequalities such as

$$-3 < 2x + 1 \quad \text{and} \quad 2x + 1 \leq 3$$

expressed as a **compound inequality**

$$-3 < 2x + 1 \leq 3.$$

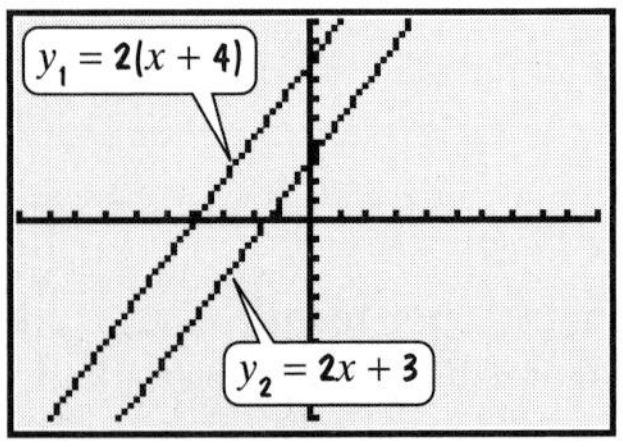

The word "and" does not appear when the inequality is written in the shorter form, although intersection is implied. The shorter form enables us to solve both inequalities at once. By performing the same operation on all three parts of the inequality, our goal is to **isolate x in the middle.**

Technology

To check Example 6, graph each part of

$$-3 < 2x + 1 \le 3.$$

Enter $y_1 = -3$. Enter $y_2 = 2x + 1$. Enter $y_3 = 3$.

The figure shows that the graph of $y_2 = 2x + 1$ lies above the graph of $y_1 = -3$ and on or below the graph of $y_3 = 3$ when x is in the interval $(-2, 1]$.

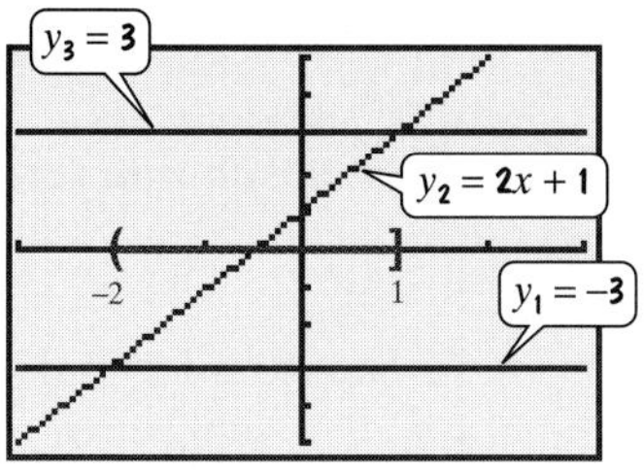

$[-3, 3, 1]$ by $[-5, 5, 1]$

EXAMPLE 6 Solving a Compound Inequality

Solve and graph the solution set on a number line:

$$-3 < 2x + 1 \le 3.$$

Solution We would like to isolate x in the middle. We can do this by first subtracting 1 from all three parts of the compound inequality. Then we isolate x from $2x$ by dividing all three parts of the inequality by 2.

$$-3 < 2x + 1 \le 3 \quad \text{This is the given inequality.}$$

$$-3 - 1 < 2x + 1 - 1 \le 3 - 1 \quad \text{Subtract 1 from all three parts.}$$

$$-4 < 2x \le 2 \quad \text{Simplify.}$$

$$\frac{-4}{2} < \frac{2x}{2} \le \frac{2}{2} \quad \text{Divide each part by 2.}$$

$$-2 < x \le 1 \quad \text{Simplify.}$$

The solution set consists of all real numbers greater than -2 and less than or equal to 1, represented by $\{x|-2 < x \le 1\}$ in set-builder notation and $(-2, 1]$ in interval notation. The graph is shown as follows:

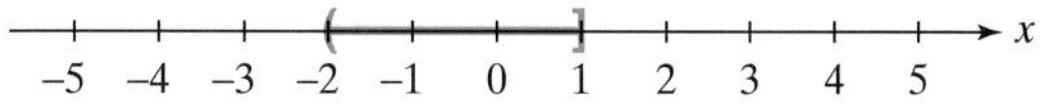

Check Point 6 Solve and graph the solution set on a number line: $1 \le 2x + 3 < 11$.

6 Solve absolute value inequalities.

Solving Inequalities with Absolute Value

We know that $|x|$ describes the distance of x from zero on a real number line. We can use this geometric interpretation to solve an inequality such as

$$|x| < 2.$$

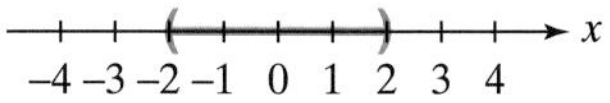

Figure 1.27 $|x| < 2$, so $-2 < x < 2$.

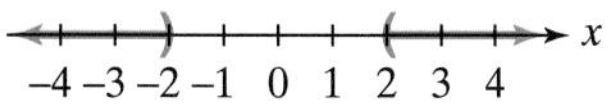

Figure 1.28 $|x| > 2$, so $x < -2$ or $x > 2$.

This means that the distance of x from 0 is *less than* 2, as shown in Figure 1.27. The interval shows values of x that lie less than 2 units from 0. Thus, x can lie between -2 and 2. That is, x is greater than -2 and less than 2. We write $(-2, 2)$ or $\{x|-2 < x < 2.\}$

Some absolute value inequalities use the "greater than" symbol. For example, $|x| > 2$ means that the distance of x from 0 is *greater than* 2, as shown in Figure 1.28. Thus, x can be less than -2 *or* greater than 2. We write $x < -2$ or $x > 2$.

These observations suggest the following principles for solving inequalities with absolute value.

Study Tip

In the $|X| < c$ case, we have one compound inequality to solve. In the $|X| > c$ case, we have two separate inequalities to solve.

Solving an Absolute Value Inequality

If X is an algebraic expression and c is a positive number,

1. The solutions of $|X| < c$ are the numbers that satisfy $-c < X < c$.
2. The solutions of $|X| > c$ are the numbers that satisfy $X < -c$ or $X > c$.

These rules are valid if $<$ is replaced by $\le$ and $>$ is replaced by $\ge$.

EXAMPLE 7 Solving an Absolute Value Inequality

Solve and graph the solution set on a number line: $|x - 4| < 3$.

Solution We rewrite the inequality without absolute value bars.

$$|x - 4| < 3 \quad \text{means} \quad -3 < x - 4 < 3.$$

We solve the compound inequality by adding 4 to all three parts.

$$-3 < x - 4 < 3$$
$$-3 + 4 < x - 4 + 4 < 3 + 4$$
$$1 < x < 7$$

The solution set is all real numbers greater than 1 and less than 7, denoted by $\{x | 1 < x < 7\}$ or $(1, 7)$. The graph of the solution set is shown as follows:

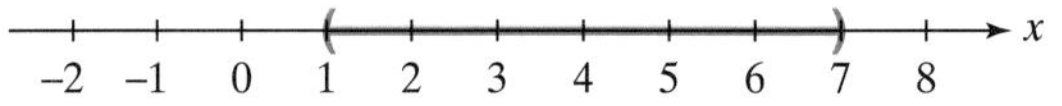

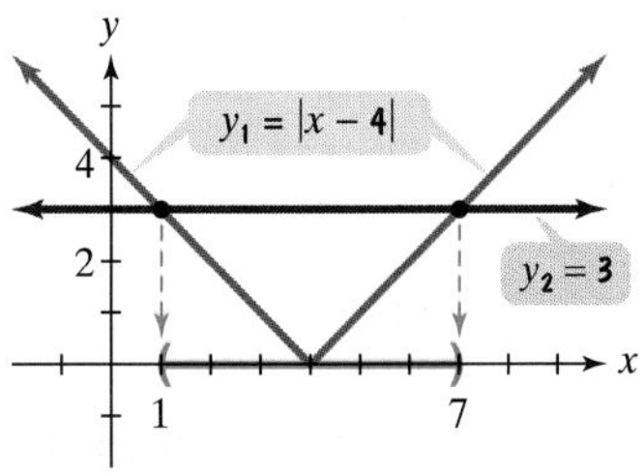

Figure 1.29 The solution set of $|x - 4| < 3$ is $(1, 7)$.

We can use the rectangular coordinate system to visualize the solution set of

$$|x - 4| < 3.$$

Figure 1.29 shows the graphs of $y_1 = |x - 4|$ and $y_2 = 3$. The solution set of $|x - 4| < 3$ consists of all values of x for which the blue graph of y_1 lies below the red graph of y_2. These x-values make up the interval $(1, 7)$, which is the solution set.

Check Point 7 Solve and graph the solution set on a number line: $|x - 2| < 5$.

EXAMPLE 8 Solving an Absolute Value Inequality

Solve and graph the solution set on a number line: $-2|3x + 5| + 7 \geq -13$.

Solution

$-2	3x + 5	+ 7 \geq -13$	This is the given inequality.

We need to isolate $|3x + 5|$, the absolute value expression.

$-2	3x + 5	+ 7 - 7 \geq -13 - 7$	Subtract 7 from both sides.
$-2	3x + 5	\geq -20$	Simplify.
$\dfrac{-2	3x + 5	}{-2} \leq \dfrac{-20}{-2}$	Divide both sides by -2 and change the sense of the inequality.
$	3x + 5	\leq 10$	Simplify.
$-10 \leq 3x + 5 \leq 10$	Rewrite without absolute value bars: $	X	\leq c$ means $-c \leq X \leq c$.

Now we need to isolate x in the middle.

$-10 - 5 \leq 3x + 5 - 5 \leq 10 - 5$	Subtract 5 from all three parts.
$-15 \leq 3x \leq 5$	Simplify.
$\dfrac{-15}{3} \leq \dfrac{3x}{3} \leq \dfrac{5}{3}$	Divide each part by 3.
$-5 \leq x \leq \dfrac{5}{3}$	Simplify.

The solution set is $\{x \mid -5 \le x \le \frac{5}{3}\}$ in set-builder notation and $\left[-5, \frac{5}{3}\right]$ in interval notation. The graph is shown as follows:

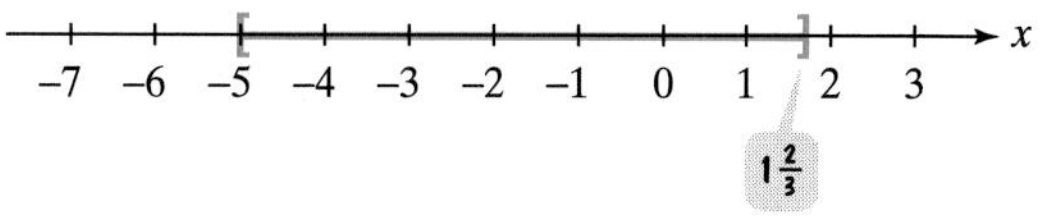

Check Point 8 Solve and graph the solution set on a number line: $-3|5x - 2| + 20 \ge -19$.

EXAMPLE 9 Solving an Absolute Value Inequality

Solve and graph the solution set on a number line: $7 < |5 - 2x|$.

Solution We begin by expressing the inequality with the absolute value expression on the left side:

$$|5 - 2x| > 7.$$

$c < |X|$ means the same thing as $|X| > c$. In both cases, the inequality symbol points to c.

We rewrite this inequality without absolute value bars.

$|X| > c$ means $X < -c$ or $X > c$.

$$|5 - 2x| > 7 \text{ means } 5 - 2x < -7 \text{ or } 5 - 2x > 7.$$

We solve each of these inequalities separately. Then we take the union of their solution sets.

$5 - 2x < -7$	or	$5 - 2x > 7$	These are the inequalities without absolute value bars.
$5 - 5 - 2x < -7 - 5$		$5 - 5 - 2x > 7 - 5$	Subtract 5 from both sides.
$-2x < -12$		$-2x > 2$	Simplify.
$\frac{-2x}{-2} > \frac{-12}{-2}$		$\frac{-2x}{-2} < \frac{2}{-2}$	Divide both sides by -2 and change the sense of the inequality.
$x > 6$		$x < -1$	Simplify.

The solution set consists of all numbers that are less than -1 or greater than 6. The solution set is $\{x \mid x < -1 \text{ or } x > 6\}$, or, in interval notation $(-\infty, -1) \cup (6, \infty)$. The graph of the solution set is shown as follows:

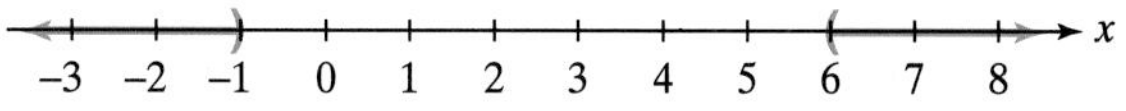

Study Tip

The graph of the solution set for $|X| > c$ will be divided into two intervals whose union cannot be represented as a single interval. The graph of the solution set for $|X| < c$ will be a single interval. Avoid the common error of rewriting $|X| > c$ as $-c < X > c$.

Check Point 9 Solve and graph the solution set on a number line: $18 < |6 - 3x|$.

Applications

Our next example shows how to use an inequality to select the better deal between two pricing options. We use our strategy for solving word problems, translating from the verbal conditions of the problem to a linear inequality.

EXAMPLE 10 Selecting the Better Deal

Acme Car rental agency charges $4 a day plus $0.15 per mile, whereas Interstate rental agency charges $20 a day and $0.05 per mile. How many miles must be driven to make the daily cost of an Acme rental a better deal than an Interstate rental?

Solution

Step 1 Let x represent one of the quantities. We are looking for the number of miles that must be driven in a day to make Acme the better deal. Thus,

$$\text{let } x = \text{the number of miles driven in a day.}$$

Step 2 Represent other quantities in terms of x. We are not asked to find another quantity, so we can skip this step.

Step 3 Write an inequality in x that models the conditions. Acme is a better deal than Interstate if the daily cost of Acme is less than the daily cost of Interstate.

$$4 \quad + \quad 0.15 \cdot x \quad\quad < \quad\quad 20 \quad + \quad 0.05 \cdot x$$

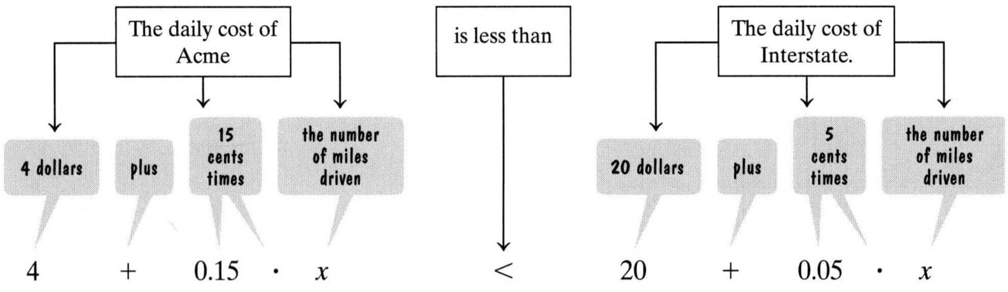

Technology

The graphs of the daily cost models for the car rental agencies

$$y_1 = 4 + 0.15x$$
$$\text{and } y_2 = 20 + 0.05x$$

are shown in a $[0, 300, 10]$ by $[0, 40, 4]$ viewing rectangle. The graphs intersect at $(160, 28)$. To the left of $x = 160$, the graph of Acme's daily cost lies below that of Interstate's daily cost. This shows that for fewer than 160 miles per day, Acme offers the better deal.

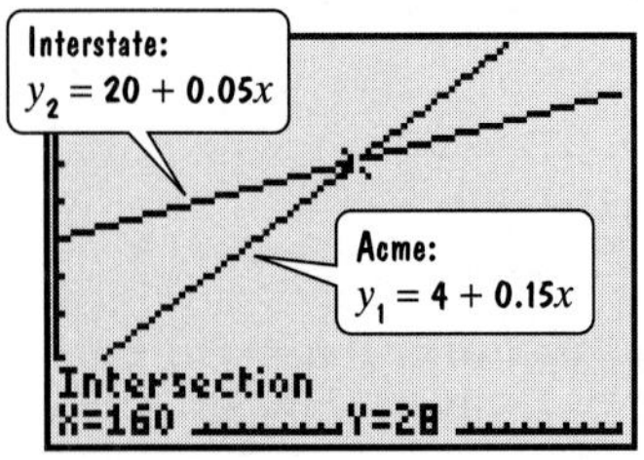

Step 4 Solve the inequality and answer the question.

$4 + 0.15x < 20 + 0.05x$	This is the inequality that models the verbal conditions.
$4 + 0.15x - 0.05x < 20 + 0.05x - 0.05x$	Subtract 0.05x from both sides.
$4 + 0.1x < 20$	Simplify.
$4 + 0.1x - 4 < 20 - 4$	Subtract 4 from both sides.
$0.1x < 16$	Simplify.
$\dfrac{0.1x}{0.1} < \dfrac{16}{0.1}$	Divide both sides by 0.1.
$x < 160$	Simplify.

Thus, driving fewer than 160 miles per day makes Acme the better deal.

Step 5 Check the proposed solution in the original wording of the problem. One way to do this is to take a mileage less than 160 miles per day to see if Acme is the better deal. Suppose that 150 miles are driven in a day.

$$\text{Cost for Acme} = 4 + 0.15(150) = 26.50$$
$$\text{Cost for Interstate} = 20 + 0.05(150) = 27.50$$

Acme has a lower daily cost, making Acme the better deal.

Check Point 10 A car can be rented from Basic Rental for $260 per week with no extra charge for mileage. Continental charges $80 per week plus 25 cents for each mile driven to rent the same car. How many miles must be driven in a week to make the rental cost for Basic Rental a better deal than Continental's?

EXERCISE SET 1.7

Practice Exercises

In Exercises 1–14, express each interval in set-builder notation and graph the interval on a number line.

1. $(1, 6]$
2. $(-2, 4]$
3. $[-5, 2)$
4. $[-4, 3)$
5. $[-3, 1]$
6. $[-2, 5]$
7. $(2, \infty)$
8. $(3, \infty)$
9. $[-3, \infty)$
10. $[-5, \infty)$
11. $(-\infty, 3)$
12. $(-\infty, 2)$
13. $(-\infty, 5.5)$
14. $(-\infty, 3.5]$

In Exercises 15–26, use graphs to find each set.

15. $(-3, 0) \cap [-1, 2]$
16. $(-4, 0) \cap [-2, 1]$
17. $(-3, 0) \cup [-1, 2]$
18. $(-4, 0) \cup [-2, 1]$
19. $(-\infty, 5) \cap [1, 8)$
20. $(-\infty, 6) \cap [2, 9)$
21. $(-\infty, 5) \cup [1, 8)$
22. $(-\infty, 6) \cup [2, 9)$
23. $[3, \infty) \cap (6, \infty)$
24. $[2, \infty) \cap (4, \infty)$
25. $[3, \infty) \cup (6, \infty)$
26. $[2, \infty) \cup (4, \infty)$

In all exercises, other than ∅, use interval notation to express solution sets and graph each solution set on a number line.

In Exercises 27–50, solve each linear inequality.

27. $5x + 11 < 26$
28. $2x + 5 < 17$
29. $3x - 7 \geq 13$
30. $8x - 2 \geq 14$
31. $-9x \geq 36$
32. $-5x \leq 30$
33. $8x - 11 \leq 3x - 13$
34. $18x + 45 \leq 12x - 8$
35. $4(x + 1) + 2 \geq 3x + 6$
36. $8x + 3 > 3(2x + 1) + x + 5$
37. $2x - 11 < -3(x + 2)$
38. $-4(x + 2) > 3x + 20$
39. $1 - (x + 3) \geq 4 - 2x$
40. $5(3 - x) \leq 3x - 1$
41. $\frac{x}{4} - \frac{3}{2} \leq \frac{x}{2} + 1$
42. $\frac{3x}{10} + 1 \geq \frac{1}{5} - \frac{x}{10}$
43. $1 - \frac{x}{2} > 4$
44. $7 - \frac{4}{5}x < \frac{3}{5}$
45. $\frac{x - 4}{6} \geq \frac{x - 2}{9} + \frac{5}{18}$
46. $\frac{4x - 3}{6} + 2 \geq \frac{2x - 1}{12}$
47. $4(3x - 2) - 3x < 3(1 + 3x) - 7$
48. $3(x - 8) - 2(10 - x) > 5(x - 1)$
49. $5(x - 2) - 3(x + 4) \geq 2x - 20$
50. $6(x - 1) - (4 - x) \geq 7x - 8$

In Exercises 51–58, solve each compound inequality.

51. $6 < x + 3 < 8$
52. $7 < x + 5 < 11$
53. $-3 \leq x - 2 < 1$
54. $-6 < x - 4 \leq 1$
55. $-11 < 2x - 1 \leq -5$
56. $3 \leq 4x - 3 < 19$
57. $-3 \leq \frac{2}{3}x - 5 < -1$
58. $-6 \leq \frac{1}{2}x - 4 < -3$

In Exercises 59–94, solve each absolute value inequality.

59. $|x| < 3$
60. $|x| < 5$
61. $|x - 1| \leq 2$
62. $|x + 3| \leq 4$
63. $|2x - 6| < 8$
64. $|3x + 5| < 17$
65. $|2(x - 1) + 4| \leq 8$
66. $|3(x - 1) + 2| \leq 20$
67. $\left|\frac{2x + 6}{3}\right| < 2$
68. $\left|\frac{3(x - 1)}{4}\right| < 6$
69. $|x| > 3$
70. $|x| > 5$
71. $|x - 1| \geq 2$
72. $|x + 3| \geq 4$
73. $|3x - 8| > 7$
74. $|5x - 2| > 13$
75. $\left|\frac{2x + 2}{4}\right| \geq 2$
76. $\left|\frac{3x - 3}{9}\right| \geq 1$
77. $\left|3 - \frac{2}{3}x\right| > 5$
78. $\left|3 - \frac{3}{4}x\right| > 9$
79. $3|x - 1| + 2 \geq 8$
80. $5|2x + 1| - 3 \geq 9$
81. $-2|x - 4| \geq -4$
82. $-3|x + 7| \geq -27$
83. $-4|1 - x| < -16$
84. $-2|5 - x| < -6$
85. $3 \leq |2x - 1|$
86. $9 \leq |4x + 7|$
87. $5 > |4 - x|$
88. $2 > |11 - x|$
89. $1 < |2 - 3x|$
90. $4 < |2 - x|$
91. $12 < \left|-2x + \frac{6}{7}\right| + \frac{3}{7}$
92. $1 < \left|x - \frac{11}{3}\right| + \frac{7}{3}$
93. $4 + \left|3 - \frac{x}{3}\right| \geq 9$
94. $\left|2 - \frac{x}{2}\right| - 1 \leq 1$

In Exercises 95–102, use interval notation to represent all values of x satisfying the given conditions.

95. $y_1 = \frac{x}{2} + 3$, $y_2 = \frac{x}{3} + \frac{5}{2}$, and $y_1 \leq y_2$.
96. $y_1 = \frac{2}{3}(6x - 9) + 4$, $y_2 = 5x + 1$, and $y_1 > y_2$.
97. $y = 1 - (x + 3) + 2x$ and y is at least 4.
98. $y = 2x - 11 + 3(x + 2)$ and y is at most 0.
99. $y = |3x - 4| + 2$ and $y < 8$.
100. $y = |2x - 5| + 1$ and $y > 9$.
101. $y = 7 - \left|\frac{x}{2} + 2\right|$ and y is at most 4.
102. $y = 8 - |5x + 3|$ and y is at least 6.

Practice Plus

In Exercises 103–104, use the graph of $y = |4 - x|$ to solve each inequality.

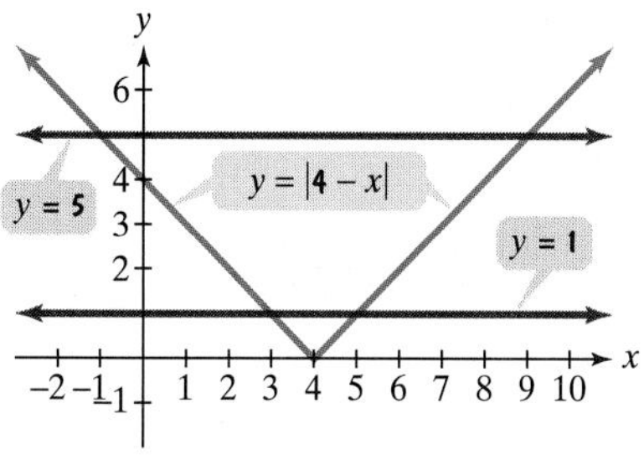

103. $|4 - x| < 5$
104. $|4 - x| \geq 5$

In Exercises 105–106, use the table to solve each inequality.

105. $-2 \le 5x + 3 < 13$

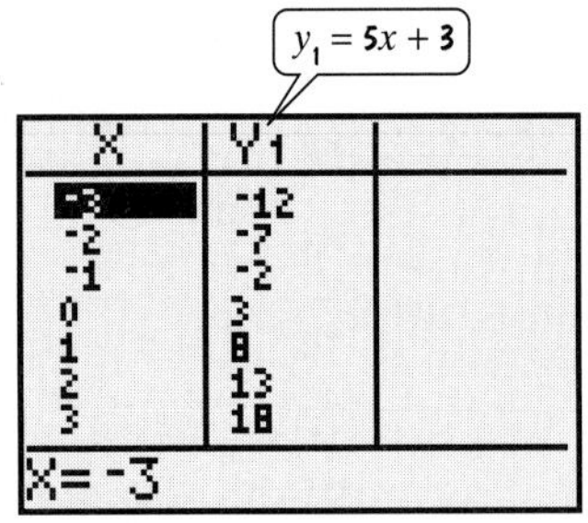

106. $-3 < 2x - 5 \le 3$

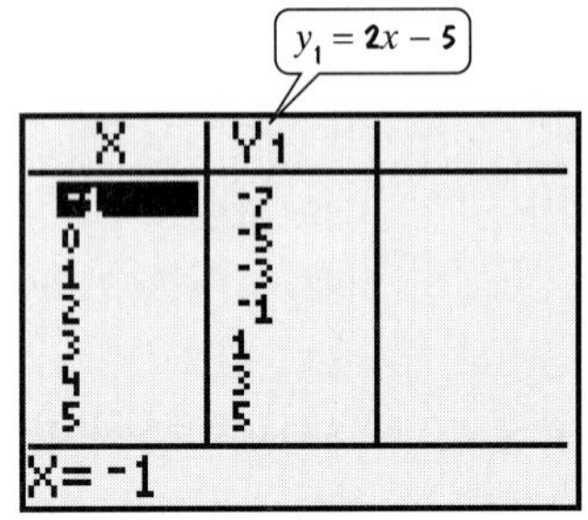

107. When 3 times a number is subtracted from 4, the absolute value of the difference is at least 5. Use interval notation to express the set of all numbers that satisfy this condition.

108. When 4 times a number is subtracted from 5, the absolute value of the difference is at most 13. Use interval notation to express the set of all numbers that satisfy this condition.

Application Exercises

The graphs show that the three components of love, namely passion, intimacy, and commitment, progress differently over time. Passion peaks early in a relationship and then declines. By contrast, intimacy and commitment build gradually. Use the graphs to solve Exercises 109–116.

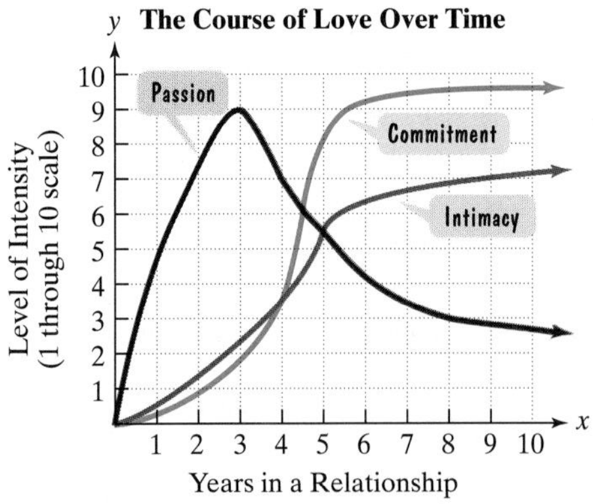

Source: R. J. Sternberg. A Triangular Theory of Love, *Psychological Review*, 93, 119–135.

109. Use interval notation to write an inequality that expresses for which years in a relationship intimacy is greater than commitment.

110. Use interval notation to write an inequality that expresses for which years in a relationship passion is greater than or equal to intimacy.

111. What is the relationship between passion and intimacy on the interval $[5, 7)$?

112. What is the relationship between intimacy and commitment on the interval $[4, 7)$?

113. What is the relationship between passion and commitment for $\{x|6 < x < 8\}$?

114. What is the relationship between passion and commitment for $\{x|7 < x < 9\}$?

115. What is the maximum level of intensity for passion? After how many years in a relationship does this occur?

116. After approximately how many years do levels of intensity for commitment exceed the maximum level of intensity for passion?

117. The percentage, P, of U.S. voters who used electronic voting systems, such as optical scans, in national elections can be modeled by the formula

$$P = 3.1x + 25.8,$$

where x is the number of years after 1994. In which years will more than 63% of U.S. voters use electronic systems?

118. The percentage, P, of U.S. voters who used punch cards or lever machines in national elections can be modeled by the formula

$$P = -2.5x + 63.1,$$

where x is the number of years after 1994. In which years will fewer than 38.1% of U.S. voters use punch cards or lever machines?

119. A basic cellular phone plan costs \$20 per month for 60 calling minutes. Additional time costs \$0.40 per minute. The formula

$$C = 20 + 0.40(x - 60)$$

gives the monthly cost for this plan, C, for x calling minutes, where $x > 60$. How many calling minutes are possible for a monthly cost of at least \$28 and at most \$40?

120. The formula for converting Fahrenheit temperature, F, to Celsius temperature, C, is

$$C = \frac{5}{9}(F - 32).$$

If Celsius temperature ranges from 15° to 35°, inclusive, what is the range for the Fahrenheit temperature? Use interval notation to express this range.

121. If a coin is tossed 100 times, we would expect approximately 50 of the outcomes to be heads. It can be demonstrated that a coin is unfair if h, the number of outcomes that result in heads, satisfies $\left|\frac{h - 50}{5}\right| \ge 1.645$. Describe the number of outcomes that determine an unfair coin that is tossed 100 times.

In Exercises 122–133, use the strategy for solving word problems, translating from the verbal conditions of the problem to a linear inequality.

122. A truck can be rented from Basic Rental for \$50 per day plus \$0.20 per mile. Continental charges \$20 per day plus \$0.50 per mile to rent the same truck. How many miles must be driven in a day to make the rental cost for Basic Rental a better deal than Continental's?

123. You are choosing between two long-distance telephone plans. Plan A has a monthly fee of \$15 with a charge of \$0.08 per minute for all long-distance calls. Plan B has a monthly fee of \$3 with a charge of \$0.12 per minute for all long-distance calls. How many minutes of long-distance calls in a month make plan A the better deal?

124. A city commission has proposed two tax bills. The first bill requires that a homeowner pay \$1800 plus 3% of the assessed home value in taxes. The second bill requires taxes of \$200 plus 8% of the assessed home value. What price range of home assessment would make the first bill a better deal?

125. A local bank charges \$8 per month plus 5¢ per check. The credit union charges \$2 per month plus 8¢ per check. How many checks should be written each month to make the credit union a better deal?

126. A company manufactures and sells blank audiocassette tapes. The weekly fixed cost is \$10,000 and it costs \$0.40 to produce each tape. The selling price is \$2.00 per tape. How many tapes must be produced and sold each week for the company to generate a profit?

127. A company manufactures and sells personalized stationery. The weekly fixed cost is \$3000 and it costs \$3.00 to produce each package of stationery. The selling price is \$5.50 per package. How many packages of stationery must be produced and sold each week for the company to generate a profit?

128. An elevator at a construction site has a maximum capacity of 2800 pounds. If the elevator operator weighs 265 pounds and each cement bag weighs 65 pounds, how many bags of cement can be safely lifted on the elevator in one trip?

129. An elevator at a construction site has a maximum capacity of 3000 pounds. If the elevator operator weighs 245 pounds and each cement bag weighs 95 pounds, how many bags of cement can be safely lifted on the elevator in one trip?

130. To earn an A in a course, you must have a final average of at least 90%. On the first four examinations, you have grades of 86%, 88%, 92%, and 84%. If the final examination counts as two grades, what must you get on the final to earn an A in the course?

131. On two examinations, you have grades of 86 and 88. There is an optional final examination, which counts as one grade. You decide to take the final in order to get a course grade of A, meaning a final average of at least 90.

a. What must you get on the final to earn an A in the course?

b. By taking the final, if you do poorly, you might risk the B that you have in the course based on the first two exam grades. If your final average is less than 80, you will lose your B in the course. Describe the grades on the final that will cause this to happen.

132. Parts for an automobile repair cost \$175. The mechanic charges \$34 per hour. If you receive an estimate for at least \$226 and at most \$294 for fixing the car, what is the time interval that the mechanic will be working on the job?

133. The toll to a bridge is \$3.00. A three-month pass costs \$7.50 and reduces the toll to \$0.50. A six-month pass costs \$30 and permits crossing the bridge for no additional fee. How many crossings per three-month period does it take for the three-month pass to be the best deal?

Writing in Mathematics

134. When graphing the solutions of an inequality, what does a parenthesis signify? What does a bracket signify?

135. Describe ways in which solving a linear inequality is similar to solving a linear equation.

136. Describe ways in which solving a linear inequality is different than solving a linear equation.

137. What is a compound inequality and how is it solved?

138. Describe how to solve an absolute value inequality involving the symbol $<$. Give an example.

139. Describe how to solve an absolute value inequality involving the symbol $>$. Give an example.

140. Explain why $|x| < -4$ has no solution.

141. Describe the solution set of $|x| > -4$.

Technology Exercises

In Exercises 142–143, solve each inequality using a graphing utility. Graph each side separately. Then determine the values of x for which the graph for the left side lies above the graph for the right side.

142. $-3(x - 6) > 2x - 2$

143. $-2(x + 4) > 6x + 16$

144. Use a graphing utility's TABLE feature to verify your work in Exercises 142–143.

145. A bank offers two checking account plans. Plan A has a base service charge of \$4.00 per month plus 10¢ per check. Plan B charges a base service charge of \$2.00 per month plus 15¢ per check.

a. Write models for the total monthly costs for each plan if x checks are written.

b. Use a graphing utility to graph the models in the same [0, 50, 10] by [0, 10, 1] viewing rectangle.

c. Use the graphs (and the intersection feature) to determine for what number of checks per month plan A will be better than plan B.

d. Verify the result of part (c) algebraically by solving an inequality.

Critical Thinking Exercises

146. Which one of the following is true?

a. The first step in solving $|2x - 3| > -7$ is to rewrite the inequality as $2x - 3 > -7$ or $2x - 3 < 7$.

b. The smallest real number in the solution set of $2x > 6$ is 4.

c. All irrational numbers satisfy $|x - 4| > 0$.

d. None of these statements is true.

147. What's wrong with this argument? Suppose x and y represent two real numbers, where $x > y$.

$2 > 1$	This is a true statement.
$2(y - x) > 1(y - x)$	Multiply both sides by $y - x$.
$2y - 2x > y - x$	Use the distributive property.
$y - 2x > -x$	Subtract y from both sides.
$y > x$	Add $2x$ to both sides.

The final inequality, $y > x$, is impossible because we were initially given $x > y$.

148. Write an absolute value inequality for which the interval shown is the solution.

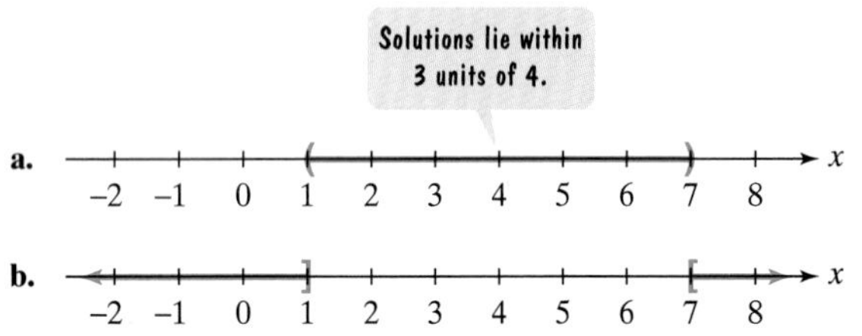

149. Here are two inequalities that describe the range of monthly average temperatures, T, in degrees Fahrenheit for two American cities:

Model 1: $|T - 57| < 7$

Model 2: $|T - 50| < 22$.

Which model describes Albany, New York, and which model describes San Francisco, California?

Group Exercise

150. Each group member should research one situation that provides two different pricing options. These can involve areas such as public transportation options (with or without coupon books), cell phone plans, long-distance telephone plans, or anything of interest. Be sure to bring in all the details for each option. At a second group meeting, select the two pricing situations that are most interesting and relevant. Using each situation, write a word problem about selecting the better of the two options. The word problem should be one that can be solved using a linear inequality. The group should turn in the two problems and their solutions.

Chapter 1 Summary, Review, and Test

Summary

1.1 Graphs and Graphing Utilities

DEFINITIONS AND CONCEPTS	EXAMPLES
a. The rectangular coordinate system consists of a horizontal number line, the x-axis, and a vertical number line, the y-axis, intersecting at their zero points, the origin. Each point in the system corresponds to an ordered pair of real numbers (x, y). The first number in the pair is the x-coordinate; the second number is the y-coordinate. See Figure 1.1 on page 84.	Ex. 1, p. 85
b. An ordered pair is a solution of an equation in two variables if replacing the variables by the corresponding coordinates results in a true statement. The ordered pair is said to satisfy the equation. The graph of the equation is the set of all points whose coordinates satisfy the equation. One method for graphing an equation is to plot ordered-pair solutions and connect them with a smooth curve or line.	Ex. 2, p. 86; Ex. 3, p. 86
c. An x-intercept of a graph is the x-coordinate of a point where the graph intersects the x-axis. The y-coordinate corresponding to an x-intercept is always zero. A y-intercept of a graph is the y-coordinate of a point where the graph intersects the y-axis. The x-coordinate corresponding to a y-intercept is always zero.	Ex. 5, p. 89

1.2 Linear Equations and Rational Equations

DEFINITIONS AND CONCEPTS	EXAMPLES
a. A linear equation in one variable x can be written in the form $ax + b = 0, a \neq 0$.	
b. The procedure for solving a linear equation is given in the box on page 97.	Ex. 1, p. 96; Ex. 2, p. 97
c. If an equation contains fractions, begin by multiplying both sides by the least common denominator, thereby clearing fractions.	Ex. 3, p. 99
d. A rational equation is an equation containing one or more rational expressions. If an equation contains rational expressions with variable denominators, avoid in the solution set any values of the variable that make a denominator zero.	Ex. 4, p. 100; Ex. 5, p. 101; Ex. 6, p. 101
e. An identity is an equation that is true for all real numbers for which both sides are defined. A conditional equation is not an identity and is true for at least one real number. An inconsistent equation is an equation that is not true for even one real number.	Ex. 7, p. 103

1.3 Models and Applications

a. A five-step procedure for solving word problems using equations that model verbal conditions is given in the box on page 108. — Ex. 1, p. 108; Ex. 2, p. 110; Ex. 3, p. 111; Ex. 4, p. 113; Ex. 5, p. 114; Ex. 6, p. 115

b. Solving a formula for a variable means rewriting the formula so that the variable is isolated on one side of the equation. — Ex. 7, p. 117; Ex. 8, p. 117

1.4 Complex Numbers

a. The imaginary unit i is defined as

$$i = \sqrt{-1}, \text{ where } i^2 = -1.$$

The set of numbers in the form $a + bi$ is called the set of complex numbers; a is the real part and b is the imaginary part. If $b = 0$, the complex number is a real number. If $b \neq 0$, the complex number is an imaginary number. Complex numbers in the form bi are called pure imaginary numbers.

b. Rules for adding and subtracting complex numbers are given in the box on page 124. — Ex. 1, p. 124

c. To multiply complex numbers, multiply as if they are polynomials. After completing the multiplication, replace i^2 with -1 and simplify. — Ex. 2, p. 125

d. The complex conjugate of $a + bi$ is $a - bi$ and vice versa. The multiplication of complex conjugates gives a real number:

$$(a + bi)(a - bi) = a^2 + b^2.$$

e. To divide complex numbers, multiply the numerator and the denominator by the complex conjugate of the denominator. — Ex. 3, p. 126

f. When performing operations with square roots of negative numbers, begin by expressing all square roots in terms of i. The principal square root of $-b$ is defined by — Ex. 4, p. 127

$$\sqrt{-b} = i\sqrt{b}.$$

1.5 Quadratic Equations

a. A quadratic equation in x can be written in the general form $ax^2 + bx + c = 0, a \neq 0$.

b. The procedure for solving a quadratic equation by factoring and the zero-product principle is given in the box on page 131. — Ex. 1, p. 131

c. The procedure for solving a quadratic equation by the square root property is given in the box on page 132. — Ex. 2, p. 133

d. All quadratic equations can be solved by completing the square. Isolate the binomial with the two variable terms on one side of the equation. If the coefficient of the x^2-term is not one, divide each side of the equation by this coefficient. Then add the square of half the coefficient of x to both sides. — Ex. 4, p. 135; Ex. 5, p. 136

e. All quadratic equations can be solved by the quadratic formula — Ex. 6, p. 138; Ex. 7, p. 139

$$x = \frac{-b \pm \sqrt{b^2 - 4ac}}{2a}.$$

The formula is derived by completing the square of the equation $ax^2 + bx + c = 0$.

f. The discriminant, $b^2 - 4ac$, indicates the number and type of solutions to the quadratic equation $ax^2 + bx + c = 0$, shown in Table 1.3 on page 140. — Ex. 8, p. 140

g. Table 1.4 on page 141 shows the most efficient technique to use when solving a quadratic equation. — Ex. 9, p. 142; Ex. 10, p. 143

1.6 Other Types of Equations

a. Some polynomial equations of degree 3 or greater can be solved by moving all terms to one side, obtaining zero on the other side, factoring, and using the zero-product principle. Factoring by grouping is often used. — Ex. 1, p. 151; Ex. 2, p. 151

b. A radical equation is an equation in which the variable occurs in a square root, cube root, and so on. A radical equation can be solved by isolating the radical and raising both sides of the equation to a power equal to the radical's index. When raising both sides to an even power, check all proposed solutions in the original equation. Eliminate extraneous solutions from the solution set. — Ex. 3, p. 153; Ex. 4, p. 154

c. A radical equation with rational exponents can be solved by isolating the expression with the rational exponent and raising both sides of the equation to a power that is the reciprocal of the rational exponent. See the details in the box on page 156. — Ex. 5, p. 156

d. An equation is quadratic in form if it can be written in the form $au^2 + bu + c = 0$, where u is an algebraic expression and $a \neq 0$. Solve for u and use the substitution that resulted in this equation to find the values for the variable in the given equation. Ex. 6, p. 157; Ex. 7, p. 158

e. Absolute value equations in the form $|X| = c, c > 0$, can be solved by rewriting the equation without absolute value bars: $X = c$ or $X = -c$. Ex. 8, p. 159; Ex. 9, p. 159

1.7 Linear Inequalities and Absolute Value Inequalities

a. Solution sets of inequalities are expressed using set-builder notation and interval notation. In interval notation, parentheses indicate endpoints that are not included in an interval. Square brackets indicate endpoints that are included in an interval. See Table 1.5 on page 165. Ex. 1, p. 166

b. A procedure for finding intersections and unions of intervals is given in the box on page 166. Ex. 2, p. 166

c. A linear inequality in one variable x can be expressed as $ax + b \leq c, ax + b < c, ax + b \geq c$, or $ax + b > c, a \neq 0$.

d. A linear inequality is solved using a procedure similar to solving a linear equation. However, when multiplying or dividing by a negative number, change the sense of the inequality. Ex. 3, p. 168; Ex. 4, p. 169; Ex. 5, p. 170

e. A compound inequality with three parts can be solved by isolating the variable in the middle. Ex. 6, p. 171

f. Inequalities involving absolute value can be solved by rewriting the inequalities without absolute value bars. The ways to do this are shown in the box on page 171. Ex. 7, p. 172; Ex. 8, p. 172; Ex. 9, p. 173

Review Exercises

1.1

Graph each equation in Exercises 1–4. Let $x = -3, -2, -1, 0, 1, 2$, and 3.

1. $y = 2x - 2$

2. $y = x^2 - 3$

3. $y = x$

4. $y = |x| - 2$

5. What does a $[-20, 40, 10]$ by $[-5, 5, 1]$ viewing rectangle mean? Draw axes with tick marks and label the tick marks to illustrate this viewing rectangle.

In Exercises 6–8, use the graph and determine the x-intercepts, if any, and the y-intercepts, if any. For each graph, tick marks along the axes represent one unit each.

6.

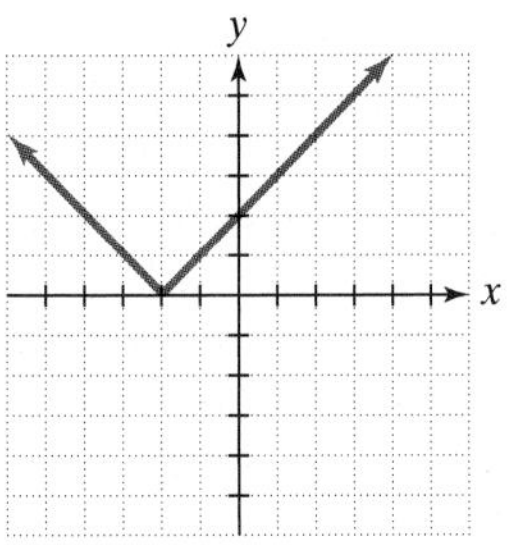

7.

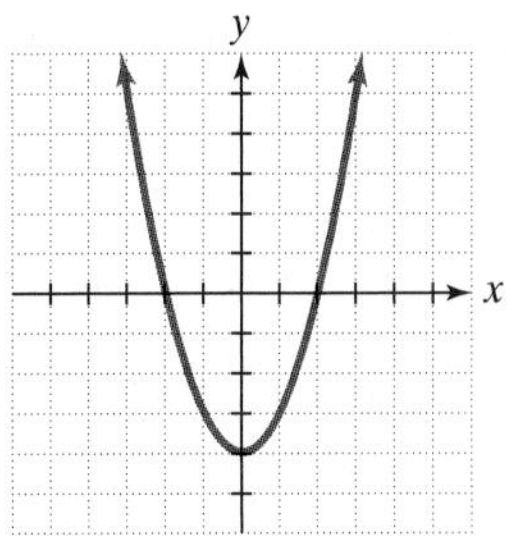

8.

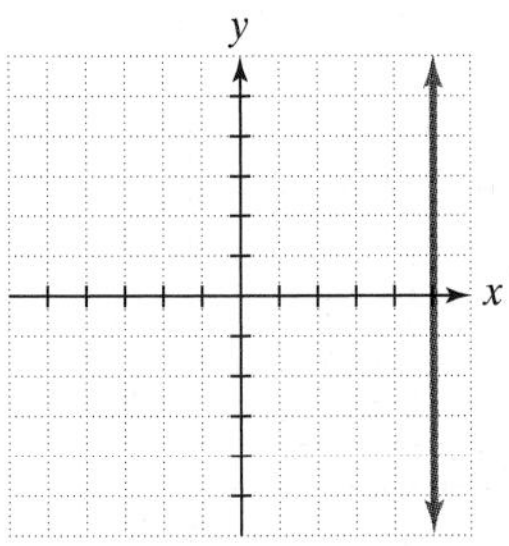

Afghanistan accounts for 76% of the world's illegal opium production. Opium-poppy cultivation nets big money in a country where most people earn less than \$1 per day. (Source: Newsweek) The line graph shows opium-poppy cultivation, in thousands of acres, in Afghanistan from 1990 through 2004. Use the graph to solve Exercises 9–14.

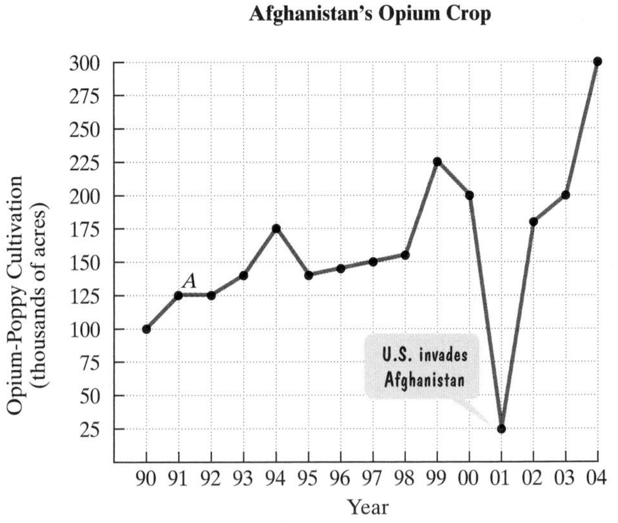

Source: U.N. Office on Drugs and Crime

9. What are the coordinates of point A? What does this mean in terms of the information given by the graph?

10. In which year were 150 thousand acres used for opium-poppy cultivation?

11. For the period shown, when did opium cultivation reach a minimum? How many thousands of acres were used to cultivate the illegal crop?

12. For the period shown, when did opium cultivation reach a maximum? How many thousands of acres were used to cultivate the illegal crop?

13. Between which two years did opium cultivation not change?

14. Between which two years did opium cultivation increase at the greatest rate? What is a reasonable estimate of the increase, in thousands of acres, used to cultivate the illegal crop during this period?

1.2

In Exercises 15–35, solve each equation. Then state whether the equation is an identity, a conditional equation, or an inconsistent equation.

15. $2x - 5 = 7$

16. $5x + 20 = 3x$

17. $7(x - 4) = x + 2$

18. $1 - 2(6 - x) = 3x + 2$

19. $2(x - 4) + 3(x + 5) = 2x - 2$

20. $2x - 4(5x + 1) = 3x + 17$

21. $7x + 5 = 5(x + 3) + 2x$

22. $7x + 13 = 2(2x - 5) + 3x + 23$

23. $\frac{2x}{3} = \frac{x}{6} + 1$

24. $\frac{x}{2} - \frac{1}{10} = \frac{x}{5} + \frac{1}{2}$

25. $\frac{2x}{3} = 6 - \frac{x}{4}$

26. $\frac{x}{4} = 2 - \frac{x - 3}{3}$

27. $\frac{3x + 1}{3} - \frac{13}{2} = \frac{1 - x}{4}$

28. $\frac{9}{4} - \frac{1}{2x} = \frac{4}{x}$

29. $\frac{7}{x - 5} + 2 = \frac{x + 2}{x - 5}$

30. $\frac{1}{x - 1} - \frac{1}{x + 1} = \frac{2}{x^2 - 1}$

31. $\frac{5}{x + 3} + \frac{1}{x - 2} = \frac{8}{x^2 + x - 6}$

32. $\frac{1}{x + 5} = 0$

33. $\frac{4}{x + 2} + \frac{3}{x} = \frac{10}{x^2 + 2x}$

34. $3 - 5(2x + 1) - 2(x - 4) = 0$

35. $\frac{x + 2}{x + 3} + \frac{1}{x^2 + 2x - 3} - 1 = 0$

1.3

In Exercises 36–43, use the five-step strategy for solving word problems.

36. The fast-food chains may be touting their "new and improved" salads, but how do they measure up in terms of calories?

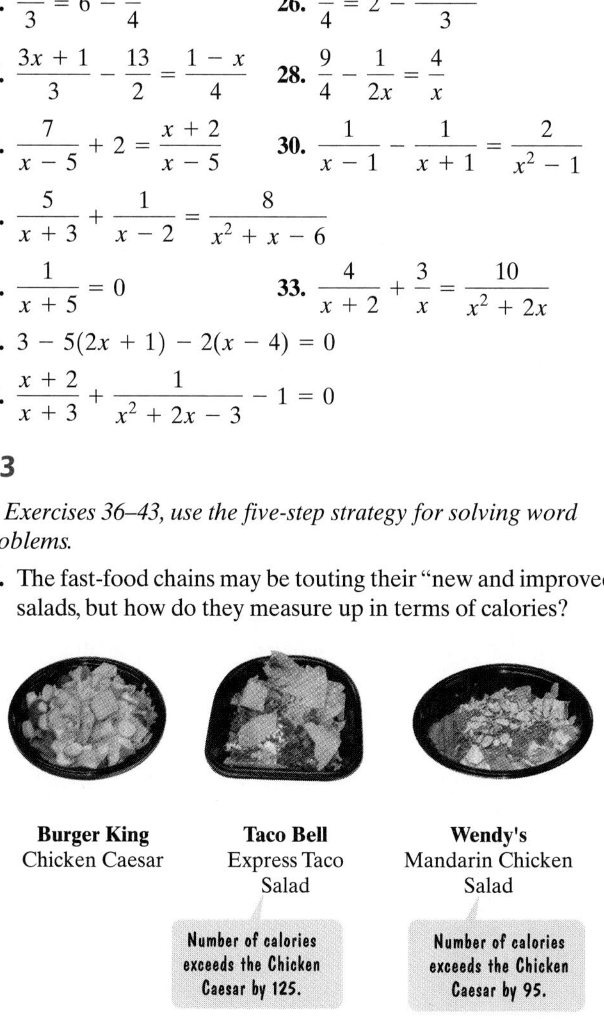
Burger King
Chicken Caesar
Taco Bell
Express Taco Salad
Wendy's
Mandarin Chicken Salad
Number of calories exceeds the Chicken Caesar by 125.
Number of calories exceeds the Chicken Caesar by 95.

Source: Newsweek

Combined, the three salads contain 1705 calories. Determine the number of calories in each salad.

37. The bar graph shows that in 1970, 37.4% of U.S. adults smoked cigarettes. For the period from 1970 through 2002, the percentage of smokers among U.S. adults decreased at an average rate of 0.5% per year. If this trend continues, when will only 18.4% of U.S. adults smoke cigarettes?

Butt Out: Percentage of Cigarette Smokers Among U.S. Adults

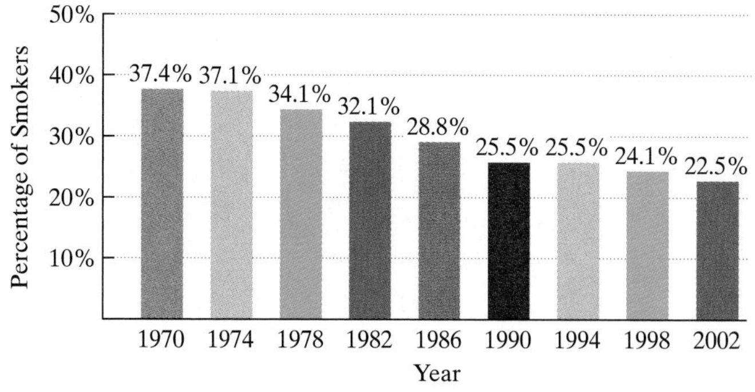

Source: Centers for Disease Control and Prevention

38. You are choosing between two long-distance telephone plans. One plan has a monthly fee of $15 with a charge of $0.05 per minute. The other plan has a monthly fee of $5 with a charge of $0.07 per minute. For how many minutes of long-distance calls will the costs for the two plans be the same?

39. After a 20% price reduction, a cordless phone sold for $48. What was the phone's price before the reduction?

40. A salesperson earns $300 per week plus 5% commission of sales. How much must be sold to earn $800 in a week?

41. You invested $9000 in two funds paying 4% and 7% annual interest, respectively. At the end of the year, the total interest from these investments was $555. How much was invested at each rate?

42. You invested $8000 in two funds paying 2% and 5% annual interest, respectively. At the end of the year, the interest from the 5% investment exceeded the interest from the 2% investment by $85. How much money was invested at each rate?

43. The length of a rectangular field is 6 yards less than triple the width. If the perimeter of the field is 340 yards, what are its dimensions?

44. In 2007, there were 14,100 students at college A, with a projected enrollment increase of 1500 students per year. In the same year, there were 41,700 students at college B, with a projected enrollment decline of 800 students per year.

   a. Let x represent the number of years after 2007. Write, but do not solve, an equation that can be used to find how many years after 2007 the colleges will have the same enrollment.

   b. The following table is based on your equation in part (a). Y_1 represents one side of the equation and Y_2 represents the other side of the equation. Use the table to answer the following questions: In which year will the colleges have the same enrollment? What will be the enrollment in each college at that time?

X	Y1	Y2
7	24600	36100
8	26100	35300
9	27600	34500
10	29100	33700
11	30600	32900
12	32100	32100
13	33600	31300

X=7

In Exercises 45–47, solve each formula for the specified variable.

45. $vt + gt^2 = s$ for g **46.** $T = gr + gvt$ for g

47. $T = \dfrac{A - P}{Pr}$ for P

1.4

In Exercises 48–57, perform the indicated operations and write the result in standard form.

48. $(8 - 3i) - (17 - 7i)$ **49.** $4i(3i - 2)$

50. $(7 - i)(2 + 3i)$ **51.** $(3 - 4i)^2$

52. $(7 + 8i)(7 - 8i)$ **53.** $\dfrac{6}{5 + i}$

54. $\dfrac{3 + 4i}{4 - 2i}$ **55.** $\sqrt{-32} - \sqrt{-18}$

56. $(-2 + \sqrt{-100})^2$ **57.** $\dfrac{4 + \sqrt{-8}}{2}$

1.5

Solve each equation in Exercises 58–59 by factoring.

58. $2x^2 + 15x = 8$ **59.** $5x^2 + 20x = 0$

Solve each equation in Exercises 60–63 by the square root property.

60. $2x^2 - 3 = 125$ **61.** $\dfrac{x^2}{2} + 5 = -3$

62. $(x + 3)^2 = -10$ **63.** $(3x - 4)^2 = 18$

In Exercises 64–65, determine the constant that should be added to the binomial so that it becomes a perfect square trinomial. Then write and factor the trinomial.

64. $x^2 + 20x$ **65.** $x^2 - 3x$

Solve each equation in Exercises 66–67 by completing the square.

66. $x^2 - 12x + 27 = 0$ **67.** $3x^2 - 12x + 11 = 0$

Solve each equation in Exercises 68–70 using the quadratic formula.

68. $x^2 = 2x + 4$ **69.** $x^2 - 2x + 19 = 0$

70. $2x^2 = 3 - 4x$

In Exercises 71–72, without solving the given quadratic equation, determine the number and type of solutions.

71. $x^2 - 4x + 13 = 0$ **72.** $9x^2 = 2 - 3x$

Solve each equation in Exercises 73–81 by the method of your choice.

73. $2x^2 - 11x + 5 = 0$ **74.** $(3x + 5)(x - 3) = 5$

75. $3x^2 - 7x + 1 = 0$ **76.** $x^2 - 9 = 0$

77. $(x - 3)^2 - 25 = 0$ **78.** $3x^2 - x + 2 = 0$

79. $3x^2 - 10x = 8$ **80.** $(x + 2)^2 + 4 = 0$

81. $\dfrac{5}{x + 1} + \dfrac{x - 1}{4} = 2$

82. The formula $W = 3t^2$ models the weight of a human fetus, W, in grams, after t weeks, where $0 \le t \le 39$. After how many weeks does the fetus weigh 588 grams?

83. In 1945, 35.4% of taxes collected by the U.S. Treasury came from corporate income taxes. Since then, corporations have worked hard to convince lawmakers that they shouldn't pay taxes. The bar graph shows the percentage of federal taxes from corporate income taxes for selected years from 1985 through 2003. The data can be modeled by the formula

$$P = -0.035x^2 + 0.65x + 7.6,$$

where P represents the percentage of federal taxes from corporations x years after 1985. If these trends continue, by which year (to the nearest year) will corporations pay no taxes?

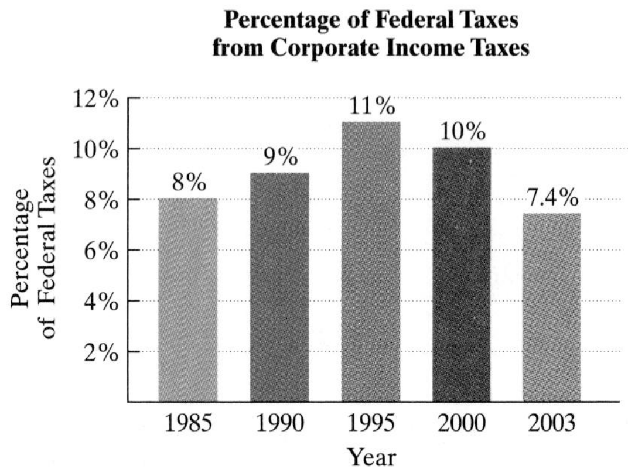

Source: White House Office of Management and Budget

84. An architect is allowed 15 square yards of floor space to add a small bedroom to a house. Because of the room's design in relationship to the existing structure, the width of the rectangular floor must be 7 yards less than two times the length. Find the length and width of the rectangular floor that the architect is permitted.

85. A building casts a shadow that is double the length of its height. If the distance from the end of the shadow to the top of the building is 300 meters, how high is the building? Round to the nearest meter.

1.6

Solve each polynomial equation in Exercises 86–87.

86. $2x^4 = 50x^2$ **87.** $2x^3 - x^2 - 18x + 9 = 0$

Solve each radical equation in Exercises 88–89.

88. $\sqrt{2x - 3} + x = 3$ **89.** $\sqrt{x - 4} + \sqrt{x + 1} = 5$

Solve the equations with rational exponents in Exercises 90–91.

90. $3x^{\frac{3}{4}} - 24 = 0$ **91.** $(x - 7)^{\frac{2}{3}} = 25$

Solve each equation in Exercises 92–93 by making an appropriate substitution.

92. $x^4 - 5x^2 + 4 = 0$ **93.** $x^{\frac{1}{2}} + 3x^{\frac{1}{4}} - 10 = 0$

Solve the equations containing absolute value in Exercises 94–95.

94. $|2x + 1| = 7$ **95.** $2|x - 3| - 6 = 10$

Solve each equation in Exercises 96–102 by the method of your choice.

96. $3x^{\frac{4}{3}} - 5x^{\frac{2}{3}} + 2 = 0$ **97.** $2\sqrt{x - 1} = x$

98. $|2x - 5| - 3 = 0$ **99.** $x^3 + 2x^2 = 9x + 18$

100. $\sqrt{8-2x} - x = 0$ **101.** $x^3 + 3x^2 - 2x - 6 = 0$

102. $-4|x+1| + 12 = 0$

103. By 2010, India could become the world's most HIV-afflicted country. The bar graph shows the increase in the country's HIV infections from 1998 through 2001. The formula $N = 0.3\sqrt{x} + 3.4$ models the number of HIV infections in India, N, in millions, x years after 1998.

AIDS in India

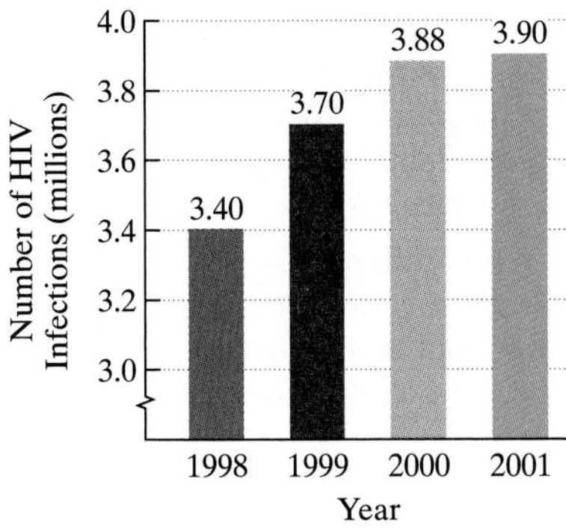

Source: UNAIDS

If trends indicated by the data continue, use the model to determine when the number of HIV infections in India will reach 4.3 million.

1.7

In Exercises 104–106, express each interval in set-builder notation and graph the interval on a number line.

104. $[-3, 5)$ **105.** $(-2, \infty)$ **106.** $(-\infty, 0]$

In Exercises 107–110, use graphs to find each set.

107. $(-2, 1] \cap [-1, 3)$ **108.** $(-2, 1] \cup [-1, 3)$

109. $[1, 3) \cap (0, 4)$ **110.** $[1, 3) \cup (0, 4)$

In Exercises 111–121, solve each inequality. Other than ∅, use interval notation to express solution sets and graph each solution set on a number line.

111. $-6x + 3 \le 15$ **112.** $6x - 9 \ge -4x - 3$

113. $\frac{x}{3} - \frac{3}{4} - 1 > \frac{x}{2}$ **114.** $6x + 5 > -2(x - 3) - 25$

115. $3(2x - 1) - 2(x - 4) \ge 7 + 2(3 + 4x)$

116. $5(x - 2) - 3(x + 4) \ge 2x - 20$

117. $7 < 2x + 3 \le 9$ **118.** $|2x + 3| \le 15$

119. $\left|\frac{2x+6}{3}\right| > 2$ **120.** $|2x + 5| - 7 \ge -6$

121. $-4|x + 2| + 5 \le -7$

In Exercises 122–123, use interval notation to represent all values of x satisfying the given conditions.

122. $y_1 = -10 - 3(2x + 1)$, $y_2 = 8x + 1$, and $y_1 > y_2$.

123. $y = 3 - |2x - 5|$ and y is at least -6.

124. A car rental agency rents a certain car for \$40 per day with unlimited mileage or \$24 per day plus \$0.20 per mile. How far can a customer drive this car per day for the \$24 option to cost no more than the unlimited mileage option?

125. To receive a B in a course, you must have an average of at least 80% but less than 90% on five exams. Your grades on the first four exams were 95%, 79%, 91%, and 86%. What range of grades on the fifth exam will result in a B for the course?

126. A retiree requires an annual income of at least \$9000 from an investment paying 7.5% annual interest. How much should the retiree invest to achieve the desired return?

Chapter 1 Test

In Exercises 1–23, solve each equation or inequality. Other than ∅, use interval notation to express solution sets of inequalities and graph these solution sets on a number line.

1. $7(x - 2) = 4(x + 1) - 21$

2. $-10 - 3(2x + 1) - 8x - 1 = 0$

3. $\frac{2x-3}{4} = \frac{x-4}{2} - \frac{x+1}{4}$

4. $\frac{2}{x-3} - \frac{4}{x+3} = \frac{8}{x^2-9}$

5. $2x^2 - 3x - 2 = 0$ **6.** $(3x - 1)^2 = 75$

7. $(x + 3)^2 + 25 = 0$ **8.** $x(x - 2) = 4$

9. $4x^2 = 8x - 5$ **10.** $x^3 - 4x^2 - x + 4 = 0$

11. $\sqrt{x-3} + 5 = x$ **12.** $\sqrt{8-2x} - x = 0$

13. $\sqrt{x+4} + \sqrt{x-1} = 5$ **14.** $5x^{\frac{3}{2}} - 10 = 0$

15. $x^{\frac{2}{3}} - 9x^{\frac{1}{3}} + 8 = 0$ **16.** $\left|\frac{2}{3}x - 6\right| = 2$

17. $-3|4x - 7| + 15 = 0$ **18.** $\frac{1}{x^2} - \frac{4}{x} + 1 = 0$

19. $\frac{2x}{x^2+6x+8} + \frac{2}{x+2} = \frac{x}{x+4}$

20. $3(x + 4) \ge 5x - 12$ **21.** $\frac{x}{6} + \frac{1}{8} \le \frac{x}{2} - \frac{3}{4}$

22. $-3 \le \frac{2x+5}{3} < 6$ **23.** $|3x + 2| \ge 3$

In Exercises 24–25, use interval notation to represent all values of x satisfying the given conditions.

24. $y = 2x - 5$, and y is at least -3 and no more than 7.

25. $y = \left|\frac{2-x}{4}\right|$ and y is at least 1.

In Exercises 26–27, use graphs to find each set.

26. $[-1, 2) \cup (0, 5]$ **27.** $[-1, 2) \cap (0, 5]$

In Exercises 28–29, solve each formula for the specified variable.

28. $V = \frac{1}{3}lwh$ for h **29.** $y - y_1 = m(x - x_1)$ for x

In Exercises 30–31, graph each equation in a rectangular coordinate system.

30. $y = 2 - |x|$ **31.** $y = x^2 - 4$

In Exercises 32–34, perform the indicated operations and write the result in standard form.

32. $(6 - 7i)(2 + 5i)$ **33.** $\frac{5}{2 - i}$

34. $2\sqrt{-49} + 3\sqrt{-64}$

Without changes, the graphs show projections for the amount being paid in Social Security benefits and the amount going into the system. All data are expressed in billions of dollars.

Social Insecurity: Projected Income and Outflow of the Social Security System

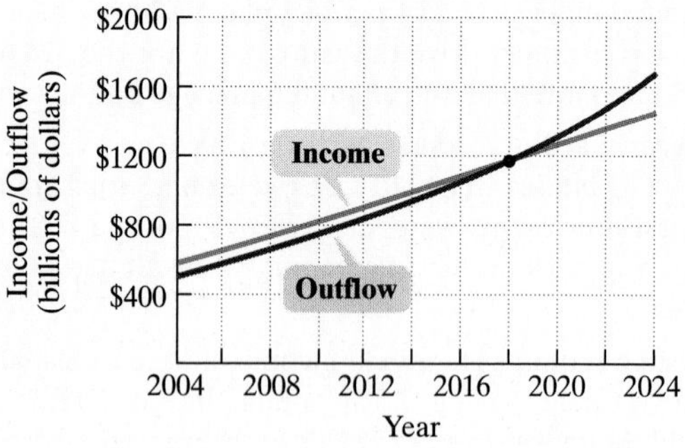

Source: 2004 Social Security Trustees Report

Exercises 35–37 are based on the data shown by the graphs.

35. In 2004, the system's income was $575 billion, projected to increase at an average rate of $43 billion per year. In which year will the system's income be $1177 billion?

36. The data for the system's outflow can be modeled by the formula

$$B = 0.07x^2 + 47.4x + 500,$$

where B represents the amount paid in benefits, in billions of dollars, x years after 2004. According to this model, when will the amount paid in benefits be $1177 billion? Round to the nearest year.

37. How well do your answers to Exercises 35 and 36 model the data shown by the graphs?

38. From 2002 through 2004, there were 2598 books categorized as U.S. politics and government. The number of books in 2003 exceeded the number in 2002 by 62 and the number in 2004 exceeded the number in 2002 by 190. How many books on U.S. politics were there for each of the three years? (*Source:* Andrew Grabois, R. R. Bowker)

39. The costs for two different kinds of heating systems for a three-bedroom home are given in the following table. After how many years will total costs for solar heating and electric heating be the same? What will be the cost at that time?

System	Cost to Install	Operating Cost/Year
Solar	$29,700	$150
Electric	$5000	$1100

40. You invested $10,000 in two accounts paying 8% and 10% annual interest, respectively. At the end of the year, the total interest from these investments was $940. How much was invested at each rate?

41. The length of a rectangular carpet is 4 feet greater than twice its width. If the area is 48 square feet, find the carpet's length and width.

42. A vertical pole is to be supported by a wire that is 26 feet long and anchored 24 feet from the base of the pole. How far up the pole should the wire be attached?

43. After a 60% reduction, a jacket sold for $20. What was the jacket's price before the reduction?

44. You are choosing between two telephone plans for local calls. Plan A charges $25 per month for unlimited calls. Plan B has a monthly fee of $13 with a charge of $0.06 per local call. How many local telephone calls in a month make plan A the better deal?

CHAPTER 2

Functions and Graphs

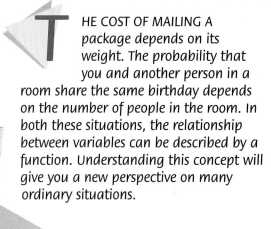

THE COST OF MAILING A package depends on its weight. The probability that you and another person in a room share the same birthday depends on the number of people in the room. In both these situations, the relationship between variables can be described by a function. Understanding this concept will give you a new perspective on many ordinary situations.

'TIS THE SEASON AND YOU'VE waited until the last minute to mail your holiday gifts. Your only option is overnight express mail. You realize that the cost of mailing a gift depends on its weight, but the mailing costs seem somewhat odd. Your packages that weigh 1.1 pounds, 1.5 pounds, and 2 pounds cost $15.75 each to send overnight. Packages that weigh 2.01 pounds and 3 pounds cost you $18.50 each. Finally, your heaviest gift is barely over 3 pounds and its mailing cost is $21.25. What sort of system is this in which costs increase by $2.75, stepping from $15.75 to $18.50 and from $18.50 to $21.25?

Graphs that ascend in steps are discussed on page 210 in Section 2.2.

SECTION 2.1 Basics of Functions and Their Graphs

Objectives

1. Find the domain and range of a relation.
2. Determine whether a relation is a function.
3. Determine whether an equation represents a function.
4. Evaluate a function.
5. Graph functions by plotting points.
6. Use the vertical line test to identify functions.
7. Obtain information about a function from its graph.
8. Identify the domain and range of a function from its graph.
9. Identify intercepts from a function's graph.

Have you ever seen a gas-guzzling car from the 1950s, with its huge fins and overstated design? The worst year for automobile fuel efficiency was 1958, when cars averaged a dismal 12.4 miles per gallon. There is a formula that approximately describes fuel efficiency of U.S. cars over time. The formula is

$$y = 0.0075x^2 - 0.2672x + 14.8.$$

The variable x represents the number of years after 1940. The variable y represents the average number of miles per gallon for U.S. automobiles.

The mathematical model for fuel efficiency indicates that miles per gallon depend on the number of years after 1940. For each value of x, or the number of years after 1940, the model gives precisely one value of y, or the average number of miles per gallon for U.S. automobiles. Under these conditions, we say that fuel efficiency is a *function* of time.

In this section, you will be introduced to the basics of functions and their graphs. Much of our work in this course will be devoted to the important topic of functions and how they model your world.

1 Find the domain and range of a relation.

Relations

Studies show that exercise can promote good long-term health no matter how much you weigh. A brisk half-hour walk each day is enough to get the benefits. Combined with a healthy diet, it also helps to stave off obesity. How many calories does your workout burn? The graph in Figure 2.1 shows the calories burned per hour in six activities.

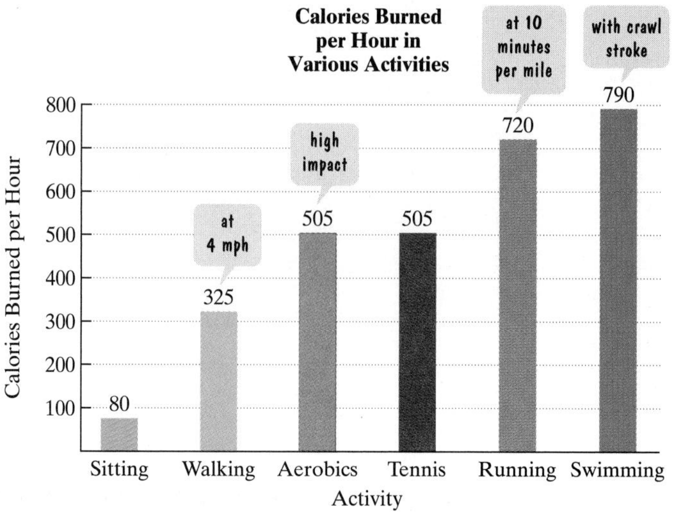

Figure 2.1 Counting calories
Source: fitresource.com

The information shown in the bar graph indicates a correspondence between the activities and calories burned per hour. We can write this correspondence using a set of ordered pairs:

{(sitting, 80), (walking, 325), (aerobics, 505), (tennis, 505), (running, 720), (swimming, 790)}.

These braces indicate that we are representing a set.

The mathematical term for a set of ordered pairs is a *relation*.

Definition of a Relation

A **relation** is any set of ordered pairs. The set of all first components of the ordered pairs is called the **domain** of the relation and the set of all second components is called the **range** of the relation.

EXAMPLE 1 Finding the Domain and Range of a Relation

Find the domain and the range of the relation:

{(sitting, 80), (walking, 325), (aerobics, 505), (tennis, 505), (running, 720), (swimming, 790)}.

Solution The domain is the set of all first components. Thus, the domain is

{sitting, walking, aerobics, tennis, running, swimming}.

The range is the set of all second components. Thus, the range is

{80, 325, 505, 720, 790}.

Although both aerobics and tennis burn 505 calories per hour, it is not necessary to list 505 twice.

Check Point 1 Find the domain and the range of the relation:

$\{(5, 12.8), (10, 16.2), (15, 18.9), (20, 20.7), (25, 21.8)\}$.

As you worked Check Point 1, did you wonder if there was a rule that assigned the "inputs" in the domain to the "outputs" in the range? For example, for the ordered pair (15, 18.9), how does the output 18.9 depend on the input 15? Think paid vacation days! The first number in each ordered pair is the number of years that a full-time employee has been employed by a medium to large U.S. company. The second number is the average number of paid vacation days each year. Consider, for example, the ordered pair (15, 18.9).

(15, 18.9)

After 15 years, workers average 18.9 paid vacation days per year.

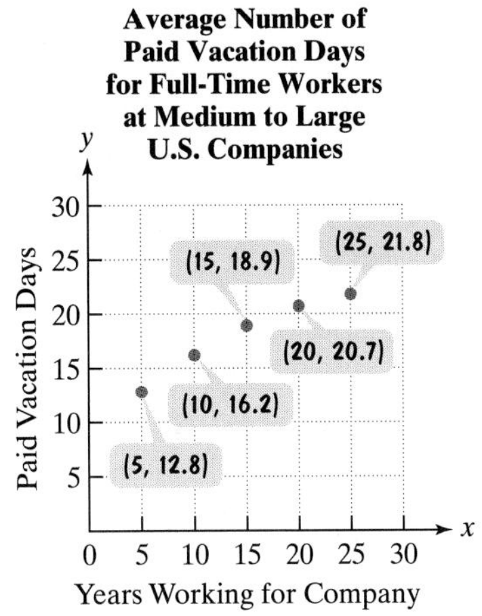

Figure 2.2 The graph of a relation showing a correspondence between years with a company and paid vacation days

Source: Bureau of Labor Statistics

The relation in the vacation-days example can be pictured as follows:

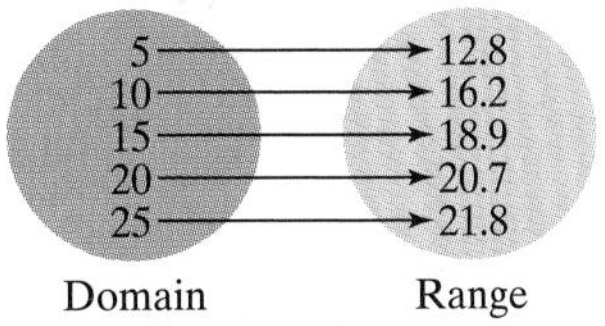

The five points in Figure 2.2 are another way to visually represent the relation.

2 Determine whether a relation is a function.

Activity	Calories Burned per hour
Sitting	80
Walking	325
Aerobics	505
Tennis	505
Running	720
Swimming	790

Functions

Shown in the margin are the calories burned per hour for the activities in the bar graph in Figure 2.1 on page 186. We've used this information to define two relations. Figure 2.3(a) shows a correspondence between activities and calories burned. Figure 2.3(b) shows a correspondence between calories burned and activities.

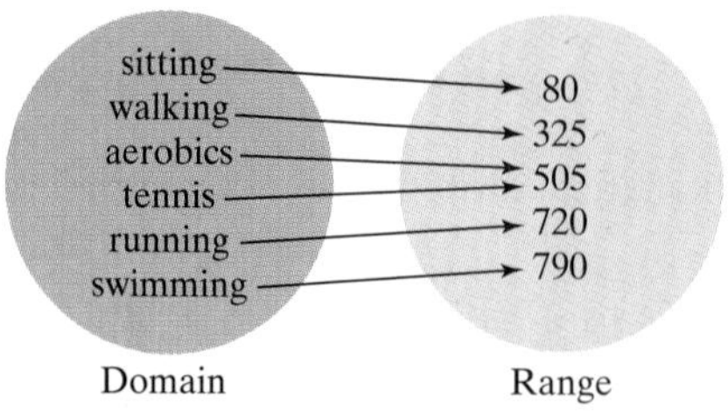

Figure 2.3(a) Activities correspond to calories burned.

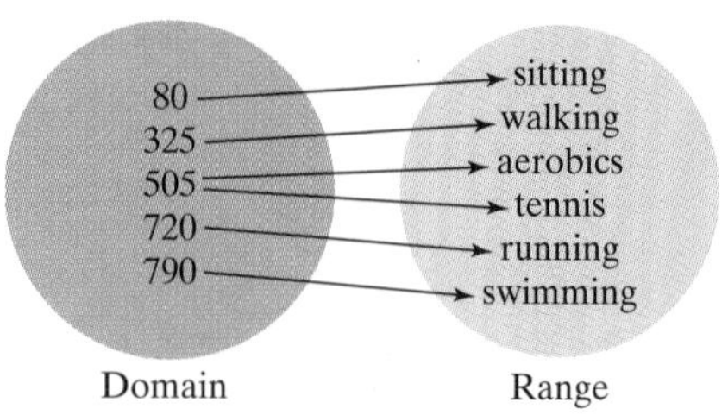

Figure 2.3(b) Calories burned correspond to activities.

A relation in which each member of the domain corresponds to exactly one member of the range is a **function**. Can you see that the relation in Figure 2.3(a) is a function? Each activity in the domain corresponds to exactly one number representing calories burned per hour in the range. If we know the activity, we know the calories burned per hour. Notice that more than one element in the domain can correspond to the same element in the range: Aerobics and tennis both burn 505 calories per hour.

Is the relation in Figure 2.3(b) a function? Does each member of the domain correspond to precisely one member of the range? This relation is not a function because there is a member of the domain that corresponds to two members of the range:

$$(505, \text{aerobics}) \quad (505, \text{tennis}).$$

The member of the domain, 505, corresponds to both aerobics and tennis. If we know the calories burned per hour, 505, we cannot be sure of the activity. Because **a function is a relation in which no two ordered pairs have the same first component and different second components**, the ordered pairs (505, aerobics) and (505, tennis) are not ordered pairs of a function.

Same first component

$$(505, \text{aerobics}) \quad (505, \text{tennis})$$

Different second components

Definition of a Function

A **function** is a correspondence from a first set, called the **domain**, to a second set, called the **range**, such that each element in the domain corresponds to *exactly one* element in the range.

Can you see that the correspondence between years worked and paid vacation days from Check Point 1 is a function?

Each element in the domain

$$\{(5, 12.8), (10, 16.2), (15, 18.9), (20, 20.7), (25, 21.8)\}$$

corresponds to exactly one element in the range.

However, Example 2 illustrates that not every correspondence between sets is a function.

EXAMPLE 2 Determining Whether a Relation Is a Function

Determine whether each relation is a function:

a. $\{(1, 6), (2, 6), (3, 8), (4, 9)\}$ **b.** $\{(6, 1), (6, 2), (8, 3), (9, 4)\}$.

Solution We begin by making a figure for each relation that shows the domain and the range (Figure 2.4).

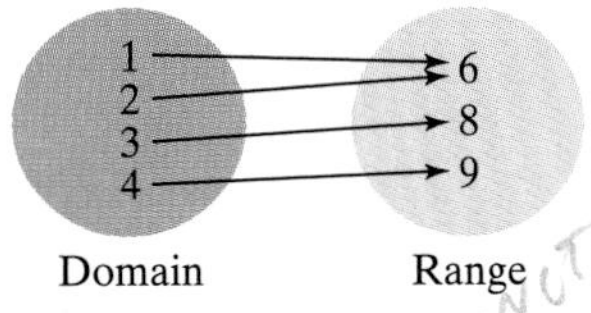

Figure 2.4(a)

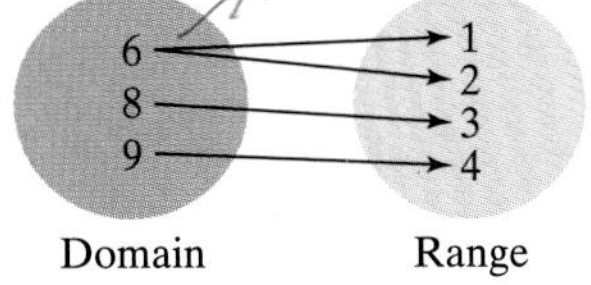

Figure 2.4(b)

a. Figure 2.4(a) shows that every element in the domain corresponds to exactly one element in the range. The element 1 in the domain corresponds to the element 6 in the range. Furthermore, 2 corresponds to 6, 3 corresponds to 8, and 4 corresponds to 9. No two ordered pairs in the given relation have the same first component and different second components. Thus, the relation is a function.

b. Figure 2.4(b) shows that 6 corresponds to both 1 and 2. If any element in the domain corresponds to more than one element in the range, the relation is not a function. This relation is not a function; two ordered pairs have the same first component and different second components.

Same first component

(6, 1) (6, 2)

Different second components

Study Tip

If a relation is a function, reversing the components in each of its ordered pairs may result in a relation that is not a function.

Look at Figure 2.4(a) again. The fact that 1 and 2 in the domain correspond to the same number, 6, in the range does not violate the definition of a function. **A function can have two different first components with the same second component.** By contrast, a relation is not a function when two different ordered pairs have the same first component and different second components. Thus, the relation in Figure 2.4(b) is not a function.

Check Point 2 Determine whether each relation is a function:

a. $\{(1, 2), (3, 4), (5, 6), (5, 8)\}$ **b.** $\{(1, 2), (3, 4), (6, 5), (8, 5)\}$.

3 Determine whether an equation represents a function.

Functions as Equations

Functions are usually given in terms of equations rather than as sets of ordered pairs. For example, here is an equation that models paid vacation days each year as a function of years working for a company:

$$y = -0.016x^2 + 0.93x + 8.5.$$

The variable x represents years working for a company. The variable y represents the average number of vacation days each year. The variable y is a function of the variable x. For each value of x, there is one and only one value of y. The variable x is called the **independent variable** because it can be assigned any value from the domain. Thus, x can be assigned any positive integer representing the number of years working for a company. The variable y is called the **dependent variable** because its value depends on x. Paid vacation days depend on years working for a company. The value of the dependent variable, y, is calculated after selecting a value for the independent variable, x.

We have seen that not every set of ordered pairs defines a function. Similarly, not all equations with the variables x and y define a function. If an equation is solved for y and more than one value of y can be obtained for a given x, then the equation does not define y as a function of x.

EXAMPLE 3 Determining Whether an Equation Represents a Function

Determine whether each equation defines y as a function of x:

a. $x^2 + y = 4$ **b.** $x^2 + y^2 = 4$.

Solution Solve each equation for y in terms of x. If two or more values of y can be obtained for a given x, the equation is not a function.

a.
$$x^2 + y = 4 \qquad \text{This is the given equation.}$$
$$x^2 + y - x^2 = 4 - x^2 \qquad \text{Solve for y by subtracting } x^2 \text{ from both sides.}$$
$$y = 4 - x^2 \qquad \text{Simplify.}$$

From this last equation we can see that for each value of x, there is one and only one value of y. For example, if $x = 1$, then $y = 4 - 1^2 = 3$. The equation defines y as a function of x.

b.
$$x^2 + y^2 = 4 \qquad \text{This is the given equation.}$$
$$x^2 + y^2 - x^2 = 4 - x^2 \qquad \text{Isolate } y^2 \text{ by subtracting } x^2 \text{ from both sides.}$$
$$y^2 = 4 - x^2 \qquad \text{Simplify.}$$
$$y = \pm\sqrt{4 - x^2} \qquad \text{Apply the square root property: If } u^2 = d, \text{ then } u = \pm\sqrt{d}.$$

The $\pm$ in this last equation shows that for certain values of x (all values between -2 and 2), there are two values of y. For example, if $x = 1$, then $y = \pm\sqrt{4 - 1^2} = \pm\sqrt{3}$. For this reason, the equation does not define y as a function of x.

Check Point 3 Solve each equation for y and then determine whether the equation defines y as a function of x:

a. $2x + y = 6$ **b.** $x^2 + y^2 = 1$.

④ Evaluate a function.

Input x

Output $f(x)$

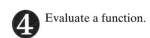

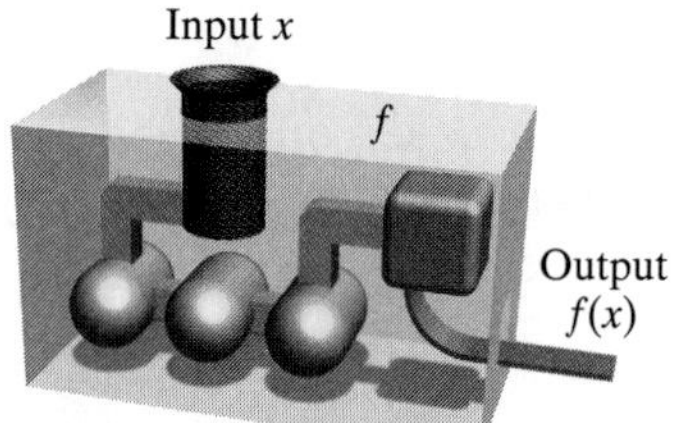

Figure 2.5 A "function machine" with inputs and outputs

Study Tip

The notation $f(x)$ does *not* mean "f times x." The notation describes the value of the function at x.

Function Notation

If an equation in x and y gives one and only one value of y for each value of x, then the variable y is a function of the variable x. When an equation represents a function, the function is often named by a letter such as f, g, h, F, G, or H. Any letter can be used to name a function. Suppose that f names a function. Think of the domain as the set of the function's inputs and the range as the set of the function's outputs. As shown in Figure 2.5, input is represented by x and the output by $f(x)$. The special notation $f(x)$, read "f of x" or "f at x," represents the **value of the function at the number x**.

 Let's make this clearer by considering a specific example. We know that the equation

$$y = -0.016x^2 + 0.93x + 8.5$$

defines y as a function of x. We'll name the function f. Now, we can apply our new function notation.

We read this equation as "f of x equals $-0.016x^2 + 0.93x + 8.5$."

Input	Output	Equation
x	$f(x)$	$f(x) = -0.016x^2 + 0.93x + 8.5$

Technology

Graphing utilities can be used to evaluate functions. The screens below show the evaluation of

$$f(x) = -0.016x^2 + 0.93x + 8.5$$

at 10 on a TI-83 Plus graphing calculator. The function f is named Y_1.

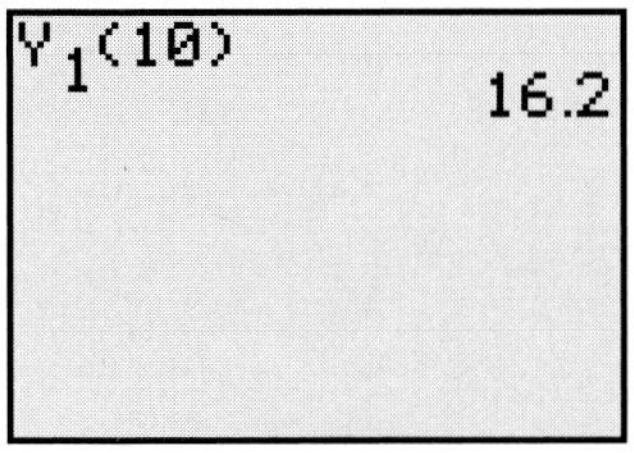

Suppose we are interested in finding $f(10)$, the function's output when the input is 10. To find the value of the function at 10, we substitute 10 for x. We are **evaluating the function** at 10.

$$\begin{aligned} f(x) &= -0.016x^2 + 0.93x + 8.5 && \text{This is the given function.} \\ f(10) &= -0.016(10)^2 + 0.93(10) + 8.5 && \text{Replace each occurrence of } x \text{ with 10.} \\ &= -0.016(100) + 0.93(10) + 8.5 && \text{Evaluate the exponential expression: } 10^2 = 100. \\ &= -1.6 + 9.3 + 8.5 && \text{Perform the multiplications.} \\ &= 16.2 && \text{Add from left to right.} \end{aligned}$$

The statement $f(10) = 16.2$, read "f of 10 equals 16.2," tells us that the value of the function at 10 is 16.2. When the function's input is 10, its output is 16.2. (After 10 years, workers average 16.2 vacation days each year.) To find other function values, such as $f(15)$, $f(20)$, or $f(23)$, substitute the specified input values for x into the function's equation.

If a function is named f and x represents the independent variable, the notation $f(x)$ corresponds to the y-value for a given x. Thus,

$$f(x) = -0.016x^2 + 0.93x + 8.5 \quad \text{and} \quad y = -0.016x^2 + 0.93x + 8.5$$

define the same function. This function may be written as

$$y = f(x) = -0.016x^2 + 0.93x + 8.5.$$

EXAMPLE 4 Evaluating a Function

If $f(x) = x^2 + 3x + 5$, evaluate each of the following:

a. $f(2)$ **b.** $f(x + 3)$ **c.** $f(-x)$.

Solution We substitute 2, $x + 3$, and $-x$ for x in the equation for f. When replacing x with a variable or an algebraic expression, you might find it helpful to think of the function's equation as

$$f(\ x\ ) = \ x\ ^2 + 3\ x\ + 5.$$

a. We find $f(2)$ by substituting 2 for x in the equation.

$$f(\ 2\ ) = \ 2\ ^2 + 3 \cdot \ 2\ + 5 = 4 + 6 + 5 = 15$$

Thus, $f(2) = 15$.

b. We find $f(x + 3)$ by substituting $x + 3$ for x in the equation.

$$f(\ x + 3\ ) = \ (x + 3)\ ^2 + 3\ (x + 3)\ + 5$$

Equivalently,

$$\begin{aligned} f(x + 3) &= (x + 3)^2 + 3(x + 3) + 5 \\ &= x^2 + 6x + 9 + 3x + 9 + 5 && \text{Square } x + 3 \text{ using } (A + B)^2 = A^2 + 2AB + B^2. \text{ Distribute 3 throughout the parentheses.} \\ &= x^2 + 9x + 23. && \text{Combine like terms.} \end{aligned}$$

c. We find $f(-x)$ by substituting $-x$ for x in the equation.

$$f(\ -x\ ) = \ (-x)\ ^2 + 3\ (-x)\ + 5$$

Equivalently,

$$\begin{aligned} f(-x) &= (-x)^2 + 3(-x) + 5 \\ &= x^2 - 3x + 5. \end{aligned}$$

Discovery

Using $f(x) = x^2 + 3x + 5$ and the answers in parts (b) and (c):

1. Is $f(x + 3)$ equal to $f(x) + f(3)$?
2. Is $f(-x)$ equal to $-f(x)$?

Check Point 4 If $f(x) = x^2 - 2x + 7$, evaluate each of the following:

a. $f(-5)$ **b.** $f(x + 4)$ **c.** $f(-x)$.

5 Graph functions by plotting points.

Graphs of Functions

The **graph of a function** is the graph of its ordered pairs. For example, the graph of $f(x) = 2x$ is the set of points (x, y) in the rectangular coordinate system satisfying $y = 2x$. Similarly, the graph of $g(x) = 2x + 4$ is the set of points (x, y) in the rectangular coordinate system satisfying the equation $y = 2x + 4$. In the next example, we graph both of these functions in the same rectangular coordinate system.

EXAMPLE 5 Graphing Functions

Graph the functions $f(x) = 2x$ and $g(x) = 2x + 4$ in the same rectangular coordinate system. Select integers for x, starting with -2 and ending with 2.

Solution We begin by setting up a partial table of coordinates for each function. Then, we plot the five points in each table and connect them, as shown in Figure 2.6. The graph of each function is a straight line. Do you see a relationship between the two graphs? The graph of g is the graph of f shifted vertically up by 4 units.

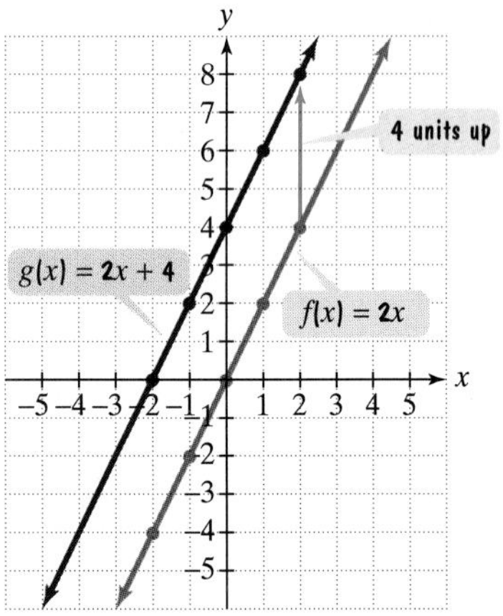

Figure 2.6

x	$f(x) = 2x$	(x, y) or $(x, f(x))$
-2	$f(-2) = 2(-2) = -4$	$(-2, -4)$
-1	$f(-1) = 2(-1) = -2$	$(-1, -2)$
0	$f(0) = 2 \cdot 0 = 0$	$(0, 0)$
1	$f(1) = 2 \cdot 1 = 2$	$(1, 2)$
2	$f(2) = 2 \cdot 2 = 4$	$(2, 4)$

Choose x. Compute $f(x)$ by evaluating f at x. Form the ordered pair.

x	$g(x) = 2x + 4$	(x, y) or $(x, g(x))$
-2	$g(-2) = 2(-2) + 4 = 0$	$(-2, 0)$
-1	$g(-1) = 2(-1) + 4 = 2$	$(-1, 2)$
0	$g(0) = 2 \cdot 0 + 4 = 4$	$(0, 4)$
1	$g(1) = 2 \cdot 1 + 4 = 6$	$(1, 6)$
2	$g(2) = 2 \cdot 2 + 4 = 8$	$(2, 8)$

Choose x. Compute $g(x)$ by evaluating g at x. Form the ordered pair.

The graphs in Example 5 are straight lines. All functions with equations of the form $f(x) = mx + b$ graph as straight lines. Such functions, called **linear functions**, will be discussed in detail in Section 2.3.

Technology

We can use a graphing utility to check the tables and the graphs in Example 5 for the functions

$$f(x) = 2x \quad \text{and} \quad g(x) = 2x + 4.$$

Enter $y_1 = 2x$ in the $\boxed{y=}$ screen.

Enter $y_2 = 2x + 4$ in the $\boxed{y=}$ screen.

We entered -2 for the starting x-value and 1 as an increment between x-values to check our tables in Example 5.

Checking Tables

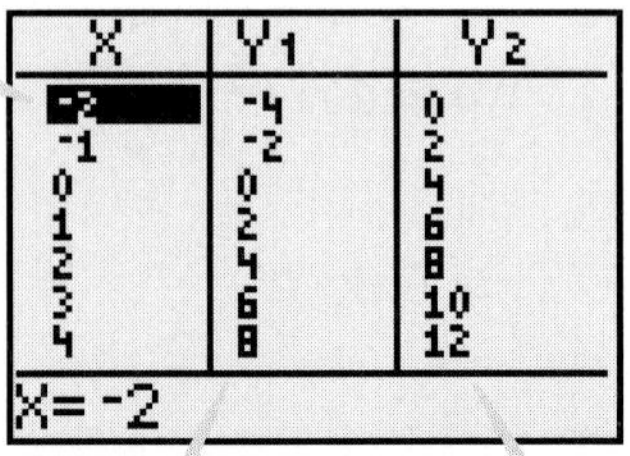

Use the first five ordered pairs (x, y_1) to check the first table.

Use the first five ordered pairs (x, y_2) to check the second table.

Checking Graphs

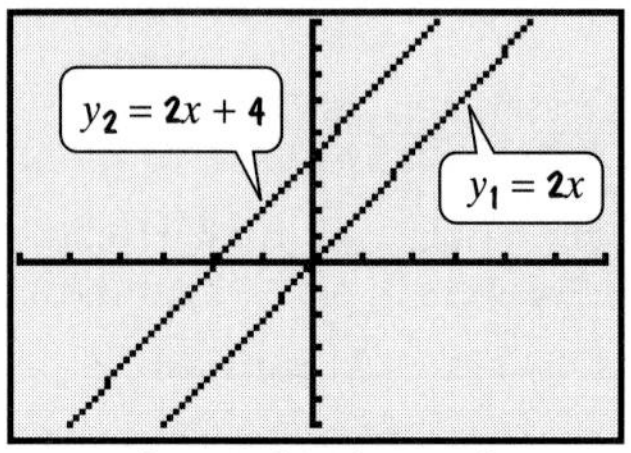

$[-6, 6, 1]$ by $[-6, 9, 1]$

We selected this viewing rectangle, or window, to match Figure 2.6.

Check Point 5 Graph the functions $f(x) = 2x$ and $g(x) = 2x - 3$ in the same rectangular coordinate system. Select integers for x, starting with -2 and ending with 2. How is the graph of g related to the graph of f?

6 Use the vertical line test to identify functions.

The Vertical Line Test

Not every graph in the rectangular coordinate system is the graph of a function. The definition of a function specifies that no value of x can be paired with two or more different values of y. Consequently, if a graph contains two or more different points with the same first coordinate, the graph cannot represent a function. This is illustrated in Figure 2.7. Observe that points sharing a common first coordinate are vertically above or below each other.

This observation is the basis of a useful test for determining whether a graph defines y as a function of x. The test is called the **vertical line test**.

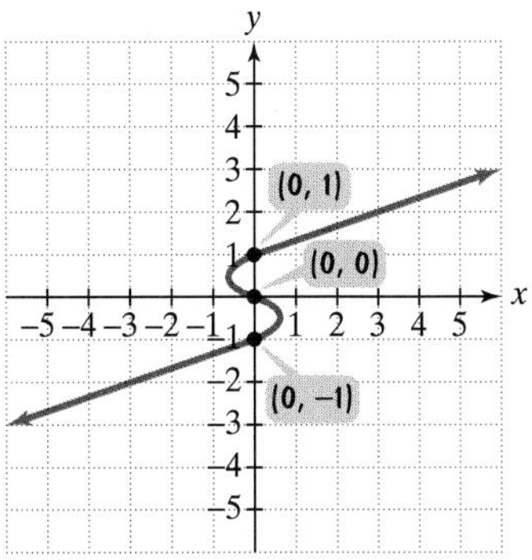

Figure 2.7 y is not a function of x because 0 is paired with three values of y, namely, 1, 0, and -1.

The Vertical Line Test for Functions

If any vertical line intersects a graph in more than one point, the graph does not define y as a function of x.

EXAMPLE 6 Using the Vertical Line Test

Use the vertical line test to identify graphs in which y is a function of x.

a.

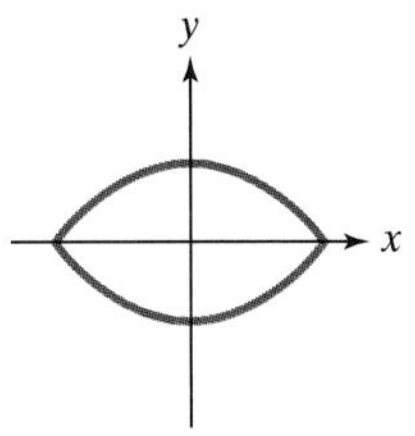

b.

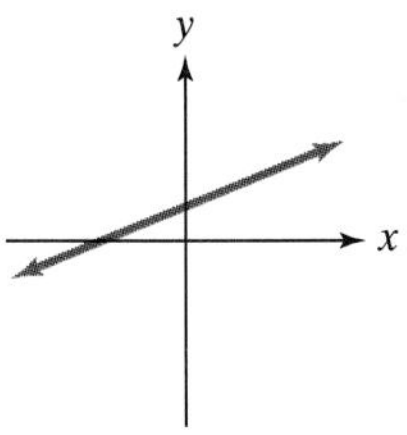

c.

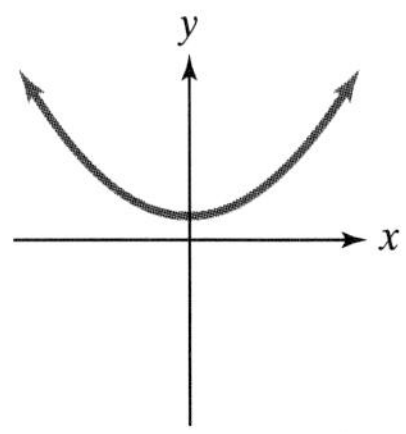

d.

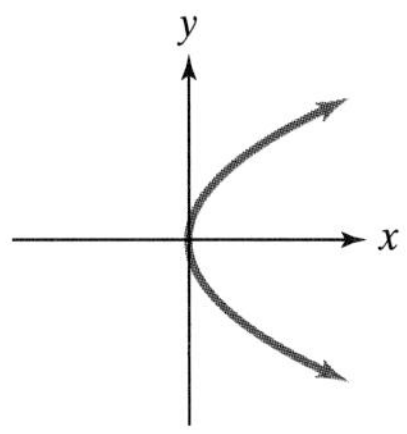

Solution y is a function of x for the graphs in (b) and (c).

a.

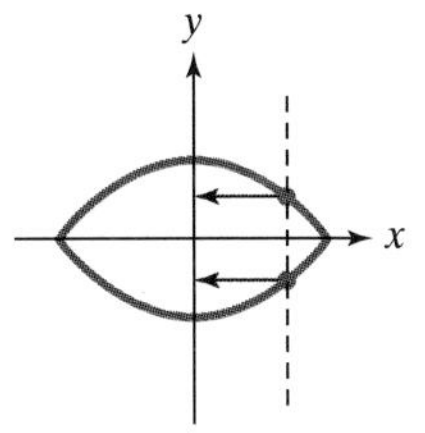

y is **not a function of** x. Two values of y correspond to an x-value.

b.

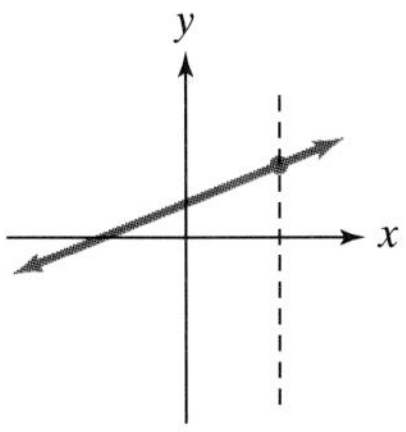

y **is a function of** x.

c.

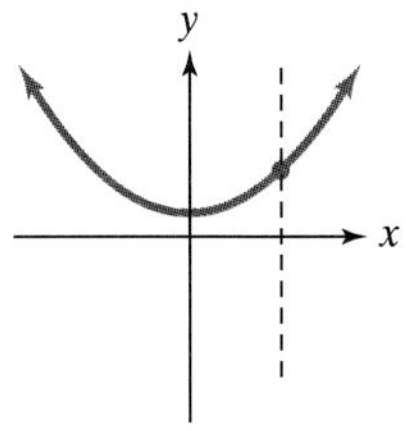

y **is a function of** x.

d.

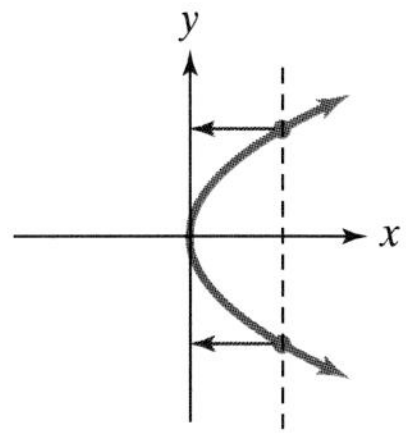

y is **not a function of** x. Two values of y correspond to an x-value.

Check Point 6 Use the vertical line test to identify graphs in which y is a function of x.

a.

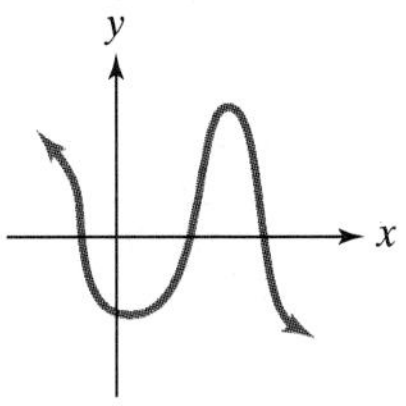

b.

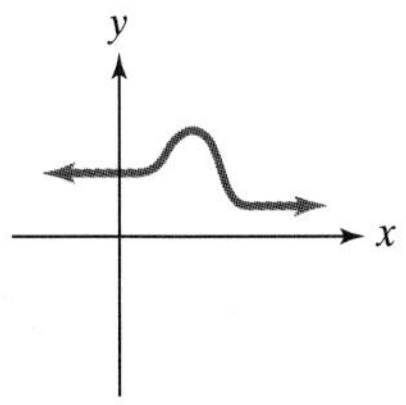

c.

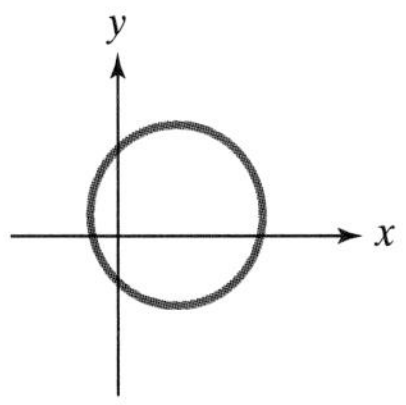

7 Obtain information about a function from its graph.

Obtaining Information from Graphs

You can obtain information about a function from its graph. At the right or left of a graph, you will find closed dots, open dots, or arrows.

- A closed dot indicates that the graph does not extend beyond this point and the point belongs to the graph.
- An open dot indicates that the graph does not extend beyond this point and the point does not belong to the graph.
- An arrow indicates that the graph extends indefinitely in the direction in which the arrow points.

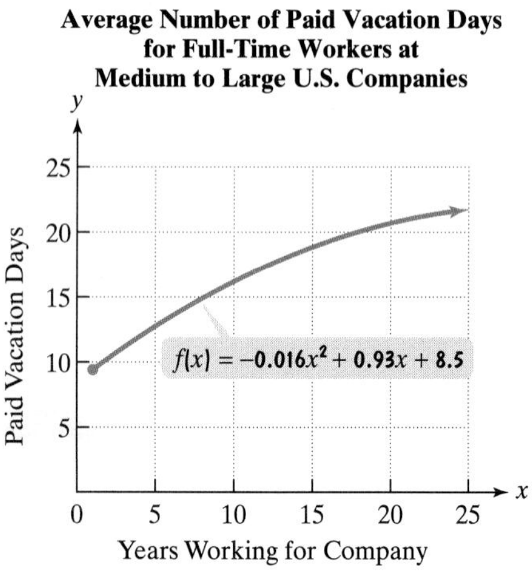

Figure 2.8

Source: Bureau of Labor Statistics

EXAMPLE 7 Analyzing the Graph of a Function

The function

$$f(x) = -0.016x^2 + 0.93x + 8.5$$

models the average number of paid vacation days each year, $f(x)$, for full-time workers at medium to large U.S. companies after x years. The graph of f is shown in Figure 2.8.

a. Explain why f represents the graph of a function.

b. Use the graph to find a reasonable estimate of $f(5)$.

c. For what value of x is $f(x) = 20$?

d. Describe the general trend shown by the graph.

Solution

a. No vertical line intersects the graph of f more than once. By the vertical line test, f represents the graph of a function.

b. To find $f(5)$, or f of 5, we locate 5 on the x-axis. The figure shows the point on the graph of f for which 5 is the first coordinate. From this point, we look to the y-axis to find the corresponding y-coordinate. A reasonable estimate of the y-coordinate is 13. Thus, $f(5) \approx 13$. After 5 years, a worker can expect approximately 13 paid vacation days.

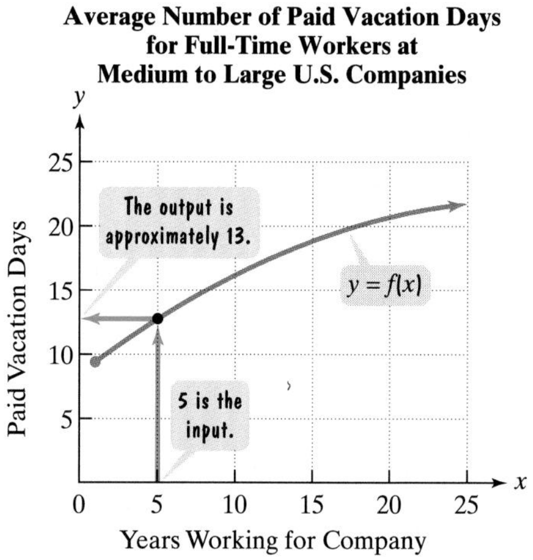

c. To find the value of x for which $f(x) = 20$, we locate 20 on the y-axis. The figure shows that there is one point on the graph of f for which 20 is the second coordinate. From this point, we look to the x-axis to find the corresponding x-coordinate. A reasonable estimate of the x-coordinate is 18. Thus, $f(x) = 20$ for $x \approx 18$. A worker with 20 paid vacation days has been with the company approximately 18 years.

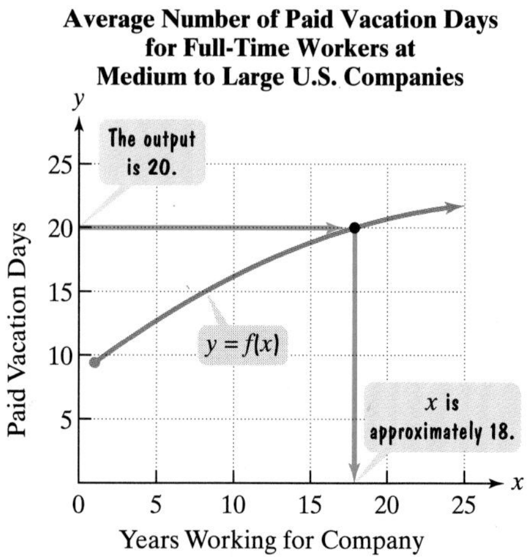

d. The graph of f in Figure 2.8 is rising from left to right. This shows that paid vacation days increase as time with the company increases. However, the rate of increase is slowing down as the graph moves to the right. This means that the increase in paid vacation days takes place more slowly the longer an employee is with the company.

Check Point 7 **a.** Use the graph of f in Figure 2.8 to find a reasonable estimate of $f(10)$.
b. For what value of x is $f(x) = 15$? Round to the nearest whole number.

8 Identify the domain and range of a function from its graph.

Identifying Domain and Range from a Function's Graph

Study Tip

Throughout this discussion, we will be using interval notation. Recall that square brackets indicate endpoints that are included in an interval. Parentheses indicate endpoints that are not included in an interval. For more detail on interval notation, see Section 1.7, pages 164–166.

Figure 2.9 illustrates how the graph of a function is used to determine the function's domain and its range.

Domain: set of inputs

Found on the x-axis

Range: set of outputs

Found on the y-axis

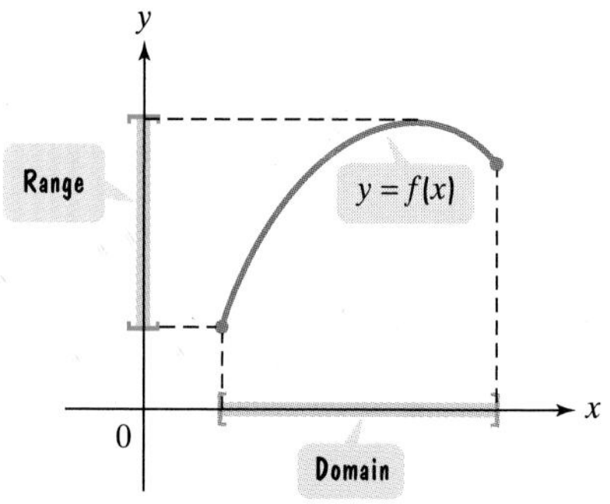

Figure 2.9 Domain and range of f

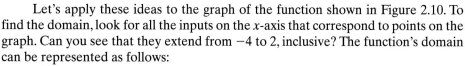

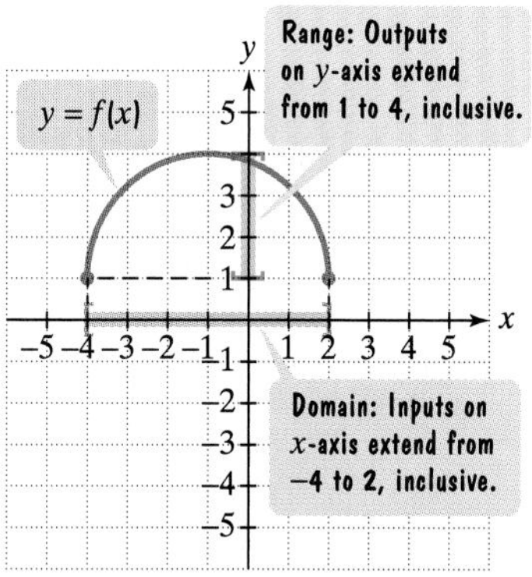

Figure 2.10 Domain and range of f

Let's apply these ideas to the graph of the function shown in Figure 2.10. To find the domain, look for all the inputs on the x-axis that correspond to points on the graph. Can you see that they extend from -4 to 2, inclusive? The function's domain can be represented as follows:

Using Set-Builder Notation	Using Interval Notation
$\{x \mid -4 \le x \le 2\}$	$[-4, 2]$.
The set of all x / such that / x is greater than or equal to -4 and less than or equal to 2.	The square brackets indicate -4 and 2 are included. Note the square brackets on the x-axis in Figure 2.10.

To find the range, look for all the outputs on the y-axis that correspond to points on the graph. They extend from 1 to 4, inclusive. The function's range can be represented as follows:

Using Set-Builder Notation	Using Interval Notation
$\{y \mid 1 \le y \le 4\}$	$[1, 4]$.
The set of all y / such that / y is greater than or equal to 1 and less than or equal to 4.	The square brackets indicate 1 and 4 are included. Note the square brackets on the y-axis in Figure 2.10.

EXAMPLE 8 Identifying the Domain and Range of a Function from Its Graph

Use the graph of each function to identify its domain and its range.

a.

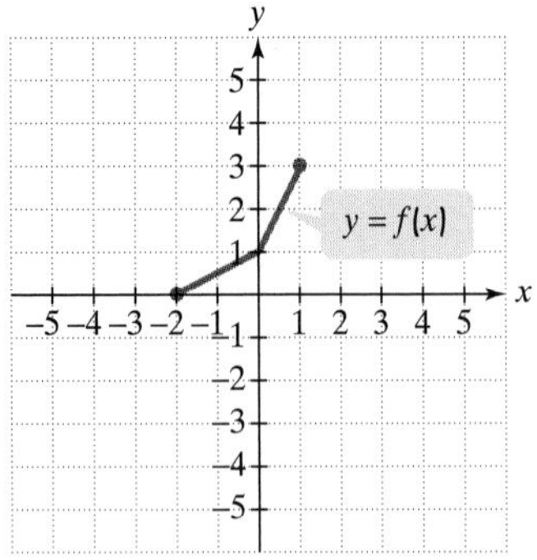

b.

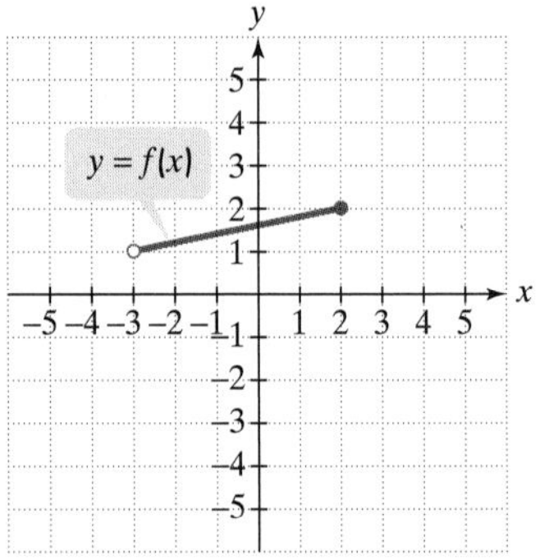

c.

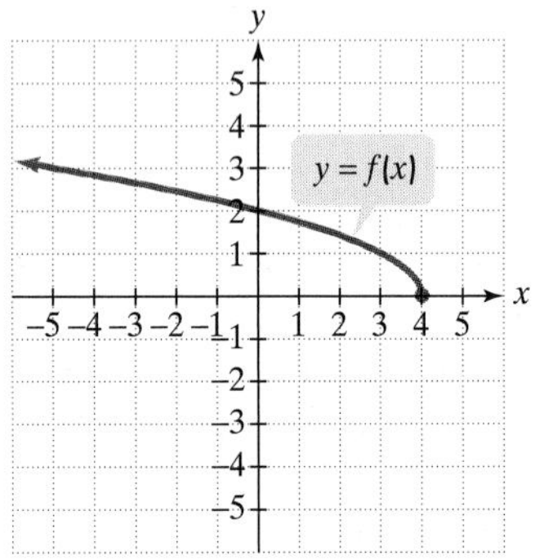

d.

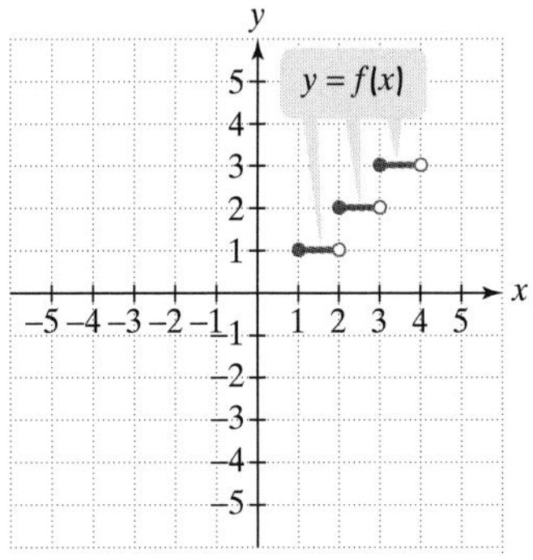

Solution For the graph of each function, the domain is highlighted in blue on the x-axis and the range is highlighted in green on the y-axis.

a.

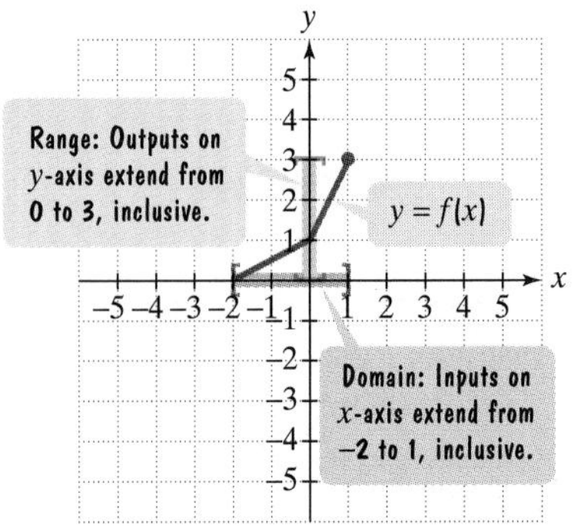

Domain $= \{x | -2 \le x \le 1\}$ or $[-2, 1]$
Range $= \{y | 0 \le y \le 3\}$ or $[0, 3]$

b.

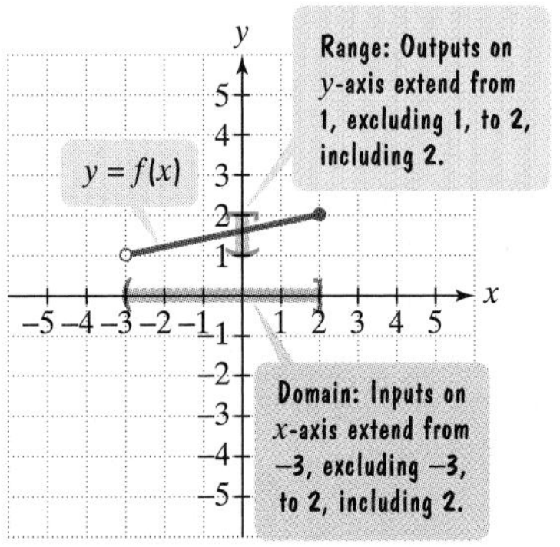

Domain $= \{x | -3 < x \le 2\}$ or $(-3, 2]$
Range $= \{y | 1 < y \le 2\}$ or $(1, 2]$

c.

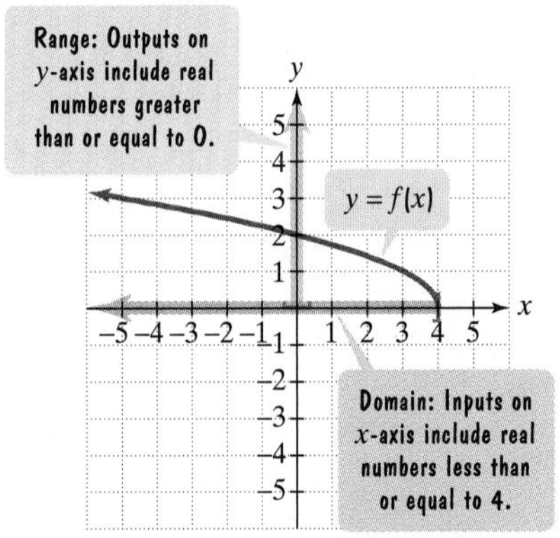

Domain $= \{x | x \le 4\}$ or $(-\infty, 4]$
Range $= \{y | y \ge 0\}$ or $[0, \infty)$

d.

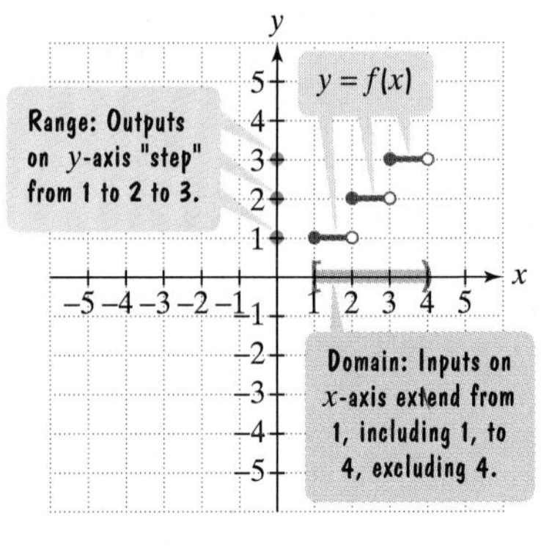

Domain $= \{x | 1 \le x < 4\}$ or $[1, 4)$
Range $= \{y | y = 1, 2, 3\}$

Check Point 8 Use the graph of each function to identify its domain and its range.

a.

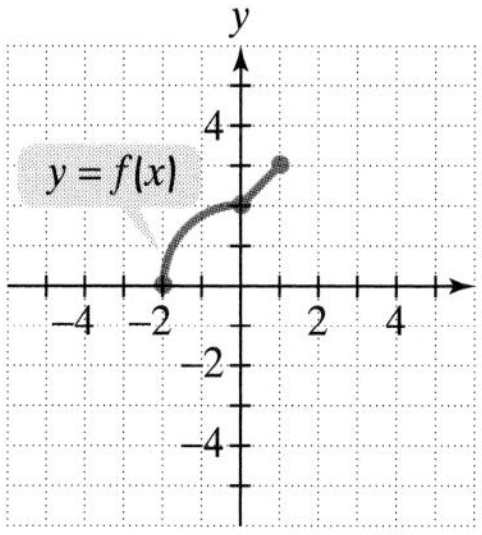

b.

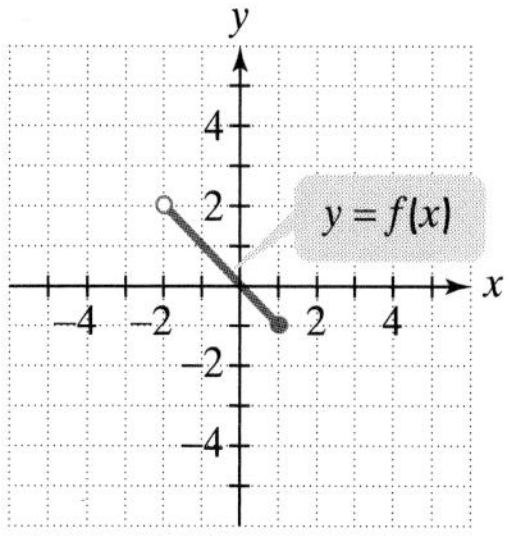

c.

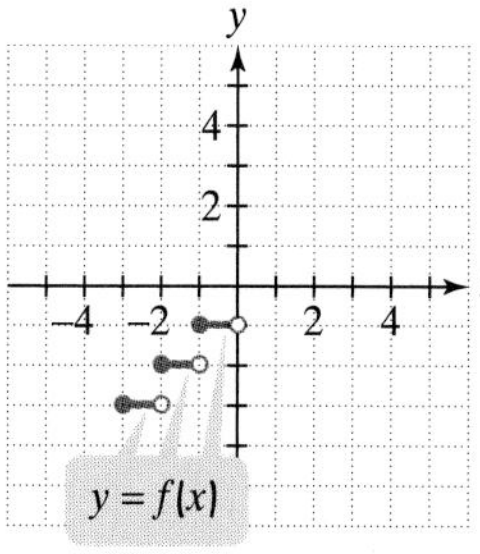

9 Identify intercepts from a function's graph.

Identifying Intercepts from a Function's Graph

Figure 2.11 illustrates how we can identify intercepts from a function's graph. To find the x-intercepts, look for the points at which the graph crosses the x-axis. There are three such points: $(-2, 0)$, $(3, 0)$, and $(5, 0)$. Thus, the x-intercepts are -2, 3, and 5. We express this in function notation by writing $f(-2) = 0$, $f(3) = 0$, and $f(5) = 0$. We say that -2, 3, and 5 are the *zeros of the function*. The **zeros of a function**, f, are the x-values for which $f(x) = 0$.

To find the y-intercept, look for the point at which the graph crosses the y-axis. This occurs at $(0, 3)$. Thus, the y-intercept is 3. We express this in function notation by writing $f(0) = 3$.

By the definition of a function, for each value of x we can have at most one value for y. What does this mean in terms of intercepts? **A function can have more than one x-intercept but at most one y-intercept.**

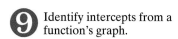

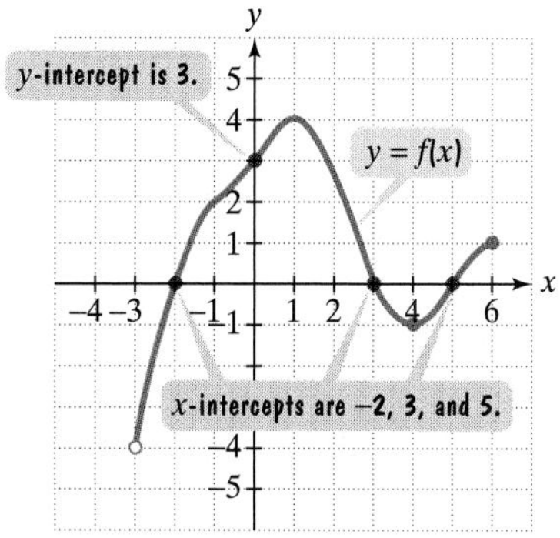

Figure 2.11 Identifying intercepts

EXERCISE SET 2.1

Practice Exercises

In Exercises 1–10, determine whether each relation is a function. Give the domain and range for each relation.

1. $\{(1, 2), (3, 4), (5, 5)\}$
2. $\{(4, 5), (6, 7), (8, 8)\}$
3. $\{(3, 4), (3, 5), (4, 4), (4, 5)\}$
4. $\{(5, 6), (5, 7), (6, 6), (6, 7)\}$
5. $\{(3, -2), (5, -2), (7, 1), (4, 9)\}$
6. $\{(10, 4), (-2, 4), (-1, 1), (5, 6)\}$
7. $\{(-3, -3), (-2, -2), (-1, -1), (0, 0)\}$
8. $\{(-7, -7), (-5, -5), (-3, -3), (0, 0)\}$
9. $\{(1, 4), (1, 5), (1, 6)\}$
10. $\{(4, 1), (5, 1), (6, 1)\}$

In Exercises 11–26, determine whether each equation defines y as a function of x.

11. $x + y = 16$
12. $x + y = 25$
13. $x^2 + y = 16$
14. $x^2 + y = 25$
15. $x^2 + y^2 = 16$
16. $x^2 + y^2 = 25$
17. $x = y^2$
18. $4x = y^2$
19. $y = \sqrt{x + 4}$
20. $y = -\sqrt{x + 4}$
21. $x + y^3 = 8$
22. $x + y^3 = 27$
23. $xy + 2y = 1$
24. $xy - 5y = 1$
25. $|x| - y = 2$
26. $|x| - y = 5$

In Exercises 27–38, evaluate each function at the given values of the independent variable and simplify.

27. $f(x) = 4x + 5$
 a. $f(6)$ **b.** $f(x + 1)$ **c.** $f(-x)$
28. $f(x) = 3x + 7$
 a. $f(4)$ **b.** $f(x + 1)$ **c.** $f(-x)$
29. $g(x) = x^2 + 2x + 3$
 a. $g(-1)$ **b.** $g(x + 5)$ **c.** $g(-x)$
30. $g(x) = x^2 - 10x - 3$
 a. $g(-1)$ **b.** $g(x + 2)$ **c.** $g(-x)$
31. $h(x) = x^4 - x^2 + 1$
 a. $h(2)$ **b.** $h(-1)$
 c. $h(-x)$ **d.** $h(3a)$
32. $h(x) = x^3 - x + 1$
 a. $h(3)$ **b.** $h(-2)$
 c. $h(-x)$ **d.** $h(3a)$
33. $f(r) = \sqrt{r + 6} + 3$
 a. $f(-6)$ **b.** $f(10)$ **c.** $f(x - 6)$

34. $f(r) = \sqrt{25 - r} - 6$

a. $f(16)$ **b.** $f(-24)$ **c.** $f(25 - 2x)$

35. $f(x) = \dfrac{4x^2 - 1}{x^2}$

a. $f(2)$ **b.** $f(-2)$ **c.** $f(-x)$

36. $f(x) = \dfrac{4x^3 + 1}{x^3}$

a. $f(2)$ **b.** $f(-2)$ **c.** $f(-x)$

37. $f(x) = \dfrac{x}{|x|}$

a. $f(6)$ **b.** $f(-6)$ **c.** $f(r^2)$

38. $f(x) = \dfrac{|x + 3|}{x + 3}$

a. $f(5)$ **b.** $f(-5)$ **c.** $f(-9 - x)$

In Exercises 39–50, graph the given functions, f and g, in the same rectangular coordinate system. Select integers for x, starting with −2 and ending with 2. Once you have obtained your graphs, describe how the graph of g is related to the graph of f.

39. $f(x) = x, g(x) = x + 3$

40. $f(x) = x, g(x) = x - 4$

41. $f(x) = -2x, g(x) = -2x - 1$

42. $f(x) = -2x, g(x) = -2x + 3$

43. $f(x) = x^2, g(x) = x^2 + 1$

44. $f(x) = x^2, g(x) = x^2 - 2$

45. $f(x) = |x|, g(x) = |x| - 2$

46. $f(x) = |x|, g(x) = |x| + 1$

47. $f(x) = x^3, g(x) = x^3 + 2$

48. $f(x) = x^3, g(x) = x^3 - 1$

49. $f(x) = 3, g(x) = 5$

50. $f(x) = -1, g(x) = 4$

In Exercises 51–54, graph the given square root functions, f and g, in the same rectangular coordinate system. Use the integer values of x given to the right of each function to obtain ordered pairs. Because only nonnegative numbers have square roots that are real numbers, be sure that each graph appears only for values of x that cause the expression under the radical sign to be greater than or equal to zero. Once you have obtained your graphs, describe how the graph of g is related to the graph of f.

51. $f(x) = \sqrt{x}$ $(x = 0, 1, 4, 9)$ and
$g(x) = \sqrt{x} - 1$ $(x = 0, 1, 4, 9)$

52. $f(x) = \sqrt{x}$ $(x = 0, 1, 4, 9)$ and
$g(x) = \sqrt{x} + 2$ $(x = 0, 1, 4, 9)$

53. $f(x) = \sqrt{x}$ $(x = 0, 1, 4, 9)$ and
$g(x) = \sqrt{x - 1}$ $(x = 1, 2, 5, 10)$

54. $f(x) = \sqrt{x}$ $(x = 0, 1, 4, 9)$ and
$g(x) = \sqrt{x + 2}$ $(x = -2, -1, 2, 7)$

In Exercises 55–64, use the vertical line test to identify graphs in which y is a function of x.

55.

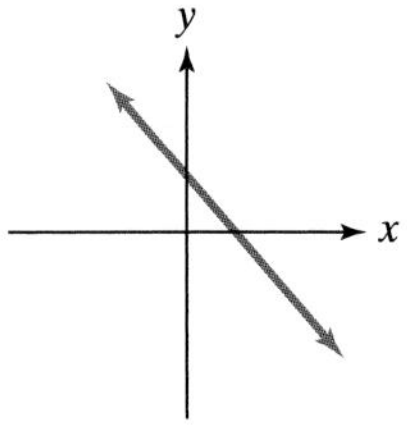

56.

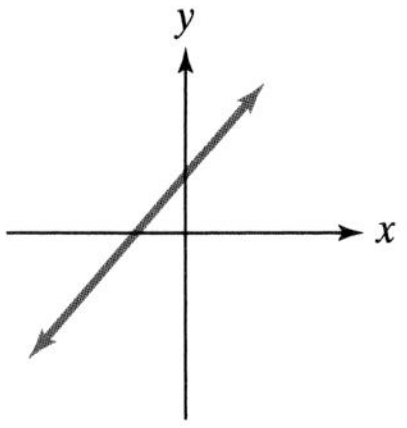

57.

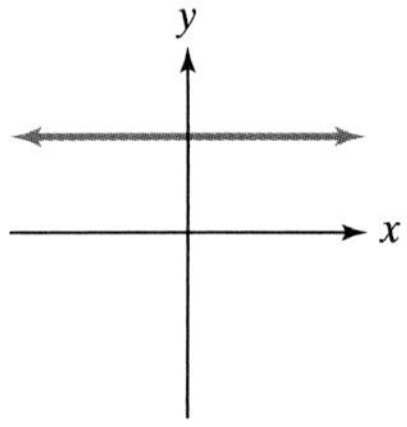

58.

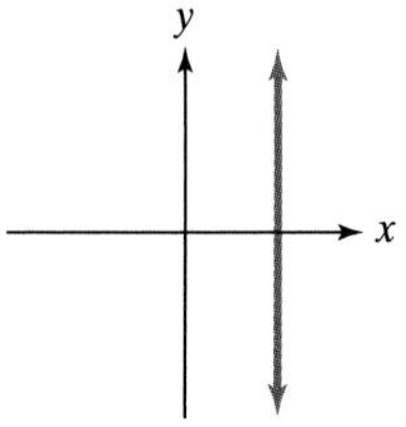

59.

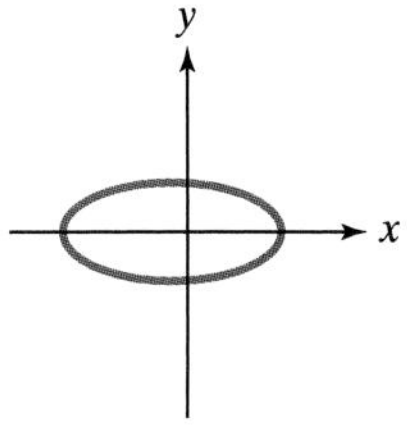

60.

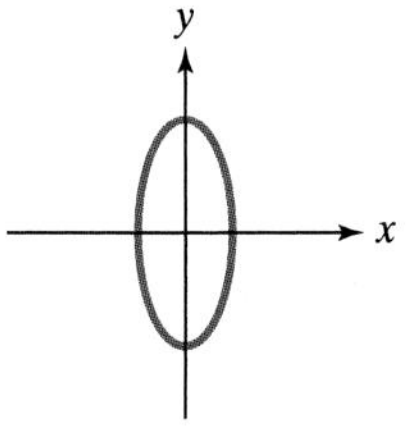

61.

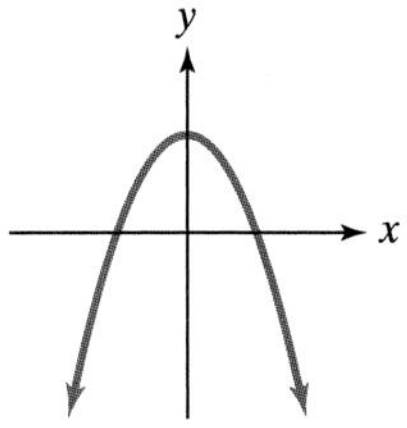

62.

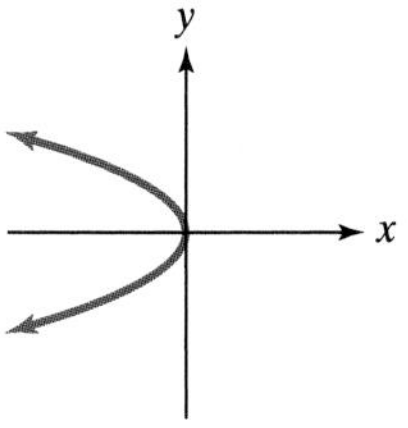

63.

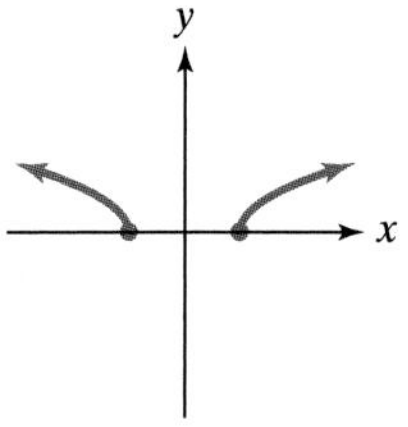

64.

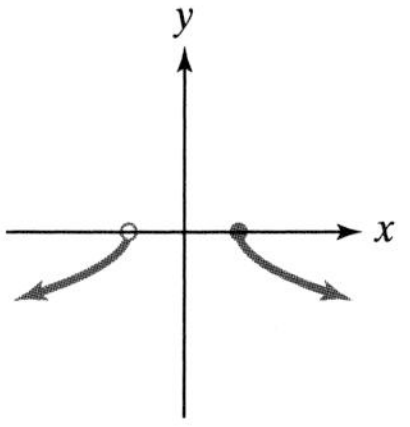

In Exercises 65–70, use the graph of f to find each indicated function value.

65. $f(-2)$

66. $f(2)$

67. $f(4)$

68. $f(-4)$

69. $f(-3)$

70. $f(-1)$

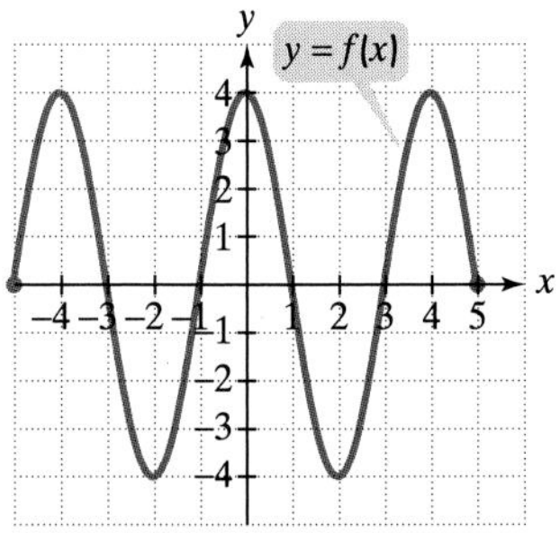

Use the graph of g to solve Exercises 71–76.

71. Find $g(-4)$.

72. Find $g(2)$.

73. Find $g(-10)$.

74. Find $g(10)$.

75. For what value of x is $g(x) = 1$?

76. For what value of x is $g(x) = -1$?

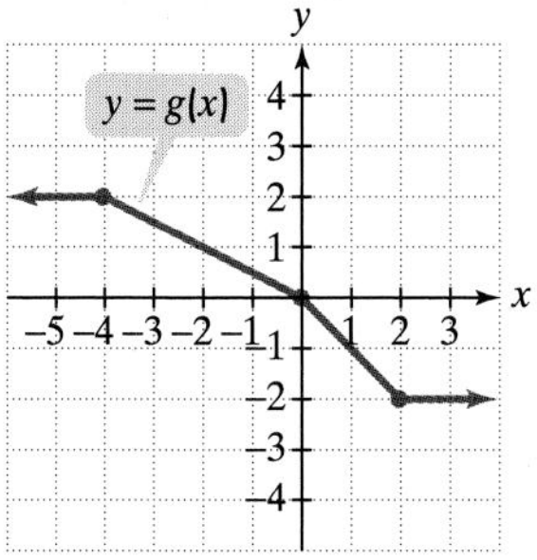

In Exercises 77–92, use the graph to determine **a.** *the function's domain;* **b.** *the function's range;* **c.** *the x-intercepts, if any;* **d.** *the y-intercept, if any; and* **e.** *the function values indicated below the graphs.*

77.

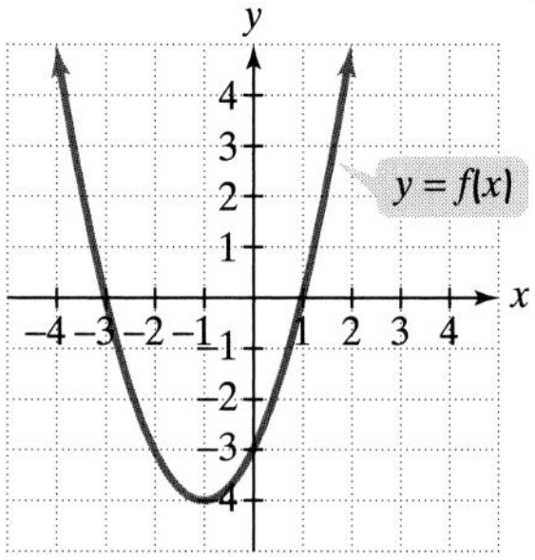

$f(-2) = ?\quad f(2) = ?$

78.

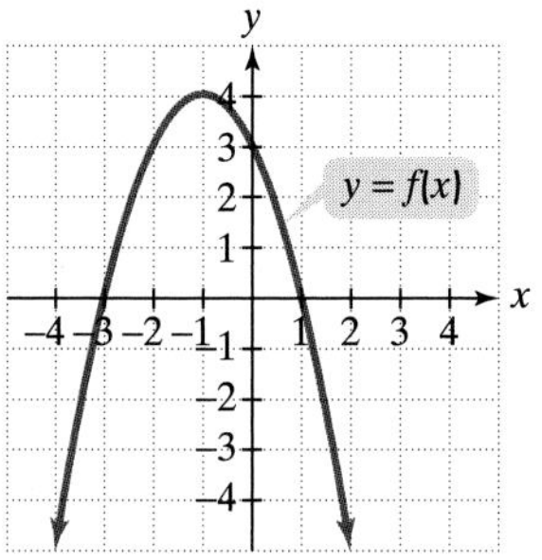

$f(-2) = ?\quad f(2) = ?$

79.

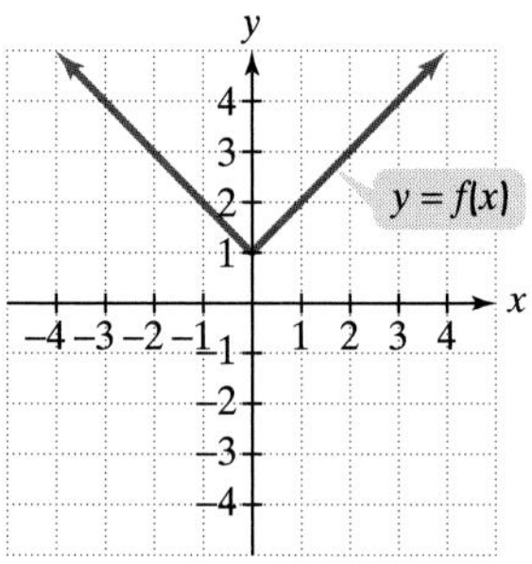

$f(-1) = ?\quad f(3) = ?$

80.

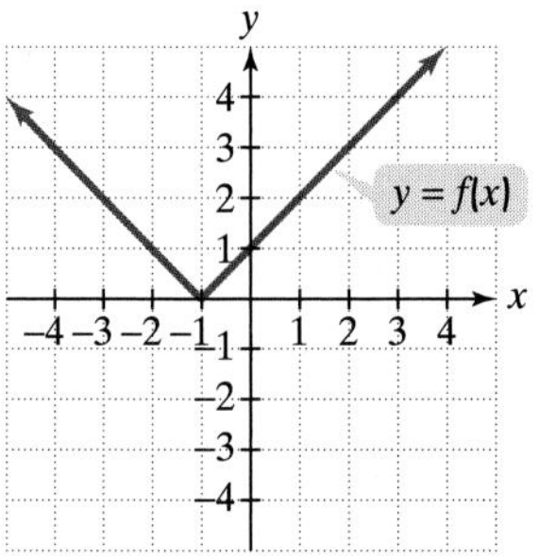

$f(-4) = ?\quad f(3) = ?$

81.

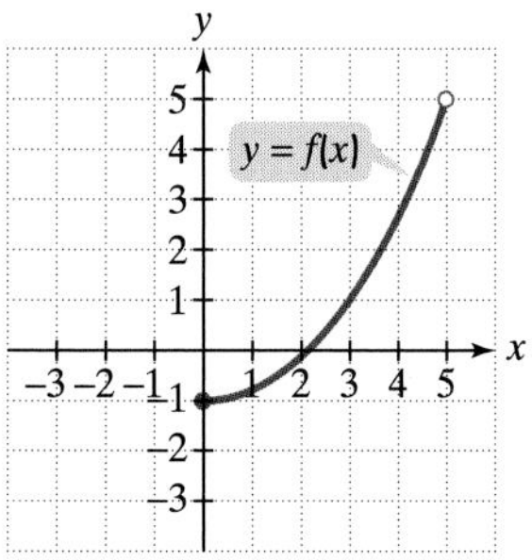

$f(3) = ?$

82.

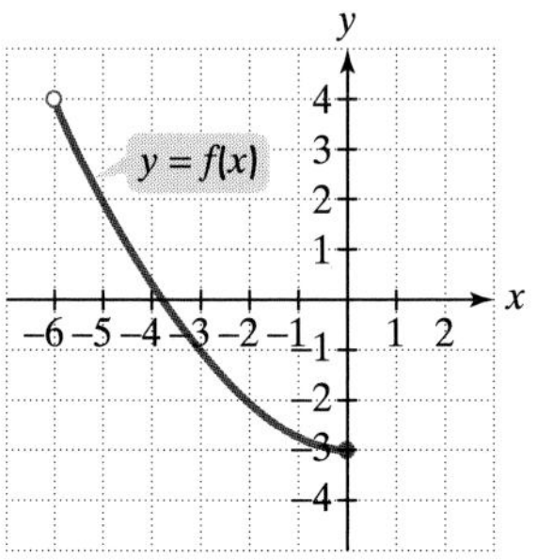

$f(-5) = ?$

83.

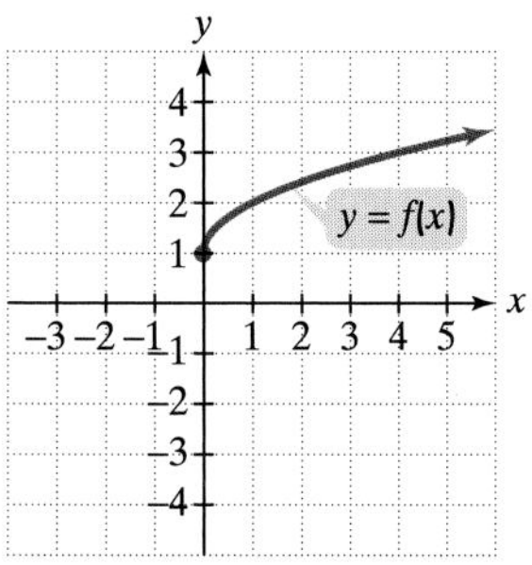

$f(4) = ?$

84.

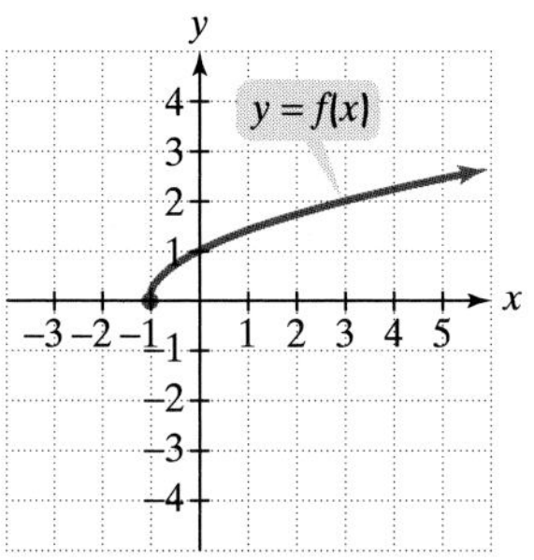

$f(3) = ?$

85.

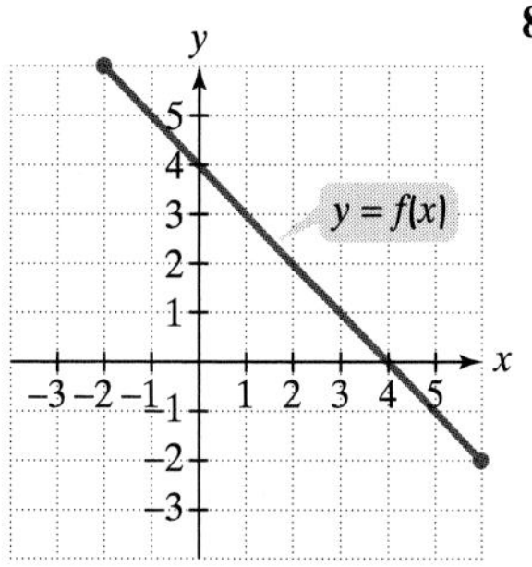

$f(-1) = ?$

86.

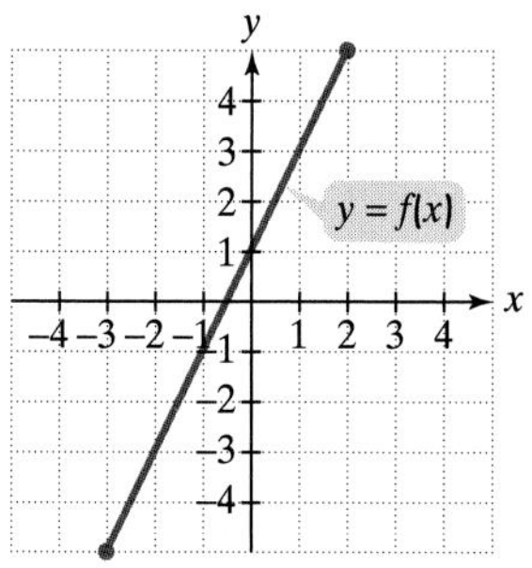

$f(-2) = ?$

87.

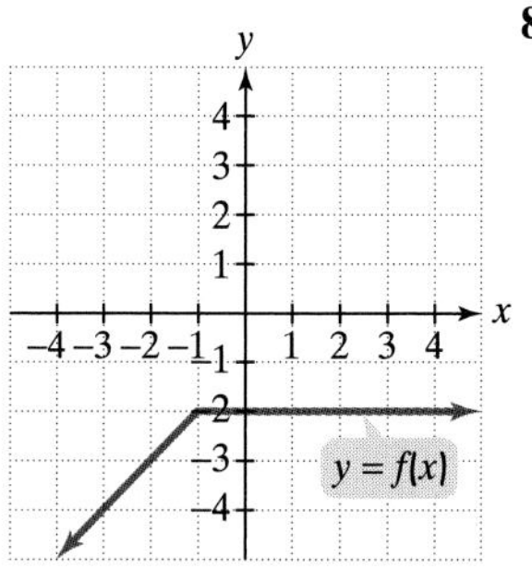

$f(-4) = ?\quad f(4) = ?$

88.

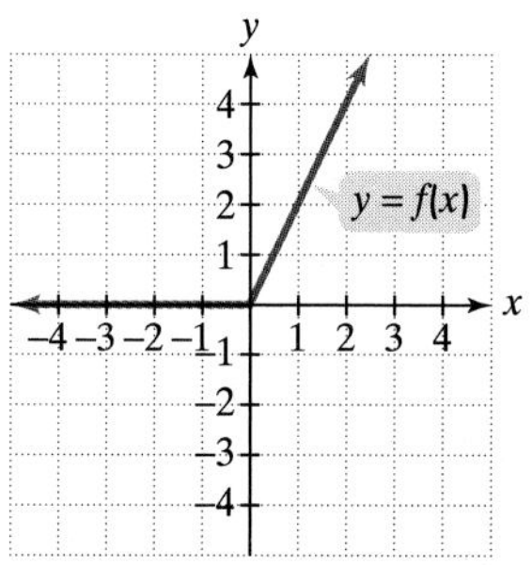

$f(-2) = ?\quad f(2) = ?$

89.

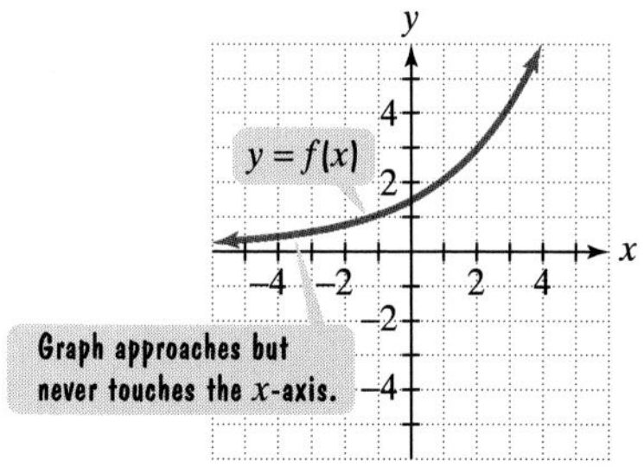

$f(4) = ?$

90.

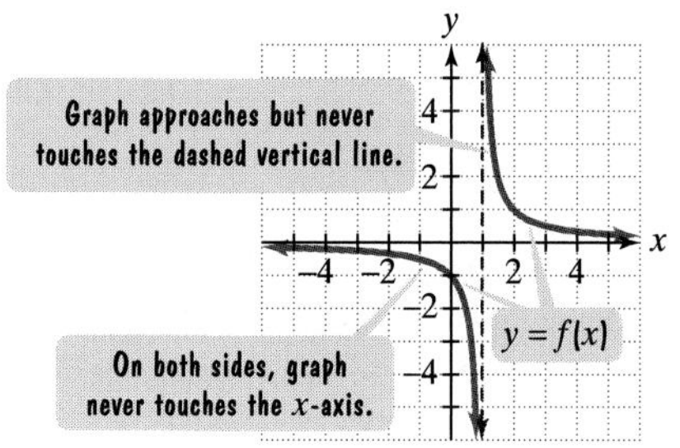

$f(2) = ?$

91.

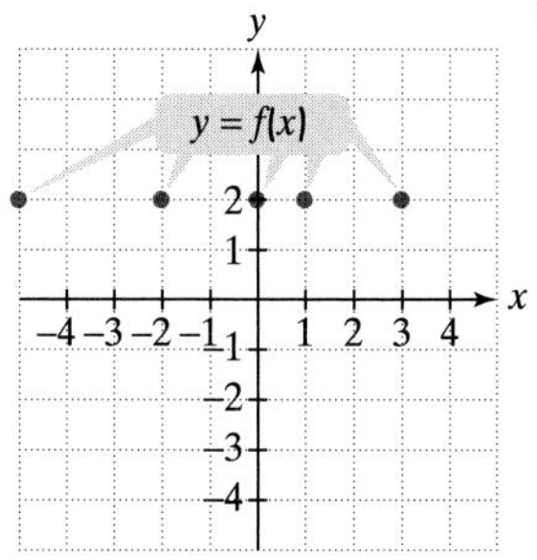

$f(-5) + f(3) = ?$

92.

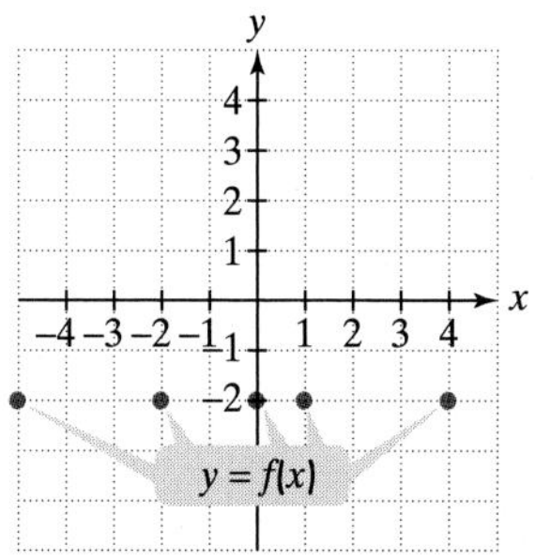

$f(-5) + f(4) = ?$

Practice Plus

In Exercises 93–94, let $f(x) = x^2 - x + 4$ *and* $g(x) = 3x - 5$.

93. Find $g(1)$ and $f(g(1))$. **94.** Find $g(-1)$ and $f(g(-1))$.

In Exercises 95–96, let f and g be defined by the following table:

x	$f(x)$	$g(x)$
−2	6	0
−1	3	4
0	−1	1
1	−4	−3
2	0	−6

95. Find $\sqrt{f(-1) - f(0)} - [g(2)]^2 + f(-2) \div g(2) \cdot g(-1)$.

96. Find $|f(1) - f(0)| - [g(1)]^2 + g(1) \div f(-1) \cdot g(2)$,

In Exercises 97–98, find $f(-x) - f(x)$ *for the given function f. Then simplify the expression.*

97. $f(x) = x^3 + x - 5$ **98.** $f(x) = x^2 - 3x + 7$

Application Exercises

99. The bar graph shows the percentage of children in the world's leading industrial countries who daydream about being rich.

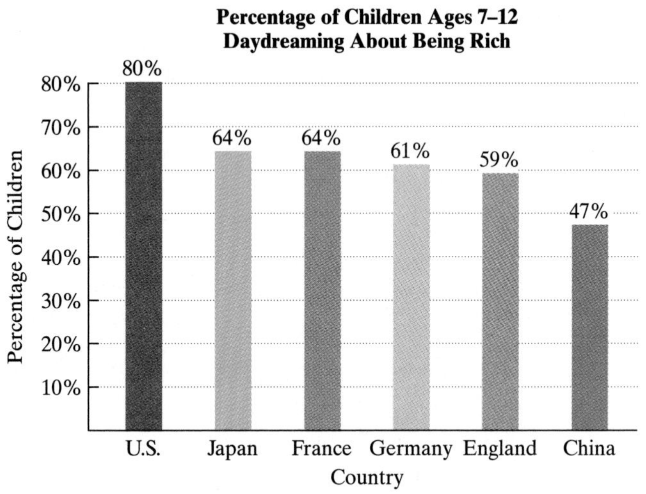

Source: Roper Starch Worldwide for A.B.C. Research

a. Write a set of six ordered pairs in which countries correspond to the percentage of children daydreaming about being rich. Each ordered pair should be in the form

(country, percent).

b. Is the relation in part (a) a function? Explain your answer.

c. Write a set of six ordered pairs in which the percentage of children daydreaming about being rich corresponds to countries. Each ordered pair should be in the form

(percent, country).

d. Is the relation in part (c) a function? Explain your answer.

100. The bar graph shows the breakdown of political ideologies in the United States.

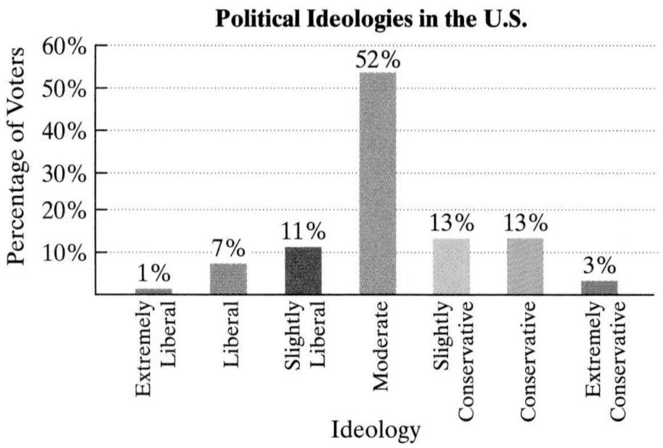

Source: Center for Political Studies, University of Michigan

a. Write a set of seven ordered pairs in which political ideologies correspond to percentages. Each ordered pair should be in the form

(ideology, percent).

Use EL, L, SL, M, SC, C, and EC to represent the respective ideologies from left to right.

b. Is the relation in part (a) a function? Explain your answer.

c. Write a set of seven ordered pairs in which percentages correspond to political ideologies. Each ordered pair should be in the form

(percent, ideology).

d. Is the relation in part (c) a function? Explain your answer.

The male minority? The graphs show enrollment in U.S. colleges, with projections through 2009. The trend indicated by the graphs is among the hottest topics of debate among college-admissions officers. Some private liberal arts colleges have quietly begun special efforts to recruit men—including admissions preferences for them.

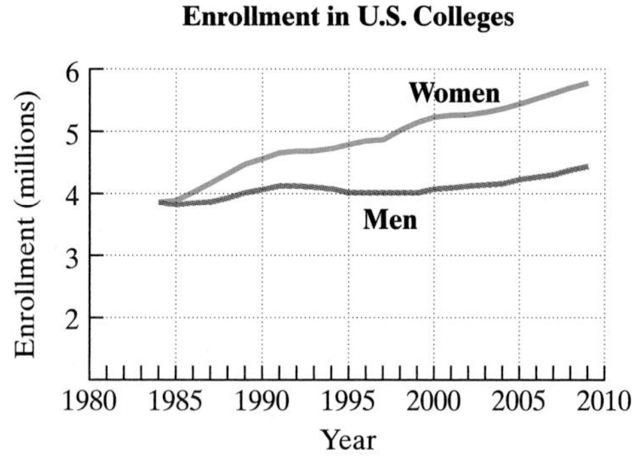

Source: Department of Education

The function

$$W(x) = 0.07x + 4.1$$

models the number of women, $W(x)$, *in millions, enrolled in U.S. colleges x years after 1984. The function*

$$M(x) = 0.01x + 3.9$$

models the number of men, $M(x)$, *in millions, enrolled in U.S. colleges x years after 1984. Use these functions to solve Exercises 101–104.*

101. Find and interpret $W(16)$. Identify this information as a point on the graph for women.

102. Find and interpret $M(16)$. Identify this information as a point on the graph for men.

103. Find and interpret $W(20) - M(20)$.

104. Find and interpret $W(25) - M(25)$.

The wage gap is used to compare the status of women's earnings relative to men's. The wage gap is expressed as a percent and is calculated by dividing the median, or middlemost, annual earnings for women by the median annual earnings for men. The line graph shows the wage gap for selected years from 1960 through 2003.

Median Women's Earnings as a Percentage of Median Men's Earnings in the U.S.

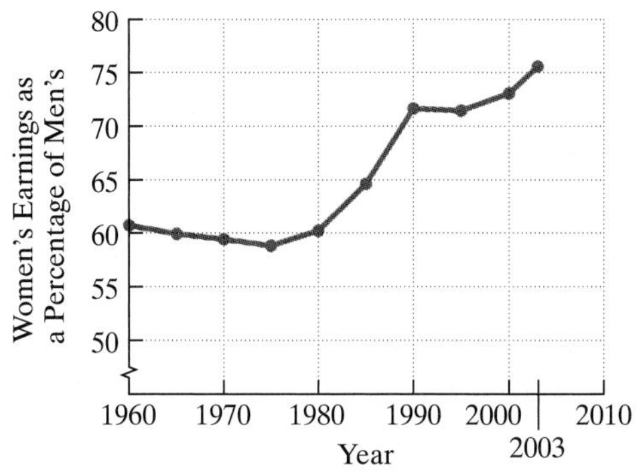

Source: U.S. Women's Bureau

The function

$$P(x) = 0.012x^2 - 0.16x + 60$$

models median women's earnings as a percentage of median men's earnings, $P(x)$, x years after 1960. Use the graph and this function to solve Exercises 105–106.

105. a. Use the graph to estimate, to the nearest percent, women's earnings as a percentage of men's in 2000.

b. Use the function to find women's earnings as a percentage of men's in 2000.

c. In 2000, median annual earnings for U.S. women and men were \$27,355 and \$37,339, respectively. What were women's earnings as a percentage of men's? Use a calculator and round to the nearest tenth of a percent. How well do your answers in parts (a) and (b) model the actual data?

106. a. Use the graph to estimate, to the nearest percent, women's earnings as a percentage of men's in 2003.

b. Use the function to find women's earnings as a percentage of men's in 2003. Round to the nearest tenth of a percent.

c. In 2003, median annual earnings for U.S. women and men were \$30,724 and \$40,668, respectively. What were women's earnings as a percentage of men's? Use a calculator and round to the nearest tenth of a percent. How well do your answers in parts (a) and (b) model the actual data?

In Exercises 107–110, you will be developing functions that model given conditions.

107. A company that manufactures bicycles has a fixed cost of \$100,000. It costs \$100 to produce each bicycle. The total cost for the company is the sum of its fixed cost and variable costs. Write the total cost, C, as a function of the number of bicycles produced, x. Then find and interpret $C(90)$.

108. A car was purchased for \$22,500. The value of the car decreases by \$3200 per year for the first six years. Write a function that describes the value of the car, V, after x years, where $0 \le x \le 7$. Then find and interpret $V(3)$.

109. You commute to work a distance of 40 miles and return on the same route at the end of the day. Your average rate on the return trip is 30 miles per hour faster than your average rate on the outgoing trip. Write the total time, T, in hours, devoted to your outgoing and return trips as a function of your rate on the outgoing trip, x. Then find and interpret $T(30)$. Hint:

$$\text{Time traveled} = \frac{\text{Distance traveled}}{\text{Rate of travel}}.$$

110. A chemist working on a flu vaccine needs to mix a 10% sodium-iodine solution with a 60% sodium-iodine solution to obtain a 50-milliliter mixture. Write the amount of sodium iodine in the mixture, S, in milliliters, as a function of the number of milliliters of the 10% solution used, x. Then find and interpret $S(30)$.

Writing in Mathematics

111. What is a relation? Describe what is meant by its domain and its range.

112. Explain how to determine whether a relation is a function. What is a function?

113. How do you determine if an equation in x and y defines y as a function of x?

114. Does $f(x)$ mean f times x when referring to a function f? If not, what does $f(x)$ mean? Provide an example with your explanation.

115. What is the graph of a function?

116. Explain how the vertical line test is used to determine whether a graph represents a function.

117. Explain how to identify the domain and range of a function from its graph.

118. For people filing a single return, federal income tax is a function of adjusted gross income because for each value of adjusted gross income there is a specific tax to be paid. By contrast, the price of a house is not a function of the lot size on which the house sits because houses on same-sized lots can sell for many different prices.

a. Describe an everyday situation between variables that is a function.

b. Describe an everyday situation between variables that is not a function.

119. Do you believe that the trend shown by the graphs for Exercises 101–104 should be reversed by providing admissions preferences for men? Explain your position on this issue.

Technology Exercise

120. Use a graphing utility to verify any five pairs of graphs that you drew by hand in Exercises 39–54.

Critical Thinking Exercises

121. Which one of the following is true based on the graph of f in the figure?

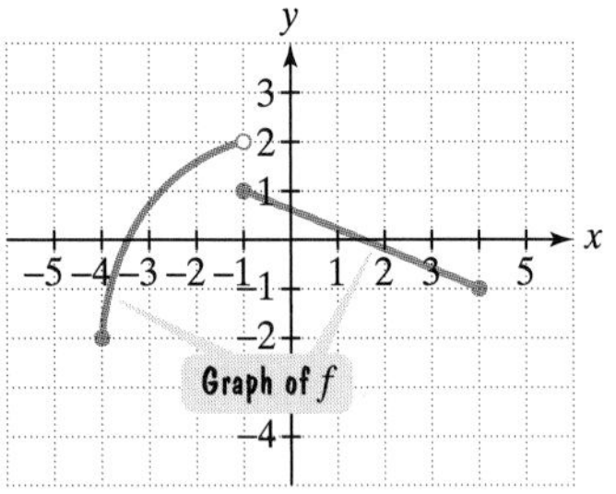

a. The domain of f is $[-4, 1) \cup (1, 4]$.
b. The range of f is $[-2, 2]$.
c. $f(-1) - f(4) = 2$
d. $f(0) = 2.1$

122. If $f(x) = 3x + 7$, find $\dfrac{f(a + h) - f(a)}{h}$.

123. Give an example of a relation with the following characteristics: The relation is a function containing two ordered pairs. Reversing the components in each ordered pair results in a relation that is not a function.

124. If $f(x + y) = f(x) + f(y)$ and $f(1) = 3$, find $f(2)$, $f(3)$, and $f(4)$. Is $f(x + y) = f(x) + f(y)$ for all functions?

SECTION 2.2 More on Functions and Their Graphs

Objectives

1. Find and simplify a function's difference quotient.
2. Understand and use piecewise functions.
3. Identify intervals on which a function increases, decreases, or is constant.
4. Use graphs to locate relative maxima or minima.
5. Identify even or odd functions and recognize their symmetries.
6. Graph step functions.

"Our relationship is just going through a phase." When that phase reaches a point where married couples cannot agree on anything else, they agree on a divorce, frequently arranged so that lawyers can live happily ever after. The graph in Figure 2.12 shows the percent distribution of divorces in the United States by number of years of marriage.

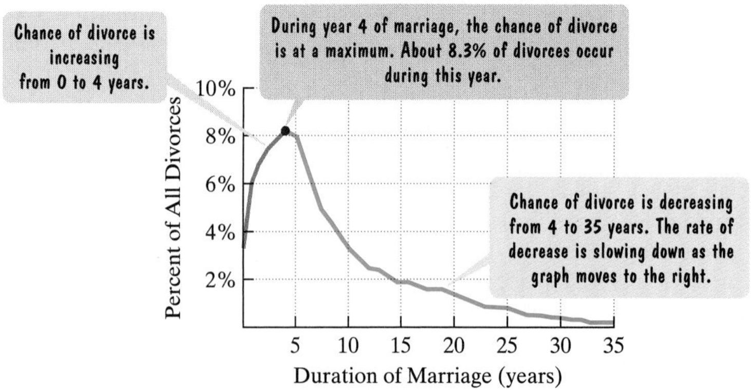

Figure 2.12
Source: Divorce Center

You are probably familiar with the words and phrases used to describe the graph in Figure 2.12:

increasing decreasing maximum slowing rate of decrease

In this section, you will enhance your intuitive understanding of ways of describing graphs by viewing these descriptions from the perspective of functions.

1 Find and simplify a function's difference quotient.

Functions and Difference Quotients

In the next section, we will be studying the average rate of change of a function. A ratio, called the *difference quotient*, plays an important role in understanding the rate at which functions change.

Definition of a Difference Quotient

The expression

$$\frac{f(x+h)-f(x)}{h}$$

for $h \neq 0$ is called the **difference quotient**.

EXAMPLE 1 Evaluating and Simplifying a Difference Quotient

If $f(x) = 2x^2 - x + 3$, find and simplify each expression:

a. $f(x+h)$ **b.** $\frac{f(x+h)-f(x)}{h}$, $h \neq 0$.

Solution

a. We find $f(x+h)$ by replacing x with $x + h$ each time that x appears in the equation.

$$f(x) = 2x^2 \quad - \quad x \quad + \quad 3$$

Replace x with $x+h$. Replace x with $x+h$. Replace x with $x+h$. Copy the 3. There is no x in this term.

$$\begin{aligned} f(x+h) &= 2(x+h)^2 - (x+h) + 3 \\ &= 2(x^2 + 2xh + h^2) - x - h + 3 \\ &= 2x^2 + 4xh + 2h^2 - x - h + 3 \end{aligned}$$

b. Using our result from part (a), we obtain the following:

This is $f(x+h)$ from part (a). This is $f(x)$ from the given equation.

$$\frac{f(x+h)-f(x)}{h} = \frac{\boxed{2x^2 + 4xh + 2h^2 - x - h + 3} - (2x^2 - x + 3)}{h}$$

$$= \frac{2x^2 + 4xh + 2h^2 - x - h + 3 - 2x^2 + x - 3}{h}$$ Remove parentheses and change the sign of each term in the parentheses.

$$= \frac{(2x^2 - 2x^2) + (-x + x) + (3 - 3) + 4xh + 2h^2 - h}{h}$$ Group like terms.

$$= \frac{4xh + 2h^2 - 1h}{h}$$ Simplify.

We wrote $-h$ as $-1h$ to avoid possible errors in the next factoring step.

$$= \frac{h(4x + 2h - 1)}{h}$$ Factor h from the numerator.

$$= 4x + 2h - 1$$ Divide out identical factors of h in the numerator and denominator.

Check Point 1 If $f(x) = -2x^2 + x + 5$, find and simplify each expression:

a. $f(x+h)$ **b.** $\frac{f(x+h)-f(x)}{h}$, $h \neq 0$.

2 Understand and use piecewise functions.

Piecewise Functions

A cellular phone company offers the following plan:

- \$20 per month buys 60 minutes.
- Additional time costs \$0.40 per minute.

We can represent this plan mathematically by writing the total monthly cost, C, as a function of the number of calling minutes, t.

$$C(t) = \begin{cases} 20 & \text{if } 0 \le t \le 60 \\ 20 + 0.40(t - 60) & \text{if } t > 60 \end{cases}$$

The cost is \$20 for up to and including 60 calling minutes.

The cost is \$20 plus \$0.40 per minute for additional time for more than 60 calling minutes.

\$20 for first 60 minutes

\$0.40 per minute

times the number of calling minutes exceeding 60

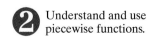

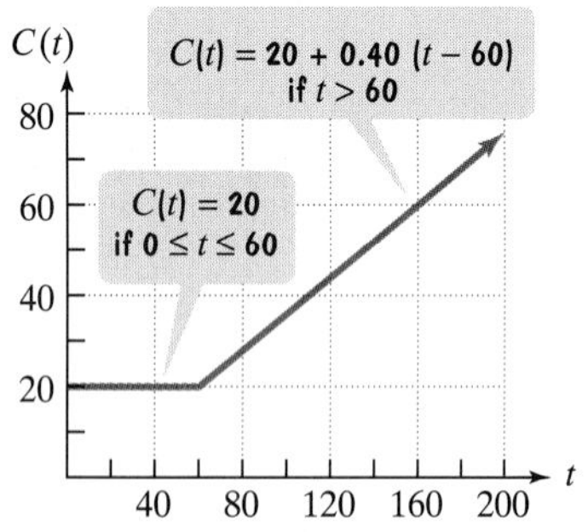

Figure 2.13

A function that is defined by two (or more) equations over a specified domain is called a **piecewise function**. Many cellular phone plans can be represented with piecewise functions. The graph of the piecewise function described above is shown in Figure 2.13.

EXAMPLE 2 Evaluating a Piecewise Function

Use the function that describes the cellular phone plan

$$C(t) = \begin{cases} 20 & \text{if } 0 \le t \le 60 \\ 20 + 0.40(t - 60) & \text{if } t > 60 \end{cases}$$

to find and interpret each of the following:

a. $C(30)$ **b.** $C(100)$.

Solution

a. To find $C(30)$, we let $t = 30$. Because 30 lies between 0 and 60, we use the first line of the piecewise function.

$C(t) = 20$ This is the function's equation for $0 \le t \le 60$.

$C(30) = 20$ Replace t with 30. Regardless of this function's input, the constant output is 20.

This means that with 30 calling minutes, the monthly cost is \$20. This can be visually represented by the point $(30, 20)$ on the first piece of the graph in Figure 2.13.

b. To find $C(100)$, we let $t = 100$. Because 100 is greater than 60, we use the second line of the piecewise function.

$C(t) = 20 + 0.40(t - 60)$ This is the function's equation for $t > 60$.

$C(100) = 20 + 0.40(100 - 60)$ Replace t with 100.

$= 20 + 0.40(40)$ Subtract within parentheses: $100 - 60 = 40$.

$= 20 + 16$ Multiply: $0.40(40) = 16$.

$= 36$ Add: $20 + 16 = 36$.

Thus, $C(100) = 36$. This means that with 100 calling minutes, the monthly cost is \$36. This can be visually represented by the point $(100, 36)$ on the second piece of the graph in Figure 2.13.

Check Point 2 Use the function in Example 2 to find and interpret each of the following:

a. $C(40)$ **b.** $C(80)$.

Identify solutions on the graph in Figure 2.13.

3 Identify intervals on which a function increases, decreases, or is constant.

Increasing and Decreasing Functions

Too late for that flu shot now! It's only 8 A.M. and you're feeling lousy. Your temperature is 101°F. Fascinated by the way that algebra models the world (your author is projecting a bit here), you decide to construct graphs showing your body temperature as a function of the time of day. You decide to let x represent the number of hours after 8 A.M. and $f(x)$ your temperature at time x.

At 8 A.M. your temperature is 101°F and you are not feeling well. However, your temperature starts to decrease. It reaches normal (98.6°F) by 11 A.M. Feeling energized, you construct the graph shown on the right, indicating decreasing temperature for $\{x|0 < x < 3\}$, or on the interval $(0, 3)$.

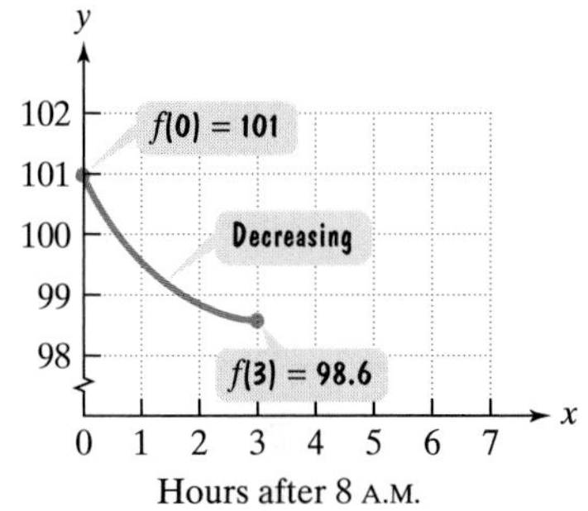

Temperature decreases on (0, 3), reaching 98.6° by 11 A.M.

Did creating that first graph drain you of your energy? Your temperature starts to rise after 11 A.M. By 1 P.M., 5 hours after 8 A.M., your temperature reaches 100°F. However, you keep plotting points on your graph. At the right, we can see that your temperature increases for $\{x|3 < x < 5\}$, or on the interval $(3, 5)$.

The graph of f is decreasing to the left of $x = 3$ and increasing to the right of $x = 3$. Thus, your temperature 3 hours after 8 A.M. was at its lowest point. Your relative minimum temperature was 98.6°.

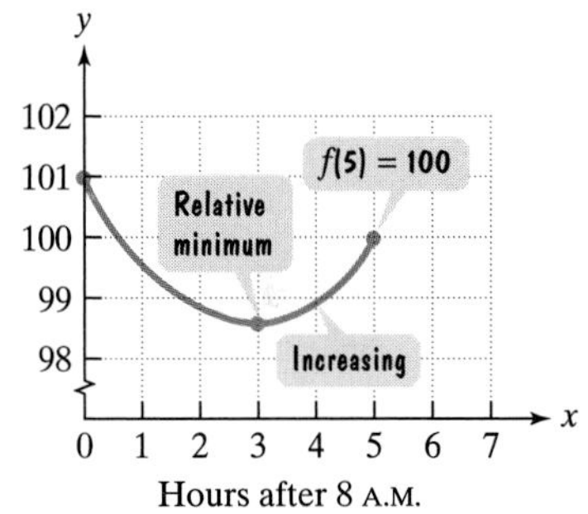

Temperature increases on (3, 5).

By 3 P.M., your temperature is no worse than it was at 1 P.M.: It is still 100°F. (Of course, it's no better, either.) Your temperature remained the same, or constant, for $\{x|5 < x < 7\}$, or on the interval $(5, 7)$.

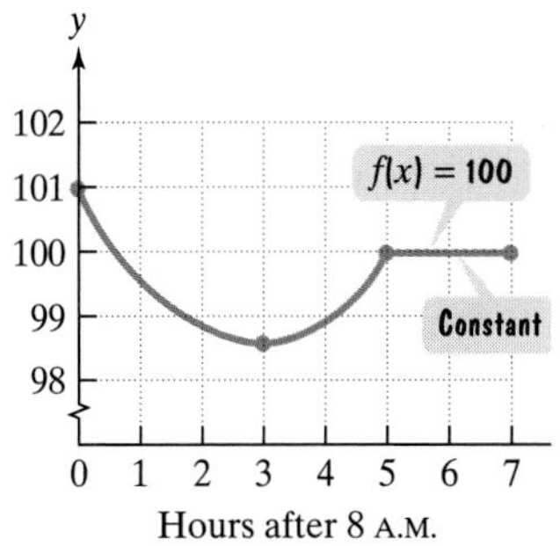

The time-temperature flu scenario illustrates that a function f is increasing when its graph rises from left to right, decreasing when its graph falls from left to right, and remains constant when it neither rises nor falls. Let's now provide a more precise algebraic description for these intuitive concepts.

Increasing, Decreasing, and Constant Functions

1. A function is **increasing** on an open interval, I, if for any x_1 and x_2 in the interval, where $x_1 < x_2$, then $f(x_1) < f(x_2)$.
2. A function is **decreasing** on an open interval, I, if for any x_1 and x_2 in the interval, where $x_1 < x_2$, then $f(x_1) > f(x_2)$.
3. A function is **constant** on an open interval, I, if for any x_1 and x_2 in the interval, where $x_1 < x_2$, then $f(x_1) = f(x_2)$.

Increasing

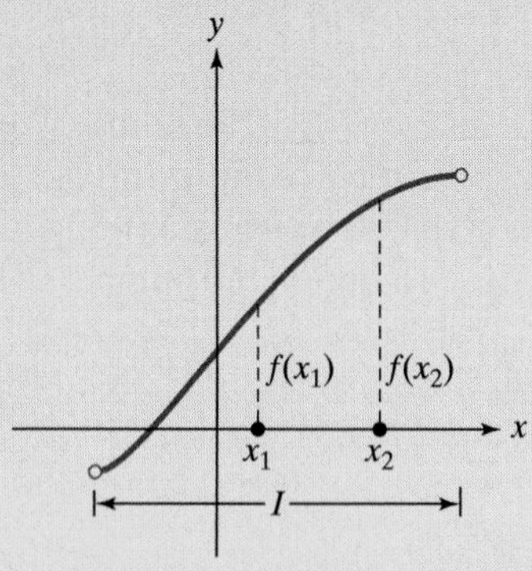

(1) For $x_1 < x_2$ in I,
$f(x_1) < f(x_2)$;
f is increasing on I.

Decreasing

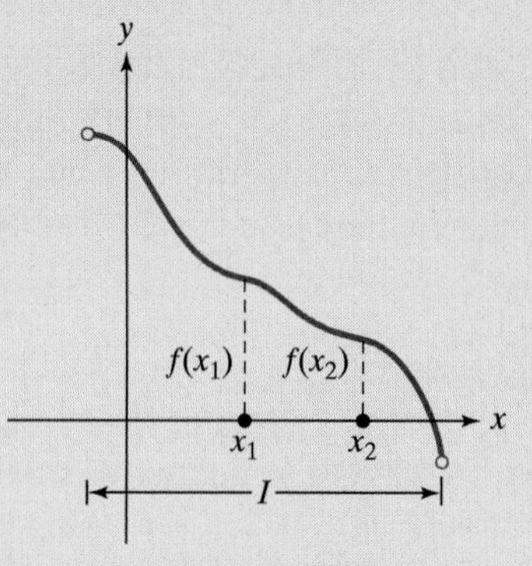

(2) For $x_1 < x_2$ in I,
$f(x_1) > f(x_2)$;
f is decreasing on I.

Constant

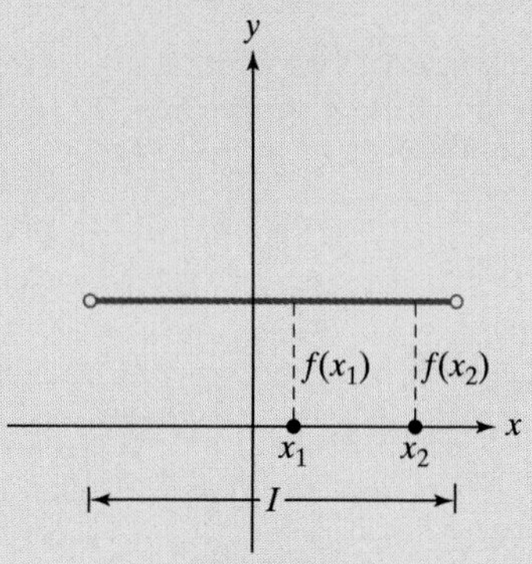

(3) For $x_1 < x_2$ in I,
$f(x_1) = f(x_2)$;
f is constant on I.

Study Tip

The open intervals describing where functions increase, decrease, or are constant, use x-coordinates and not the y-coordinates.

EXAMPLE 3 Intervals on Which a Function Increases, Decreases, or Is Constant

State the intervals on which each given function is increasing, decreasing, or constant.

a.

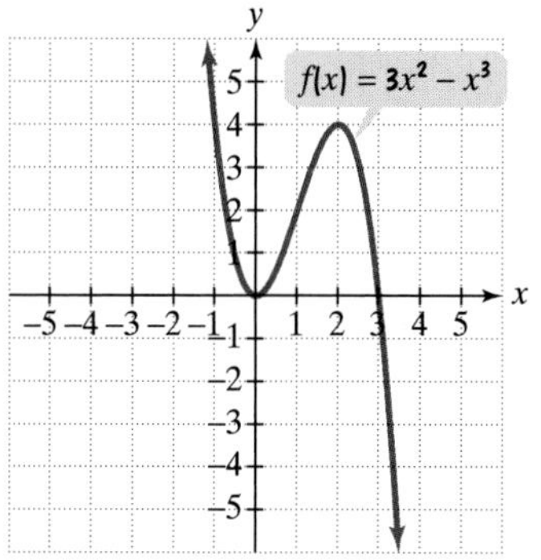

b.

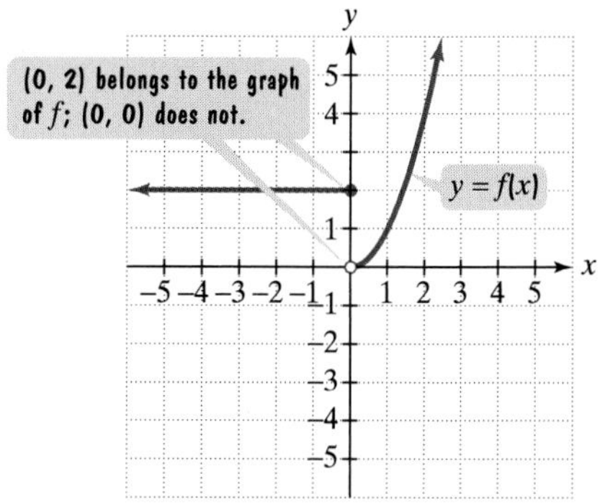

Solution

a. The function is decreasing on the interval $(-\infty, 0)$, increasing on the interval $(0, 2)$, and decreasing on the interval $(2, \infty)$.

b. Although the function's equations are not given, the graph indicates that the function is defined in two pieces. The part of the graph to the left of the y-axis shows that the function is constant on the interval $(-\infty, 0)$. The part to the right of the y-axis shows that the function is increasing on the interval $(0, \infty)$.

Check Point 3 State the intervals on which the given function is increasing, decreasing, or constant.

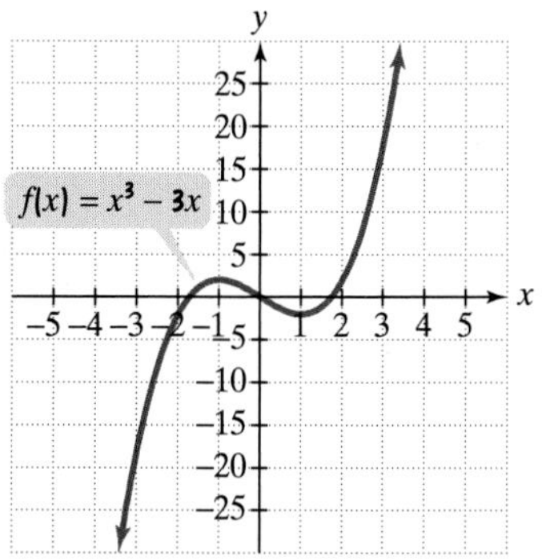

4 Use graphs to locate relative maxima or minima.

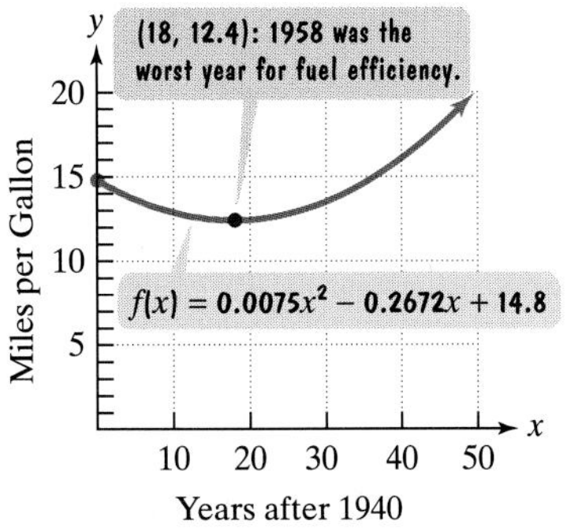

Figure 2.14 Fuel efficiency of U.S. automobiles over time

Relative Maxima and Relative Minima

The points at which a function changes its increasing or decreasing behavior can be used to find the *relative maximum* or *relative minimum* values of the function. For example, consider the function with which we opened the previous section:

$$f(x) = 0.0075x^2 - 0.2672x + 14.8.$$

Recall that the function models the average number of miles per gallon of U.S. automobiles, $f(x)$, x years after 1940. The graph of this function is shown as a continuous curve in Figure 2.14. (It can also be shown as a series of points, each point representing a year and miles per gallon for that year.)

The graph of f is decreasing to the left of $x = 18$ and increasing to the right of $x = 18$. Thus, 18 years after 1940, in 1958, fuel efficiency was at a minimum. We say that the relative minimum fuel efficiency is $f(18)$, or approximately 12.4 miles per gallon. Mathematicians use the word "relative" to suggest that relative to an open interval about 18, the value $f(18)$ is smallest.

Definitions of Relative Maximum and Relative Minimum

1. A function value $f(a)$ is a **relative maximum** of f if there exists an open interval about a such that $f(a) > f(x)$ for all x in the open interval.
2. A function value $f(b)$ is a **relative minimum** of f if there exists an open interval about b such that $f(b) < f(x)$ for all x in the open interval.

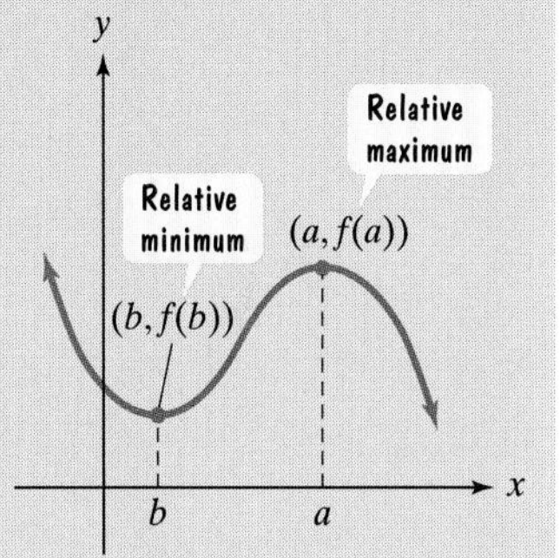

Study Tip

The word *local* is sometimes used instead of *relative* when describing maxima or minima. If f has a relative, or local, maximum at a, $f(a)$ is greater than the values of f near a. If f has a relative, or local, minimum at b, $f(b)$ is less than the values of f near b.

If the graph of a function is given, we can often visually locate the number(s) at which the function has a relative maximum or a relative minimum. For example, the graph of f in Figure 2.15 shows that

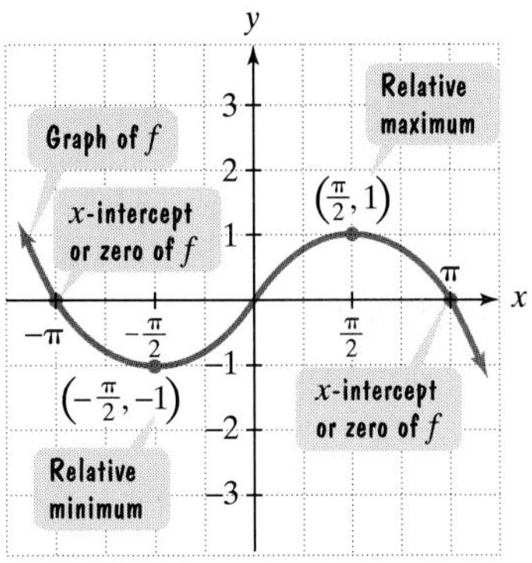

Figure 2.15 Using a graph to locate where f has a relative maximum or minimum

- f has a relative maximum at $\frac{\pi}{2}$.

  The relative maximum is $f\left(\frac{\pi}{2}\right) = 1$.

- f has a relative minimum at $-\frac{\pi}{2}$.

  The relative minimum is $f\left(-\frac{\pi}{2}\right) = -1$.

Notice that f does not have a relative maximum or minimum at $-\pi$ and π, the x-intercepts, or zeros, of the function.

5 Identify even or odd functions and recognize their symmetries.

Even and Odd Functions and Symmetry

Is beauty in the eye of the beholder? Or are there certain objects (or people) that are so well balanced and proportioned that they are universally pleasing to the eye? What constitutes an attractive human face? In Figure 2.16, we've drawn lines between paired features and marked the midpoints. Notice how the features line up almost perfectly. Each half of the face is a mirror image of the other half through the white vertical line.

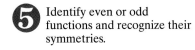

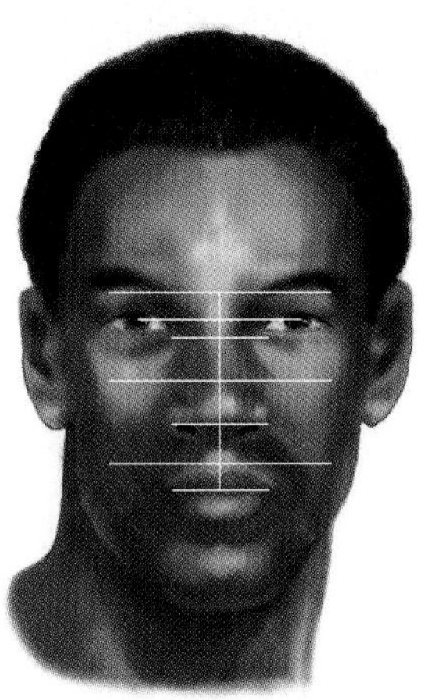

Figure 2.16 To most people, an attractive face is one in which each half is an almost perfect mirror image of the other half.

Did you know that graphs of some equations exhibit exactly the kind of symmetry shown by the attractive face in Figure 2.16? The word *symmetry* comes from the Greek *symmetria*, meaning "the same measure." We can identify graphs with symmetry by looking at a function's equation and determining if the function is *even* or *odd*.

Definition of Even and Odd Functions

The function f is an **even function** if

$$f(-x) = f(x) \quad \text{for all } x \text{ in the domain of } f.$$

The right side of the equation of an even function does not change if x is replaced with $-x$.

The function f is an **odd function** if

$$f(-x) = -f(x) \quad \text{for all } x \text{ in the domain of } f.$$

Every term in the right side of the equation of an odd function changes its sign if x is replaced with $-x$.

EXAMPLE 4 Identifying Even or Odd Functions

Determine whether each of the following functions is even, odd, or neither:

a. $f(x) = x^3 - 6x$ **b.** $g(x) = x^4 - 2x^2$ **c.** $h(x) = x^2 + 2x + 1$.

Solution In each case, replace x with $-x$ and simplify. If the right side of the equation stays the same, the function is even. If every term on the right changes sign, the function is odd.

a. We use the given function's equation, $f(x) = x^3 - 6x$, to find $f(-x)$.

Use $f(x) = x^3 - 6x$.

Replace x with $-x$.

$$f(-x) = (-x)^3 - 6(-x) = (-x)(-x)(-x) - 6(-x) = -x^3 + 6x$$

There are two terms on the right side of the given equation, $f(x) = x^3 - 6x$, and each term changed its sign when we replaced x with $-x$. Because $f(-x) = -f(x)$, f is an odd function.

b. We use the given function's equation, $g(x) = x^4 - 2x^2$, to find $g(-x)$.

Use $g(x) = x^4 - 2x^2$.

Replace x with $-x$.

$$g(-x) = (-x)^4 - 2(-x)^2 = (-x)(-x)(-x)(-x) - 2(-x)(-x)$$
$$= x^4 - 2x^2$$

The right side of the equation of the given function, $g(x) = x^4 - 2x^2$, did not change when we replaced x with $-x$. Because $g(-x) = g(x)$, g is an even function.

c. We use the given function's equation, $h(x) = x^2 + 2x + 1$, to find $h(-x)$.

Use $h(x) = x^2 + 2x + 1$.

Replace x with $-x$.

$$h(-x) = (-x)^2 + 2(-x) + 1 = x^2 - 2x + 1$$

The right side of the equation of the given function, $h(x) = x^2 + 2x + 1$, changed when we replaced x with $-x$. Thus, $h(-x) \neq h(x)$, so h is not an even function. The sign of *each* of the three terms in the equation for $h(x)$ did not change when we replaced x with $-x$. Only the second term changed signs. Thus, $h(-x) \neq -h(x)$, so h is not an odd function. We conclude that h is neither an even nor an odd function.

Check Point 4 Determine whether each of the following functions is even, odd, or neither:

a. $f(x) = x^2 + 6$ **b.** $g(x) = 7x^3 - x$ **c.** $h(x) = x^5 + 1$.

Now, let's see what even and odd functions tell us about a function's graph. Begin with the even function $f(x) = x^2 - 4$, shown in Figure 2.17. The function is even because

$$f(-x) = (-x)^2 - 4 = x^2 - 4 = f(x).$$

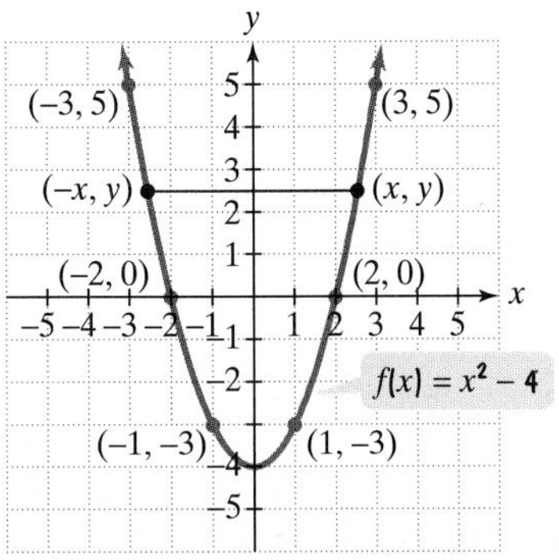

Figure 2.17 y-axis symmetry with $f(-x) = f(x)$

Examine the pairs of points shown, such as $(3, 5)$ and $(-3, 5)$. Notice that we obtain the same y-coordinate whenever we evaluate the function at a value of x and the value of its opposite, $-x$. Like the attractive face, each half of the graph is a mirror image of the other half through the y-axis. If we were to fold the paper along the y-axis, the two halves of the graph would coincide. This causes the graph to be *symmetric with respect to the y-axis*. A graph is **symmetric with respect to the y-axis** if, for every point (x, y) on the graph, the point $(-x, y)$ is also on the graph. All even functions have graphs with this kind of symmetry.

Even Functions and y-Axis Symmetry

The graph of an even function in which $f(-x) = f(x)$ is symmetric with respect to the y-axis.

Now, consider the graph of the function $f(x) = x^3$, shown in Figure 2.18. The function is odd because

$$f(-x) = (-x)^3 = (-x)(-x)(-x) = -x^3 = -f(x).$$

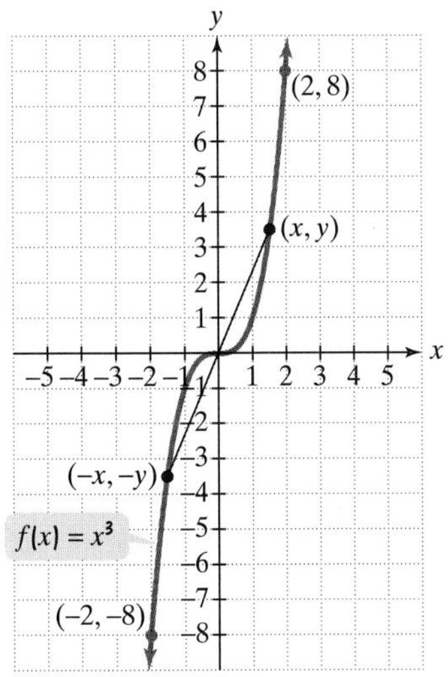

Figure 2.18 Origin symmetry with $f(-x) = -f(x)$

Although the graph in Figure 2.18 is not symmetric with respect to the y-axis, it is symmetric in another way. Look at the pairs of points, such as $(2, 8)$ and $(-2, -8)$. For each point (x, y) on the graph, the point $(-x, -y)$ is also on the graph. The points $(2, 8)$ and $(-2, -8)$ are reflections of one another about the origin. This means that

- the points are the same distance from the origin, and
- the points lie on a line through the origin.

A graph is **symmetric with respect to the origin** if, for every point (x, y) on the graph, the point $(-x, -y)$ is also on the graph. Observe that the first- and third-quadrant portions of $f(x) = x^3$ are reflections of one another with respect to the origin. Notice that $f(x)$ and $f(-x)$ have opposite signs, so that $f(-x) = -f(x)$. All odd functions have graphs with origin symmetry.

Odd Functions and Origin Symmetry

The graph of an odd function in which $f(-x) = -f(x)$ is symmetric with respect to the origin.

6 Graph step functions.

Table 2.1 Cost of First-Class Mail (Effective June 30, 2002)

Weight Not Over	Cost
1 ounce	$0.37
2 ounces	0.60
3 ounces	0.83
4 ounces	1.06
5 ounces	1.29

Source: U.S. Postal Service

Step Functions

Have you ever mailed a letter that seemed heavier than usual? Perhaps you worried that the letter would not have enough postage. Costs for mailing a letter weighing up to 5 ounces are given in Table 2.1. If your letter weighs an ounce or less, the cost is $0.37. If your letter weighs 1.05 ounces, 1.50 ounces, 1.90 ounces, or 2.00 ounces, the cost "steps" to $0.60. The cost does not take on any value between $0.37 and $0.60. If your letter weighs 2.05 ounces, 2.50 ounces, 2.90 ounces, or 3 ounces, the cost "steps" to $0.83. Cost increases are $0.23 per step.

Now, let's see what the graph of the function that models this situation looks like. Let

$$x = \text{the weight of the letter, in ounces, and}$$
$$y = f(x) = \text{the cost of mailing a letter weighing } x \text{ ounces.}$$

The graph is shown in Figure 2.19. Notice how it consists of a series of steps that jump vertically 0.23 unit at each integer. The graph is constant between each pair of consecutive integers.

Mathematicians have defined functions that describe situations where function values graphically form discontinuous steps. One such function is called the **greatest integer function**, symbolized by $\text{int}(x)$ or $[\![x]\!]$. And what is $\text{int}(x)$?

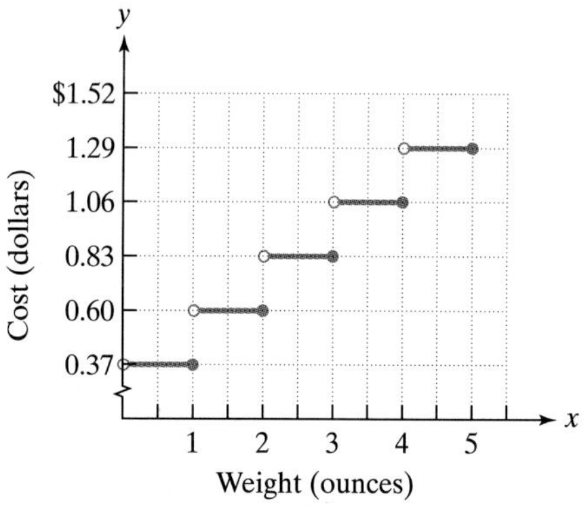

Figure 2.19

$$\text{int}(x) = \text{the greatest integer that is less than or equal to } x$$

For example,

$$\text{int}(1) = 1, \quad \text{int}(1.3) = 1, \quad \text{int}(1.5) = 1, \quad \text{int}(1.9) = 1.$$

1 is the greatest integer that is less than or equal to 1, 1.3, 1.5, and 1.9.

Here are some additional examples:

$$\text{int}(2) = 2, \quad \text{int}(2.3) = 2, \quad \text{int}(2.5) = 2, \quad \text{int}(2.9) = 2.$$

2 is the greatest integer that is less than or equal to 2, 2.3, 2.5, and 2.9.

Notice how we jumped from 1 to 2 in the function values for $\text{int}(x)$. In particular,

$$\text{If } 1 \le x < 2, \quad \text{then} \quad \text{int}(x) = 1.$$
$$\text{If } 2 \le x < 3, \quad \text{then} \quad \text{int}(x) = 2.$$

The graph of $f(x) = \text{int}(x)$ is shown in Figure 2.20. The graph of the greatest integer function jumps vertically one unit at each integer. However, the graph is constant between each pair of consecutive integers. The rightmost horizontal step shown in the graph illustrates that

$$\text{If } 5 \le x < 6, \quad \text{then} \quad \text{int}(x) = 5.$$

In general,

$$\text{If } n \le x < n + 1, \text{ where } n \text{ is an integer,} \quad \text{then} \quad \text{int}(x) = n.$$

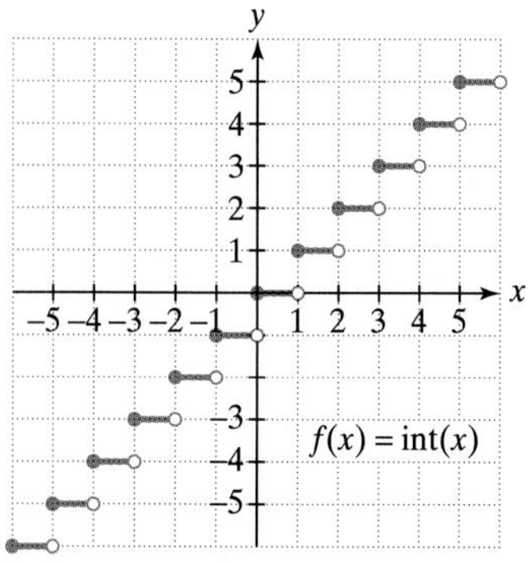

Figure 2.20 The graph of the greatest integer function

By contrast to the graph for the cost of first-class mail, the graph of the greatest integer function includes the point on the left of each horizontal step, but does not include the point on the right. The domain of $f(x) = \text{int}(x)$ is the set of all real numbers, $(-\infty, \infty)$. The range is the set of all integers.

Technology

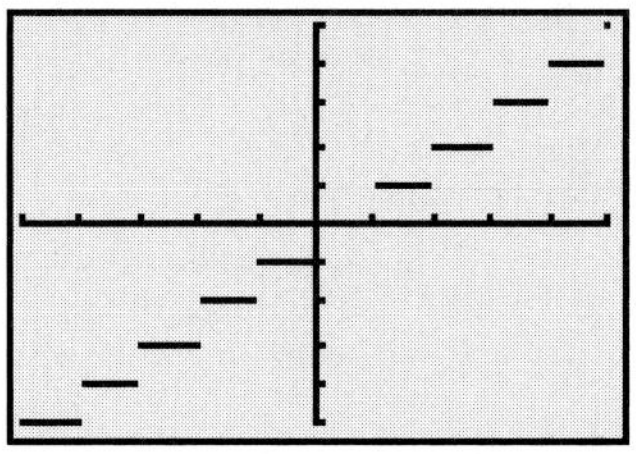

The graph of $f(x) = \text{int}(x)$, shown on the left, was obtained with a graphing utility. By graphing in "dot" mode, we can see the discontinuities at the integers. By looking at the graph, it is impossible to tell that, for each step, the point on the left is included and the point on the right is not. We must trace along the graph to obtain such information.

EXERCISE SET 2.2

Practice Exercises

In Exercises 1–22, find and simplify the difference quotient

$$\frac{f(x+h) - f(x)}{h},\; h \neq 0$$

for the given function.

1. $f(x) = 4x$ **2.** $f(x) = 7x$

3. $f(x) = 3x + 7$ **4.** $f(x) = 6x + 1$

5. $f(x) = x^2$ **6.** $f(x) = 2x^2$

7. $f(x) = x^2 - 4x + 3$ **8.** $f(x) = x^2 - 5x + 8$

9. $f(x) = 2x^2 + x - 1$ **10.** $f(x) = 3x^2 + x + 5$

11. $f(x) = -x^2 + 2x + 4$ **12.** $f(x) = -x^2 - 3x + 1$

13. $f(x) = -2x^2 + 5x + 7$ **14.** $f(x) = -3x^2 + 2x - 1$

15. $f(x) = -2x^2 - x + 3$ **16.** $f(x) = -3x^2 + x - 1$

17. $f(x) = 6$ **18.** $f(x) = 7$

19. $f(x) = \frac{1}{x}$ **20.** $f(x) = \frac{1}{2x}$

21. $f(x) = \sqrt{x}$ **22.** $f(x) = \sqrt{x - 1}$

In Exercises 23–28, evaluate each piecewise function at the given values of the independent variable.

23. $f(x) = \begin{cases} 3x + 5 & \text{if } x < 0 \\ 4x + 7 & \text{if } x \geq 0 \end{cases}$

a. $f(-2)$ **b.** $f(0)$ **c.** $f(3)$

24. $f(x) = \begin{cases} 6x - 1 & \text{if } x < 0 \\ 7x + 3 & \text{if } x \geq 0 \end{cases}$

a. $f(-3)$ **b.** $f(0)$ **c.** $f(4)$

25. $g(x) = \begin{cases} x + 3 & \text{if } x \geq -3 \\ -(x + 3) & \text{if } x < -3 \end{cases}$

a. $g(0)$ **b.** $g(-6)$ **c.** $g(-3)$

26. $g(x) = \begin{cases} x + 5 & \text{if } x \geq -5 \\ -(x + 5) & \text{if } x < -5 \end{cases}$

a. $g(0)$ **b.** $g(-6)$ **c.** $g(-5)$

27. $h(x) = \begin{cases} \frac{x^2 - 9}{x - 3} & \text{if } x \neq 3 \\ 6 & \text{if } x = 3 \end{cases}$

a. $h(5)$ **b.** $h(0)$ **c.** $h(3)$

28. $h(x) = \begin{cases} \frac{x^2 - 25}{x - 5} & \text{if } x \neq 5 \\ 10 & \text{if } x = 5 \end{cases}$

a. $h(7)$ **b.** $h(0)$ **c.** $h(5)$

In Exercises 29–40, use the graph to determine

a. *intervals on which the function is increasing, if any.*

b. *intervals on which the function is decreasing, if any.*

c. *intervals on which the function is constant, if any.*

29.

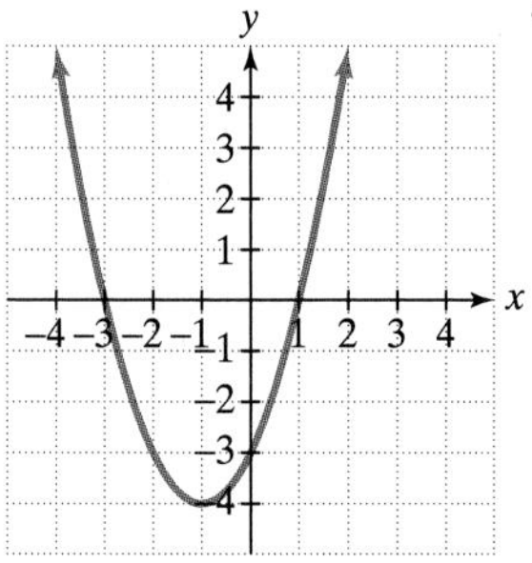

30.

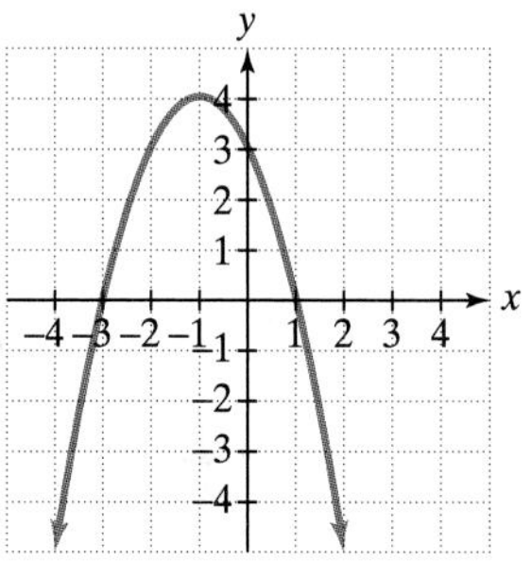

31.

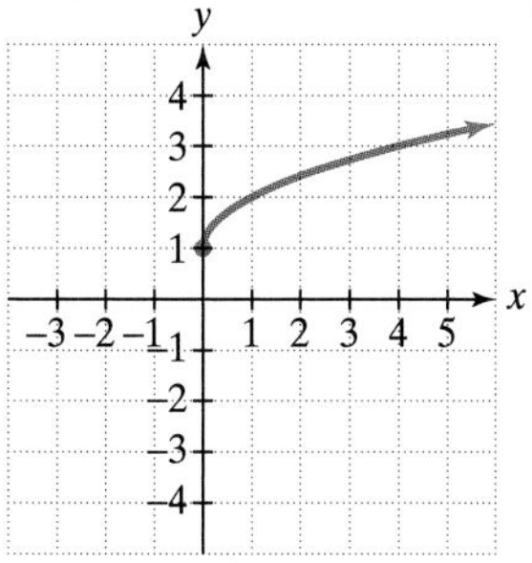

32.

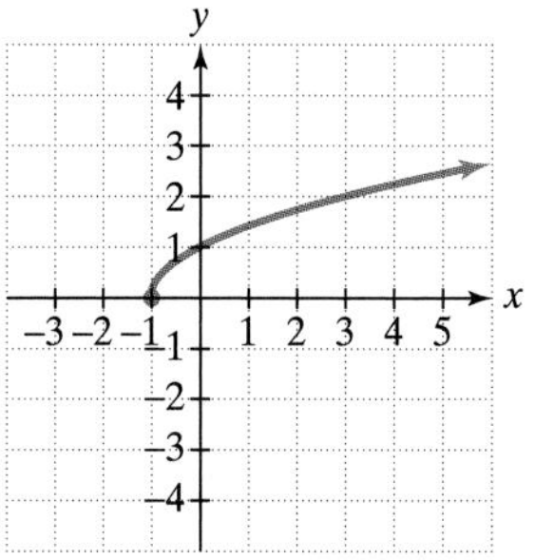

33.

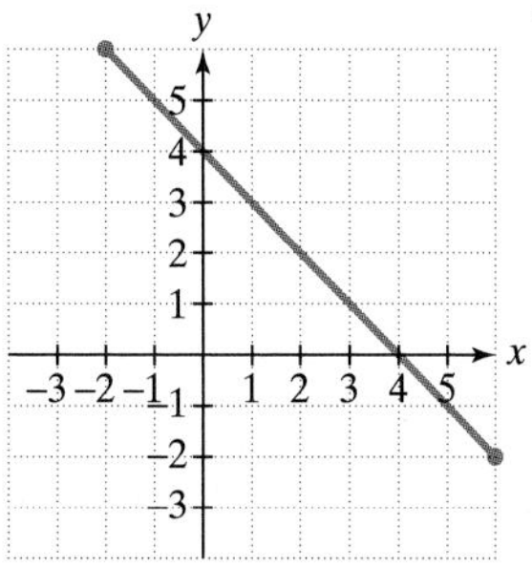

34.

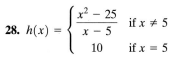

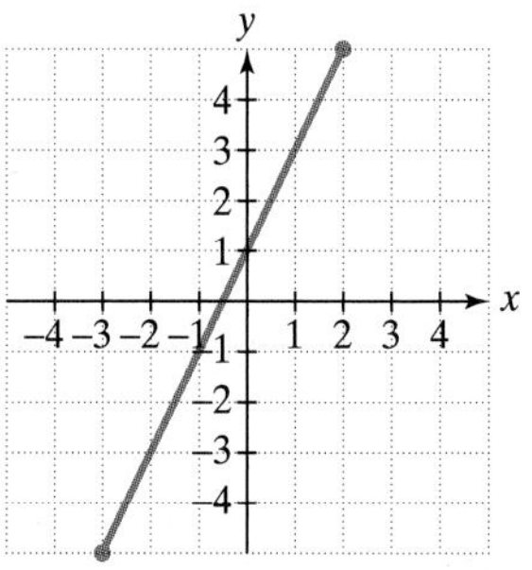

35.

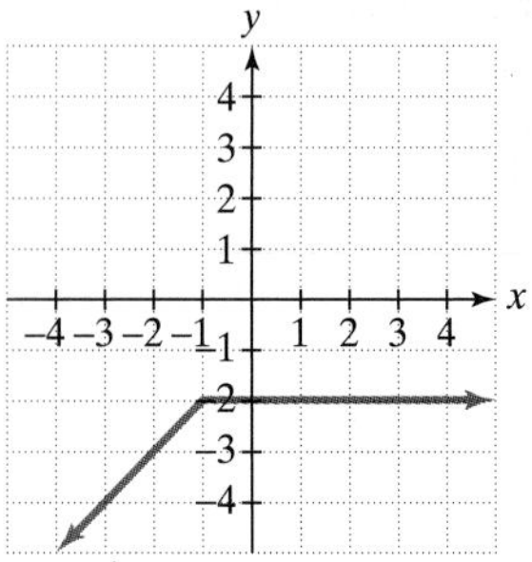

36.

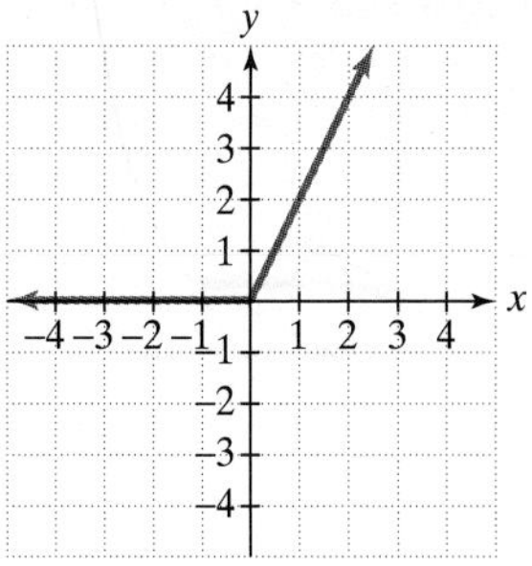

42.

37.

43.

$$f(x) = 2x^3 + 3x^2 - 12x + 1$$

[−4, 4, 1] by [−15, 25, 5]

38.

44.

$$f(x) = 2x^3 - 15x^2 + 24x + 19$$

[−2, 6, 1] by [−15, 35, 5]

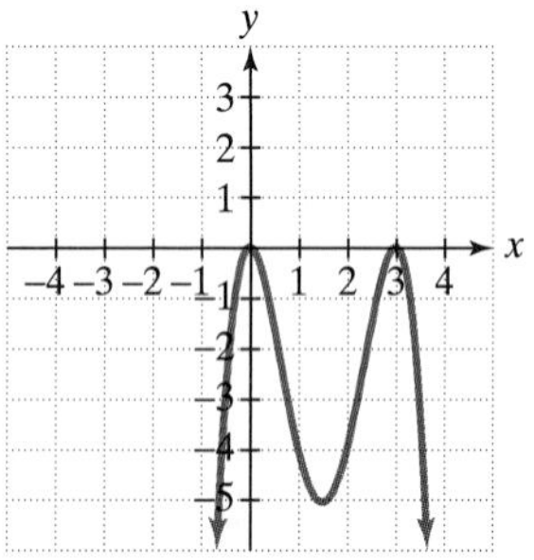

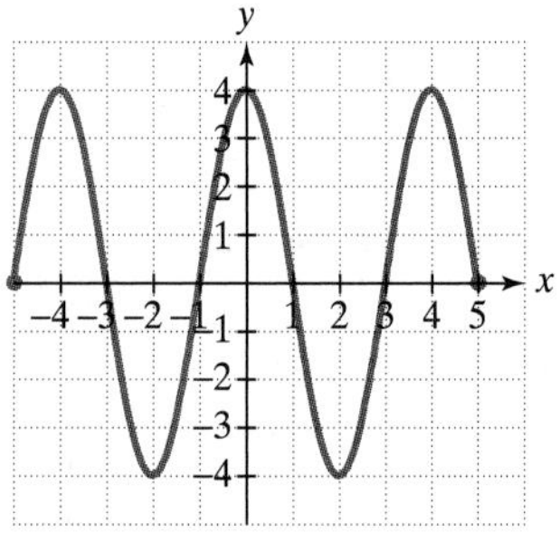

39.

40.

In Exercises 45–56, determine whether each function is even, odd, or neither.

45. $f(x) = x^3 + x$ **46.** $f(x) = x^3 - x$

47. $g(x) = x^2 + x$ **48.** $g(x) = x^2 - x$

49. $h(x) = x^2 - x^4$ **50.** $h(x) = 2x^2 + x^4$

51. $f(x) = x^2 - x^4 + 1$ **52.** $f(x) = 2x^2 + x^4 + 1$

53. $f(x) = \frac{1}{5}x^6 - 3x^2$ **54.** $f(x) = 2x^3 - 6x^5$

55. $f(x) = x\sqrt{1 - x^2}$ **56.** $f(x) = x^2\sqrt{1 - x^2}$

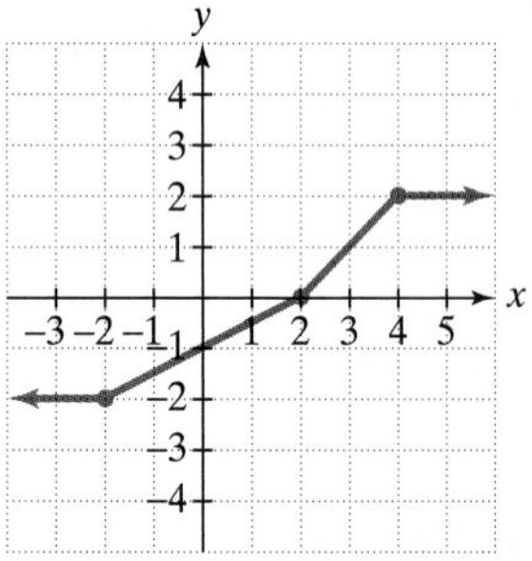

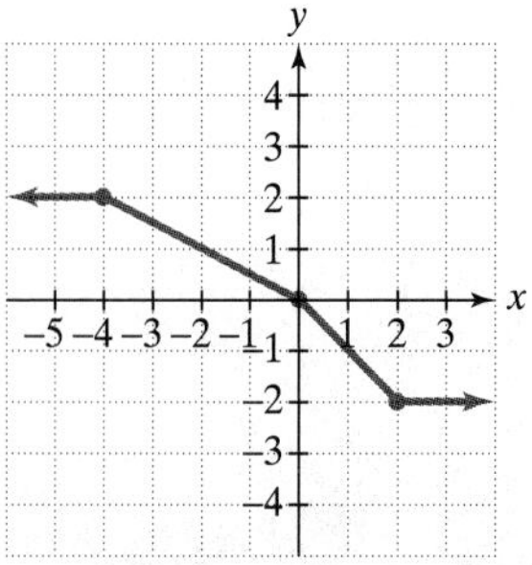

In Exercises 41–44, the graph of a function f is given. Use the graph to find each of the following:

 a. The numbers, if any, at which f has a relative maximum. What are these relative maxima?

 b. The numbers, if any, at which f has a relative minimum. What are these relative minima?

In Exercises 57–60, use possible symmetry to determine whether each graph is the graph of an even function, an odd function, or a function that is neither even nor odd.

41.

57.

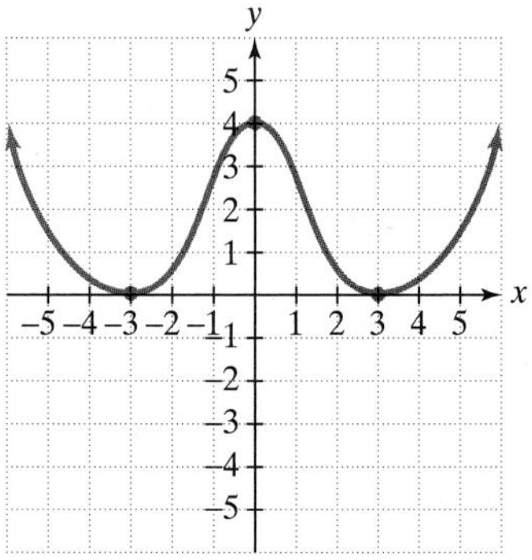

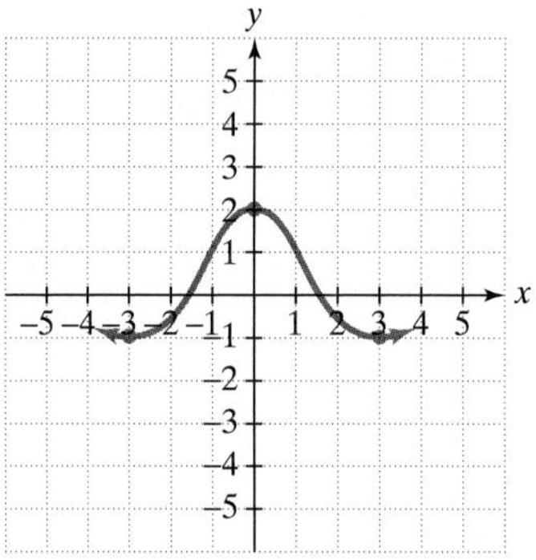

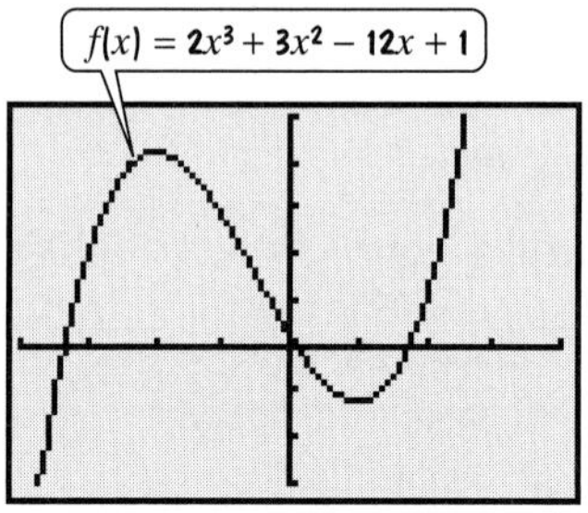

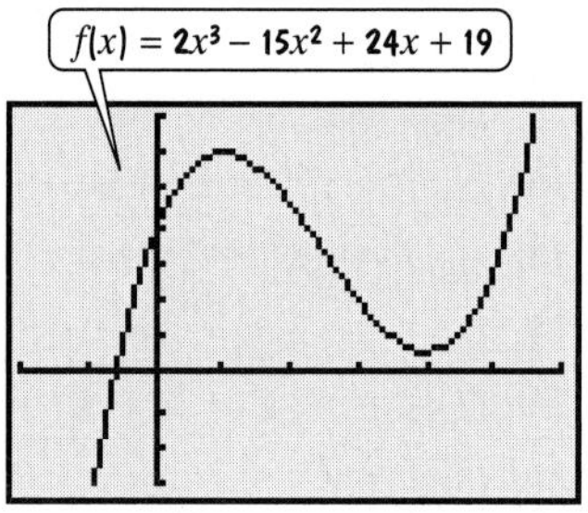

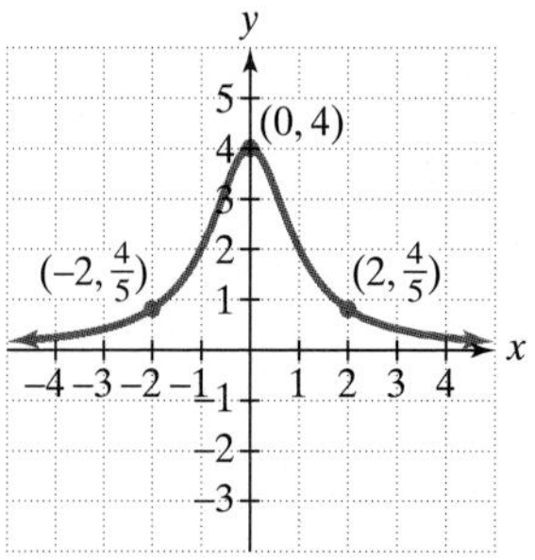

58.

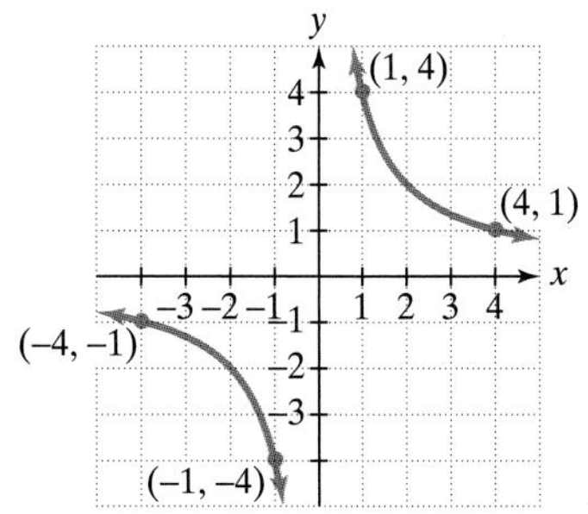

59.

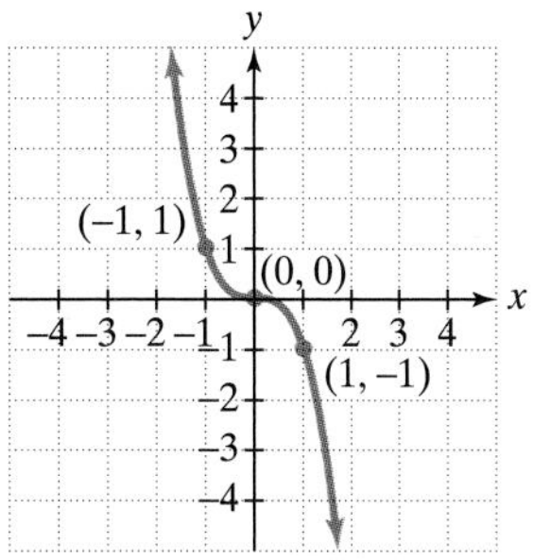

60.

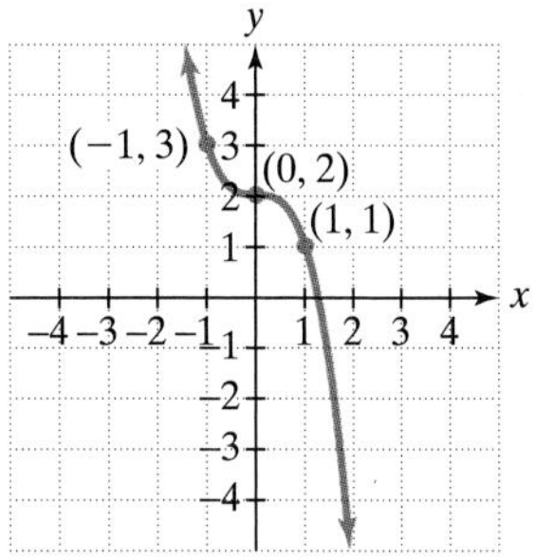

61. Use the graph of f to determine each of the following. Where applicable, use interval notation.

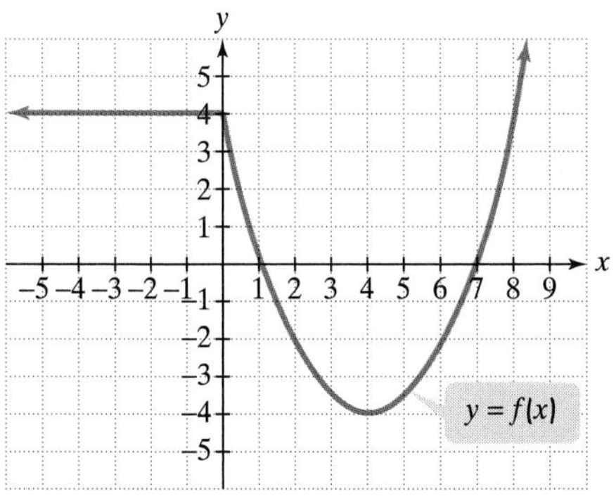

a. the domain of f
b. the range of f
c. the x-intercepts
d. the y-intercept
e. intervals on which f is increasing
f. intervals on which f is decreasing
g. intervals on which f is constant
h. the number at which f has a relative minimum
i. the relative minimum of f
j. $f(-3)$
k. the values of x for which $f(x) = -2$
l. Is f even, odd, or neither?

62. Use the graph of f to determine each of the following. Where applicable, use interval notation.

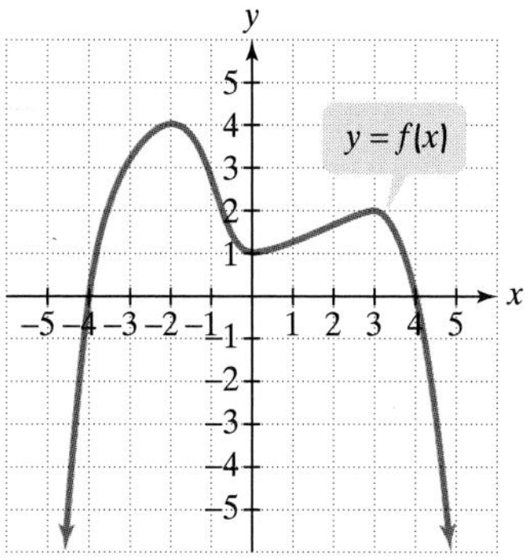

a. the domain of f
b. the range of f
c. the x-intercepts
d. the y-intercept
e. intervals on which f is increasing
f. intervals on which f is decreasing
g. values of x for which $f(x) \le 0$
h. the numbers at which f has a relative maximum
i. the relative maxima of f
j. $f(-2)$
k. the values of x for which $f(x) = 0$
l. Is f even, odd, or neither?

63. Use the graph of f to determine each of the following. Where applicable, use interval notation.

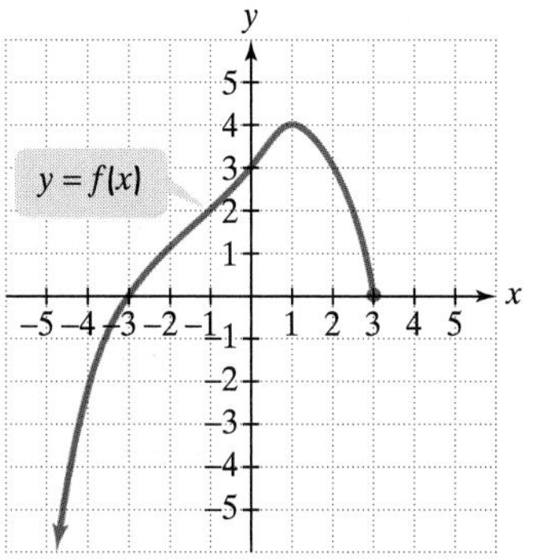

a. the domain of f
b. the range of f
c. the zeros of f
d. $f(0)$
e. intervals on which f is increasing
f. intervals on which f is decreasing
g. values of x for which $f(x) \le 0$
h. any relative maxima and the numbers at which they occur
i. the value of x for which $f(x) = 4$
j. Is $f(-1)$ positive or negative?

64. Use the graph of f to determine each of the following. Where applicable, use interval notation.

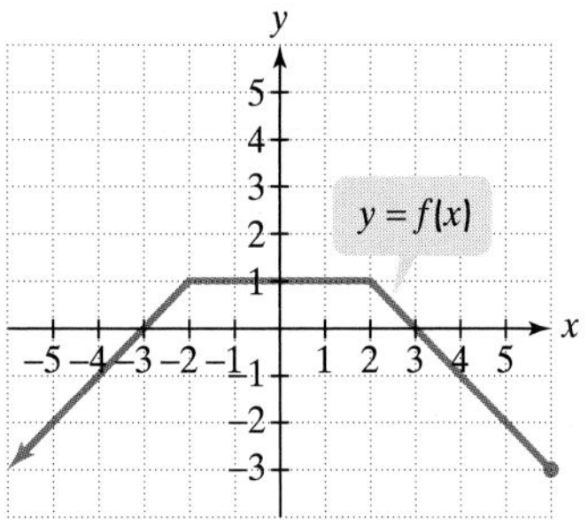

a. the domain of f
b. the range of f
c. the zeros of f
d. $f(0)$
e. intervals on which f is increasing
f. intervals on which f is decreasing
g. intervals on which f is constant
h. values of x for which $f(x) > 0$
i. values of x for which $f(x) = -2$
j. Is $f(4)$ positive or negative?
k. Is f even, odd, or neither?
l. Is $f(2)$ a relative maximum?

In Exercises 65–70, if $f(x) = int(x)$, find each function value.

65. $f(1.06)$ **66.** $f(2.99)$ **67.** $f(\frac{1}{3})$

68. $f(-1.5)$ **69.** $f(-2.3)$ **70.** $f(-99.001)$

Practice Plus

In Exercises 71–72, let f be defined by the following graph:

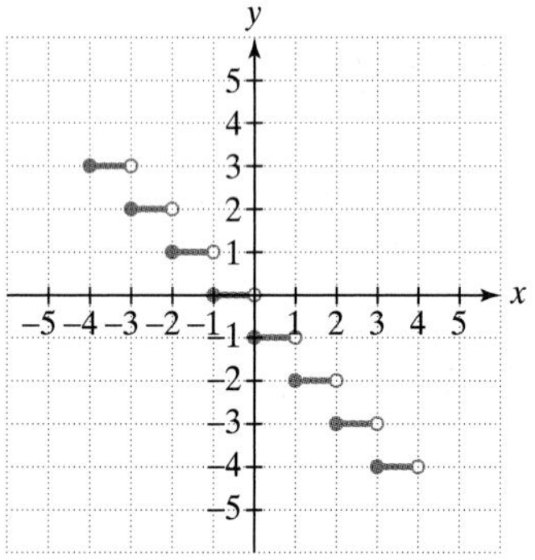

71. Find
$$\sqrt{f(-1.5) + f(-0.9)} - [f(\pi)]^2 + f(-3) \div f(1) \cdot f(-\pi).$$

72. Find
$$\sqrt{f(-2.5) - f(1.9)} - [f(-\pi)]^2 + f(-3) \div f(1) \cdot f(\pi).$$

A cellular phone company offers the following plans. Also given are the piecewise functions that describe these plans. Use this information to solve Exercises 73–74.

Plan A

- $30 per month buys 120 minutes.
- Additional time costs $0.30 per minute.

$$C(t) = \begin{cases} 30 & \text{if } 0 \le t \le 120 \\ 30 + 0.30(t - 120) & \text{if } t > 120 \end{cases}$$

Plan B

- $40 per month buys 200 minutes.
- Additional time costs $0.30 per minute.

$$C(t) = \begin{cases} 40 & \text{if } 0 \le t \le 200 \\ 40 + 0.30(t - 200) & \text{if } t > 200 \end{cases}$$

73. Simplify the algebraic expression in the second line of the piecewise function for plan A. Then use point-plotting to graph the function.

74. Simplify the algebraic expression in the second line of the piecewise function for plan B. Then use point-plotting to graph the function.

In Exercises 75–76, write a piecewise function that describes each cellular phone billing plan. Then graph the function.

75. $50 per month buys 400 minutes. Additional time costs $0.30 per minute.

76. $60 per month buys 450 minutes. Additional time costs $0.35 per minute.

Application Exercises

The figure shows the percentage of Jewish Americans in the U.S. population, $f(x)$, x years after 1900. Use the graph to solve Exercises 77–84.

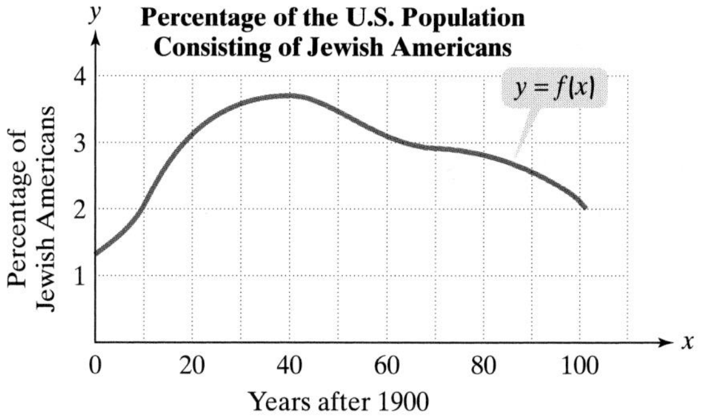

Source: American Jewish Yearbook

77. Use the graph to find a reasonable estimate of $f(60)$. What does this mean in terms of the variables in this situation?

78. Use the graph to find a reasonable estimate of $f(100)$. What does this mean in terms of the variables in this situation?

79. For what value or values of x is $f(x) = 3$? Round to the nearest year. What does this mean in terms of the variables in this situation?

80. For what value or values of x is $f(x) = 2.5$? Round to the nearest year. What does this mean in terms of the variables in this situation?

81. In which year did the percentage of Jewish Americans in the U.S. population reach a maximum? What is a reasonable estimate of the percentage for that year?

82. In which year was the percentage of Jewish Americans in the U.S. population at a minimum? What is a reasonable estimate of the percentage for that year?

83. Explain why f represents the graph of a function.

84. Describe the general trend shown by the graph.

The function

$$f(x) = 0.4x^2 - 36x + 1000$$

models the number of accidents, $f(x)$, per 50 million miles driven as a function of a driver's age, x, in years, where x includes drivers from ages 16 through 74, inclusive. The graph of f is shown. Use the graph of f, and possibly the equation, to solve Exercises 85–88.

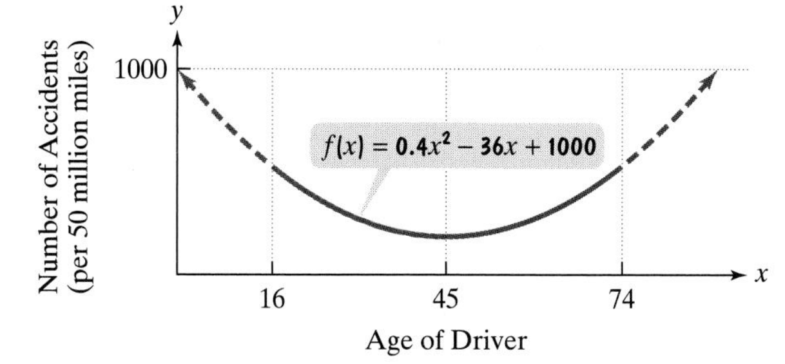

85. State the intervals on which the function is increasing and decreasing. Describe what this means in terms of the variables modeled by the function.

86. For what value of x does the graph reach its lowest point? Use the equation for f to find the minimum value of y. Describe the practical significance of this minimum value.

87. Use the graph to identify two different ages for which drivers have the same number of accidents. Use the equation for f to find the number of accidents for drivers at each of these ages.

88. Use the equation for f to find and interpret $f(50)$. Identify this information as a point on the graph of f.

The graph shows cigarette consumption per U.S. adult from 1910 through 2003. The data can be modeled by the piecewise function

$$f(x) = \begin{cases} 61.9x + 132 & \text{if } 0 \le x \le 30 \\ -2.2x^2 + 256x - 3503 & \text{if } 30 < x \le 93, \end{cases}$$

where x represents years after 1910 and $f(x)$ represents cigarette consumption per U.S. adult. Use this information to solve Exercises 89–92.

Cigarette Consumption per U.S. Adult

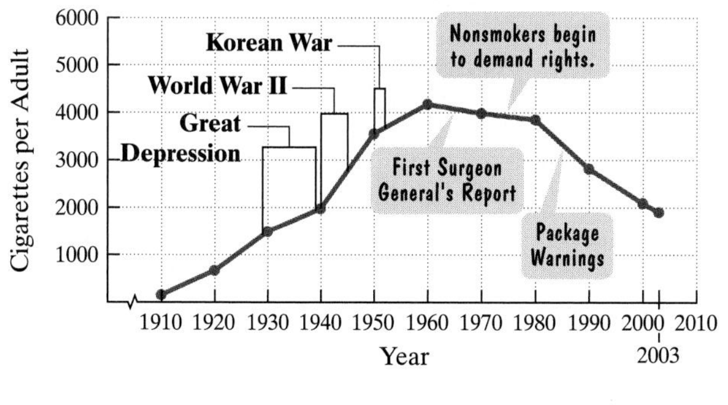

Source: U.S. Department of Health and Human Services

89. Use the piecewise function that models the data to find cigarette consumption in 1940. How well does the function describe the actual consumption for that year shown by the line graph?

90. Use the piecewise function that models the data to find cigarette consumption in 1990. How well does the function describe the actual consumption for that year shown by the line graph?

91. For the period shown, in which year was cigarette consumption at a maximum? Use the graph to find a reasonable estimate of consumption for that year. How well does the piecewise function model this estimate?

92. For the period shown, in which year was cigarette consumption at a minimum? Use the graph to find a reasonable estimate of consumption for that year. How well does the piecewise function model this estimate?

93. The cost of a telephone call between two cities is \$0.10 for the first minute and \$0.05 for each additional minute or portion of a minute. Draw a graph of the cost, C, in dollars, of the phone call as a function of time, t, in minutes, on the interval $(0, 5]$.

94. A cargo service charges a flat fee of \$4 plus \$1 for each pound or fraction of a pound to mail a package. Let $C(x)$ represent the cost to mail a package that weighs x pounds. Graph the cost function on the interval $(0, 5]$.

Writing in Mathematics

95. Explain how to find the difference quotient, $\frac{f(x + h) - f(x)}{h}$, if a function's equation is given.

96. What is a piecewise function?

97. What does it mean if a function f is increasing on an interval?

98. Suppose that a function f is increasing on (a, b), decreasing on (b, c), and defined at b. Describe what occurs at $x = b$. What does the function value $f(b)$ represent?

99. If you are given a function's equation, how do you determine if the function is even, odd, or neither?

100. If you are given a function's graph, how do you determine if the function is even, odd, or neither?

101. What is a step function? Give an example of an everyday situation that can be modeled using such a function. Do not use the cost-of-mail example.

102. Explain how to find $\text{int}(-3.000004)$.

Technology Exercises

103. The function

$$f(x) = -0.00002x^3 + 0.008x^2 - 0.3x + 6.95$$

models the number of annual physician visits, $f(x)$, by a person of age x. Graph the function in a $[0, 100, 5]$ by $[0, 40, 2]$ viewing rectangle. What does the shape of the graph indicate about the relationship between one's age and the number of annual physician visits? Use the TRACE or minimum function capability to find the coordinates of the minimum point on the graph of the function. What does this mean?

In Exercises 104–109, use a graphing utility to graph each function. Use a $[-5, 5, 1]$ by $[-5, 5, 1]$ viewing rectangle. Then find the intervals on which the function is increasing, decreasing, or constant.

104. $f(x) = x^3 - 6x^2 + 9x + 1$

105. $g(x) = |4 - x^2|$

106. $h(x) = |x - 2| + |x + 2|$

107. $f(x) = x^{\frac{1}{3}}(x - 4)$

108. $g(x) = x^{\frac{2}{3}}$ **109.** $h(x) = 2 - x^{\frac{2}{5}}$

110. a. Graph the functions $f(x) = x^n$ for $n = 2, 4$, and 6 in a $[-2, 2, 1]$ by $[-1, 3, 1]$ viewing rectangle.

b. Graph the functions $f(x) = x^n$ for $n = 1, 3$, and 5 in a $[-2, 2, 1]$ by $[-2, 2, 1]$ viewing rectangle.

c. If n is even, where is the graph of $f(x) = x^n$ increasing and where is it decreasing?

d. If n is odd, what can you conclude about the graph of $f(x) = x^n$ in terms of increasing or decreasing behavior?

e. Graph all six functions in a $[-1, 3, 1]$ by $[-1, 3, 1]$ viewing rectangle. What do you observe about the graphs in terms of how flat or how steep they are?

Critical Thinking Exercises

111. Sketch the graph of f using the following properties. (More than one correct graph is possible.) f is a piecewise function that is decreasing on $(-\infty, 2)$, $f(2) = 0$, f is increasing on $(2, \infty)$, and the range of f is $[0, \infty)$.

112. Define a piecewise function on the intervals $(-\infty, 2]$, $(2, 5)$, and $[5, \infty)$ that does not "jump" at 2 or 5 such that one piece is a constant function, another piece is an increasing function, and the third piece is a decreasing function.

113. Suppose that $h(x) = \frac{f(x)}{g(x)}$. The function f can be even, odd, or neither. The same is true for the function g.

a. Under what conditions is h definitely an even function?

b. Under what conditions is h definitely an odd function?

114. Take another look at the cost of first-class mail and its graph (Table 2.1 and Figure 2.19 on page 210. Change the description of the heading in the left column of Table 2.1 so that the graph includes the point on the left of each horizontal step, but does not include the point on the right.

Group Exercise

115. (For assistance with this exercise, refer to the discussion of piecewise functions on page 204, as well as to Exercises 73–74.)

Group members who have cellular phone plans should describe the total monthly cost of the plan as follows:

$_____ per month buys _____ minutes. Additional time costs $ _____ per minute.

(For simplicity, ignore off-peak rates, roaming charges, etc.) The group should select any three plans, from "basic" to "premier." For each plan selected, write a piecewise function that describes the plan and graph the function. Graph the three functions in the same rectangular coordinate system. Now examine the graphs. For any given number of calling minutes, the best plan is the one whose graph is lowest at that point. Compare the three calling plans. Over how many minutes does one plan become better than another? (You can check out cellular phone plans by visiting www.point.com.)

SECTION 2.3 Linear Functions and Slope

Objectives

1. Calculate a line's slope.
2. Write the point-slope form of the equation of a line.
3. Write and graph the slope-intercept form of the equation of a line.
4. Graph horizontal or vertical lines.
5. Recognize and use the general form of a line's equation.
6. Use intercepts to graph the general form of a line's equation.
7. Model data with linear functions and make predictions.

Is there a relationship between literacy and child mortality? As the percentage of adult females who are literate increases, does the mortality of children under five decrease? Figure 2.21, based on data from the United Nations, indicates that this is, indeed, the case. Each point in the figure represents one country.

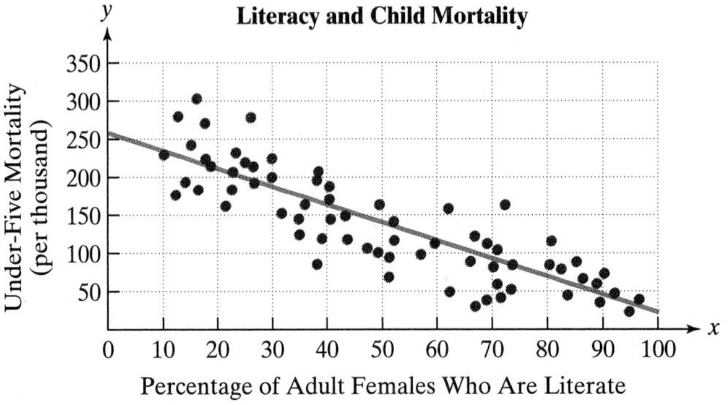

Figure 2.21

Source: United Nations

Data presented in a visual form as a set of points is called a **scatter plot**. Also shown in Figure 2.21 is a line that passes through or near the points. A line that best fits the data points in a scatter plot is called a **regression line**. By writing the equation of this line, we can obtain a model for the data and make predictions about child mortality based on the percentage of literate adult females in a country.

Data often fall on or near a line. In this section, we will use functions to model such data and make predictions. We begin with a discussion of a line's steepness.

1 Calculate a line's slope.

The Slope of a Line

Mathematicians have developed a useful measure of the steepness of a line, called the *slope* of the line. Slope compares the vertical change (the **rise**) to the horizontal change (the **run**) when moving from one fixed point to another along the line. To calculate the slope of a line, we use a ratio that compares the change in y (the rise) to the corresponding change in x (the run).

Slope and the Streets of San Francisco

San Francisco's Filbert Street has a slope of 0.613, meaning that for every horizontal distance of 100 feet, the street ascends 61.3 feet vertically. With its 31.5° angle of inclination, the street is too steep to pave and is only accessible by wooden stairs.

Definition of Slope

The **slope** of the line through the distinct points (x_1, y_1) and (x_2, y_2) is

$$\frac{\text{Change in } y}{\text{Change in } x} = \frac{\text{Rise}}{\text{Run}} = \frac{y_2 - y_1}{x_2 - x_1}$$

where $x_2 - x_1 \neq 0$.

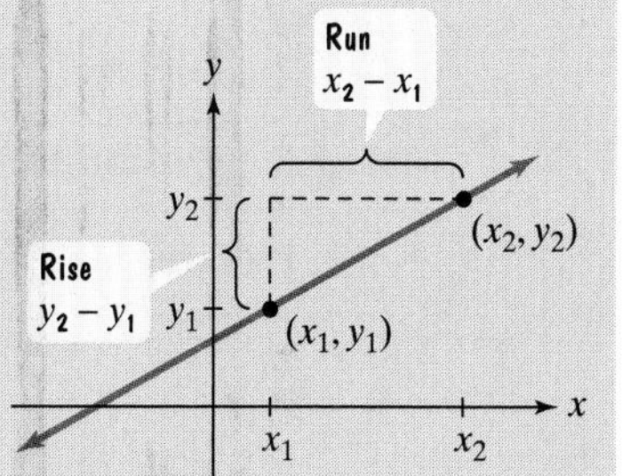

It is common notation to let the letter m represent the slope of a line. The letter m is used because it is the first letter of the French verb *monter*, meaning to rise, or to ascend.

EXAMPLE 1 Using the Definition of Slope

Find the slope of the line passing through each pair of points:

a. $(-3, -1)$ and $(-2, 4)$ **b.** $(-3, 4)$ and $(2, -2)$.

Solution

a. Let $(x_1, y_1) = (-3, -1)$ and $(x_2, y_2) = (-2, 4)$. We obtain the slope as follows:

$$m = \frac{\text{Change in } y}{\text{Change in } x} = \frac{y_2 - y_1}{x_2 - x_1} = \frac{4 - (-1)}{-2 - (-3)} = \frac{5}{1} = 5.$$

The situation is illustrated in Figure 2.22(a). The slope of the line is 5, indicating that there is a vertical change, a rise, of 5 units for each horizontal change, a run, of 1 unit. The slope is positive, and the line rises from left to right.

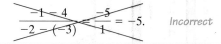

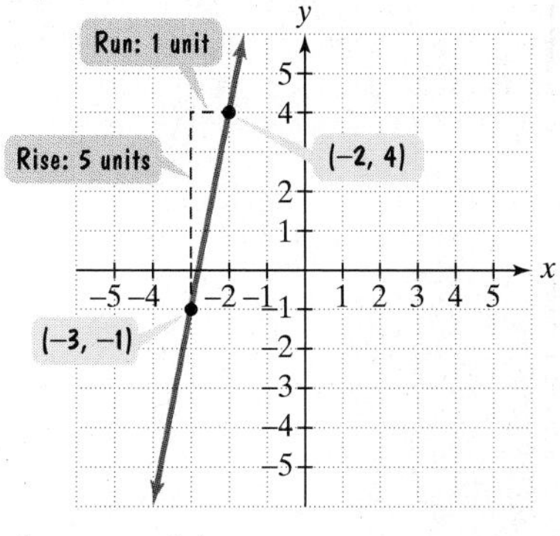

Figure 2.22(a) Visualizing slope

Study Tip

When computing slope, it makes no difference which point you call (x_1, y_1) and which point you call (x_2, y_2). If we let $(x_1, y_1) = (-2, 4)$ and $(x_2, y_2) = (-3, -1)$, the slope is still 5:

$$m = \frac{\text{Change in } y}{\text{Change in } x} = \frac{y_2 - y_1}{x_2 - x_1} = \frac{-1 - 4}{-3 - (-2)} = \frac{-5}{-1} = 5.$$

However, you should not subtract in one order in the numerator $(y_2 - y_1)$ and then in a different order in the denominator $(x_1 - x_2)$. The slope is *not* -5:

$$\frac{-1 - 4}{-2 - (-3)} = \frac{-5}{1} = -5. \quad \text{Incorrect}$$

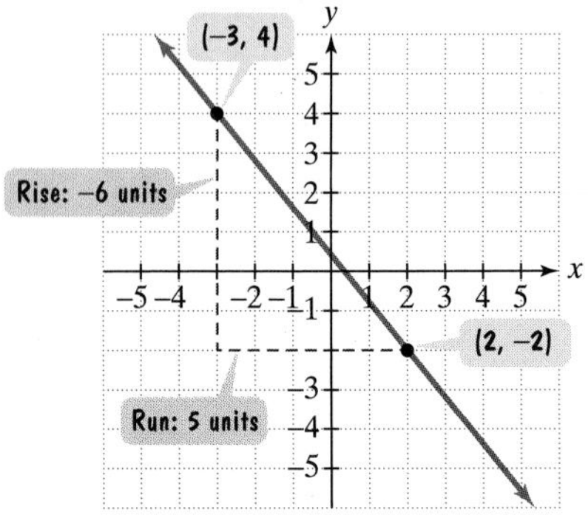

Figure 2.22(b)

b. We can let $(x_1, y_1) = (-3, 4)$ and $(x_2, y_2) = (2, -2)$. The slope of the line shown in Figure 2.22(b) is computed as follows:

$$m = \frac{\text{Change in } y}{\text{Change in } x} = \frac{y_2 - y_1}{x_2 - x_1} = \frac{-2 - 4}{2 - (-3)} = \frac{-6}{5} = -\frac{6}{5}.$$

The slope of the line is $-\frac{6}{5}$. For every vertical change of -6 units (6 units down), there is a corresponding horizontal change of 5 units. The slope is negative and the line falls from left to right.

Check Point 1 Find the slope of the line passing through each pair of points:

a. $(-3, 4)$ and $(-4, -2)$ **b.** $(4, -2)$ and $(-1, 5)$.

Example 1 illustrates that a line with a positive slope is rising from left to right and a line with a negative slope is falling from left to right. By contrast, a horizontal line neither rises nor falls and has a slope of zero. A vertical line has no horizontal change, so $x_2 - x_1 = 0$ in the formula for slope. Because we cannot divide by zero, the slope of a vertical line is undefined. This discussion is summarized in Table 2.2.

Table 2.2 Possibilities for a Line's Slope

Positive Slope	Negative Slope	Zero Slope	Undefined Slope
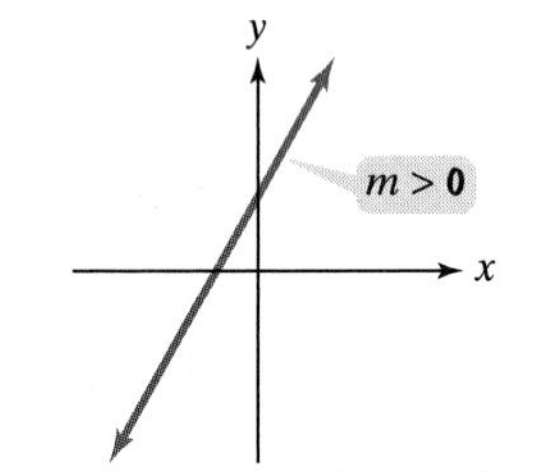	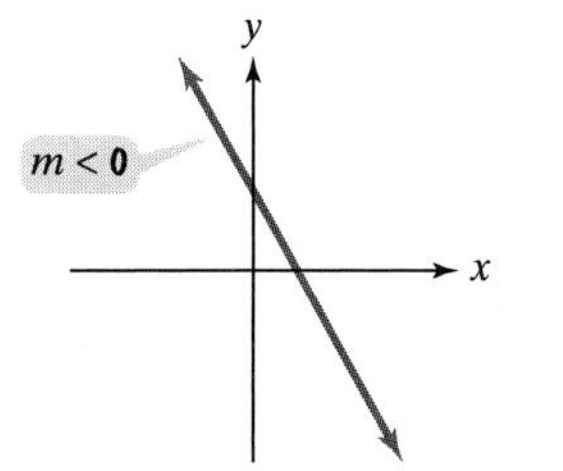	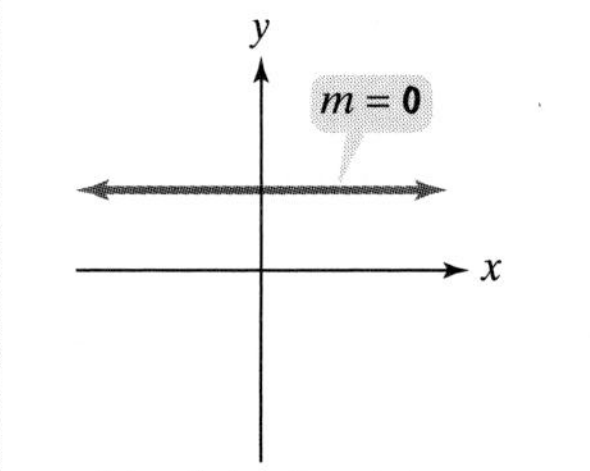	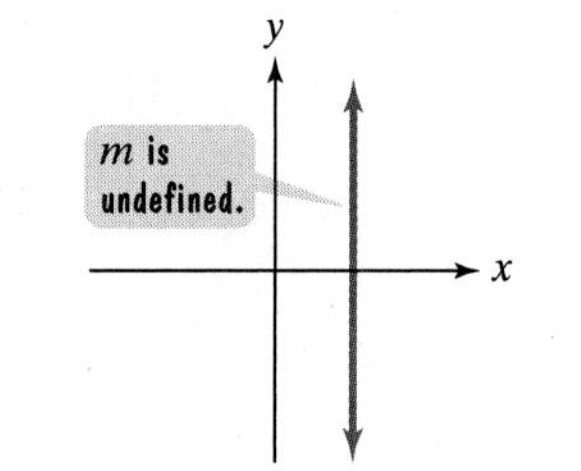
Line rises from left to right.	Line falls from left to right.	Line is horizontal.	Line is vertical.

Study Tip

Always be clear in the way you use language, especially in mathematics. For example, it's not a good idea to say that a line has "no slope." This could mean that the slope is zero or that the slope is undefined.

2 Write the point-slope form of the equation of a line.

The Point-Slope Form of the Equation of a Line

We can use the slope of a line to obtain various forms of the line's equation. For example, consider a nonvertical line that has slope m and that contains the point (x_1, y_1). Now, let (x, y) represent any other point on the line, shown in Figure 2.23. Keep in mind that the point (x, y) is arbitrary and is not in one fixed position. By contrast, the point (x_1, y_1) is fixed.

Regardless of where the point (x, y) is located, the steepness of the line in Figure 2.23 remains the same. Thus, the ratio for the slope stays a constant m. This means that for all points along the line

$$m = \frac{\text{Change in } y}{\text{Change in } x} = \frac{y - y_1}{x - x_1}.$$

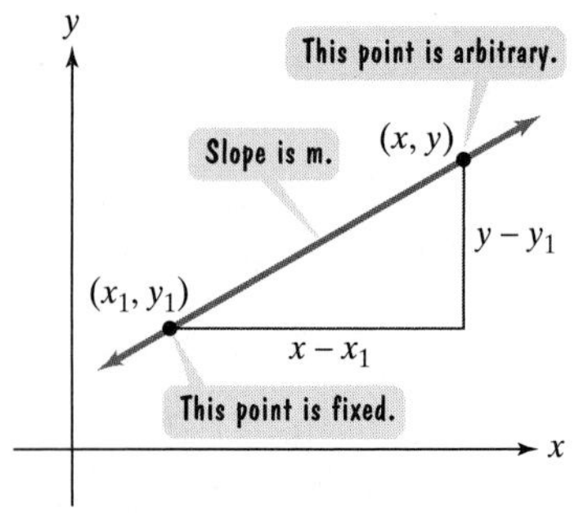

Figure 2.23 A line passing through (x_1, y_1) with slope m

We can clear the fraction by multiplying both sides by $x - x_1$, the least common denominator.

$$m = \frac{y - y_1}{x - x_1} \quad \text{This is the slope of the line in Figure 2.23.}$$

$$m(x - x_1) = \frac{y - y_1}{x - x_1} \cdot x - x_1 \quad \text{Multiply both sides by } x - x_1.$$

$$m(x - x_1) = y - y_1 \quad \text{Simplify: } \frac{y - y_1}{\cancel{x - x_1}} \cdot \cancel{x - x_1} = y - y_1.$$

Now, if we reverse the two sides, we obtain the *point-slope form* of the equation of a line.

Point-Slope Form of the Equation of a Line

The **point-slope form of the equation** of a nonvertical line with slope m that passes through the point (x_1, y_1) is

$$y - y_1 = m(x - x_1).$$

For example, the point-slope form of the equation of the line passing through $(1, 5)$ with slope 2; $(m = 2)$ is

$$y - 5 = 2(x - 1).$$

We will soon be expressing the equation of a nonvertical line in function notation. To do so, we need to solve the point-slope form of a line's equation for y. Example 2 illustrates how to isolate y on one side of the equal sign.

EXAMPLE 2 Writing the Point-Slope Form of the Equation of a Line

Write the point-slope form of the equation of the line with slope 4 that passes through the point $(-1, 3)$. Then solve the equation for y.

Solution We use the point-slope form of the equation of a line with $m = 4$, $x_1 = -1$, and $y_1 = 3$.

$$y - y_1 = m(x - x_1)$$ This is the point-slope form of the equation.

$$y - 3 = 4[x - (-1)]$$ Substitute the given values.

$$y - 3 = 4(x + 1)$$ We now have the point-slope form of the equation of the given line.

We can solve this equation for y by first applying the distributive property on the right side.

$$y - 3 = 4x + 4$$

Finally, we add 3 to both sides.

$$y = 4x + 7$$

Check Point 2 Write the point-slope form of the equation of the line with slope 6 that passes through the point $(2, -5)$. Then solve the equation for y.

EXAMPLE 3 Writing the Point-Slope Form of the Equation of a Line

Write the point-slope form of the equation of the line passing through the points $(4, -3)$ and $(-2, 6)$. (See Figure 2.24.) Then solve the equation for y.

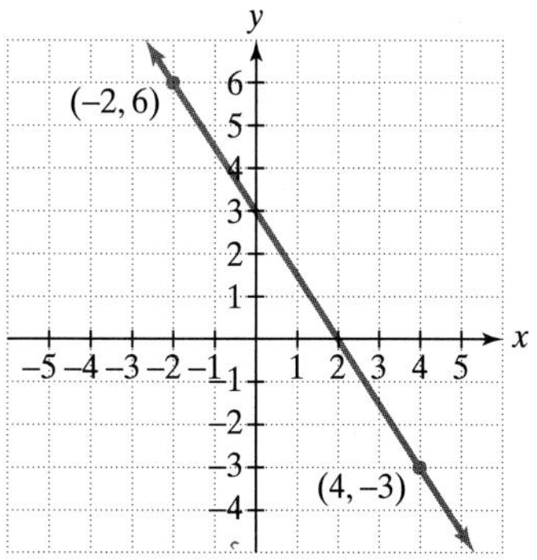

Figure 2.24 Write the point-slope form of the equation of this line.

Solution To use the point-slope form, we need to find the slope. The slope is the change in the y-coordinates divided by the corresponding change in the x-coordinates.

$$m = \frac{6 - (-3)}{-2 - 4} = \frac{9}{-6} = -\frac{3}{2}$$ This is the definition of slope using $(4, -3)$ and $(-2, 6)$.

We can take either point on the line to be (x_1, y_1). Let's use $(x_1, y_1) = (4, -3)$. Now, we are ready to write the point-slope form of the equation.

$$y - y_1 = m(x - x_1)$$ This is the point-slope form of the equation.

$$y - (-3) = -\tfrac{3}{2}(x - 4)$$ Substitute: $(x_1, y_1) = (4, -3)$ and $m = -\frac{3}{2}$.

$$y + 3 = -\tfrac{3}{2}(x - 4)$$ Simplify.

We now have the point-slope form of the equation of the line shown in Figure 2.24. Now, we solve this equation for y.

Discovery

You can use either point for (x_1, y_1) when you write a line's point-slope equation. Rework Example 3 using $(-2, 6)$ for (x_1, y_1). Once you solve for y, you should still obtain

$$y = -\frac{3}{2}x + 3.$$

We need to isolate y.

$$y + 3 = -\frac{3}{2}(x - 4) \quad \text{This is the point-slope form of the equation.}$$
$$y + 3 = -\frac{3}{2}x + 6 \quad \text{Use the distributive property.}$$
$$y = -\frac{3}{2}x + 3 \quad \text{Subtract 3 from both sides.}$$

Check Point 3 Write the point-slope form of the equation of the line passing through the points $(-2, -1)$ and $(-1, -6)$. Then solve the equation for y.

3 Write and graph the slope-intercept form of the equation of a line.

The Slope-Intercept Form of the Equation of a Line

Let's write the point-slope form of the equation of a nonvertical line with slope m and y-intercept b. The line is shown in Figure 2.25. Because the y-intercept is b, the line passes through $(0, b)$. We use the point-slope form with $x_1 = 0$ and $y_1 = b$.

$$y - y_1 = m(x - x_1)$$

Let $y_1 = b$. Let $x_1 = 0$.

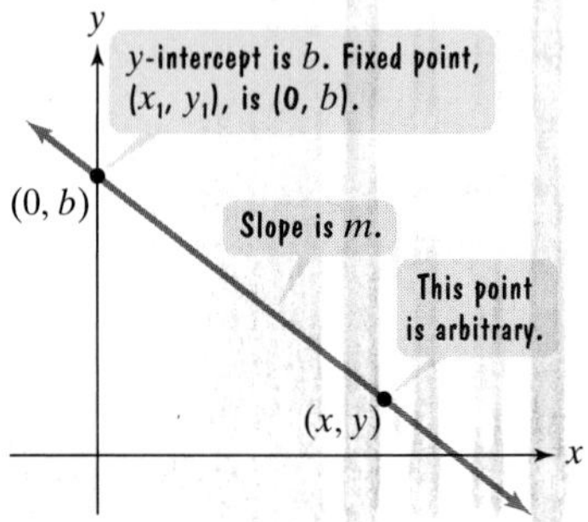

Figure 2.25 A line with slope m and y-intercept b

We obtain

$$y - b = m(x - 0).$$

Simplifying on the right side gives us

$$y - b = mx.$$

Finally, we solve for y by adding b to both sides.

$$y = mx + b$$

Thus, if a line's equation is written with y isolated on one side, the x-coefficient is the line's slope and the constant term is the y-intercept. This form of a line's equation is called the *slope-intercept form* of the line.

Slope-Intercept Form of the Equation of a Line

The **slope-intercept form of the equation** of a nonvertical line with slope m and y-intercept b is

$$y = mx + b.$$

The slope-intercept form of a line's equation, $y = mx + b$, can be expressed in function notation by replacing y with $f(x)$:

$$f(x) = mx + b.$$

We have seen that functions in this form are called **linear functions**. Thus, in the equation of a linear function, the x-coefficient is the line's slope and the constant term is the y-intercept. Here are two examples:

$$y = 2x - 4 \qquad\qquad f(x) = \frac{1}{2}x + 2.$$

The slope is 2. The y-intercept is -4. The slope is $\frac{1}{2}$. The y-intercept is 2.

If a linear function's equation is in slope-intercept form, we can use the y-intercept and the slope to obtain its graph.

Graphing $y = mx + b$ Using the Slope and y-Intercept

1. Plot the point containing the y-intercept on the y-axis. This is the point $(0, b)$.
2. Obtain a second point using the slope, m. Write m as a fraction, and use rise over run, starting at the point containing the y-intercept, to plot this point.
3. Use a straightedge to draw a line through the two points. Draw arrowheads at the ends of the line to show that the line continues indefinitely in both directions.

EXAMPLE 4 Graphing Using the Slope and y-Intercept

Graph the linear function: $f(x) = -\frac{3}{2}x + 2$.

Solution The equation of the line is in the form $f(x) = mx + b$. We can find the slope, m, by identifying the coefficient of x. We can find the y-intercept, b, by identifying the constant term.

$$f(x) = -\frac{3}{2}x + 2$$

The slope is $-\frac{3}{2}$.

The y-intercept is 2.

Now that we have identified the slope and the y-intercept, we use the three-step procedure to graph the equation.

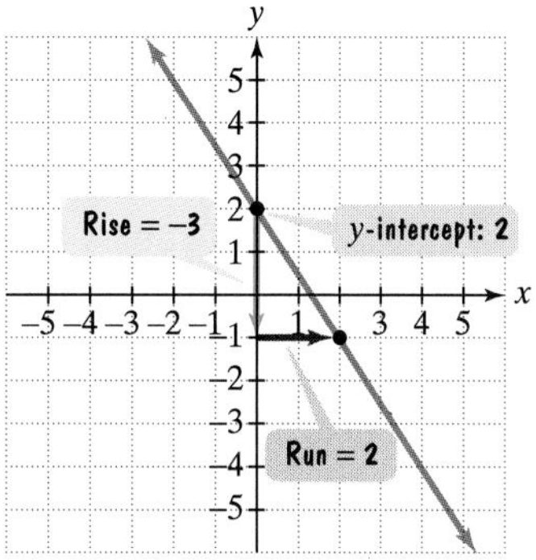

Figure 2.26 The graph of $f(x) = -\frac{3}{2}x + 2$

Step 1 Plot the point containing the y-intercept on the y-axis. The y-intercept is 2. We plot $(0, 2)$, shown in Figure 2.26.

Step 2 Obtain a second point using the slope, m. Write m as a fraction, and use rise over run, starting at the point containing the y-intercept, to plot this point. The slope, $-\frac{3}{2}$, is already written as a fraction.

$$m = -\frac{3}{2} = \frac{-3}{2} = \frac{\text{Rise}}{\text{Run}}$$

We plot the second point on the line by starting at $(0, 2)$, the first point. Based on the slope, we move 3 units *down* (the rise) and 2 units to the *right* (the run). This puts us at a second point on the line, $(2, -1)$, shown in Figure 2.26.

Step 3 Use a straightedge to draw a line through the two points. The graph of the linear function $f(x) = -\frac{3}{2}x + 2$ is shown as a blue line in Figure 2.26.

Check Point 4 Graph the linear function: $f(x) = \frac{3}{5}x + 1$.

4 Graph horizontal or vertical lines.

Equations of Horizontal and Vertical Lines

Some things change very little. For example, from 1997 through 2003, the federal minimum wage remained constant at \$5.15 per hour, indicated by the green bars in Figure 2.27. These bars show the minimum wage before it was adjusted for inflation. Also shown in the figure is a blue horizontal line segment that passes through the tops of the seven green bars.

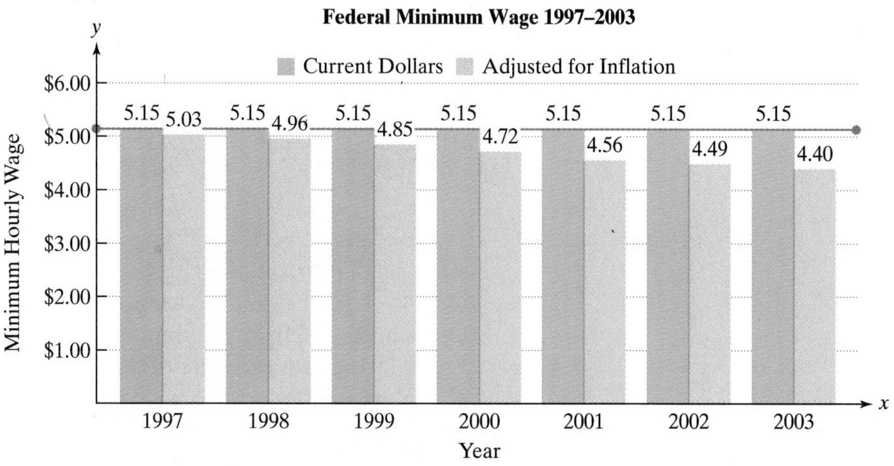

Figure 2.27

Source: www.dol.gov/esa/public/minwage

We can use $y = mx + b$, the slope-intercept form of a line's equation, to obtain an equation that models the federal minimum wage, y, in current dollars, in year x, where x is between 1997 and 2003, inclusive. The horizontal blue line segment in Figure 2.27 on the previous page provides the values for m and b:

$$y = mx + b.$$

Because the line segment is horizontal, $m = 0$.

The y-intercept is shown as \$5.15, so $b = 5.15$.

Thus, an equation that models the federal minimum wage between 1997 and 2003, inclusive, is

$$y = 0x + 5.15, \quad \text{or } y = 5.15.$$

The federal minimum wage remained constant at \$5.15 per hour. Using function notation, we can write

$$f(x) = 5.15.$$

For all year inputs, x, in the domain from 1997 through 2003, inclusive,

the output is a constant 5.15.

In general, if a line is horizontal, its slope is zero: $m = 0$. Thus, the equation $y = mx + b$ becomes $y = b$, where b is the y-intercept. For example, the graph of $y = -4$ is a horizontal line with a y-intercept of -4. The graph is shown in Figure 2.28. Three of the points along the line are shown and labeled.

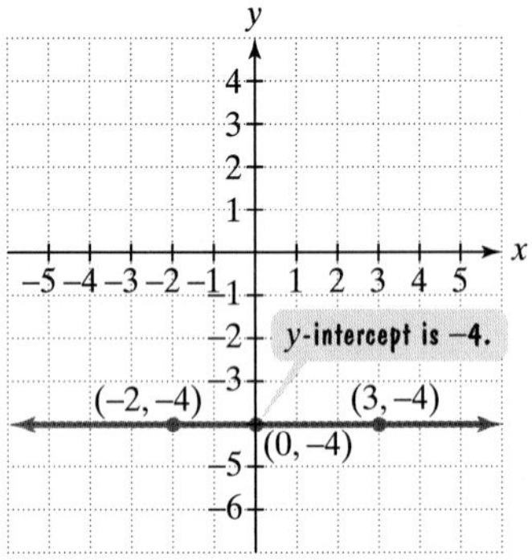

Figure 2.28 The graph of $y = -4$ or $f(x) = -4$

x	$y = -4$	(x, y)
−2	−4	(−2, −4)
0	−4	(0, −4)
3	−4	(3, −4)

For all choices of x,

y is a constant −4.

No matter what the x-coordinate is, the corresponding y-coordinate for every point on the line in Figure 2.28 is -4.

Equation of a Horizontal Line

A horizontal line is given by an equation of the form

$$y = b,$$

where b is the y-intercept.

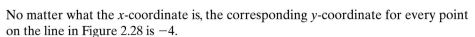

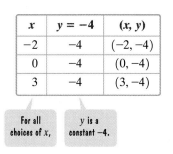

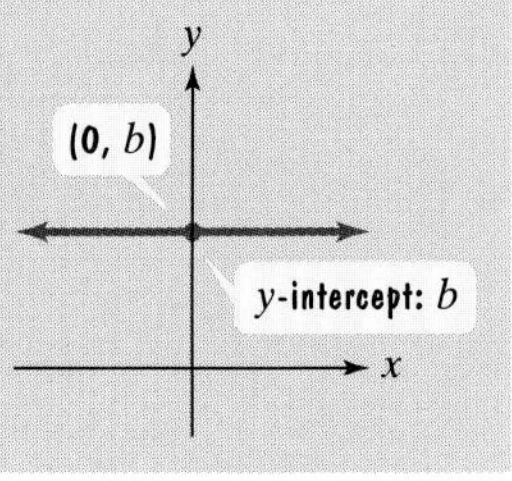

Because any vertical line can intersect the graph of a horizontal line $y = b$ only once, a horizontal line is the graph of a function. Thus, we can express the equation $y = b$ as $f(x) = b$. This linear function is often called a **constant function**. The function modeling the federal minimum wage from 1997 through 2003, namely $f(x) = 5.15$, is an example of a constant function.

Next, let's see what we can discover about the graph of an equation of the form $x = a$ by looking at an example.

EXAMPLE 5 Graphing a Vertical Line

Graph the linear equation: $x = 2$.

Solution All ordered pairs that are solutions of $x = 2$ have a value of x that is always 2. Any value can be used for y. Let's select three of the possible values for y: -2, 0, and 3.

For all choices of y,

$x = 2$	y	(x, y)
2	-2	$(2, -2)$
2	0	$(2, 0)$
2	3	$(2, 3)$

x is always 2.

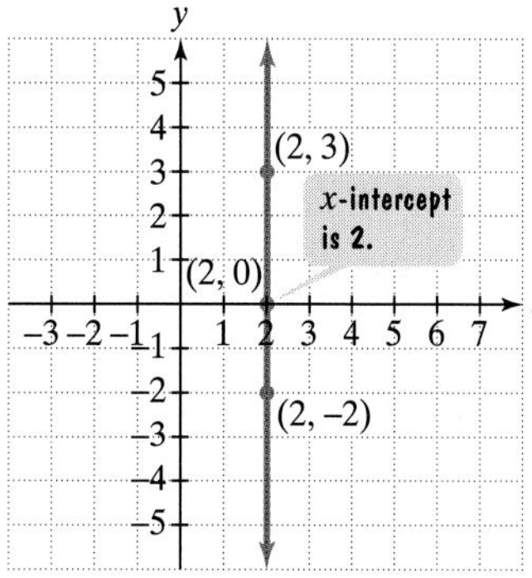

Figure 2.29 The graph of $x = 2$

The table shows that three ordered pairs that are solutions of $x = 2$ are $(2, -2)$, $(2, 0)$, and $(2, 3)$. Drawing a line that passes through the three points gives the vertical line shown in Figure 2.29.

Equation of a Vertical Line

A vertical line is given by an equation of the form

$$x = a,$$

where a is the x-intercept.

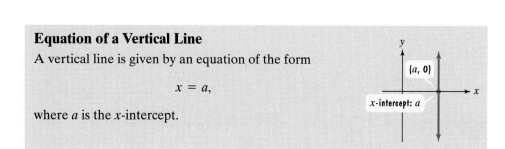

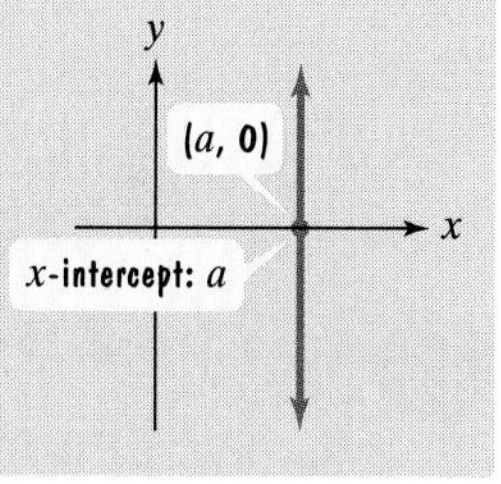

Does a vertical line represent the graph of a linear function? No. Look at the graph of $x = 2$ in Figure 2.29. A vertical line drawn through $(2, 0)$ intersects the graph infinitely many times. This shows that infinitely many outputs are associated with the input 2. **No vertical line is a linear function.**

Check Point 5 Graph the linear equation: $x = -3$.

5 Recognize and use the general form of a line's equation.

The General Form of the Equation of a Line

The vertical line whose equation is $x = 5$ cannot be written in slope-intercept form, $y = mx + b$, because its slope is undefined. However, every line has an equation that can be expressed in the form $Ax + By + C = 0$. For example, $x = 5$ can be expressed as $1x + 0y - 5 = 0$, or $x - 5 = 0$. The equation $Ax + By + C = 0$ is called the *general form* of the equation of a line.

General Form of the Equation of a Line

Every line has an equation that can be written in the **general form**

$$Ax + By + C = 0,$$

where A, B, and C are real numbers, and A and B are not both zero.

If the equation of a line is given in general form, it is possible to find the slope, m, and the y-intercept, b, for the line. We solve the equation for y, transforming it into the slope–intercept form $y = mx + b$. In this form, the coefficient of x is the slope of the line and the constant term is its y-intercept.

EXAMPLE 6 Finding the Slope and the y-Intercept

Find the slope and the y-intercept of the line whose equation is $3x + 2y - 4 = 0$.

Solution The equation is given in general form. We begin by rewriting it in the form $y = mx + b$. We need to solve for y.

Our goal is to isolate y.

$$3x + 2y - 4 = 0 \quad \text{This is the given equation.}$$

$$2y = -3x + 4 \quad \text{Isolate the term containing } y \text{ by adding } -3x + 4 \text{ to both sides.}$$

$$\frac{2y}{2} = \frac{-3x + 4}{2} \quad \text{Divide both sides by 2.}$$

$$y = -\frac{3}{2}x + 2 \quad \text{On the right, divide each term in the numerator by 2 to obtain slope-intercept form.}$$

slope: $-\frac{3}{2}$ y-intercept: 2

The coefficient of x, $-\frac{3}{2}$, is the slope and the constant term, 2, is the y-intercept. This is the form of the equation that we graphed in Figure 2.26 on page 221.

Check Point 6 Find the slope and the y-intercept of the line whose equation is $3x + 6y - 12 = 0$. Then use the y-intercept and the slope to graph the equation.

6 Use intercepts to graph the general form of a line's equation.

Using Intercepts to Graph $Ax + By + C = 0$

Example 6 and Check Point 6 illustrate that one way to graph the general form of a line's equation is to convert to slope-intercept form, $y = mx + b$. Then use the slope and the y-intercept to obtain the graph.

A second method for graphing $Ax + By + C = 0$ uses intercepts. This method does not require rewriting the general form in a different form.

Using Intercepts to Graph $Ax + By + C = 0$

1. Find the x-intercept. Let $y = 0$ and solve for x. Plot the point containing the x-intercept on the x-axis.
2. Find the y-intercept. Let $x = 0$ and solve for y. Plot the point containing the y-intercept on the y-axis.
3. Use a straightedge to draw a line through the two points containing the intercepts. Draw arrowheads at the ends of the line to show that the line continues indefinitely in both directions.

EXAMPLE 7 Using Intercepts to Graph a Linear Equation

Graph using intercepts: $4x - 3y - 6 = 0$.

Solution

Step 1 Find the x-intercept. Let $y = 0$ and solve for x.

$$4x - 3 \cdot 0 - 6 = 0 \quad \text{Replace } y \text{ with 0 in } 4x - 3y - 6 = 0.$$

$$4x - 6 = 0 \quad \text{Simplify.}$$

$$4x = 6 \quad \text{Add 6 to both sides.}$$

$$x = \frac{6}{4} = \frac{3}{2} \quad \text{Divide both sides by 4.}$$

The x-intercept is $\frac{3}{2}$, so the line passes through $\left(\frac{3}{2}, 0\right)$ or $(1.5, 0)$, as shown in Figure 2.30.

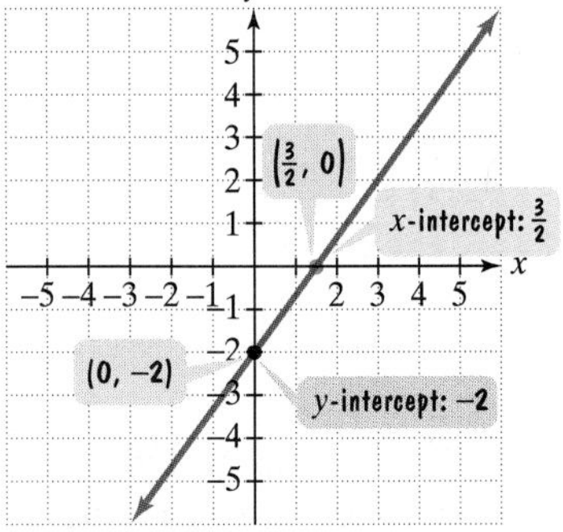

Figure 2.30 The graph of $4x - 3y - 6 = 0$

Step 2 Find the y-intercept. Let $x = 0$ and solve for y.

$$4 \cdot 0 - 3y - 6 = 0 \qquad \text{\color{gray}Replace x with 0 in 4x − 3y − 6 = 0.}$$
$$-3y - 6 = 0 \qquad \text{\color{gray}Simplify.}$$
$$-3y = 6 \qquad \text{\color{gray}Add 6 to both sides.}$$
$$y = -2 \qquad \text{\color{gray}Divide both sides by −3.}$$

The y-intercept is -2, so the line passes through $(0, -2)$, as shown in Figure 2.30.

Step 3 Graph the equation by drawing a line through the two points containing the intercepts. The graph of $4x - 3y - 6 = 0$ is shown in Figure 2.30.

Check Point 7 Graph using intercepts: $3x - 2y - 6 = 0$.

We've covered a lot of territory. Let's take a moment to summarize the various forms for equations of lines.

Equations of Lines

1. Point-slope form:		$y - y_1 = m(x - x_1)$
2. Slope-intercept form:		$y = mx + b$ or $f(x) = mx + b$
3. Horizontal line:		$y = b$
4. Vertical line:		$x = a$
5. General form:		$Ax + By + C = 0$

7 Model data with linear functions and make predictions.

Technology

You can use a graphing utility to obtain a model for a scatter plot in which the data points fall on or near a straight line. After entering the data in Figure 2.31(b), a graphing utility displays a scatter plot of the data and the regression line, that is, the line that best fits the data.

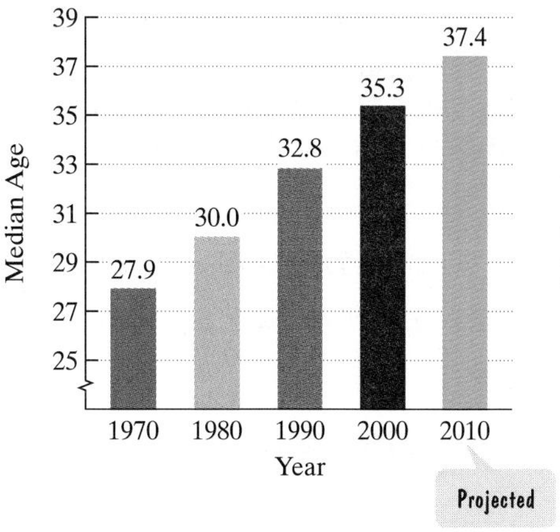

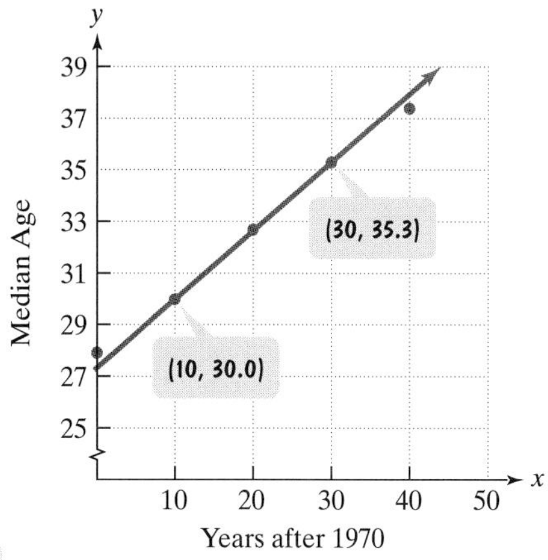

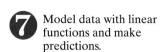

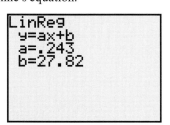

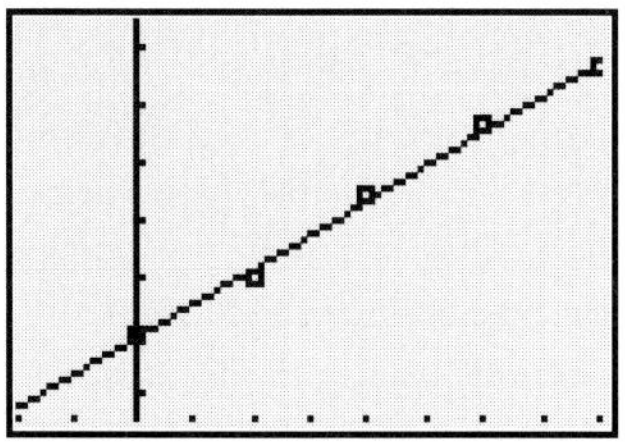

[−10, 40, 5] by [25, 39, 2]

Also displayed is the regression line's equation.

Applications

Linear functions are useful for modeling data that fall on or near a line. For example, the bar graph in Figure 2.31(a) gives the median age of the U.S. population in the indicated year. (The median age is the age in the middle when all the ages of the U.S. population are arranged from youngest to oldest.) The data are displayed as a set of five points in a rectangular coordinate system in Figure 2.31(b).

The Graying of America: Median Age of the U.S. Population

Figure 2.31(a) **Figure 2.31(b)**

Source: U.S. Census Bureau

Also shown on the scatter plot in Figure 2.31(b) is a line that passes through or near the five points. By writing the equation of this line, we can obtain a model of the data and make predictions about the median age of the U.S. population in the future.

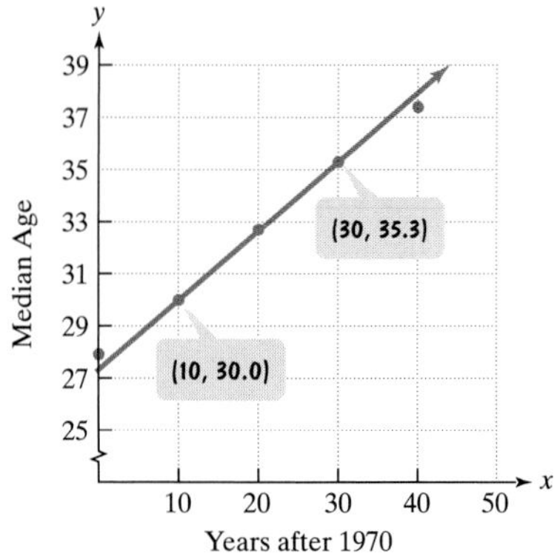

Figure 2.31(b) (repeated)

EXAMPLE 8 Modeling the Graying of America

Write the slope-intercept equation of the line shown in Figure 2.31(b). Use the equation to predict the median age of the U.S. population in 2020.

Solution The line in Figure 2.31(b) passes through (10, 30.0) and (30, 35.3). We start by finding its slope.

$$m = \frac{\text{Change in } y}{\text{Change in } x} = \frac{35.3 - 30.0}{30 - 10} = \frac{5.3}{20} = 0.265$$

The slope indicates that each year the median age of the U.S. population is increasing by 0.265 years.

Now, we write the line's slope-intercept equation.

$y - y_1 = m(x - x_1)$	Begin with the point-slope form.
$y - 30.0 = 0.265(x - 10)$	Either ordered pair can be (x_1, y_1). Let $(x_1, y_1) = (10, 30.0)$. From above, $m = 0.265$.
$y - 30.0 = 0.265x - 2.65$	Apply the distributive property.
$y = 0.265x + 27.35$	Add 30 to both sides and solve for y.

A linear function that models the median age of the U.S. population, $f(x)$, x years after 1970 is

$$f(x) = 0.265x + 27.35.$$

Now, let's use this function to predict the median age in 2020. Because 2020 is 50 years after 1970, we substitute 50 for x and evaluate the function at 50.

$$f(50) = 0.265(50) + 27.35 = 40.6$$

Our model predicts that the median age of the U.S. population in 2020 will be 40.6.

Check Point 8 Use the data points (10, 30.0) and (20, 32.8) from Figure 2.31(b) to write a slope-intercept equation that models the median age of the U.S. population x years after 1970. Use this model to predict the median age in 2020.

Cigarettes and Lung Cancer

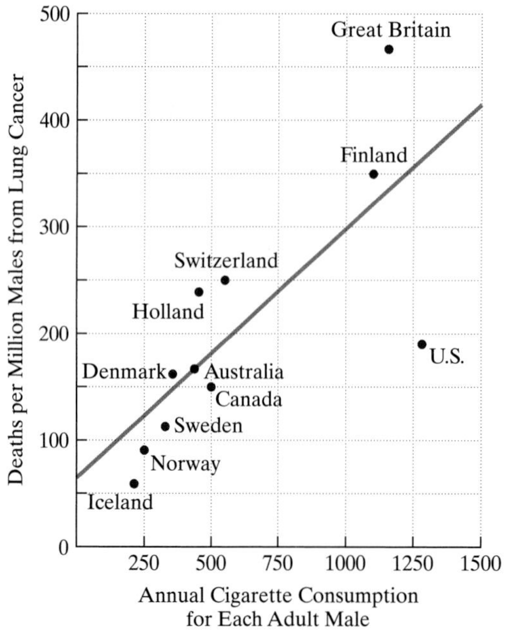

This scatter plot shows a relationship between cigarette consumption among males and deaths due to lung cancer per million males. The data are from 11 countries and date back to a 1964 report by the U.S. Surgeon General. The scatter plot can be modeled by a line whose slope indicates an increasing death rate from lung cancer with increased cigarette consumption. At that time, the tobacco industry argued that in spite of this regression line, tobacco use is not the cause of cancer. Recent data do, indeed, show a causal effect between tobacco use and numerous diseases.

Source: Smoking and Health, Washington, D.C., 1964

EXERCISE SET 2.3

Practice Exercises

In Exercises 1–10, find the slope of the line passing through each pair of points or state that the slope is undefined. Then indicate whether the line through the points rises, falls, is horizontal, or is vertical.

1. $(4, 7)$ and $(8, 10)$
2. $(2, 1)$ and $(3, 4)$
3. $(-2, 1)$ and $(2, 2)$
4. $(-1, 3)$ and $(2, 4)$
5. $(4, -2)$ and $(3, -2)$
6. $(4, -1)$ and $(3, -1)$
7. $(-2, 4)$ and $(-1, -1)$
8. $(6, -4)$ and $(4, -2)$
9. $(5, 3)$ and $(5, -2)$
10. $(3, -4)$ and $(3, 5)$

In Exercises 11–38, use the given conditions to write an equation for each line in point-slope form and slope-intercept form.

11. Slope $= 2$, passing through $(3, 5)$
12. Slope $= 4$, passing through $(1, 3)$
13. Slope $= 6$, passing through $(-2, 5)$
14. Slope $= 8$, passing through $(4, -1)$
15. Slope $= -3$, passing through $(-2, -3)$
16. Slope $= -5$, passing through $(-4, -2)$
17. Slope $= -4$, passing through $(-4, 0)$
18. Slope $= -2$, passing through $(0, -3)$
19. Slope $= -1$, passing through $\left(-\frac{1}{2}, -2\right)$
20. Slope $= -1$, passing through $\left(-4, -\frac{1}{4}\right)$
21. Slope $= \frac{1}{2}$, passing through the origin
22. Slope $= \frac{1}{3}$, passing through the origin
23. Slope $= -\frac{2}{3}$, passing through $(6, -2)$
24. Slope $= -\frac{3}{5}$, passing through $(10, -4)$
25. Passing through $(1, 2)$ and $(5, 10)$
26. Passing through $(3, 5)$ and $(8, 15)$
27. Passing through $(-3, 0)$ and $(0, 3)$
28. Passing through $(-2, 0)$ and $(0, 2)$
29. Passing through $(-3, -1)$ and $(2, 4)$
30. Passing through $(-2, -4)$ and $(1, -1)$
31. Passing through $(-3, -2)$ and $(3, 6)$
32. Passing through $(-3, 6)$ and $(3, -2)$
33. Passing through $(-3, -1)$ and $(4, -1)$
34. Passing through $(-2, -5)$ and $(6, -5)$
35. Passing through $(2, 4)$ with x-intercept $= -2$
36. Passing through $(1, -3)$ with x-intercept $= -1$
37. x-intercept $= -\frac{1}{2}$ and y-intercept $= 4$
38. x-intercept $= 4$ and y-intercept $= -2$

In Exercises 39–48, give the slope and y-intercept of each line whose equation is given. Then graph the linear function.

39. $y = 2x + 1$
40. $y = 3x + 2$
41. $f(x) = -2x + 1$
42. $f(x) = -3x + 2$
43. $f(x) = \frac{3}{4}x - 2$
44. $f(x) = \frac{3}{4}x - 3$
45. $y = -\frac{3}{5}x + 7$
46. $y = -\frac{2}{5}x + 6$
47. $g(x) = -\frac{1}{2}x$
48. $g(x) = -\frac{1}{3}x$

In Exercises 49–58, graph each equation in a rectangular coordinate system.

49. $y = -2$
50. $y = 4$
51. $x = -3$
52. $x = 5$
53. $y = 0$
54. $x = 0$
55. $f(x) = 1$
56. $f(x) = 3$
57. $3x - 18 = 0$
58. $3x + 12 = 0$

In Exercises 59–66,

a. *Rewrite the given equation in slope-intercept form.*
b. *Give the slope and y-intercept.*
c. *Use the slope and y-intercept to graph the linear function.*

59. $3x + y - 5 = 0$
60. $4x + y - 6 = 0$
61. $2x + 3y - 18 = 0$
62. $4x + 6y + 12 = 0$
63. $8x - 4y - 12 = 0$
64. $6x - 5y - 20 = 0$
65. $3y - 9 = 0$
66. $4y + 28 = 0$

In Exercises 67–72, use intercepts to graph each equation.

67. $6x - 2y - 12 = 0$
68. $6x - 9y - 18 = 0$
69. $2x + 3y + 6 = 0$
70. $3x + 5y + 15 = 0$
71. $8x - 2y + 12 = 0$
72. $6x - 3y + 15 = 0$

Practice Plus

In Exercises 73–76, find the slope of the line passing through each pair of points or state that the slope is undefined. Assume that all variables represent positive real numbers. Then indicate whether the line through the points rises, falls, is horizontal, or is vertical.

73. $(0, a)$ and $(b, 0)$
74. $(-a, 0)$ and $(0, -b)$
75. (a, b) and $(a, b + c)$
76. $(a - b, c)$ and $(a, a + c)$

In Exercises 77–78, give the slope and y-intercept of each line whose equation is given. Assume that $B \neq 0$.

77. $Ax + By = C$ **78.** $Ax = By - C$

In Exercises 79–80, find the value of y if the line through the two given points is to have the indicated slope.

79. $(3, y)$ and $(1, 4)$, $m = -3$

80. $(-2, y)$ and $(4, -4)$, $m = \frac{1}{3}$

In Exercises 81–82, graph each linear function.

81. $3x - 4f(x) - 6 = 0$ **82.** $6x - 5f(x) - 20 = 0$

83. If one point on a line is $(3, -1)$ and the line's slope is -2, find the y-intercept.

84. If one point on a line is $(2, -6)$ and the line's slope is $-\frac{3}{2}$, find the y-intercept.

Use the figure to make the lists in Exercises 85–86.

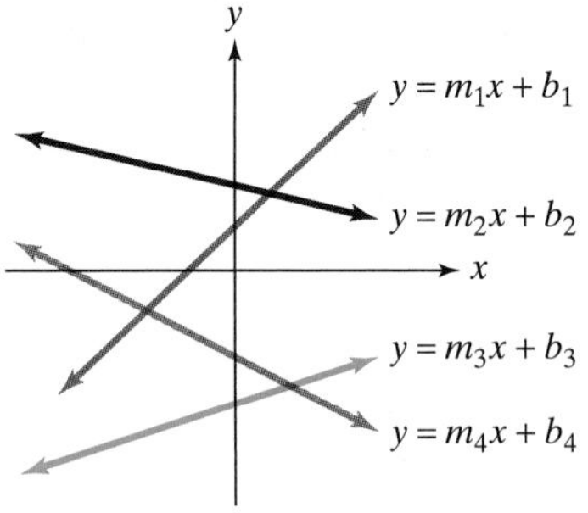

85. List the slopes m_1, m_2, m_3, and m_4 in order of decreasing size.

86. List the y-intercepts b_1, b_2, b_3, and b_4 in order of decreasing size.

Application Exercises

Though increasing numbers of Americans are obese, fewer are trimming down by watching what they eat. The bar graph shows the percentage of American adults on weight-loss diets for four selected years. The data are displayed as two sets of four points each, one scatter plot for the percentage of dieting women and one for the percentage of dieting men. Also shown in each scatter plot is a line that passes through or near the four points. Use these lines to solve Exercises 87–88.

Percentage of American Adults on Weight-Loss Diets

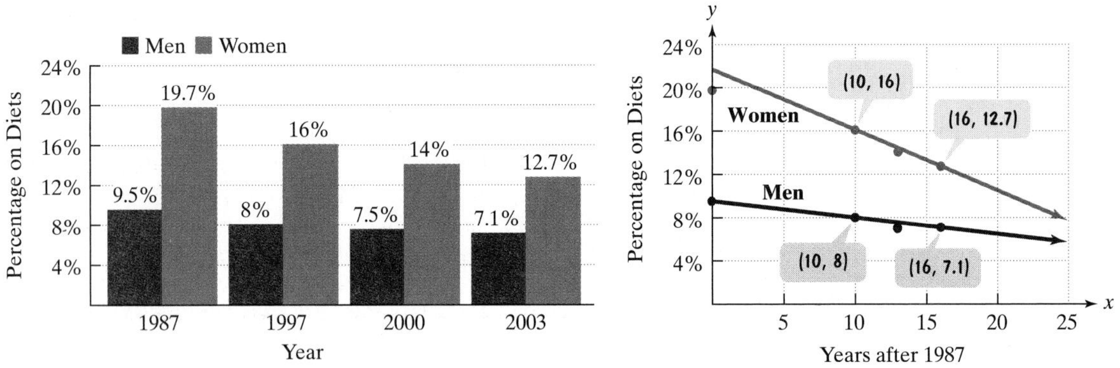

Source: Mediamark Research, American Demographics

87. In this exercise, you will use the blue line for the women shown on the scatter plot to develop a model for the percentage of dieting American women.

a. Use the two points whose coordinates are shown by the voice balloons to find the point-slope form of the equation of the line that models the percentage of adult women on diets, y, x years after 1987.

b. Write the equation in part (a) in slope-intercept form. Use function notation.

c. Use the linear function to predict the percentage of adult women on weight-loss diets in 2007.

88. In this exercise, you will use the red line for men shown on the scatter plot to develop a model for the percentage of dieting American men.

a. Use the two points whose coordinates are shown by the voice balloons to find the point-slope form of the equation of the line that models the percentage of adult men on diets, y, x years after 1987.

b. Write the equation in part (a) in slope-intercept form. Use function notation.

c. Use the linear function to predict the percentage of adult men on weight-loss diets in 2007.

89. The bar graph shows life expectancies for Americans born in seven selected years.

Life Expectancy in the U.S. by Birth Year

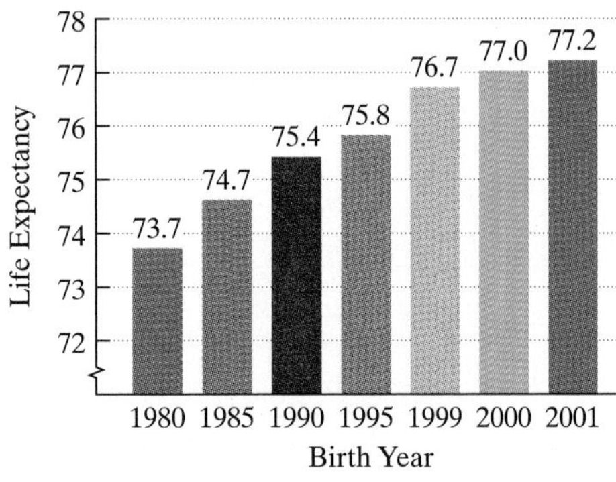

Source: National Center for Health Statistics

a. Let x represent the number of birth years after 1980 and let y represent life expectancy. Create a scatter plot that displays the data as a set of seven points in a rectangular coordinate system.

b. Draw a line through the two points that show life expectancies for 1985 and 2000. Use the coordinates of these points to write the line's equation in point-slope form and slope-intercept form. Round the slope to two decimal places.

c. Write a linear function that models life expectancy, $E(x)$, for Americans born x years after 1980. Then use this function to predict the life expectancy of an American born in 2020.

90. The bar graph shows the number of global HIV/AIDS cases, in millions, from 1999 through 2003.

Millions of Worldwide HIV/AIDS Cases

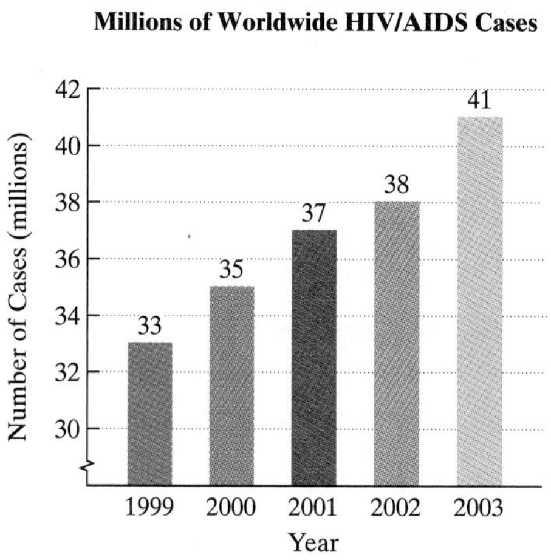

Source: UNAIDS

a. Let x represent the number of years after 1999 and let y represent the number of HIV/AIDS cases worldwide, in millions. Create a scatter plot that displays the data as a set of five points in a rectangular coordinate system.

b. Draw a line through the two points that show the number of cases in 2000 and 2003. Use the coordinates of these points to write the line's equation in point-slope form and slope-intercept form.

c. Write a linear function that models the number of HIV/AIDS cases worldwide, $A(x)$, in millions, x years after 1999. Then use this function to predict the number of cases in 2010.

91. Shown, again, is the scatter plot that indicates a relationship between the percentage of adult females in a country who are literate and the mortality of children under five. Also

Literacy and Child Mortality

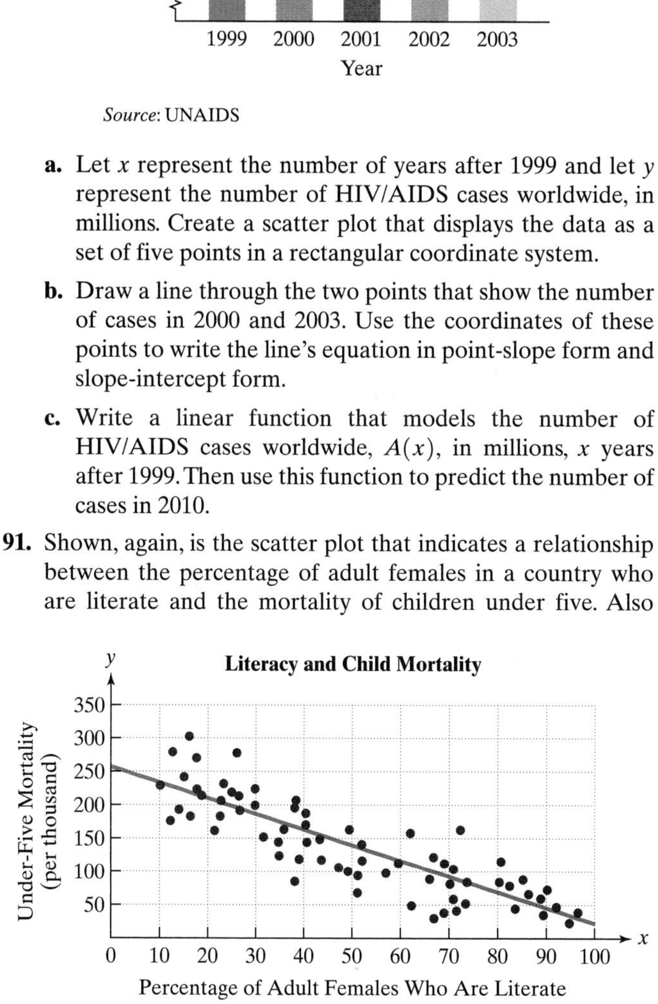

Source: United Nations

shown is a line that passes through or near the points. Find a linear function that models the data by finding the slope-intercept form of the line's equation. Use the function to make a prediction about child mortality based on the percentage of adult females in a country who are literate.

92. Just as money doesn't buy happiness for individuals, the two don't necessarily go together for countries either. However, the scatter plot does show a relationship between a country's annual per capita income and the percentage of people in that country who call themselves "happy."

Per Capita Income and National Happiness

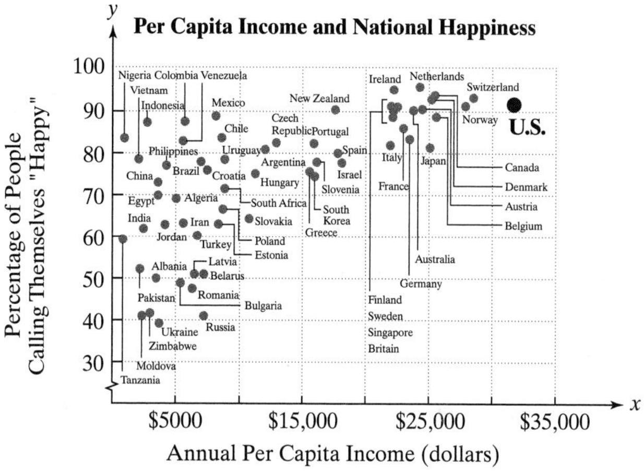

Source: Richard Layard, *Happiness: Lessons from a New Science,* Penguin, 2005

Draw a line that fits the data so that the spread of the data points around the line is as small as possible. Use the coordinates of two points along your line to write the slope-intercept form of its equation. Express the equation in function notation and use the linear function to make a prediction about national happiness based on per capita income.

Writing in Mathematics

93. What is the slope of a line and how is it found?

94. Describe how to write the equation of a line if two points along the line are known.

95. Explain how to derive the slope-intercept form of a line's equation, $y = mx + b$, from the point-slope form

$$y - y_1 = m(x - x_1).$$

96. Explain how to graph the equation $x = 2$. Can this equation be expressed in slope-intercept form? Explain.

97. Explain how to use the general form of a line's equation to find the line's slope and y-intercept.

98. Explain how to use intercepts to graph the general form of a line's equation.

99. Take another look at the scatter plot in Exercise 91. Although there is a relationship between literacy and child mortality, we cannot conclude that increased literacy causes child mortality to decrease. Offer two or more possible explanations for the data in the scatter plot.

Technology Exercises

Use a graphing utility to graph each equation in Exercises 100–103. Then use the TRACE *feature to trace along the line and find the coordinates of two points. Use these points to compute the line's slope. Check your result by using the coefficient of x in the line's equation.*

100. $y = 2x + 4$ **101.** $y = -3x + 6$

102. $y = -\frac{1}{2}x - 5$ **103.** $y = \frac{3}{4}x - 2$

104. Is there a relationship between alcohol from moderate wine consumption and heart disease death rate? The table gives data from 19 developed countries.

France

Country	A	B	C	D	E	F	G
Liters of alcohol from drinking wine, per person per year (x)	2.5	3.9	2.9	2.4	2.9	0.8	9.1
Deaths from heart disease, per 100,000 people per year (y)	211	167	131	191	220	297	71

U.S.

Country	H	I	J	K	L	M	N	O	P	Q	R	S
(x)	0.8	0.7	7.9	1.8	1.9	0.8	6.5	1.6	5.8	1.3	1.2	2.7
(y)	211	300	107	167	266	227	86	207	115	285	199	172

Source: New York Times, December 28, 1994

a. Use the statistical menu of your graphing utility to enter the 19 ordered pairs of data items shown in the table.

b. Use the DRAW menu and the scatter plot capability to draw a scatter plot of the data.

c. Select the linear regression option. Use your utility to obtain values for a and b for the equation of the regression line, $y = ax + b$. You may also be given a **correlation coefficient**, r. Values of r close to 1 indicate that the points can be described by a linear relationship and the regression line has a positive slope. Values of r close to -1 indicate that the points can be described by a linear relationship and the regression line has a negative slope. Values of r close to 0 indicate no linear relationship between the variables. In this case, a linear model does not accurately describe the data.

d. Use the appropriate sequence (consult your manual) to graph the regression equation on top of the points in the scatter plot.

Critical Thinking Exercises

105. Which one of the following is true?

a. A linear function with nonnegative slope has a graph that rises from left to right.

b. Every line in the rectangular coordinate system has an equation that can be expressed in slope-intercept form.

c. The graph of the linear function $5x + 6y = 30$ is a line passing through the point $(6, 0)$ with slope $-\frac{5}{6}$.

d. The graph of $x = 7$ in the rectangular coordinate system is the single point $(7, 0)$.

In Exercises 106–107, find the coefficients that must be placed in each shaded area so that the function's graph will be a line satisfying the specified conditions.

106. $\square x + \square y = 12$; x-intercept $= -2$; y-intercept $= 4$

107. $\square x + \square y = 12$; y-intercept $= -6$; slope $= \frac{1}{2}$

108. Prove that the equation of a line passing through $(a, 0)$ and $(0, b)$ $(a \neq 0, b \neq 0)$ can be written in the form $\frac{x}{a} + \frac{y}{b} = 1$. Why is this called the *intercept form* of a line?

109. Excited about the success of celebrity stamps, post office officials were rumored to have put forth a plan to institute two new types of thermometers. On these new scales, $°E$ represents degrees Elvis and $°M$ represents degrees Madonna. If it is known that $40°E = 25°M$, $280°E = 125°M$, and degrees Elvis is linearly related to degrees Madonna, write an equation expressing E in terms of M.

Group Exercise

110. In Example 8 on page 226, we used the data in Figure 2.31 on page 225 to develop a linear function that modeled the graying of America. For this group exercise, you might find it helpful to pattern your work after Figure 2.31 and the solution to Example 8. Group members should begin by consulting an almanac, newspaper, magazine, or the Internet to find data that appear to lie approximately on or near a line. Working by hand or using a graphing utility, group members should construct scatter plots for the data that were assembled. If working by hand, draw a line that approximately fits the data in each scatter plot and then write its equation as a function in slope-intercept form. If using a graphing utility, obtain the equation of each regression line. Then use each linear function's equation to make predictions about what might occur in the future. Are there circumstances that might affect the accuracy of the prediction? List some of these circumstances.

SECTION 2.4 More on Slope

Objectives

1. Find slopes and equations of parallel and perpendicular lines.
2. Interpret slope as rate of change.
3. Find a function's average rate of change.

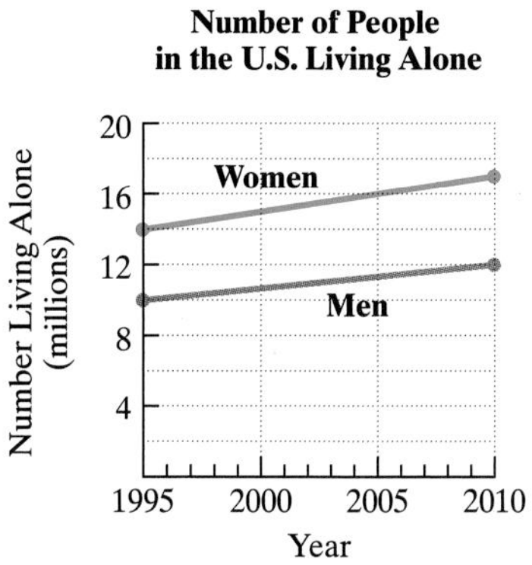

Figure 2.32

Source: Forrester Research

A best guess at the look of our nation in the next decades indicates that the number of men and women living alone will increase each year. Figure 2.32 shows that by 2010, approximately 12 million men and 17 million women will be living alone.

By looking at Figure 2.32, can you tell that the green graph representing women has a greater slope than the blue graph representing men? This indicates a greater yearly rate of change in the millions of women living alone than in the millions of men living alone. In this section, you will learn to interpret slope as a rate of change. You will also explore the relationships between slopes of parallel and perpendicular lines.

1 Find slopes and equations of parallel and perpendicular lines.

Parallel and Perpendicular Lines

Two nonintersecting lines that lie in the same plane are **parallel**. If two lines do not intersect, the ratio of the vertical change to the horizontal change is the same for each line. Because two parallel lines have the same "steepness," they must have the same slope.

Slope and Parallel Lines

1. If two nonvertical lines are parallel, then they have the same slope.
2. If two distinct nonvertical lines have the same slope, then they are parallel.
3. Two distinct vertical lines, both with undefined slopes, are parallel.

EXAMPLE 1 Writing Equations of a Line Parallel to a Given Line

Write an equation of the line passing through $(-3, 1)$ and parallel to the line whose equation is $y = 2x + 1$. Express the equation in point-slope form and slope-intercept form.

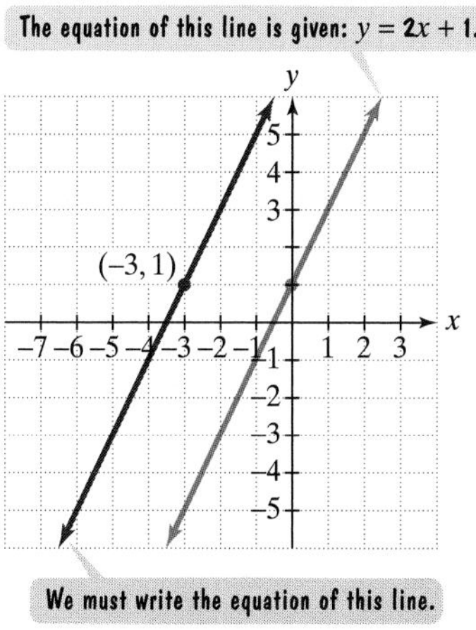

Figure 2.33

Solution The situation is illustrated in Figure 2.33. We are looking for the equation of the red line shown on the left. How do we obtain this equation? Notice that the line passes through the point $(-3, 1)$. Using the point-slope form of the line's equation, we have $x_1 = -3$ and $y_1 = 1$.

$$y - y_1 = m(x - x_1)$$

$y_1 = 1$ $x_1 = -3$

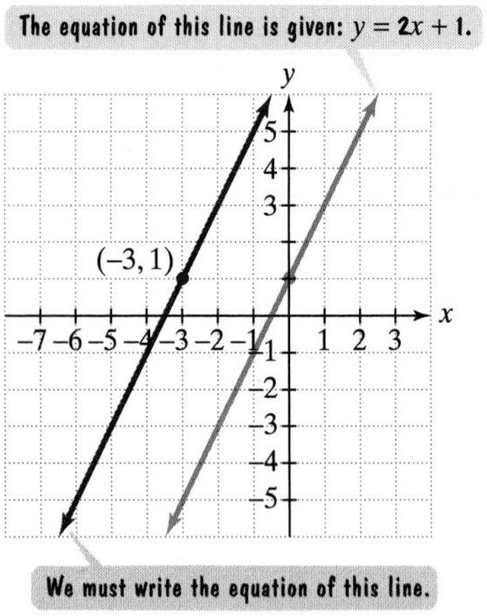

Figure 2.33 (repeated)

With $(x_1, y_1) = (-3, 1)$, the only thing missing from the equation of the red line is m, the slope. Do we know anything about the slope of either line in Figure 2.33? The answer is yes; we know the slope of the blue line on the right, whose equation is given.

$$y = 2x + 1$$

The slope of the blue line on the right in Figure 2.33 is 2.

Parallel lines have the same slope. Because the slope of the blue line is 2, the slope of the red line, the line whose equation we must write, is also 2: $m = 2$. We now have values for x_1, y_1, and m for the red line.

$$y - y_1 = m(x - x_1)$$

$y_1 = 1$ $m = 2$ $x_1 = -3$

The point-slope form of the red line's equation is

$$y - 1 = 2[x - (-3)] \text{ or}$$
$$y - 1 = 2(x + 3).$$

Solving for y, we obtain the slope-intercept form of the equation.

$y - 1 = 2x + 6$ Apply the distributive property.

$y = 2x + 7$ Add 1 to both sides. This is the slope-intercept form, $y = mx + b$, of the equation. Using function notation, the equation is $f(x) = 2x + 7$.

Check Point 1 Write an equation of the line passing through $(-2, 5)$ and parallel to the line whose equation is $y = 3x + 1$. Express the equation in point-slope form and slope-intercept form.

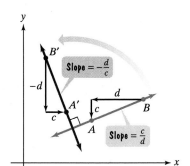

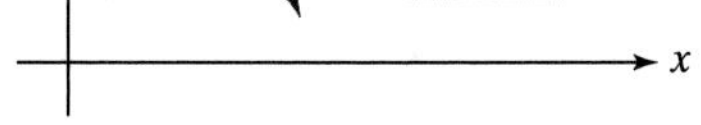

Figure 2.34 Slopes of perpendicular lines

Two lines that intersect at a right angle (90°) are said to be **perpendicular**, shown in Figure 2.34. The relationship between the slopes of perpendicular lines is not as obvious as the relationship between parallel lines. Figure 2.34 shows line AB, with slope $\frac{c}{d}$. Rotate line AB through 90° to the left to obtain line $A'B'$, perpendicular to line AB. The figure indicates that the rise and the run of the new line are reversed from the original line, but the rise is now negative. This means that the slope of the new line is $-\frac{d}{c}$. Notice that the product of the slopes of the two perpendicular lines is -1:

$$\left(\frac{c}{d}\right)\left(-\frac{d}{c}\right) = -1.$$

This relationship holds for all perpendicular lines and is summarized in the following box:

Slope and Perpendicular Lines

1. If two nonvertical lines are perpendicular, then the product of their slopes is -1.
2. If the product of the slopes of two lines is -1, then the lines are perpendicular.
3. A horizontal line having zero slope is perpendicular to a vertical line having undefined slope.

An equivalent way of stating this relationship is to say that **one line is perpendicular to another line if its slope is the *negative reciprocal* of the slope of the other line.** For example, if a line has slope 5, any line having slope $-\frac{1}{5}$ is perpendicular to it. Similarly, if a line has slope $-\frac{3}{4}$, any line having slope $\frac{4}{3}$ is perpendicular to it.

EXAMPLE 2 Writing Equations of a Line Perpendicular to a Given Line

a. Find the slope of any line that is perpendicular to the line whose equation is $x + 4y - 8 = 0$.

b. Write the equation of the line passing through $(3, -5)$ and perpendicular to the line whose equation is $x + 4y - 8 = 0$. Express the equation in general form.

Solution

a. We begin by writing the equation of the given line, $x + 4y - 8 = 0$, in slope-intercept form. Solve for y.

$x + 4y - 8 = 0$ — This is the given equation.

$4y = -x + 8$ — To isolate the y-term, subtract x and add 8 on both sides.

$y = -\frac{1}{4}x + 2$ — Divide both sides by 4.

Slope is $-\frac{1}{4}$.

The given line has slope $-\frac{1}{4}$. Any line perpendicular to this line has a slope that is the negative reciprocal of $-\frac{1}{4}$. Thus, the slope of any perpendicular line is 4.

b. Let's begin by writing the point-slope form of the perpendicular line's equation. Because the line passes through the point $(3, -5)$, we have $x_1 = 3$ and $y_1 = -5$. In part (a), we determined that the slope of any line perpendicular to $x + 4y - 8 = 0$ is 4, so the slope of this particular perpendicular line must also be 4: $m = 4$.

$$y - y_1 = m(x - x_1)$$

$y_1 = -5$ $m = 4$ $x_1 = 3$

The point-slope form of the perpendicular line's equation is

$$y - (-5) = 4(x - 3) \text{ or}$$
$$y + 5 = 4(x - 3).$$

How can we express this equation in general form $(Ax + By + C = 0)$? We need to obtain zero on one side of the equation. Let's do this and keep A, the coefficient of x, positive.

$y + 5 = 4(x - 3)$ — This is the point-slope form of the line's equation.

$y + 5 = 4x - 12$ — Apply the distributive property.

$y - y + 5 - 5 = 4x - y - 12 - 5$ — To obtain 0 on the left, subtract y and subtract 5 on both sides.

$0 = 4x - y - 17$ — Simplify.

The general form of the perpendicular line's equation is $4x - y - 17 = 0$.

Check Point 2

a. Find the slope of any line that is perpendicular to the line whose equation is $x + 3y - 12 = 0$.

b. Write the equation of the line passing through $(-2, -6)$ and perpendicular to the line whose equation is $x + 3y - 12 = 0$. Express the equation in general form.

2 Interpret slope as rate of change.

Slope as Rate of Change

Slope is defined as the ratio of a change in y to a corresponding change in x. It describes how fast y is changing with respect to x. For a linear function, slope may be interpreted as the rate of change of the dependent variable per unit change in the independent variable.

Our next example shows how slope can be interpreted as a rate of change in an applied situation. When calculating slope in applied problems, keep track of the units in the numerator and the denominator.

EXAMPLE 3 Slope as a Rate of Change

The line graphs for the number of women and men living alone are shown again in Figure 2.35. Find the slope of the line segment for the women. Describe what this slope represents.

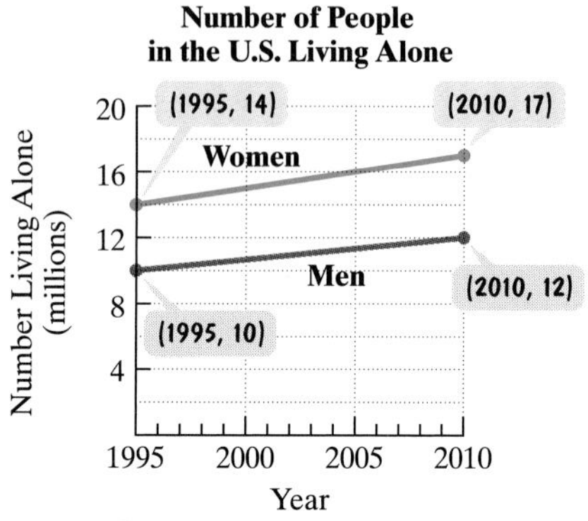

Figure 2.35
Source: Forrester Research

Solution We let x represent a year and y the number of women living alone in that year. The two points shown on the line segment for women have the following coordinates:

$$(1995, 14) \quad \text{and} \quad (2010, 17).$$

In 1995, 14 million U.S. women lived alone.

In 2010, 17 million U.S. women are projected to live alone.

Now we compute the slope:

$$m = \frac{\text{Change in } y}{\text{Change in } x} = \frac{17 - 14}{2010 - 1995}$$

$$= \frac{3}{15} = \frac{1}{5} = \frac{0.2 \text{ million women}}{\text{year}}.$$

The unit in the numerator is *million women.*

The unit in the denominator is *year.*

The slope indicates that the number of U.S. women living alone is projected to increase by 0.2 million each year. The rate of change is 0.2 million women per year.

Check Point 3 Use the graph in Figure 2.35 to find the slope of the line segment for the men. Express the slope correct to two decimal places and describe what it represents.

In Check Point 3 did you find that the slope of the line segment for the men is different from that of the women? The rate of change for men living alone is not equal to the rate of change for women living alone. Because of these different slopes, if you extend the line segments in Figure 2.35, the resulting lines will intersect. They are not parallel.

3 Find a function's average rate of change.

The Average Rate of Change of a Function

If the graph of a function is not a straight line, the **average rate of change** between any two points is the slope of the line containing the two points. This line is called a **secant line**. For example, Figure 2.36 shows the graph of a particular man's height, in inches, as a function of his age, in years. Two points on the graph are labeled: (13, 57) and (18, 76). At age 13, this man was 57 inches tall and at age 18, he was 76 inches tall.

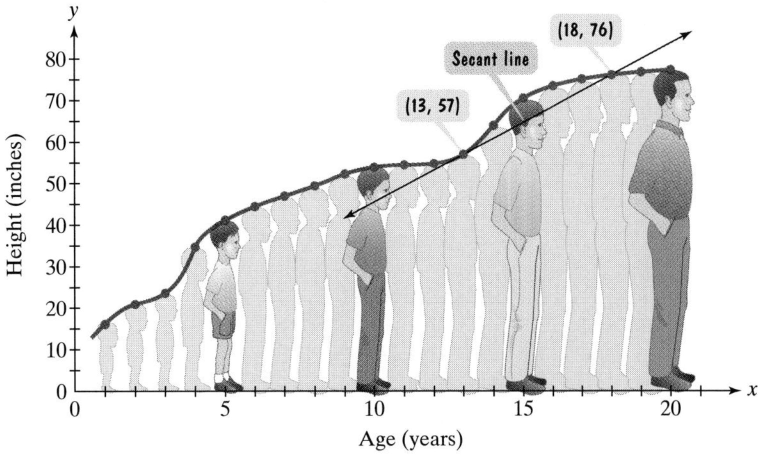

Figure 2.36 Height as a function of age

The man's average growth rate between ages 13 and 18 is the slope of the secant line containing (13, 57) and (18, 76):

$$m = \frac{\text{Change in } y}{\text{Change in } x} = \frac{76 - 57}{18 - 13} = \frac{19}{5} = 3\frac{4}{5}.$$

This man's average rate of change, or average growth rate, from age 13 to age 18 was $3\frac{4}{5}$, or 3.8, inches per year.

The Average Rate of Change of a Function

Let $(x_1, f(x_1))$ and $(x_2, f(x_2))$ be distinct points on the graph of a function f. (See Figure 2.37.) The **average rate of change of f** from x_1 to x_2 is

$$\frac{f(x_2) - f(x_1)}{x_2 - x_1}.$$

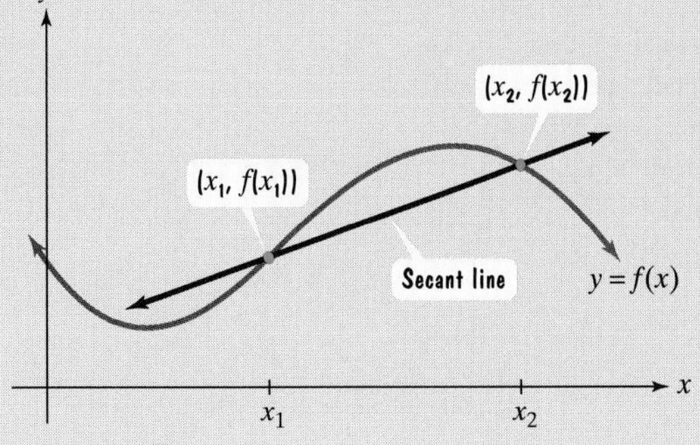

Figure 2.37

EXAMPLE 4 Finding the Average Rate of Change

Find the average rate of change of $f(x) = x^2$ from

a. $x_1 = 0$ to $x_2 = 1$ **b.** $x_1 = 1$ to $x_2 = 2$ **c.** $x_1 = -2$ to $x_2 = 0$.

Solution

a. The average rate of change of $f(x) = x^2$ from $x_1 = 0$ to $x_2 = 1$ is

$$\frac{f(x_2) - f(x_1)}{x_2 - x_1} = \frac{f(1) - f(0)}{1 - 0} = \frac{1^2 - 0^2}{1} = 1.$$

Figure 2.38(a) shows the secant line of $f(x) = x^2$ from $x_1 = 0$ to $x_2 = 1$. The average rate of change is positive and the function is increasing on the interval $(0, 1)$.

b. The average rate of change of $f(x) = x^2$ from $x_1 = 1$ to $x_2 = 2$ is

$$\frac{f(x_2) - f(x_1)}{x_2 - x_1} = \frac{f(2) - f(1)}{2 - 1} = \frac{2^2 - 1^2}{1} = 3.$$

Figure 2.38(b) shows the secant line of $f(x) = x^2$ from $x_1 = 1$ to $x_2 = 2$. The average rate of change is positive and the function is increasing on the interval $(1, 2)$. Can you see that the graph rises more steeply on the interval $(1, 2)$ than on $(0, 1)$? This is because the average rate of change from $x_1 = 1$ to $x_2 = 2$ is greater than the average rate of change from $x_1 = 0$ to $x_2 = 1$.

c. The average rate of change of $f(x) = x^2$ from $x_1 = -2$ to $x_2 = 0$ is

$$\frac{f(x_2) - f(x_1)}{x_2 - x_1} = \frac{f(0) - f(-2)}{0 - (-2)} = \frac{0^2 - (-2)^2}{2} = \frac{-4}{2} = -2.$$

Figure 2.38(c) shows the secant line of $f(x) = x^2$ from $x_1 = -2$ to $x_2 = 0$. The average rate of change is negative and the function is decreasing on the interval $(-2, 0)$.

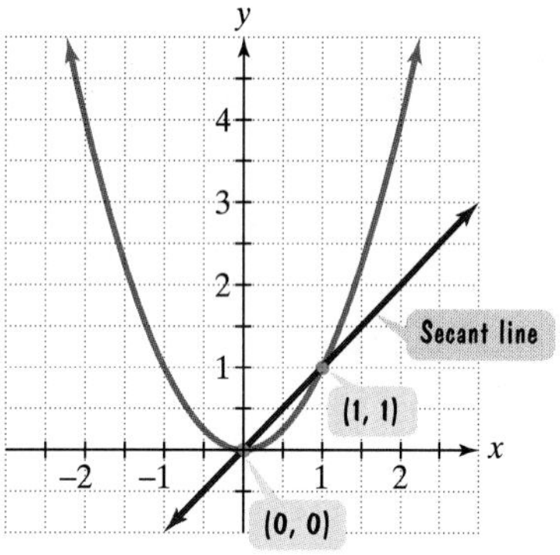

Figure 2.38(a) The secant line of $f(x) = x^2$ from $x_1 = 0$ to $x_2 = 1$

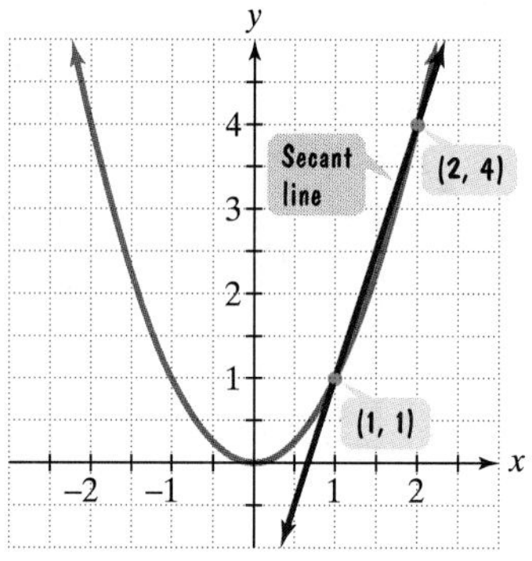

Figure 2.38(b) The secant line of $f(x) = x^2$ from $x_1 = 1$ to $x_2 = 2$

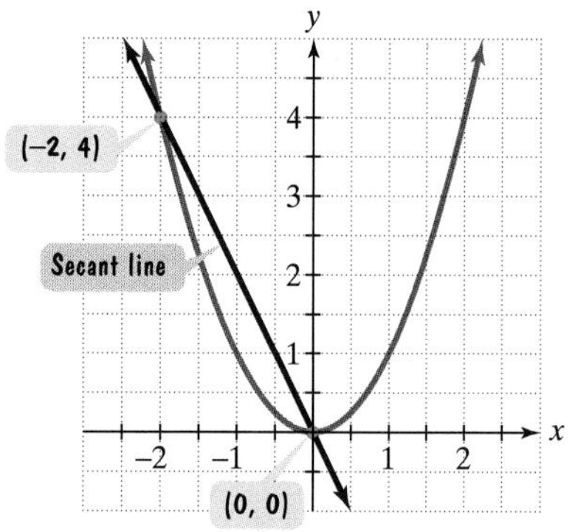

Figure 2.38(c) The secant line of $f(x) = x^2$ from $x_1 = -2$ to $x_2 = 0$

Check Point 4 Find the average rate of change of $f(x) = x^3$ from

a. $x_1 = 0$ to $x_2 = 1$ **b.** $x_1 = 1$ to $x_2 = 2$ **c.** $x_1 = -2$ to $x_2 = 0$.

Suppose we are interested in the average rate of change of f from $x_1 = x$ to $x_2 = x + h$. In this case, the average rate of change is

$$\frac{f(x_2) - f(x_1)}{x_2 - x_1} = \frac{f(x + h) - f(x)}{x + h - x} = \frac{f(x + h) - f(x)}{h}.$$

Do you recognize the last expression? It is the difference quotient that you used in Section 2.2. Thus, the difference quotient gives the average rate of change of a function from x to $x + h$. In the difference quotient, h is thought of as a number very close to 0. In this way, the average rate of change can be found for a very short interval.

EXAMPLE 5 Finding the Average Rate of Change

When a person receives a drug injected into a muscle, the concentration of the drug in the body, measured in milligrams per 100 milliliters, is a function of the time elapsed after the injection, measured in hours. Figure 2.39 shows the graph of such a function, where x represents hours after the injection and $f(x)$ is the drug's concentration at time x. Find the average rate of change in the drug's concentration between 3 and 7 hours.

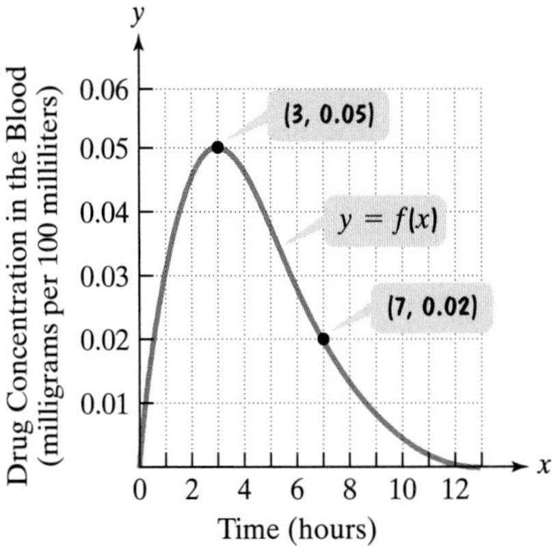

Figure 2.39 Concentration of a drug as a function of time

Solution At 3 hours, the drug's concentration is 0.05 and at 7 hours, the concentration is 0.02. The average rate of change in its concentration between 3 and 7 hours is

$$\frac{f(x_2) - f(x_1)}{x_2 - x_1} = \frac{f(7) - f(3)}{7 - 3} = \frac{0.02 - 0.05}{7 - 3} = \frac{-0.03}{4} = -0.0075.$$

The average rate of change is -0.0075. This means that the drug's concentration is decreasing at an average rate of 0.0075 milligrams per 100 milliliters per hour.

Study Tip

Units used to describe x and y tend to "pile up" when expressing the rate of change of y with respect to x. The unit used to express the rate of change of y with respect to x is

the unit used to describe y **per** the unit used to describe x.

In Figure 2.39, y, or drug concentration, is described in milligrams per 100 milliliters.

In Figure 2.39, x, or time, is described in hours.

In Figure 2.39, the rate of change is described in terms of milligrams per 100 milliliters per hour.

Check Point 5 Use Figure 2.39 to find the average rate of change in the drug's concentration between 1 hour and 3 hours.

How Calculus Studies Change

Calculus allows motion and change to be analyzed by "freezing the frame" of a continuous changing process, instant by instant. For example, Figure 2.40 shows a male's changing height over intervals of time. Over the period of time from P to D, his average rate of growth is his change in height—that is, his height at time D minus his height at time P—divided by the change in time from P to D. This is the slope of secant line PD.

The secant lines PD, PC, PB, and PA shown in Figure 2.40 have slopes that show average growth rates for successively shorter periods of time. Calculus makes these time frames so small that they approach a single point—that is, a single instant in time. This point is shown as point P in Figure 2.40. The slope of the line that touches the graph at P gives the male's growth rate at one instant in time, P.

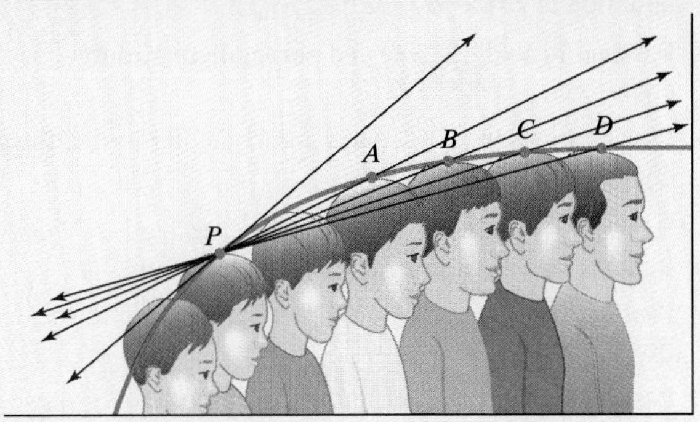

Figure 2.40 Analyzing continuous growth over intervals of time and at an instant in time

EXERCISE SET 2.4

Practice Exercises

In Exercises 1–4, write an equation for line L in point-slope form and slope-intercept form.

1.

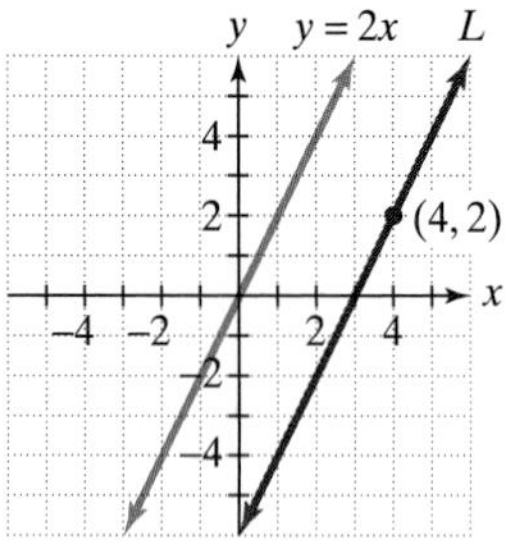

L is parallel to $y = 2x$.

2.

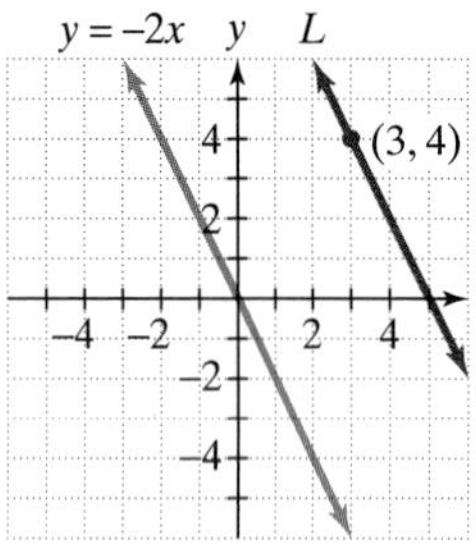

L is parallel to $y = -2x$.

3.

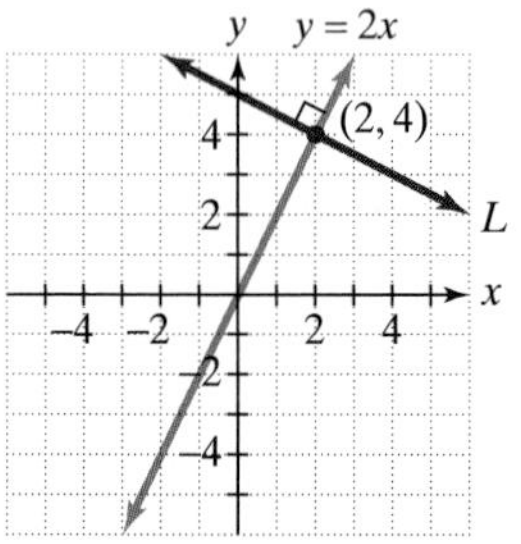

L is perpendicular to $y = 2x$.

4.

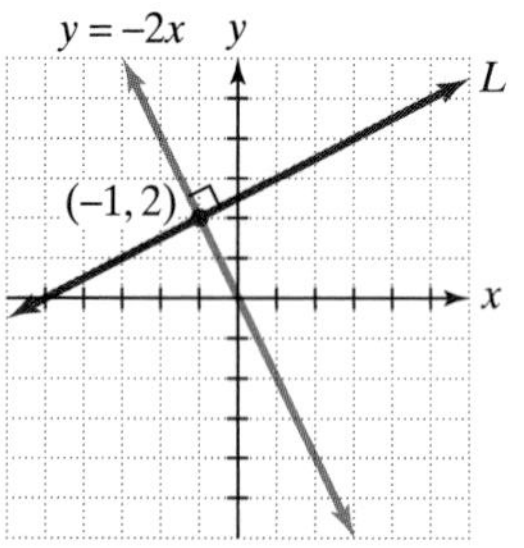

L is perpendicular to $y = -2x$.

In Exercises 5–8, use the given conditions to write an equation for each line in point-slope form and slope-intercept form.

5. Passing through $(-8, -10)$ and parallel to the line whose equation is $y = -4x + 3$

6. Passing through $(-2, -7)$ and parallel to the line whose equation is $y = -5x + 4$

7. Passing through $(2, -3)$ and perpendicular to the line whose equation is $y = \frac{1}{5}x + 6$

8. Passing through $(-4, 2)$ and perpendicular to the line whose equation is $y = \frac{1}{3}x + 7$

In Exercises 9–12, use the given conditions to write an equation for each line in point-slope form and general form.

9. Passing through $(-2, 2)$ and parallel to the line whose equation is $2x - 3y - 7 = 0$

10. Passing through $(-1, 3)$ and parallel to the line whose equation is $3x - 2y - 5 = 0$

11. Passing through $(4, -7)$ and perpendicular to the line whose equation is $x - 2y - 3 = 0$

12. Passing through $(5, -9)$ and perpendicular to the line whose equation is $x + 7y - 12 = 0$

In Exercises 13–18, find the average rate of change of the function from x_1 to x_2.

13. $f(x) = 3x$ from $x_1 = 0$ to $x_2 = 5$

14. $f(x) = 6x$ from $x_1 = 0$ to $x_2 = 4$

15. $f(x) = x^2 + 2x$ from $x_1 = 3$ to $x_2 = 5$

16. $f(x) = x^2 - 2x$ from $x_2 = 3$ to $x_2 = 6$

17. $f(x) = \sqrt{x}$ from $x_1 = 4$ to $x_2 = 9$

18. $f(x) = \sqrt{x}$ from $x_1 = 9$ to $x_2 = 16$

Practice Plus

In Exercises 19–24, write the slope-intercept equation of a function f whose graph satisfies the given conditions.

19. The graph of f passes through $(-1, 5)$ and is perpendicular to the line whose equation is $x = 6$.

20. The graph of f passes through $(-2, 6)$ and is perpendicular to the line whose equation is $x = -4$.

21. The graph of f passes through $(-6, 4)$ and is perpendicular to the line that has an x-intercept of 2 and a y-intercept of -4.

22. The graph of f passes through $(-5, 6)$ and is perpendicular to the line that has an x-intercept of 3 and a y-intercept of -9.

23. The graph of f is perpendicular to the line whose equation is $3x - 2y - 4 = 0$ and has the same y-intercept as this line.

24. The graph of f is perpendicular to the line whose equation is $4x - y - 6 = 0$ and has the same y-intercept as this line.

Application Exercises

In Exercises 25–28, a linear function that models data is described. Find the slope of each model. Then describe what this means in terms of the rate of change of the dependent variable per unit change in the independent variable.

25. The linear function $f(x) = 0.01x + 57.7$ models the global average temperature of Earth, $f(x)$, in degrees Fahrenheit, x years after 1995.

26. The linear function $f(x) = 2x + 10$ models the amount, $f(x)$, in billions of dollars, that the drug industry spent on marketing information about drugs to doctors x years after 2000. (*Source:* IMS Health)

27. The linear function $f(x) = -0.52x + 24.7$ models the percentage of U.S. adults who smoked cigarettes, $f(x)$, x years after 1997. (*Source:* National Center for Health Statistics)

28. The linear function $f(x) = -0.28x + 1.7$ models the percentage of U.S. taxpayers who were audited by the IRS, $f(x)$, x years after 1996. (*Source:* IRS)

The bar graph shows the average amount that U.S. consumers spent on four pieces of the entertainment pie from 2002 through 2004.

Average Amount U.S. Consumers Spent on Entertainment

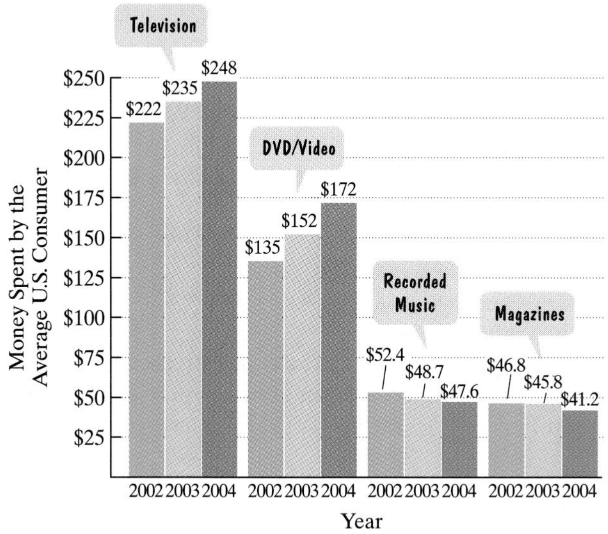

Source: Veronis, Suhler, Stevenson, Communications Industry Forecast and Report

In Exercises 29–32, find a linear function in slope-intercept form that models the given description. Each function should model the average amount, $f(x)$, that U.S. consumers spent on the mode of entertainment x years after 2002.

29. In 2002, the average U.S. consumer spent $222 on television (broadcast, cable, and satellite) and this amount has increased at an average rate of $13 per year since then.

30. In 2002, the average U.S. consumer spent $135 on DVDs and videos, and this amount has increased at an average rate of $18.50 per year since then.

31. In 2002, the average U.S. consumer spent $52.40 on recorded music and this amount has decreased at an average rate of $2.40 per year since then.

32. In 2002, the average U.S. consumer spent $46.80 on magazines and this amount has decreased at an average rate of $2.80 per year since then.

The graph shows the percentage of sales of recorded music in the United States for rock and rap/hip-hop from 1997 through 2003. Use the information shown to solve Exercises 33–34.

Sales of Recorded Music in the U.S.

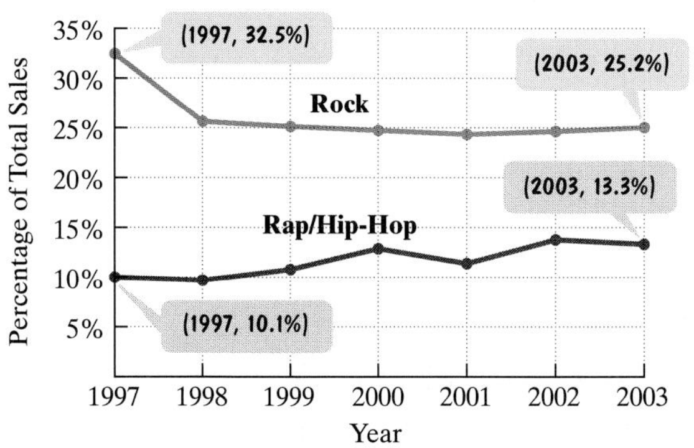

Source: RIAA

33. Find the average rate of change in the percentage of total sales of rock from 1997 through 2003. Round to the nearest hundredth of a percent.

34. Find the average rate of change in the percentage of total sales of rap/hip-hop from 1997 through 2003. Round to the nearest hundredth of a percent.

Writing in Mathematics

35. If two lines are parallel, describe the relationship between their slopes.

36. If two lines are perpendicular, describe the relationship between their slopes.

37. If you know a point on a line and you know the equation of a line perpendicular to this line, explain how to write the line's equation.

38. A formula in the form $y = mx + b$ models the cost, y, of a four-year college x years after 2005. Would you expect m to be positive, negative, or zero? Explain your answer.

39. What is a secant line?

40. What is the average rate of change of a function?

Technology Exercise

41. **a.** Why are the lines whose equations are $y = \frac{1}{3}x + 1$ and $y = -3x - 2$ perpendicular?

b. Use a graphing utility to graph the equations in a $[-10, 10, 1]$ by $[-10, 10, 1]$ viewing rectangle. Do the lines appear to be perpendicular?

c. Now use the zoom square feature of your utility. Describe what happens to the graphs. Explain why this is so.

Critical Thinking Exercises

In Exercises 42–43, draw a graph that illustrates each data description.

42. From 1971 through 1980, the percentage of Americans who were obese held constant at 15%. After 1980, this percentage increased at a rate of 0.8% per year.
(*Source:* National Center for Health Statistics)

43. In 1970, the daily calories in the U.S. food supply was 3300 per person. From 1970 through 1975, daily calories in the food supply decreased at a rate of 20 calories per person per year. From 1975 through the present, this number has increased at a rate of 28 calories per person per year.
(*Source:* USDA, Economic Research Service)

44. What is the slope of a line that is perpendicular to the line whose equation is $Ax + By + C = 0$, $A \neq 0$ and $B \neq 0$?

45. Determine the value of A so that the line whose equation is $Ax + y - 2 = 0$ is perpendicular to the line containing the points $(1, -3)$ and $(-2, 4)$.

CHAPTER 2
MID-CHAPTER CHECK POINT

What You Know: We learned that a function is a relation in which no two ordered pairs have the same first component and different second components. We represented functions as equations and used function notation. We graphed functions and applied the vertical line test to identify graphs of functions. We determined the domain and range of a function from its graph, using inputs on the x-axis for the domain and outputs on the y-axis for the range. We used graphs to identify intervals on which functions increase, decrease, or are constant, as well as to locate relative maxima or minima. We identified even functions [$f(-x) = f(x)$: y-axis symmetry] and odd functions [$f(-x) = -f(x)$: origin symmetry]. Finally, we studied linear functions and slope, using slope (change in y divided by change in x) to develop various forms for equations of lines:

Point-slope form	Slope-intercept form	Horizontal line	Vertical line	General form
$y - y_1 = m(x - x_1)$	$y = f(x) = mx + b$	$y = f(x) = b$	$x = a$	$Ax + By + C = 0$

We saw that parallel lines have the same slope and that perpendicular lines have slopes that are negative reciprocals. For linear functions, slope was interpreted as the rate of change of the dependent variable per unit change in the independent variable. For nonlinear functions, the slope of the secant line between $(x_1, f(x_1))$ and $(x_2, f(x_2))$ described the average rate of change of f from x_1 to x_2: $\dfrac{f(x_2) - f(x_1)}{x_2 - x_1}$.

In Exercises 1–6, determine whether each relation is a function. Give the domain and range for each relation.

1. $\{(2, 6), (1, 4), (2, -6)\}$
2. $\{(0, 1), (2, 1), (3, 4)\}$

3.
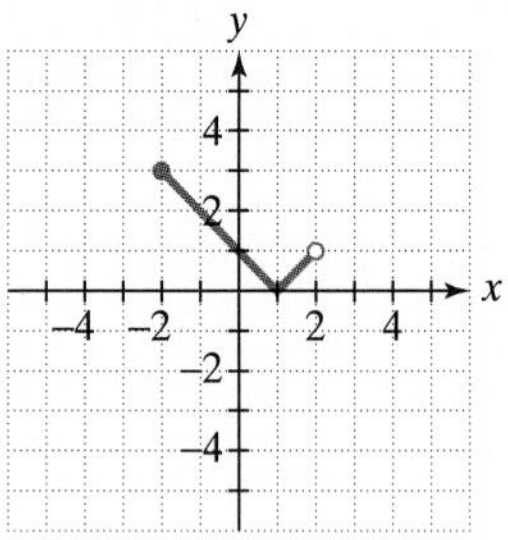

4.
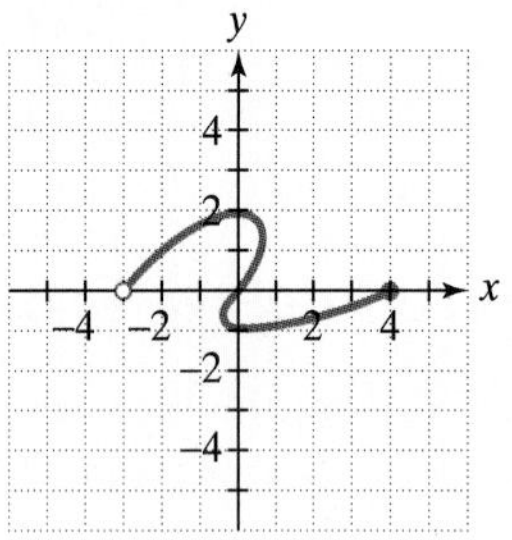

5.
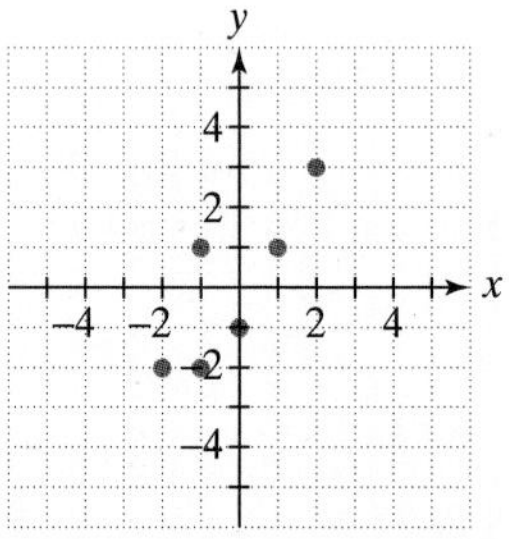

6.
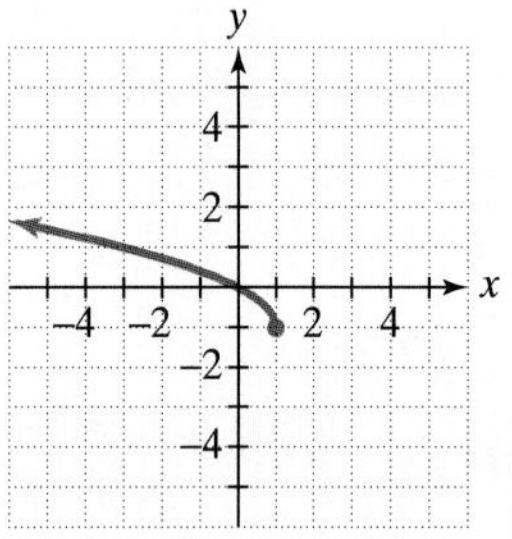

In Exercises 7–8, determine whether each equation defines y as a function of x.

7. $x^2 + y = 5$
8. $x + y^2 = 5$

Use the graph of f to solve Exercises 9–24. Where applicable, use interval notation.

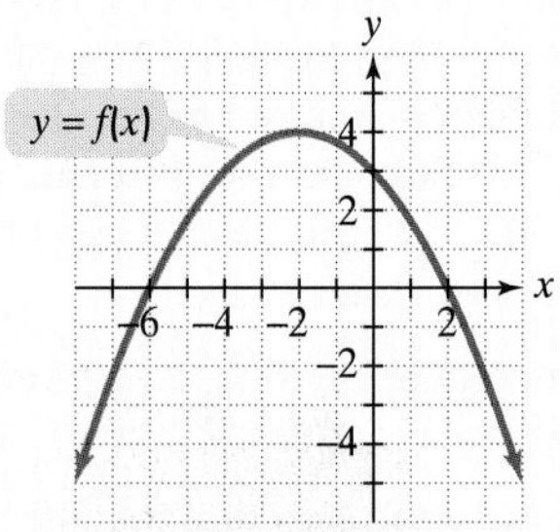

9. Explain why f represents the graph of a function.
10. Find the domain of f.
11. Find the range of f.
12. Find the x-intercept(s).
13. Find the y-intercept.
14. Find the interval(s) on which f is increasing.
15. Find the interval(s) on which f is decreasing.
16. At what number does f have a relative maximum?
17. What is the relative maximum of f?
18. Find $f(-4)$.
19. For what value or values of x is $f(x) = -2$?
20. For what value or values of x is $f(x) = 0$?
21. For what values of x is $f(x) > 0$?
22. Is $f(100)$ positive or negative?
23. Is f even, odd, or neither?
24. Find the average rate of change of f from $x_1 = -4$ to $x_2 = 4$.

In Exercises 25–36, graph each equation in a rectangular coordinate system.

25. $y = -2x$
26. $y = -2$
27. $x + y = -2$
28. $y = \frac{1}{3}x - 2$
29. $x = 3.5$
30. $4x - 2y = 8$
31. $f(x) = x^2 - 4$
32. $f(x) = x - 4$
33. $f(x) = |x| - 4$
34. $5y = -3x$
35. $5y = 20$
36. $f(x) = \begin{cases} -1 & \text{if } x \le 0 \\ 1 & \text{if } x > 0 \end{cases}$
37. Let $f(x) = -2x^2 + x - 5$.
    a. Find $f(-x)$. Is f even, odd, or neither?
    b. Find $\dfrac{f(x + h) - f(x)}{h}$, $h \neq 0$.

38. Let $C(x) = \begin{cases} 30 & \text{if} \quad 0 \le t \le 200 \\ 30 + 0.40(t - 200) & \text{if} \quad t > 200 \end{cases}$.

a. Find $C(150)$. **b.** Find $C(250)$.

In Exercises 39–42, write a function in slope-intercept form whose graph satisfies the given conditions.

39. Slope $= -2$, passing through $(-4, 3)$

40. Passing through $(-1, -5)$ and $(2, 1)$

41. Passing through $(3, -4)$ and parallel to the line whose equation is $3x - y - 5 = 0$

42. Passing through $(-4, -3)$ and perpendicular to the line whose equation is $2x - 5y - 10 = 0$

43. Determine whether the line through $(2, -4)$ and $(7, 0)$ is parallel to a second line through $(-4, 2)$ and $(1, 6)$.

44. The graph shows the percentage of U.S. colleges that offered distance learning by computer for selected years from 1995 through 2002.

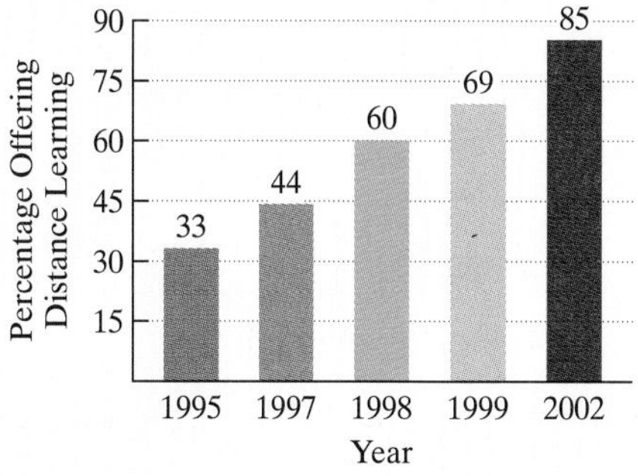

Source: International Data Corporation

The data can be modeled by the linear function $f(x) = 7.8x + 33$, where x is the number of years after 1995 and $f(x)$ is the percentage of U.S. colleges offering distance learning. Find the slope of this function and describe its meaning as a rate of change.

45. Find the average rate of change of $f(x) = 3x^2 - x$ from $x_1 = -1$ to $x_2 = 2$.

SECTION 2.5 Transformations of Functions

Objectives

1. Recognize graphs of common functions.
2. Use vertical shifts to graph functions.
3. Use horizontal shifts to graph functions.
4. Use reflections to graph functions.
5. Use vertical stretching and shrinking to graph functions.
6. Use horizontal stretching and shrinking to graph functions.
7. Graph functions involving a sequence of transformations.

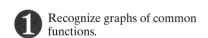

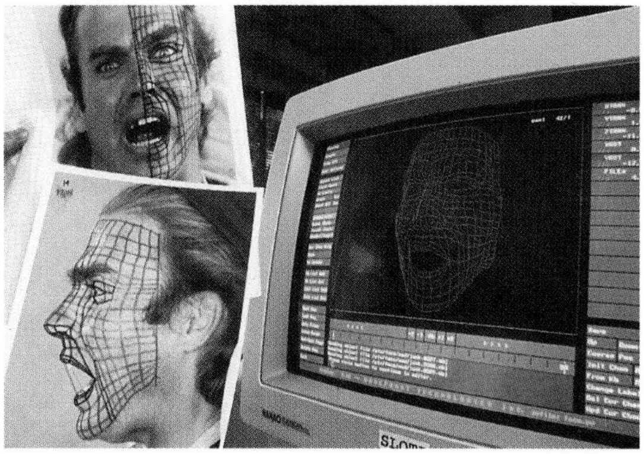

Have you seen *Terminator 2*, *The Mask*, or *The Matrix*? These were among the first films to use spectacular effects in which a character or object having one shape was transformed in a fluid fashion into a quite different shape. The name for such a transformation is **morphing**. The effect allows a real actor to be seamlessly transformed into a computer-generated animation. The animation can be made to perform impossible feats before it is morphed back to the conventionally filmed image.

Like transformed movie images, the graph of one function can be turned into the graph of a different function. To do this, we need to rely on a function's equation. Knowing that a graph is a transformation of a familiar graph makes graphing easier.

1 Recognize graphs of common functions.

Graphs of Common Functions

Table 2.3 on the next page gives names to seven frequently encountered functions in algebra. The table shows each function's graph and lists characteristics of the function. Study the shape of each graph and take a few minutes to verify the function's characteristics from its graph. Knowing these graphs is essential for analyzing their transformations into more complicated graphs.

Table 2.3 Algebra's Common Graphs

Constant Function

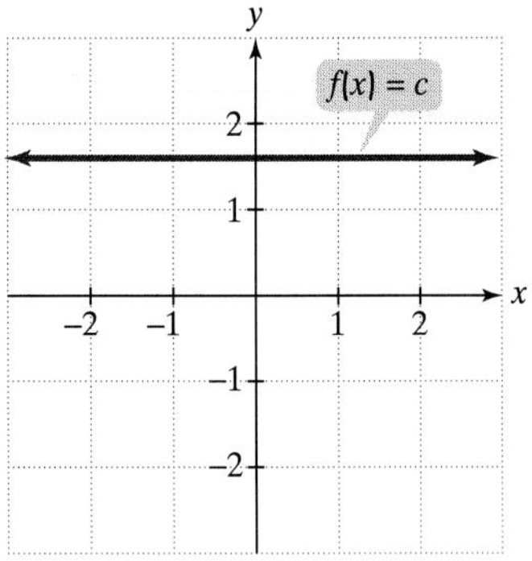

- Domain: $(-\infty, \infty)$
- Range: the single number c
- Constant on $(-\infty, \infty)$
- Even function

Identity Function

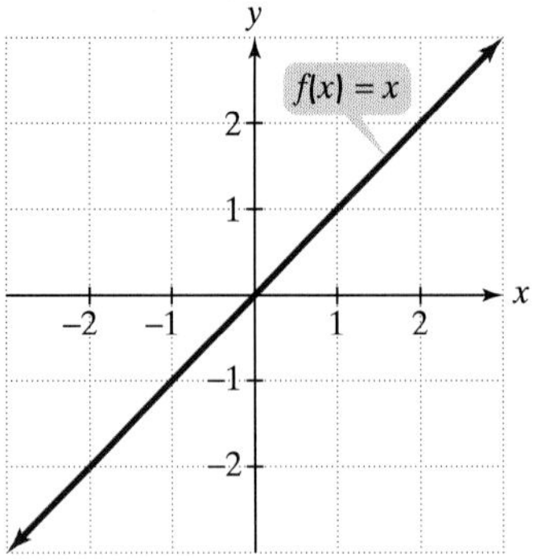

- Domain: $(-\infty, \infty)$
- Range: $(-\infty, \infty)$
- Increasing on $(-\infty, \infty)$
- Odd function

Absolute Value Function

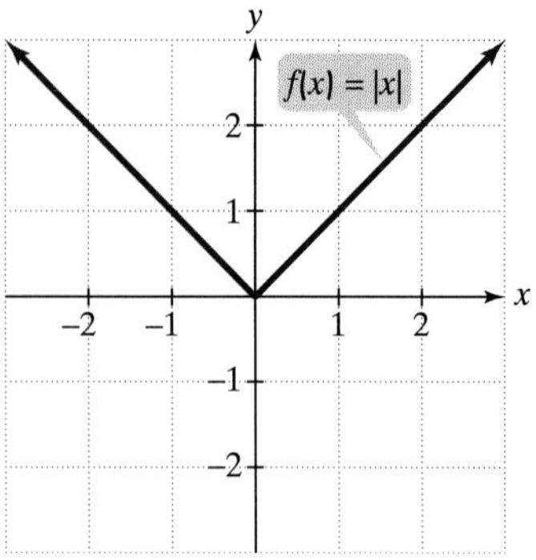

- Domain: $(-\infty, \infty)$
- Range: $[0, \infty)$
- Decreasing on $(-\infty, 0)$ and increasing on $(0, \infty)$
- Even function

Standard Quadratic Function

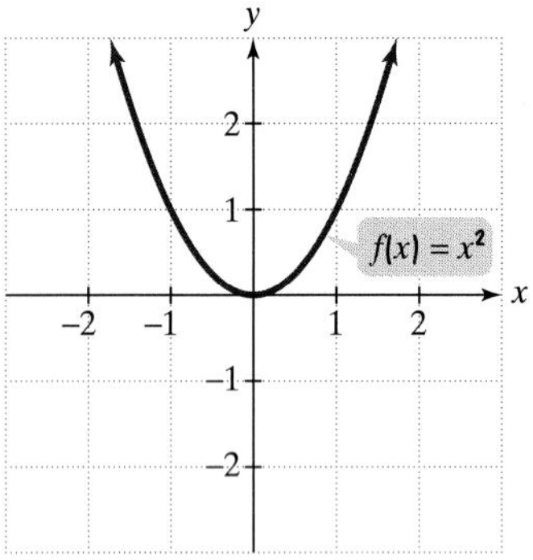

- Domain: $(-\infty, \infty)$
- Range: $[0, \infty)$
- Decreasing on $(-\infty, 0)$ and increasing on $(0, \infty)$
- Even function

Square Root Function

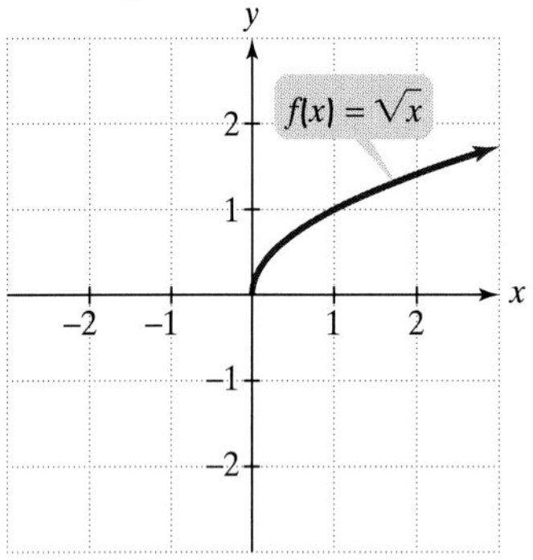

- Domain: $[0, \infty)$
- Range: $[0, \infty)$
- Increasing on $(0, \infty)$
- Neither even nor odd

Standard Cubic Function

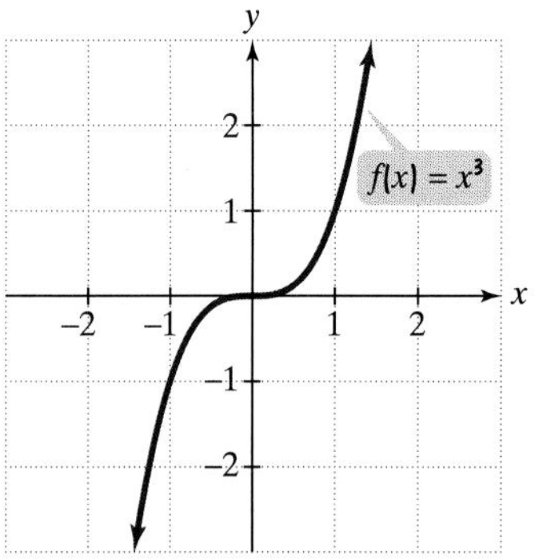

- Domain: $(-\infty, \infty)$
- Range: $(-\infty, \infty)$
- Increasing on $(-\infty, \infty)$
- Odd function

Cube Root Function

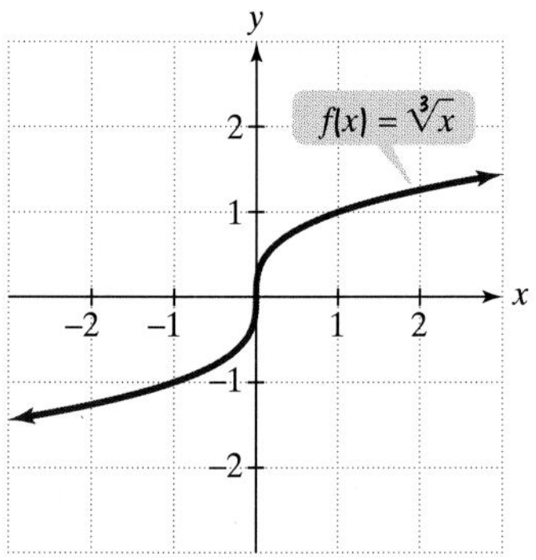

- Domain: $(-\infty, \infty)$
- Range: $(-\infty, \infty)$
- Increasing on $(-\infty, \infty)$
- Odd function

Discovery

The study of how changing a function's equation can affect its graph can be explored with a graphing utility. Use your graphing utility to verify the hand-drawn graphs as you read this section.

2 Use vertical shifts to graph functions.

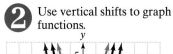

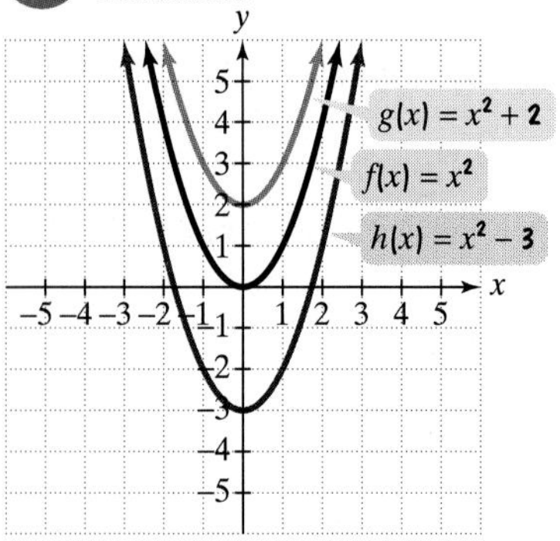

Figure 2.41 Vertical shifts

Vertical Shifts

Let's begin by looking at three graphs whose shapes are the same. Figure 2.41 shows the graphs. The black graph in the middle is the standard quadratic function, $f(x) = x^2$. Now, look at the blue graph on the top. The equation of this graph, $g(x) = x^2 + 2$, adds 2 to the right side of $f(x) = x^2$. The y-coordinate of each point of g is 2 more than the corresponding y-coordinate of each point of f. What effect does this have on the graph of f? It shifts the graph vertically up by 2 units.

$$g(x) = x^2 + 2 = f(x) + 2$$

The graph of g — shifts the graph of f up 2 units.

Finally, look at the red graph on the bottom in Figure 2.41. The equation of this graph, $h(x) = x^2 - 3$, subtracts 3 from the right side of $f(x) = x^2$. The y-coordinate of each point of h is 3 less than the corresponding y-coordinate of each point of f. What effect does this have on the graph of f? It shifts the graph vertically down by 3 units.

$$h(x) = x^2 - 3 = f(x) - 3$$

The graph of h shifts the graph of f down 3 units.

In general, if c is positive, $y = f(x) + c$ shifts the graph of f upward c units and $y = f(x) - c$ shifts the graph of f downward c units. These are called **vertical shifts** of the graph of f.

Vertical Shifts

Let f be a function and c a positive real number.

- The graph of $y = f(x) + c$ is the graph of $y = f(x)$ shifted c units vertically upward.
- The graph of $y = f(x) - c$ is the graph of $y = f(x)$ shifted c units vertically downward.

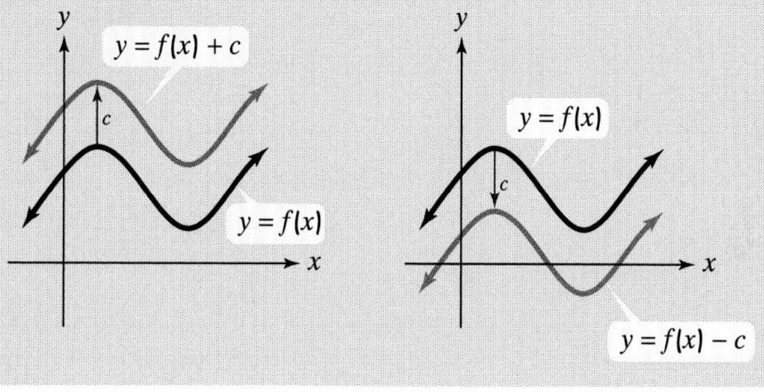

Study Tip

To keep track of transformations, identify a number of points on the given function's graph. Then analyze what happens to the coordinates of these points with each transformation.

EXAMPLE 1 Vertical Shift Down

Use the graph of $f(x) = |x|$ to obtain the graph of $g(x) = |x| - 4$.

Solution The graph of $g(x) = |x| - 4$ has the same shape as the graph of $f(x) = |x|$. However, it is shifted down vertically 4 units.

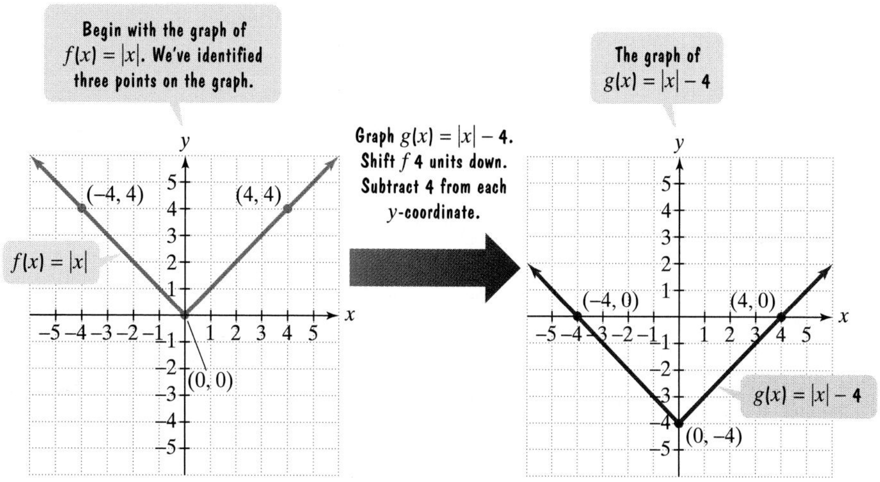

Check Point 1 Use the graph of $f(x) = |x|$ to obtain the graph of $g(x) = |x| + 3$.

3 Use horizontal shifts to graph functions.

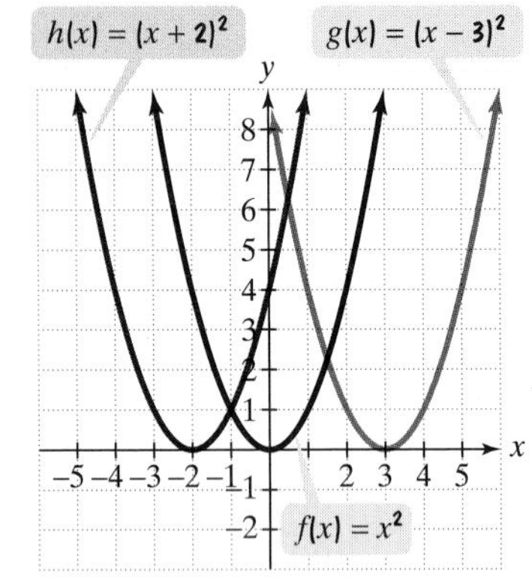

Figure 2.42 Horizontal shifts

Horizontal Shifts

We return to the graph of $f(x) = x^2$, the standard quadratic function. In Figure 2.42, the graph of function f is in the middle of the three graphs. By contrast to the vertical shift situation, this time there are graphs to the left and to the right of the graph of f. Look at the blue graph on the right. The equation of this graph, $g(x) = (x - 3)^2$, subtracts 3 from each value of x before squaring it. What effect does this have on the graph of $f(x) = x^2$? It shifts the graph horizontally to the right by 3 units.

$$g(x) = (x - 3)^2 = f(x - 3)$$

The graph of g — shifts the graph of f 3 units to the right.

Does it seem strange that *subtracting* 3 in the domain causes a shift of 3 units to the *right*? Perhaps a partial table of coordinates for each function will numerically convince you of this shift.

x	$f(x) = x^2$
−2	$(-2)^2 = 4$
−1	$(-1)^2 = 1$
0	$0^2 = 0$
1	$1^2 = 1$
2	$2^2 = 4$

x	$g(x) = (x - 3)^2$
1	$(1 - 3)^2 = (-2)^2 = 4$
2	$(2 - 3)^2 = (-1)^2 = 1$
3	$(3 - 3)^2 = 0^2 = 0$
4	$(4 - 3)^2 = 1^2 = 1$
5	$(5 - 3)^2 = 2^2 = 4$

Notice that for the values of $f(x)$ and $g(x)$ to be the same, the values of x used in graphing g must each be 3 units greater than those used to graph f. For this reason, the graph of g is the graph of f shifted 3 units to the right.

Now, look at the red graph on the left in Figure 2.42. The equation of this graph, $h(x) = (x + 2)^2$, adds 2 to each value of x before squaring it. What effect does this have on the graph of $f(x) = x^2$? It shifts the graph horizontally to the left by 2 units.

$$h(x) = (x + 2)^2 = f(x + 2)$$

The graph of h — shifts the graph of f 2 units to the left.

In general, if c is positive, $y = f(x + c)$ shifts the graph of f to the left c units and $y = f(x - c)$ shifts the graph of f to the right c units. These are called **horizontal shifts** of the graph of f.

Study Tip

On a number line, if x represents a number and c is positive, then $x + c$ lies c units to the right of x and $x - c$ lies c units to the left of x. This orientation does not apply to horizontal shifts: $f(x + c)$ causes a shift of c units to the left and $f(x - c)$ causes a shift of c units to the right.

Horizontal Shifts

Let f be a function and c a positive real number.

- The graph of $y = f(x + c)$ is the graph of $y = f(x)$ shifted to the left c units.
- The graph of $y = f(x - c)$ is the graph of $y = f(x)$ shifted to the right c units.

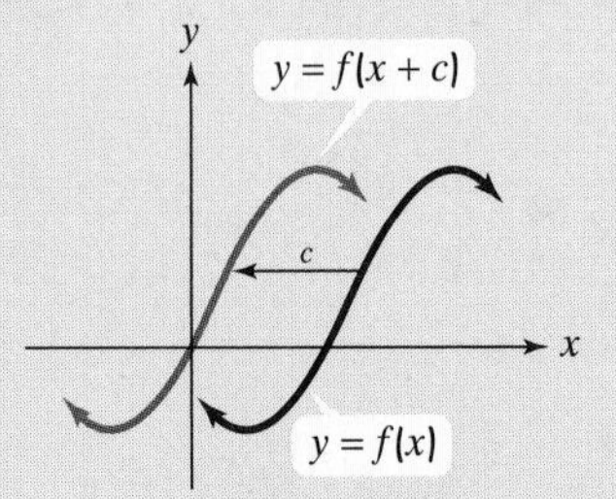

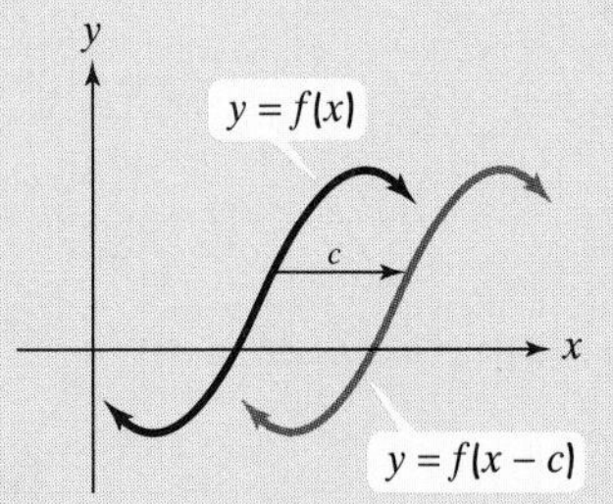

EXAMPLE 2 Horizontal Shift to the Left

Use the graph of $f(x) = \sqrt{x}$ to obtain the graph of $g(x) = \sqrt{x + 5}$.

Solution Compare the equations for $f(x) = \sqrt{x}$ and $g(x) = \sqrt{x + 5}$. The equation for g adds 5 to each value of x before taking the square root.

$$y = g(x) = \sqrt{x + 5} = f(x + 5)$$

The graph of g | shifts the graph of f 5 units to the left.

The graph of $g(x) = \sqrt{x + 5}$ has the same shape as the graph of $f(x) = \sqrt{x}$. However, it is shifted horizontally to the left 5 units.

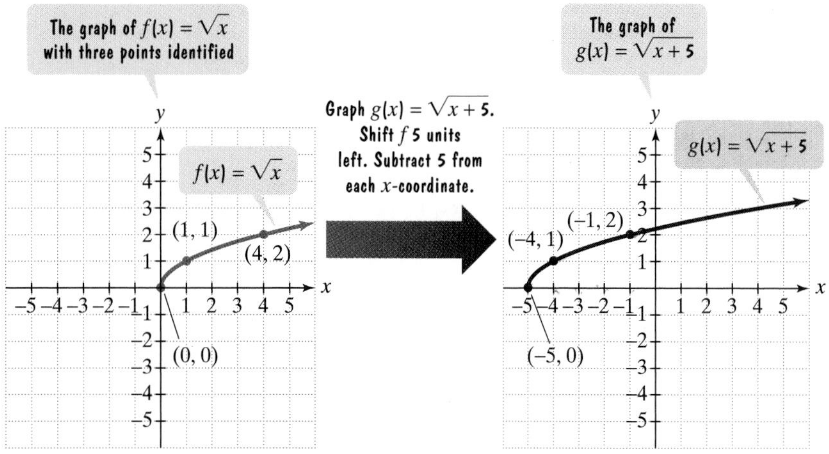

Check Point 2 Use the graph of $f(x) = \sqrt{x}$ to obtain the graph of $g(x) = \sqrt{x - 4}$.

Some functions can be graphed by combining horizontal and vertical shifts. These functions will be variations of a function whose equation you know how to graph, such as the standard quadratic function, the standard cubic function, the square root function, the cube root function, or the absolute value function.

In our next example, we will use the graph of the standard quadratic function, $f(x) = x^2$, to obtain the graph of $h(x) = (x + 1)^2 - 3$. We will graph three functions:

$$f(x) = x^2 \qquad g(x) = (x + 1)^2 \qquad h(x) = (x + 1)^2 - 3.$$

Start by graphing the standard quadratic function. | Shift the graph of f horizontally one unit to the left. | Shift the graph of g vertically down 3 units.

EXAMPLE 3 Combining Horizontal and Vertical Shifts

Use the graph of $f(x) = x^2$ to obtain the graph of $h(x) = (x + 1)^2 - 3$.

Solution

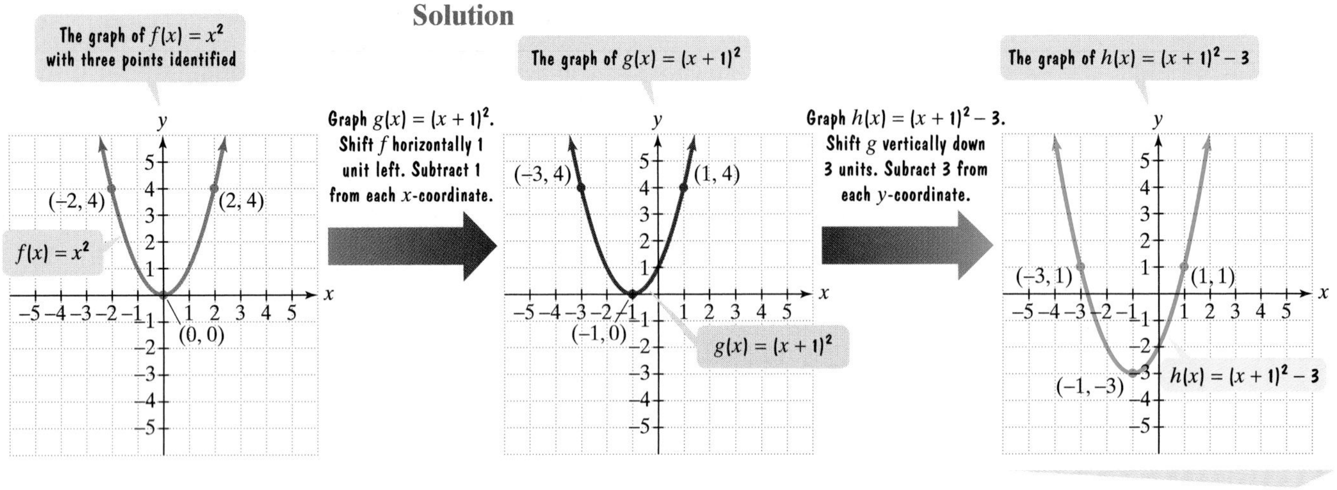

Discovery

Work Example 3 by first shifting the graph of $f(x) = x^2$ three units down, graphing $g(x) = x^2 - 3$. Now, shift this graph one unit left to graph $h(x) = (x + 1)^2 - 3$. Did you obtain the last graph shown in the solution of Example 3? What can you conclude?

Check Point 3 Use the graph of $f(x) = \sqrt{x}$ to obtain the graph of $h(x) = \sqrt{x - 1} - 2$.

4 Use reflections to graph functions.

Reflections of Graphs

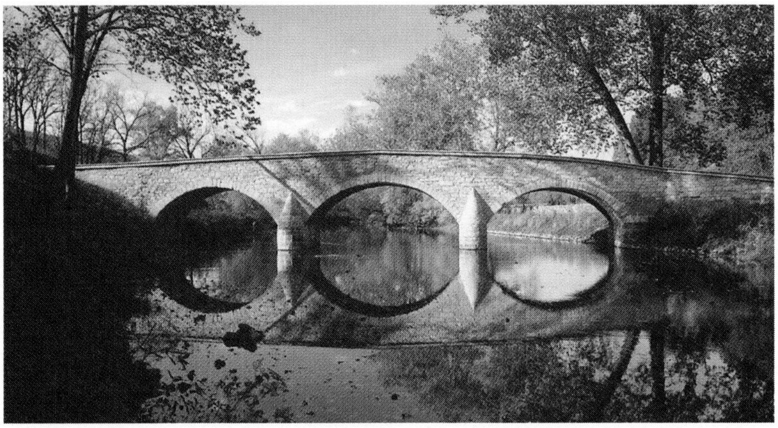

This photograph shows a reflection of an old bridge in a Maryland river. This perfect reflection occurs because the surface of the water is absolutely still. A mild breeze rippling the water's surface would distort the reflection.

Is it possible for graphs to have mirror-like qualities? Yes. Figure 2.43 shows the graphs of $f(x) = x^2$ and $g(x) = -x^2$. The graph of g is a **reflection about the x-axis** of the graph of f. For corresponding values of x, the y-coordinates of g are the opposites of the y-coordinates of f. In general, the graph of $y = -f(x)$ reflects the graph of f about the x-axis. Thus, the graph of g is a reflection of the graph of f about the x-axis because

$$g(x) = -x^2 = -f(x).$$

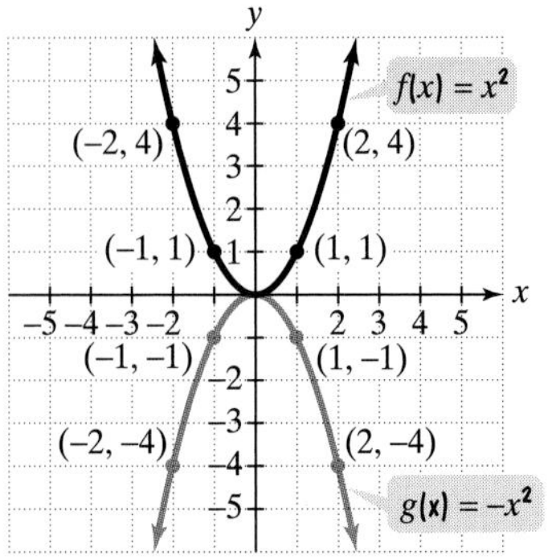

Figure 2.43 Reflection about the x-axis

Reflection about the x-Axis

The graph of $y = -f(x)$ is the graph of $y = f(x)$ reflected about the x-axis.

EXAMPLE 4 Reflection about the *x*-Axis

Use the graph of $f(x) = \sqrt[3]{x}$ to obtain the graph of $g(x) = -\sqrt[3]{x}$.

Solution Compare the equations for $f(x) = \sqrt[3]{x}$ and $g(x) = -\sqrt[3]{x}$. The graph of g is a reflection about the x-axis of the graph of f because

$$g(x) = -\sqrt[3]{x} = -f(x).$$

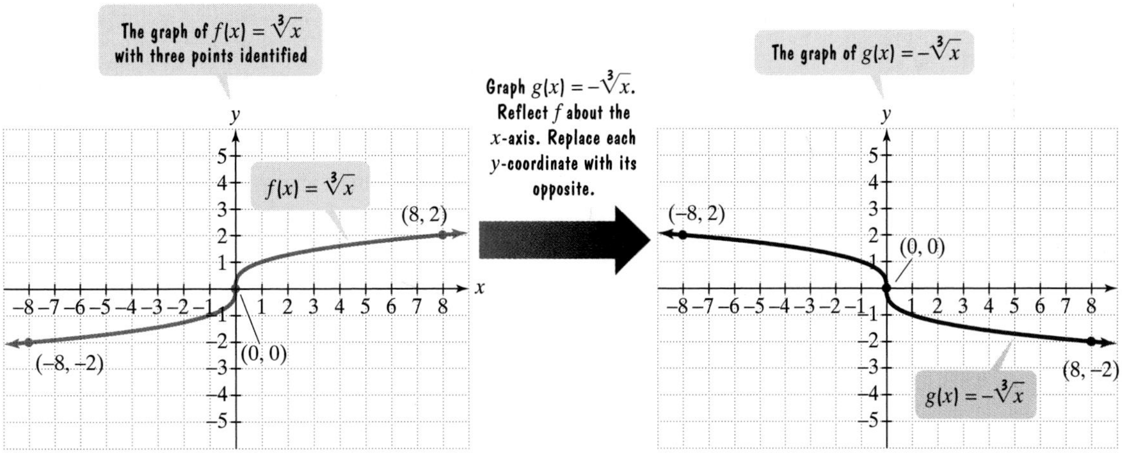

Check Point 4 Use the graph of $f(x) = |x|$ to obtain the graph of $g(x) = -|x|$.

It is also possible to reflect graphs about the y-axis.

Reflection about the *y*-Axis

The graph of $y = f(-x)$ is the graph of $y = f(x)$ reflected about the y-axis.

For corresponding values of y, the x-coordinates of $y = f(-x)$ are the opposite of those of $y = f(x)$.

EXAMPLE 5 Reflection about the *y*-Axis

Use the graph of $f(x) = \sqrt{x}$ to obtain the graph of $h(x) = \sqrt{-x}$.

Solution Compare the equations for $f(x) = \sqrt{x}$ and $h(x) = \sqrt{-x}$. The graph of h is a reflection about the y-axis of the graph of f because

$$h(x) = \sqrt{-x} = f(-x).$$

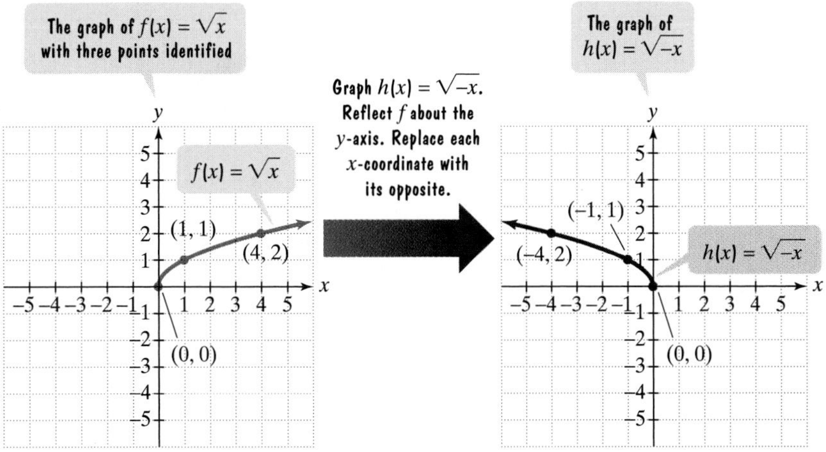

Check Point 5 Use the graph of $f(x) = \sqrt[3]{x}$ to obtain the graph of $h(x) = \sqrt[3]{-x}$.

5 Use vertical stretching and shrinking to graph functions.

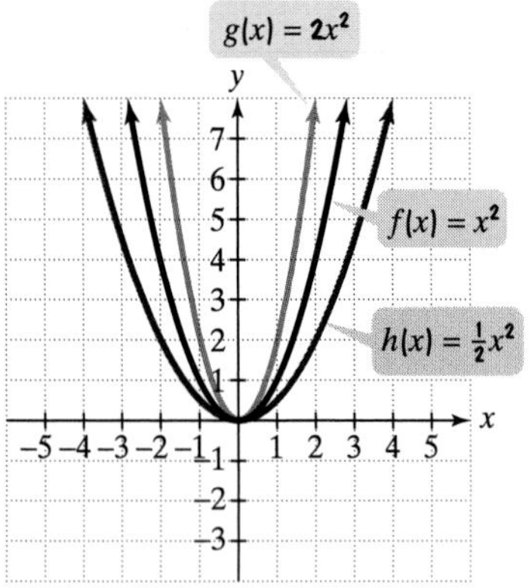

Figure 2.44 Vertically stretching and shrinking $f(x) = x^2$

Vertical Stretching and Shrinking

Morphing does much more than move an image horizontally, vertically, or about an axis. An object having one shape is transformed into a different shape. Horizontal shifts, vertical shifts, and reflections do not change the basic shape of a graph. Graphs remain rigid and proportionally the same when they undergo these transformations. How can we shrink and stretch graphs, thereby altering their basic shapes?

Look at the three graphs in Figure 2.44. The black graph in the middle is the graph of the standard quadratic function, $f(x) = x^2$. Now, look at the blue graph on the top. The equation of this graph is $g(x) = 2x^2$, or $g(x) = 2f(x)$. Thus, for each x, the y-coordinate of g is 2 times as large as the corresponding y-coordinate on the graph of f. The result is a narrower graph because the values of y are rising faster. We say that the graph of g is obtained by vertically *stretching* the graph of f. Now, look at the red graph on the bottom. The equation of this graph is $h(x) = \frac{1}{2}x^2$, or $h(x) = \frac{1}{2}f(x)$. Thus, for each x, the y-coordinate of h is one-half as large as the corresponding y-coordinate on the graph of f. The result is a wider graph because the values of y are rising more slowly. We say that the graph of h is obtained by vertically *shrinking* the graph of f.

These observations can be summarized as follows:

Vertically Stretching and Shrinking Graphs

Let f be a function and c a positive real number.

- If $c > 1$, the graph of $y = cf(x)$ is the graph of $y = f(x)$ vertically stretched by multiplying each of its y-coordinates by c.
- If $0 < c < 1$, the graph of $y = cf(x)$ is the graph of $y = f(x)$ vertically shrunk by multiplying each of its y-coordinates by c.

Stretching: $c > 1$ **Shrinking**: $0 < c < 1$

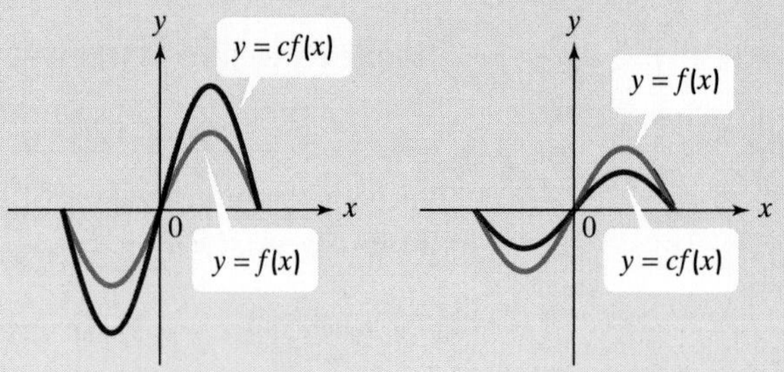

EXAMPLE 6 Vertically Shrinking a Graph

Use the graph of $f(x) = x^3$ to obtain the graph of $h(x) = \frac{1}{2}x^3$.

Solution The graph of $h(x) = \frac{1}{2}x^3$ is obtained by vertically shrinking the graph of $f(x) = x^3$.

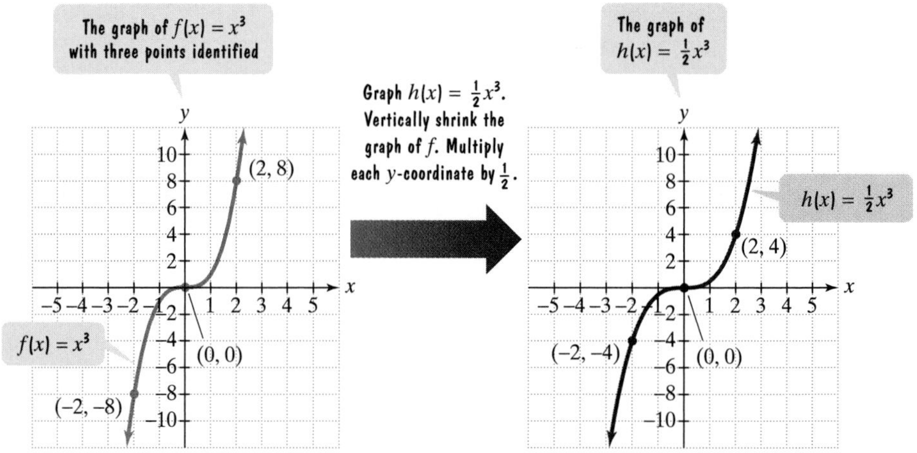

Check Point 6 Use the graph of $f(x) = |x|$ to obtain the graph of $g(x) = 2|x|$.

6 Use horizontal stretching and shrinking to graph functions.

Horizontal Stretching and Shrinking

It is also possible to horizontally stretch and shrink graphs.

Horizontally Stretching and Shrinking Graphs

Let f be a function and c a positive real number.

- If $c > 1$, the graph of $y = f(cx)$ is the graph of $y = f(x)$ horizontally shrunk by dividing each of its x-coordinates by c.
- If $0 < c < 1$, the graph of $y = f(cx)$ is the graph of $y = f(x)$ horizontally stretched by dividing each of its x-coordinates by c.

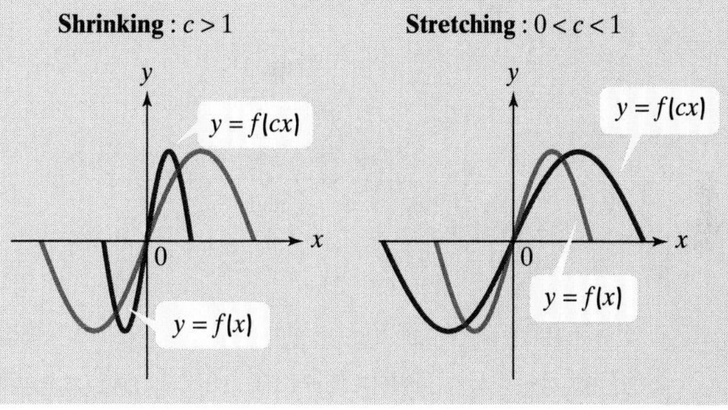

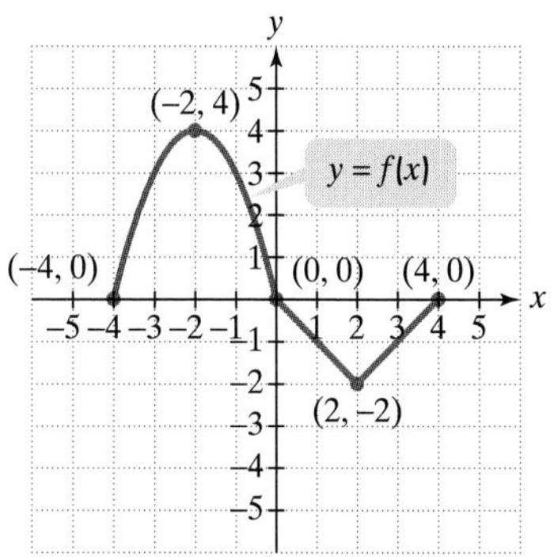

Figure 2.45

EXAMPLE 7 Horizontally Stretching and Shrinking a Graph

Use the graph of $y = f(x)$ in Figure 2.45 to obtain each of the following graphs:

a. $g(x) = f(2x)$ **b.** $h(x) = f\left(\frac{1}{2}x\right)$.

Solution

a. The graph of $g(x) = f(2x)$ is obtained by horizontally shrinking the graph of $y = f(x)$.

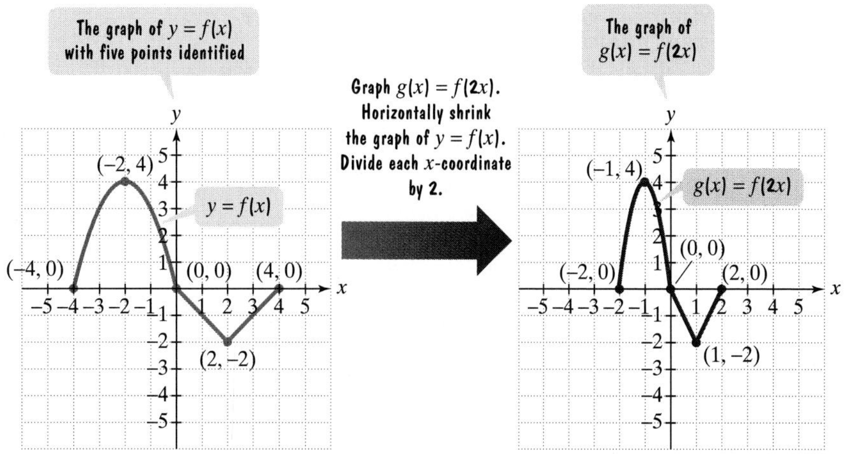

b. The graph of $h(x) = f\left(\frac{1}{2}x\right)$ is obtained by horizontally stretching the graph of $y = f(x)$.

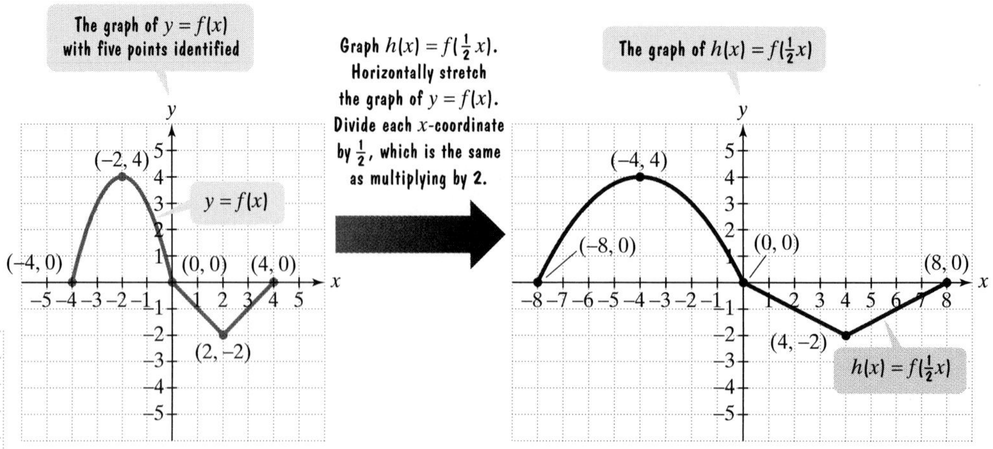

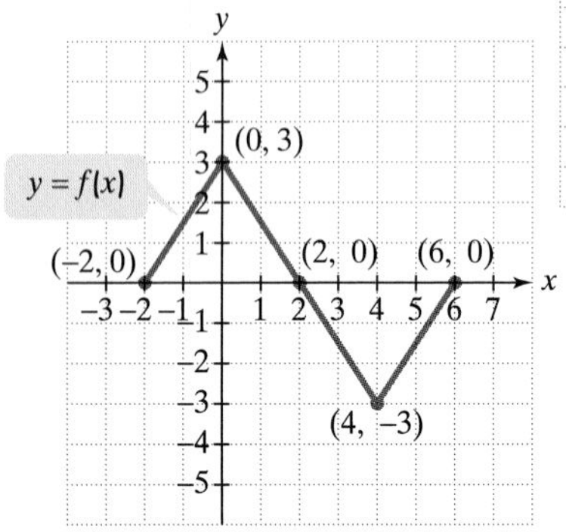

Figure 2.46

Check Point 7 Use the graph of $y = f(x)$ in Figure 2.46 to obtain each of the following graphs:

a. $g(x) = f(2x)$ **b.** $h(x) = f\left(\frac{1}{2}x\right)$.

⑦ Graph functions involving a sequence of transformations.

Sequences of Transformations

Table 2.4 summarizes the procedures for transforming the graph of $y = f(x)$.

Table 2.4 Summary of Transformations
In each case, c represents a positive real number.

To Graph:	Draw the Graph of f and:	Changes in the Equation of $y = f(x)$
Vertical shifts $y = f(x) + c$ $y = f(x) - c$	Raise the graph of f by c units. Lower the graph of f by c units.	c is added to $f(x)$. c is subtracted from $f(x)$.
Horizontal shifts $y = f(x + c)$ $y = f(x - c)$	Shift the graph of f to the left c units. Shift the graph of f to the right c units.	x is replaced with $x + c$. x is replaced with $x - c$.
Reflection about the x-axis $y = -f(x)$	Reflect the graph of f about the x-axis.	$f(x)$ is multiplied by -1.
Reflection about the y-axis $y = f(-x)$	Reflect the graph of f about the y-axis.	x is replaced with $-x$.
Vertical stretching or shrinking $y = cf(x), c > 1$ $y = cf(x), 0 < c < 1$	Multiply each y-coordinate of $y = f(x)$ by c, vertically stretching the graph of f. Multiply each y-coordinate of $y = f(x)$ by c, vertically shrinking the graph of f.	$f(x)$ is multiplied by $c, c > 1$. $f(x)$ is multiplied by $c, 0 < c < 1$.
Horizontal stretching or shrinking $y = f(cx), c > 1$ $y = f(cx), 0 < c < 1$	Divide each x-coordinate of $y = f(x)$ by c, horizontally shrinking the graph of f. Divide each x-coordinate of $y = f(x)$ by c, horizontally stretching the graph of f.	x is replaced with $cx, c > 1$. x is replaced with $cx, 0 < c < 1$.

A function involving more than one transformation can be graphed by performing transformations in the following order:

1. Horizontal shifting
2. Stretching or shrinking
3. Reflecting
4. Vertical shifting

EXAMPLE 8 Graphing Using a Sequence of Transformations

Use the graph of $y = f(x)$ given in Figure 2.45 of Example 7 on page 249, and repeated below, to graph $y = -\frac{1}{2}f(x-1)+3$.

Solution Our graphs will evolve in the following order:

1. Horizontal shifting: Graph $y = f(x-1)$ by shifting the graph of $y = f(x)$ 1 unit to the right.
2. Shrinking: Graph $y = \frac{1}{2}f(x-1)$ by shrinking the previous graph by a factor of $\frac{1}{2}$.
3. Reflecting: Graph $y = -\frac{1}{2}f(x-1)$ by reflecting the previous graph about the x-axis.
4. Vertical shifting: Graph $y = -\frac{1}{2}f(x-1)+3$ by shifting the previous graph up 3 units.

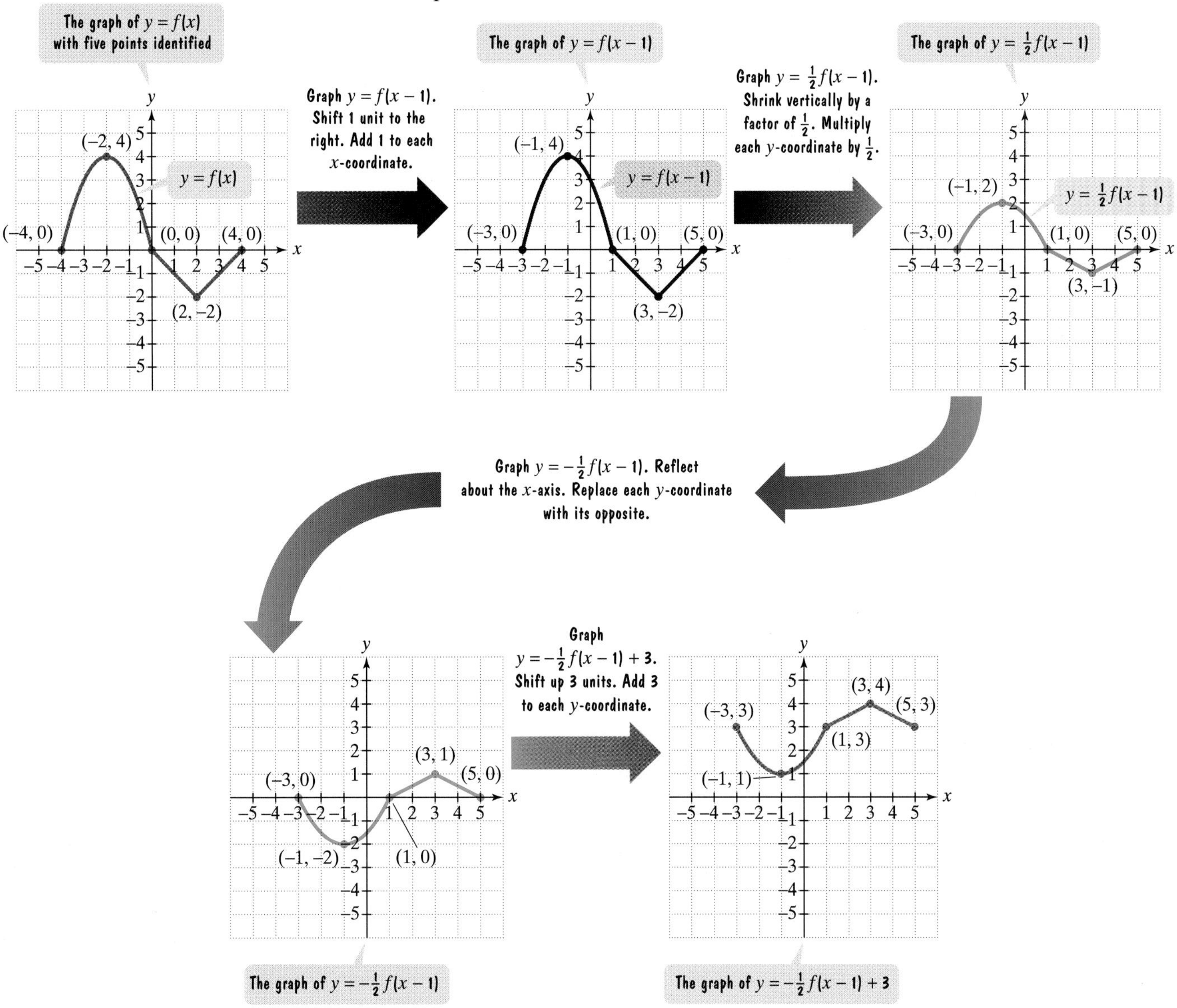

Check Point 8 Use the graph of $y = f(x)$ given in Figure 2.46 of Check Point 7 to graph $y = -\frac{1}{3}f(x+1)-2$.

EXAMPLE 9 Graphing Using a Sequence of Transformations

Use the graph of $f(x) = x^2$ to graph $g(x) = 2(x + 3)^2 - 1$.

Solution Our graphs will evolve in the following order:

1. Horizontal shifting: Graph $y = (x + 3)^2$ by shifting the graph of $f(x) = x^2$ three units to the left.
2. Stretching: Graph $y = 2(x + 3)^2$ by stretching the previous graph by a factor of 2.
3. Vertical shifting: Graph $g(x) = 2(x + 3)^2 - 1$ by shifting the previous graph down 1 unit.

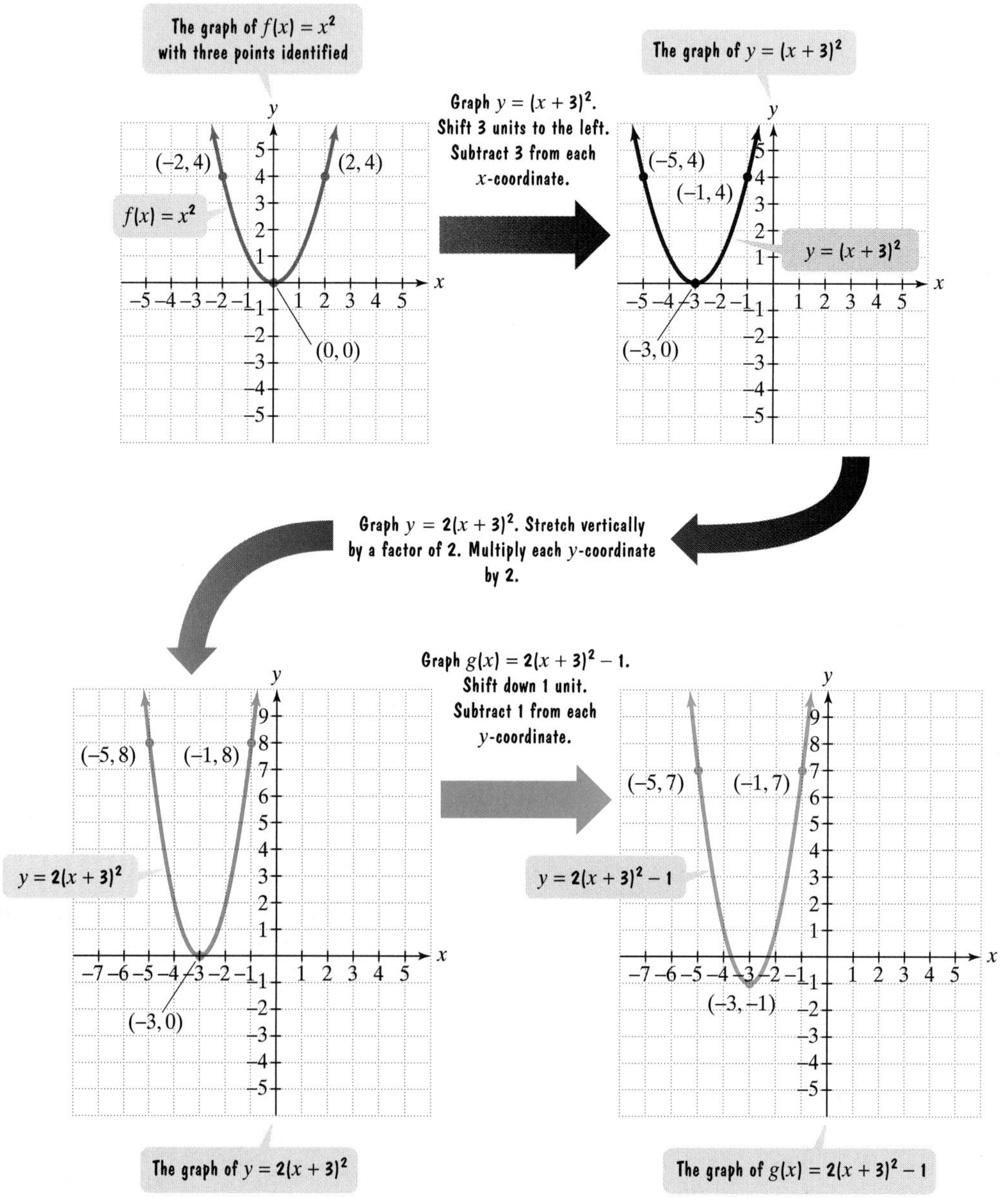

The graph of f(x) = x² with three points identified
(−2, 4)
(2, 4)
(0, 0)
f(x) = x²
Graph y = (x + 3)². Shift 3 units to the left. Subtract 3 from each x-coordinate.
The graph of y = (x + 3)²
(−5, 4)
(−1, 4)
(−3, 0)
y = (x + 3)²
Graph y = 2(x + 3)². Stretch vertically by a factor of 2. Multiply each y-coordinate by 2.
(−5, 8)
(−1, 8)
y = 2(x + 3)²
(−3, 0)
Graph g(x) = 2(x + 3)² − 1. Shift down 1 unit. Subtract 1 from each y-coordinate.
(−5, 7)
(−1, 7)
y = 2(x + 3)² − 1
(−3, −1)
The graph of y = 2(x + 3)²
The graph of g(x) = 2(x + 3)² − 1

Check Point 9 Use the graph of $f(x) = x^2$ to graph $g(x) = 2(x - 1)^2 + 3$.

EXERCISE SET 2.5

Practice Exercises

In Exercises 1–16, use the graph of $y = f(x)$ to graph each function g.

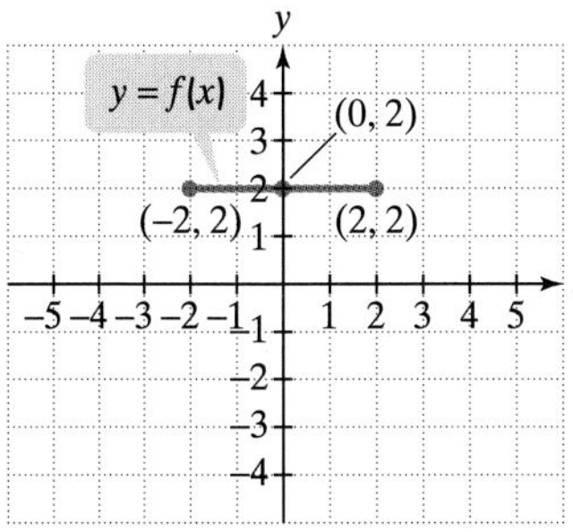

1. $g(x) = f(x) + 1$
2. $g(x) = f(x) - 1$
3. $g(x) = f(x + 1)$
4. $g(x) = f(x - 1)$
5. $g(x) = f(x - 1) - 2$
6. $g(x) = f(x + 1) + 2$
7. $g(x) = f(-x)$
8. $g(x) = -f(x)$
9. $g(x) = -f(x) + 3$
10. $g(x) = f(-x) + 3$
11. $g(x) = \frac{1}{2}f(x)$
12. $g(x) = 2f(x)$
13. $g(x) = f\left(\frac{1}{2}x\right)$
14. $g(x) = f(2x)$
15. $g(x) = -f\left(\frac{1}{2}x\right) + 1$
16. $g(x) = -f(2x) - 1$

In Exercises 17–32, use the graph of $y = f(x)$ to graph each function g.

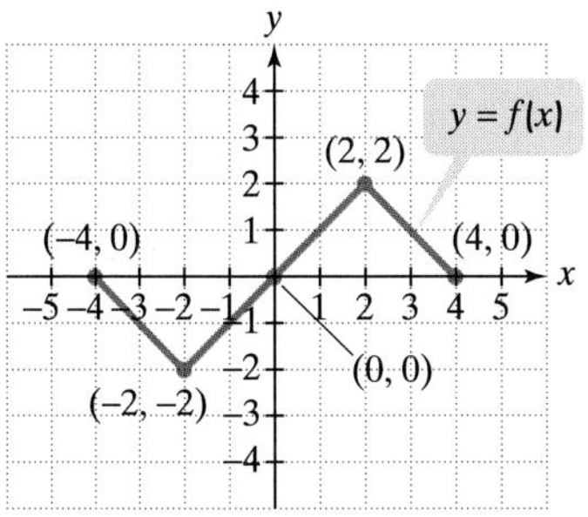

17. $g(x) = f(x) - 1$
18. $g(x) = f(x) + 1$
19. $g(x) = f(x - 1)$
20. $g(x) = f(x + 1)$
21. $g(x) = f(x - 1) + 2$
22. $g(x) = f(x + 1) - 2$
23. $g(x) = -f(x)$
24. $g(x) = f(-x)$
25. $g(x) = f(-x) + 1$
26. $g(x) = -f(x) + 1$
27. $g(x) = 2f(x)$
28. $g(x) = \frac{1}{2}f(x)$
29. $g(x) = f(2x)$
30. $g(x) = f\left(\frac{1}{2}x\right)$
31. $g(x) = 2f(x + 2) + 1$
32. $g(x) = 2f(x + 2) - 1$

In Exercises 33–44, use the graph of $y = f(x)$ to graph each function g.

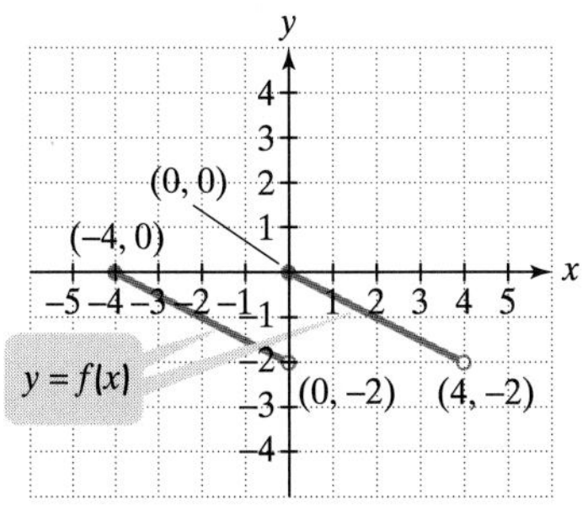

33. $g(x) = f(x) + 2$
34. $g(x) = f(x) - 2$
35. $g(x) = f(x + 2)$
36. $g(x) = f(x - 2)$
37. $g(x) = -f(x + 2)$
38. $g(x) = -f(x - 2)$
39. $g(x) = -\frac{1}{2}f(x + 2)$
40. $g(x) = -\frac{1}{2}f(x - 2)$
41. $g(x) = -\frac{1}{2}f(x + 2) - 2$
42. $g(x) = -\frac{1}{2}f(x - 2) + 2$
43. $g(x) = \frac{1}{2}f(2x)$
44. $g(x) = 2f\left(\frac{1}{2}x\right)$

In Exercises 45–52, use the graph of $y = f(x)$ to graph each function g.

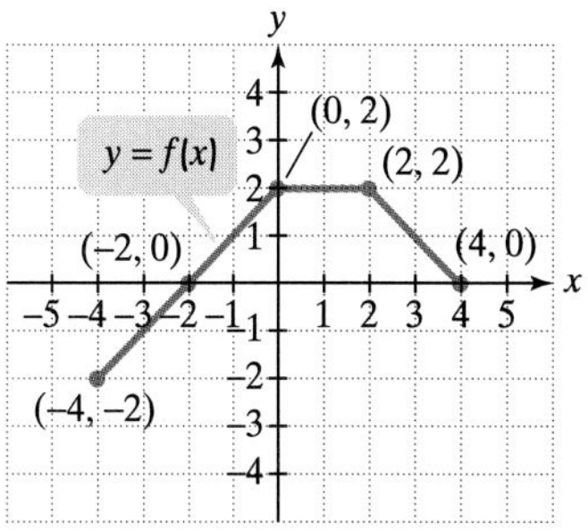

45. $g(x) = f(x - 1) - 1$
46. $g(x) = f(x + 1) + 1$
47. $g(x) = -f(x - 1) + 1$
48. $g(x) = -f(x + 1) - 1$
49. $g(x) = 2f\left(\frac{1}{2}x\right)$
50. $g(x) = \frac{1}{2}f(2x)$
51. $g(x) = \frac{1}{2}f(x + 1)$
52. $g(x) = 2f(x - 1)$

In Exercises 53–66, begin by graphing the standard quadratic function, $f(x) = x^2$. Then use transformations of this graph to graph the given function.

53. $g(x) = x^2 - 2$
54. $g(x) = x^2 - 1$
55. $g(x) = (x - 2)^2$
56. $g(x) = (x - 1)^2$
57. $h(x) = -(x - 2)^2$
58. $h(x) = -(x - 1)^2$
59. $h(x) = (x - 2)^2 + 1$
60. $h(x) = (x - 1)^2 + 2$
61. $g(x) = 2(x - 2)^2$
62. $g(x) = \frac{1}{2}(x - 1)^2$
63. $h(x) = 2(x - 2)^2 - 1$
64. $h(x) = \frac{1}{2}(x - 1)^2 - 1$
65. $h(x) = -2(x + 1)^2 + 1$
66. $h(x) = -2(x + 2)^2 + 1$

In Exercises 67–80, begin by graphing the square root function, $f(x) = \sqrt{x}$. Then use transformations of this graph to graph the given function.

67. $g(x) = \sqrt{x} + 2$
68. $g(x) = \sqrt{x} + 1$
69. $g(x) = \sqrt{x + 2}$
70. $g(x) = \sqrt{x + 1}$
71. $h(x) = -\sqrt{x + 2}$
72. $h(x) = -\sqrt{x + 1}$
73. $h(x) = \sqrt{-x + 2}$
74. $h(x) = \sqrt{-x + 1}$
75. $g(x) = \frac{1}{2}\sqrt{x + 2}$
76. $g(x) = 2\sqrt{x + 1}$
77. $h(x) = \sqrt{x + 2} - 2$
78. $h(x) = \sqrt{x + 1} - 1$
79. $g(x) = 2\sqrt{x + 2} - 2$
80. $g(x) = 2\sqrt{x + 1} - 1$

In Exercises 81–94, begin by graphing the absolute value function, $f(x) = |x|$. Then use transformations of this graph to graph the given function.

81. $g(x) = |x| + 4$
82. $g(x) = |x| + 3$
83. $g(x) = |x + 4|$
84. $g(x) = |x + 3|$
85. $h(x) = |x + 4| - 2$
86. $h(x) = |x + 3| - 2$
87. $h(x) = -|x + 4|$
88. $h(x) = -|x + 3|$

89. $g(x) = -|x + 4| + 1$ **90.** $g(x) = -|x + 4| + 2$

91. $h(x) = 2|x + 4|$ **92.** $h(x) = 2|x + 3|$

93. $g(x) = -2|x + 4| + 1$ **94.** $g(x) = -2|x + 3| + 2$

In Exercises 95–106, begin by graphing the standard cubic function, $f(x) = x^3$. Then use transformations of this graph to graph the given function.

95. $g(x) = x^3 - 3$ **96.** $g(x) = x^3 - 2$

97. $g(x) = (x - 3)^3$ **98.** $g(x) = (x - 2)^3$

99. $h(x) = -x^3$ **100.** $h(x) = -(x - 2)^3$

101. $h(x) = \frac{1}{2}x^3$ **102.** $h(x) = \frac{1}{4}x^3$

103. $r(x) = (x - 3)^3 + 2$ **104.** $r(x) = (x - 2)^3 + 1$

105. $h(x) = \frac{1}{2}(x - 3)^3 - 2$ **106.** $h(x) = \frac{1}{2}(x - 2)^3 - 1$

In Exercises 107–118, begin by graphing the cube root function, $f(x) = \sqrt[3]{x}$. Then use transformations of this graph to graph the given function.

107. $g(x) = \sqrt[3]{x} + 2$ **108.** $g(x) = \sqrt[3]{x} - 2$

109. $g(x) = \sqrt[3]{x + 2}$ **110.** $g(x) = \sqrt[3]{x - 2}$

111. $h(x) = \frac{1}{2}\sqrt[3]{x + 2}$ **112.** $h(x) = \frac{1}{2}\sqrt[3]{x - 2}$

113. $r(x) = \frac{1}{2}\sqrt[3]{x + 2} - 2$ **114.** $r(x) = \frac{1}{2}\sqrt[3]{x - 2} + 2$

115. $h(x) = -\sqrt[3]{x + 2}$ **116.** $h(x) = -\sqrt[3]{x - 2}$

117. $g(x) = \sqrt[3]{-x - 2}$ **118.** $g(x) = \sqrt[3]{-x + 2}$

Practice Plus

In Exercises 119–122, use transformations of the graph of the greatest integer function, $f(x) = \text{int}(x)$, to graph each function. (The graph of $f(x) = \text{int}(x)$ is shown in Figure 2.20 on page 210.)

119. $g(x) = 2\,\text{int}\,(x + 1)$ **120.** $g(x) = 3\,\text{int}\,(x - 1)$

121. $h(x) = \text{int}(-x) + 1$ **122.** $h(x) = \text{int}(-x) - 1$

In Exercises 123–126, write a possible equation for the function whose graph is shown. Each graph shows a transformation of a common function.

123.

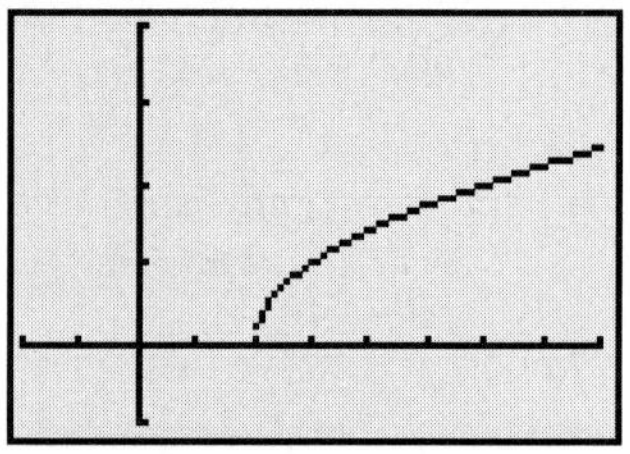

[−2, 8, 1] by [−1, 4, 1]

124.

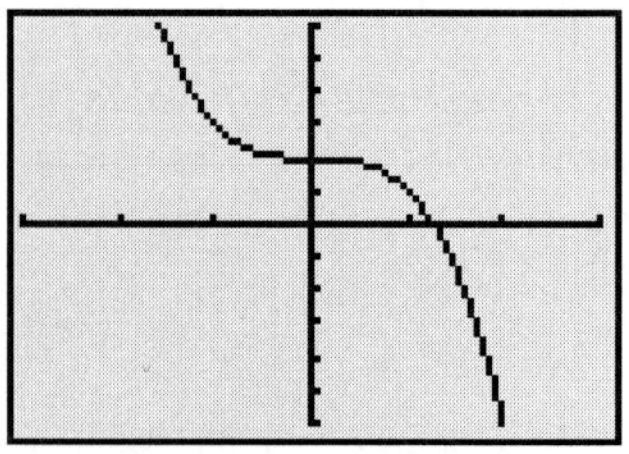

[−3, 3, 1] by [−6, 6, 1]

125.

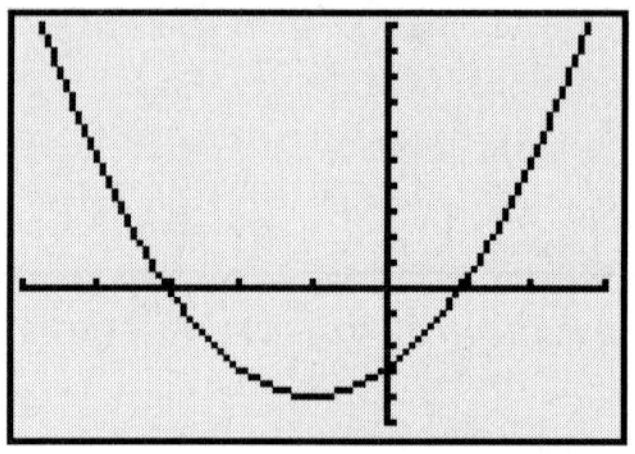

[−5, 3, 1] by [−5, 10, 1]

126.

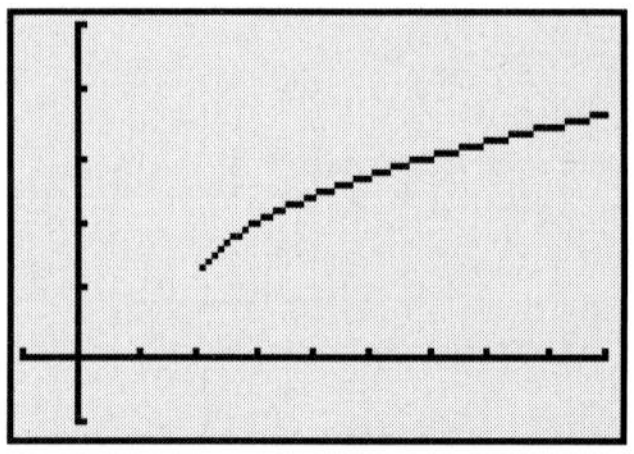

[−1, 9, 1] by [−1, 5, 1]

Application Exercises

127. The function $f(x) = 2.9\sqrt{x} + 20.1$ models the median height, $f(x)$, in inches, of boys who are x months of age. The graph of f is shown.

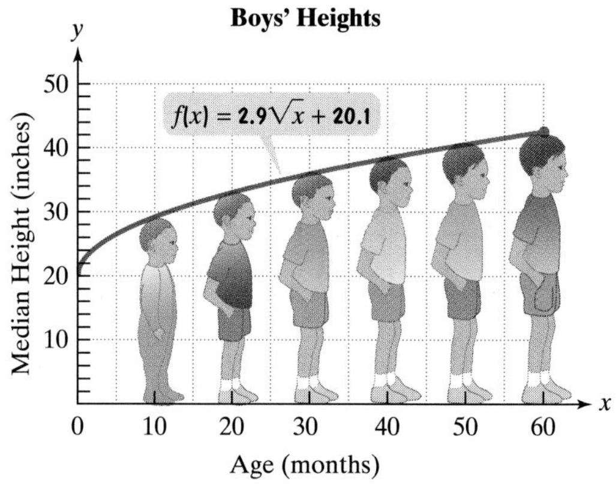

Source: Laura Walther Nathanson, *The Portable Pediatrician for Parents*

a. Describe how the graph can be obtained using transformations of the square root function $f(x) = \sqrt{x}$.

b. According to the model, what is the median height of boys who are 48 months, or four years, old? Use a calculator and round to the nearest tenth of an inch. The actual median height for boys at 48 months is 40.8 inches. How well does the model describe the actual height?

c. Use the model to find the average rate of change, in inches per month, between birth and 10 months. Round to the nearest tenth.

d. Use the model to find the average rate of change, in inches per month, between 50 and 60 months. Round to the nearest tenth. How does this compare with your answer in part (c)? How is this difference shown by the graph?

128. The function $f(x) = 3.1\sqrt{x} + 19$ models the median height, $f(x)$, in inches, of girls who are x months of age. The graph of f is shown.

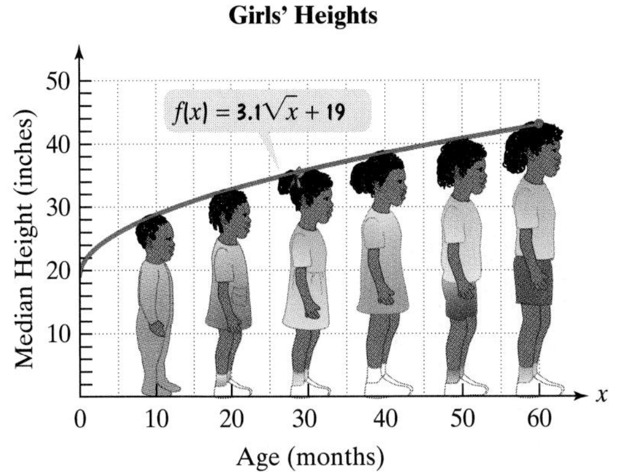

Source: Laura Walther Nathanson, *The Portable Pediatrician for Parents*

a. Describe how the graph can be obtained using transformations of the square root function $f(x) = \sqrt{x}$.

b. According to the model, what is the median height of girls who are 48 months, or four years, old? Use a calculator and round to the nearest tenth of an inch. The actual median height for girls at 48 months is 40.2 inches. How well does the model describe the actual height?

c. Use the model to find the average rate of change, in inches per month, between birth and 10 months. Round to the nearest tenth.

d. Use the model to find the average rate of change, in inches per month, between 50 and 60 months. Round to the nearest tenth. How does this compare with your answer in part (c)? How is this difference shown by the graph?

Writing in Mathematics

129. What must be done to a function's equation so that its graph is shifted vertically upward?

130. What must be done to a function's equation so that its graph is shifted horizontally to the right?

131. What must be done to a function's equation so that its graph is reflected about the x-axis?

132. What must be done to a function's equation so that its graph is reflected about the y-axis?

133. What must be done to a function's equation so that its graph is stretched vertically?

134. What must be done to a function's equation so that its graph is shrunk horizontally?

Technology Exercises

135. a. Use a graphing utility to graph $f(x) = x^2 + 1$.

b. Graph $f(x) = x^2 + 1$, $g(x) = f(2x)$, $h(x) = f(3x)$, and $k(x) = f(4x)$ in the same viewing rectangle.

c. Describe the relationship among the graphs of f, g, h, and k, with emphasis on different values of x for points on all four graphs that give the same y-coordinate.

d. Generalize by describing the relationship between the graph of f and the graph of g, where $g(x) = f(cx)$ for $c > 1$.

e. Try out your generalization by sketching the graphs of $f(cx)$ for $c = 1$, $c = 2$, $c = 3$, and $c = 4$ for a function of your choice.

136. a. Use a graphing utility to graph $f(x) = x^2 + 1$.

b. Graph $f(x) = x^2 + 1$, $g(x) = f\left(\frac{1}{2}x\right)$, and $h(x) = f\left(\frac{1}{4}x\right)$ in the same viewing rectangle.

c. Describe the relationship among the graphs of f, g, and h, with emphasis on different values of x for points on all three graphs that give the same y-coordinate.

d. Generalize by describing the relationship between the graph of f and the graph of g, where $g(x) = f(cx)$ for $0 < c < 1$.

e. Try out your generalization by sketching the graphs of $f(cx)$ for $c = 1$, and $c = \frac{1}{2}$, and $c = \frac{1}{4}$ for a function of your choice.

Critical Thinking Exercises

137. Which one of the following is true?

a. If $f(x) = |x|$ and $g(x) = |x + 3| + 3$, then the graph of g is a translation of the graph of f three units to the right and three units upward.

b. If $f(x) = -\sqrt{x}$ and $g(x) = \sqrt{-x}$, then f and g have identical graphs.

c. If $f(x) = x^2$ and $g(x) = 5(x^2 - 2)$, then the graph of g can be obtained from the graph of f by stretching f five units followed by a downward shift of two units.

d. If $f(x) = x^3$ and $g(x) = -(x - 3)^3 - 4$, then the graph of g can be obtained from the graph of f by moving f three units to the right, reflecting about the x-axis, and then moving the resulting graph down four units.

In Exercises 138–141, functions f and g are graphed in the same rectangular coordinate system. If g is obtained from f through a sequence of transformations, find an equation for g.

138.

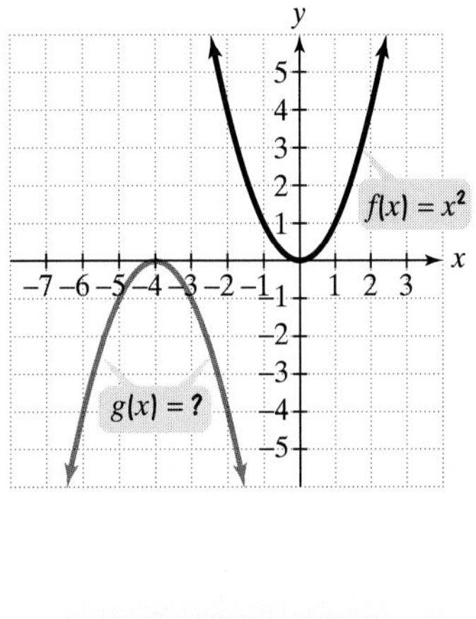

139.

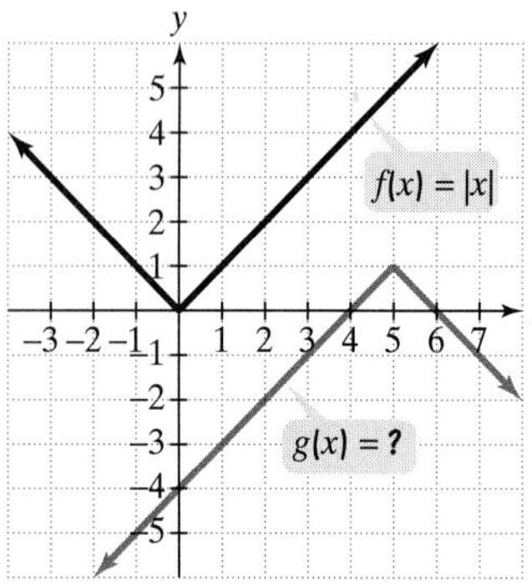

140.

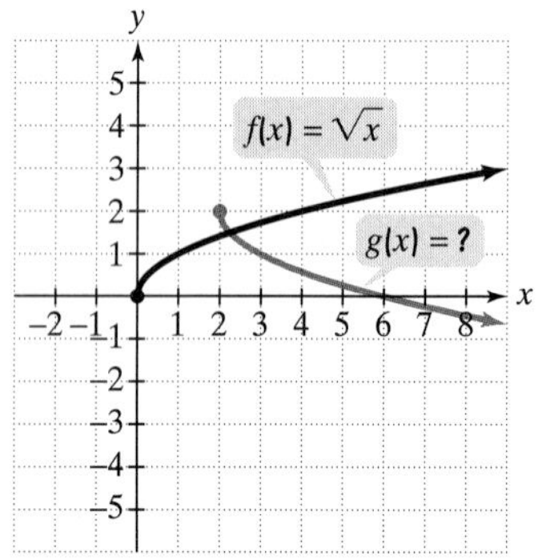

141.

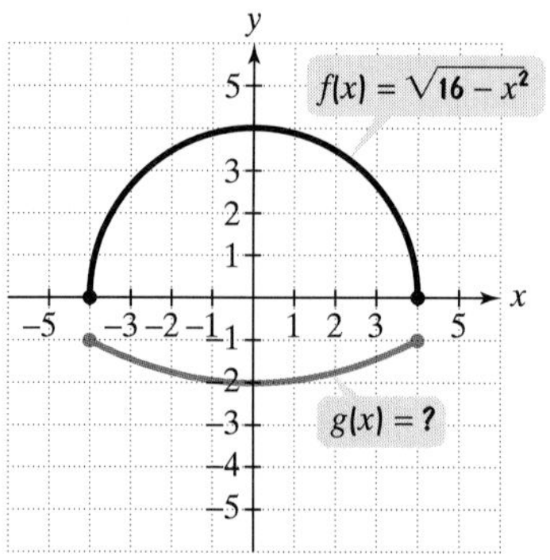

For Exercises 142–145, assume that (a, b) is a point on the graph of f. What is the corresponding point on the graph of each of the following functions?

142. $y = f(-x)$

143. $y = 2f(x)$

144. $y = f(x - 3)$

145. $y = f(x) - 3$

SECTION 2.6 Combinations of Functions; Composite Functions

Objectives

1. Find the domain of a function.
2. Combine functions using the algebra of functions, specifying domains.
3. Form composite functions.
4. Determine domains for composite functions.
5. Write functions as compositions.

America's big three automakers, GM, Ford, and Chrysler, know that consumers have always been willing to pay more for cool design and a hot car. In 2004, Detroit gave consumers that opportunity, unleashing 40 new cars or updated models. The Big Three's discovery of the automobile in 2004 might seem odd, but from 1990 through 2003, Detroit focused much of its energy and money on SUVs and trucks, which commanded high prices and high profits, and saw less competition from imports. The line graphs in Figure 2.47 show the number, in millions, of cars and SUVs sold by the Big Three from 1990 through 2003. In this section, we will look at these data from the perspective of functions. By considering total sales of cars and SUVs, you will see that functions can be combined using procedures that will remind you of combining algebraic expressions.

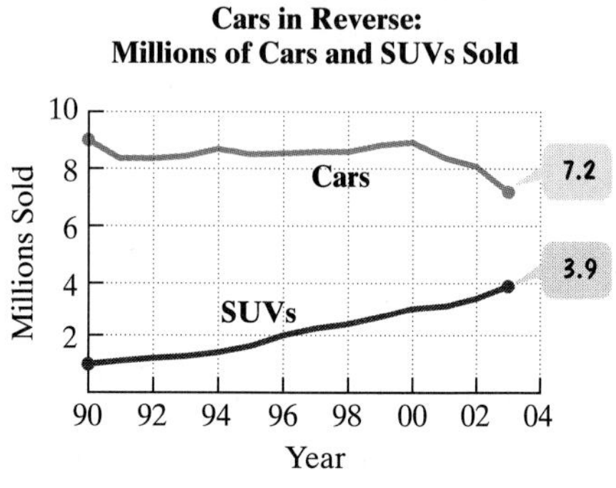

Figure 2.47 Sales by America's Big Three automakers

Study Tip

Throughout this section, we will be using the intersection of sets expressed in interval notation. Recall that the intersection of sets A and B, written $A \cap B$, is the set of elements common to both set A and set B. When sets A and B are in interval notation, to find the intersection, graph each interval and take the portion of the number line that the two graphs have in common. We will also be using notation involving the union of sets A and B, $A \cup B$, meaning the set of elements in A or in B or in both. For more detail, see Section P.1, pages 5–6 and Section 1.7, pages 166–167.

1 Find the domain of a function.

The Domain of a Function

We begin with two functions that model the data in Figure 2.47.

$$C(x) = -0.14x + 9 \qquad S(x) = 0.22x + 1$$

Car sales, $C(x)$, in millions, x years after 1990

SUV sales, $S(x)$, in millions, x years after 1990

How far beyond 1990 should we extend these models? The trend in Figure 2.47 shows decreasing car sales and increasing SUV sales. Because the three automakers focused on SUVs from 1990 through 2003 and launched a fleet of new cars in 2004, the trend shown by the data changed in 2004. Thus, we should not extend the models beyond 2003. Because x represents the number of years after 1990,

$$\text{Domain of } C = \{x | x = 0, 1, 2, 3, \ldots, 13\}$$

and

$$\text{Domain of } S = \{x | x = 0, 1, 2, 3, \ldots, 13\}.$$

Functions that model data often have their domains explicitly given with the function's equation. However, for most functions, only an equation is given and the domain is not specified. In cases like this, the domain of a function f is the largest set of real numbers for which the value of $f(x)$ is a real number. For example, consider the function

$$f(x) = \frac{1}{x - 3}.$$

Because division by 0 is undefined (and not a real number), the denominator, $x - 3$, cannot be 0. Thus, x cannot equal 3. The domain of the function consists of all real numbers other than 3, represented by

$$\text{Domain of } f = \{x | x \text{ is a real number and } x \neq 3\}.$$

Using interval notation,

$$\text{Domain of } f = (-\infty, 3) \cup (3, \infty).$$

All real numbers less than 3 — or — All real numbers greater than 3

Now consider a function involving a square root:

$$g(x) = \sqrt{x - 3}.$$

Because only nonnegative numbers have square roots that are real numbers, the expression under the square root sign, $x - 3$, must be nonnegative. We can use inspection to see that $x - 3 \geq 0$ if $x \geq 3$. The domain of g consists of all real numbers that are greater than or equal to 3:

$$\text{Domain of } g = \{x | x \geq 3\} \text{ or } [3, \infty).$$

Finding a Function's Domain

If a function f does not model data or verbal conditions, its domain is the largest set of real numbers for which the value of $f(x)$ is a real number. Exclude from a function's domain real numbers that cause division by zero and real numbers that result in a square root of a negative number.

EXAMPLE 1 Finding the Domain of a Function

Find the domain of each function:

a. $f(x) = x^2 - 7x$ **b.** $g(x) = \dfrac{3x + 2}{x^2 - 2x - 3}$ **c.** $h(x) = \sqrt{3x + 12}$.

Solution

a. The function $f(x) = x^2 - 7x$ contains neither division nor a square root. For every real number, x, the algebraic expression $x^2 - 7x$ represents a real number. Thus, the domain of f is the set of all real numbers.

$$\text{Domain of } f = (-\infty, \infty)$$

b. The function $g(x) = \dfrac{3x + 2}{x^2 - 2x - 3}$ contains division. Because division by 0 is undefined, we must exclude from the domain the values of x that cause the denominator, $x^2 - 2x - 3$, to be 0. We can identify these values by setting $x^2 - 2x - 3$ equal to 0.

$$x^2 - 2x - 3 = 0 \quad \text{Set the function's denominator equal to 0.}$$

$$(x + 1)(x - 3) = 0 \quad \text{Factor.}$$

$$x + 1 = 0 \quad \text{or} \quad x - 3 = 0 \quad \text{Set each factor equal to 0.}$$

$$x = -1 \qquad x = 3 \quad \text{Solve the resulting equations.}$$

We must exclude -1 and 3 from the domain of g.

$$\text{Domain of } g = (-\infty, -1) \cup (-1, 3) \cup (3, \infty)$$

c. The function $h(x) = \sqrt{3x + 12}$ contains an even root. Because only nonnegative numbers have real square roots, the quantity under the radical sign, $3x + 12$, must be greater than or equal to 0.

$$3x + 12 \geq 0 \quad \text{Set the function's radicand greater than or equal to 0.}$$

$$3x \geq -12 \quad \text{Subtract 12 from both sides.}$$

$$x \geq -4 \quad \text{Divide both sides by 3. Division by a positive number preserves the sense of the inequality.}$$

The domain of h consists of all real numbers greater than or equal to -4.

$$\text{Domain of } h = [-4, \infty)$$

The domain is highlighted on the x-axis in Figure 2.48.

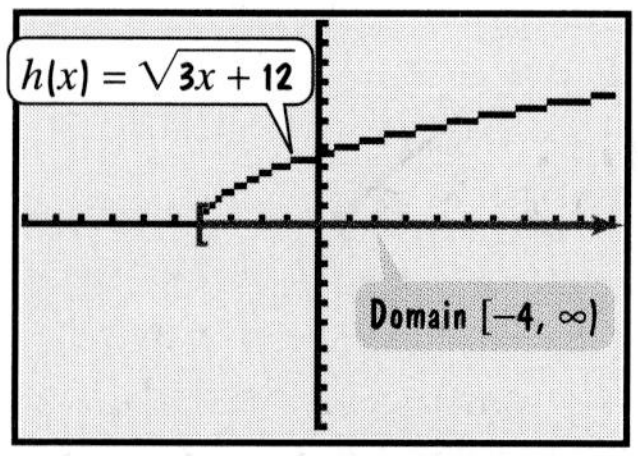

[−10, 10, 1] by [−10, 10, 1]

Figure 2.48

Check Point 1 Find the domain of each function:

a. $f(x) = x^2 + 3x - 17$ **b.** $g(x) = \dfrac{5x}{x^2 - 49}$

c. $h(x) = \sqrt{9x - 27}$.

The Algebra of Functions

We return to the functions that model millions of car and SUV sales from 1990 through 2003:

$$C(x) = -0.14x + 9 \qquad S(x) = 0.22x + 1.$$

Car sales, $C(x)$, in millions, x years after 1990

SUV sales, $S(x)$, in millions, x years after 1990

How can we use these functions to find total sales of cars and SUVs in 2003? Because 2003 is 13 years after 1990 and 13 is in the domain of each function, we need to find the sum of two function values:

$$C(13) + S(13).$$

Here is how it's done:

$$C(13) = -0.14(13) + 9 = 7.18 \qquad S(13) = 0.22(13) + 1 = 3.86$$

Substitute 13 for x in $C(x) = -0.14x + 9$.

7.18 million cars were sold in 2003.

Substitute 13 for x in $S(x) = 0.22x + 1$.

3.86 million SUVs were sold in 2003.

$$C(13) + S(13) = 7.18 + 3.86 = 11.04.$$

Thus, a total of 11.04 million cars and SUVs were sold in 2003.

There is a second way that we can obtain this number. We can first add the functions C and S to obtain a new function, $C + S$. To do so, we add the terms to the right of the equal sign for $C(x)$ to the terms to the right of the equal sign for $S(x)$:

$$\begin{aligned}(C + S)(x) &= C(x) + S(x)\\ &= (-0.14x + 9) + (0.22x + 1) && \text{Add terms for } C(x) \text{ and } S(x).\\ &= 0.08x + 10. && \text{Combine like terms.}\end{aligned}$$

Thus,

$$(C + S)(x) = 0.08x + 10.$$

Total car and SUV sales, in millions, x years after 1990

Do you see how we can use this new function to find total car and SUV sales in 2003? Substitute 13 for x in the equation for $C + S$:

$$(C + S)(13) = 0.08(13) + 10 = 11.04.$$

Substitute 13 for x in $(C + S)(x) = 0.08x + 10$.

As we found above, a total of 11.04 million cars and SUVs were sold in 2003.

The domain of the new function, $C + S$, consists of the numbers x that are in the domain of C **and** in the domain of S. If D_C represents the domain of C and D_S represents the domain of S, the domain of $C + S$ is $D_C \cap D_S$. Because both C and S model data from 1990 through 2003,

$$\text{Domain of } C + S = \{0, 1, 2, 3, \ldots, 13\}.$$

The function that models total car and SUV sales illustrates that functions can be added algebraically. We can also combine functions using subtraction, multiplication, and division by performing operations with the algebraic expressions that appear on the right side of the equations. The domain for each of these functions consists of all real numbers that are common to the domains of the functions being combined. Furthermore, when combining functions using division, values that make the divisor zero must be excluded from the domain.

The following definitions summarize our discussion:

2 Combine functions using the algebra of functions, specifying domains.

The Algebra of Functions: Sum, Difference, Product, and Quotient of Functions

Let f and g be two functions. The **sum** $f + g$, the **difference** $f - g$, the **product** fg, and the **quotient** $\frac{f}{g}$ are functions whose domains are the set of all real numbers common to the domains of f and g $(D_f \cap D_g)$, defined as follows:

1. Sum: $(f + g)(x) = f(x) + g(x)$
2. Difference: $(f - g)(x) = f(x) - g(x)$
3. Product: $(fg)(x) = f(x) \cdot g(x)$
4. Quotient: $\left(\frac{f}{g}\right)(x) = \frac{f(x)}{g(x)}$, provided $g(x) \neq 0$.

EXAMPLE 2 Combining Functions

Let $f(x) = 2x - 1$ and $g(x) = x^2 + x - 2$. Find each of the following functions:

a. $(f + g)(x)$ **b.** $(f - g)(x)$ **c.** $(fg)(x)$ **d.** $\left(\frac{f}{g}\right)(x)$.

Determine the domain for each function.

Solution

a. $(f + g)(x) = f(x) + g(x)$ — This is the definition of the sum $f + g$.

$= (2x - 1) + (x^2 + x - 2)$ — Substitute the given functions.

$= x^2 + 3x - 3$ — Remove parentheses and combine like terms.

b. $(f - g)(x) = f(x) - g(x)$ — This is the definition of the difference $f - g$.

$= (2x - 1) - (x^2 + x - 2)$ — Substitute the given functions.

$= 2x - 1 - x^2 - x + 2$ — Remove parentheses and change the sign of each term in the second set of parentheses.

$= -x^2 + x + 1$ — Combine like terms and arrange terms in descending powers of x.

c. $(fg)(x) = f(x) \cdot g(x)$ — This is the definition of the product fg.

$= (2x - 1)(x^2 + x - 2)$ — Substitute the given functions.

$= 2x(x^2 + x - 2) - 1(x^2 + x - 2)$ — Multiply each term in the second factor by $2x$ and -1, respectively.

$= 2x^3 + 2x^2 - 4x - x^2 - x + 2$ — Use the distributive property.

$= 2x^3 + (2x^2 - x^2) + (-4x - x) + 2$ — Rearrange terms so that like terms are adjacent.

$= 2x^3 + x^2 - 5x + 2$ — Combine like terms.

d. $\left(\frac{f}{g}\right)(x) = \frac{f(x)}{g(x)}$ — This is the definition of the quotient $\frac{f}{g}$.

$= \frac{2x - 1}{x^2 + x - 2}$ — Substitute the given functions. This rational expression cannot be simplified.

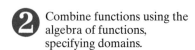

Study Tip

If the function $\frac{f}{g}$ can be simplified, determine the domain *before* simplifying.

Example:

$$f(x) = x^2 - 4 \text{ and}$$
$$g(x) = x - 2$$

$$\left(\frac{f}{g}\right)(x) = \frac{x^2-4}{x-2}$$

$x \neq 2$. The domain of $\frac{f}{g}$ is $(-\infty, 2) \cup (2, \infty)$.

$$= \frac{(x+2)\overset{1}{\cancel{(x-2)}}}{\underset{1}{\cancel{(x-2)}}} = x + 2$$

Because the equations for f and g do not involve division or contain even roots, the domain of both f and g is the set of all real numbers. Thus, the domain of $f + g$, $f - g$, and fg is the set of all real numbers, $(-\infty, \infty)$.

The function $\frac{f}{g}$ contains division. We must exclude from its domain values of x that cause the denominator, $x^2 + x - 2$, to be 0. Let's identify these values.

$x^2 + x - 2 = 0$	Set the denominator of $\frac{f}{g}$ equal to 0.
$(x + 2)(x - 1) = 0$	Factor.
$x + 2 = 0$ or $x - 1 = 0$	Set each factor equal to 0.
$x = -2$ $\quad$ $x = 1$	Solve the resulting equations.

We must exclude -2 and 1 from the domain of $\frac{f}{g}$.

$$\text{Domain of } \frac{f}{g} = (-\infty, -2) \cup (-2, 1) \cup (1, \infty)$$

Check Point 2 Let $f(x) = x - 5$ and $g(x) = x^2 - 1$. Find each of the following functions:

a. $(f + g)(x)$ **b.** $(f - g)(x)$ **c.** $(fg)(x)$ **d.** $\left(\frac{f}{g}\right)(x)$.

Determine the domain for each function.

EXAMPLE 3 Adding Functions and Determining the Domain

Let $f(x) = \sqrt{x + 3}$ and $g(x) = \sqrt{x - 2}$. Find each of the following:

a. $(f + g)(x)$ **b.** the domain of $f + g$.

Solution

a. $(f + g)(x) = f(x) + g(x) = \sqrt{x + 3} + \sqrt{x - 2}$

b. The domain of $f + g$ is the set of all real numbers that are common to the domain of f and the domain of g. Thus, we must find the domains of f and g before finding their intersection. We will do so for f first.

Note that $f(x) = \sqrt{x + 3}$ is a function involving the square root of $x + 3$. Because the square root of a negative quantity is not a real number, the value of $x + 3$ must be nonnegative. Thus, the domain of f is all x such that $x + 3 \geq 0$. Equivalently, the domain is $\{x | x \geq -3\}$, or $[-3, \infty)$.

Likewise, $g(x) = \sqrt{x - 2}$ is also a square root function. Because the square root of a negative quantity is not a real number, the value of $x - 2$ must be nonnegative. Thus, the domain of g is all x such that $x - 2 \geq 0$. Equivalently, the domain is $\{x | x \geq 2\}$, or $[2, \infty)$.

Now, we can use a number line to determine $D_f \cap D_g$, the domain of $f + g$. Figure 2.49 shows the domain of f in blue and the domain of g in red. Can you see that all real numbers greater than or equal to 2 are common to both domains? This is shown in purple on the number line. Thus, the domain of $f + g$ is $[2, \infty)$.

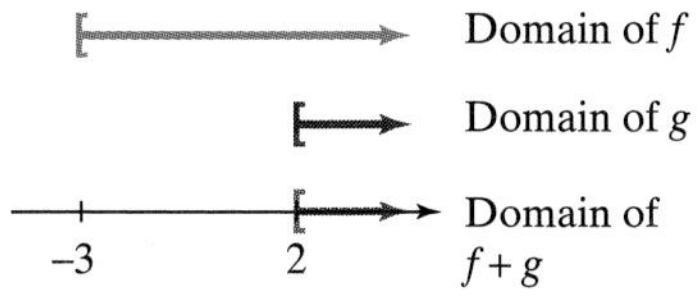

Figure 2.49 Finding the domain of the sum $f + g$

Technology

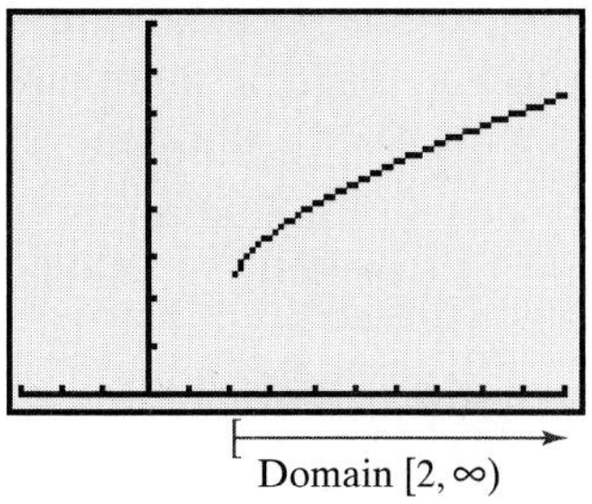

The graph on the left is the graph of

$$y = \sqrt{x + 3} + \sqrt{x - 2}$$

in a $[-3, 10, 1]$ by $[0, 8, 1]$ viewing rectangle. The graph reveals what we discovered algebraically in Example 3(b). The domain of this function is $[2, \infty)$.

Check Point 3 Let $f(x) = \sqrt{x-3}$ and $g(x) = \sqrt{x+1}$. Find each of the following:

a. $(f+g)(x)$ **b.** the domain of $f+g$.

3 Form composite functions.

Composite Functions

There is another way of combining two functions. To help understand this new combination, suppose that your local computer store is having a sale. The models that are on sale cost either \$300 less than the regular price or 85% of the regular price. If x represents the computer's regular price, the discounts can be described with the following functions:

$$f(x) = x - 300 \qquad g(x) = 0.85x.$$

The computer is on sale for \$300 less than its regular price.

The computer is on sale for 85% of its regular price.

At the store, you bargain with the salesperson. Eventually, she makes an offer you can't refuse. The sale price will be 85% of the regular price followed by a \$300 reduction:

$$0.85x - 300.$$

85% of the regular price

followed by a \$300 reduction

In terms of the functions f and g, this offer can be obtained by taking the output of $g(x) = 0.85x$, namely $0.85x$, and using it as the input of f:

$$f(x) = x - 300$$

Replace x with $0.85x$, the output of $g(x) = 0.85x$.

$$f(0.85x) = 0.85x - 300.$$

Because $0.85x$ is $g(x)$, we can write this last equation as

$$f(g(x)) = 0.85x - 300.$$

We read this equation as "f of g of x is equal to $0.85x - 300$." We call $f(g(x))$ the **composition of the function f with g**, or a **composite function**. This composite function is written $f \circ g$. Thus,

$$(f \circ g)(x) = f(g(x)) = 0.85x - 300.$$

This can be read "f of g of x" or "f composed with g of x."

Like all functions, we can evaluate $f \circ g$ for a specified value of x in the function's domain. For example, here's how to find the value of the composite function describing the offer you cannot refuse at 1400:

$$(f \circ g)(x) = 0.85x - 300$$

Replace x with 1400.

$$(f \circ g)(1400) = 0.85(1400) - 300 = 1190 - 300 = 890.$$

This means that a computer that regularly sells for \$1400 is on sale for \$890 subject to both discounts. We can use a partial table of coordinates for each of the discount functions, g and f, to numerically verify this result.

Computer's regular price; 85% of the regular price

x	$g(x) = 0.85x$
1200	1020
1300	1105
1400	1190

85% of the regular price; \$300 reduction

x	$f(x) = x - 300$
1020	720
1105	805
1190	890

Using these tables, we can find $(f \circ g)(1400)$:

$$(f \circ g)(1400) = f(g(1400)) = f(1190) = 890.$$

The table for g shows that $g(1400) = 1190$.

The table for f shows that $f(1190) = 890$.

This verifies that a computer that regularly sells for \$1400 is on sale for \$890 subject to both discounts.

Before you run out to buy a computer, let's generalize our discussion of the computer's double discount and define the composition of any two functions.

The Composition of Functions

The **composition of the function f with g** is denoted by $f \circ g$ and is defined by the equation

$$(f \circ g)(x) = f(g(x)).$$

The **domain of the composite function $f \circ g$** is the set of all x such that

1. x is in the domain of g and
2. $g(x)$ is in the domain of f.

The composition of f with g, $f \circ g$, is pictured as a machine with inputs and outputs in Figure 2.50. The diagram indicates that the output of g, or $g(x)$, becomes the input for "machine" f. If $g(x)$ is not in the domain of f, it cannot be input into machine f, and so $g(x)$ must be discarded.

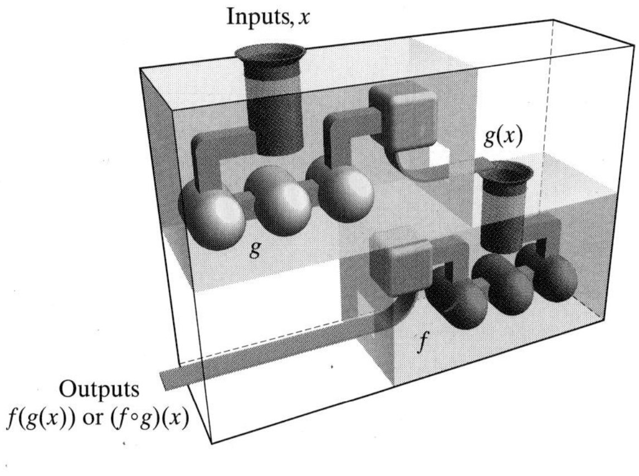

Figure 2.50 Inputting one function into a second function

EXAMPLE 4 Forming Composite Functions

Given $f(x) = 3x - 4$ and $g(x) = x^2 - 2x + 6$, find each of the following composite functions:

a. $(f \circ g)(x)$ **b.** $(g \circ f)(x)$.

Solution

a. We begin with $(f \circ g)(x)$, the composition of f with g. Because $(f \circ g)(x)$ means $f(g(x))$, we must replace each occurrence of x in the equation for f with $g(x)$.

$$f(x) = 3x - 4$$ This is the given equation for f.

Replace x with $g(x)$.

$$(f \circ g)(x) = f(g(x)) = 3g(x) - 4$$

$$= 3(x^2 - 2x + 6) - 4$$ Because $g(x) = x^2 - 2x + 6$, replace $g(x)$ with $x^2 - 2x + 6$.

$$= 3x^2 - 6x + 18 - 4$$ Use the distributive property.

$$= 3x^2 - 6x + 14$$ Simplify.

Thus, $(f \circ g)(x) = 3x^2 - 6x + 14$.

b. Next, we find $(g \circ f)(x)$, the composition of g with f. Because $(g \circ f)(x)$ means $g(f(x))$, we must replace each occurrence of x in the equation for g with $f(x)$.

$$g(x) = x^2 - 2x + 6$$ This is the equation for g.

Replace x with $f(x)$.

$$(g \circ f)(x) = g(f(x)) = (f(x))^2 - 2f(x) + 6$$

$$= (3x - 4)^2 - 2(3x - 4) + 6$$ Because $f(x) = 3x - 4$, replace $f(x)$ with $3x - 4$.

$$= 9x^2 - 24x + 16 - 6x + 8 + 6$$ Use $(A - B)^2 = A^2 - 2AB + B^2$ to square $3x - 4$.

$$= 9x^2 - 30x + 30$$ Simplify: $-24x - 6x = -30x$ and $16 + 8 + 6 = 30$.

Thus, $(g \circ f)(x) = 9x^2 - 30x + 30$. **Notice that $(f \circ g)(x)$ is not the same function as $(g \circ f)(x)$.**

Check Point 4 Given $f(x) = 5x + 6$ and $g(x) = 2x^2 - x - 1$, find each of the following composite functions:

a. $(f \circ g)(x)$ **b.** $(g \circ f)(x)$.

4 Determine domains for composite functions.

We need to be careful in determining the domain for a composite function.

Excluding Values from the Domain of $(f \circ g)(x) = f(g(x))$

The following values must be excluded from the input x:

- If x is not in the domain of g, it must not be in the domain of $f \circ g$.
- Any x for which $g(x)$ is not in the domain of f must not be in the domain of $f \circ g$.

EXAMPLE 5 Forming a Composite Function and Finding Its Domain

Given $f(x) = \frac{2}{x-1}$ and $g(x) = \frac{3}{x}$, find each of the following:

a. $(f \circ g)(x)$ **b.** the domain of $f \circ g$.

Solution

a. Because $(f \circ g)(x)$ means $f(g(x))$, we must replace x in $f(x) = \frac{2}{x-1}$ with $g(x)$.

Study Tip

The procedure for simplifying complex fractions can be found in Section P.6, pages 75–76.

$$(f \circ g)(x) = f(g(x)) = \frac{2}{g(x)-1} = \frac{2}{\frac{3}{x}-1} = \frac{2}{\frac{3}{x}-1} \cdot \frac{x}{x} = \frac{2x}{3-x}$$

$g(x) = \frac{3}{x}$

Simplify the complex fraction by multiplying by $\frac{x}{x}$, or 1.

Thus, $(f \circ g)(x) = \frac{2x}{3-x}$.

b. We determine values to exclude from the domain of $(f \circ g)(x)$ in two steps.

Rules for Excluding Numbers from the Domain of $(f \circ g)(x) = f(g(x))$	Applying the Rules to $f(x) = \frac{2}{x-1}$ and $g(x) = \frac{3}{x}$
If x is not in the domain of g, it must not be in the domain of $f \circ g$.	Because $g(x) = \frac{3}{x}$, 0 is not in the domain of g. Thus, 0 must be excluded from the domain of $f \circ g$.
Any x for which $g(x)$ is not in the domain of f must not be in the domain of $f \circ g$.	Because $f(g(x)) = \frac{2}{g(x)-1}$, we must exclude from the domain of $f \circ g$ any x for which $g(x) = 1$. $\frac{3}{x} = 1$ Set $g(x)$ equal to 1. $3 = x$ Multiply both sides by x. 3 must be excluded from the domain of $f \circ g$.

We see that 0 and 3 must be excluded from the domain of $f \circ g$. The domain of $f \circ g$ is

$$(-\infty, 0) \cup (0, 3) \cup (3, \infty).$$

Check Point 5 Given $f(x) = \frac{4}{x+2}$ and $g(x) = \frac{1}{x}$, find each of the following:

a. $(f \circ g)(x)$ **b.** the domain of $f \circ g$.

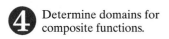

5 Write functions as compositions.

Decomposing Functions

When you form a composite function, you "compose" two functions to form a new function. It is also possible to reverse this process. That is, you can "decompose" a given function and express it as a composition of two functions. Although there is more than one way to do this, there is often a "natural" selection that comes to mind first. For example, consider the function h defined by

$$h(x) = (3x^2 - 4x + 1)^5.$$

The function h takes $3x^2 - 4x + 1$ and raises it to the power 5. A natural way to write h as a composition of two functions is to raise the function $g(x) = 3x^2 - 4x + 1$ to the power 5. Thus, if we let

$$f(x) = x^5 \text{ and } g(x) = 3x^2 - 4x + 1, \text{ then}$$
$$(f \circ g)(x) = f(g(x)) = f(3x^2 - 4x + 1) = (3x^2 - 4x + 1)^5.$$

EXAMPLE 6 Writing a Function as a Composition

Express $h(x)$ as a composition of two functions:

$$h(x) = \sqrt[3]{x^2 + 1}.$$

Solution The function h takes $x^2 + 1$ and takes its cube root. A natural way to write h as a composition of two functions is to take the cube root of the function $g(x) = x^2 + 1$. Thus, we let

$$f(x) = \sqrt[3]{x} \text{ and } g(x) = x^2 + 1.$$

We can check this composition by finding $(f \circ g)(x)$. This should give the original function, namely $h(x) = \sqrt[3]{x^2 + 1}$.

$$(f \circ g)(x) = f(g(x)) = f(x^2 + 1) = \sqrt[3]{x^2 + 1} = h(x)$$

Study Tip

Suppose the form of function h is $h(x) = (\text{algebraic expression})^{\text{power}}$. Function h can be expressed as a composition, $f \circ g$, using

$f(x) = x^{\text{power}}$
$g(x) = \text{algebraic expression}$.

Check Point 6 Express $h(x)$ as a composition of two functions:

$$h(x) = \sqrt{x^2 + 5}.$$

EXERCISE SET 2.6

Practice Exercises

In Exercises 1–30, find the domain of each function.

1. $f(x) = 3(x - 4)$
2. $f(x) = 2(x + 5)$
3. $g(x) = \dfrac{3}{x - 4}$
4. $g(x) = \dfrac{2}{x + 5}$
5. $f(x) = x^2 - 2x - 15$
6. $f(x) = x^2 + x - 12$
7. $g(x) = \dfrac{3}{x^2 - 2x - 15}$
8. $g(x) = \dfrac{2}{x^2 + x - 12}$
9. $f(x) = \dfrac{1}{x + 7} + \dfrac{3}{x - 9}$
10. $f(x) = \dfrac{1}{x + 8} + \dfrac{3}{x - 10}$
11. $g(x) = \dfrac{1}{x^2 + 1} - \dfrac{1}{x^2 - 1}$
12. $g(x) = \dfrac{1}{x^2 + 4} - \dfrac{1}{x^2 - 4}$
13. $h(x) = \dfrac{4}{\dfrac{3}{x} - 1}$
14. $h(x) = \dfrac{5}{\dfrac{4}{x} - 1}$
15. $f(x) = \dfrac{1}{\dfrac{4}{x - 1} - 2}$
16. $f(x) = \dfrac{1}{\dfrac{4}{x - 2} - 3}$
17. $f(x) = \sqrt{x - 3}$
18. $f(x) = \sqrt{x + 2}$
19. $g(x) = \dfrac{1}{\sqrt{x - 3}}$
20. $g(x) = \dfrac{1}{\sqrt{x + 2}}$
21. $g(x) = \sqrt{5x + 35}$
22. $g(x) = \sqrt{7x - 70}$
23. $f(x) = \sqrt{24 - 2x}$
24. $f(x) = \sqrt{84 - 6x}$
25. $h(x) = \sqrt{x - 2} + \sqrt{x + 3}$
26. $h(x) = \sqrt{x - 3} + \sqrt{x + 4}$
27. $g(x) = \dfrac{\sqrt{x - 2}}{x - 5}$
28. $g(x) = \dfrac{\sqrt{x - 3}}{x - 6}$

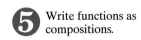

29. $f(x) = \dfrac{2x + 7}{x^3 - 5x^2 - 4x + 20}$

30. $f(x) = \dfrac{7x + 2}{x^3 - 2x^2 - 9x + 18}$

In Exercises 31–48, find $f + g$, $f - g$, fg, and $\frac{f}{g}$. Determine the domain for each function.

31. $f(x) = 2x + 3,\ g(x) = x - 1$

32. $f(x) = 3x - 4,\ g(x) = x + 2$

33. $f(x) = x - 5,\ g(x) = 3x^2$

34. $f(x) = x - 6,\ g(x) = 5x^2$

35. $f(x) = 2x^2 - x - 3,\ g(x) = x + 1$

36. $f(x) = 6x^2 - x - 1,\ g(x) = x - 1$

37. $f(x) = 3 - x^2,\ g(x) = x^2 + 2x - 15$

38. $f(x) = 5 - x^2,\ g(x) = x^2 + 4x - 12$

39. $f(x) = \sqrt{x},\ g(x) = x - 4$

40. $f(x) = \sqrt{x},\ g(x) = x - 5$

41. $f(x) = 2 + \dfrac{1}{x},\ g(x) = \dfrac{1}{x}$

42. $f(x) = 6 - \dfrac{1}{x},\ g(x) = \dfrac{1}{x}$

43. $f(x) = \dfrac{5x + 1}{x^2 - 9},\ g(x) = \dfrac{4x - 2}{x^2 - 9}$

44. $f(x) = \dfrac{3x + 1}{x^2 - 25},\ g(x) = \dfrac{2x - 4}{x^2 - 25}$

45. $f(x) = \sqrt{x + 4},\ g(x) = \sqrt{x - 1}$

46. $f(x) = \sqrt{x + 6},\ g(x) = \sqrt{x - 3}$

47. $f(x) = \sqrt{x - 2},\ g(x) = \sqrt{2 - x}$

48. $f(x) = \sqrt{x - 5},\ g(x) = \sqrt{5 - x}$

In Exercises 49–64, find

a. $(f \circ g)(x)$; **b.** $(g \circ f)(x)$; **c.** $(f \circ g)(2)$.

49. $f(x) = 2x,\ g(x) = x + 7$

50. $f(x) = 3x,\ g(x) = x - 5$

51. $f(x) = x + 4,\ g(x) = 2x + 1$

52. $f(x) = 5x + 2,\ g(x) = 3x - 4$

53. $f(x) = 4x - 3,\ g(x) = 5x^2 - 2$

54. $f(x) = 7x + 1,\ g(x) = 2x^2 - 9$

55. $f(x) = x^2 + 2,\ g(x) = x^2 - 2$

56. $f(x) = x^2 + 1,\ g(x) = x^2 - 3$

57. $f(x) = 4 - x,\ g(x) = 2x^2 + x + 5$

58. $f(x) = 5x - 2,\ g(x) = -x^2 + 4x - 1$

59. $f(x) = \sqrt{x},\ g(x) = x - 1$

60. $f(x) = \sqrt{x},\ g(x) = x + 2$

61. $f(x) = 2x - 3,\ g(x) = \dfrac{x + 3}{2}$

62. $f(x) = 6x - 3,\ g(x) = \dfrac{x + 3}{6}$

63. $f(x) = \dfrac{1}{x},\ g(x) = \dfrac{1}{x}$

64. $f(x) = \dfrac{2}{x},\ g(x) = \dfrac{2}{x}$

In Exercises 65–72, find

a. $(f \circ g)(x)$; **b.** *the domain of* $f \circ g$.

65. $f(x) = \dfrac{2}{x + 3},\ g(x) = \dfrac{1}{x}$

66. $f(x) = \dfrac{5}{x + 4},\ g(x) = \dfrac{1}{x}$

67. $f(x) = \dfrac{x}{x + 1},\ g(x) = \dfrac{4}{x}$

68. $f(x) = \dfrac{x}{x + 5},\ g(x) = \dfrac{6}{x}$

69. $f(x) = \sqrt{x},\ g(x) = x - 2$

70. $f(x) = \sqrt{x},\ g(x) = x - 3$

71. $f(x) = x^2 + 4,\ g(x) = \sqrt{1 - x}$

72. $f(x) = x^2 + 1,\ g(x) = \sqrt{2 - x}$

In Exercises 73–80, express the given function h as a composition of two functions f and g so that $h(x) = (f \circ g)(x)$.

73. $h(x) = (3x - 1)^4$

74. $h(x) = (2x - 5)^3$

75. $h(x) = \sqrt[3]{x^2 - 9}$

76. $h(x) = \sqrt{5x^2 + 3}$

77. $h(x) = |2x - 5|$

78. $h(x) = |3x - 4|$

79. $h(x) = \dfrac{1}{2x - 3}$

80. $h(x) = \dfrac{1}{4x + 5}$

Practice Plus

Use the graphs of f and g to solve Exercises 81–88.

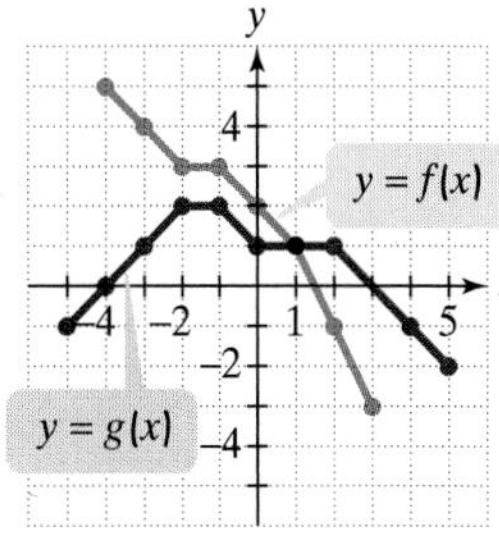

81. Find $(f + g)(-3)$.

82. Find $(g - f)(-2)$.

83. Find $(fg)(2)$.

84. Find $\left(\dfrac{g}{f}\right)(3)$.

85. Find the domain of $f + g$.

86. Find the domain of $\dfrac{f}{g}$.

87. Graph $f + g$.

88. Graph $f - g$.

In Exercises 89–92, use the graphs of f and g to evaluate each composite function.

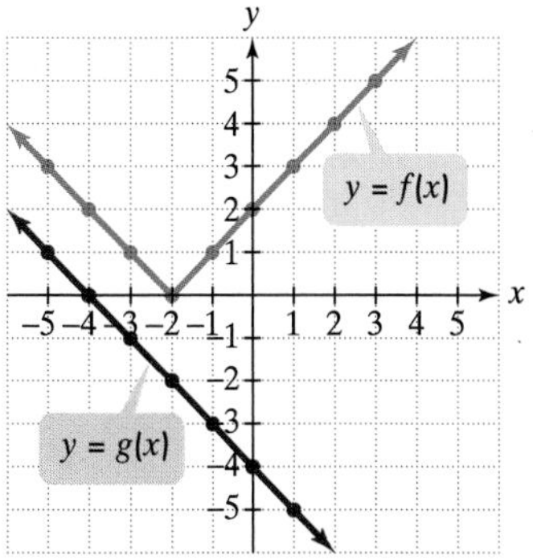

89. $(f \circ g)(-1)$

90. $(f \circ g)(1)$

91. $(g \circ f)(0)$

92. $(g \circ f)(-1)$

In Exercises 93–94, find all values of x satisfying the given conditions.

93. $f(x) = 2x - 5$, $g(x) = x^2 - 3x + 8$, and $(f \circ g)(x) = 7$.

94. $f(x) = 1 - 2x$, $g(x) = 3x^2 + x - 1$, and $(f \circ g)(x) = -5$.

Application Exercises

The table shows the total number of births and the total number of deaths in the United States from 1995 through 2003.

Births and Deaths in the U.S.

Year	Births	Deaths
1995	3,899,589	2,312,132
1996	3,891,494	2,314,690
1997	3,880,894	2,314,245
1998	3,941,553	2,337,256
1999	3,959,417	2,391,399
2000	4,058,814	2,403,351
2001	4,025,933	2,416,425
2002	4,022,000	2,436,000
2003	4,093,000	2,423,000

Source: Department of Health and Human Services

The data can be modeled by the following functions:

Number of births $B(x) = 26{,}208x + 3{,}869{,}910$

Number of deaths $D(x) = 17{,}964x + 2{,}300{,}198.$

In each function, x represents the number of years after 1995. Assume that the functions apply only to the years shown in the table. Use these functions to solve Exercises 95–98.

95. Find the domain of B.

96. Find the domain of D.

97. a. Find $(B - D)(x)$. What does this function represent?

b. Use the function in part (a) to find $(B - D)(8)$. What does this mean in terms of the U.S. population and to which year does this apply?

c. Use the data shown in the table to find $(B - D)(8)$. How well does the difference of functions used in part (b) model this number?

98. a. Find $(B - D)(x)$. What does this function represent?

b. Use the function in part (a) to find $(B - D)(6)$. What does this mean in terms of the U.S. population and to which year does this apply?

c. Use the data shown in the table to find $(B - D)(6)$. How well does the difference of functions used in part (b) model this number?

Consider the following functions:

$f(x)$ = *population of the world's more developed regions in year x*

$g(x)$ = *population of the world's less developed regions in year x*

$h(x)$ = *total world population in year x.*

Use these functions and the graphs shown to answer Exercises 99–102.

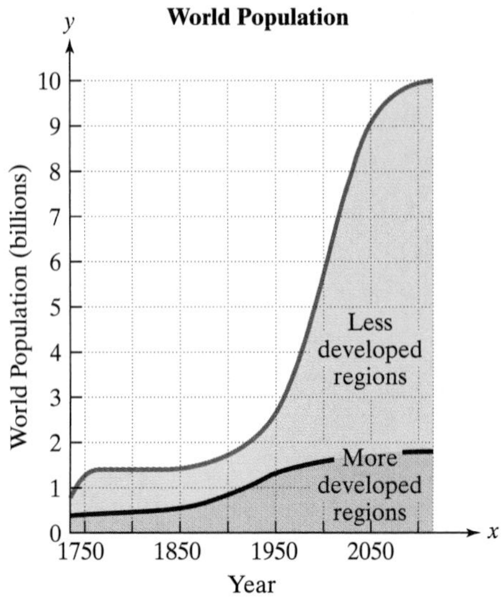

Source: Population Reference Bureau

99. What does the function $f + g$ represent?

100. What does the function $h - g$ represent?

101. Use the graph to estimate $(f + g)(2000)$.

102. Use the graph to estimate $(h - g)(2000)$.

103. A company that sells radios has yearly fixed costs of \$600,000. It costs the company \$45 to produce each radio. Each radio will sell for \$65. The company's costs and revenue are modeled by the following functions:

$C(x) = 600{,}000 + 45x$ This function models the company's costs.

$R(x) = 65x.$ This function models the company's revenue.

Find and interpret $(R - C)(20{,}000)$, $(R - C)(30{,}000)$, and $(R - C)(40{,}000)$.

104. A department store has two locations in a city. From 2000 through 2004, the profits for each of the store's two branches are modeled by the functions $f(x) = -0.44x + 13.62$ and $g(x) = 0.51x + 11.14$. In each model, x represents the number of years after 2000, and f and g represent the profit, in millions of dollars.

a. What is the slope of f? Describe what this means.

b. What is the slope of g? Describe what this means.

c. Find $f + g$. What is the slope of this function? What does this mean?

105. The regular price of a computer is x dollars. Let $f(x) = x - 400$ and $g(x) = 0.75x$.

a. Describe what the functions f and g model in terms of the price of the computer.

b. Find $(f \circ g)(x)$ and describe what this models in terms of the price of the computer.

c. Repeat part (b) for $(g \circ f)(x)$.

d. Which composite function models the greater discount on the computer, $f \circ g$ or $g \circ f$? Explain.

106. The regular price of a pair of jeans is x dollars. Let $f(x) = x - 5$ and $g(x) = 0.6x$.

a. Describe what functions f and g model in terms of the price of the jeans.

b. Find $(f \circ g)(x)$ and describe what this models in terms of the price of the jeans.

c. Repeat part (b) for $(g \circ f)(x)$.

d. Which composite function models the greater discount on the jeans, $f \circ g$ or $g \circ f$? Explain.

Writing in Mathematics

107. If a function is defined by an equation, explain how to find its domain.

108. If equations for f and g are given, explain how to find $f - g$.

109. If equations for two functions are given, explain how to obtain the quotient function and its domain.

110. Describe a procedure for finding $(f \circ g)(x)$. What is the name of this function?

111. Describe the values of x that must be excluded from the domain of $(f \circ g)(x)$.

112. We opened the section with two functions that modeled the data in Figure 2.47 on page 256. Car sales, $C(x)$, in millions, x years after 1990 were modeled by $C(x) = -0.14x + 9$. SUV sales, $S(x)$, in millions, x years after 1990 were modeled by $S(x) = 0.22x + 1$. Explain how these models were obtained from Figure 2.47.

Technology Exercises

113. The function $f(t) = -0.14t^2 + 0.51t + 31.6$ models the U.S. population ages 65 and older, $f(t)$, in millions, t years after 1990. The function $g(t) = 0.54t^2 + 12.64t + 107.1$ models the total yearly cost of Medicare, $g(t)$, in billions of dollars, t years after 1990. Graph the function $\frac{g}{f}$ in a $[0, 15, 1]$ by $[0, 60, 10]$ viewing rectangle. What does the shape of the graph indicate about the per capita costs of Medicare for the U.S. population ages 65 and over with increasing time?

114. Graph $y_1 = x^2 - 2x$, $y_2 = x$, and $y_3 = y_1 \div y_2$ in the same $[-10, 10, 1]$ by $[-10, 10, 1]$ viewing rectangle. Then use the TRACE feature to trace along y_3. What happens at $x = 0$? Explain why this occurs.

115. Graph $y_1 = \sqrt{2 - x}$, $y_2 = \sqrt{x}$, and $y_3 = \sqrt{2 - y_2}$ in the same $[-4, 4, 1]$ by $[0, 2, 1]$ viewing rectangle. If y_1 represents f and y_2 represents g, use the graph of y_3 to find the domain of $f \circ g$. Then verify your observation algebraically.

Critical Thinking Exercises

116. Which one of the following is true?

a. If $f(x) = x^2 - 4$ and $g(x) = \sqrt{x^2 - 4}$, then $(f \circ g)(x) = -x^2$ and $(f \circ g)(5) = -25$.

b. There can never be two functions f and g, where $f \neq g$, for which $(f \circ g)(x) = (g \circ f)(x)$.

c. If $f(7) = 5$ and $g(4) = 7$, then $(f \circ g)(4) = 35$.

d. If $f(x) = \sqrt{x}$ and $g(x) = 2x - 1$, then $(f \circ g)(5) = g(2)$.

117. Prove that if f and g are even functions, then fg is also an even function.

118. Define two functions f and g so that $f \circ g = g \circ f$.

119. Use the graphs given in Exercises 99–102 to create a graph that shows the population, in billions, of less developed regions from 1950 through 2050.

SECTION 2.7 Distance and Midpoint Formulas; Circles

Objectives

1. Find the distance between two points.
2. Find the midpoint of a line segment.
3. Write the standard form of a circle's equation.
4. Give the center and radius of a circle whose equation is in standard form.
5. Convert the general form of a circle's equation to standard form.

It's a good idea to know your way around a circle. Clocks, angles, maps, and compasses are based on circles. Circles occur everywhere in nature: in ripples on water, patterns on a moth's wings, and cross sections of trees. Some consider the circle to be the most pleasing of all shapes.

The rectangular coordinate system gives us a unique way of knowing a circle. It enables us to translate a circle's geometric definition into an algebraic equation. To do this, we must first develop a formula for the distance between any two points in rectangular coordinates.

1 Find the distance between two points.

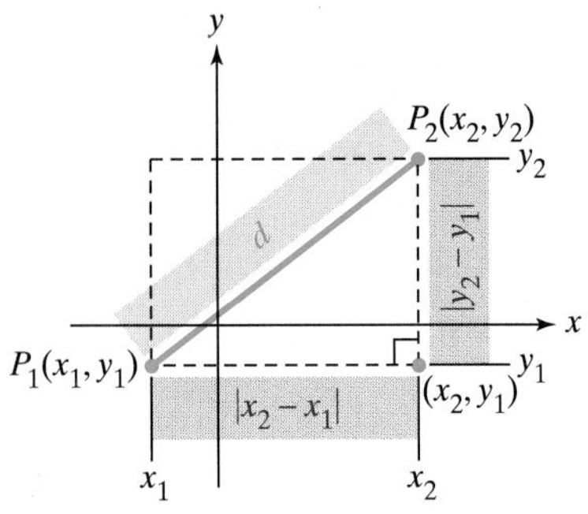

Figure 2.51

The Distance Formula

Using the Pythagorean Theorem, we can find the distance between the two points $P_1(x_1, y_1)$ and $P_2(x_2, y_2)$ in the rectangular coordinate system. The two points are illustrated in Figure 2.51.

The distance that we need to find is represented by d and shown in blue. Notice that the distance between two points on the dashed horizontal line is the absolute value of the difference between the x-coordinates of the two points. This distance, $|x_2 - x_1|$, is shown in pink. Similarly, the distance between two points on the dashed vertical line is the absolute value of the difference between the y-coordinates of the two points. This distance, $|y_2 - y_1|$, is also shown in pink.

Because the dashed lines are horizontal and vertical, a right triangle is formed. Thus, we can use the Pythagorean Theorem to find the distance d. Squaring the lengths of the triangle's sides results in positive numbers, so absolute value notation is not necessary.

$$d^2 = (x_2 - x_1)^2 + (y_2 - y_1)^2$$ Apply the Pythagorean Theorem to the right triangle in Figure 2.51.

$$d = \pm\sqrt{(x_2 - x_1)^2 + (y_2 - y_1)^2}$$ Apply the square root property.

$$d = \sqrt{(x_2 - x_1)^2 + (y_2 - y_1)^2}$$ Because distance is nonnegative, write only the principal square root.

This result is called the **distance formula**.

> **The Distance Formula**
>
> The distance, d, between the points (x_1, y_1) and (x_2, y_2) in the rectangular coordinate system is
>
> $$d = \sqrt{(x_2 - x_1)^2 + (y_2 - y_1)^2}.$$
>
> To compute the distance between two points, find the square of the difference between the x-coordinates plus the square of the difference between the y-coordinates. The principal square root of this sum is the distance.

When using the distance formula, it does not matter which point you call (x_1, y_1) and which you call (x_2, y_2).

EXAMPLE 1 Using the Distance Formula

Find the distance between $(-1, 4)$ and $(3, -2)$.

Solution We will let $(x_1, y_1) = (-1, 4)$ and $(x_2, y_2) = (3, -2)$.

$$d = \sqrt{(x_2 - x_1)^2 + (y_2 - y_1)^2}$$ Use the distance formula.

$$= \sqrt{(-2 - 4)^2 + [3 - (-1)]^2}$$ Substitute the given values.

$$= \sqrt{(-6)^2 + 4^2}$$ Perform operations inside grouping symbols: $-2 - 4 = -6$ and $3 - (-1) = 3 + 1 = 4$.

$$= \sqrt{36 + 16}$$ Square 2 6 and 4.

Caution: This does not equal $\sqrt{36} + \sqrt{16}$.

$$= \sqrt{52}$$ Add.

$$= \sqrt{4 \cdot 13} = 2\sqrt{13} \approx 7.21$$ $\sqrt{52} = \sqrt{4 \cdot 13} = \sqrt{4}\sqrt{13} = 2\sqrt{13}$

The distance between the given points is $2\sqrt{13}$ units, or approximately 7.21 units. The situation is illustrated in Figure 2.52.

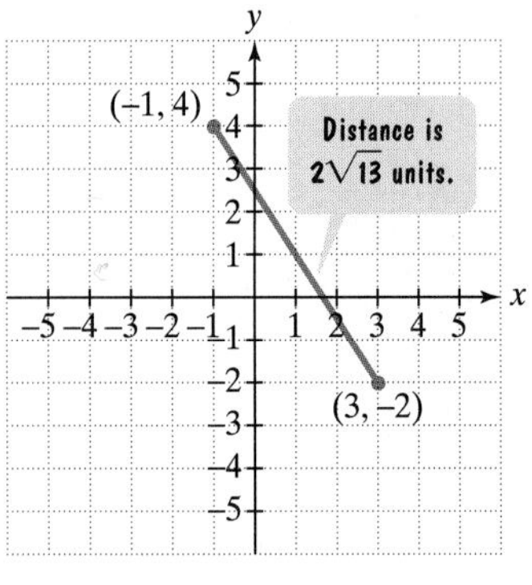

Figure 2.52 Finding the distance between two points

Check Point 1 Find the distance between $(-4, 9)$ and $(1, -3)$.

Find the midpoint of a line segment.

The Midpoint Formula

The distance formula can be used to derive a formula for finding the midpoint of a line segment between two given points. The formula is given as follows:

The Midpoint Formula

Consider a line segment whose endpoints are (x_1, y_1) and (x_2, y_2). The coordinates of the segment's midpoint are

$$\left(\frac{x_1 + x_2}{2}, \frac{y_1 + y_2}{2}\right).$$

To find the midpoint, take the average of the two x-coordinates and the average of the two y-coordinates.

Study Tip

The midpoint formula requires finding the *sum* of coordinates. By contrast, the distance formula requires finding the *difference* of coordinates:

Midpoint: Sum of coordinates

Distance: Difference of coordinates

$$\left(\frac{x_1 + x_2}{2}, \frac{y_1 + y_2}{2}\right) \qquad \sqrt{(x_2 - x_1)^2 + (y_2 - y_1)^2}$$

It's easy to confuse the two formulas. Be sure to use addition, not subtraction, when applying the midpoint formula.

EXAMPLE 2 Using the Midpoint Formula

Find the midpoint of the line segment with endpoints $(1, -6)$ and $(-8, -4)$.

Solution To find the coordinates of the midpoint, we average the coordinates of the endpoints.

$$\text{Midpoint} = \left(\frac{1 + (-8)}{2}, \frac{-6 + (-4)}{2}\right) = \left(\frac{-7}{2}, \frac{-10}{2}\right) = \left(-\frac{7}{2}, -5\right)$$

Average the x-coordinates. Average the y-coordinates.

Figure 2.53 illustrates that the point $\left(-\frac{7}{2}, -5\right)$ is midway between the points $(1, -6)$ and $(-8, -4)$.

Check Point 2 Find the midpoint of the line segment with endpoints $(1, 2)$ and $(7, -3)$.

$$\frac{1+7}{2}, \frac{7+(-3)}{2} = \frac{8}{2}, \frac{4}{2} = (4, 2)$$

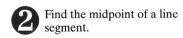

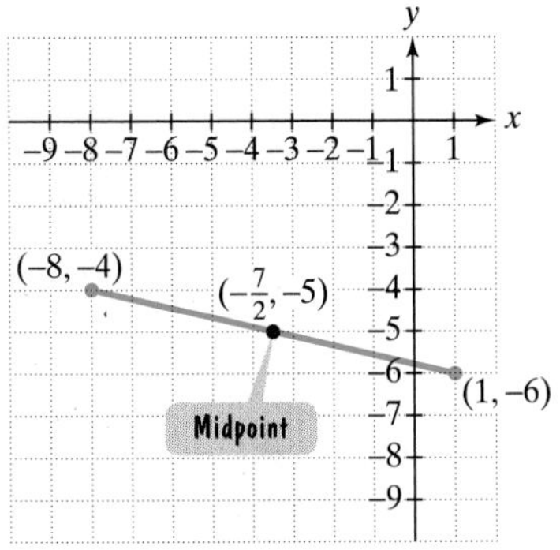

Figure 2.53 Finding a line segment's midpoint

(-8, -4) $\left(-\frac{7}{2}, -5\right)$ (1, -6) Midpoint

Circles

Our goal is to translate a circle's geometric definition into an equation. We begin with this geometric definition.

Definition of a Circle

A **circle** is the set of all points in a plane that are equidistant from a fixed point, called the **center**. The fixed distance from the circle's center to any point on the circle is called the **radius**.

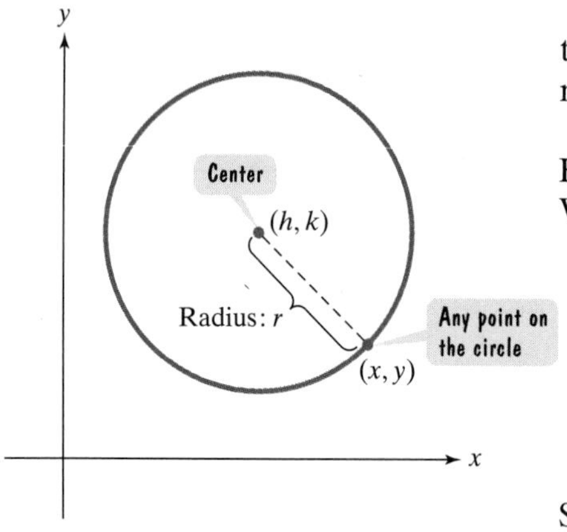

Figure 2.54 A circle centered at (h, k) with radius r

Figure 2.54 is our starting point for obtaining a circle's equation. We've placed the circle into a rectangular coordinate system. The circle's center is (h, k) and its radius is r. We let (x, y) represent the coordinates of any point on the circle.

What does the geometric definition of a circle tell us about point (x, y) in Figure 2.54? The point is on the circle if and only if its distance from the center is r. We can use the distance formula to express this idea algebraically:

The distance between (x, y) and (h, k) is always r.

$$\sqrt{(x-h)^2+(y-k)^2} = r.$$

Squaring both sides of $\sqrt{(x-h)^2+(y-k)^2} = r$ yields the *standard form of the equation of a circle.*

3 Write the standard form of a circle's equation.

The Standard Form of the Equation of a Circle

The **standard form of the equation of a circle** with center (h, k) and radius r is

$$(x-h)^2+(y-k)^2=r^2.$$

EXAMPLE 3 Finding the Standard Form of a Circle's Equation

Write the standard form of the equation of the circle with center $(0, 0)$ and radius 2. Graph the circle.

Solution The center is $(0, 0)$. Because the center is represented as (h, k) in the standard form of the equation, $h = 0$ and $k = 0$. The radius is 2, so we will let $r = 2$ in the equation.

$(x-h)^2+(y-k)^2=r^2$ This is the standard form of a circle's equation.

$(x-0)^2+(y-0)^2=2^2$ Substitute 0 for h, 0 for k, and 2 for r.

$x^2+y^2=4$ Simplify.

The standard form of the equation of the circle is $x^2+y^2=4$. Figure 2.55 shows the graph.

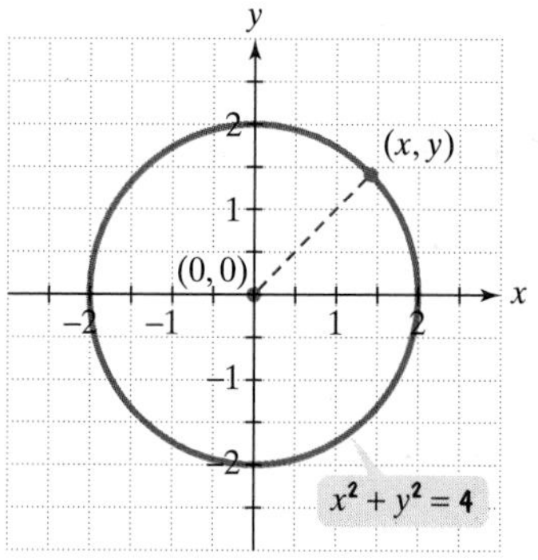

Figure 2.55 The graph of $x^2+y^2=4$

Check Point 3 Write the standard form of the equation of the circle with center $(0, 0)$ and radius 4.

Technology

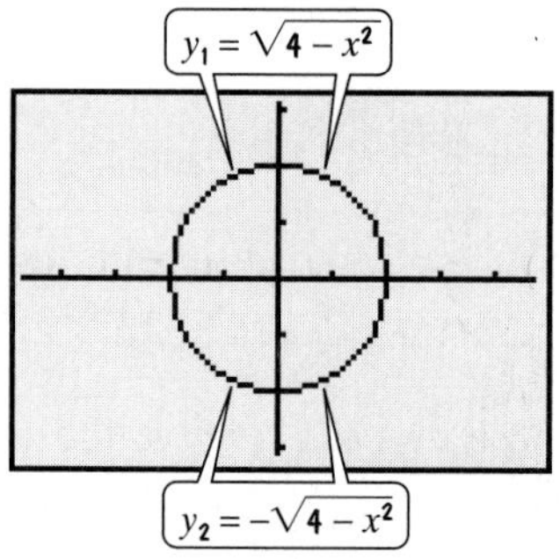

To graph a circle with a graphing utility, first solve the equation for y.

$$x^2+y^2=4$$
$$y^2=4-x^2$$
$$y=\pm\sqrt{4-x^2}$$

y is not a function of x.

Graph the two equations

$$y_1=\sqrt{4-x^2} \quad \text{and} \quad y_2=-\sqrt{4-x^2}$$

in the same viewing rectangle. The graph of $y_1=\sqrt{4-x^2}$ is the top semicircle because y is always positive. The graph of $y_2=-\sqrt{4-x^2}$ is the bottom semicircle because y is always negative. Use a ZOOM SQUARE setting so that the circle looks like a circle. (Many graphing utilities have problems connecting the two semicircles because the segments directly across horizontally from the center become nearly vertical.)

Example 3 and Check Point 3 involved circles centered at the origin. The standard form of the equation of all such circles is $x^2 + y^2 = r^2$, where r is the circle's radius. Now, let's consider a circle whose center is not at the origin.

EXAMPLE 4 Finding the Standard Form of a Circle's Equation

Write the standard form of the equation of the circle with center $(-2, 3)$ and radius 4.

Solution The center is $(-2, 3)$. Because the center is represented as (h, k) in the standard form of the equation, $h = -2$ and $k = 3$. The radius is 4, so we will let $r = 4$ in the equation.

$$(x - h)^2 + (y - k)^2 = r^2 \quad \text{This is the standard form of a circle's equation.}$$

$$[x - (-2)]^2 + (y - 3)^2 = 4^2 \quad \text{Substitute } -2 \text{ for } h, 3 \text{ for } k, \text{ and } 4 \text{ for } r.$$

$$(x + 2)^2 + (y - 3)^2 = 16 \quad \text{Simplify.}$$

The standard form of the equation of the circle is $(x + 2)^2 + (y - 3)^2 = 16$.

Check Point 4 Write the standard form of the equation of the circle with center $(5, -6)$ and radius 10.

4 Give the center and radius of a circle whose equation is in standard form.

EXAMPLE 5 Using the Standard Form of a Circle's Equation to Graph the Circle

a. Find the center and radius of the circle whose equation is

$$(x - 2)^2 + (y + 4)^2 = 9.$$

b. Graph the equation.

c. Use the graph to identify the relation's domain and range.

Solution

a. We begin by finding the circle's center, (h, k), and its radius, r. We can find the values for h, k, and r by comparing the given equation to the standard form of the equation of a circle, $(x - h)^2 + (y - k)^2 = r^2$.

$$(x - 2)^2 + (y + 4)^2 = 9$$

$$(x - 2)^2 + (y - (-4))^2 = 3^2$$

This is $(x - h)^2$, with $h = 2$. This is $(y - k)^2$, with $k = -4$. This is r^2, with $r = 3$.

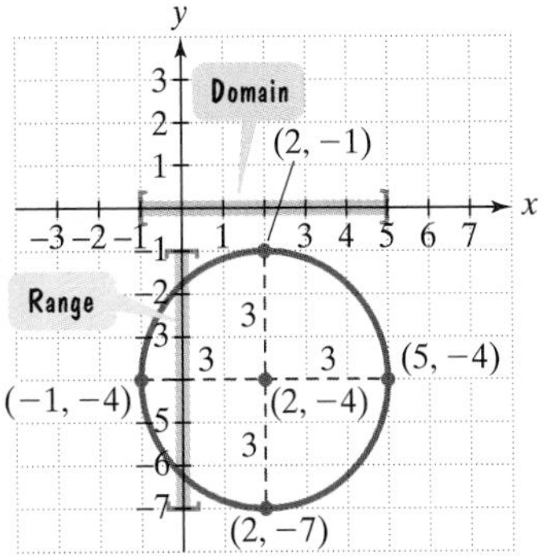

Figure 2.56 The graph of $(x - 2)^2 + (y + 4)^2 = 9$

We see that $h = 2$, $k = -4$, and $r = 3$. Thus, the circle has center $(h, k) = (2, -4)$ and a radius of 3 units.

b. To graph this circle, first plot the center $(2, -4)$. Because the radius is 3, you can locate at least four points on the circle by going out three units to the right, to the left, up, and down from the center.

The points three units to the right and to the left of $(2, -4)$ are $(5, -4)$ and $(-1, -4)$, respectively. The points three units up and down from $(2, -4)$ are $(2, -1)$ and $(2, -7)$, respectively.

Using these points, we obtain the graph in Figure 2.56.

c. The four points that we located on the circle can be used to determine the relation's domain and range. The points $(-1, -4)$ and $(5, -4)$ show that values of x extend from -1 to 5, inclusive:

$$\text{Domain} = [-1, 5].$$

The points $(2, -7)$ and $(2, -1)$ show that values of y extend from -7 to -1, inclusive:

$$\text{Range} = [-7, -1].$$

Check Point 5 **a.** Find the center and radius of the circle whose equation is

$$(x + 3)^2 + (y - 1)^2 = 4.$$

b. Graph the equation.

c. Use the graph to identify the relation's domain and range.

If we square $x - 2$ and $y + 4$ in the standard form of the equation from Example 5, we obtain another form for the circle's equation.

$(x - 2)^2 + (y + 4)^2 = 9$	This is the standard form of the equation from Example 5.
$x^2 - 4x + 4 + y^2 + 8y + 16 = 9$	Square $x - 2$ and $y + 4$.
$x^2 + y^2 - 4x + 8y + 20 = 9$	Combine constants and rearrange terms.
$x^2 + y^2 - 4x + 8y + 11 = 0$	Subtract 9 from both sides.

This result suggests that an equation in the form $x^2 + y^2 + Dx + Ey + F = 0$ can represent a circle. This is called the *general form of the equation of a circle.*

The General Form of the Equation of a Circle

The **general form of the equation of a circle** is

$$x^2 + y^2 + Dx + Ey + F = 0$$

where D, E, and F are real numbers.

5 Convert the general form of a circle's equation to standard form.

We can convert the general form of the equation of a circle to the standard form $(x - h)^2 + (y - k)^2 = r^2$. We do so by completing the square on x and y. Let's see how this is done.

EXAMPLE 6 Converting the General Form of a Circle's Equation to Standard Form and Graphing the Circle

Study Tip

To review completing the square, see Section 1.5, pages 134–136.

Write in standard form and graph: $x^2 + y^2 + 4x - 6y - 23 = 0.$

Solution Because we plan to complete the square on both x and y, let's rearrange the terms so that x-terms are arranged in descending order, y-terms are arranged in descending order, and the constant term appears on the right.

$x^2 + y^2 + 4x - 6y - 23 = 0$	This is the given equation.
$(x^2 + 4x \quad\;) + (y^2 - 6y \quad\;) = 23$	Rewrite in anticipation of completing the square.
$(x^2 + 4x + 4) + (y^2 - 6y + 9) = 23 + 4 + 9$	Complete the square on x: $\frac{1}{2} \cdot 4 = 2$ and $2^2 = 4$, so add 4 to both sides. Complete the square on y: $\frac{1}{2} 1 - 62 = -3$and $1-32^2 = 9$, so add 9 to both sides.
$(x + 2)^2 + (y - 3)^2 = 36$	Factor on the left and add on the right.

Remember that numbers added on the left side must also be added on the right side.

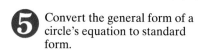

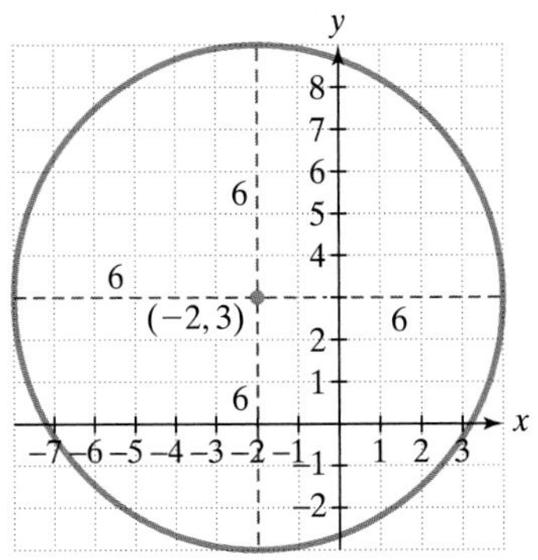

Figure 2.57 The graph of $(x + 2)^2 + (y - 3)^2 = 36$

This last equation, $(x + 2)^2 + (y - 3)^2 = 36$, is in standard form. We can identify the circle's center and radius by comparing this equation to the standard form of the equation of a circle, $(x - h)^2 + (y - k)^2 = r^2$.

$$(x + 2)^2 + (y - 3)^2 = 36$$

$$(x - (-2))^2 + (y - 3)^2 = 6^2$$

This is $(x - h)^2$, with $h = -2$. This is $(y - k)^2$, with $k = 3$. This is r^2, with $r = 6$.

We use the center, $(h, k) = (-2, 3)$, and the radius, $r = 6$, to graph the circle. The graph is shown in Figure 2.57.

Technology

To graph $x^2 + y^2 + 4x - 6y - 23 = 0$, rewrite the equation as a quadratic equation in y.

$$y^2 - 6y + (x^2 + 4x - 23) = 0$$

Now solve for y using the quadratic formula, with $a = 1$, $b = -6$, and $c = x^2 + 4x - 23$.

$$y = \frac{-b \pm \sqrt{b^2 - 4ac}}{2a} = \frac{-(-6) \pm \sqrt{(-6)^2 - 4 \cdot 1(x^2 + 4x - 23)}}{2 \cdot 1} = \frac{6 \pm \sqrt{36 - 4(x^2 + 4x - 23)}}{2}$$

Because we will enter these equations, there is no need to simplify. Enter

$$y_1 = \frac{6 + \sqrt{36 - 4(x^2 + 4x - 23)}}{2}$$

and

$$y_2 = \frac{6 - \sqrt{36 - 4(x^2 + 4x - 23)}}{2}.$$

Use a ZOOM SQUARE setting. The graph is shown on the right.

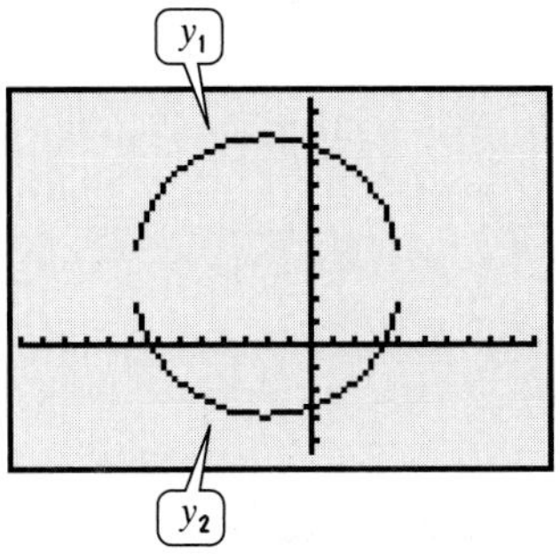

Check Point 6 Write in standard form and graph:

$$x^2 + y^2 + 4x - 4y - 1 = 0.$$

EXERCISE SET 2.7

Practice Exercises

In Exercises 1–18, find the distance between each pair of points. If necessary, round answers to two decimals places.

1. $(2, 3)$ and $(14, 8)$
2. $(5, 1)$ and $(8, 5)$
3. $(4, -1)$ and $(-6, 3)$
4. $(2, -3)$ and $(-1, 5)$
5. $(0, 0)$ and $(-3, 4)$
6. $(0, 0)$ and $(3, -4)$
7. $(-2, -6)$ and $(3, -4)$
8. $(-4, -1)$ and $(2, -3)$
9. $(0, -3)$ and $(4, 1)$
10. $(0, -2)$ and $(4, 3)$
11. $(3.5, 8.2)$ and $(-0.5, 6.2)$
12. $(2.6, 1.3)$ and $(1.6, -5.7)$
13. $(0, -\sqrt{3})$ and $(\sqrt{5}, 0)$
14. $(0, -\sqrt{2})$ and $(\sqrt{7}, 0)$
15. $(3\sqrt{3}, \sqrt{5})$ and $(-\sqrt{3}, 4\sqrt{5})$
16. $(2\sqrt{3}, \sqrt{6})$ and $(-\sqrt{3}, 5\sqrt{6})$
17. $\left(\frac{7}{3}, \frac{1}{5}\right)$ and $\left(\frac{1}{3}, \frac{6}{5}\right)$
18. $\left(-\frac{1}{4}, -\frac{1}{7}\right)$ and $\left(\frac{3}{4}, \frac{6}{7}\right)$

In Exercises 19–30, find the midpoint of each line segment with the given endpoints.

19. $(6, 8)$ and $(2, 4)$
20. $(10, 4)$ and $(2, 6)$
21. $(-2, -8)$ and $(-6, -2)$
22. $(-4, -7)$ and $(-1, -3)$
23. $(-3, -4)$ and $(6, -8)$
24. $(-2, -1)$ and $(-8, 6)$
25. $\left(-\frac{7}{2}, \frac{3}{2}\right)$ and $\left(-\frac{5}{2}, -\frac{11}{2}\right)$
26. $\left(-\frac{2}{5}, \frac{7}{15}\right)$ and $\left(-\frac{2}{5}, -\frac{4}{15}\right)$
27. $(8, 3\sqrt{5})$ and $(-6, 7\sqrt{5})$
28. $(7\sqrt{3}, -6)$ and $(3\sqrt{3}, -2)$
29. $(\sqrt{18}, -4)$ and $(\sqrt{2}, 4)$
30. $(\sqrt{50}, -6)$ and $(\sqrt{2}, 6)$

In Exercises 31–40, write the standard form of the equation of the circle with the given center and radius.

31. Center $(0, 0)$, $r = 7$ **32.** Center $(0, 0)$, $r = 8$

33. Center $(3, 2)$, $r = 5$ **34.** Center $(2, -1)$, $r = 4$

35. Center $(-1, 4)$, $r = 2$ **36.** Center $(-3, 5)$, $r = 3$

37. Center $(-3, -1)$, $r = \sqrt{3}$

38. Center $(-5, -3)$, $r = \sqrt{5}$

39. Center $(-4, 0)$, $r = 10$ **40.** Center $(-2, 0)$, $r = 6$

In Exercises 41–48, give the center and radius of the circle described by the equation and graph each equation. Use the graph to identify the relation's domain and range.

41. $x^2 + y^2 = 16$ **42.** $x^2 + y^2 = 49$

43. $(x - 3)^2 + (y - 1)^2 = 36$

44. $(x - 2)^2 + (y - 3)^2 = 16$

45. $(x + 3)^2 + (y - 2)^2 = 4$

46. $(x + 1)^2 + (y - 4)^2 = 25$

47. $(x + 2)^2 + (y + 2)^2 = 4$

48. $(x + 4)^2 + (y + 5)^2 = 36$

In Exercises 49–60, complete the square and write the equation in standard form. Then give the center and radius of each circle and graph the equation.

49. $x^2 + y^2 + 6x + 2y + 6 = 0$

50. $x^2 + y^2 + 8x + 4y + 16 = 0$

51. $x^2 + y^2 - 10x - 6y - 30 = 0$

52. $x^2 + y^2 - 4x - 12y - 9 = 0$

53. $x^2 + y^2 + 8x - 2y - 8 = 0$

54. $x^2 + y^2 + 12x - 6y - 4 = 0$

55. $x^2 - 2x + y^2 - 15 = 0$

56. $x^2 + y^2 - 6y - 7 = 0$

57. $x^2 + y^2 - x + 2y + 1 = 0$

58. $x^2 + y^2 + x + y - \frac{1}{2} = 0$

59. $x^2 + y^2 + 3x - 2y - 1 = 0$

60. $x^2 + y^2 + 3x + 5y + \frac{9}{4} = 0$

Practice Plus

In Exercises 61–62, a line segment through the center of each circle intersects the circle at the points shown.

a. *Find the coordinates of the circle's center.*

b. *Find the radius of the circle.*

c. *Use your answers from parts (a) and (b) to write the standard form of the circle's equation.*

61.

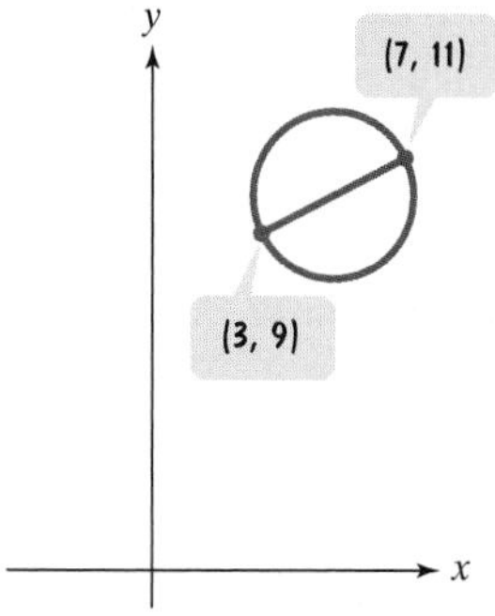

62.

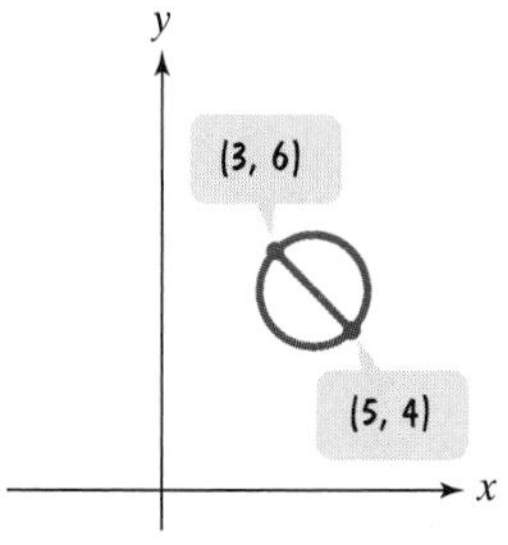

In Exercises 63–66, graph both equations in the same rectangular coordinate system and find all points of intersection. Then show that these ordered pairs satisfy the equations.

63. $x^2 + y^2 = 16$

$x - y = 4$

64. $x^2 + y^2 = 9$

$x - y = 3$

65. $(x - 2)^2 + (y + 3)^2 = 4$

$y = x - 3$

66. $(x - 3)^2 + (y + 1)^2 = 9$

$y = x - 1$

Application Exercises

67. A rectangular coordinate system with coordinates in miles is placed on the map in the figure shown. Bangkok has coordinates $(-115, 170)$ and Phnom Penh has coordinates $(65, 70)$. How long will it take a plane averaging 400 miles per hour to fly directly from one city to the other? Round to the nearest tenth of an hour. Approximately how many minutes is the flight?

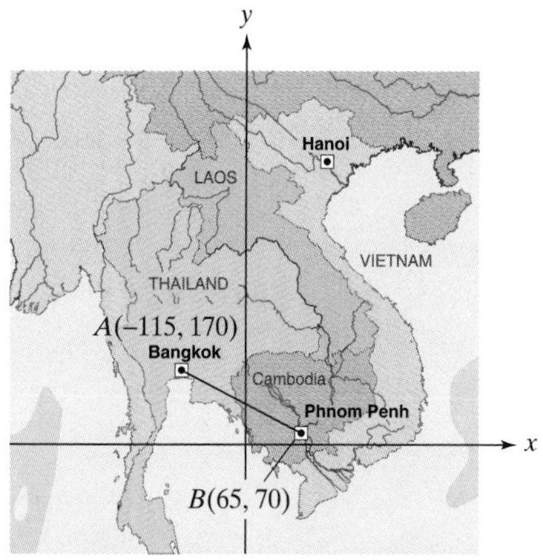

68. The Ferris wheel in the figure has a radius of 68 feet. The clearance between the wheel and the ground is 14 feet. The rectangular coordinate system shown has its origin on the ground directly below the center of the wheel. Use the coordinate system to write the equation of the circular wheel.

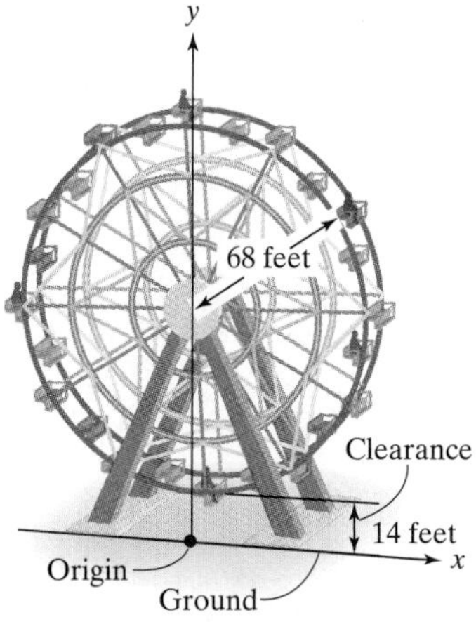

69. A rectangular coordinate system with coordinates in miles is placed with the origin at the center of Los Angeles. The figure indicates that the University of Southern California is located 2.4 miles west and 2.7 miles south of central Los Angeles. A seismograph on the campus shows that a small earthquake occurred. The quake's epicenter is estimated to be approximately 30 miles from the university. Write the standard form of the equation for the set of points that could be the epicenter of the quake.

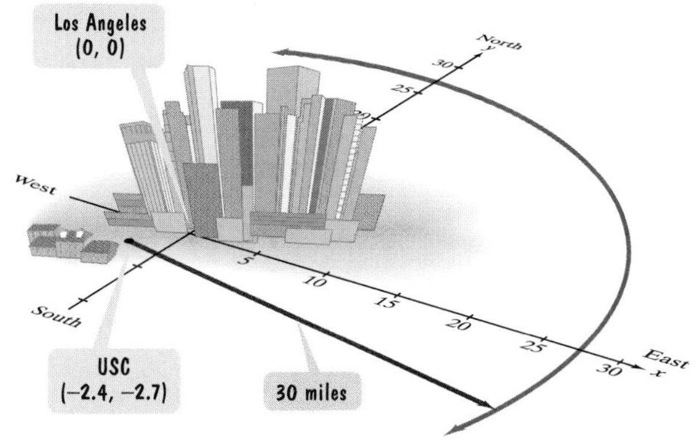

Writing in Mathematics

70. In your own words, describe how to find the distance between two points in the rectangular coordinate system.

71. In your own words, describe how to find the midpoint of a line segment if its endpoints are known.

72. What is a circle? Without using variables, describe how the definition of a circle can be used to obtain a form of its equation.

73. Give an example of a circle's equation in standard form. Describe how to find the center and radius for this circle.

74. How is the standard form of a circle's equation obtained from its general form?

75. Does $(x - 3)^2 + (y - 5)^2 = 0$ represent the equation of a circle? If not, describe the graph of this equation.

76. Does $(x - 3)^2 + (y - 5)^2 = -25$ represent the equation of a circle? What sort of set is the graph of this equation?

Technology Exercises

In Exercises 77–79, use a graphing utility to graph each circle whose equation is given.

77. $x^2 + y^2 = 25$

78. $(y + 1)^2 = 36 - (x - 3)^2$

79. $x^2 + 10x + y^2 - 4y - 20 = 0$

Critical Thinking Exercises

80. Which one of the following is true?

a. The equation of the circle whose center is at the origin with radius 16 is $x^2 + y^2 = 16$.

b. The graph of $(x - 3)^2 + (y + 5)^2 = 36$ is a circle with radius 6 centered at $(-3, 5)$.

c. The graph of $(x - 4) + (y + 6) = 25$ is a circle with radius 5 centered at $(4, -6)$.

d. None of the above is true.

81. Show that the points $A(1, 1 + d)$, $B(3, 3 + d)$, and $C(6, 6 + d)$ are collinear (lie along a straight line) by showing that the distance from A to B plus the distance from B to C equals the distance from A to C.

82. Prove the midpoint formula by using the following procedure.

a. Show that the distance between (x_1, y_1) and $\left(\frac{x_1 + x_2}{2}, \frac{y_1 + y_2}{2}\right)$ is equal to the distance between (x_2, y_2) and $\left(\frac{x_1 + x_2}{2}, \frac{y_1 + y_2}{2}\right)$.

b. Use the procedure from Exercise 81 and the distances from part (a) to show that the points (x_1, y_1), $\left(\frac{x_1 + x_2}{2}, \frac{y_1 + y_2}{2}\right)$, and (x_2, y_2) are collinear.

83. Find the area of the donut-shaped region bounded by the graphs of $(x - 2)^2 + (y + 3)^2 = 25$ and $(x - 2)^2 + (y + 3)^2 = 36$.

84. A **tangent line** to a circle is a line that intersects the circle at exactly one point. The tangent line is perpendicular to the radius of the circle at this point of contact. Write the point-slope form of the equation of a line tangent to the circle whose equation is $x^2 + y^2 = 25$ at the point $(3, -4)$.

Chapter 2
Summary, Review, and Test

Summary

DEFINITIONS AND CONCEPTS	EXAMPLES
2.1 Basics of Functions and Their Graphs	
a. A relation is any set of ordered pairs. The set of first components is the domain of the relation and the set of second components is the range.	Ex. 1, p. 187
b. A function is a correspondence from a first set, called the domain, to a second set, called the range, such that each element in the domain corresponds to exactly one element in the range. If any element in a relation's domain corresponds to more than one element in the range, the relation is not a function.	Ex. 2, p. 189

DEFINITIONS AND CONCEPTS	**EXAMPLES**
c. Functions are usually given in terms of equations involving x and y, in which x is the independent variable and y is the dependent variable. If an equation is solved for y and more than one value of y can be obtained for a given x, then the equation does not define y as a function of x. If an equation defines a function, the value of the function at x, $f(x)$, often replaces y.	Ex. 3, p. 190; Ex. 4, p. 191
d. The graph of a function is the graph of its ordered pairs.	Ex. 5, p. 192
e. The vertical line test for functions: If any vertical line intersects a graph in more than one point, the graph does not define y as a function of x.	Ex. 6, p. 193
f. The graph of a function can be used to determine the function's domain and its range. To find the domain, look for all the inputs on the x-axis that correspond to points on the graph. To find the range, look for all the outputs on the y-axis that correspond to points on the graph.	Ex. 8, p. 196
g. The zeros of a function, f, are the values of x for which $f(x) = 0$. At these values, the graph of f has x-intercepts. A function can have more than one x-intercept but at most one y-intercept.	Figure 2.11, p. 197

2.2 More on Functions and Their Graphs

a. The difference quotient is $$\frac{f(x + h) - f(x)}{h}, h \neq 0.$$	Ex. 1, p. 203
b. Piecewise functions are defined by two (or more) equations over a specified domain.	Ex. 2, p. 204
c. A function is increasing on intervals where its graph rises, decreasing on intervals where it falls, and constant on intervals where it neither rises nor falls. Precise definitions are given in the box on page 206.	Ex. 3, p. 206
d. If the graph of a function is given, we can often visually locate the number(s) at which the function has a relative maximum or relative minimum. Precise definitions are given in the box on page 207.	Figure 2.15, p. 207
e. The graph of an even function in which $f(-x) = f(x)$ is symmetric with respect to the y-axis. The graph of an odd function in which $f(-x) = -f(x)$ is symmetric with respect to the origin.	Ex. 4, p. 208
f. The graph of $f(x) = \text{int}(x)$, where $\text{int}(x)$ is the greatest integer that is less than or equal to x, has function values that form discontinuous steps, shown in Figure 2.20 on page 210. If $n \leq x < n + 1$, where n is an integer, then $\text{int}(x) = n$.	

2.3 Linear Functions and Slope

a. The slope, m, of the line through (x_1, y_1) and (x_2, y_2) is $m = \dfrac{y_2 - y_1}{x_2 - x_1}$.	Ex. 1, p. 217
b. Equations of lines include point-slope form, $y - y_1 = m(x - x_1)$, slope-intercept form, $y = mx + b$, and general form, $Ax + By + C = 0$. The equation of a horizontal line is $y = b$; a vertical line is $x = a$. A vertical line is not a linear function.	Ex. 2, p. 219; Ex. 3, p. 219; Ex. 5, p. 223
c. Linear functions in the form $f(x) = mx + b$ can be graphed using the slope, m, and the y-intercept, b. (See the box on page 220.) Linear equations in the general form $Ax + By + C = 0$ can be solved for y and graphed using the slope and the y-intercept. Intercepts can also be used to graph $Ax + By + C = 0$. (See the box on page 224.)	Ex. 4, p. 221; Ex. 6, p. 224; Ex. 7, p. 224

2.4 More on Slope

a. Parallel lines have equal slopes. Perpendicular lines have slopes that are negative reciprocals.	Ex. 1, p. 231; Ex. 2, p. 233
b. The slope of a linear function is the rate of change of the dependent variable per unit change of the independent variable.	Ex. 3, p. 234
c. The average rate of change of f from x_1 to x_2 is $$\frac{f(x_2) - f(x_1)}{x_2 - x_1}.$$	Ex. 4, p. 235; Ex. 5, p. 237

DEFINITIONS AND CONCEPTS	EXAMPLES
2.5 Transformations of Functions	
a. Table 2.3 on page 242 shows the graphs of the constant function, $f(x) = c$, the identity function, $f(x) = x$, the absolute value function, $f(x) = \lvert x \rvert$, the standard quadratic function, $f(x) = x^2$, the square root function, $f(x) = \sqrt{x}$, the standard cubic function, $f(x) = x^3$, and the cube root function, $f(x) = \sqrt[3]{x}$. The table also lists characteristics of each function.	Ex. 1, p. 243;
b. Table 2.4 on page 250 summarizes how to graph a function using vertical shifts, $y = f(x) \pm c$, horizontal shifts, $y = f(x \pm c)$, reflections about the x-axis, $y = -f(x)$, reflections about the y-axis, $y = f(-x)$, vertical stretching, $y = cf(x), c > 1$, vertical shrinking, $y = cf(x), 0 < c < 1$, horizontal shrinking, $y = f(cx), c > 1$, and horizontal stretching, $y = f(cx), 0 < c < 1$.	Ex. 2, p. 245; Ex. 3, p. 246; Ex. 4, p. 247; Ex. 5, p. 247; Ex. 6, p. 248; Ex. 7, p. 249
c. A function involving more than one transformation can be graphed in the following order: (1) horizontal shifting; (2) stretching or shrinking; (3) reflecting; (4) vertical shifting.	Ex. 8, p. 251; Ex. 9, p. 252
2.6 Combinations of Functions; Composite Functions	
a. If a function f does not model data or verbal conditions, its domain is the largest set of real numbers for which the value of $f(x)$ is a real number. Exclude from a function's domain real numbers that cause division by zero and real numbers that result in a square root of a negative number.	Ex. 1, p. 258
b. When functions are given as equations, they can be added, subtracted, multiplied, or divided by performing operations with the algebraic expressions that appear on the right side of the equations. Definitions for the sum $f + g$, the difference $f - g$, the product fg, and the quotient $\frac{f}{g}$ functions, with domains $D_f \cap D_g$, and $g(x) \neq 0$ for the quotient function, are given in the box on page 260.	Ex. 2, p. 260; Ex. 3, p. 261
c. The composition of functions f and g, $f \circ g$, is defined by $(f \circ g)(x) = f(g(x))$. The domain of the composite function $f \circ g$ is given in the box on page 263. This composite function is obtained by replacing each occurrence of x in the equation for f with $g(x)$.	Ex. 4, p. 264; Ex. 5, p. 265
2.7 Distance and Midpoint Formulas; Circles	
a. The distance, d, between the points (x_1, y_1) and (x_2, y_2) is given by $d = \sqrt{(x_2 - x_1)^2 + (y_2 - y_1)^2}$.	Ex. 1, p. 270
b. The midpoint of the line segment whose endpoints are (x_1, y_1) and (x_2, y_2) is the point with coordinates $\left(\frac{x_1 + x_2}{2}, \frac{y_1 + y_2}{2}\right)$.	Ex. 2, p. 271
c. The standard form of the equation of a circle with center (h, k) and radius r is $(x - h)^2 + (y - k)^2 = r^2$.	Ex. 3, p. 272; Ex. 4, p. 273; Ex. 5, p. 273
d. The general form of the equation of a circle is $x^2 + y^2 + Dx + Ey + F = 0$.	
e. To convert from the general form to the standard form of a circle's equation, complete the square on x and y.	Ex. 6, p. 274

Review Exercises

2.1 and 2.2

In Exercises 1–3, determine whether each relation is a function. Give the domain and range for each relation.

1. $\{(2, 7), (3, 7), (5, 7)\}$

2. $\{(1, 10), (2, 500), (13, \pi)\}$

3. $\{(12, 13), (14, 15), (12, 19)\}$

In Exercises 4–6, determine whether each equation defines y as a function of x.

4. $2x + y = 8$ **5.** $3x^2 + y = 14$

6. $2x + y^2 = 6$

In Exercises 7–10, evaluate each function at the given values of the independent variable and simplify.

7. $f(x) = 5 - 7x$

a. $f(4)$ **b.** $f(x + 3)$ **c.** $f(-x)$

8. $g(x) = 3x^2 - 5x + 2$

a. $g(0)$ **b.** $g(-2)$

c. $g(x - 1)$ **d.** $g(-x)$

9. $g(x) = \begin{cases} \sqrt{x - 4} & \text{if } x \geq 4 \\ 4 - x & \text{if } x < 4 \end{cases}$

a. $g(13)$ **b.** $g(0)$ **c.** $g(-3)$

10. $f(x) = \begin{cases} \dfrac{x^2 - 1}{x - 1} & \text{if } x \neq 1 \\ 12 & \text{if } x = 1 \end{cases}$

a. $f(-2)$ **b.** $f(1)$ **c.** $f(2)$

In Exercises 11–16, use the vertical line test to identify graphs in which y is a function of x.

11.

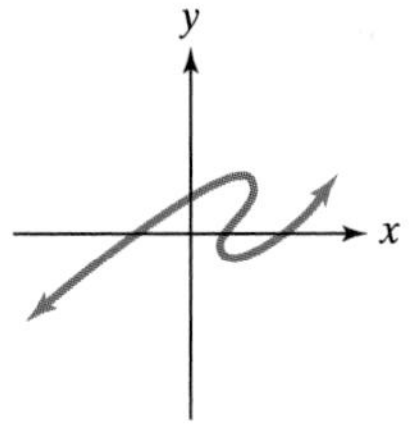

12.

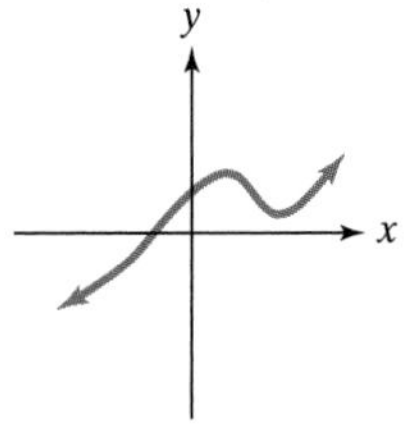

13.

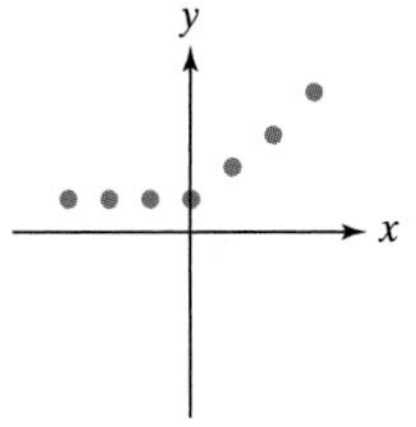

14.

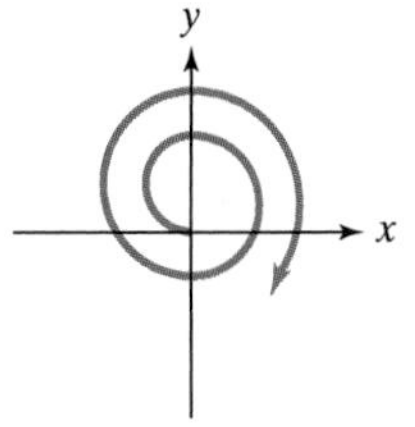

15.

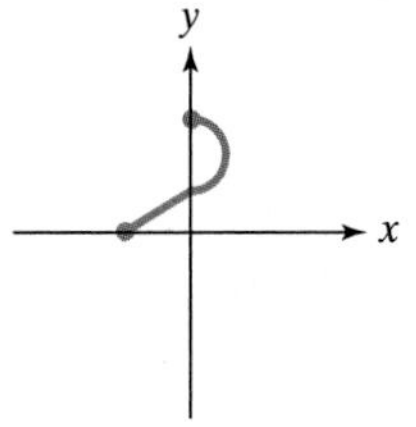

16.

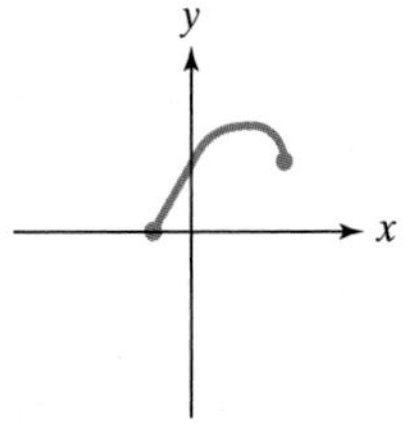

In Exercises 17–18, find and simplify the difference quotient

$$\frac{f(x + h) - f(x)}{h}, \quad h \neq 0$$

for the given function.

17. $f(x) = 8x - 11$ **18.** $f(x) = -2x^2 + x + 10$

In Exercises 19–21, use the graph to determine **a.** *the function's domain;* **b.** *the function's range;* **c.** *the x-intercepts, if any;* **d.** *the y-intercept, if any;* **e.** *intervals on which the function is increasing, decreasing, or constant; and* **f.** *the function values indicated below the graphs.*

19.

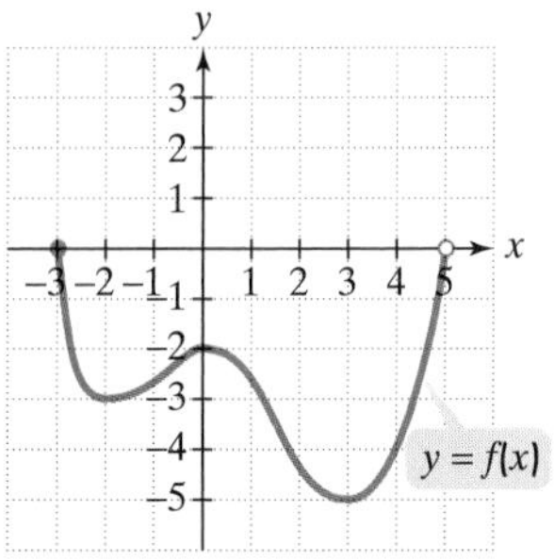

$f(-2) = ?$ $f(3) = ?$

20.

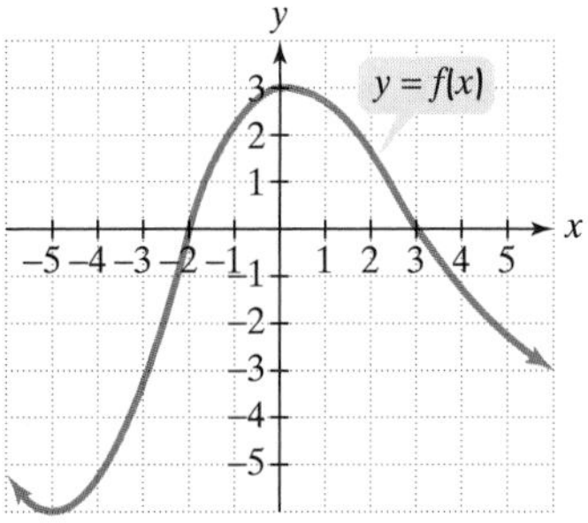

$f(-2) = ?$ $f(6) = ?$

21.

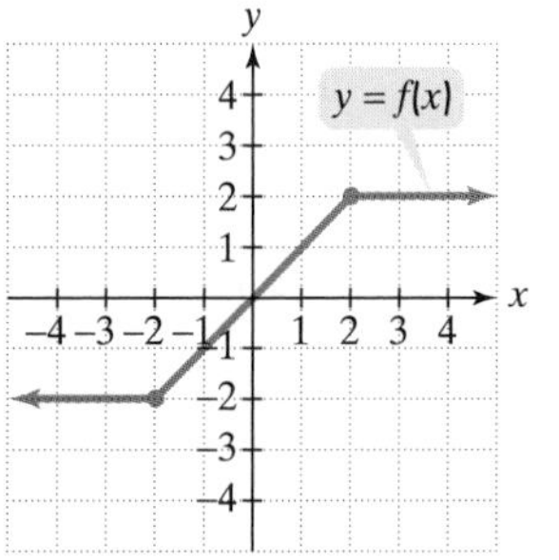

$f(-9) = ?$ $f(14) = ?$

In Exercises 22–23, find each of the following:

a. *The numbers, if any, at which f has a relative maximum. What are these relative maxima?*

b. *The numbers, if any, at which f has a relative minimum. What are these relative minima?*

22. Use the graph in Exercise 19.

23. Use the graph in Exercise 20.

In Exercises 24–26, determine whether each function is even, odd, or neither. State each function's symmetry. If you are using a graphing utility, graph the function and verify its possible symmetry.

24. $f(x) = x^3 - 5x$ **25.** $f(x) = x^4 - 2x^2 + 1$

26. $f(x) = 2x\sqrt{1 - x^2}$

27. The graph shows the height, in meters, of an eagle in terms of its time, in seconds, in flight.

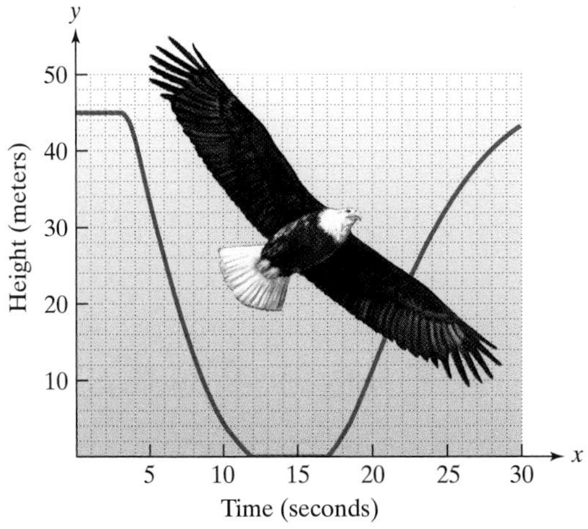

a. Is the eagle's height a function of time? Use the graph to explain why or why not.

b. On which interval is the function decreasing? Describe what this means in practical terms.

c. On which intervals is the function constant? What does this mean for each of these intervals?

d. On which interval is the function increasing? What does this mean?

28. A cargo service charges a flat fee of \$5 plus \$1.50 for each pound or fraction of a pound. Graph shipping cost, $C(x)$, in dollars, as a function of weight, x, in pounds, for $0 < x \le 5$.

2.3 and 2.4

In Exercises 29–32, find the slope of the line passing through each pair of points or state that the slope is undefined. Then indicate whether the line through the points rises, falls, is horizontal, or is vertical.

29. $(3, 2)$ and $(5, 1)$

30. $(-1, -2)$ and $(-3, -4)$

31. $\left(-3, \frac{1}{4}\right)$ and $\left(6, \frac{1}{4}\right)$

32. $(-2, 5)$ and $(-2, 10)$

In Exercises 33–36, use the given conditions to write an equation for each line in point-slope form and slope-intercept form.

33. Passing through $(-3, 2)$ with slope -6

34. Passing through $(1, 6)$ and $(-1, 2)$

35. Passing through $(4, -7)$ and parallel to the line whose equation is $3x + y - 9 = 0$

36. Passing through $(-3, 6)$ and perpendicular to the line whose equation is $y = \frac{1}{3}x + 4$

37. Write the general form of the equation of the line passing through $(-12, -1)$ and perpendicular to the line whose equation is $6x - y - 4 = 0$.

In Exercises 38–41, give the slope and y-intercept of each line whose equation is given. Then graph the line.

38. $y = \frac{2}{5}x - 1$

39. $f(x) = -4x + 5$

40. $2x + 3y + 6 = 0$

41. $2y - 8 = 0$

42. Graph using intercepts: $2x - 5y - 10 = 0$.

43. Graph: $2x - 10 = 0$.

44. You can click a mouse and bet the house. The points in the graph show the dizzying growth of online gambling. With more than 1800 sites, the industry has become the Web's biggest moneymaker.

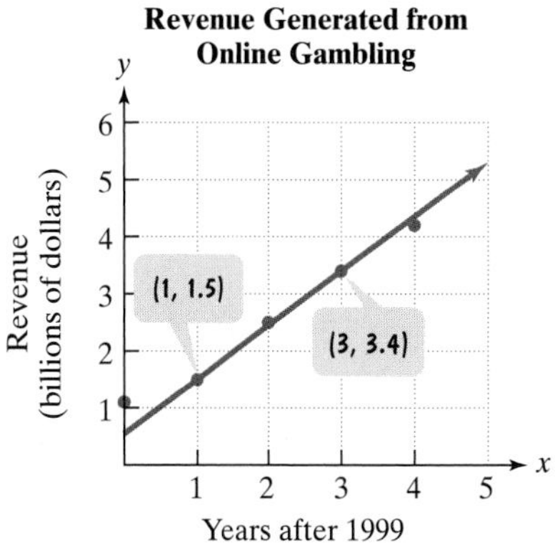

Source: Newsweek

a. Use the two points whose coordinates are shown by the voice balloons to find the point-slope form of the equation of the line that models revenue from online gambling, y, in billions of dollars, x years after 1999.

b. Write the equation in part (a) in slope-intercept form.

c. In 2003, nearly \$3.5 billion was lost on Internet bets, triggering a sharp backlash that threatened to shut down Internet wagering. If this crackdown on the industry is not successful, use your slope-intercept model to predict the billions of dollars in revenue from online gambling in 2009.

45. The graph shows new AIDS diagnoses among the general U.S. population, y, for year x, where $1999 \le x \le 2003$.

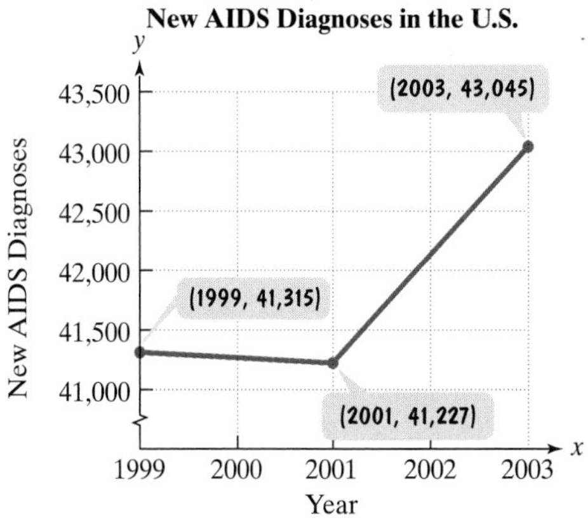

Source: Centers for Disease Control

a. Find the slope of the line passing through (1999, 41,315) and (2001, 41,227). Then express the slope as a rate of change with the proper units attached.

b. Find the slope of the line passing through (2001, 41,227) and (2003, 43,045). Then express the slope as a rate of change.

c. Draw a line passing through (1999, 41,315) and (2003, 43,045) and find its slope. Is the slope the average of the slopes of the lines that you found in parts (a) and (b)? Explain your answer.

46. Find the average rate of change of $f(x) = x^2 - 4x$ from $x_1 = 5$ to $x_2 = 9$.

2.5

In Exercises 47–51, use the graph of $y = f(x)$ to graph each function g.

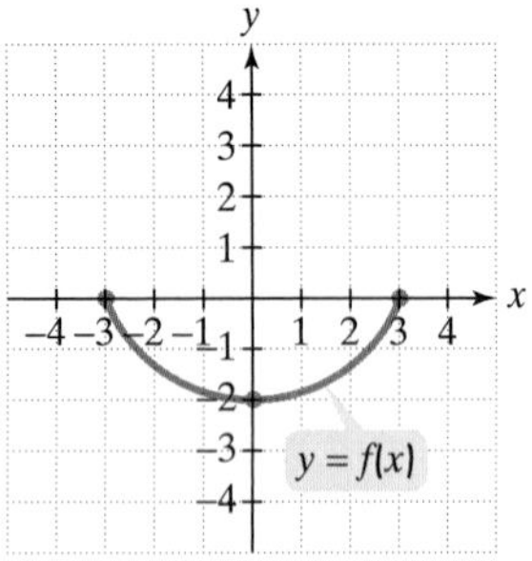

47. $g(x) = f(x + 2) + 3$ **48.** $g(x) = \frac{1}{2}f(x - 1)$

49. $g(x) = -f(2x)$ **50.** $g(x) = 2f\left(\frac{1}{2}x\right)$

51. $g(x) = -f(-x) - 1$

In Exercises 52–55, begin by graphing the standard quadratic function, $f(x) = x^2$. Then use transformations of this graph to graph the given function.

52. $g(x) = x^2 + 2$ **53.** $h(x) = (x + 2)^2$

54. $r(x) = -(x + 1)^2$ **55.** $y(x) = \frac{1}{2}(x - 1)^2 + 1$

In Exercises 56–58, begin by graphing the square root function, $f(x) = \sqrt{x}$. Then use transformations of this graph to graph the given function.

56. $g(x) = \sqrt{x + 3}$ **57.** $h(x) = \sqrt{3 - x}$

58. $r(x) = 2\sqrt{x + 2}$

In Exercises 59–61, begin by graphing the absolute value function, $f(x) = |x|$. Then use transformations of this graph to graph the given function.

59. $g(x) = |x + 2| - 3$ **60.** $h(x) = -|x - 1| + 1$

61. $r(x) = \frac{1}{2}|x + 2|$

In Exercises 62–64, begin by graphing the standard cubic function, $f(x) = x^3$. Then use transformations of this graph to graph the given function.

62. $g(x) = \frac{1}{2}(x - 1)^3$ **63.** $h(x) = -(x + 1)^3$

64. $r(x) = \frac{1}{4}x^3 - 1$

In Exercises 65–67, begin by graphing the cube root function, $f(x) = \sqrt[3]{x}$. Then use transformations of this graph to graph the given function.

65. $g(x) = \sqrt[3]{x + 2} - 1$ **66.** $h(x) = -\sqrt[3]{2x}$

67. $r(x) = -2\sqrt[3]{-x}$

2.6

In Exercises 68–73, find the domain of each function.

68. $f(x) = x^2 + 6x - 3$ **69.** $g(x) = \frac{4}{x - 7}$

70. $h(x) = \sqrt{8 - 2x}$ **71.** $f(x) = \frac{x}{x^2 + 4x - 21}$

72. $g(x) = \frac{\sqrt{x - 2}}{x - 5}$ **73.** $f(x) = \sqrt{x - 1} + \sqrt{x + 5}$

In Exercises 74–76, find $f + g$, $f - g$, fg, and $\frac{f}{g}$. Determine the domain for each function.

74. $f(x) = 3x - 1, \quad g(x) = x - 5$

75. $f(x) = x^2 + x + 1, \quad g(x) = x^2 - 1$

76. $f(x) = \sqrt{x + 7}, \quad g(x) = \sqrt{x - 2}$

In Exercises 77–78, find **a.** $(f \circ g)(x)$; **b.** $(g \circ f)(x)$; **c.** $(f \circ g)(3)$.

77. $f(x) = x^2 + 3, \quad g(x) = 4x - 1$

78. $f(x) = \sqrt{x}, \quad g(x) = x + 1$

In Exercises 79–80, find **a.** $(f \circ g)(x)$; **b.** *the domain of* $(f \circ g)$.

79. $f(x) = \frac{x + 1}{x - 2}, \quad g(x) = \frac{1}{x}$

80. $f(x) = \sqrt{x - 1}, \quad g(x) = x + 3$

In Exercises 81–82, express the given function h as a composition of two functions f and g so that $h(x) = (f \circ g)(x)$.

81. $h(x) = (x^2 + 2x - 1)^4$

82. $h(x) = \sqrt[3]{7x + 4}$

2.7

In Exercises 83–84, find the distance between each pair of points. If necessary, round answers to two decimal places.

83. $(-2, 3)$ and $(3, -9)$ **84.** $(-4, 3)$ and $(-2, 5)$

In Exercises 85–86, find the midpoint of each line segment with the given endpoints.

85. $(2, 6)$ and $(-12, 4)$ **86.** $(4, -6)$ and $(-15, 2)$

In Exercises 87–88, write the standard form of the equation of the circle with the given center and radius.

87. Center $(0, 0)$, $r = 3$ **88.** Center $(-2, 4)$, $r = 6$

In Exercises 89–91, give the center and radius of each circle and graph its equation. Use the graph to identify the relation's domain and range.

89. $x^2 + y^2 = 1$ **90.** $(x + 2)^2 + (y - 3)^2 = 9$

91. $x^2 + y^2 - 4x + 2y - 4 = 0$

Chapter 2 Test

1. List by letter all relations that are not functions.

a. $\{(7, 5), (8, 5), (9, 5)\}$

b. $\{(5, 7), (5, 8), (5, 9)\}$

c.

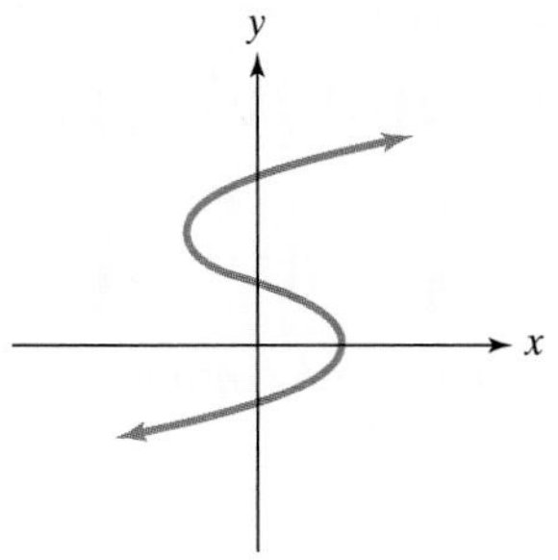

d. $x^2 + y^2 = 100$

e.

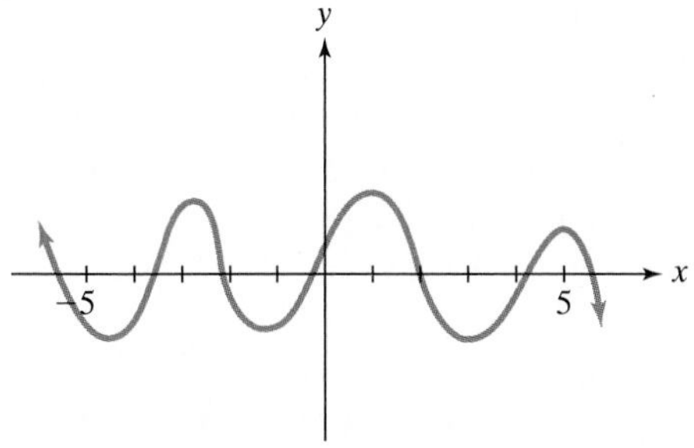

2. Use the graph of $y = f(x)$ to solve this exercise.

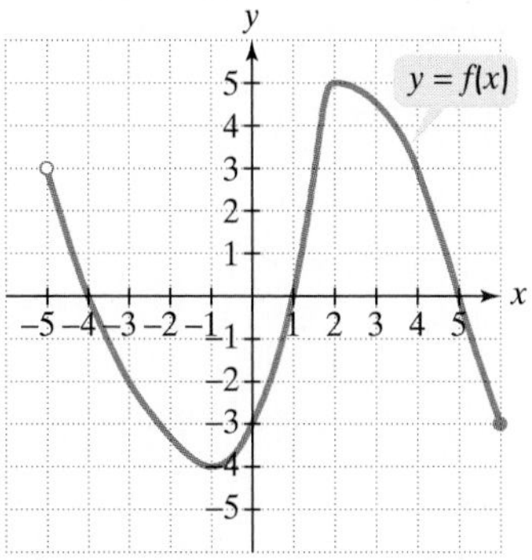

a. What is $f(4) - f(-3)$?

b. What is the domain of f?

c. What is the range of f?

d. On which interval or intervals is f increasing?

e. On which interval or intervals is f decreasing?

f. For what number does f have a relative maximum? What is the relative maximum?

g. For what number does f have a relative minimum? What is the relative minimum?

h. What are the x-intercepts?

i. What is the y-intercept?

3. Use the graph of $y = f(x)$ to solve this exercise.

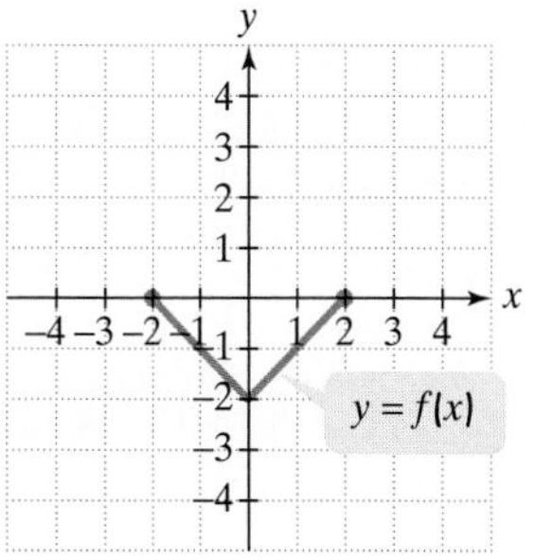

a. What are the zeros of f?

b. Find the value(s) of x for which $f(x) = -1$.

c. Find the value(s) of x for which $f(x) = -2$.

d. Is f even, odd, or neither?

e. Is $f(0)$ a relative maximum, a relative minimum, or neither?

f. Graph $g(x) = f(x + 1) - 1$.

g. Graph $h(x) = \frac{1}{2}f\left(\frac{1}{2}x\right)$.

h. Graph $r(x) = -f(-x) + 1$.

i. Find the average rate of change of f from $x_1 = -2$ to $x_2 = 1$.

In Exercises 4–12, graph each equation in a rectangular coordinate system. If two functions are indicated, graph both in the same system. Then use your graphs to identify each relation's domain and range.

4. $x + y = 4$

5. $x^2 + y^2 = 4$

6. $f(x) = 4$

7. $f(x) = -\frac{1}{3}x + 2$

8. $(x + 2)^2 + (y - 1)^2 = 9$

9. $f(x) = \begin{cases} 2 & \text{if } x \le 0 \\ -1 & \text{if } x > 0 \end{cases}$

10. $x^2 + y^2 + 4x - 6y - 3 = 0$

11. $f(x) = |x|$ and $g(x) = \frac{1}{2}|x + 1| - 2$

12. $f(x) = x^2$ and $g(x) = -(x - 1)^2 + 4$

In Exercises 13–20, let $f(x) = x^2 - x - 4$ and $g(x) = 2x - 6$.

13. Find $f(x - 1)$.

14. Find $\dfrac{f(x + h) - f(x)}{h}$.

15. Find $(g - f)(x)$.

16. Find $\left(\dfrac{f}{g}\right)(x)$ and its domain.

17. Find $(f \circ g)(x)$.

18. Find $(g \circ f)(x)$.

19. Find $g(f(-1))$.

20. Find $f(-x)$. Is f even, odd, or neither?

In Exercises 21–22, use the given conditions to write an equation for each line in point-slope form and slope-intercept form.

21. Passing through $(2, 1)$ and $(-1, -8)$

22. Passing through $(-4, 6)$ and perpendicular to the line whose equation is $y = -\frac{1}{4}x + 5$

23. Write the general form of the equation of the line passing through $(-7, -10)$ and parallel to the line whose equation is $4x + 2y - 5 = 0$.

24. When adjusted for inflation, the federal minimum wage from 1997 through 2003 continued to decrease. The points in the scatter plot show the minimum hourly inflation-adjusted wage for this period. Also shown is a line that passes through or near the points.

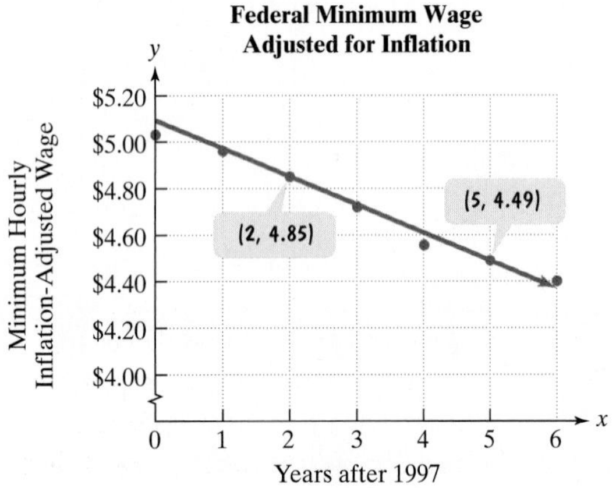

Source: www.dul.gov/esa/pudha/minwage

a. Use the two points whose coordinates are shown by the voice balloons to find the point-slope form of the equation of the line that models the minimum hourly inflation-adjusted wage, y, x years after 1997.

b. Write the equation in part (a) in slope-intercept form. Use function notation.

c. Use the linear function to predict the minimum hourly inflation-adjusted wage in 2007.

25. Find the average rate of change of $f(x) = 3x^2 - 5$ from $x_1 = 6$ to $x_2 = 10$.

26. If $g(x) = \begin{cases} \sqrt{x - 3} & \text{if } x \geq 3 \\ 3 - x & \text{if } x < 3 \end{cases}$, find $g(-1)$ and $g(7)$.

In Exercises 27–28, find the domain of each function.

27. $f(x) = \dfrac{3}{x + 5} + \dfrac{7}{x - 1}$

28. $f(x) = 3\sqrt{x + 5} + 7\sqrt{x - 1}$

29. If $f(x) = \dfrac{7}{x - 4}$ and $g(x) = \dfrac{2}{x}$, find $(f \circ g)(x)$ and the domain of $f \circ g$.

30. Express $h(x) = (2x + 3)^7$ as a composition of two functions f and g so that $h(x) = (f \circ g)(x)$.

31. Find the length and the midpoint of the line segment whose endpoints are $(2, -2)$ and $(5, 2)$.

Cumulative Review Exercises (Chapters 1–2)

Use the graph of $y = f(x)$ to solve Exercises 1–5.

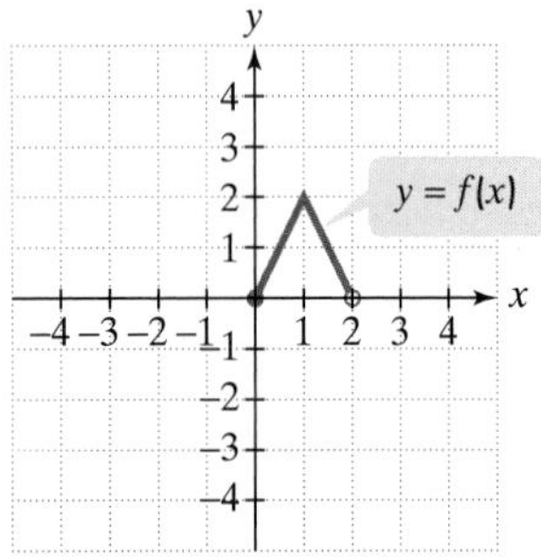

1. Find the domain and the range of f.

2. For what value(s) of x is $f(x) = 1$?

3. Find the relative maximum.

4. Graph $g(x) = f(x - 1) + 1$.

5. Graph $h(x) = -2f\left(\frac{1}{2}x\right)$.

In Exercises 6–10, solve each equation or inequality.

6. $(x + 3)(x - 4) = 8$

7. $3(4x - 1) = 4 - 6(x - 3)$

8. $\sqrt{x} + 2 = x$

9. $x^{\frac{2}{3}} - x^{\frac{1}{3}} - 6 = 0$

10. $\dfrac{x}{2} - 3 \leq \dfrac{x}{4} + 2$

In Exercises 11–13, graph each equation in a rectangular coordinate system. If two functions are indicated, graph both in the same system. Then use your graphs to identify each relation's domain and range.

11. $3x - 6y - 12 = 0$

12. $(x - 2)^2 + (y + 1)^2 = 4$

13. $f(x) = \sqrt[3]{x}$ and $g(x) = \sqrt[3]{x - 3} + 4$

In Exercises 14–15, let $f(x) = 4 - x^2$ and $g(x) = x + 5$.

14. Find $\dfrac{f(x + h) - f(x)}{h}$ and simplify.

15. Find all values of x satisfying $(f \circ g)(x) = 0$.

16. Write the point-slope form, the slope-intercept form, and the general form of the line passing through $(-2, 5)$ and perpendicular to the line whose equation is $y = -\frac{1}{4}x + \frac{1}{3}$.

17. You invested \$6000 in two accounts paying 7% and 9% annual interest, respectively. At the end of the year, the total interest from these investments was \$510. How much was invested at each rate?

18. For a summer sales job, you are choosing between two pay arrangements: a weekly salary of \$200 plus 5% commission on sales, or a straight 15% commission. For how many dollars of sales will the earnings be the same regardless of the pay arrangement?

19. The length of a rectangular garden is 2 feet more than twice its width. If 22 feet of fencing is needed to enclose the garden, what are its dimensions?

CHAPTER 3

Systems of Equations and Inequalities

MOST THINGS IN LIFE DEPEND ON *many variables. Temperature and precipitation are two variables that have a critical effect on whether regions are forests, grasslands, or deserts. Airlines deal with numerous variables during weather disruptions at large connecting airports. They must solve the problem of putting their operations back together again to minimize the cost of the disruption and passenger inconvenience. In this chapter, forests, grasslands, and airline service are viewed in the same way—situations with several variables. You will learn methods for modeling and solving problems in these situations.*

A MAJOR WEATHER DISRUPTION delayed your flight for hours, but you finally made it. You are in Yosemite National Park in California, surrounded by evergreen forests, alpine meadows, and sheer walls of granite. Soaring cliffs, plunging waterfalls, gigantic trees, rugged canyons, mountains, and valleys stand in stark contrast to the angry chaos at the airport. This is so different from where you live and attend college, a region in which grasslands predominate.

SECTION 3.1 Systems of Linear Equations in Two Variables

Objectives

1. Decide whether an ordered pair is a solution of a linear system.
2. Solve linear systems by substitution.
3. Solve linear systems by addition.
4. Identify systems that do not have exactly one ordered-pair solution.
5. Solve problems using systems of linear equations.

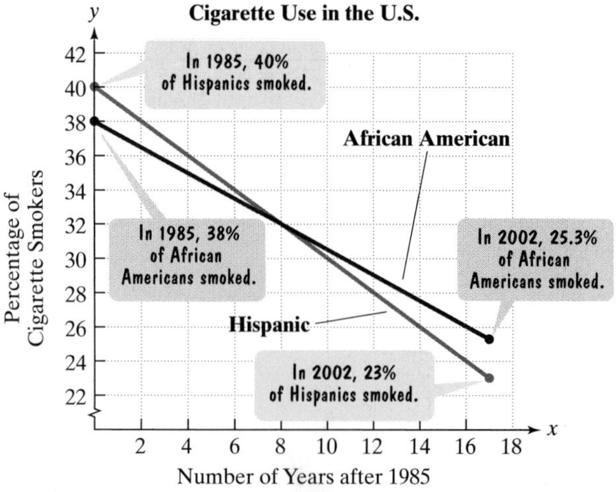

Figure 3.1

Source: Dept. of Health and Human Services

Although we still see celebrities smoking in movies, in music videos, and on television, there has been a remarkable decline in the percentage of cigarette smokers in the United States. The decline among African Americans and Hispanics, illustrated in Figure 3.1, can be analyzed using a pair of linear models in two variables.

In the first two sections of this chapter, you will learn to model your world with two equations in two variables and three equations in three variables. The methods you learn for solving these systems provide the foundation for solving complex problems involving thousands of equations containing thousands of variables. In the exercise set, you will apply these methods to analyze the linear decrease in cigarette use among whites, African Americans, and Hispanics.

1 Decide whether an ordered pair is a solution of a linear system.

Systems of Linear Equations and Their Solutions

We have seen that all equations in the form $Ax + By = C$ are straight lines when graphed. Two such equations are called a **system of linear equations** or a **linear system**. **A solution to a system of linear equations in two variables** is an ordered pair that satisfies both equations in the system. For example, $(3, 4)$ satisfies the system

$$x + y = 7 \qquad (3 + 4 \text{ is, indeed, } 7.)$$
$$x - y = -1. \qquad (3 - 4 \text{ is, indeed, } -1.)$$

Thus, $(3, 4)$ satisfies both equations and is a solution of the system. The solution can be described by saying that $x = 3$ and $y = 4$. The solution can also be described using set notation. The solution set to the system is $\{(3, 4)\}$—that is, the set consisting of the ordered pair $(3, 4)$.

A system of linear equations can have exactly one solution, no solution, or infinitely many solutions. We begin with systems that have exactly one solution.

EXAMPLE 1 Determining Whether Ordered Pairs Are Solutions of a System

Consider the system:

$$x + 2y = 2$$
$$x - 2y = 6.$$

Determine if each ordered pair is a solution of the system:

a. $(4, -1)$ **b.** $(-4, 3)$.

Solution

a. We begin by determining whether $(4, -1)$ is a solution. Because 4 is the x-coordinate and -1 is the y-coordinate of $(4, -1)$, we replace x with 4 and y with -1.

$$\begin{aligned} x + 2y &= 2 \\ 4 + 2(-1) &\stackrel{?}{=} 2 \\ 4 + (-2) &\stackrel{?}{=} 2 \\ 2 &= 2, \quad \text{true} \end{aligned} \qquad \begin{aligned} x - 2y &= 6 \\ 4 - 2(-1) &\stackrel{?}{=} 6 \\ 4 - (-2) &\stackrel{?}{=} 6 \\ 4 + 2 &\stackrel{?}{=} 6 \\ 6 &= 6, \quad \text{true} \end{aligned}$$

The pair $(4, -1)$ satisfies both equations: It makes each equation true. Thus, the ordered pair is a solution of the system.

b. To determine whether $(-4, 3)$ is a solution, we replace x with -4 and y with 3.

$$\begin{aligned} x + 2y &= 2 \\ -4 + 2 \cdot 3 &\stackrel{?}{=} 2 \\ -4 + 6 &\stackrel{?}{=} 2 \\ 2 &= 2, \quad \text{true} \end{aligned} \qquad \begin{aligned} x - 2y &= 6 \\ -4 - 2 \cdot 3 &\stackrel{?}{=} 6 \\ -4 - 6 &\stackrel{?}{=} 6 \\ -10 &= 6, \quad \text{false} \end{aligned}$$

The pair $(-4, 3)$ fails to satisfy *both* equations: It does not make both equations true. Thus, the ordered pair is not a solution of the system.

Study Tip

When solving linear systems by graphing, neatly drawn graphs are essential for determining points of intersection.

- Use rectangular coordinate graph paper.
- Use a ruler or straightedge.
- Use a pencil with a sharp point.

The solution of a system of linear equations can sometimes be found by graphing both of the equations in the same rectangular coordinate system. For a system with one solution, the **coordinates of the point of intersection give the system's solution**. For example, the system in Example 1,

$$\begin{aligned} x + 2y &= 2 \\ x - 2y &= 6 \end{aligned}$$

is graphed in Figure 3.2. The solution of the system, $(4, -1)$, corresponds to the point of intersection of the lines.

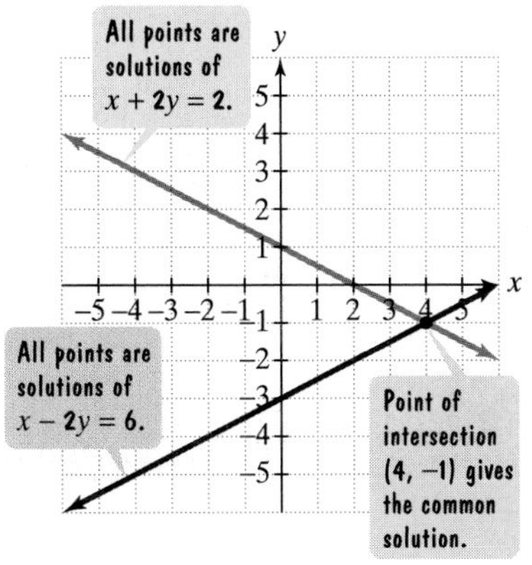

Figure 3.2 Visualizing a system's solution

Check Point 1 Consider the system:

$$\begin{aligned} 2x - 3y &= -4 \\ 2x + y &= 4. \end{aligned}$$

Determine if each ordered pair is a solution of the system:

a. $(1, 2)$ **b.** $(7, 6)$.

2 Solve linear systems by substitution.

Eliminating a Variable Using the Substitution Method

Finding the solution to a linear system by graphing equations may not be easy to do. For example, a solution of $\left(-\frac{2}{3}, \frac{157}{29}\right)$ would be difficult to "see" as an intersection point on a graph.

Let's consider a method that does not depend on finding a system's solution visually: the substitution method. This method involves converting the system to one equation in one variable by an appropriate substitution.

Study Tip

In step 1, you can choose which variable to isolate in which equation. If possible, solve for a variable whose coefficient is 1 or −1 to avoid working with fractions.

Solving Linear Systems by Substitution

1. Solve either of the equations for one variable in terms of the other. (If one of the equations is already in this form, you can skip this step.)
2. Substitute the expression found in step 1 into the *other* equation. This will result in an equation in one variable.
3. Solve the equation containing one variable.
4. Back-substitute the value found in step 3 into one of the original equations. Simplify and find the value of the remaining variable.
5. Check the proposed solution in both of the system's given equations.

EXAMPLE 2 Solving a System by Substitution

Solve by the substitution method:

$$5x - 4y = 9$$
$$x - 2y = -3.$$

Solution

Step 1 Solve either of the equations for one variable in terms of the other. We begin by isolating one of the variables in either of the equations. By solving for x in the second equation, which has a coefficient of 1, we can avoid fractions.

$x - 2y = -3$	This is the second equation in the given system.
$x = 2y - 3$	Solve for x by adding 2y to both sides.

Step 2 Substitute the expression from step 1 into the other equation. We substitute $2y - 3$ for x in the first equation.

$$x = \boxed{2y - 3} \qquad 5\boxed{x} - 4y = 9$$

This gives us an equation in one variable, namely

$$5(2y - 3) - 4y = 9.$$

The variable x has been eliminated.

Step 3 Solve the resulting equation containing one variable.

$5(2y - 3) - 4y = 9$	This is the equation containing one variable.
$10y - 15 - 4y = 9$	Apply the distributive property.
$6y - 15 = 9$	Combine like terms.
$6y = 24$	Add 15 to both sides.
$y = 4$	Divide both sides by 6.

Study Tip

The equation from step 1, in which one variable is expressed in terms of the other, is equivalent to one of the original equations. It is often easiest to back-substitute an obtained value into this equation to find the value of the other variable. After obtaining both values, get into the habit of checking the ordered-pair solution in *both* equations of the system.

Step 4 Back-substitute the obtained value into one of the original equations. We back-substitute 4 for y into one of the original equations to find x. Let's use both equations to show that we obtain the same value for x in either case.

Using the first equation:	**Using the second equation:**
$5x - 4y = 9$	$x - 2y = -3$
$5x - 4(4) = 9$	$x - 2(4) = -3$
$5x - 16 = 9$	$x - 8 = -3$
$5x = 25$	$x = 5$
$x = 5$	

With $x = 5$ and $y = 4$, the proposed solution is $(5, 4)$.

Step 5 Check. Take a moment to show that $(5, 4)$ satisfies both given equations. The solution set is $\{(5, 4)\}$.

Technology

A graphing utility can be used to solve the system in Example 2. Solve each equation for y, graph the equations, and use the intersection feature. The utility displays the solution `15,42` as `x = 5,y = 4`.

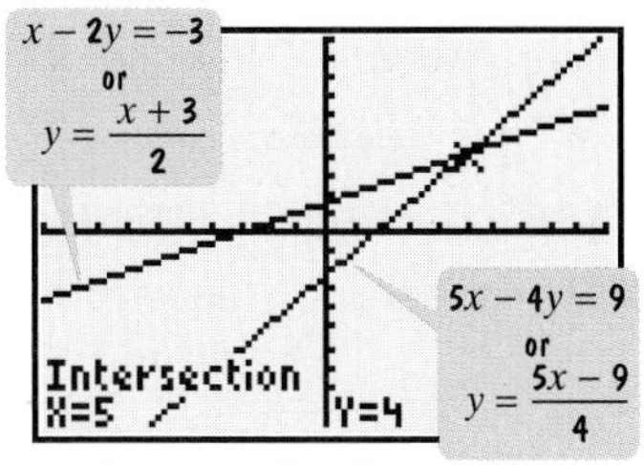

[−10, 10, 1] by [−10, 10, 1]

Check Point 2 Solve by the substitution method:

$$\begin{aligned} 3x + 2y &= 4 \\ 2x + y &= 1. \end{aligned}$$

3 Solve linear systems by addition.

Eliminating a Variable Using the Addition Method

The substitution method is most useful if one of the given equations has an isolated variable. A second, and frequently the easiest, method for solving a linear system is the addition method. Like the substitution method, the addition method involves eliminating a variable and ultimately solving an equation containing only one variable. However, this time we eliminate a variable by adding the equations.

For example, consider the following system of linear equations:

$$\begin{aligned} 3x - 4y &= 11 \\ -3x + 2y &= -7. \end{aligned}$$

When we add these two equations, the x-terms are eliminated. This occurs because the coefficients of the x-terms, 3 and -3, are opposites (additive inverses) of each other:

$$\begin{aligned} 3x - 4y &= 11 \\ \underline{-3x + 2y} &= \underline{-7} \\ \text{Add:}\quad -2y &= 4 \\ y &= -2 \end{aligned}$$

The sum is an equation in one variable.

Solve for y by dividing both sides by -2.

Now we can back-substitute -2 for y into one of the original equations to find x. It does not matter which equation you use; you will obtain the same value for x in either case. If we use either equation, we can show that $x = 1$ and the solution $(1, -2)$ satisfies both equations in the system.

When we use the addition method, we want to obtain two equations whose sum is an equation containing only one variable. The key step is to **obtain, for one of the variables, coefficients that differ only in sign**. To do this, we may need to multiply one or both equations by some nonzero number so that the coefficients of one of the variables, x or y, become opposites. Then when the two equations are added, this variable is eliminated.

Study Tip

Although the addition method is also known as the elimination method, variables are eliminated when using both the substitution and addition methods. The name *addition method* specifically tells us that the elimination of a variable is accomplished by adding two equations.

Solving Linear Systems by Addition

1. If necessary, rewrite both equations in the form $Ax + By = C$.
2. If necessary, multiply either equation or both equations by appropriate nonzero numbers so that the sum of the x-coefficients or the sum of the y-coefficients is 0.
3. Add the equations in step 2. The sum is an equation in one variable.
4. Solve the equation in one variable.
5. Back-substitute the value obtained in step 4 into either of the given equations and solve for the other variable.
6. Check the solution in both of the original equations.

EXAMPLE 3 Solving a System by the Addition Method

Solve by the addition method:

$$\begin{aligned} 3x + 2y &= 48 \\ 9x - 8y &= -24. \end{aligned}$$

Solution

Step 1 Rewrite both equations in the form $Ax + By = C$. Both equations are already in this form. Variable terms appear on the left and constants appear on the right.

Step 2 If necessary, multiply either equation or both equations by appropriate numbers so that the sum of the x-coefficients or the sum of the y-coefficients is 0. We can eliminate x or y. Let's eliminate x. Consider the terms in x in each equation, that is, $3x$ and $9x$. To eliminate x, we can multiply each term of the first equation by -3 and then add the equations.

$$\begin{aligned} 3x + 2y &= 48 \quad \xrightarrow{\text{Multiply by } -3.} \quad -9x - 6y = -144 \\ 9x - 8y &= -24 \quad \xrightarrow{\text{No change}} \quad \underline{9x - 8y = -24} \end{aligned}$$

Step 3 Add the equations. Add: $-14y = -168$

Step 4 Solve the equation in one variable. We solve $-14y = -168$ by dividing both sides by -14.

$$\frac{-14y}{-14} = \frac{-168}{-14} \quad \text{Divide both sides by } -14.$$

$$y = 12 \quad \text{Simplify.}$$

Step 5 Back-substitute and find the value for the other variable. We can back-substitute 12 for y into either one of the given equations. We'll use the first one.

$$\begin{aligned} 3x + 2y &= 48 && \text{This is the first equation in the given system.} \\ 3x + 2(12) &= 48 && \text{Substitute 12 for } y. \\ 3x + 24 &= 48 && \text{Multiply.} \\ 3x &= 24 && \text{Subtract 24 from both sides.} \\ x &= 8 && \text{Divide both sides by 3.} \end{aligned}$$

We found that $y = 12$ and $x = 8$. The proposed solution is $(8, 12)$.

Step 6 Check. Take a few minutes to show that $(8, 12)$ satisfies both of the original equations in the system. The solution set is $\{(8, 12)\}$.

Check Point 3 Solve by the addition method:

$$\begin{aligned} 4x + 5y &= 3 \\ 2x - 3y &= 7. \end{aligned}$$

Some linear systems have solutions that are not integers. If the value of one variable turns out to be a "messy" fraction, back-substitution might lead to cumbersome arithmetic. If this happens, you can return to the original system and use the addition method to find the value of the other variable.

EXAMPLE 4 Solving a System by the Addition Method

Solve by the addition method:

$$2x = 7y - 17$$
$$5y = 17 - 3x.$$

Solution

Step 1 Rewrite both equations in the form $Ax + By = C$. We first arrange the system so that variable terms appear on the left and constants appear on the right. We obtain

$$2x - 7y = -17 \quad \text{Subtract } 7y \text{ from both sides of the first equation.}$$
$$3x + 5y = 17. \quad \text{Add } 3x \text{ to both sides of the second equation.}$$

Step 2 If necessary, multiply either equation or both equations by appropriate numbers so that the sum of the x-coefficients or the sum of the y-coefficients is 0. We can eliminate x or y. Let's eliminate x by multiplying the first equation by 3 and the second equation by -2.

$$2x - 7y = -17 \xrightarrow{\text{Multiply by 3.}} 6x - 21y = -51$$
$$3x + 5y = 17 \xrightarrow{\text{Multiply by } -2.} \underline{-6x - 10y = -34}$$

Step 3 Add the equations. Add: $-31y = -85$

Step 4 Solve the equation in one variable. We solve $-31y = -85$ by dividing both sides by -31.

$$\frac{-31y}{-31} = \frac{-85}{-31} \quad \text{Divide both sides by } -31.$$
$$y = \frac{85}{31} \quad \text{Simplify.}$$

Step 5 Back-substitute and find the value for the other variable. Back-substitution of $\frac{85}{31}$ for y into either of the given equations results in cumbersome arithmetic. Instead, let's use the addition method on the given system in the form $Ax + By = C$ to find the value for x. Thus, we eliminate y by multiplying the first equation by 5 and the second equation by 7.

$$2x - 7y = -17 \xrightarrow{\text{Multiply by 5.}} 10x - 35y = -85$$
$$3x + 5y = 17 \xrightarrow{\text{Multiply by 7.}} \underline{21x + 35y = 119}$$
$$\text{Add: } 31x = 34$$
$$x = \frac{34}{31} \quad \text{Divide both sides by 31.}$$

We found that $y = \frac{85}{31}$ and $x = \frac{34}{31}$. The proposed solution is $\left(\frac{34}{31}, \frac{85}{31}\right)$.

Step 6 Check. For this system, a calculator is helpful in showing that $\left(\frac{34}{31}, \frac{85}{31}\right)$ satisfies both of the original equations in the system. The solution set is $\left\{\left(\frac{34}{31}, \frac{85}{31}\right)\right\}$.

Check Point 4 Solve by the addition method:

$$2x = 9 + 3y$$
$$4y = 8 - 3x.$$

4 Identify systems that do not have exactly one ordered-pair solution.

Linear Systems Having No Solution or Infinitely Many Solutions

We have seen that a system of linear equations in two variables represents a pair of lines. The lines either intersect at one point, are parallel, or are identical. Thus, there are three possibilities for the number of solutions to a system of two linear equations.

The Number of Solutions to a System of Two Linear Equations

The number of solutions to a system of two linear equations in two variables is given by one of the following. (See Figure 3.3.)

Number of Solutions	What This Means Graphically
Exactly one ordered pair solution	The two lines intersect at one point.
No solution	The two lines are parallel.
Infinitely many solutions	The two lines are identical.

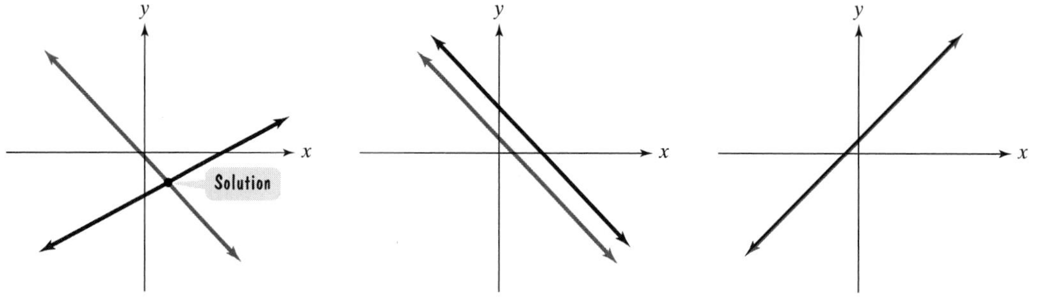

Exactly one solution — No solution (parallel lines) — Infinitely many solutions (lines coincide)

Figure 3.3 Possible graphs for a system of two linear equations in two variables

A linear system with no solution is called an **inconsistent system**. If you attempt to solve such a system by substitution or addition, you will eliminate both variables. A false statement, such as $0 = 12$, will be the result.

EXAMPLE 5 A System with No Solution

Solve the system:

$$4x + 6y = 12$$
$$6x + 9y = 12.$$

Solution Because no variable is isolated, we will use the addition method. To obtain coefficients of x that differ only in sign, we multiply the first equation by 3 and multiply the second equation by -2.

$4x + 6y = 12$ $\xrightarrow{\text{Multiply by 3.}}$ $12x + 18y = 36$

$6x + 9y = 12$ $\xrightarrow{\text{Multiply by } -2.}$ $-12x - 18y = -24$

Add: $0 = 12$

There are no values of x and y for which $0 = 12$. No values of x and y satisfy $0x + 0y = 12$.

The false statement $0 = 12$ indicates that the system is inconsistent and has no solution. The solution set is the empty set, $\varnothing$.

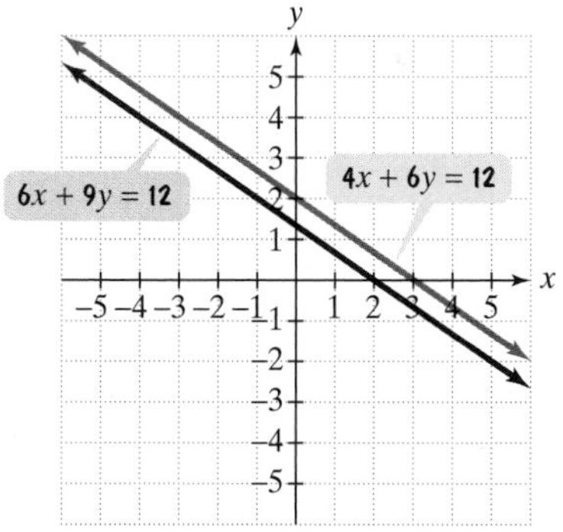

Figure 3.4 The graph of an inconsistent system

The lines corresponding to the two equations in Example 5 are shown in Figure 3.4. The lines are parallel and have no point of intersection.

Discovery

Show that the graphs of $4x + 6y = 12$ and $6x + 9y = 12$ must be parallel lines by solving each equation for y. What is the slope and y-intercept for each line? What does this mean? If a linear system is inconsistent, what must be true about the slopes and y-intercepts for the system's graphs?

Check Point 5 Solve the system:

$$5x - 2y = 4$$
$$-10x + 4y = 7.$$

A linear system that has at least one solution is called a **consistent system**. Lines that intersect and lines that coincide both represent consistent systems. If the lines coincide, then the consistent system has infinitely many solutions, represented by every point on either line.

The equations in a linear system with infinitely many solutions are called **dependent**. If you attempt to solve such a system by substitution or addition, you will eliminate both variables. However, a true statement, such as $10 = 10$, will be the result.

EXAMPLE 6 A System with Infinitely Many Solutions

Solve the system:

$$y = 3x - 2$$
$$15x - 5y = 10.$$

Solution Because the variable y is isolated in $y = 3x - 2$, the first equation, we can use the substitution method. We substitute the expression for y into the second equation.

$y = \boxed{3x - 2}$ $\quad 15x - 5\boxed{y} = 10$ Substitute $3x - 2$ for y.

$15x - 5(3x - 2) = 10$ The substitution results in an equation in one variable.

$15x - 15x + 10 = 10$ Apply the distributive property.

$10 = 10$ Simplify.

This statement is true for all values of x and y.

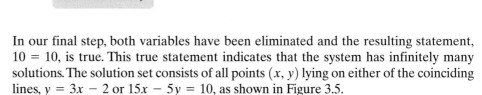

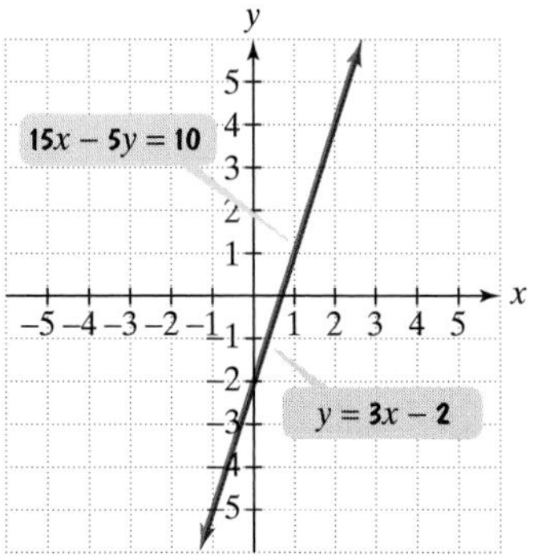

Figure 3.5 The graph of a system with infinitely many solutions

In our final step, both variables have been eliminated and the resulting statement, $10 = 10$, is true. This true statement indicates that the system has infinitely many solutions. The solution set consists of all points (x, y) lying on either of the coinciding lines, $y = 3x - 2$ or $15x - 5y = 10$, as shown in Figure 3.5.

We express the solution set for the system in one of two equivalent ways:

$$\{(x, y) \mid y = 3x - 2\} \quad \text{or} \quad \{(x, y) \mid 15x - 5y = 10\}.$$

The set of all ordered pairs (x, y) such that $y = 3x - 2$

The set of all ordered pairs (x, y) such that $15x - 5y = 10$

Study Tip

Although the system in Example 6 has infinitely many solutions, this does not mean that any ordered pair of numbers you can form will be a solution. The ordered pair (x, y) must satisfy one of the system's equations, $y = 3 - 2x$ or $15x - 5y = 10$, and there are infinitely many such ordered pairs. Because the graphs are coinciding lines, the ordered pairs that are solutions of one of the equations are also solutions of the other equation.

Check Point 6 Solve the system:

$$x = 4y - 8$$
$$5x - 20y = -40.$$

5 Solve problems using systems of linear equations.

Functions of Business: Break-Even Analysis

Suppose that a company produces and sells x units of a product. Its *revenue function* is the money generated by selling x units of the product. Its *cost function* is the cost of producing x units of the product.

Revenue and Cost Functions

A company produces and sells x units of a product.

Revenue Function

$$R(x) = (\text{price per unit sold})x$$

Cost Function

$$C(x) = \text{fixed cost} + (\text{cost per unit produced})x$$

The point of intersection of the graphs of the revenue and cost functions is called the **break-even point.** The x-coordinate of the point reveals the number of units that a company must produce and sell so that money coming in, the revenue, is equal to money going out, the cost. The y-coordinate of the break-even point gives the amount of money coming in and going out. Example 7 illustrates the use of the substitution method in determining a company's break-even point.

EXAMPLE 7 Finding a Break-Even Point

A company is planning to manufacture radically different wheelchairs. Fixed cost will be \$500,000 and it will cost \$400 to produce each wheelchair. Each wheelchair will be sold for \$600.

a. Write the cost function, C, of producing x wheelchairs.

b. Write the revenue function, R, from the sale of x wheelchairs.

c. Determine the break-even point. Describe what this means.

Solution

a. The cost function is the sum of the fixed cost and variable cost.

Fixed cost of \$500,000 | plus | Variable cost: \$400 for each chair produced

$$C(x) = 500{,}000 + 400x$$

b. The revenue function is the money generated from the sale of x wheelchairs.

Revenue per chair, \$600, times | the number of chairs sold

$$R(x) = 600x$$

c. The break-even point occurs where the graphs of C and R intersect. Thus, we find this point by solving the system

$$C(x) = 500{,}000 + 400x \qquad\qquad y = 500{,}000 + 400x$$
$$\qquad\qquad\text{or}$$
$$R(x) = 600x \qquad\qquad y = 600x.$$

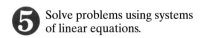

Using substitution, we can substitute $600x$ for y in the first equation:

$$600x = 500{,}000 + 400x \quad \text{Substitute } 600x \text{ for } y \text{ in } y = 500{,}000 + 400x.$$

$$200x = 500{,}000 \quad \text{Subtract } 400x \text{ from both sides.}$$

$$x = 2500 \quad \text{Divide both sides by } 200.$$

Back-substituting 2500 for x in either of the system's equations (or functions), we obtain

$$R(2500) = 600(2500) = 1{,}500{,}000.$$

We used $R(x) = 600x$.

The break-even point is (2500, 1,500,000). This means that the company will break even if it produces and sells 2500 wheelchairs. At this level, the money coming in is equal to the money going out: \$1,500,000.

Figure 3.6 shows the graphs of the revenue and cost functions for the wheelchair business. Similar graphs and models apply no matter how small or large a business venture may be.

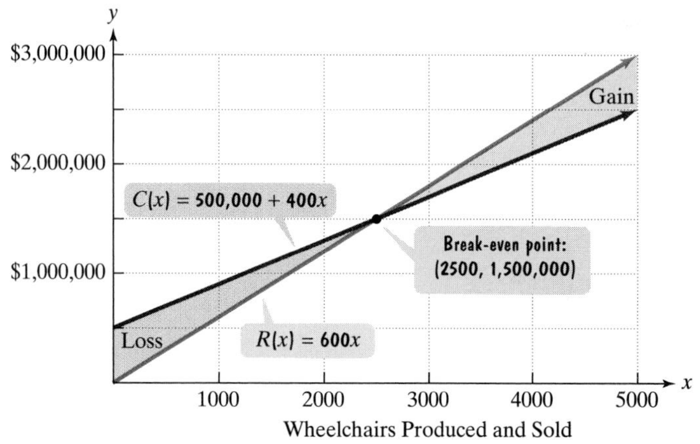

Figure 3.6

The intersection point confirms that the company breaks even by producing and selling 2500 wheelchairs. Can you see what happens for $x < 2500$? The red cost graph lies above the blue revenue graph. The cost is greater than the revenue and the business is losing money. Thus, if they sell fewer than 2500 wheelchairs, the result is a *loss*. By contrast, look at what happens for $x > 2500$. The blue revenue graph lies above the red cost graph. The revenue is greater than the cost and the business is making money. Thus, if they sell more than 2500 wheelchairs, the result is a *gain*.

Check Point 7 A company that manufactures running shoes has a fixed cost of \$300,000. Additionally, it costs \$30 to produce each pair of shoes. They are sold at \$80 per pair.

a. Write the cost function, C, of producing x pairs of running shoes.

b. Write the revenue function, R, from the sale of x pairs of running shoes.

c. Determine the break-even point. Describe what this means.

What does every entrepreneur, from a kid selling lemonade to Donald Trump, want to do? Generate profit, of course. The *profit* made is the money taken in, or the revenue, minus the money spent, or the cost. This relationship between revenue and cost allows us to define the *profit function, P(x).*

The Profit Function

The profit, $P(x)$, generated after producing and selling x units of a product is given by the **profit function**

$$P(x) = R(x) - C(x),$$

where R and C are the revenue and cost functions, respectively.

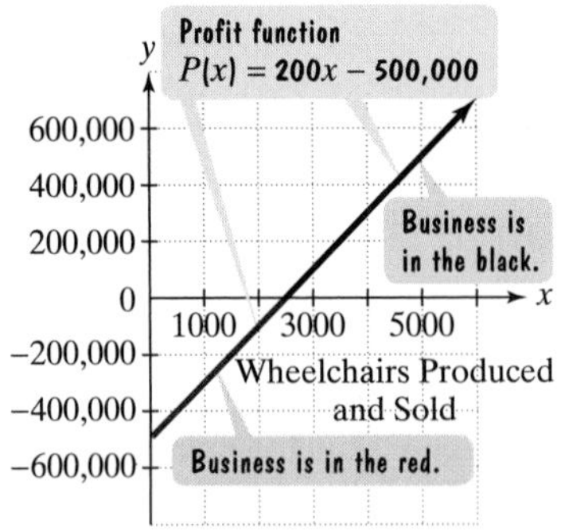

Figure 3.7

The profit function for the wheelchair business in Example 7 is

$$\begin{aligned} P(x) &= R(x) - C(x) \\ &= 600x - (500{,}000 + 400x) \\ &= 200x - 500{,}000. \end{aligned}$$

The graph of this profit function is shown in Figure 3.7. The red portion lies below the x-axis and shows a loss when fewer than 2500 wheelchairs are sold. The business is "in the red." The black portion lies above the x-axis and shows a gain when more than 2500 wheelchairs are sold. The wheelchair business is "in the black."

EXERCISE SET 3.1

Practice Exercises

In Exercises 1–4, determine whether the given ordered pair is a solution of the system.

1. $(2, 3)$
$x + 3y = 11$
$x - 5y = -13$

2. $(-3, 5)$
$9x + 7y = 8$
$8x - 9y = -69$

3. $(2, 5)$
$2x + 3y = 17$
$x + 4y = 16$

4. $(8, 5)$
$5x - 4y = 20$
$3y = 2x + 1$

In Exercises 5–18, solve each system by the substitution method.

5. $x + y = 4$
$y = 3x$

6. $x + y = 6$
$y = 2x$

7. $x + 3y = 8$
$y = 2x - 9$

8. $2x - 3y = -13$
$y = 2x + 7$

9. $x = 4y - 2$
$x = 6y + 8$

10. $x = 3y + 7$
$x = 2y - 1$

11. $5x + 2y = 0$
$x - 3y = 0$

12. $4x + 3y = 0$
$2x - y = 0$

13. $2x + 5y = -4$
$3x - y = 11$

14. $2x + 5y = 1$
$-x + 6y = 8$

15. $2x - 3y = 8 - 2x$
$3x + 4y = x + 3y + 14$

16. $3x - 4y = x - y + 4$
$2x + 6y = 5y - 4$

17. $y = \frac{1}{3}x + \frac{2}{3}$
$y = \frac{5}{7}x - 2$

18. $y = -\frac{1}{2}x + 2$
$y = \frac{3}{4}x + 7$

In Exercises 19–30, solve each system by the addition method.

19. $x + y = 1$
$x - y = 3$

20. $x + y = 6$
$x - y = -2$

21. $2x + 3y = 6$
$2x - 3y = 6$

22. $3x + 2y = 14$
$3x - 2y = 10$

23. $x + 2y = 2$
$-4x + 3y = 25$

24. $2x - 7y = 2$
$3x + y = -20$

25. $4x + 3y = 15$
$2x - 5y = 1$

26. $3x - 7y = 13$
$6x + 5y = 7$

27. $3x - 4y = 11$
$2x + 3y = -4$

28. $2x + 3y = -16$
$5x - 10y = 30$

29. $3x = 4y + 1$
$3y = 1 - 4x$

30. $5x = 6y + 40$
$2y = 8 - 3x$

In Exercises 31–42, solve by the method of your choice. Identify systems with no solution and systems with infinitely many solutions, using set notation to express their solution sets.

31. $x = 9 - 2y$
$x + 2y = 13$

32. $6x + 2y = 7$
$y = 2 - 3x$

33. $y = 3x - 5$
$21x - 35 = 7y$

34. $9x - 3y = 12$
$y = 3x - 4$

35. $3x - 2y = -5$
$4x + y = 8$

36. $2x + 5y = -4$
$3x - y = 11$

37. $x + 3y = 2$
$3x + 9y = 6$

38. $4x - 2y = 2$
$2x - y = 1$

39. $\frac{x}{4} - \frac{y}{4} = -1$
$x + 4y = -9$

40. $\frac{x}{6} - \frac{y}{2} = \frac{1}{3}$
$x + 2y = -3$

41. $2x = 3y + 4$
$4x = 3 - 5y$

42. $4x = 3y + 8$
$2x = -14 + 5y$

In Exercises 43–46, let x represent one number and let y represent the other number. Use the given conditions to write a system of equations. Solve the system and find the numbers.

43. The sum of two numbers is 7. If one number is subtracted from the other, their difference is -1. Find the numbers.

44. The sum of two numbers is 2. If one number is subtracted from the other, their difference is 8. Find the numbers.

45. Three times a first number decreased by a second number is 1. The first number increased by twice the second number is 12. Find the numbers.

46. The sum of three times a first number and twice a second number is 8. If the second number is subtracted from twice the first number, the result is 3. Find the numbers.

Practice Plus

In Exercises 47–48, solve each system by the method of your choice.

47. $\frac{x+2}{2} - \frac{y+4}{3} = 3$

$\frac{x+y}{5} = \frac{x-y}{2} - \frac{5}{2}$

48. $\frac{x-y}{3} = \frac{x+y}{2} - \frac{1}{2}$

$\frac{x+2}{2} - 4 = \frac{y+4}{3}$

In Exercises 49–50, solve each system for x and y, expressing either value in terms of a or b, if necessary. Assume that $a \neq 0$ and $b \neq 0$.

49. $5ax + 4y = 17$

$ax + 7y = 22$

50. $4ax + by = 3$

$6ax + 5by = 8$

51. For the linear function $f(x) = mx + b$, $f(-2) = 11$ and $f(3) = -9$. Find m and b.

52. For the linear function $f(x) = mx + b$, $f(-3) = 23$ and $f(2) = -7$. Find m and b.

Use the graphs of the linear functions to solve Exercises 53–54.

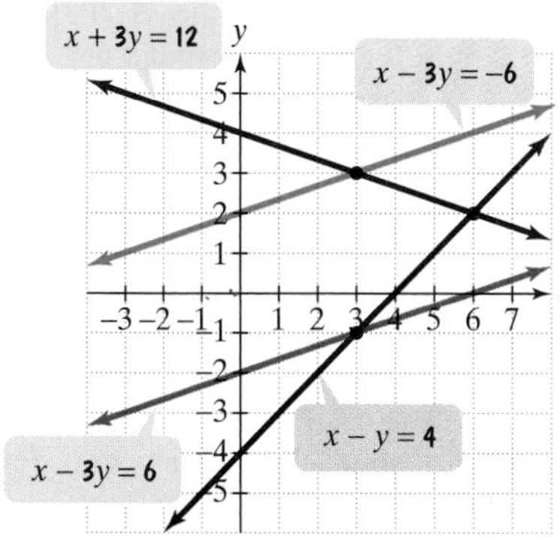

53. Write the linear system whose solution set is $\{(6, 2)\}$. Express each equation in the system in slope-intercept form.

54. Write the linear system whose solution set is $\varnothing$. Express each equation in the system in slope-intercept form.

Application Exercises

The figure shows the graphs of the cost and revenue functions for a company that manufactures and sells small radios. Use the information in the figure to solve Exercises 55–60.

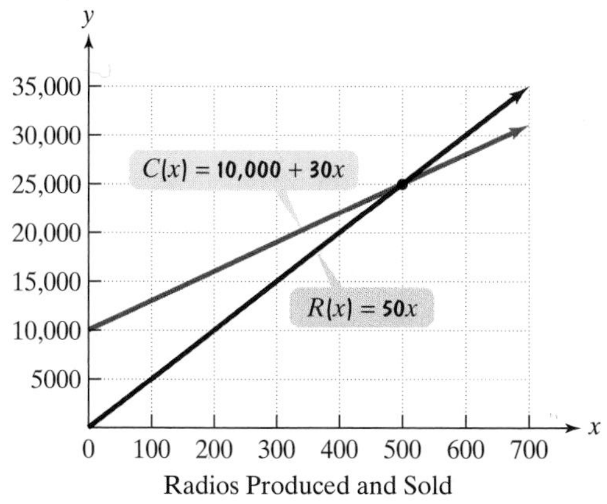

55. How many radios must be produced and sold for the company to break even?

56. More than how many radios must be produced and sold for the company to have a profit?

57. Use the formulas shown in the voice balloons to find $R(200) - C(200)$. Describe what this means for the company.

58. Use the formulas shown in the voice balloons to find $R(300) - C(300)$. Describe what this means for the company.

59. a. Use the formulas shown in the voice balloons to write the company's profit function, P, from producing and selling x radios.

b. Find the company's profit if 10,000 radios are produced and sold.

60. a. Use the formulas shown in the voice balloons to write the company's profit function, P, from producing and selling x radios.

b. Find the company's profit if 20,000 radios are produced and sold.

Exercises 61–64 describe a number of business ventures. For each exercise,

a. *Write the cost function, C.*

b. *Write the revenue function, R.*

c. *Determine the break-even point. Describe what this means.*

61. A company that manufactures small canoes has a fixed cost of \$18,000. It costs \$20 to produce each canoe. The selling price is \$80 per canoe. (In solving this exercise, let x represent the number of canoes produced and sold.)

62. A company that manufactures bicycles has a fixed cost of \$100,000. It costs \$100 to produce each bicycle. The selling price is \$300 per bike. (In solving this exercise, let x represent the number of bicycles produced and sold.)

63. You invest in a new play. The cost includes an overhead of \$30,000, plus production costs of \$2500 per performance. A sold-out performance brings in \$3125. (In solving this exercise, let x represent the number of sold-out performances.)

64. You invested \$30,000 and started a business writing greeting cards. Supplies cost 2¢ per card and you are selling each card for 50¢. (In solving this exercise, let x represent the number of cards produced and sold.)

An important application of systems of equations arises in connection with supply and demand. As the price of a product increases, the demand for that product decreases. However, at higher prices, suppliers are willing to produce greater quantities of the product. Exercises 65–66 involve supply and demand.

65. A chain of electronics stores sells hand-held color televisions. The weekly demand and supply models are given as follows:

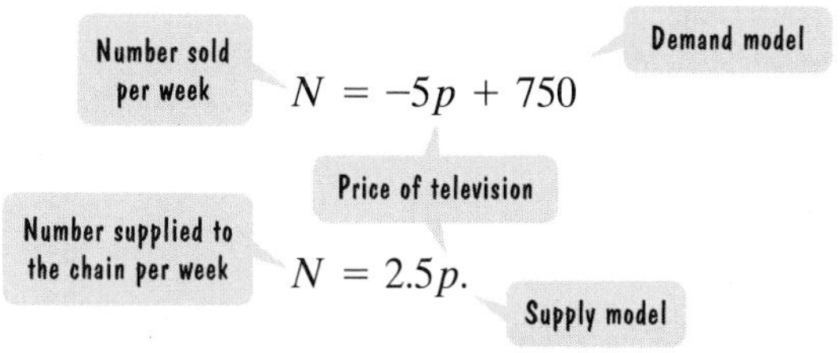
Number sold per week
Demand model
N = −5p + 750
Price of television
Number supplied to the chain per week
N = 2.5p.
Supply model

a. How many hand-held color televisions can be sold and supplied at \$120 per television?

b. Find the price at which supply and demand are equal. At this price, how many televisions can be supplied and sold each week?

66. At a price of p dollars per ticket, the number of tickets to a rock concert that can be sold is given by the demand model $N = -25p + 7800$. At a price of p dollars per ticket, the number of tickets that the concert's promoters are willing to make available is given by the supply model $N = 5p + 6000$.

a. How many tickets can be sold and supplied for \$50 per ticket?

b. Find the ticket price at which supply and demand are equal. At this price, how many tickets will be supplied and sold?

67. The graphs shown below are based on 543 adults polled nationally by *Newsweek*.

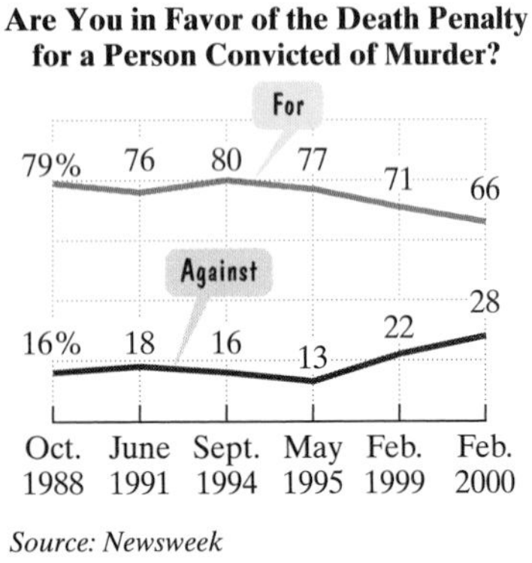

Source: Newsweek

The function $13x + 12y = 992$ models the percent, y, in favor of the death penalty x years after 1988. The function $-x + y = 16$ models the percent, y, against the death penalty x years after 1988. If the trends shown by the graphs continue, in which year will the percentage of Americans in favor of the death penalty be the same as the percentage of Americans who oppose it? For that year, what percent will be for the death penalty and what percent will be against it?

68. One of the most dramatic developments in the work force has been the increase in the number of women, at approximately $\frac{1}{2}\%$ per year. By contrast, the percentage of men is decreasing by $\frac{1}{4}\%$ per year. The graphs shown below illustrate these changes.

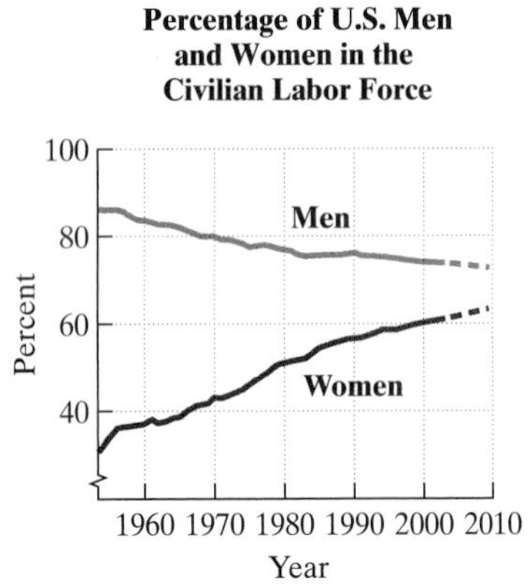

Source: U.S. Department of Labor

The function $y = 0.52x + 35.7$ models the percentage, y, of U.S. women in the work force x years after 1955. The function $0.25x + y = 85.4$ models the percentage, y, of U.S. men in the work force x years after 1955. Use these models to determine when the percentage of women in the work force will be the same as the percentage of men in the work force. Round to the nearest year. What percentage of women and what percentage of men will be in the work force at that time?

69. Although Social Security is a problem, some projections indicate that there's a much bigger time bomb ticking in the federal budget, and that's Medicare. In 2000, the cost of Social Security was 5.48% of the gross domestic product, increasing by 0.04% of the GDP per year. In 2000, the cost of Medicare was 1.84% of the gross domestic product, increasing by 0.17% of the GDP per year.

(*Source:* Congressional Budget Office)

a. Write a function that models the cost of Social Security as a percentage of the GDP x years after 2000.

b. Write a function that models the cost of Medicare as a percentage of the GDP x years after 2000.

c. In which year will the cost of Medicare and Social Security be the same? For that year, what will be the cost of each program as a percentage of the GDP? Which program will have the greater cost after that year?

70. The graph indicates that in 1984, there were 72 meals per person at take-out restaurants. For the period shown, this number increased by an average of 2.25 meals per person per year. In 1984, there were 94 meals per person at on-premise dining facilities and this number decreased by an average of 0.55 meals per person per year.

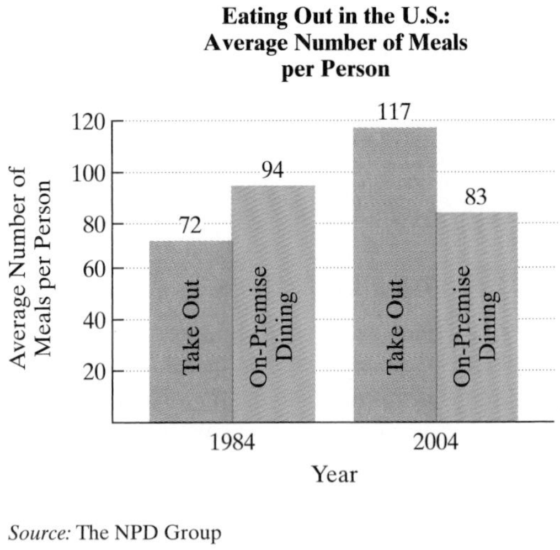

Source: The NPD Group

a. Write a function that models the average number of meals per person at take-out restaurants x years after 1984.

b. Write a function that models the average number of meals per person at on-premise dining facilities x years after 1984.

c. In which year, to the nearest whole year, was the average number of meals per person for take-out and on-premise restaurants the same? For that year, how many meals per person, to the nearest whole number, were there for each kind of restaurant? Which kind of restaurant had the greater number of meals per person after that year?

The bar graph shows the percentage of Americans who used cigarettes, by ethnicity, in 1985 and 2002. For each of the groups shown, cigarette use has been linearly decreasing. Use this information to solve Exercises 71–72.

Cigarette Use in the U.S.

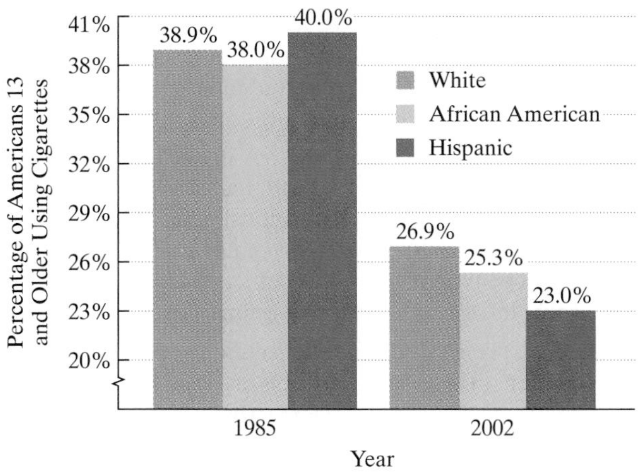

Source: Department of Health and Human Services

71. In this exercise, let x represent the number of years after 1985 and let y represent the percentage of Americans in one of the groups shown who used cigarettes.

a. Use the data points $(0, 38)$ and $(17, 25.3)$ to find the slope-intercept equation of the line that models the percentage of African Americans who used cigarettes, y, x years after 1985. Round the value of m to two decimal places.

b. Use the data points $(0, 40)$ and $(17, 23)$ to find the slope-intercept equation of the line that models the percentage of Hispanics who used cigarettes, y, x years after 1985.

c. Use the models from parts (a) and (b) to find the year during which cigarette use was the same for African Americans and Hispanics. What percentage of each group used cigarettes during that year?

72. In this exercise, let x represent the number of years after 1985 and let y represent the percentage of Americans in one of the groups shown who used cigarettes.

a. Use the data points $(0, 38.9)$ and $(17, 26.9)$ to find the slope-intercept equation of the line that models the percentage of whites who used cigarettes, y, x years after 1985. Round the value of m to two decimal places.

b. Use the data points $(0, 40)$ and $(17, 23)$ to find the slope-intercept equation of the line that models the percentage of Hispanics who used cigarettes, y, x years after 1985.

c. Use the models from parts (a) and (b) to find the year, to the nearest whole year, during which cigarette use was the same for whites and Hispanics. What percentage of each group, to the nearest percent, used cigarettes during that year?

Use a system of linear equations to solve Exercises 73–84.

The graph shows the calories in some favorite fast foods. Use the information in Exercises 73–74 to find the exact caloric content of the specified foods.

Calories in Some Favorite Fast Foods

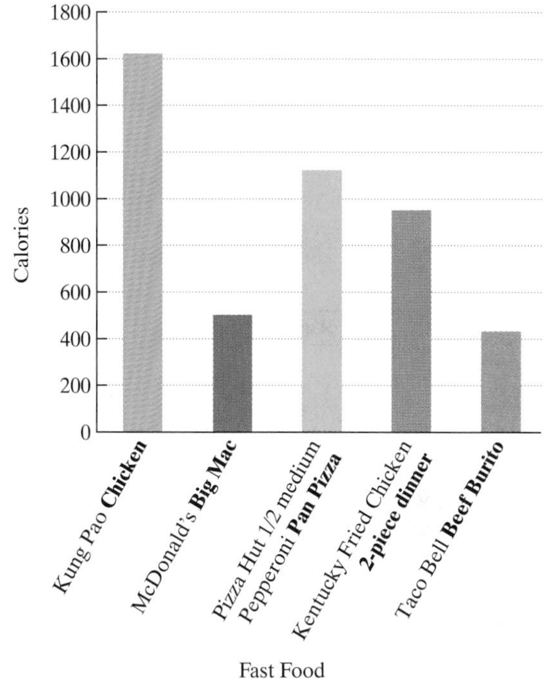

Source: Center for Science in the Public Interest

73. One pan pizza and two beef burritos provide 1980 calories. Two pan pizzas and one beef burrito provide 2670 calories. Find the caloric content of each item.

74. One Kung Pao chicken and two Big Macs provide 2620 calories. Two Kung Pao chickens and one Big Mac provide 3740 calories. Find the caloric content of each item.

75. Cholesterol intake should be limited to 300 mg or less each day. One serving of scrambled eggs from McDonalds and one Double Beef Whopper from Burger King exceed this intake by 241 mg. Two servings of scrambled eggs and three Double Beef Whoppers provide 1257 mg of cholesterol. Determine the cholesterol content in each item.

76. Two medium eggs and three cups of ice cream contain 701 milligrams of cholesterol. One medium egg and one cup of ice cream exceed the suggested daily cholesterol intake of 300 milligrams by 25 milligrams. Determine the cholesterol content in each item.

77. A hotel has 200 rooms. Those with kitchen facilities rent for \$100 per night and those without kitchen facilities rent for \$80 per night. On a night when the hotel was completely occupied, revenues were \$17,000. How many of each type of room does the hotel have?

78. A new restaurant is to contain two-seat tables and four-seat tables. Fire codes limit the restaurant's maximum occupancy to 56 customers. If the owners have hired enough servers to handle 17 tables of customers, how many of each kind of table should they purchase?

79. A rectangular lot whose perimeter is 360 feet is fenced along three sides. An expensive fencing along the lot's length costs \$20 per foot and an inexpensive fencing along the two side widths costs only \$8 per foot. The total cost of the fencing along the three sides comes to \$3280. What are the lot's dimensions?

80. A rectangular lot whose perimeter is 320 feet is fenced along three sides. An expensive fencing along the lot's length costs \$16 per foot and an inexpensive fencing along the two side widths costs only \$5 per foot. The total cost of the fencing along the three sides comes to \$2140. What are the lot's dimensions?

81. When a crew rows with the current, it travels 16 miles in 2 hours. Against the current, the crew rows 8 miles in 2 hours. Let $x =$ the crew's rowing rate in still water and let $y =$ the rate of the current. The following chart summarizes this information:

	Rate	×	Time	=	Distance
Rowing with current	$x + y$		2		16
Rowing against current	$x - y$		2		8

Find the rate of rowing in still water and the rate of the current.

82. When an airplane flies with the wind, it travels 800 miles in 4 hours. Against the wind, it takes 5 hours to cover the same distance. Find the plane's rate in still air and the rate of the wind.

In Exercises 83–84, an isosceles triangle containing two angles with equal measure is shown. The degree measure of each triangle's three interior angles and an exterior angle is represented with variables. Find the measure of the three interior angles.

83.

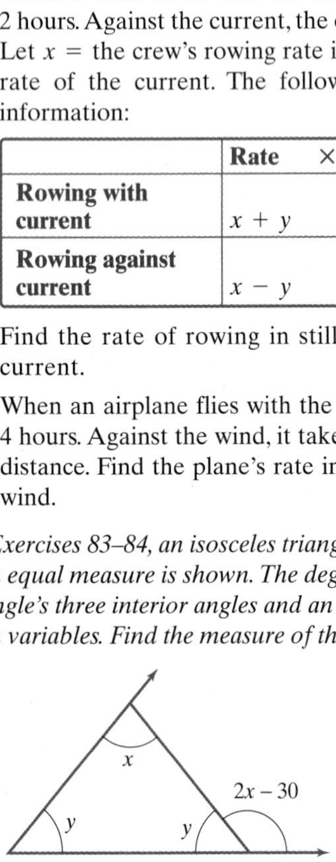

84.

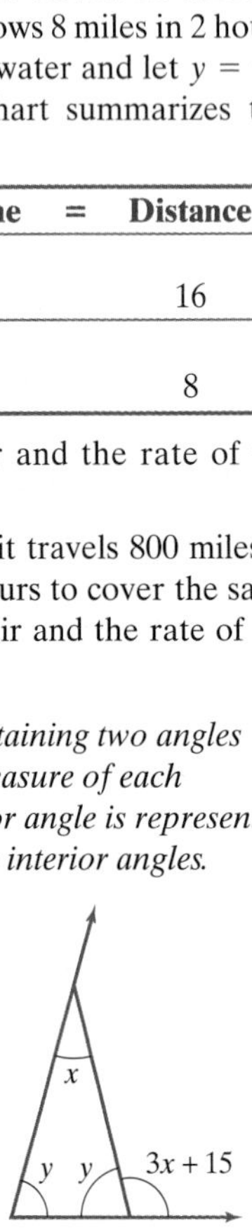

Writing in Mathematics

85. What is a system of linear equations? Provide an example with your description.

86. What is the solution of a system of linear equations?

87. Explain how to solve a system of equations using the substitution method. Use $y = 3 - 3x$ and $3x + 4y = 6$ to illustrate your explanation.

88. Explain how to solve a system of equations using the addition method. Use $3x + 5y = -2$ and $2x + 3y = 0$ to illustrate your explanation.

89. When is it easier to use the addition method rather than the substitution method to solve a system of equations?

90. When using the addition or substitution method, how can you tell if a system of linear equations has infinitely many solutions? What is the relationship between the graphs of the two equations?

91. When using the addition or substitution method, how can you tell if a system of linear equations has no solution? What is the relationship between the graphs of the two equations?

92. Describe the break-even point for a business.

Technology Exercises

93. Verify your solutions to any five exercises in Exercises 5–42 by using a graphing utility to graph the two equations in the system in the same viewing rectangle. Then use the intersection feature to display the solution.

94. Some graphing utilities can give the solution to a linear system of equations. (Consult your manual for details.) This capability is usually accessed with the SIMULT (simultaneous equations) feature. First, you will enter 2, for two equations in two variables. With each equation in $Ax + By = C$ form, you will then enter the coefficients for x and y and the constant term, one equation at a time. After entering all six numbers, press SOLVE. The solution will be displayed on the screen. (The x-value may be displayed as $x_1 =$ and the y-value as $x_2 =$.) Use this capability to verify the solution to any five of the exercises you solved in the practice exercises of this exercise set. Describe what happens when you use your graphing utility on a system with no solution or infinitely many solutions.

Critical Thinking Exercises

95. Write a system of equations having $\{(-2, 7)\}$ as a solution set. (More than one system is possible.)

96. Solve the system for x and y in terms of a_1, b_1, c_1, a_2, b_2, and c_2:

$$a_1x + b_1y = c_1$$
$$a_2x + b_2y = c_2.$$

97. Two identical twins can only be distinguished by the characteristic that one always tells the truth and the other always lies. One twin tells you of a lucky number pair: "When I multiply my first lucky number by 3 and my second lucky number by 6, the addition of the resulting numbers produces a sum of 12. When I add my first lucky number and twice my second lucky number, the sum is 5." Which twin is talking?

98. A marching band has 52 members and there are 24 in the pom-pom squad. They wish to form several hexagons and squares like those diagrammed below. Can it be done with no people left over?

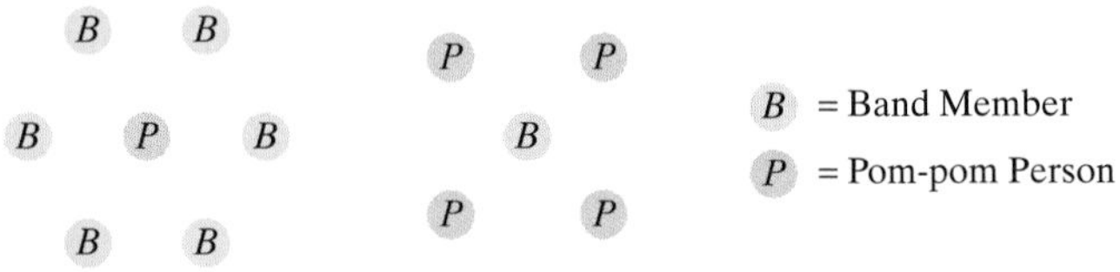

Group Exercise

99. The group should write four different word problems that can be solved using a system of linear equations in two variables. All of the problems should be on different topics. The group should turn in the four problems and their algebraic solutions.

SECTION 3.2 Systems of Linear Equations in Three Variables

Objectives

1. Verify the solution of a system of linear equations in three variables.
2. Solve systems of linear equations in three variables.
3. Solve problems using systems in three variables.

All animals sleep, but the length of time they sleep varies widely: Cattle sleep for only a few minutes at a time. We humans seem to need more sleep than other animals, up to eight hours a day. Without enough sleep, we have difficulty concentrating, make mistakes in routine tasks, lose energy, and feel bad-tempered. There is a relationship between hours of sleep and death rate per year per 100,000 people. How many hours of sleep will put you in the group with the minimum death rate? In this section, we will answer this question by solving a system of linear equations with more than two variables.

1 Verify the solution of a system of linear equations in three variables.

Systems of Linear Equations in Three Variables and Their Solutions

An equation such as $x + 2y - 3z = 9$ is called a *linear equation in three variables*. In general, any equation of the form

$$Ax + By + Cz = D,$$

where A, B, C, and D are real numbers such that A, B, and C are not all 0, is a **linear equation in three variables: x, y, and z.** The graph of this linear equation in three variables is a plane in three-dimensional space.

The process of solving a system of three linear equations in three variables is geometrically equivalent to finding the point of intersection (assuming that there is one) of three planes in space. (See Figure 3.8.) A **solution** of a system of linear equations in three variables is an ordered triple of real numbers that satisfies all equations of the system. The **solution set** of the system is the set of all its solutions.

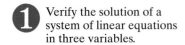

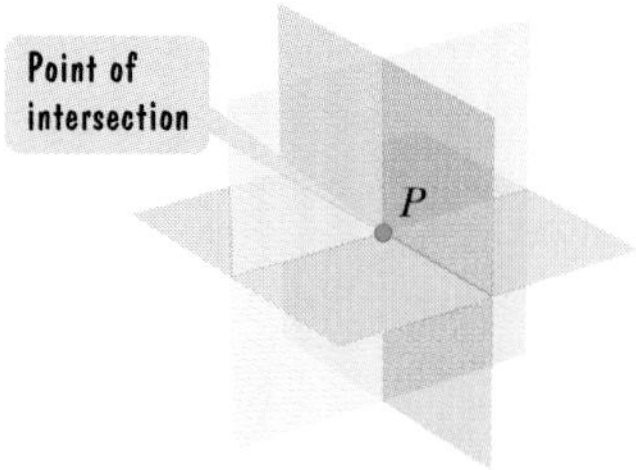

Figure 3.8

EXAMPLE 1 Determining Whether an Ordered Triple Satisfies a System

Show that the ordered triple $(-1, 2, -2)$ is a solution of the system:

$$\begin{aligned} x + 2y - 3z &= 9 \\ 2x - y + 2z &= -8 \\ -x + 3y - 4z &= 15. \end{aligned}$$

Solution Because -1 is the x-coordinate, 2 is the y-coordinate, and -2 is the z-coordinate of $(-1, 2, -2)$, we replace x with -1, y with 2, and z with -2 in each of the three equations.

$$\begin{aligned} x + 2y - 3z &= 9 \\ -1 + 2(2) - 3(-2) &\stackrel{?}{=} 9 \\ -1 + 4 + 6 &\stackrel{?}{=} 9 \\ 9 &= 9, \quad \text{true} \end{aligned}$$

$$\begin{aligned} 2x - y + 2z &= -8 \\ 2(-1) - 2 + 2(-2) &\stackrel{?}{=} -8 \\ -2 - 2 - 4 &\stackrel{?}{=} -8 \\ -8 &= -8, \quad \text{true} \end{aligned}$$

$$\begin{aligned} -x + 3y - 4z &= 15 \\ -(-1) + 3(2) - 4(-2) &\stackrel{?}{=} 15 \\ 1 + 6 + 8 &\stackrel{?}{=} 15 \\ 15 &= 15, \quad \text{true} \end{aligned}$$

The ordered triple $(-1, 2, -2)$ satisfies the three equations: It makes each equation true. Thus, the ordered triple is a solution of the system.

Check Point 1 Show that the ordered triple $(-1, -4, 5)$ is a solution of the system:

$$\begin{aligned} x - 2y + 3z &= 22 \\ 2x - 3y - z &= 5 \\ 3x + y - 5z &= -32. \end{aligned}$$

2 Solve systems of linear equations in three variables.

Solving Systems of Linear Equations in Three Variables by Eliminating Variables

The method for solving a system of linear equations in three variables is similar to that used on systems of linear equations in two variables. We use addition to eliminate any variable, reducing the system to two equations in two variables. Once we obtain a system of two equations in two variables, we use addition or substitution to eliminate a variable. The result is a single equation in one variable. We solve this equation to get the value of the remaining variable. Other variable values are found by back-substitution.

Study Tip

It does not matter which variable you eliminate, as long as you do it in two different pairs of equations.

Solving Linear Systems in Three Variables by Eliminating Variables

1. Reduce the system to two equations in two variables. This is usually accomplished by taking two different pairs of equations and using the addition method to eliminate the same variable from both pairs.
2. Solve the resulting system of two equations in two variables using addition or substitution. The result is an equation in one variable that gives the value of that variable.
3. Back-substitute the value of the variable found in step 2 into either of the equations in two variables to find the value of the second variable.
4. Use the values of the two variables from steps 2 and 3 to find the value of the third variable by back-substituting into one of the original equations.
5. Check the proposed solution in each of the original equations.

EXAMPLE 2 Solving a System in Three Variables

Solve the system:

$$\begin{aligned} 5x - 2y - 4z &= 3 && \text{Equation 1} \\ 3x + 3y + 2z &= -3 && \text{Equation 2} \\ -2x + 5y + 3z &= 3. && \text{Equation 3} \end{aligned}$$

Solution There are many ways to proceed. Because our initial goal is to reduce the system to two equations in two variables, **the central idea is to take two different pairs of equations and eliminate the same variable from both pairs.**

Step 1 Reduce the system to two equations in two variables. We choose any two equations and use the addition method to eliminate a variable. Let's eliminate z using Equations 1 and 2. We do so by multiplying Equation 2 by 2. Then we add equations.

$$\begin{aligned} &\text{(Equation 1)}\quad 5x - 2y - 4z = 3 \xrightarrow{\text{No change}} & 5x - 2y - 4z &= 3 \\ &\text{(Equation 2)}\quad 3x + 3y + 2z = -3 \xrightarrow{\text{Multiply by 2.}} & 6x + 6y + 4z &= -6 \\ &\text{Add:} & 11x + 4y \quad &= -3 \quad \text{Equation 4} \end{aligned}$$

Now we must eliminate the *same* variable using another pair of equations. We can eliminate z from Equations 2 and 3. First, we multiply Equation 2 by -3. Next, we multiply Equation 3 by 2. Finally, we add equations.

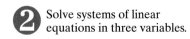

(Equation 2)	$3x + 3y + 2z = -3$	Multiply by −3. $\rightarrow$	$-9x - 9y - 6z = 9$
(Equation 3)	$-2x + 5y + 3z = 3$	Multiply by 2. $\rightarrow$	$-4x + 10y + 6z = 6$
		Add:	$-13x + y = 15$ Equation 5

Equations 4 and 5 give us a system of two equations in two variables:

$$11x + 4y = -3 \quad \text{Equation 4}$$
$$-13x + y = 15. \quad \text{Equation 5}$$

Step 2 Solve the resulting system of two equations in two variables. We will use the addition method to solve Equations 4 and 5 for x and y. To do so, we multiply Equation 5 on both sides by -4 and add this to Equation 4.

(Equation 4)	$11x + 4y = -3$	No change $\rightarrow$	$11x + 4y = -3$
(Equation 5)	$-13x + y = 15$	Multiply by −4. $\rightarrow$	$52x - 4y = -60$
		Add:	$63x = -63$
			$x = -1$ Divide both sides by 63.

Step 3 Use back-substitution in one of the equations in two variables to find the value of the second variable. We back-substitute -1 for x in either Equation 4 or 5 to find the value of y.

$$-13x + y = 15 \quad \text{Equation 5}$$
$$-13(-1) + y = 15 \quad \text{Substitute } -1 \text{ for } x.$$
$$13 + y = 15 \quad \text{Multiply.}$$
$$y = 2 \quad \text{Subtract 13 from both sides.}$$

Step 4 Back-substitute the values found for two variables into one of the original equations to find the value of the third variable. We can now use any one of the original equations and back-substitute the values of x and y to find the value for z. We will use Equation 2.

$$3x + 3y + 2z = -3 \quad \text{Equation 2}$$
$$3(-1) + 3(2) + 2z = -3 \quad \text{Substitute } -1 \text{ for } x \text{ and 2 for } y.$$
$$3 + 2z = -3 \quad \text{Multiply and then add: } 3(-1) + 3(2) = -3 + 6 = 3.$$
$$2z = -6 \quad \text{Subtract 3 from both sides.}$$
$$z = -3 \quad \text{Divide both sides by 2.}$$

With $x = -1$, $y = 2$, and $z = -3$, the proposed solution is the ordered triple $(-1, 2, -3)$.

Step 5 Check. Check the proposed solution, $(-1, 2, -3)$, by substituting the values for x, y, and z into each of the three original equations. These substitutions yield three true statements. Thus, the solution set is $\{(-1, 2, -3)\}$.

Check Point 2 Solve the system:

$$x + 4y - z = 20$$
$$3x + 2y + z = 8$$
$$2x - 3y + 2z = -16.$$

In some examples, one of the variables is already eliminated from a given equation. In this case, the same variable should be eliminated from the other two equations, thereby making it possible to omit one of the elimination steps. We illustrate this idea in Example 3.

EXAMPLE 3 Solving a System of Equations with a Missing Term

Solve the system:

$$\begin{aligned} x + \quad\;\; z &= 8 && \text{Equation 1} \\ x + y + 2z &= 17 && \text{Equation 2} \\ x + 2y + z &= 16. && \text{Equation 3} \end{aligned}$$

Solution

Step 1 Reduce the system to two equations in two variables. Because Equation 1 contains only x and z, we could omit one of the elimination steps by eliminating y using Equations 2 and 3. This will give us two equations in x and z. To eliminate y using Equations 2 and 3, we multiply Equation 2 by -2 and add Equation 3.

$$\begin{aligned} &(\text{Equation 2})\quad x + y + 2z = 17 \xrightarrow{\text{Multiply by } -2.} && -2x - 2y - 4z = -34 \\ &(\text{Equation 3})\quad x + 2y + z = 16 \xrightarrow{\text{No change}} && \underline{\;x + 2y + z = 16\;} \\ &\text{Add:} && -x \qquad\quad - 3z = -18 \quad \text{Equation 4} \end{aligned}$$

Equation 4 and the given Equation 1 provide us with a system of two equations in two variables:

$$\begin{aligned} x + z &= 8 && \text{Equation 1} \\ -x - 3z &= -18. && \text{Equation 4} \end{aligned}$$

Step 2 Solve the resulting system of two equations in two variables. We will solve Equations 1 and 4 for x and z.

$$\begin{aligned} x + z &= 8 && \text{Equation 1} \\ \underline{-x - 3z} &= \underline{-18} && \text{Equation 4} \\ \text{Add:} \quad -2z &= -10 \\ z &= 5 && \text{Divide both sides by } -2. \end{aligned}$$

Step 3 Use back-substitution in one of the equations in two variables to find the value of the second variable. To find x, we back-substitute 5 for z in either Equation 1 or 4. We will use Equation 1.

$$\begin{aligned} x + z &= 8 && \text{Equation 1} \\ x + 5 &= 8 && \text{Substitute 5 for z.} \\ x &= 3 && \text{Subtract 5 from both sides.} \end{aligned}$$

Step 4 Back-substitute the values found for two variables into one of the original equations to find the value of the third variable. To find y, we back-substitute 3 for x and 5 for z into Equation 2 or 3. We cannot use Equation 1 because y is missing in this equation. We will use Equation 2.

$$\begin{aligned} x + y + 2z &= 17 && \text{Equation 2} \\ 3 + y + 2(5) &= 17 && \text{Substitute 3 for x and 5 for z.} \\ y + 13 &= 17 && \text{Multiply and add.} \\ y &= 4 && \text{Subtract 13 from both sides.} \end{aligned}$$

We found that $z = 5$, $x = 3$, and $y = 4$. Thus, the proposed solution is the ordered triple $(3, 4, 5)$.

Step 5 Check. Substituting 3 for x, 4 for y, and 5 for z into each of the three original equations yields three true statements. Consequently, the solution set is $\{(3, 4, 5)\}$.

Check Point 3 Solve the system:

$$\begin{aligned} 2y - z &= 7 \\ x + 2y + z &= 17 \\ 2x - 3y + 2z &= -1. \end{aligned}$$

A system of linear equations in three variables represents three planes. The three planes may not always intersect at one point. The planes may have no common point of intersection and represent an inconsistent system with no solution. By contrast, the planes may coincide or intersect along a line. In these cases, the planes have infinitely many points in common and represent systems with infinitely many solutions.

③ Solve problems using systems in three variables.

Applications

Systems of equations may allow us to find models for data without using a graphing utility. Three data points that do not lie on or near a line determine the graph of a quadratic function of the form $y = ax^2 + bx + c, a \neq 0$. Quadratic functions often model situations in which values of y are decreasing and then increasing, suggesting the cuplike shape of a parabola.

EXAMPLE 4 Modeling Data Relating Sleep and Death Rate

In a study relating sleep and death rate, the following data were obtained. Use the function $y = ax^2 + bx + c$ to model the data.

x (Average Number of Hours of Sleep)	y (Death Rate per Year per 100,000 Males)
4	1682
7	626
9	967

Solution We need to find values for a, b, and c in $y = ax^2 + bx + c$. We can do so by solving a system of three linear equations in a, b, and c. We obtain the three equations by using the values of x and y from the data as follows:

$$y = ax^2 + bx + c \quad \text{Use the quadratic function to model the data.}$$

When x = 4, y = 1682: $1682 = a \cdot 4^2 + b \cdot 4 + c$ or $16a + 4b + c = 1682$

When x = 7, y = 626: $626 = a \cdot 7^2 + b \cdot 7 + c$ or $49a + 7b + c = 626$

When x = 9, y = 967: $967 = a \cdot 9^2 + b \cdot 9 + c$ or $81a + 9b + c = 967$.

The easiest way to solve this system is to eliminate c from two pairs of equations, obtaining two equations in a and b. Solving this system gives $a = 104.5$, $b = -1501.5$, and $c = 6016$. We now substitute the values for a, b, and c into $y = ax^2 + bx + c$. The function that models the given data is

$$y = 104.5x^2 - 1501.5x + 6016.$$

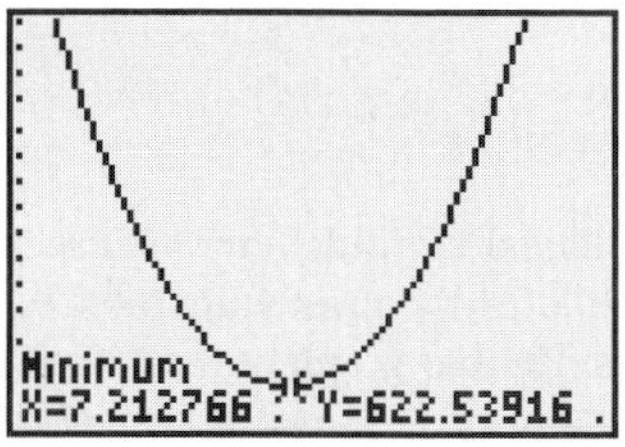

We can use the model that we obtained in Example 4 to find the death rate of males who average, say, 6 hours of sleep. First, write the model in function notation:

$$f(x) = 104.5x^2 - 1501.5x + 6016.$$

Substitute 6 for x:

$$f(6) = 104.5(6)^2 - 1501.5(6) + 6016 = 769.$$

According to the model, the death rate for males who average 6 hours of sleep is 769 deaths per 100,000 males.

Technology

The graph of
$$y = 104.5x^2 - 1501.5x + 6016$$
is displayed in a $[3, 12, 1]$ by $[500, 2000, 100]$ viewing rectangle. The minimum function feature shows that the lowest point on the graph, the vertex, is approximately $(7.2, 622.5)$. Men who average 7.2 hours of sleep are in the group with the lowest death rate, approximately 622.5 deaths per 100,000 males.

Check Point 4 Find the quadratic function $y = ax^2 + bx + c$ whose graph passes through the points $(1, 4)$, $(2, 1)$, and $(3, 4)$.

EXERCISE SET 3.2

Practice Exercises

In Exercises 1–4, determine if the given ordered triple is a solution of the system.

1. $(2, -1, 3)$
$$\begin{aligned} x + y + z &= 4 \\ x - 2y - z &= 1 \\ 2x - y - 2z &= -1 \end{aligned}$$

2. $(5, -3, -2)$
$$\begin{aligned} x + y + z &= 0 \\ x + 2y - 3z &= 5 \\ 3x + 4y + 2z &= -1 \end{aligned}$$

3. $(4, 1, 2)$
$$\begin{aligned} x - 2y &= 2 \\ 2x + 3y &= 11 \\ y - 4z &= -7 \end{aligned}$$

4. $(-1, 3, 2)$
$$\begin{aligned} x - 2z &= -5 \\ y - 3z &= -3 \\ 2x - z &= -4 \end{aligned}$$

Solve each system in Exercises 5–18.

5.
$$\begin{aligned} x + y + 2z &= 11 \\ x + y + 3z &= 14 \\ x + 2y - z &= 5 \end{aligned}$$

6.
$$\begin{aligned} 2x + y - 2z &= -1 \\ 3x - 3y - z &= 5 \\ x - 2y + 3z &= 6 \end{aligned}$$

7.
$$\begin{aligned} 4x - y + 2z &= 11 \\ x + 2y - z &= -1 \\ 2x + 2y - 3z &= -1 \end{aligned}$$

8.
$$\begin{aligned} x - y + 3z &= 8 \\ 3x + y - 2z &= -2 \\ 2x + 4y + z &= 0 \end{aligned}$$

9.
$$\begin{aligned} 3x + 2y - 3z &= -2 \\ 2x - 5y + 2z &= -2 \\ 4x - 3y + 4z &= 10 \end{aligned}$$

10.
$$\begin{aligned} 2x + 3y + 7z &= 13 \\ 3x + 2y - 5z &= -22 \\ 5x + 7y - 3z &= -28 \end{aligned}$$

11.
$$\begin{aligned} 2x - 4y + 3z &= 17 \\ x + 2y - z &= 0 \\ 4x - y - z &= 6 \end{aligned}$$

12.
$$\begin{aligned} x + z &= 3 \\ x + 2y - z &= 1 \\ 2x - y + z &= 3 \end{aligned}$$

13.
$$\begin{aligned} 2x + y &= 2 \\ x + y - z &= 4 \\ 3x + 2y + z &= 0 \end{aligned}$$

14.
$$\begin{aligned} x + 3y + 5z &= 20 \\ y - 4z &= -16 \\ 3x - 2y + 9z &= 36 \end{aligned}$$

15.
$$\begin{aligned} x + y &= -4 \\ y - z &= 1 \\ 2x + y + 3z &= -21 \end{aligned}$$

16.
$$\begin{aligned} x + y &= 4 \\ x + z &= 4 \\ y + z &= 4 \end{aligned}$$

17.
$$\begin{aligned} 3(2x + y) + 5z &= -1 \\ 2(x - 3y + 4z) &= -9 \\ 4(1 + x) &= -3(z - 3y) \end{aligned}$$

18.
$$\begin{aligned} 7z - 3 &= 2(x - 3y) \\ 5y + 3z - 7 &= 4x \\ 4 + 5z &= 3(2x - y) \end{aligned}$$

In Exercises 19–22, find the quadratic function $y = ax^2 + bx + c$ whose graph passes through the given points.

19. $(-1, 6), (1, 4), (2, 9)$ **20.** $(-2, 7), (1, -2), (2, 3)$

21. $(-1, -4), (1, -2), (2, 5)$ **22.** $(1, 3), (3, -1), (4, 0)$

In Exercises 23–24, let x represent the first number, y the second number, and z the third number. Use the given conditions to write a system of equations. Solve the system and find the numbers.

23. The sum of three numbers is 16. The sum of twice the first number, 3 times the second number, and 4 times the third number is 46. The difference between 5 times the first number and the second number is 31. Find the three numbers.

24. The following is known about three numbers: Three times the first number plus the second number plus twice the third number is 5. If 3 times the second number is subtracted from the sum of the first number and 3 times the third number, the result is 2. If the third number is subtracted from 2 times the first number and 3 times the second number, the result is 1. Find the numbers.

Practice Plus

Solve each system in Exercises 25–26.

25.
$$\begin{aligned} \frac{x+2}{6} - \frac{y+4}{3} + \frac{z}{2} &= 0 \\ \frac{x+1}{2} + \frac{y-1}{2} - \frac{z}{4} &= \frac{9}{2} \\ \frac{x-5}{4} + \frac{y+1}{3} + \frac{z-2}{2} &= \frac{19}{4} \end{aligned}$$

26.
$$\begin{aligned} \frac{x+3}{2} - \frac{y-1}{2} + \frac{z+2}{4} &= \frac{3}{2} \\ \frac{x-5}{2} + \frac{y+1}{3} - \frac{z}{4} &= -\frac{25}{6} \\ \frac{x-3}{4} - \frac{y+1}{2} + \frac{z-3}{2} &= -\frac{5}{2} \end{aligned}$$

In Exercises 27–28, find the equation of the quadratic function $y = ax^2 + bx + c$ whose graph is shown. Select three points whose coordinates appear to be integers.

27.

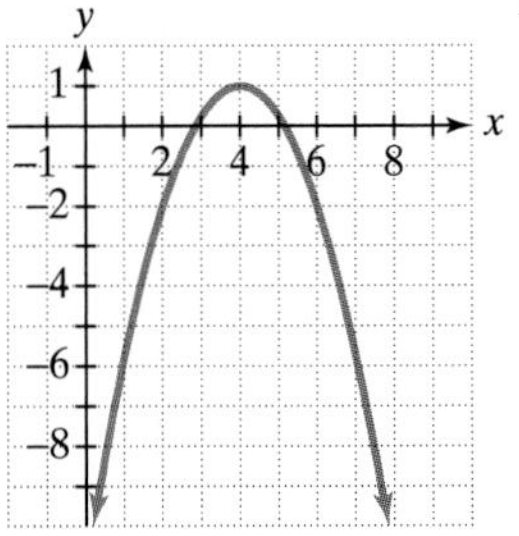

28.

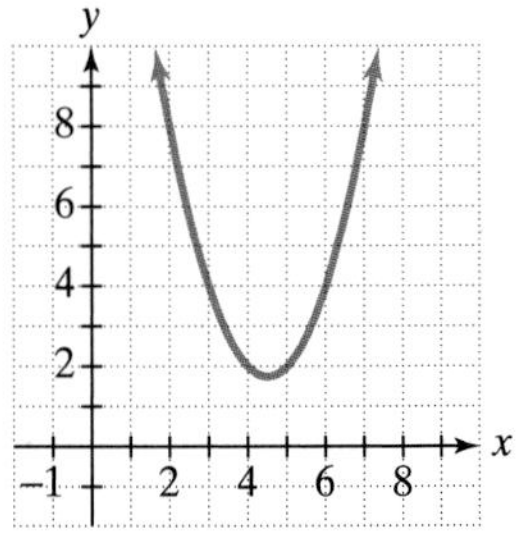

In Exercises 29–30, solve each system for (x, y, z) in terms of the nonzero constants a, b, and c.

29.
$$\begin{aligned} ax - by - 2cz &= 21 \\ ax + by + cz &= 0 \\ 2ax - by + cz &= 14 \end{aligned}$$

30.
$$\begin{aligned} ax - by + 2cz &= -4 \\ ax + 3by - cz &= 1 \\ 2ax + by + 3cz &= 2 \end{aligned}$$

Application Exercises

31. Although headlines about illegal steroids have focused on professional and Olympic athletes, the most vulnerable users may be high school students. The bar graph at the top of the next page shows the percentage of U.S. high school seniors who had taken steroids from 2000 through 2003.

Percentage of U.S. High School Seniors Who Had Taken Steroids

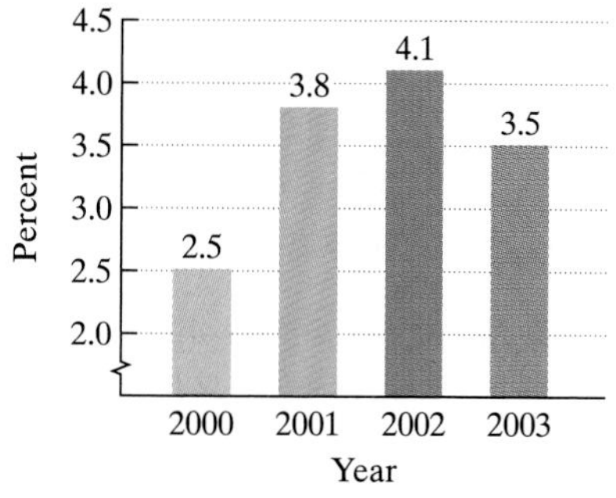

Source: University of Michigan

a. Write the data for 2000, 2002, and 2003 as ordered pairs (x, y), where x is the number of years after 2000 and y is the percentage of seniors who had taken steroids in that year.

b. The three data points in part (a) can be modeled by the quadratic function $y = ax^2 + bx + c$. Substitute each ordered pair into this function, one ordered pair at a time, and write a system of linear equations in three variables that can be used to find values for a, b, and c.

c. Solve the system in part (b) and write a quadratic function that models the percentage of U.S. high school seniors who had taken steroids x years after 2000.

32. The bar graph shows the percentage of people in the United States living below the poverty level for selected years from 1990 through 2003.

Percentage of People in the U.S. Living Below the Poverty Level

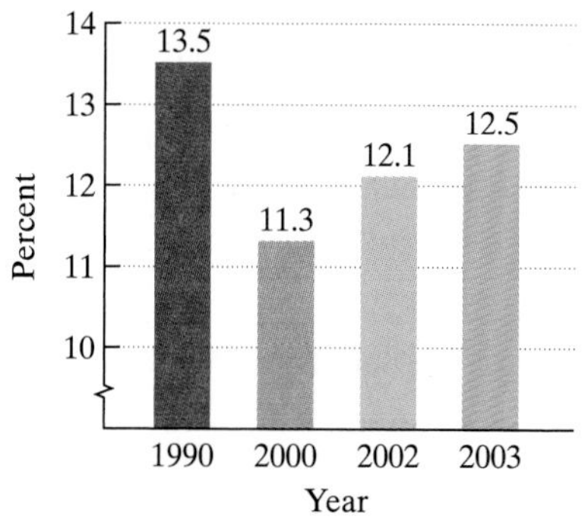

Source: Department of Health and Human Services

a. Write the data for 1990, 2002, and 2003 as ordered pairs (x, y), where x is the number of years after 1990 and y is the percentage of people living below the poverty level.

b. The three data points in part (a) can be modeled by the quadratic function $y = ax^2 + bx + c$. Substitute each ordered pair into this function, one ordered pair at a time, and write a system of linear equations in three variables that can be used to find values for a, b, and c. It is not necessary to solve the system.

33. You throw a ball straight up from a rooftop. The ball misses the rooftop on its way down and eventually strikes the ground. A mathematical model can be used to describe the relationship for the ball's height above the ground, y, after x seconds. Consider the following data:

x, seconds after the ball is thrown	y, ball's height, in feet, above the ground
1	224
3	176
4	104

a. Find the quadratic function $y = ax^2 + bx + c$ whose graph passes through the given points.

b. Use the function in part (a) to find the value for y when $x = 5$. Describe what this means.

34. A mathematical model can be used to describe the relationship between the number of feet a car travels once the brakes are applied, y, and the number of seconds the car is in motion after the brakes are applied, x. A research firm collects the following data:

x, seconds in motion after brakes are applied	y, feet car travels once the brakes are applied
1	46
2	84
3	114

a. Find the quadratic function $y = ax^2 + bx + c$ whose graph passes through the given points.

b. Use the function in part (a) to find the value for y when $x = 6$. Describe what this means.

Use a system of linear equations in three variables to solve Exercises 35–41.

35. In current U.S. dollars, John D. Rockefeller's 1913 fortune of \$900 million would be worth about \$189 billion. The bar graph shows that Rockefeller is the wealthiest among the world's five richest people of all time. The combined estimated wealth, in current billions of U.S. dollars, of Andrew Carnegie, Cornelius Vanderbilt, and Bill Gates is \$244 billion. The difference between Carnegie's estimated wealth and Vanderbilt's is \$4 billion. The difference between Vanderbilt's estimated wealth and Gates's is \$48 billion. Find the estimated wealth, in current billions of U.S. dollars, of Carnegie, Vanderbilt, and Gates.

The Richest People of All Time Estimated Wealth, in Current Billions of U.S. Dollars

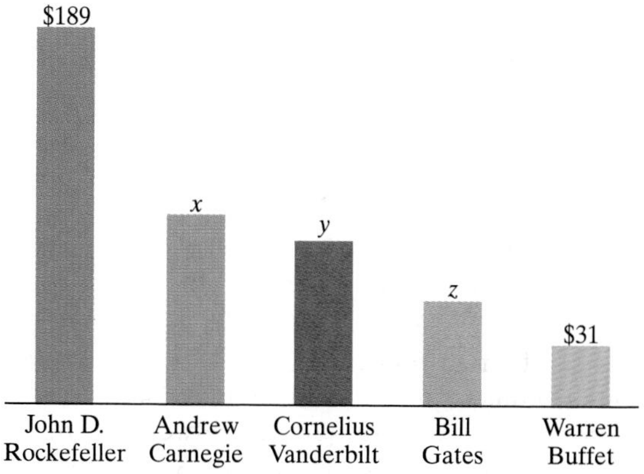

Source: Scholastic Book of World Records

36. The circle graph shows the percentage of Americans who drink caffeinated beverages on a daily basis and the number of cups consumed per day.

A Wired Nation: Percentage of American Adults Drinking Caffeinated Beverages

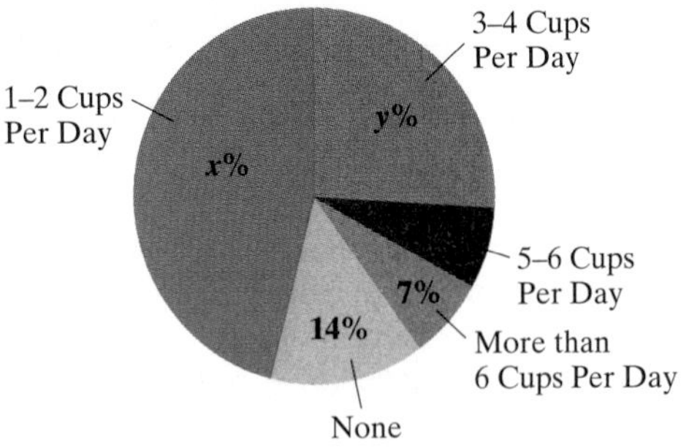

Source: Harris Interactive

72% of American adults drink from one to four cups of caffeinated beverages per day and 40% drink three or more cups per day. Find the percentage who drink from one to two cups, from three to four cups, and from five to six cups of caffeinated beverages per day.

37. At a college production of *Streetcar Named Desire*, 400 tickets were sold. The ticket prices were \$8, \$10, and \$12, and the total income from ticket sales was \$3700. How many tickets of each type were sold if the combined number of \$8 and \$10 tickets sold was 7 times the number of \$12 tickets sold?

38. A certain brand of razor blades comes in packages of 6, 12, and 24 blades, costing \$2, \$3, and \$4 per package, respectively. A store sold 12 packages containing a total of 162 razor blades and took in \$35. How many packages of each type were sold?

39. A person invested \$6700 for one year, part at 8%, part at 10%, and the remainder at 12%. The total annual income from these investments was \$716. The amount of money invested at 12% was \$300 more than the amount invested at 8% and 10% combined. Find the amount invested at each rate.

40. A person invested \$17,000 for one year, part at 10%, part at 12%, and the remainder at 15%. The total annual income from these investments was \$2110. The amount of money invested at 12% was \$1000 less than the amount invested at 10% and 15% combined. Find the amount invested at each rate.

41. In the following triangle, the degree measures of the three interior angles and two of the exterior angles are represented with variables. Find the measure of each interior angle.

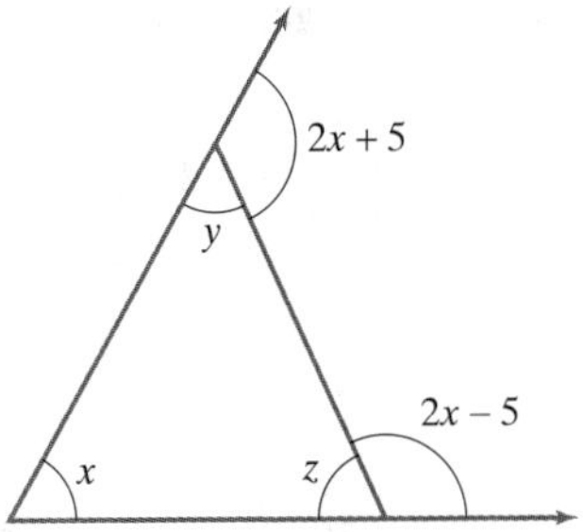

Writing in Mathematics

42. What is a system of linear equations in three variables?

43. How do you determine whether a given ordered triple is a solution of a system in three variables?

44. Describe in general terms how to solve a system in three variables.

45. AIDS is taking a deadly toll on southern Africa. Describe how to use the techniques that you learned in this section to obtain a model for African life span using projections with AIDS, shown by the red graph in the figure. Let x represent the number of years after 1985 and let y represent African life span in that year.

African Life Span

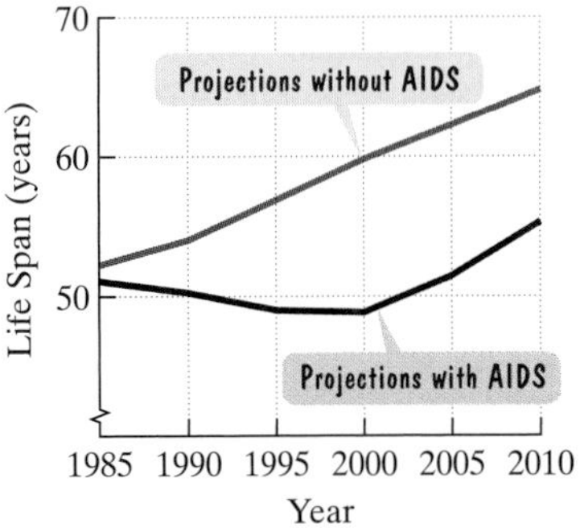

Source: United Nations

Technology Exercises

46. Does your graphing utility have a feature that allows you to solve linear systems by entering coefficients and constant terms? If so, use this feature to verify the solutions to any five exercises that you worked by hand from Exercises 5–16.

47. Verify your results in Exercises 19–22 by using a graphing utility to graph the resulting parabola. Trace along the curve and convince yourself that the three points given in the exercise lie on the parabola.

Critical Thinking Exercises

48. Describe how the system

$$\begin{aligned} x + y - z - 2w &= -8 \\ x - 2y + 3z + w &= 18 \\ 2x + 2y + 2z - 2w &= 10 \\ 2x + y - z + w &= 3 \end{aligned}$$

could be solved. Is it likely that in the near future a graphing utility will be available to provide a geometric solution (using intersecting graphs) to this system? Explain.

49. A modernistic painting consists of triangles, rectangles, and pentagons, all drawn so as to not overlap or share sides. Within each rectangle are drawn 2 red roses and each pentagon contains 5 carnations. How many triangles, rectangles, and pentagons appear in the painting if the painting contains a total of 40 geometric figures, 153 sides of geometric figures, and 72 flowers?

Group Exercise

50. Group members should develop appropriate functions that model each of the projections shown in Exercise 45.

SECTION 3.3 Matrix Solutions to Linear Systems

Objectives

1. Write the augmented matrix for a linear system.
2. Perform matrix row operations.
3. Use matrices and Gaussian elimination to solve systems.
4. Use matrices and Gauss-Jordan elimination to solve systems.

Yes, we overindulged, but it was delicious. Anyway, a few hours of moderate activity and we'll just burn off those extra calories. The following chart should help. We see that the number of calories burned per hour depends on our weight. Four hours of tennis and we'll be as good as new!

How Fast You Burn Off Calories

	Weight (pounds)					
	110	**132**	**154**	**176**	**187**	**209**
Activity	**Calories Burned per Hour**					
Housework	175	210	245	285	300	320
Cycling	190	215	245	270	280	295
Tennis	335	380	425	470	495	520
Watching TV	60	70	80	85	90	95

The 24 numbers inside the red brackets are arranged in four rows and six columns. This rectangular array of 24 numbers, arranged in rows and columns and placed in brackets, is an example of a **matrix** (plural: **matrices**). The numbers inside the brackets are called **elements** of the matrix. Matrices are used to display information and to solve systems of linear equations. Because systems involving two equations in two variables can easily be solved by substitution or addition, we will focus on matrix solutions to systems of linear equations in three or more variables.

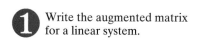

1 Write the augmented matrix for a linear system.

Solving Linear Systems Using Matrices

A matrix gives us a shortened way of writing a system of equations. The first step in solving a system of linear equations using matrices is to write the *augmented matrix*. An **augmented matrix** has a vertical bar separating the columns of the matrix into two groups. The coefficients of each variable are placed to the left of the vertical line and the constants are placed to the right. If any variable is missing, its coefficient is 0. Here are two examples:

System of Linear Equations | **Augmented Matrix**

$$\begin{aligned} 3x + y + 2z &= 31 \\ x + y + 2z &= 19 \\ x + 3y + 2z &= 25 \end{aligned} \qquad \left[\begin{array}{ccc|c} 3 & 1 & 2 & 31 \\ 1 & 1 & 2 & 19 \\ 1 & 3 & 2 & 25 \end{array}\right]$$

$$\begin{aligned} x + 2y - 5z &= -19 \\ y + 3z &= 9 \\ z &= 4 \end{aligned} \qquad \left[\begin{array}{ccc|c} 1 & 2 & -5 & -19 \\ 0 & 1 & 3 & 9 \\ 0 & 0 & 1 & 4 \end{array}\right].$$

Notice how the second matrix contains 1s down the diagonal from upper left to lower right, called the **main diagonal**, and 0s below the 1s. This arrangement makes it easy to find the solution of the system of equations, as Example 1 shows.

EXAMPLE 1 Solving a System Using a Matrix

Write the solution set for a system of equations represented by the matrix

$$\left[\begin{array}{ccc|c} 1 & 2 & -5 & -19 \\ 0 & 1 & 3 & 9 \\ 0 & 0 & 1 & 4 \end{array}\right].$$

Solution The system represented by the given matrix is

$$\left[\begin{array}{ccc|c} 1 & 2 & -5 & -19 \\ 0 & 1 & 3 & 9 \\ 0 & 0 & 1 & 4 \end{array}\right] \rightarrow \begin{aligned} 1x + 2y - 5z &= -19 \\ 0x + 1y + 3z &= 9. \\ 0x + 0y + 1z &= 4 \end{aligned}$$

This system can be simplified as follows.

$$\begin{aligned} x + 2y - 5z &= -19 && \text{Equation 1} \\ y + 3z &= 9 && \text{Equation 2} \\ z &= 4 && \text{Equation 3} \end{aligned}$$

The value of z is known. We can find y by back-substitution.

$$\begin{aligned} y + 3z &= 9 && \text{Equation 2} \\ y + 3(4) &= 9 && \text{Substitute 4 for } z. \\ y + 12 &= 9 && \text{Multiply.} \\ y &= -3 && \text{Subtract 12 from both sides.} \end{aligned}$$

With values for y and z, we can now use back-substitution to find x.

$$\begin{aligned} x + 2y - 5z &= -19 && \text{Equation 1} \\ x + 2(-3) - 5(4) &= -19 && \text{Substitute } -3 \text{ for } y \text{ and 4 for } z. \\ x - 6 - 20 &= -19 && \text{Multiply.} \\ x - 26 &= -19 && \text{Add.} \\ x &= 7 && \text{Add 26 to both sides.} \end{aligned}$$

We see that $x = 7$, $y = -3$, and $z = 4$. The solution set for the system is $\{(7, -3, 4)\}$.

Check Point 1 Write the solution set for a system of equations represented by the matrix

$$\left[\begin{array}{ccc|c} 1 & -1 & 1 & 8 \\ 0 & 1 & -12 & -15 \\ 0 & 0 & 1 & 1 \end{array}\right].$$

Our goal in solving a system of linear equations in three variables using matrices is to produce a matrix with 1s down the main diagonal and 0s below the 1s. In general, the matrix will be of the form

$$\left[\begin{array}{ccc|c} 1 & a & b & c \\ 0 & 1 & d & e \\ 0 & 0 & 1 & f \end{array}\right]$$

where a through f represent real numbers. The third row of this matrix gives us the value of one variable. The other variables can then be found by back-substitution.

2 Perform matrix row operations.

A matrix with 1s down the main diagonal and 0s below the 1s is said to be in **row-echelon form**. How do we produce a matrix in this form? We use **row operations** on the augmented matrix. These row operations are just like what you did when solving a linear system by the addition method. The difference is that we no longer write the variables, usually represented by x, y, and z.

Matrix Row Operations

The following row operations produce matrices that represent systems with the same solution set:

1. Two rows of a matrix may be interchanged. This is the same as interchanging two equations in a linear system.
2. The elements in any row may be multiplied by a nonzero number. This is the same as multiplying both sides of an equation by a nonzero number.
3. The elements in any row may be multiplied by a nonzero number, and these products may be added to the corresponding elements in any other row. This is the same as multiplying both sides of an equation by a nonzero number and then adding equations to eliminate a variable.

Two matrices are **row equivalent** if one can be obtained from the other by a sequence of row operations.

Study Tip

When performing the row operation

$$kR_i + R_j,$$

we use row i to find the products. However, **elements in row i do not change. It is the elements in row j that change:** Add k times the elements in row i to the corresponding elements in row j. Replace elements in row j by these sums.

Each matrix row operation in the preceding box can be expressed symbolically as follows:

1. Interchange the elements in the ith and jth rows: $R_i \leftrightarrow R_j$.
2. Multiply each element in the ith row by k: kR_i.
3. Add k times the elements in row i to the corresponding elements in row j: $kR_i + R_j$.

EXAMPLE 2 Performing Matrix Row Operations

Use the matrix

$$\left[\begin{array}{rrr|r} 3 & 18 & -12 & 21 \\ 1 & 2 & -3 & 5 \\ -2 & -3 & 4 & -6 \end{array}\right]$$

and perform each indicated row operation:

a. $R_1 \leftrightarrow R_2$ **b.** $\frac{1}{3}R_1$ **c.** $2R_2 + R_3$.

Solution

a. The notation $R_1 \leftrightarrow R_2$ means to interchange the elements in row 1 and row 2. This results in the row-equivalent matrix

$$\left[\begin{array}{rrr|r} 1 & 2 & -3 & 5 \\ 3 & 18 & -12 & 21 \\ -2 & -3 & 4 & -6 \end{array}\right].$$

This was row 2; now it's row 1.

This was row 1; now it's row 2.

b. The notation $\frac{1}{3}R_1$ means to multiply each element in row 1 by $\frac{1}{3}$. This results in the row-equivalent matrix

$$\left[\begin{array}{rrr|r} \frac{1}{3}(3) & \frac{1}{3}(18) & \frac{1}{3}(-12) & \frac{1}{3}(21) \\ 1 & 2 & -3 & 5 \\ -2 & -3 & 4 & -6 \end{array}\right] = \left[\begin{array}{rrr|r} 1 & 6 & -4 & 7 \\ 1 & 2 & -3 & 5 \\ -2 & -3 & 4 & -6 \end{array}\right].$$

c. The notation $2R_2 + R_3$ means to add 2 times the elements in row 2 to the corresponding elements in row 3. Replace the elements in row 3 by these sums. First, we find 2 times the elements in row 2, namely, 1, 2, −3 and 5:

$$2(1) \text{ or } 2, \quad 2(2) \text{ or } 4, \quad 2(-3) \text{ or } -6, \quad 2(5) \text{ or } 10.$$

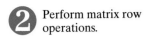

Now we add these products to the corresponding elements in row 3. Although we use row 2 to find the products, row 2 does not change. It is the elements in row 3 that change, resulting in the row-equivalent matrix

Replace row 3 by the sum of itself and 2 times row 2.

$$\left[\begin{array}{ccc|c} 3 & 18 & -12 & 21 \\ 1 & 2 & -3 & 5 \\ -2+2=0 & -3+4=1 & 4+(-6)=-2 & -6+10=4 \end{array}\right] = \left[\begin{array}{ccc|c} 3 & 18 & -12 & 21 \\ 1 & 2 & -3 & 5 \\ 0 & 1 & -2 & 4 \end{array}\right].$$

Check Point 2 Use the matrix

$$\left[\begin{array}{ccc|c} 4 & 12 & -20 & 8 \\ 1 & 6 & -3 & 7 \\ -3 & -2 & 1 & -9 \end{array}\right]$$

and perform each indicated row operation:

a. $R_1 \leftrightarrow R_2$ **b.** $\frac{1}{4}R_1$ **c.** $3R_2 + R_3$.

3 Use matrices and Gaussian elimination to solve systems.

The process that we use to solve linear systems using matrix row operations is called **Gaussian elimination**, after the German mathematician Carl Friedrich Gauss (1777–1855). Here are the steps used in Gaussian elimination:

Solving Linear Systems Using Gaussian Elimination

1. Write the augmented matrix for the system.
2. Use matrix row operations to simplify the matrix to a row-equivalent matrix in row-echelon form, with 1s down the main diagonal from upper left to lower right, and 0s below the 1s.

$$\left[\begin{array}{ccc|c} 1 & * & * & * \\ * & * & * & * \\ * & * & * & * \end{array}\right] \rightarrow \left[\begin{array}{ccc|c} 1 & * & * & * \\ 0 & * & * & * \\ 0 & * & * & * \end{array}\right] \rightarrow \left[\begin{array}{ccc|c} 1 & * & * & * \\ 0 & 1 & * & * \\ 0 & * & * & * \end{array}\right] \rightarrow \left[\begin{array}{ccc|c} 1 & * & * & * \\ 0 & 1 & * & * \\ 0 & 0 & * & * \end{array}\right] \rightarrow \left[\begin{array}{ccc|c} 1 & * & * & * \\ 0 & 1 & * & * \\ 0 & 0 & 1 & * \end{array}\right]$$

Get 1 in the upper left-hand corner. Use the 1 in the first column to get 0s below it. Get 1 in the second row, second column position. Use the 1 in the second column to get 0 below it. Get 1 in the third row, third column position.

3. Write the system of linear equations corresponding to the matrix in step 2 and use back-substitution to find the system's solution.

EXAMPLE 3 Gaussian Elimination with Back-Substitution

Use matrices to solve the system:

$$\begin{aligned} 3x + y + 2z &= 31 \\ x + y + 2z &= 19 \\ x + 3y + 2z &= 25. \end{aligned}$$

Solution

Step 1 Write the augmented matrix for the system.

Linear System

$$\begin{aligned} 3x + y + 2z &= 31 \\ x + y + 2z &= 19 \\ x + 3y + 2z &= 25 \end{aligned}$$

Augmented Matrix

$$\left[\begin{array}{ccc|c} 3 & 1 & 2 & 31 \\ 1 & 1 & 2 & 19 \\ 1 & 3 & 2 & 25 \end{array}\right]$$

Step 2 Use matrix row operations to simplify the matrix to row-echelon form, with 1s down the main diagonal from upper left to lower right, and 0s below the 1s. Our first step in achieving this goal is to get 1 in the top position of the first column.

We want 1 in this position.

$$\left[\begin{array}{ccc|c} 3 & 1 & 2 & 31 \\ 1 & 1 & 2 & 19 \\ 1 & 3 & 2 & 25 \end{array}\right]$$

To get 1 in this position, we interchange row 1 and row 2: $R_1 \leftrightarrow R_2$. (We could also interchange row 1 and row 3 to attain our goal.)

$$\left[\begin{array}{ccc|c} 1 & 1 & 2 & 19 \\ 3 & 1 & 2 & 31 \\ 1 & 3 & 2 & 25 \end{array}\right]$$

This was row 2; now it's row 1.

This was row 1; now it's row 2.

Now we want to get 0s below the 1 in the first column.

We want 0 in these positions.

$$\left[\begin{array}{ccc|c} 1 & 1 & 2 & 19 \\ 3 & 1 & 2 & 31 \\ 1 & 3 & 2 & 25 \end{array}\right]$$

To get a 0 where there is now a 3, multiply the top row of numbers by -3 and add these products to the second row of numbers: $-3R_1 + R_2$. To get a 0 where there is now a 1, multiply the top row of numbers by -1 and add these products to the third row of numbers: $-1R_1 + R_3$. Although we are using row 1 to find the products, the numbers in row 1 do not change.

Replace row 2 by $-3R_1 + R_2$.

Replace row 3 by $-1R_1 + R_3$.

$$\left[\begin{array}{ccc|c} 1 & 1 & 2 & 19 \\ -3(1)+3 & -3(1)+1 & -3(2)+2 & -3(19)+31 \\ -1(1)+1 & -1(1)+3 & -1(2)+2 & -1(19)+25 \end{array}\right] = \left[\begin{array}{ccc|c} 1 & 1 & 2 & 19 \\ 0 & -2 & -4 & -26 \\ 0 & 2 & 0 & 6 \end{array}\right]$$

We want 1 in this position.

We move on to the second column. To get 1 in the desired position, we multiply -2 by its reciprocal, $-\frac{1}{2}$. Therefore, we multiply all the numbers in the second row by $-\frac{1}{2}$: $-\frac{1}{2}R_2$.

$-\frac{1}{2}R_2$

$$\left[\begin{array}{ccc|c} 1 & 1 & 2 & 19 \\ -\frac{1}{2}(0) & -\frac{1}{2}(-2) & -\frac{1}{2}(-4) & -\frac{1}{2}(-26) \\ 0 & 2 & 0 & 6 \end{array}\right] = \left[\begin{array}{ccc|c} 1 & 1 & 2 & 19 \\ 0 & 1 & 2 & 13 \\ 0 & 2 & 0 & 6 \end{array}\right].$$

We want 0 in this position.

We are not yet done with the second column. The voice balloon shows that we want to get a 0 where there is now a 2. If we multiply the second row of numbers by -2 and add these products to the third row of numbers, we will get 0 in this position: $-2R_2 + R_3$. Although we are using the numbers in row 2 to find the products, the numbers in row 2 do not change.

Replace row 3 by $-2R_2 + R_3$.

$$\left[\begin{array}{ccc|c} 1 & 1 & 2 & 19 \\ 0 & 1 & 2 & 13 \\ -2(0)+0 & -2(1)+2 & -2(2)+0 & -2(13)+6 \end{array}\right] = \left[\begin{array}{ccc|c} 1 & 1 & 2 & 19 \\ 0 & 1 & 2 & 13 \\ 0 & 0 & -4 & -20 \end{array}\right]$$

We want 1 in this position.

We move on to the third column. To get 1 in the desired position, we multiply -4 by its reciprocal, $-\frac{1}{4}$. Therefore, we multiply all the numbers in the third row by $-\frac{1}{4}$: $-\frac{1}{4}R_3$.

$-\frac{1}{4}R_3$

$$\left[\begin{array}{ccc|c} 1 & 1 & 2 & 19 \\ 0 & 1 & 2 & 13 \\ -\frac{1}{4}(0) & -\frac{1}{4}(0) & -\frac{1}{4}(-4) & -\frac{1}{4}(-20) \end{array}\right] = \left[\begin{array}{ccc|c} 1 & 1 & 2 & 19 \\ 0 & 1 & 2 & 13 \\ 0 & 0 & 1 & 5 \end{array}\right].$$

We now have the desired matrix in row-echelon form, with 1s down the main diagonal and 0s below the 1s.

Step 3 Write the system of linear equations corresponding to the matrix in step 2 and use back-substitution to find the system's solution. The system represented by the matrix in step 2 is

$$\left[\begin{array}{ccc|c} 1 & 1 & 2 & 19 \\ 0 & 1 & 2 & 13 \\ 0 & 0 & 1 & 5 \end{array}\right] \rightarrow \begin{aligned} 1x + 1y + 2z &= 19 \\ 0x + 1y + 2z &= 13 \\ 0x + 0y + 1z &= 5 \end{aligned} \quad \text{or} \quad \begin{aligned} x + y + 2z &= 19 & (1)\\ y + 2z &= 13. & (2)\\ z &= 5 & (3) \end{aligned}$$

We immediately see from equation (3) that the value for z is 5. To find y, we back-substitute 5 for z in the second equation.

$$\begin{aligned} y + 2z &= 13 && \text{Equation (2)} \\ y + 2(5) &= 13 && \text{Substitute 5 for } z. \\ y &= 3 && \text{Solve for } y. \end{aligned}$$

Finally, back-substitute 3 for y and 5 for z in the first equation.

$$\begin{aligned} x + y + 2z &= 19 && \text{Equation (1)} \\ x + 3 + 2(5) &= 19 && \text{Substitute 3 for } y \text{ and 5 for } z. \\ x + 13 &= 19 && \text{Multiply and add.} \\ x &= 6 && \text{Subtract 13 from both sides.} \end{aligned}$$

The solution set of the original system is $\{(6, 3, 5)\}$. Check to see that the solution satisfies all three equations in the given system.

Technology

Most graphing utilities can convert an augmented matrix to row-echelon form, with 1s down the main diagonal and 0s below the 1s. However, row-echelon form is not unique. Your graphing utility might give a row-echelon form different from the one you obtained by hand. However, all row-echelon forms for a given system's augmented matrix produce the same solution to the system. Enter the augmented matrix and name it A. Then use the REF (row-echelon form) command on matrix A.

Check Point 3 Use matrices to solve the system:

$$\begin{aligned} 2x + y + 2z &= 18 \\ x - y + 2z &= 9 \\ x + 2y - z &= 6. \end{aligned}$$

Modern supercomputers are capable of solving systems with more than 600,000 variables. The augmented matrices for such systems are huge, but the solution using matrices is exactly like what we did in Example 3. Work with the augmented matrix, one column at a time. First, get 1 in the desired position. Then get 0s below the 1. Let's see how this works for a linear system involving four equations in four variables.

EXAMPLE 4 Gaussian Elimination with Back-Substitution

Use matrices to solve the system:

$$\begin{aligned} 2w + x + 3y - z &= 6 \\ w - x + 2y - 2z &= -1 \\ w - x - y + z &= -4 \\ -w + 2x - 2y - z &= -7. \end{aligned}$$

Solution

Step 1 Write the augmented matrix for the system.

Linear System	Augmented Matrix
$\begin{aligned} 2w + x + 3y - z &= 6 \\ w - x + 2y - 2z &= -1 \\ w - x - y + z &= -4 \\ -w + 2x - 2y - z &= -7 \end{aligned}$	$\left[\begin{array}{cccc|c} 2 & 1 & 3 & -1 & 6 \\ 1 & -1 & 2 & -2 & -1 \\ 1 & -1 & -1 & 1 & -4 \\ -1 & 2 & -2 & -1 & -7 \end{array}\right]$

Step 2 Use matrix row operations to simplify the matrix to row-echelon form, with 1s down the diagonal from upper left to lower right, and 0s below the 1s. Working one column at a time, we must obtain 1 in the diagonal position. Then we use this 1 to get 0s below it. Thus, our first step in achieving this goal is to get 1 in the top position of the first column. To do this, we interchange row 1 and row 2: $R_1 \leftrightarrow R_2$.

$$\left[\begin{array}{cccc|c} 1 & -1 & 2 & -2 & -1 \\ 2 & 1 & 3 & -1 & 6 \\ 1 & -1 & -1 & 1 & -4 \\ -1 & 2 & -2 & -1 & -7 \end{array}\right]$$

This was row 2; now it's row 1.

This was row 1; now it's row 2.

We want 0s in these positions.

Now we use the 1 at the top of the first column to get 0s below it.

Use the previous matrix and:
Replace row 2 by $-2R_1 + R_2$.
Replace row 3 by $-1R_1 + R_3$.
Replace row 4 by $1R_1 + R_4$.

$$\left[\begin{array}{cccc|c} 1 & -1 & 2 & -2 & -1 \\ 0 & 3 & -1 & 3 & 8 \\ 0 & 0 & -3 & 3 & -3 \\ 0 & 1 & 0 & -3 & -8 \end{array}\right]$$

We want 1 in this position.

We move on to the second column. We can obtain 1 in the desired position by multiplying the numbers in the second row by $\frac{1}{3}$, the reciprocal of 3.

$$\left[\begin{array}{cccc|c} 1 & -1 & 2 & -2 & -1 \\ \frac{1}{3}(0) & \frac{1}{3}(3) & \frac{1}{3}(-1) & \frac{1}{3}(3) & \frac{1}{3}(8) \\ 0 & 0 & -3 & 3 & -3 \\ 0 & 1 & 0 & -3 & -8 \end{array}\right] = \left[\begin{array}{cccc|c} 1 & -1 & 2 & -2 & -1 \\ 0 & 1 & -\frac{1}{3} & 1 & \frac{8}{3} \\ 0 & 0 & -3 & 3 & -3 \\ 0 & 1 & 0 & -3 & -8 \end{array}\right] \quad \frac{1}{3}R_2$$

We want 0s in these positions. The top position already has a 0.

Now we use the 1 in the second row, second column position to get 0s below it.

Replace row 4 in the previous matrix by $-1R_2 + R_4$.

$$\left[\begin{array}{cccc|c} 1 & -1 & 2 & -2 & -1 \\ 0 & 1 & -\frac{1}{3} & 1 & \frac{8}{3} \\ 0 & 0 & -3 & 3 & -3 \\ 0 & 0 & \frac{1}{3} & -4 & -\frac{32}{3} \end{array}\right]$$

We want 1 in this position.

We move on to the third column. We can obtain 1 in the desired position by multiplying the numbers in the third row by $-\frac{1}{3}$, the reciprocal of -3.

$$\left[\begin{array}{cccc|c} 1 & -1 & 2 & -2 & -1 \\ 0 & 1 & -\frac{1}{3} & 1 & \frac{8}{3} \\ -\frac{1}{3}(0) & -\frac{1}{3}(0) & -\frac{1}{3}(-3) & -\frac{1}{3}(3) & -\frac{1}{3}(-3) \\ 0 & 0 & \frac{1}{3} & -4 & -\frac{32}{3} \end{array}\right] = \left[\begin{array}{cccc|c} 1 & -1 & 2 & -2 & -1 \\ 0 & 1 & -\frac{1}{3} & 1 & \frac{8}{3} \\ 0 & 0 & 1 & -1 & 1 \\ 0 & 0 & \frac{1}{3} & -4 & -\frac{32}{3} \end{array}\right] \quad -\frac{1}{3}R_3$$

We want 0 in this position.

Now we use the 1 in the third column to get 0 below it.

Replace row 4 in the previous matrix by $-\frac{1}{3}R_3 + R_4$.

$$\left[\begin{array}{cccc|c} 1 & -1 & 2 & -2 & -1 \\ 0 & 1 & -\frac{1}{3} & 1 & \frac{8}{3} \\ 0 & 0 & 1 & -1 & 1 \\ 0 & 0 & 0 & -\frac{11}{3} & -11 \end{array}\right]$$

We want 1 in this position.

We move on to the fourth column. Because we want 1s down the diagonal from upper left to lower right, we want 1 where there is now $-\frac{11}{3}$. We can obtain 1 in this position by multiplying the numbers in the fourth row by $-\frac{3}{11}$.

$$\left[\begin{array}{cccc|c} 1 & -1 & 2 & -2 & -1 \\ 0 & 1 & -\frac{1}{3} & 1 & \frac{8}{3} \\ 0 & 0 & 1 & -1 & 1 \\ -\frac{3}{11}(0) & -\frac{3}{11}(0) & -\frac{3}{11}(0) & -\frac{3}{11}(-\frac{11}{3}) & -\frac{3}{11}(-11) \end{array}\right]$$

$$= \left[\begin{array}{cccc|c} 1 & -1 & 2 & -2 & -1 \\ 0 & 1 & -\frac{1}{3} & 1 & \frac{8}{3} \\ 0 & 0 & 1 & -1 & 1 \\ 0 & 0 & 0 & 1 & 3 \end{array}\right] \quad -\tfrac{3}{11}R_4$$

We now have the desired matrix in row-echelon form, with 1s down the main diagonal and 0s below the 1s. An equivalent row-echelon matrix can be obtained using a graphing utility and the REF command on the augmented matrix.

Step 3 Write the system of linear equations corresponding to the matrix in step 2 and use back-substitution to find the system's solution. The system represented by the matrix in step 2 is

$$\left[\begin{array}{cccc|c} 1 & -1 & 2 & -2 & -1 \\ 0 & 1 & -\frac{1}{3} & 1 & \frac{8}{3} \\ 0 & 0 & 1 & -1 & 1 \\ 0 & 0 & 0 & 1 & 3 \end{array}\right] \rightarrow \begin{aligned} 1w - 1x + 2y - 2z &= -1 \\ 0w + 1x - \tfrac{1}{3}y + 1z &= \tfrac{8}{3} \\ 0w + 0x + 1y - 1z &= 1 \\ 0w + 0x + 0y + 1z &= 3 \end{aligned} \quad \text{or} \quad \begin{aligned} w - x + 2y - 2z &= -1 \\ x - \tfrac{1}{3}y + z &= \tfrac{8}{3} \\ y - z &= 1 \\ z &= 3. \end{aligned}$$

We immediately see that the value for z is 3. We can now use back-substitution to find the values for y, x, and w.

These are the four equations from the last column.

$$z = 3$$

$$\begin{aligned} y - z &= 1 \\ y - 3 &= 1 \\ y &= 4 \end{aligned}$$

$$\begin{aligned} x - \frac{1}{3}y + z &= \frac{8}{3} \\ x - \frac{1}{3}(4) + 3 &= \frac{8}{3} \\ x + \frac{5}{3} &= \frac{8}{3} \\ x &= 1 \end{aligned}$$

$$\begin{aligned} w - x + 2y - 2z &= -1 \\ w - 1 + 2(4) - 2(3) &= -1 \\ w - 1 + 8 - 6 &= -1 \\ w + 1 &= -1 \\ w &= -2 \end{aligned}$$

Let's agree to write the solution set for the system in the alphabetical order in which the variables for the given system appeared from left to right, namely (w, x, y, z). Thus, the solution set is $\{(-2, 1, 4, 3)\}$. We can verify this solution set by substituting the value for each variable into the original system of equations and obtaining four true statements.

Check Point 4 Use matrices to solve the system:

$$\begin{aligned} w - 3x - 2y + z &= -3 \\ 2w - 7x - y + 2z &= 1 \\ 3w - 7x - 3y + 3z &= -5 \\ 5w + x + 4y - 2z &= 18. \end{aligned}$$

4 Use matrices and Gauss-Jordan elimination to solve systems.

Gauss-Jordan Elimination

Using Gaussian elimination, we obtain a matrix in row-echelon form, with 1s down the main diagonal and 0s below the 1s. A second method, called **Gauss-Jordan elimination**, after Carl Friedrich Gauss and Wilhelm Jordan (1842–1899), continues the process until a matrix with 1s down the main diagonal and 0s in every position *above and below* each 1 is found. Such a matrix is said to be in **reduced row-echelon form**. For a system of linear equations in three variables, x, y, and z, we must get the augmented matrix into the form

$$\left[\begin{array}{ccc|c} 1 & 0 & 0 & a \\ 0 & 1 & 0 & b \\ 0 & 0 & 1 & c \end{array}\right].$$

Based on this matrix, we conclude that $x = a$, $y = b$, and $z = c$.

Solving Linear Systems Using Gauss-Jordan Elimination

1. Write the augmented matrix for the system.
2. Use matrix row operations to simplify the matrix to a row-equivalent matrix in reduced row-echelon form, with 1s down the main diagonal from upper left to lower right, and 0s above and below the 1s.
 a. Get 1 in the upper left-hand corner.
 b. Use the 1 in the first column to get 0s below it.
 c. Get 1 in the second row, second column.
 d. Use the 1 in the second column to make the remaining entries in the second column 0.
 e. Get 1 in the third row, third column.
 f. Use the 1 in the third column to make the remaining entries in the third column 0.
 g. Continue this procedure as far as possible.
3. Use the reduced row-echelon form of the matrix in step 2 to write the system's solution set. (Back-substitution is not necessary.)

Technology

Most graphing utilities can convert a matrix to reduced row-echelon form. Enter the system's augmented matrix and name it A. Then use the [RREF] (reduced row-echelon form) command on matrix A.

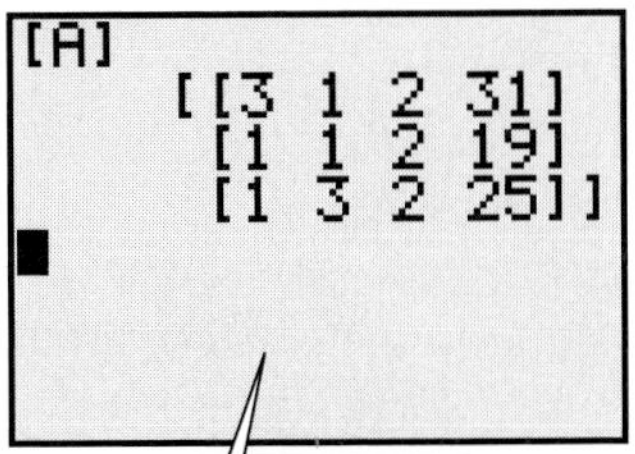

This is the augmented matrix for the system in Example 5.

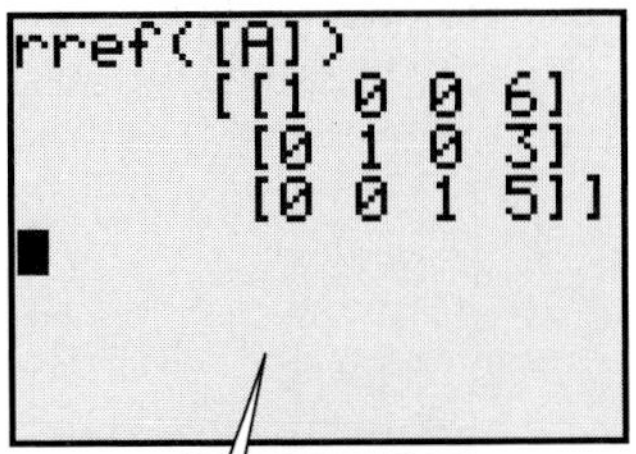

This is the matrix in reduced row-echelon form we obtained in Example 5.

EXAMPLE 5 Using Gauss-Jordan Elimination

Use Gauss-Jordan elimination to solve the system:

$$\begin{aligned} 3x + y + 2z &= 31 \\ x + y + 2z &= 19 \\ x + 3y + 2z &= 25. \end{aligned}$$

Solution In Example 3, we used Gaussian elimination to obtain the following matrix:

$$\begin{array}{l} \text{We want} \\ \text{0s in these} \\ \text{positions.} \end{array} \left[\begin{array}{ccc|c} 1 & 1 & 2 & 19 \\ 0 & 1 & 2 & 13 \\ 0 & 0 & 1 & 5 \end{array}\right].$$

To use Gauss-Jordan elimination, we need 0s both below and above the 1s in the main diagonal. We use the 1 in the second row, second column to get a 0 above it.

$$\begin{array}{l} \text{Replace row 1} \\ \text{in the previous} \\ \text{matrix by} \\ -1R_2 + R_1. \end{array} \left[\begin{array}{ccc|c} 1 & 0 & 0 & 6 \\ 0 & 1 & 2 & 13 \\ 0 & 0 & 1 & 5 \end{array}\right] \begin{array}{l} \text{We want} \\ \text{0s in these} \\ \text{positions.} \end{array}$$

We use the 1 in the third column to get 0s above it.

$$\left[\begin{array}{ccc|c} 1 & 0 & 0 & 6 \\ 0 & 1 & 0 & 3 \\ 0 & 0 & 1 & 5 \end{array}\right] \begin{array}{l} \text{Replace row 2 in the previous} \\ \text{matrix by } -2R_3 + R_2. \end{array}$$

This last matrix corresponds to

$$x = 6, \quad y = 3, \quad z = 5.$$

As we found in Example 3, the solution set is $\{(6, 3, 5)\}$.

Check Point 5 Solve the system in Check Point 3 using Gauss-Jordan elimination. Begin by working with the matrix that you obtained in Check Point 3.

EXERCISE SET 3.3

Practice Exercises

In Exercises 1–8, write the augmented matrix for each system of linear equations.

1. $\begin{aligned} 2x + y + 2z &= 2 \\ 3x - 5y - z &= 4 \\ x - 2y - 3z &= -6 \end{aligned}$

2. $\begin{aligned} 3x - 2y + 5z &= 31 \\ x + 3y - 3z &= -12 \\ -2x - 5y + 3z &= 11 \end{aligned}$

3. $\begin{aligned} x - y + z &= 8 \\ y - 12z &= -15 \\ z &= 1 \end{aligned}$

4. $\begin{aligned} x - 2y + 3z &= 9 \\ y + 3z &= 5 \\ z &= 2 \end{aligned}$

5. $\begin{aligned} 5x - 2y - 3z &= 0 \\ x + y &= 5 \\ 2x - 3z &= 4 \end{aligned}$

6. $\begin{aligned} x - 2y + z &= 10 \\ 3x + y &= 5 \\ 7x + 2z &= 2 \end{aligned}$

7. $\begin{aligned} 2w + 5x - 3y + z &= 2 \\ 3x + y &= 4 \\ w - x + 5y &= 9 \\ 5w - 5x - 2y &= 1 \end{aligned}$

8. $\begin{aligned} 4w + 7x - 8y + z &= 3 \\ 5x + y &= 5 \\ w - x - y &= 17 \\ 2w - 2x + 11y &= 4 \end{aligned}$

In Exercises 9–12, write the system of linear equations represented by the augmented matrix. Use x, y, z, and, if necessary, w, x, y, and z, for the variables.

9. $\left[\begin{array}{ccc|c} 5 & 0 & 3 & -11 \\ 0 & 1 & -4 & 12 \\ 7 & 2 & 0 & 3 \end{array}\right]$

10. $\left[\begin{array}{ccc|c} 7 & 0 & 4 & -13 \\ 0 & 1 & -5 & 11 \\ 2 & 7 & 0 & 6 \end{array}\right]$

11. $\left[\begin{array}{cccc|c} 1 & 1 & 4 & 1 & 3 \\ -1 & 1 & -1 & 0 & 7 \\ 2 & 0 & 0 & 5 & 11 \\ 0 & 0 & 12 & 4 & 5 \end{array}\right]$

12. $\left[\begin{array}{cccc|c} 4 & 1 & 5 & 1 & 6 \\ 1 & -1 & 0 & -1 & 8 \\ 3 & 0 & 0 & 7 & 4 \\ 0 & 0 & 11 & 5 & 3 \end{array}\right]$

In Exercises 13–18, write the system of linear equations represented by the augmented matrix. Use x, y, z, and, if necessary, w, x, y, and z, for the variables. Once the system is written, use back-substitution to find its solution.

13. $\left[\begin{array}{ccc|c} 1 & 0 & -4 & 5 \\ 0 & 1 & -12 & 13 \\ 0 & 0 & 1 & -\frac{1}{2} \end{array}\right]$

14. $\left[\begin{array}{ccc|c} 1 & 2 & 1 & 0 \\ 0 & 1 & 0 & -2 \\ 0 & 0 & 1 & 3 \end{array}\right]$

15. $\left[\begin{array}{ccc|c} 1 & \frac{1}{2} & 1 & \frac{11}{2} \\ 0 & 1 & \frac{3}{2} & 7 \\ 0 & 0 & 1 & 4 \end{array}\right]$

16. $\left[\begin{array}{ccc|c} 1 & 1 & 0 & 3 \\ 0 & 1 & \frac{3}{2} & -2 \\ 0 & 0 & 1 & 0 \end{array}\right]$

17. $\left[\begin{array}{cccc|c} 1 & -1 & 1 & 1 & 3 \\ 0 & 1 & -2 & -1 & 0 \\ 0 & 0 & 1 & 6 & 17 \\ 0 & 0 & 0 & 1 & 3 \end{array}\right]$

18. $\left[\begin{array}{cccc|c} 1 & 2 & -1 & 0 & 2 \\ 0 & 1 & 1 & -2 & -3 \\ 0 & 0 & 1 & -1 & -2 \\ 0 & 0 & 0 & 1 & 3 \end{array}\right]$

In Exercises 19–24, perform each matrix row operation and write the new matrix.

19. $\left[\begin{array}{ccc|c} 2 & -6 & 4 & 10 \\ 1 & 5 & -5 & 0 \\ 3 & 0 & 4 & 7 \end{array}\right] \quad \frac{1}{2}R_1$

20. $\left[\begin{array}{ccc|c} 3 & -12 & 6 & 9 \\ 1 & -4 & 4 & 0 \\ 2 & 0 & 7 & 4 \end{array}\right] \quad \frac{1}{3}R_1$

21. $\left[\begin{array}{ccc|c} 1 & -3 & 2 & 0 \\ 3 & 1 & -1 & 7 \\ 2 & -2 & 1 & 3 \end{array}\right] \quad -3R_1 + R_2$

22. $\left[\begin{array}{ccc|c} 1 & -1 & 5 & -6 \\ 3 & 3 & -1 & 10 \\ 1 & 3 & 2 & 5 \end{array}\right] \quad -3R_1 + R_2$

23. $\left[\begin{array}{cccc|c} 1 & -1 & 1 & 1 & 3 \\ 0 & 1 & -2 & -1 & 0 \\ 2 & 0 & 3 & 4 & 11 \\ 5 & 1 & 2 & 4 & 6 \end{array}\right] \quad \begin{array}{l} -2R_1 + R_3 \\ -5R_1 + R_4 \end{array}$

24. $\left[\begin{array}{cccc|c} 1 & -5 & 2 & -2 & 4 \\ 0 & 1 & -3 & -1 & 0 \\ 3 & 0 & 2 & -1 & 6 \\ -4 & 1 & 4 & 2 & -3 \end{array}\right] \quad \begin{array}{l} -3R_1 + R_3 \\ 4R_1 + R_4 \end{array}$

In Exercises 25–26, a few steps in the process of simplifying the given matrix to row-echelon form, with 1s down the diagonal from upper left to lower right, and 0s below the 1s, are shown. Fill in the missing numbers in the steps that are shown.

25. $\left[\begin{array}{ccc|c} 1 & -1 & 1 & 8 \\ 2 & 3 & -1 & -2 \\ 3 & -2 & -9 & 9 \end{array}\right] \rightarrow \left[\begin{array}{ccc|c} 1 & -1 & 1 & 8 \\ 0 & 5 & \square & \square \\ 0 & 1 & \square & \square \end{array}\right]$

$\rightarrow \left[\begin{array}{ccc|c} 1 & -1 & 1 & 8 \\ 0 & 1 & \square & \square \\ 0 & 1 & \square & \square \end{array}\right]$

26. $\left[\begin{array}{ccc|c} 1 & -2 & 3 & 4 \\ 2 & 1 & -4 & 3 \\ -3 & 4 & -1 & -2 \end{array}\right] \rightarrow \left[\begin{array}{ccc|c} 1 & -2 & 3 & 4 \\ 0 & 5 & \square & \square \\ 0 & -2 & \square & \square \end{array}\right]$

$\rightarrow \left[\begin{array}{ccc|c} 1 & -2 & 3 & 4 \\ 0 & 1 & \square & \square \\ 0 & -2 & \square & \square \end{array}\right]$

In Exercises 27–44, solve each system of equations using matrices. Use Gaussian elimination with back-substitution or Gauss-Jordan elimination.

27. $\begin{aligned} x + y - z &= -2 \\ 2x - y + z &= 5 \\ -x + 2y + 2z &= 1 \end{aligned}$

28. $\begin{aligned} x - 2y - z &= 2 \\ 2x - y + z &= 4 \\ -x + y - 2z &= -4 \end{aligned}$

29. $\begin{aligned} x + 3y \qquad &= 0 \\ x + y + z &= 1 \\ 3x - y - z &= 11 \end{aligned}$

30. $\begin{aligned} 3y - z &= -1 \\ x + 5y - z &= -4 \\ -3x + 6y + 2z &= 11 \end{aligned}$

31. $\begin{aligned} 2x - y - z &= 4 \\ x + y - 5z &= -4 \\ x - 2y \qquad &= 4 \end{aligned}$

32. $\begin{aligned} x \qquad - 3z &= -2 \\ 2x + 2y + z &= 4 \\ 3x + y - 2z &= 5 \end{aligned}$

33. $\begin{aligned} x + y + z &= 4 \\ x - y - z &= 0 \\ x - y + z &= 2 \end{aligned}$

34. $\begin{aligned} 3x + y - z &= 0 \\ x + y + 2z &= 6 \\ 2x + 2y + 3z &= 10 \end{aligned}$

35. $\begin{aligned} x + 2y &= z - 1 \\ x &= 4 + y - z \\ x + y - 3z &= -2 \end{aligned}$

36. $\begin{aligned} 2x + y &= z + 1 \\ 2x &= 1 + 3y - z \\ x + y + z &= 4 \end{aligned}$

37. $\begin{aligned} 3a - b - 4c &= 3 \\ 2a - b + 2c &= -8 \\ a + 2b - 3c &= 9 \end{aligned}$

38. $\begin{aligned} 3a + b - c &= 0 \\ 2a + 3b - 5c &= 1 \\ a - 2b + 3c &= -4 \end{aligned}$

39. $\begin{aligned} 2x + 2y + 7z &= -1 \\ 2x + y + 2z &= 2 \\ 4x + 6y + z &= 15 \end{aligned}$

40. $\begin{aligned} 3x + 2y + 3z &= 3 \\ 4x - 5y + 7z &= 1 \\ 2x + 3y - 2z &= 6 \end{aligned}$

41. $\begin{aligned} w + x + y + z &= 4 \\ 2w + x - 2y - z &= 0 \\ w - 2x - y - 2z &= -2 \\ 3w + 2x + y + 3z &= 4 \end{aligned}$

42. $\begin{aligned} w + x + y + z &= 5 \\ w + 2x - y - 2z &= -1 \\ w - 3x - 3y - z &= -1 \\ 2w - x + 2y - z &= -2 \end{aligned}$

43. $\begin{aligned} 3w - 4x + y + z &= 9 \\ w + x - y - z &= 0 \\ 2w + x + 4y - 2z &= 3 \\ -w + 2x + y - 3z &= 3 \end{aligned}$

44. $\begin{aligned} 2w + \qquad y - 3z &= 8 \\ w - x + \qquad 4z &= -10 \\ 3w + 5x - y - z &= 20 \\ w + x - y - z &= 6 \end{aligned}$

Practice Plus

45. Find the quadratic function $f(x) = ax^2 + bx + c$ for which $f(-2) = -4$, $f(1) = 2$, and $f(2) = 0$.

46. Find the quadratic function $f(x) = ax^2 + bx + c$ for which $f(-1) = 5$, $f(1) = 3$, and $f(2) = 5$.

47. Find the cubic function $f(x) = ax^3 + bx^2 + cx + d$ for which $f(-1) = 0$, $f(1) = 2$, $f(2) = 3$, and $f(3) = 12$.

48. Find the cubic function $f(x) = ax^3 + bx^2 + cx + d$ for which $f(-1) = 3$, $f(1) = 1$, $f(2) = 6$, and $f(3) = 7$.

49. Solve the system:

$$\begin{aligned} 2\ln w + \ln x + 3\ln y - 2\ln z &= -6 \\ 4\ln w + 3\ln x + \ln y - \ln z &= -2 \\ \ln w + \ln x + \ln y + \ln z &= -5 \\ \ln w + \ln x - \ln y - \ln z &= 5. \end{aligned}$$

(*Hint:* Let $A = \ln w$, $B = \ln x$, $C = \ln y$, and $D = \ln z$. Solve the system for A, B, C, and D. Then use the logarithmic equations to find w, x, y, and z.)

50. Solve the system:

$$\begin{aligned} \ln w + \ln x + \ln y + \ln z &= -1 \\ -\ln w + 4\ln x + \ln y - \ln z &= 0 \\ \ln w - 2\ln x + \ln y - 2\ln z &= 11 \\ -\ln w - 2\ln x + \ln y + 2\ln z &= -3. \end{aligned}$$

(*Hint:* Let $A = \ln w$, $B = \ln x$, $C = \ln y$, and $D = \ln z$. Solve the system for A, B, C, and D. Then use the logarithmic equations to find w, x, y, and z.)

Application Exercises

51. A ball is thrown straight upward. A position function

$$s(t) = \frac{1}{2}at^2 + v_0t + s_0$$

can be used to describe the ball's height, $s(t)$, in feet, after t seconds.

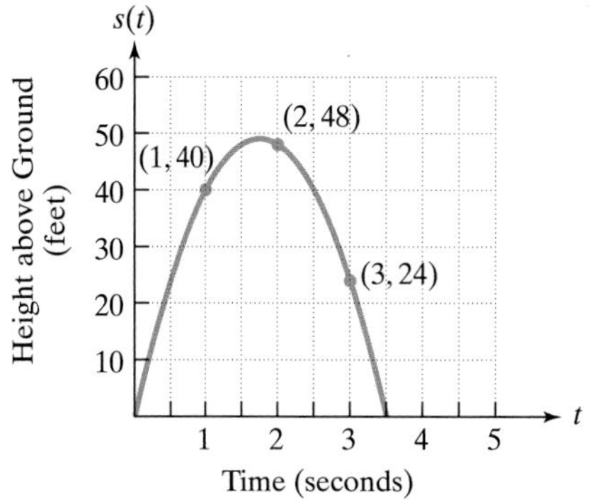

a. Use the points labeled in the graph to find the values of a, v_0, and s_0. Solve the system of linear equations involving a, v_0, and s_0 using matrices.

b. Find and interpret $s(3.5)$. Identify your solution as a point on the graph shown.

c. After how many seconds does the ball reach its maximum height? What is its maximum height?

52. A football is kicked straight upward. A position function

$$s(t) = \frac{1}{2}at^2 + v_0t + s_0$$

can be used to describe the ball's height, $s(t)$, in feet, after t seconds.

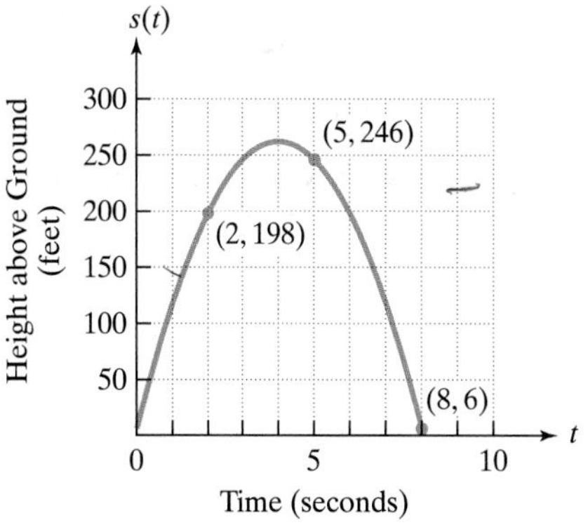

a. Use the points labeled in the graph to find the values of a, v_0, and s_0. Solve the system of linear equations involving a, v_0, and s_0 using matrices.

b. Find and interpret $s(7)$. Identify your solution as a point on the graph shown.

c. After how many seconds does the ball reach its maximum height? What is its maximum height?

Write a system of linear equations in three variables to solve Exercises 53–56. Then use matrices to solve the system.

Exercises 53–54 are based on a Time/CNN telephone poll that included never-married single women between the ages of 18 and 49 and never-married men between the ages of 18 and 49. The circle graphs show the results for one of the questions in the poll.

If You Couldn't Find the Perfect Mate, Would You Marry Someone Else?

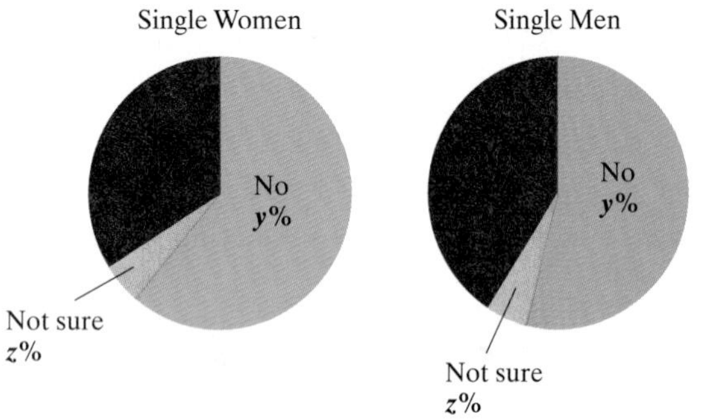

53. For single women in the poll, the percentage who said no exceeded the combined percentages for those who said yes and those who said not sure by 22%. If the percentage who said yes is doubled, it is 7% more than the percentage who said no. Find the percentage of single women who responded yes, no, and not sure.

54. For single men in the poll, the percentage who said no exceeded the combined percentages for those who said yes and those who said not sure by 8%. If the percentage who said yes is doubled, it is 28% more than the percentage who said no. Find the percentage of single men who responded yes, no, and not sure.

55. Three foods have the following nutritional content per ounce.

	Calories	Protein (in grams)	Vitamin C (in milligrams)
Food *A*	40	5	30
Food *B*	200	2	10
Food *C*	400	4	300

If a meal consisting of the three foods allows exactly 660 calories, 25 grams of protein, and 425 milligrams of vitamin C, how many ounces of each kind of food should be used?

56. A furniture company produces three types of desks: a children's model, an office model, and a deluxe model. Each desk is manufactured in three stages: cutting, construction, and finishing. The time requirements for each model and manufacturing stage are given in the following table.

	Children's model	Office model	Deluxe model
Cutting	2 hr	3 hr	2 hr
Construction	2 hr	1 hr	3 hr
Finishing	1 hr	1 hr	2 hr

Each week the company has available a maximum of 100 hours for cutting, 100 hours for construction, and 65 hours for finishing. If all available time must be used, how many of each type of desk should be produced each week?

Writing in Mathematics

57. What is a matrix?

58. Describe what is meant by the augmented matrix of a system of linear equations.

59. In your own words, describe each of the three matrix row operations. Give an example with each of the operations.

60. Describe how to use row operations and matrices to solve a system of linear equations.

61. What is the difference between Gaussian elimination and Gauss-Jordan elimination?

Technology Exercises

62. Most graphing utilities can perform row operations on matrices. Consult the owner's manual for your graphing utility to learn proper keystrokes for performing these operations. Then duplicate the row operations of any three exercises that you solved from Exercises 19–24.

63. If your graphing utility has a REF (row-echelon form) command or a RREF (reduced row-echelon form) command, use this feature to verify your work with any five systems that you solved from Exercises 27–44.

64. Solve using a graphing utility's REF or RREF command:

$$\begin{aligned} 2x_1 - 2x_2 + 3x_3 - x_4 \qquad &= 12 \\ x_1 + 2x_2 - x_3 + 2x_4 - x_5 &= -7 \\ x_1 + \qquad x_3 + x_4 - 5x_5 &= 1 \\ -x_1 + x_2 - x_3 - 2x_4 - 3x_5 &= 0 \\ x_1 - x_2 - \qquad x_4 + x_5 &= 4. \end{aligned}$$

Critical Thinking Exercises

65. Which one of the following is true?

a. A matrix row operation such as $-\frac{4}{5}R_1 + R_2$ is not permitted because of the negative fraction.

b. The augmented matrix for the system

$$\begin{aligned} x - 3y &= 5 \\ y - 2z &= 7 \\ 2x + z &= 4 \end{aligned} \quad \text{is} \quad \left[\begin{array}{cc|c} 1 & -3 & 5 \\ 1 & -2 & 7 \\ 2 & 1 & 4 \end{array}\right].$$

c. In solving a linear system of three equations in three variables, we begin with the augmented matrix and use row operations to obtain a row-equivalent matrix with 0s down the diagonal from left to right and 1s below each 0.

d. None of the above is true.

66. The table shows the daily production level and profit for a business.

x **(Number of Units Produced Daily)**	**30**	**50**	**100**
y **(Daily Profit)**	$5900	$7500	$4500

Use the quadratic function $y = ax^2 + bx + c$ to determine the number of units that should be produced each day for maximum profit. What is the maximum daily profit?

SECTION 3.4 Determinants and Cramer's Rule

Objectives

1. Evaluate a second-order determinant.
2. Solve a system of linear equations in two variables using Cramer's rule.
3. Evaluate a third-order determinant.
4. Solve a system of linear equations in three variables using Cramer's rule.
5. Use determinants to identify inconsistent
6. Evaluate higher-order determinants.

A portion of Charles Babbage's unrealized Difference Engine

As cyberspace absorbs more and more of our work, play, shopping, and socializing, where will it all end? Which activities will still be offline in 2025?

Our technologically transformed lives can be traced back to the English inventor Charles Babbage (1792–1871). Babbage knew of a method for solving linear systems called *Cramer's rule*, in honor of the Swiss geometer Gabriel Cramer (1704–1752). Cramer's rule was simple, but involved numerous multiplications for large systems. Babbage designed a machine, called the "difference engine," that consisted of toothed wheels on shafts for performing these multiplications. Despite the fact that only one-seventh of the functions ever worked, Babbage's invention demonstrated how complex calculations could be handled mechanically. In 1944, scientists at IBM used the lessons of the difference engine to create the world's first computer.

Those who invented computers hoped to relegate the drudgery of repeated computation to a machine. In this section, we look at a method for solving linear systems that played a critical role in this process. The method uses real numbers, called *determinants,* that are associated with arrays of numbers. As with matrix methods, solutions are obtained by writing down the coefficients and constants of a linear system and performing operations with them.

1 Evaluate a second-order determinant.

The Determinant of a 2 × 2 Matrix

Associated with every square matrix is a real number, called its **determinant**. The determinant for a 2 × 2 square matrix is defined as follows:

Study Tip

To evaluate a second-order determinant, find the difference of the product of the two diagonals.

$$\begin{vmatrix} a_1 & b_1 \\ a_2 & b_2 \end{vmatrix} = a_1b_2 - a_2b_1$$

Definition of the Determinant of a 2 × 2 Matrix

The determinant of the matrix $\begin{bmatrix} a_1 & b_1 \\ a_2 & b_2 \end{bmatrix}$ is denoted by $\begin{vmatrix} a_1 & b_1 \\ a_2 & b_2 \end{vmatrix}$ and is defined by

$$\begin{vmatrix} a_1 & b_1 \\ a_2 & b_2 \end{vmatrix} = a_1b_2 - a_2b_1.$$

We also say that the **value** of the **second-order determinant** $\begin{vmatrix} a_1 & b_1 \\ a_2 & b_2 \end{vmatrix}$ is $a_1b_2 - a_2b_1$.

Example 1 illustrates that the determinant of a matrix may be positive or negative. The determinant can also have 0 as its value.

EXAMPLE 1 Evaluating the Determinant of a 2 × 2 Matrix

Evaluate the determinant of each of the following matrices:

$$\textbf{a.} \begin{bmatrix} 5 & 6 \\ 7 & 3 \end{bmatrix} \quad \textbf{b.} \begin{bmatrix} 2 & 4 \\ -3 & -5 \end{bmatrix}.$$

Solution We multiply and subtract as indicated.

$$\textbf{a.} \begin{vmatrix} 5 & 6 \\ 7 & 3 \end{vmatrix} = 5 \cdot 3 - 7 \cdot 6 = 15 - 42 = -27$$

The value of the second-order determinant is −27.

$$\textbf{b.} \begin{vmatrix} 2 & 4 \\ -3 & -5 \end{vmatrix} = 2(-5) - (-3)(4) = -10 + 12 = 2$$

The value of the second-order determinant is 2.

Discovery

Write and then evaluate three determinants, one whose value is positive, one whose value is negative, and one whose value is 0.

Check Point 1 Evaluate the determinant of each of the following matrices:

$$\textbf{a.} \begin{bmatrix} 10 & 9 \\ 6 & 5 \end{bmatrix} \quad \textbf{b.} \begin{bmatrix} 4 & 3 \\ -5 & -8 \end{bmatrix}.$$

② Solve a system of linear equations in two variables using Cramer's rule.

Solving Systems of Linear Equations in Two Variables Using Determinants

Determinants can be used to solve a linear system in two variables. In general, such a system appears as

$$a_1 x + b_1 y = c_1$$
$$a_2 x + b_2 y = c_2.$$

Let's first solve this system for x using the addition method. We can solve for x by eliminating y from the equations. Multiply the first equation by b_2 and the second equation by $-b_1$. Then add the two equations:

$$a_1 x + b_1 y = c_1 \quad \xrightarrow{\text{Multiply by } b_2.} \quad a_1 b_2 x + b_1 b_2 y = c_1 b_2$$
$$a_2 x + b_2 y = c_2 \quad \xrightarrow{\text{Multiply by } -b_1.} \quad -a_2 b_1 x - b_1 b_2 y = -c_2 b_1$$
$$\text{Add:} \quad (a_1 b_2 - a_2 b_1) x = c_1 b_2 - c_2 b_1$$
$$x = \frac{c_1 b_2 - c_2 b_1}{a_1 b_2 - a_2 b_1}$$

Because

$$\begin{vmatrix} c_1 & b_1 \\ c_2 & b_2 \end{vmatrix} = c_1 b_2 - c_2 b_1 \quad \text{and} \quad \begin{vmatrix} a_1 & b_1 \\ a_2 & b_2 \end{vmatrix} = a_1 b_2 - a_2 b_1,$$

we can express our answer for x as the quotient of two determinants:

$$x = \frac{\begin{vmatrix} c_1 & b_1 \\ c_2 & b_2 \end{vmatrix}}{\begin{vmatrix} a_1 & b_1 \\ a_2 & b_2 \end{vmatrix}}.$$

Similarly, we could use the addition method to solve our system for y, again expressing y as the quotient of two determinants. This method of using determinants to solve the linear system, called **Cramer's rule**, is summarized in the box at the top of the next page.

Solving a Linear System in Two Variables Using Determinants

Cramer's Rule

If

$$a_1x + b_1y = c_1$$
$$a_2x + b_2y = c_2$$

then

$$x = \frac{\begin{vmatrix} c_1 & b_1 \\ c_2 & b_2 \end{vmatrix}}{\begin{vmatrix} a_1 & b_1 \\ a_2 & b_2 \end{vmatrix}} \quad \text{and} \quad y = \frac{\begin{vmatrix} a_1 & c_1 \\ a_2 & c_2 \end{vmatrix}}{\begin{vmatrix} a_1 & b_1 \\ a_2 & b_2 \end{vmatrix}}$$

where

$$\begin{vmatrix} a_1 & b_1 \\ a_2 & b_2 \end{vmatrix} \neq 0.$$

Here are some helpful tips when solving

$$a_1x + b_1y = c_1$$
$$a_2x + b_2y = c_2$$

using determinants:

1. Three different determinants are used to find x and y. The determinants in the denominators for x and y are identical. The determinants in the numerators for x and y differ. In abbreviated notation, we write

$$x = \frac{D_x}{D} \quad \text{and} \quad y = \frac{D_y}{D}, \text{ where } D \neq 0.$$

2. The elements of D, the determinant in the denominator, are the coefficients of the variables in the system.

$$D = \begin{vmatrix} a_1 & b_1 \\ a_2 & b_2 \end{vmatrix}$$

3. D_x, the determinant in the numerator of x, is obtained by replacing the x-coefficients, in D, a_1 and a_2, with the constants on the right sides of the equations, c_1 and c_2.

$$D = \begin{vmatrix} a_1 & b_1 \\ a_2 & b_2 \end{vmatrix} \quad \text{and} \quad D_x = \begin{vmatrix} c_1 & b_1 \\ c_2 & b_2 \end{vmatrix}$$

Replace the column with a_1 and a_2 with the constants c_1 and c_2 to get D_x.

4. D_y, the determinant in the numerator for y, is obtained by replacing the y-coefficients, in D, b_1 and b_2, with the constants on the right sides of the equations, c_1 and c_2.

$$D = \begin{vmatrix} a_1 & b_1 \\ a_2 & b_2 \end{vmatrix} \quad \text{and} \quad D_y = \begin{vmatrix} a_1 & c_1 \\ a_2 & c_2 \end{vmatrix}$$

Replace the column with b_1 and b_2 with the constants c_1 and c_2 to get D_y.

EXAMPLE 2 Using Cramer's Rule to Solve a Linear System

Use Cramer's rule to solve the system:

$$5x - 4y = 2$$
$$6x - 5y = 1.$$

Solution Because

$$x = \frac{D_x}{D} \quad \text{and} \quad y = \frac{D_y}{D},$$

we will set up and evaluate the three determinants D, D_x, and D_y.

1. D, the determinant in both denominators, consists of the x- and y-coefficients.

$$D = \begin{vmatrix} 5 & -4 \\ 6 & -5 \end{vmatrix} = (5)(-5) - (6)(-4) = -25 + 24 = -1$$

Because this determinant is not zero, we continue to use Cramer's rule to solve the system.

2. D_x, the determinant in the numerator for x, is obtained by replacing the x-coefficients in D, 5 and 6, by the constants on the right sides of the equations, 2 and 1.

$$D_x = \begin{vmatrix} 2 & -4 \\ 1 & -5 \end{vmatrix} = (2)(-5) - (1)(-4) = -10 + 4 = -6$$

3. D_y, the determinant in the numerator for y, is obtained by replacing the y-coefficients in D, -4 and -5, by the constants on the right sides of the equations, 2 and 1.

$$D_y = \begin{vmatrix} 5 & 2 \\ 6 & 1 \end{vmatrix} = (5)(1) - (6)(2) = 5 - 12 = -7$$

4. Thus,

$$x = \frac{D_x}{D} = \frac{-6}{-1} = 6 \quad \text{and} \quad y = \frac{D_y}{D} = \frac{-7}{-1} = 7.$$

As always, the solution $(6, 7)$ can be checked by substituting these values into the original equations. The solution set is $\{(6, 7)\}$.

Check Point 2 Use Cramer's rule to solve the system:

$$5x + 4y = 12$$
$$3x - 6y = 24.$$

③ Evaluate a third-order determinant.

The Determinant of a 3 × 3 Matrix

Associated with every square matrix is a real number called its determinant. The determinant for a 3 × 3 matrix is defined as follows:

Definition of a Third-Order Determinant

$$\begin{vmatrix} a_1 & b_1 & c_1 \\ a_2 & b_2 & c_2 \\ a_3 & b_3 & c_3 \end{vmatrix} = a_1 b_2 c_3 + b_1 c_2 a_3 + c_1 a_2 b_3 - a_3 b_2 c_1 - b_3 c_2 a_1 - c_3 a_2 b_1$$

The six terms and the three factors in each term in this complicated evaluation formula can be rearranged, and then we can apply the distributive property. We obtain

$$a_1 b_2 c_3 - a_1 b_3 c_2 - a_2 b_1 c_3 + a_2 b_3 c_1 + a_3 b_1 c_2 - a_3 b_2 c_1$$
$$= a_1(b_2 c_3 - b_3 c_2) - a_2(b_1 c_3 - b_3 c_1) + a_3(b_1 c_2 - b_2 c_1)$$
$$= a_1 \begin{vmatrix} b_2 & c_2 \\ b_3 & c_3 \end{vmatrix} - a_2 \begin{vmatrix} b_1 & c_1 \\ b_3 & c_3 \end{vmatrix} + a_3 \begin{vmatrix} b_1 & c_1 \\ b_2 & c_2 \end{vmatrix}.$$

You can evaluate each of the second-order determinants and obtain the three expressions in parentheses in the second step.

In summary, we now have arranged the definition of a third-order determinant as follows:

Definition of the Determinant of a 3 × 3 Matrix

A third-order determinant is defined by

Subtract. Add.

$$\begin{vmatrix} a_1 & b_1 & c_1 \\ a_2 & b_2 & c_2 \\ a_3 & b_3 & c_3 \end{vmatrix} = a_1 \begin{vmatrix} b_2 & c_2 \\ b_3 & c_3 \end{vmatrix} - a_2 \begin{vmatrix} b_1 & c_1 \\ b_3 & c_3 \end{vmatrix} + a_3 \begin{vmatrix} b_1 & c_1 \\ b_2 & c_2 \end{vmatrix}.$$

Each a on the right comes from the first column.

Here are some tips that may be helpful when evaluating the determinant of a 3 × 3 matrix:

Evaluating the Determinant of a 3 × 3 Matrix

1. Each of the three terms in the definition contains two factors—a numerical factor and a second-order determinant.
2. The numerical factor in each term is an element from the first column of the third-order determinant.
3. The minus sign precedes the second term.
4. The second-order determinant that appears in each term is obtained by crossing out the row and the column containing the numerical factor.

$$a_1 \begin{vmatrix} b_2 & c_2 \\ b_3 & c_3 \end{vmatrix} - a_2 \begin{vmatrix} b_1 & c_1 \\ b_3 & c_3 \end{vmatrix} + a_3 \begin{vmatrix} b_1 & c_1 \\ b_2 & c_2 \end{vmatrix}$$

$$\begin{vmatrix} a_1 & b_1 & c_1 \\ a_2 & b_2 & c_2 \\ a_3 & b_3 & c_3 \end{vmatrix} \quad \begin{vmatrix} a_1 & b_1 & c_1 \\ a_2 & b_2 & c_2 \\ a_3 & b_3 & c_3 \end{vmatrix} \quad \begin{vmatrix} a_1 & b_1 & c_1 \\ a_2 & b_2 & c_2 \\ a_3 & b_3 & c_3 \end{vmatrix}$$

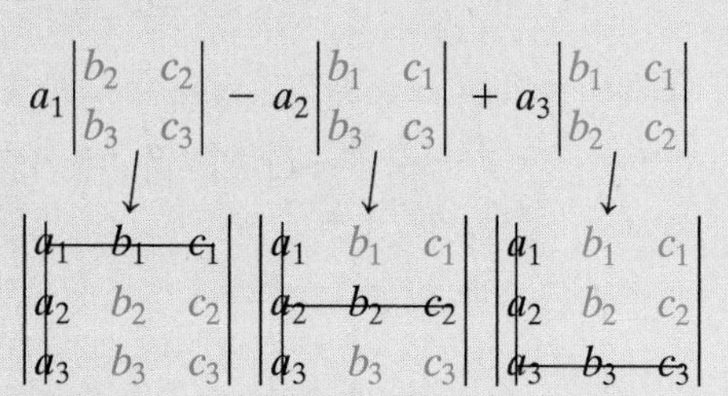

The **minor** of an element is the determinant that remains after deleting the row and column of that element. For this reason, we call this method **expansion by minors**.

EXAMPLE 3 Evaluating the Determinant of a 3 × 3 Matrix

Evaluate the determinant of the following matrix:

$$\begin{bmatrix} 4 & 1 & 0 \\ -9 & 3 & 4 \\ -3 & 8 & 1 \end{bmatrix}.$$

Solution We know that each of the three terms in the determinant contains a numerical factor and a second-order determinant. The numerical factors are from the first column of the determinant of the given matrix. They are highlighted in the following matrix:

$$\begin{vmatrix} 4 & 1 & 0 \\ -9 & 3 & 4 \\ -3 & 8 & 1 \end{vmatrix}.$$

We find the minor for each numerical factor by deleting the row and column of that element:

$$\begin{bmatrix} 4 & 1 & 0 \\ -9 & 3 & 4 \\ -3 & 8 & 1 \end{bmatrix} \quad \begin{bmatrix} 4 & 1 & 0 \\ -9 & 3 & 4 \\ -3 & 8 & 1 \end{bmatrix} \quad \begin{bmatrix} 4 & 1 & 0 \\ -9 & 3 & 4 \\ -3 & 8 & 1 \end{bmatrix}$$

The minor for 4 is $\begin{vmatrix} 3 & 4 \\ 8 & 1 \end{vmatrix}$.

The minor for −9 is $\begin{vmatrix} 1 & 0 \\ 8 & 1 \end{vmatrix}$.

The minor for −3 is $\begin{vmatrix} 1 & 0 \\ 3 & 4 \end{vmatrix}$.

Now we have three numerical factors, 4, −9, and −3, and three second-order determinants. We multiply each numerical factor by its second-order determinant to find the three terms of the third-order determinant:

$$4\begin{vmatrix} 3 & 4 \\ 8 & 1 \end{vmatrix}, \quad -9\begin{vmatrix} 1 & 0 \\ 8 & 1 \end{vmatrix}, \quad -3\begin{vmatrix} 1 & 0 \\ 3 & 4 \end{vmatrix}.$$

Based on the preceding definition, we subtract the second term from the first term and add the third term:

Don't forget to supply the minus sign.

$$\begin{vmatrix} 4 & 1 & 0 \\ -9 & 3 & 4 \\ -3 & 8 & 1 \end{vmatrix} = 4\begin{vmatrix} 3 & 4 \\ 8 & 1 \end{vmatrix} - (-9)\begin{vmatrix} 1 & 0 \\ 8 & 1 \end{vmatrix} - 3\begin{vmatrix} 1 & 0 \\ 3 & 4 \end{vmatrix}$$ Begin by evaluating the three second-order determinants.

$$= 4(3\cdot 1 - 8\cdot 4) + 9(1\cdot 1 - 8\cdot 0) - 3(1\cdot 4 - 3\cdot 0)$$

$$= 4(3 - 32) + 9(1 - 0) - 3(4 - 0)$$ Multiply within parentheses.

$$= 4(-29) + 9(1) - 3(4)$$ Subtract within parentheses.

$$= -116 + 9 - 12$$ Multiply.

$$= -119$$ Add and subtract as indicated.

Technology

A graphing utility can be used to evaluate the determinant of a matrix. Enter the matrix and call it A. Then use the determinant command. The screen below verifies our result in Example 3.

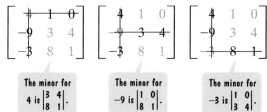

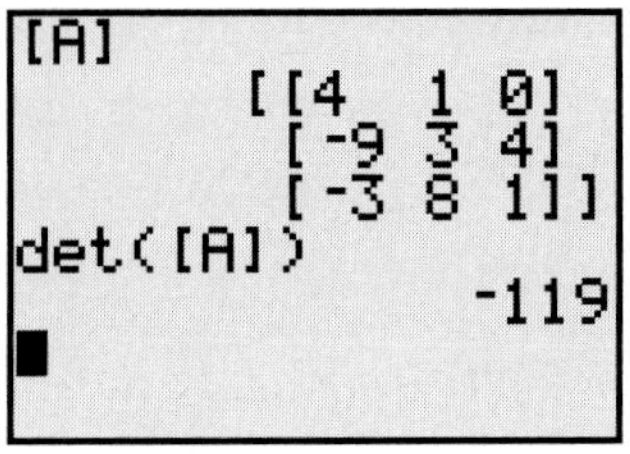

Check Point 3 Evaluate the determinant of the following matrix:

$$\begin{bmatrix} 2 & 1 & 7 \\ -5 & 6 & 0 \\ -4 & 3 & 1 \end{bmatrix}.$$

The six terms in the definition of a third-order determinant can be rearranged and factored in a variety of ways. Thus, it is possible to expand a determinant by minors about any row or any column. *Minus signs must be supplied preceding any element appearing in a position where the sum of its row and its column is an odd number.* For example, expanding about the elements in column 2 gives us

$$\begin{vmatrix} a_1 & b_1 & c_1 \\ a_2 & b_2 & c_2 \\ a_3 & b_3 & c_3 \end{vmatrix} = -b_1\begin{vmatrix} a_2 & c_2 \\ a_3 & c_3 \end{vmatrix} + b_2\begin{vmatrix} a_1 & c_1 \\ a_3 & c_3 \end{vmatrix} - b_3\begin{vmatrix} a_1 & c_1 \\ a_2 & c_2 \end{vmatrix}.$$

Minus sign is supplied because b_1 appears in row 1 and column 2; $1 + 2 = 3$, an odd number.

Minus sign is supplied because b_3 appears in row 3 and column 2; $3 + 2 = 5$, an odd number.

Expanding by minors about column 3, we obtain

$$\begin{vmatrix} a_1 & b_1 & c_1 \\ a_2 & b_2 & c_2 \\ a_3 & b_3 & c_3 \end{vmatrix} = c_1\begin{vmatrix} a_2 & b_2 \\ a_3 & b_3 \end{vmatrix} - c_2\begin{vmatrix} a_1 & b_1 \\ a_3 & b_3 \end{vmatrix} + c_3\begin{vmatrix} a_1 & b_1 \\ a_2 & b_2 \end{vmatrix}.$$

Minus sign must be supplied because c_2 appears in row 2 and column 3; $2 + 3 = 5$, an odd number.

When evaluating a 3×3 determinant using expansion by minors, you can expand about any row or column. To simplify the arithmetic, if a row or column contains one or more 0s, expand about that row or column.

Study Tip

Keep in mind that you can expand a determinant by minors about any row or column. Use alternating plus and minus signs to precede the numerical factors of the minors according to the following sign array:

$$\begin{vmatrix} + & - & + \\ - & + & - \\ + & - & + \end{vmatrix}.$$

EXAMPLE 4 Evaluating a Third-Order Determinant

Evaluate:

$$\begin{vmatrix} 9 & 5 & 0 \\ -2 & -3 & 0 \\ 1 & 4 & 2 \end{vmatrix}.$$

Solution Note that the last column has two 0s. We will expand the determinant about the elements in that column.

$$\begin{vmatrix} 9 & 5 & 0 \\ -2 & -3 & 0 \\ 1 & 4 & 2 \end{vmatrix} = 0\begin{vmatrix} -2 & -3 \\ 1 & 4 \end{vmatrix} - 0\begin{vmatrix} 9 & 5 \\ 1 & 4 \end{vmatrix} + 2\begin{vmatrix} 9 & 5 \\ -2 & -3 \end{vmatrix}$$

$$= 0 - 0 + 2[9(-3) - (-2)\cdot 5]$$
$$= 2(-27 + 10)$$
$$= 2(-17)$$
$$= -34$$

Evaluate the second-order determinant whose numerical factor is not 0.

Check Point 4 Evaluate:

$$\begin{vmatrix} 6 & 4 & 0 \\ -3 & -5 & 3 \\ 1 & 2 & 0 \end{vmatrix}.$$

4 Solve a system of linear equations in three variables using Cramer's rule.

Solving Systems of Linear Equations in Three Variables Using Determinants

Cramer's rule can be applied to solving systems of linear equations in three variables. The determinants in the numerator and denominator of all variables are third-order determinants.

Solving Three Equations in Three Variables Using Determinants

Cramer's Rule

If

$$a_1x + b_1y + c_1z = d_1$$
$$a_2x + b_2y + c_2z = d_2$$
$$a_3x + b_3y + c_3z = d_3$$

then

$$x = \frac{D_x}{D}, y = \frac{D_y}{D}, \text{ and } z = \frac{D_z}{D}.$$

These four third-order determinants are given by

$$D = \begin{vmatrix} a_1 & b_1 & c_1 \\ a_2 & b_2 & c_2 \\ a_3 & b_3 & c_3 \end{vmatrix}$$ These are the coefficients of the variables x, y and z. $D \neq 0$

$$D_x = \begin{vmatrix} d_1 & b_1 & c_1 \\ d_2 & b_2 & c_2 \\ d_3 & b_3 & c_3 \end{vmatrix}$$ Replace x-coefficients in D with the constants on the right of the three equations.

$$D_y = \begin{vmatrix} a_1 & d_1 & c_1 \\ a_2 & d_2 & c_2 \\ a_3 & d_3 & c_3 \end{vmatrix}$$ Replace y-coefficients in D with the constants on the right of the three equations.

$$D_z = \begin{vmatrix} a_1 & b_1 & d_1 \\ a_2 & b_2 & d_2 \\ a_3 & b_3 & d_3 \end{vmatrix}.$$ Replace z-coefficients in D with the constants on the right of the three equations.

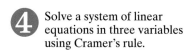

EXAMPLE 5 Using Cramer's Rule to Solve a Linear System in Three Variables

Use Cramer's rule to solve:

$$\begin{aligned} x + 2y - z &= -4 \\ x + 4y - 2z &= -6 \\ 2x + 3y + z &= 3. \end{aligned}$$

Solution Because

$$x = \frac{D_x}{D}, \quad y = \frac{D_y}{D}, \quad \text{and} \quad z = \frac{D_z}{D},$$

we need to set up and evaluate four determinants.

Step 1 Set up the determinants.

1. D, the determinant in all three denominators, consists of the x-, y-, and z-coefficients.

$$D = \begin{vmatrix} 1 & 2 & -1 \\ 1 & 4 & -2 \\ 2 & 3 & 1 \end{vmatrix}$$

2. D_x, the determinant in the numerator for x, is obtained by replacing the x-coefficients in D, 1, 1, and 2, with the constants on the right sides of the equations, -4, -6, and 3.

$$D_x = \begin{vmatrix} -4 & 2 & -1 \\ -6 & 4 & -2 \\ 3 & 3 & 1 \end{vmatrix}$$

3. D_y, the determinant in the numerator for y, is obtained by replacing the y-coefficients in D, 2, 4, and 3, with the constants on the right sides of the equations, -4, -6, and 3.

$$D_y = \begin{vmatrix} 1 & -4 & -1 \\ 1 & -6 & -2 \\ 2 & 3 & 1 \end{vmatrix}$$

4. D_z, the determinant in the numerator for z, is obtained by replacing the z-coefficients in D, -1, -2, and 1, with the constants on the right sides of the equations, -4, -6, and 3.

$$D_z = \begin{vmatrix} 1 & 2 & -4 \\ 1 & 4 & -6 \\ 2 & 3 & 3 \end{vmatrix}$$

Step 2 Evaluate the four determinants.

$$D = \begin{vmatrix} 1 & 2 & -1 \\ 1 & 4 & -2 \\ 2 & 3 & 1 \end{vmatrix} = 1\begin{vmatrix} 4 & -2 \\ 3 & 1 \end{vmatrix} - 1\begin{vmatrix} 2 & -1 \\ 3 & 1 \end{vmatrix} + 2\begin{vmatrix} 2 & -1 \\ 4 & -2 \end{vmatrix}$$

$$= 1(4 + 6) - 1(2 + 3) + 2(-4 + 4)$$

$$= 1(10) - 1(5) + 2(0) = 5$$

Using the same technique to evaluate each determinant, we obtain

$$D_x = -10, \quad D_y = 5, \quad \text{and} \quad D_z = 20.$$

Study Tip

To find D_x, D_y, and D_z, you'll need to apply the evaluation process for a 3×3 determinant three times. The values of D_x, D_y, and D_z cannot be obtained from the numbers that occur in the computation of D.

Step 3 Substitute these four values and solve the system.

$$x = \frac{D_x}{D} = \frac{-10}{5} = -2$$
$$y = \frac{D_y}{D} = \frac{5}{5} = 1$$
$$z = \frac{D_z}{D} = \frac{20}{5} = 4$$

The solution $(-2, 1, 4)$ can be checked by substitution into the original three equations. The solution set is $\{(-2, 1, 4)\}$.

Check Point 5 Use Cramer's rule to solve the system:

$$\begin{aligned} 3x - 2y + z &= 16 \\ 2x + 3y - z &= -9 \\ x + 4y + 3z &= 2. \end{aligned}$$

5 Use determinants to identify inconsistent systems and systems with dependent equations.

Cramer's Rule with Inconsistent and Dependent Systems

If D, the determinant in the denominator, is 0, the variables described by the quotient of determinants are not real numbers. However, when $D = 0$, this indicates that the system is either inconsistent or contains dependent equations. This gives rise to the following two situations:

Discovery

Write a system of two equations that is inconsistent. Now use determinants and the result boxed on the right to verify that this is truly an inconsistent system. Repeat the same process for a system with two dependent equations.

Determinants: Inconsistent and Dependent Systems

1. If $D = 0$ and at least one of the determinants in the numerator is not 0, then the system is inconsistent. The solution set is $\emptyset$.
2. If $D = 0$ and all the determinants in the numerators are 0, then the equations in the system are dependent. The system has infinitely many solutions.

Although we have focused on applying determinants to solve linear systems, they have other applications, some of which we consider in the exercise set that follows Example 6.

6 Evaluate higher-order determinants.

The Determinant of Any $n \times n$ Matrix

The determinant of a matrix with n rows and n columns is said to be an ***n*th-order determinant**. The value of an nth-order determinant $(n > 2)$ can be found in terms of determinants of order $n - 1$. For example, we found the value of a third-order determinant in terms of determinants of order 2.

We can generalize this idea for fourth-order determinants and higher. We have seen that the **minor** of the element a_{ij} is the determinant obtained by deleting the ith row and the jth column in the given array of numbers. The **cofactor** of the element a_{ij} is $(-1)^{i+j}$ times the minor of the a_{ij}th entry. If the sum of the row and column $(i + j)$ is even, the cofactor is the same as the minor. If the sum of the row and column $(i + j)$ is odd, the cofactor is the opposite of the minor.

Let's see what this means in the case of a fourth-order determinant.

EXAMPLE 6 Evaluating the Determinant of a 4×4 Matrix

Evaluate the determinant of the following matrix:

$$A = \begin{bmatrix} 1 & -2 & 3 & 0 \\ -1 & 1 & 0 & 2 \\ 0 & 2 & 0 & -3 \\ 2 & 3 & -4 & 1 \end{bmatrix}.$$

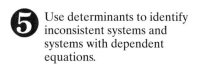

Solution

$$|A| = \begin{vmatrix} 1 & -2 & 3 & 0 \\ -1 & 1 & 0 & 2 \\ 0 & 2 & 0 & -3 \\ 2 & 3 & -4 & 1 \end{vmatrix}$$

With two 0s in the third column, we will expand along the third column.

$$= (-1)^{1+3}(3)\begin{vmatrix} -1 & 1 & 2 \\ 0 & 2 & -3 \\ 2 & 3 & 1 \end{vmatrix} + (-1)^{4+3}(-4)\begin{vmatrix} 1 & -2 & 0 \\ -1 & 1 & 2 \\ 0 & 2 & -3 \end{vmatrix}$$

3 is in row 1, column 3.

−4 is in row 4, column 3.

$$= 3\begin{vmatrix} -1 & 1 & 2 \\ 0 & 2 & -3 \\ 2 & 3 & 1 \end{vmatrix} + 4\begin{vmatrix} 1 & -2 & 0 \\ -1 & 1 & 2 \\ 0 & 2 & -3 \end{vmatrix}$$

The determinant that follows 3 is obtained by crossing out the row and the column (row 1, column 3) in the original determinant. The minor for −4 is obtained in a similar manner.

Evaluate the two third-order determinants to get

$$|A| = 3(-25) + 4(-1) = -79.$$

Check Point 6 Evaluate the determinant of the following matrix:

$$A = \begin{bmatrix} 0 & 4 & 0 & -3 \\ -1 & 1 & 5 & 2 \\ 1 & -2 & 0 & 6 \\ 3 & 0 & 0 & 1 \end{bmatrix}.$$

If a linear system has n equations, Cramer's rule requires you to compute $n + 1$ determinants of nth order. The excessive number of calculations required to perform Cramer's rule for systems with four or more equations makes it an inefficient method for solving large systems.

EXERCISE SET 3.4

Practice Exercises

Evaluate each determinant in Exercises 1–10.

1. $\begin{vmatrix} 5 & 7 \\ 2 & 3 \end{vmatrix}$

2. $\begin{vmatrix} 4 & 8 \\ 5 & 6 \end{vmatrix}$

3. $\begin{vmatrix} -4 & 1 \\ 5 & 6 \end{vmatrix}$

4. $\begin{vmatrix} 7 & 9 \\ -2 & -5 \end{vmatrix}$

5. $\begin{vmatrix} -7 & 14 \\ 2 & -4 \end{vmatrix}$

6. $\begin{vmatrix} 1 & -3 \\ -8 & 2 \end{vmatrix}$

7. $\begin{vmatrix} -5 & -1 \\ -2 & -7 \end{vmatrix}$

8. $\begin{vmatrix} \frac{1}{5} & \frac{1}{6} \\ -6 & 5 \end{vmatrix}$

9. $\begin{vmatrix} \frac{1}{2} & \frac{1}{2} \\ \frac{1}{8} & -\frac{3}{4} \end{vmatrix}$

10. $\begin{vmatrix} \frac{2}{3} & \frac{1}{3} \\ -\frac{1}{2} & \frac{3}{4} \end{vmatrix}$

For Exercises 11–26, use Cramer's rule to solve each system or to determine that the system is inconsistent or contains dependent equations.

11. $x + y = 7$
 $x - y = 3$

12. $2x + y = 3$
 $x - y = 3$

13. $12x + 3y = 15$
 $2x - 3y = 13$

14. $x - 2y = 5$
 $5x - y = -2$

15. $4x - 5y = 17$
 $2x + 3y = 3$

16. $3x + 2y = 2$
 $2x + 2y = 3$

17. $x + 2y = 3$
 $5x + 10y = 15$

18. $2x - 9y = 5$
 $3x - 3y = 11$

19. $3x - 4y = 4$
 $2x + 2y = 12$

20. $3x = 7y + 1$
 $2x = 3y - 1$

21. $2x = 3y + 2$
 $5x = 51 - 4y$

22. $y = -4x + 2$
 $2x = 3y + 8$

23. $3x = 2 - 3y$
$2y = 3 - 2x$

24. $x + 2y - 3 = 0$
$12 = 8y + 4x$

25. $4y = 16 - 3x$
$6x = 32 - 8y$

26. $2x = 7 + 3y$
$4x - 6y = 3$

Evaluate each determinant in Exercises 27–32.

27. $\begin{vmatrix} 3 & 0 & 0 \\ 2 & 1 & -5 \\ 2 & 5 & -1 \end{vmatrix}$

28. $\begin{vmatrix} 4 & 0 & 0 \\ 3 & -1 & 4 \\ 2 & -3 & 5 \end{vmatrix}$

29. $\begin{vmatrix} 3 & 1 & 0 \\ -3 & 4 & 0 \\ -1 & 3 & -5 \end{vmatrix}$

30. $\begin{vmatrix} 2 & -4 & 2 \\ -1 & 0 & 5 \\ 3 & 0 & 4 \end{vmatrix}$

31. $\begin{vmatrix} 1 & 1 & 1 \\ 2 & 2 & 2 \\ -3 & 4 & -5 \end{vmatrix}$

32. $\begin{vmatrix} 1 & 2 & 3 \\ 2 & 2 & -3 \\ 3 & 2 & 1 \end{vmatrix}$

In Exercises 33–40, use Cramer's rule to solve each system.

33. $x + y + z = 0$
$2x - y + z = -1$
$-x + 3y - z = -8$

34. $x - y + 2z = 3$
$2x + 3y + z = 9$
$-x - y + 3z = 11$

35. $4x - 5y - 6z = -1$
$x - 2y - 5z = -12$
$2x - y = 7$

36. $x - 3y + z = -2$
$x + 2y = 8$
$2x - y = 1$

37. $x + y + z = 4$
$x - 2y + z = 7$
$x + 3y + 2z = 4$

38. $2x + 2y + 3z = 10$
$4x - y + z = -5$
$5x - 2y + 6z = 1$

39. $x + 2z = 4$
$2y - z = 5$
$2x + 3y = 13$

40. $3x + 2z = 4$
$5x - y = -4$
$4y + 3z = 22$

Evaluate each determinant in Exercises 41–44.

41. $\begin{vmatrix} 4 & 2 & 8 & -7 \\ -2 & 0 & 4 & 1 \\ 5 & 0 & 0 & 5 \\ 4 & 0 & 0 & -1 \end{vmatrix}$

42. $\begin{vmatrix} 3 & -1 & 1 & 2 \\ -2 & 0 & 0 & 0 \\ 2 & -1 & -2 & 3 \\ 1 & 4 & 2 & 3 \end{vmatrix}$

43. $\begin{vmatrix} -2 & -3 & 3 & 5 \\ 1 & -4 & 0 & 0 \\ 1 & 2 & 2 & -3 \\ 2 & 0 & 1 & 1 \end{vmatrix}$

44. $\begin{vmatrix} 1 & -3 & 2 & 0 \\ -3 & -1 & 0 & -2 \\ 2 & 1 & 3 & 1 \\ 2 & 0 & -2 & 0 \end{vmatrix}$

Practice Plus

In Exercises 45–46, evaluate each determinant.

45. $\begin{vmatrix} \begin{vmatrix} 3 & 1 \\ -2 & 3 \end{vmatrix} & \begin{vmatrix} 7 & 0 \\ 1 & 5 \end{vmatrix} \\ \begin{vmatrix} 3 & 0 \\ 0 & 7 \end{vmatrix} & \begin{vmatrix} 9 & -6 \\ 3 & 5 \end{vmatrix} \end{vmatrix}$

46. $\begin{vmatrix} \begin{vmatrix} 5 & 0 \\ 4 & -3 \end{vmatrix} & \begin{vmatrix} -1 & 0 \\ 0 & -1 \end{vmatrix} \\ \begin{vmatrix} 7 & -5 \\ 4 & 6 \end{vmatrix} & \begin{vmatrix} 4 & 1 \\ -3 & 5 \end{vmatrix} \end{vmatrix}$

In Exercises 47–48, write the system of linear equations for which Cramer's rule yields the given determinants.

47. $D = \begin{vmatrix} 2 & -4 \\ 3 & 5 \end{vmatrix}, \quad D_x = \begin{vmatrix} 8 & -4 \\ -10 & 5 \end{vmatrix}$

48. $D = \begin{vmatrix} 2 & -3 \\ 5 & 6 \end{vmatrix}, \quad D_x = \begin{vmatrix} 8 & -3 \\ 11 & 6 \end{vmatrix}$

In Exercises 49–52, solve each equation for x.

49. $\begin{vmatrix} -2 & x \\ 4 & 6 \end{vmatrix} = 32$

50. $\begin{vmatrix} x + 3 & -6 \\ x - 2 & -4 \end{vmatrix} = 28$

51. $\begin{vmatrix} 1 & x & -2 \\ 3 & 1 & 1 \\ 0 & -2 & 2 \end{vmatrix} = -8$

52. $\begin{vmatrix} 2 & x & 1 \\ -3 & 1 & 0 \\ 2 & 1 & 4 \end{vmatrix} = 39$

Application Exercises

Determinants are used to find the area of a triangle whose vertices are given by three points in a rectangular coordinate system. The area of a triangle with vertices (x_1, y_1), (x_2, y_2), and (x_3, y_3) is

$$\text{Area} = \pm\frac{1}{2}\begin{vmatrix} x_1 & y_1 & 1 \\ x_2 & y_2 & 1 \\ x_3 & y_3 & 1 \end{vmatrix}$$

where the $\pm$ symbol indicates that the appropriate sign should be chosen to yield a positive area. Use this information to work Exercises 53–54.

53. Use determinants to find the area of the triangle whose vertices are $(3, -5)$, $(2, 6)$, and $(-3, 5)$.

54. Use determinants to find the area of the triangle whose vertices are $(1, 1)$, $(-2, -3)$, and $(11, -3)$.

Determinants are used to show that three points lie on the same line (are collinear). If

$$\begin{vmatrix} x_1 & y_1 & 1 \\ x_2 & y_2 & 1 \\ x_3 & y_3 & 1 \end{vmatrix} = 0,$$

then the points (x_1, y_1), (x_2, y_2), and (x_3, y_3) are collinear. If the determinant does not equal 0, then the points are not collinear. Use this information to work Exercises 55–56.

55. Are the points $(3, -1)$, $(0, -3)$, and $(12, 5)$ collinear?

56. Are the points $(-4, -6)$, $(1, 0)$, and $(11, 12)$ collinear?

Determinants are used to write an equation of a line passing through two points. An equation of the line passing through the distinct points (x_1, y_1) and (x_2, y_2) is given by

$$\begin{vmatrix} x & y & 1 \\ x_1 & y_1 & 1 \\ x_2 & y_2 & 1 \end{vmatrix} = 0.$$

Use this information to work Exercises 57–58.

57. Use the determinant to write an equation of the line passing through $(3, -5)$ and $(-2, 6)$. Then expand the determinant, expressing the line's equation in slope-intercept form.

58. Use the determinant to write an equation of the line passing through $(-1, 3)$ and $(2, 4)$. Then expand the determinant, expressing the line's equation in slope-intercept form.

Writing in Mathematics

59. Explain how to evaluate a second-order determinant.

60. Describe the determinants D_x and D_y in terms of the coefficients and constants in a system of two equations in two variables.

61. Explain how to evaluate a third-order determinant.

62. When expanding a determinant by minors, when is it necessary to supply minus signs?

63. Without going into too much detail, describe how to solve a linear system in three variables using Cramer's rule.

64. In applying Cramer's rule, what does it mean if $D = 0$?

65. The process of solving a linear system in three variables using Cramer's rule can involve tedious computation. Is there a way of speeding up this process, perhaps using Cramer's rule to find the value for only one of the variables? Describe how this process might work, presenting a specific example with your description. Remember that your goal is still to find the value for each variable in the system.

66. If you could use only one method to solve linear systems in three variables, which method would you select? Explain why this is so.

Technology Exercises

67. Use the feature of your graphing utility that evaluates the determinant of a square matrix to verify any five of the determinants that you evaluated by hand in Exercises 1–10, 27–32, or 41–44.

In Exercises 68–69, use a graphing utility to evaluate the determinant for the given matrix.

68. $\begin{bmatrix} 3 & -2 & -1 & 4 \\ -5 & 1 & 2 & 7 \\ 2 & 4 & 5 & 0 \\ -1 & 3 & -6 & 5 \end{bmatrix}$

69. $\begin{bmatrix} 8 & 2 & 6 & -1 & 0 \\ 2 & 0 & -3 & 4 & 7 \\ 2 & 1 & -3 & 6 & -5 \\ -1 & 2 & 1 & 5 & -1 \\ 4 & 5 & -2 & 3 & -8 \end{bmatrix}$

70. What is the fastest method for solving a linear system with your graphing utility?

Critical Thinking Exercises

71. **a.** Evaluate: $\begin{vmatrix} a & a \\ 0 & a \end{vmatrix}$.

b. Evaluate: $\begin{vmatrix} a & a & a \\ 0 & a & a \\ 0 & 0 & a \end{vmatrix}$.

c. Evaluate: $\begin{vmatrix} a & a & a & a \\ 0 & a & a & a \\ 0 & 0 & a & a \\ 0 & 0 & 0 & a \end{vmatrix}$.

d. Describe the pattern in the given determinants.

e. Describe the pattern in the evaluations.

72. Evaluate: $\begin{vmatrix} 2 & 0 & 0 & 0 & 0 \\ 0 & 3 & 0 & 0 & 0 \\ 0 & 0 & 2 & 0 & 0 \\ 0 & 0 & 0 & 1 & 0 \\ 0 & 0 & 0 & 0 & 4 \end{vmatrix}$.

73. What happens to the value of a second-order determinant if the two columns are interchanged?

74. Consider the system

$$a_1x + b_1y = c_1$$
$$a_2x + b_2y = c_2.$$

Use Cramer's rule to prove that if the first equation of the system is replaced by the sum of the two equations, the resulting system has the same solution as the original system.

75. Show that the equation of a line through (x_1, y_1) and (x_2, y_2) is given by the determinant equation in Exercises 57–58.

Group Exercise

76. We have seen that determinants can be used to solve linear equations, give areas of triangles in rectangular coordinates, and determine equations of lines. Not impressed with these applications? Members of the group should research an application of determinants that they find intriguing. The group should then present a seminar to the class about this application.

Chapter 3
Summary, Review, and Test

Summary

DEFINITIONS AND CONCEPTS	EXAMPLES
3.1 Systems of Linear Equations in Two Variables	
a. Two equations in the form $Ax + By = C$ are called a system of linear equations. A solution of the system is an ordered pair that satisfies both equations in the system.	Ex. 1, p. 286
b. Systems of linear equations in two variables can be solved by eliminating a variable, using the substitution method (see the box on page 288) or the addition method (see the box on page 289).	Ex. 2, p. 288; Ex. 3, p. 290; Ex. 4, p. 291
c. Some linear systems have no solution and are called inconsistent systems; others have infinitely many solutions. The equations in a linear system with infinitely many solutions are called dependent. For details, see the box on page 292.	Ex. 5, p. 292; Ex. 6, p. 293
d. Functions of Business	Ex. 7, p. 294; Figure 3.7, p. 296

Revenue Function

$$R(x) = (\text{price per unit sold})x$$

Cost Function

$$C(x) = \text{fixed cost} + (\text{cost per unit produced})x$$

Profit Function

$$P(x) = R(x) - C(x)$$

The point of intersection of the graphs of R and C is the break-even point. The x-coordinate of the point reveals the number of units that a company must produce and sell so that the money coming in, the revenue, is equal to the money going out, the cost. The y-coordinate gives the amount of money coming in and going out.

DEFINITIONS AND CONCEPTS	EXAMPLES
3.2 Systems of Linear Equations in Three Variables	
a. Three equations in the form $Ax + By + Cz = D$ are called a system of linear equations in three variables. A solution of the system is an ordered triple that satisfies all three equations in the system.	Ex. 1, p. 301
b. A system of linear equations in three variables can be solved by eliminating variables. Use the addition method to eliminate any variable, reducing the system to two equations in two variables. Use substitution or the addition method to solve the resulting system in two variables. Details are found in the box on page 744.	Ex. 2, p. 302; Ex. 3, p. 304
c. Three points that do not lie on a line determine the graph of a quadratic function $y = ax^2 + bx + c$. Use the three given points to create a system of three equations. Solve the system to find a, b, and c.	Ex 4, p. 305
3.3 Matrix Solutions to Linear Systems	
a. Matrix row operations are described in the box on page 311.	Ex. 2, p. 311
b. To solve a linear system using Gaussian elimination, begin with the system's augmented matrix. Use matrix row operations to get 1s down the main diagonal from upper left to lower right, and 0s below the 1s. Such a matrix is in row-echelon form. Details are in the box on page 312.	Ex. 3, p. 312; Ex. 4, p. 314
c. To solve a linear system using Gauss-Jordan elimination, use the procedure of Gaussian elimination, but obtain 0s above and below the 1s in the main diagonal from upper left to lower right. Such a matrix is in reduced row-echelon form. Details are in the box on page 317.	Ex. 5, p. 317

3.4 Determinants and Cramer's Rule

a. Value of a Second-Order Determinant: Ex. 1, p. 322

$$\begin{vmatrix} a_1 & b_1 \\ a_2 & b_2 \end{vmatrix} = a_1b_2 - a_2b_1$$

b. Cramer's rule for solving systems of linear equations in two variables uses three second-order determinants and is stated in the box on page 323. Ex. 2, p. 323

c. To evaluate an nth-order determinant, where $n > 2$, Ex. 3, p. 325; Ex. 4, p. 327; Ex. 6, p. 329

1. Select a row or column about which to expand.
2. Multiply each element a_{ij} in the row or column by $(-1)^{i+j}$ times the determinant obtained by deleting the ith row and the jth column in the given array of numbers.
3. The value of the determinant is the sum of the products found in step 2.

d. Cramer's rule for solving systems of linear equations in three variables uses four third-order determinants and is stated in the box on page 327. Ex. 5, p. 328

e. Cramer's rule with inconsistent and dependent systems is summarized by the two situations in the box on page 329.

Review Exercises

3.1

In Exercises 1–5, solve by the method of your choice. Identify systems with no solution and systems with infinitely many solutions, using set notation to express their solution sets.

1. $y = 4x + 1$
$3x + 2y = 13$

2. $x + 4y = 14$
$2x - y = 1$

3. $5x + 3y = 1$
$3x + 4y = -6$

4. $2y - 6x = 7$
$3x - y = 9$

5. $4x - 8y = 16$
$3x - 6y = 12$

6. A company is planning to manufacture computer desks. The fixed cost will be \$60,000 and it will cost \$200 to produce each desk. Each desk will be sold for \$450.

a. Write the cost function, C, of producing x desks.

b. Write the revenue function, R, from the sale of x desks.

c. Determine the break-even point. Describe what this means.

7. The bar graph shows the five countries with the longest healthy life expectancy at birth. Combined, people in Japan and Switzerland can expect to spend 146.4 years in good health. The difference between healthy life expectancy between these two countries is 0.8 years. Find the healthy life expectancy at birth in Japan and Switzerland.

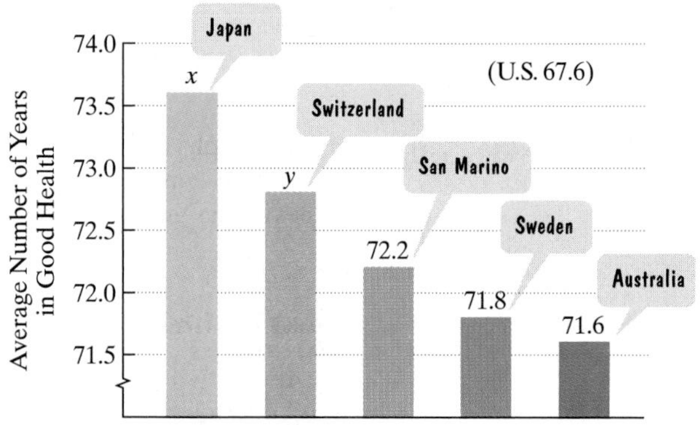

Source: World Health Organization

8. The perimeter of a rectangular table top is 34 feet. The difference between 4 times the length and 3 times the width is 33 feet. Find the dimensions.

9. A travel agent offers two package vacation plans. The first plan costs \$360 and includes 3 days at a hotel and a rental car for 2 days. The second plan costs \$500 and includes 4 days at a hotel and a rental car for 3 days. The daily charge for the hotel is the same under each plan, as is the daily charge for the car. Find the cost per day for the hotel and for the car.

10. The calorie-nutrient information for an apple and an avocado is given in the table. How many of each should be eaten to get exactly 1000 calories and 100 grams of carbohydrates?

	One Apple	One Avocado
Calories	100	350
Carbohydrates (grams)	24	14

3.2

Solve each system in Exercises 11–12.

11. $2x - y + z = 1$
$3x - 3y + 4z = 5$
$4x - 2y + 3z = 4$

12. $x + 2y - z = 5$
$2x - y + 3z = 0$
$2y + z = 1$

13. Find the quadratic function $y = ax^2 + bx + c$ whose graph passes through the points $(1, 4)$, $(3, 20)$, and $(-2, 25)$.

14. The bar graph shows that the U.S. divorce rate increased from 1970 to 1985 and then decreased from 1985 to 2003.

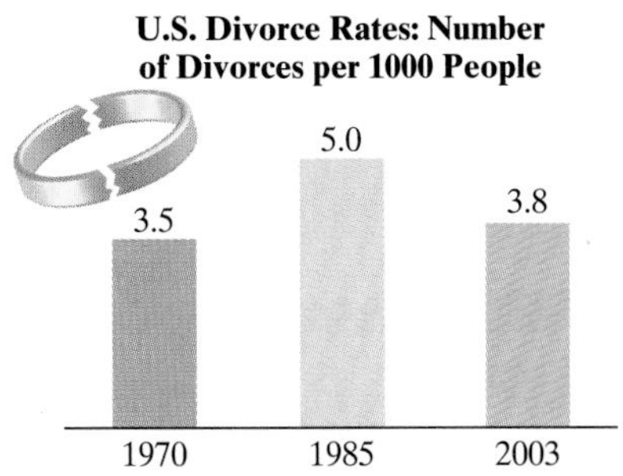
U.S. Divorce Rates: Number of Divorces per 1000 People
3.5
5.0
3.8
1970
1985
2003

Source: U.S. Census Bureau

a. Write the data for 1970, 1985, and 2003 as ordered pairs (x, y), where x is the number of years after 1970 and y is that year's divorce rate.

b. The three data points in part (a) can be modeled by the quadratic function $y = ax^2 + bx + c$. Write a system of linear equations in three variables that can be used to find values for a, b, and c. It is not necessary to solve the system.

15. The bar graph shows the top five purebred dogs in the United States in 2004 compared with how many there were a decade earlier.

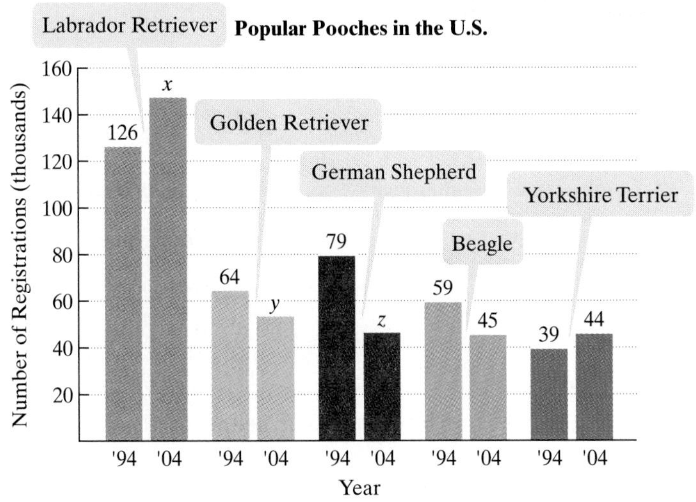
Popular Pooches in the U.S.
Labrador Retriever
Golden Retriever
German Shepherd
Yorkshire Terrier
Beagle
Number of Registrations (thousands)
160
140
120
100
80
60
40
20
126
x
64
y
79
z
59
45
39
44
'94 '04
'94 '04
'94 '04
'94 '04
'94 '04
Year

Source: American Kennel Club

In 2004, for the 15th year in a row, the Labrador retriever was the most popular purebred dog. The number of Labs exceeded the number of Golden retrievers and German shepherds combined by 48 thousand. Furthermore, the number of Labs was 9 thousand more than three times the number of German shepherds. If there were 246 thousand registrations for Labrador retrievers, Golden retrievers, and German shepherds, how many registrations, in thousands, were there for each of these breeds?

3.3

In Exercises 16–17, write the system of linear equations represented by the augmented matrix. Use x, y, z, and, if necessary, w, x, y, and z, for the variables. Once the system is written, use back-substitution to find its solution.

16. $\left[\begin{array}{ccc|c} 1 & 1 & 3 & 12 \\ 0 & 1 & -2 & -4 \\ 0 & 0 & 1 & 3 \end{array}\right]$

17. $\left[\begin{array}{cccc|c} 1 & 0 & -2 & 2 & 1 \\ 0 & 1 & 1 & -1 & 0 \\ 0 & 0 & 1 & -\frac{7}{3} & -\frac{1}{3} \\ 0 & 0 & 0 & 1 & 1 \end{array}\right]$

In Exercises 18–19, perform each matrix row operation and write the new matrix.

18. $\left[\begin{array}{ccc|c} 1 & 2 & 2 & 2 \\ 0 & 1 & -1 & 2 \\ 0 & 5 & 4 & 1 \end{array}\right]$ $\quad -5R_2 + R_3$

19. $\left[\begin{array}{ccc|c} 2 & -2 & 1 & -1 \\ 1 & 2 & -1 & 2 \\ 6 & 4 & 3 & 5 \end{array}\right]$ $\quad \frac{1}{2}R_1$

In Exercises 20–22, solve each system of equations using matrices. Use Gaussian elimination with back-substitution or Gauss-Jordan elimination.

20. $x + 2y + 3z = -5$
$2x + y + z = 1$
$x + y - z = 8$

21. $x - 2y + z = 0$
$y - 3z = -1$
$2y + 5z = -2$

22. $3x_1 + 5x_2 - 8x_3 + 5x_4 = -8$
$x_1 + 2x_2 - 3x_3 + x_4 = -7$
$2x_1 + 3x_2 - 7x_3 + 3x_4 = -11$
$4x_1 + 8x_2 - 10x_3 + 7x_4 = -10$

23. The table shows the pollutants in the air in a city on a typical summer day.

x (Hours after 6 A.M.)	y (Amount of Pollutants in the Air, in parts per million)
2	98
4	138
10	162

a. Use the function $y = ax^2 + bx + c$ to model the data. Use either Gaussian elimination with back-substitution or Gauss-Jordan elimination to find the values for a, b, and c.

b. Use the function to find the time of day at which the city's air pollution level is at a maximum. What is the maximum level?

3.4

In Exercises 24–29, evaluate each determinant.

24. $\begin{vmatrix} 3 & 2 \\ -1 & 5 \end{vmatrix}$

25. $\begin{vmatrix} -2 & -3 \\ -4 & -8 \end{vmatrix}$

26. $\begin{vmatrix} 2 & 4 & -3 \\ 1 & -1 & 5 \\ -2 & 4 & 0 \end{vmatrix}$

27. $\begin{vmatrix} 4 & 7 & 0 \\ -5 & 6 & 0 \\ 3 & 2 & -4 \end{vmatrix}$

28. $\begin{vmatrix} 1 & 1 & 0 & 2 \\ 0 & 3 & 2 & 1 \\ 0 & -2 & 4 & 0 \\ 0 & 3 & 0 & 1 \end{vmatrix}$

29. $\begin{vmatrix} 2 & 2 & 2 & 2 \\ 0 & 2 & 2 & 2 \\ 0 & 0 & 2 & 2 \\ 0 & 0 & 0 & 2 \end{vmatrix}$

In Exercises 30–33, use Cramer's rule to solve each system.

30. $x - 2y = 8$
$3x + 2y = -1$

31. $7x + 2y = 0$
$2x + y = -3$

32. $x + 2y + 2z = 5$
$2x + 4y + 7z = 19$
$-2x - 5y - 2z = 8$

33. $2x + y = -4$
$y - 2z = 0$
$3x - 2z = -11$

34. Use the quadratic function $y = ax^2 + bx + c$ to model the following data:

x (Age of a Driver)	y (Average Number of Automobile Accidents per Day in the United States)
20	400
40	150
60	400

Use Cramer's rule to determine values for a, b, and c. Then use the model to write a statement about the average number of automobile accidents in which 30-year-olds and 50-year-olds are involved daily.

Chapter 3 Test

In Exercises 1–3, solve the system.

1. $x = y + 4$
$3x + 7y = -18$

2. $2x + 5y = -2$
$3x - 4y = 20$

3. $x + y + z = 6$
$3x + 4y - 7z = 1$
$2x - y + 3z = 5$

4. A company is planning to produce and sell a new line of computers. The fixed cost will be \$360,000 and it will cost \$850 to produce each computer. Each computer will be sold for \$1150.

a. Write the cost function, C, of producing x computers.

b. Write the revenue function, R, from the sale of x computers.

c. Determine the break-even point. Describe what this means.

5. Find the quadratic function whose graph passes through the points $(-1, -2)$, $(2, 1)$, and $(-2, 1)$.

In Exercise 6, solve the system of equations using matrices.

6. $x + 2y - z = -3$
$2x - 4y + z = -7$
$-2x + 2y - 3z = 4$

7. Evaluate: $\begin{vmatrix} 4 & -1 & 3 \\ 0 & 5 & -1 \\ 5 & 2 & 4 \end{vmatrix}$.

8. Solve for x only using Cramer's rule:

$3x + y - 2z = -3$
$2x + 7y + 3z = 9$
$4x - 3y - z = 7$.

Cumulative Review Exercises (Chapters 1–3)

The figure shows the graph of $y = f(x)$ and its two vertical asymptotes. Use the graph to solve Exercises 1–9.

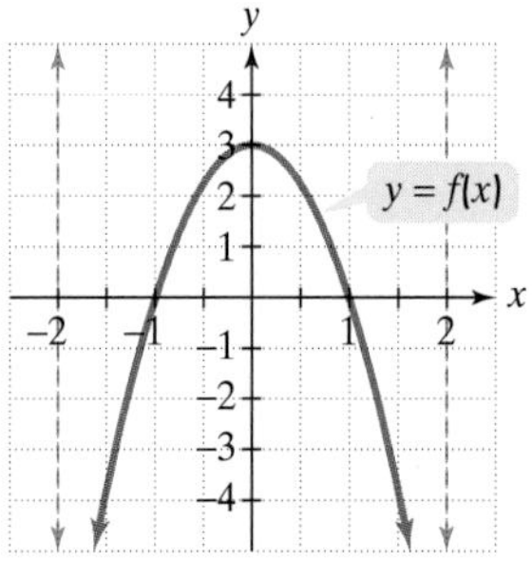

1. Find the domain and the range of f.

2. Find the zeros and the least possible multiplicity of each zero.

3. What is the relative maximum and where does it occur?

4. Find the interval(s) on which f is decreasing.

5. Is $f(-0.7)$ positive or negative?

6. Find $(f \circ f)(-1)$.

7. Does f appear to be even, odd, or neither?

8. Graph $g(x) = f(x + 2) - 1$.

9. Graph $h(x) = \frac{1}{2}f\left(\frac{1}{2}x\right)$.

In Exercises 10–15, solve each equation, inequality, or system of equations.

10. $\sqrt{x^2 - 3x} = 2x - 6$ **11.** $4x^2 = 8x - 7$

12. $\left|\frac{x}{3} + 2\right| < 4$ **13.** $6x - 3(5x + 2) = 4(1 - x)$

14. $x^{\frac{1}{2}} - 2x^{\frac{1}{4}} - 15 = 0$

15. $$\begin{aligned} x + 2y + 3z &= -2 \\ 3x + 3y + 10z &= -2 \\ 2y - 5z &= 6 \end{aligned}$$

In Exercises 16–17, graph each equation, function, or inequality in a rectangular coordinate system. If two functions are indicated, graph both in the same system.

16. $f(x) = (x + 2)^2 - 4$

17. $f(x) = |x|$ and $g(x) = -|x - 2|$

In Exercises 18–19, let $f(x) = 2x^2 - x - 1$ and $g(x) = 1 - x$.

18. Find $(f \circ g)(x)$ and $(g \circ f)(x)$.

19. Find $\frac{f(x + h) - f(x)}{h}$ and simplify.

In Exercises 20–21, write the linear function in slope-intercept form satisfying the given conditions.

20. Graph of f passes through $(2, 4)$ and $(4, -2)$.

21. Graph of g passes through $(-1, 0)$ and is perpendicular to the line whose equation is $x + 3y - 6 = 0$.

22. You invested \$4000 in two stocks paying 12% and 14% annual interest, respectively. At the end of the year, the total interest from these investments was \$508. How much was invested at each rate?

23. The length of a rectangle is 1 meter more than twice the width. If the rectangle's area is 36 square meters, find its dimensions.

Solve each equation or inequality in Exercises 24–26.

24. $2x^2 = 4 - x$ **25.** $5x + 8 \le 7(1 + x)$

26. $\sqrt{2x + 4} - \sqrt{x + 3} - 1 = 0$

27. Use matrices to solve this system:

$$\begin{aligned} x - y + z &= 17 \\ 2x + 3y + z &= 8 \\ -4x + y + 5z &= -2. \end{aligned}$$

28. Solve for y using Cramer's rule:

$$\begin{aligned} x - 2y + z &= 7 \\ 2x + y - z &= 0 \\ 3x + 2y - 2z &= -2. \end{aligned}$$

In Exercises 29–31, graph each equation, function, or inequality in a rectangular coordinate system.

29. $y = -\frac{2}{3}x - 1$

30. $f(x) = x^2 - 2x - 3$

31. $(x - 1)^2 + (y + 1)^2 = 9$

CHAPTER 4

Trigonometric Functions

HAVE YOU HAD DAYS WHERE your physical, intellectual, and emotional potentials were all at their peak? Then there are those other days when we feel we should not even bother getting out of bed. Do our potentials run in oscillating cycles like the tides? Can they be described mathematically? In this chapter, you will encounter functions that enable us to model phenomena that occur in cycles.

WHAT A DAY! IT STARTED WHEN YOU added two miles to your morning run. You've experienced a feeling of peak physical well-being ever since. College was wonderful: You actually enjoyed two difficult lectures and breezed through a math test that had you worried. Now you're having dinner with a group of old friends. You experience the warmth from bonds of friendship filling the room.

SECTION 4.1 Angles and Radian Measure

Objectives

1. Recognize and use the vocabulary of angles.
2. Use degree measure.
3. Use radian measure.
4. Convert between degrees and radians.
5. Draw angles in standard position.
6. Find coterminal angles.
7. Find the length of a circular arc.
8. Use linear and angular speed to describe motion on a circular path.

The San Francisco Museum of Modern Art was constructed in 1995 to illustrate how art and architecture can enrich one another. The exterior involves geometric shapes, symmetry, and unusual facades. Although there are no windows, natural light streams in through a truncated cylindrical skylight that crowns the building. The architect worked with a scale model of the museum at the site and observed how light hit it during different times of the day. These observations were used to cut the cylindrical skylight at an angle that maximizes sunlight entering the interior.

Angles play a critical role in creating modern architecture. They are also fundamental in trigonometry. In this section, we begin our study of trigonometry by looking at angles and methods for measuring them.

1 Recognize and use the vocabulary of angles.

Angles

The hour hand of a clock suggests a **ray**, a part of a line that has only one endpoint and extends forever in the opposite direction. An **angle** is formed by two rays that have a common endpoint. One ray is called the **initial side** and the other the **terminal side**.

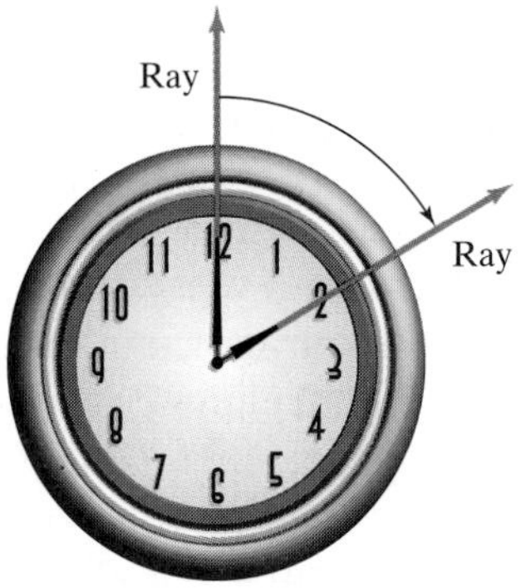

Figure 4.1 Clock with hands forming an angle

A rotating ray is often a useful way to think about angles. The ray in Figure 4.1 rotates from 12 to 2. The ray pointing to 12 is the **initial side** and the ray pointing to 2 is the **terminal side**. The common endpoint of an angle's initial side and terminal side is the **vertex** of the angle.

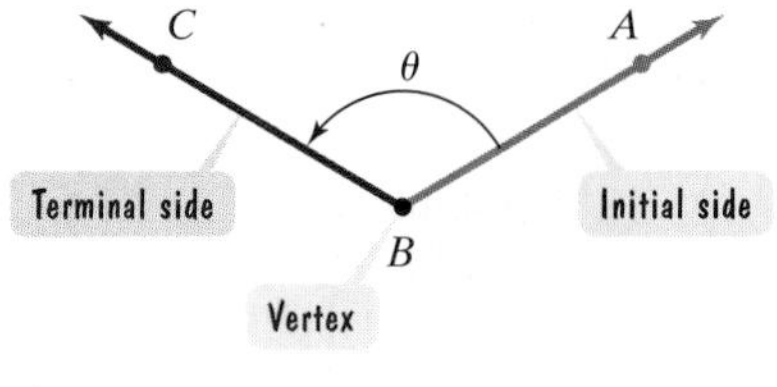

Figure 4.2 An angle; two rays with a common endpoint

Figure 4.2 shows an angle. The arrow near the vertex shows the direction and the amount of rotation from the initial side to the terminal side. Several methods can be used to name an angle. Lowercase Greek letters, such as α (alpha), β (beta), γ (gamma), and θ (theta), are often used.

An angle is in **standard position** if

- its vertex is at the origin of a rectangular coordinate system and
- its initial side lies along the positive x-axis.

The angles in Figure 4.3 at the top of the next page are both in standard position.

When we see an initial side and a terminal side in place, there are two kinds of rotation that could have generated the angle. The arrow in Figure 4.3(a) indicates

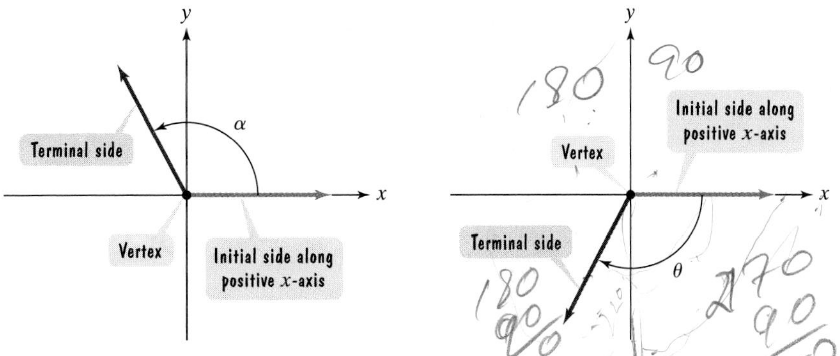

(a) α in standard position;
 α positive

(b) θ in standard position;
 θ negative

Figure 4.3 Two angles in standard position

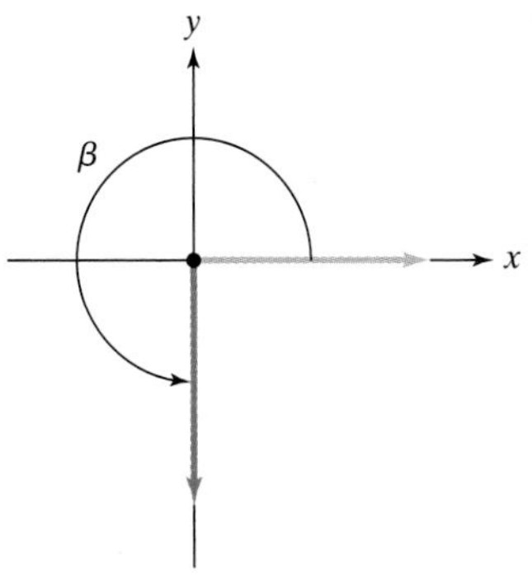

Figure 4.4 b is a quadrantal angle.

Use degree measure.

A complete 360° rotation

that the rotation from the initial side to the terminal side is in the counterclockwise direction. **Positive angles** are generated by counterclockwise rotation. Thus, angle α is positive. By contrast, the arrow in Figure 4.3(b) shows that the rotation from the initial side to the terminal side is in the clockwise direction. **Negative angles** are generated by clockwise rotation. Thus, angle θ is negative.

When an angle is in standard position, its terminal side can lie in a quadrant. We say that the angle **lies in that quadrant**. For example, in Figure 4.3(a), the terminal side of angle α lies in quadrant II. Thus, angle α lies in quadrant II. By contrast, in Figure 4.3(b), the terminal side of angle θ lies in quadrant III. Thus, angle θ lies in quadrant III.

Must all angles in standard position lie in a quadrant? The answer is no. The terminal side can lie on the x-axis or the y-axis. For example, angle β in Figure 4.4 has a terminal side that lies on the negative y-axis. An angle is called a **quadrantal angle** if its terminal side lies on the x-axis or the y-axis. Angle β in Figure 4.4 is an example of a quadrantal angle.

Measuring Angles Using Degrees

Angles are measured by determining the amount of rotation from the initial side to the terminal side. One way to measure angles is in **degrees**, symbolized by a small, raised circle °. Think of the hour hand of a clock. From 12 noon to 12 midnight, the hour hand moves around in a complete circle. By definition, the ray has rotated through 360 degrees, or 360°. Using 360° as the amount of rotation of a ray back onto itself, a degree, 1°, is $\frac{1}{360}$ of a complete rotation.

Figure 4.5 shows that certain angles have special names. An **acute angle** measures less than 90° [see Figure 4.5(a)]. A **right angle**, one quarter of a complete rotation, measures 90° [Figure 4.5(b)]. Examine the right angle—do you see a small square at the vertex? This symbol is used to indicate a right angle. An **obtuse angle** measures more than 90°, but less than 180° [Figure 4.5(c)]. Finally, a **straight angle**,

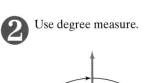

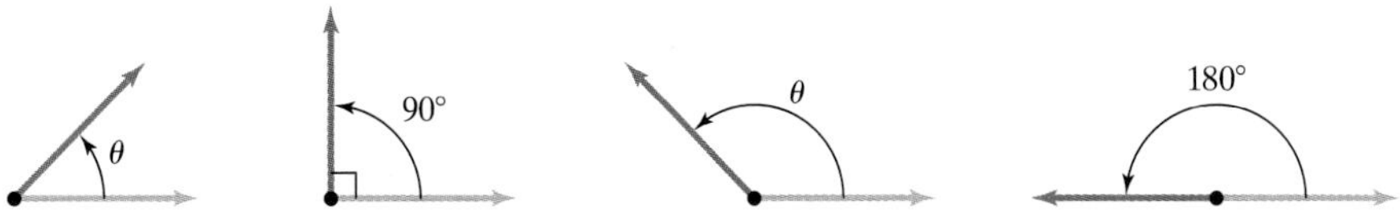

(a) **Acute angle**
$(0° < \theta < 90°)$

(b) **Right angle**
$(\frac{1}{4}$ rotation$)$

(c) **Obtuse angle**
$(90° < \theta < 180°)$

(d) **Straight angle**
$(\frac{1}{2}$ rotation$)$

Figure 4.5 Classifying angles by their degree measurement

one-half a complete rotation, measures 180° [Figure 4.5(d)].

We will be using notation such as $\theta = 60°$ to refer to an angle θ whose measure is 60°. We also refer to *an angle of* 60° or a 60° *angle*, rather than using the more precise (but cumbersome) phrase *an angle whose measure is* 60°.

Technology

Fractional parts of degrees are measured in minutes and seconds. One minute, written $1'$, is $\frac{1}{60}$ degree: $1' = \frac{1}{60}°$.

One second, written $1''$, is $\frac{1}{3600}$ degree: $1'' = \frac{1}{3600}°$.

For example,

$$31°47'12'' = \left(31 + \frac{47}{60} + \frac{12}{3600}\right)° \approx 31.787°.$$

Many calculators have keys for changing an angle from degree-minute-second notation (D°M′S″) to a decimal form and vice versa.

3 Use radian measure.

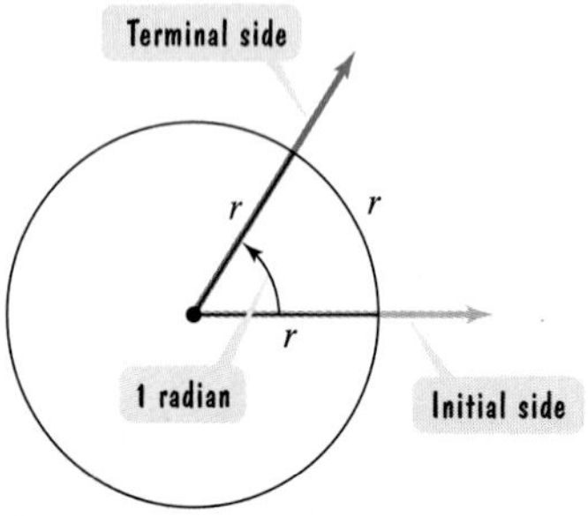

Figure 4.6 For a 1-radian angle, the intercepted arc and the radius are equal.

Measuring Angles Using Radians

Another way to measure angles is in *radians*. Let's first define an angle measuring **1 radian**. We use a circle of radius r. In Figure 4.6, we've constructed an angle whose vertex is at the center of the circle. Such an angle is called a **central angle**. Notice that this central angle intercepts an arc along the circle measuring r units. The radius of the circle is also r units. The measure of such an angle is 1 radian.

Definition of a Radian

One radian is the measure of the central angle of a circle that intercepts an arc equal in length to the radius of the circle.

The **radian measure** of any central angle is the length of the intercepted arc divided by the circle's radius. In Figure 4.7(a), the length of the arc intercepted by angle β is double the radius, r. We find the measure of angle β in radians by dividing the length of the intercepted arc by the radius.

$$\beta = \frac{\text{length of the intercepted arc}}{\text{radius}} = \frac{2r}{r} = 2$$

Thus, angle β measures 2 radians.

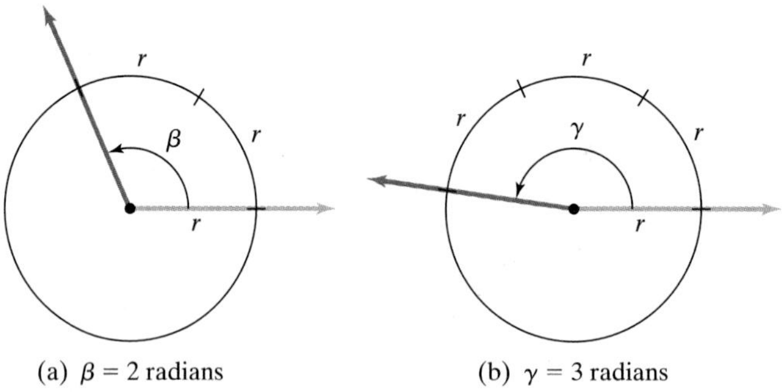

Figure 4.7 Two central angles measured in radians

In Figure 4.7(b), the length of the intercepted arc is triple the radius, r. Let us find the measure of angle γ:

$$\gamma = \frac{\text{length of the intercepted arc}}{\text{radius}} = \frac{3r}{r} = 3.$$

Thus, angle γ measures 3 radians.

Radian Measure

Consider an arc of length s on a circle of radius r. The measure of the central angle, θ, that intercepts the arc is

$$\theta = \frac{s}{r} \text{ radians.}$$

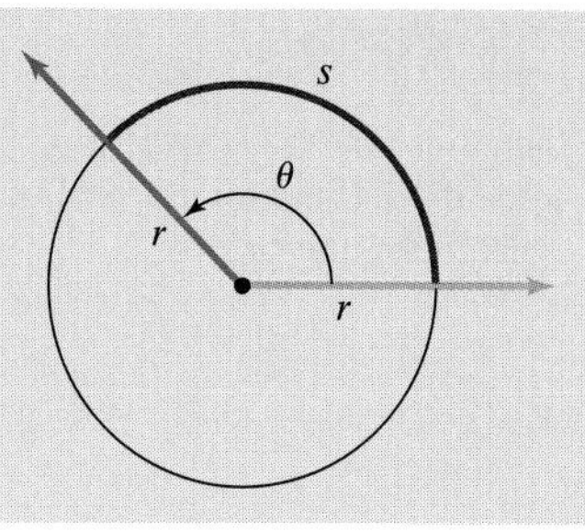

EXAMPLE 1 Computing Radian Measure

A central angle, θ, in a circle of radius 6 inches intercepts an arc of length 15 inches. What is the radian measure of θ?

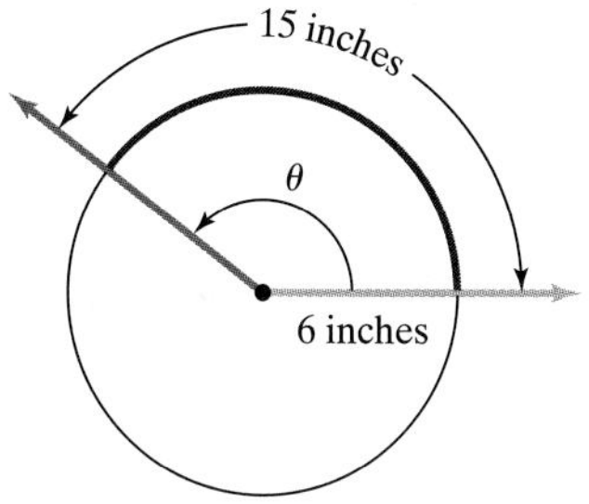

Figure 4.8

Solution Angle θ is shown in Figure 4.8. The radian measure of a central angle is the length of the intercepted arc, s, divided by the circle's radius, r. The length of the intercepted arc is 15 inches: $s = 15$ inches. The circle's radius is 6 inches: $r = 6$ inches. Now we use the formula for radian measure to find the radian measure of θ.

$$\theta = \frac{s}{r} = \frac{15 \text{ inches}}{6 \text{ inches}} = 2.5$$

Thus, the radian measure of θ is 2.5.

Study Tip

Before applying the formula for radian measure, be sure that the same unit of length is used for the intercepted arc, s, and the radius, r.

In Example 1, notice that the units (inches) cancel when we use the formula for radian measure. We are left with a number with no units. Thus, if an angle θ has a measure of 2.5 radians, we can write $\theta = 2.5$ radians or $\theta = 2.5$. We will often include the word *radians* simply for emphasis. There should be no confusion as to whether radian or degree measure is being used. Why is this so? If θ has a degree measure of, say, 2.5°, we must include the degree symbol and write $\theta = 2.5°$, and *not* $\theta = 2.5$.

Check Point 1 A central angle, θ, in a circle of radius 12 feet intercepts an arc of length 42 feet. What is the radian measure of θ?

4 Convert between degrees and radians.

Relationship between Degrees and Radians

How can we obtain a relationship between degrees and radians? We compare the number of degrees and the number of radians in one complete rotation, shown in Figure 4.9. We know that 360° is the amount of rotation of a ray back onto itself. The length of the intercepted arc is equal to the circumference of the circle. Thus, the radian measure of this central angle is the circumference of the circle divided by the circle's radius, r. The circumference of a circle of radius r is $2\pi r$. We use the formula for radian measure to find the radian measure of the 360° angle.

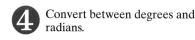

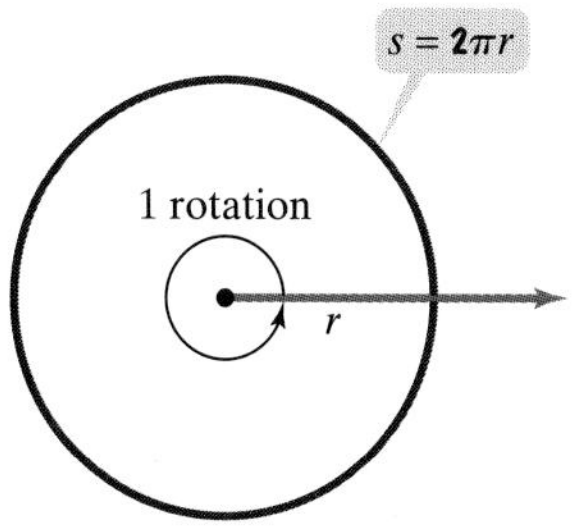

Figure 4.9 A complete rotation

$$\theta = \frac{s}{r} = \frac{\text{the circle's circumference}}{r} = \frac{2\pi r}{r} = 2\pi$$

Because one complete rotation measures 360° and 2π radians,

$$360° = 2\pi \text{ radians.}$$

Dividing both sides by 2, we have

$$180° = \pi \text{ radians.}$$

Dividing this last equation by 180° or π gives the conversion rules in the box on the next page.

Study Tip

The unit you are converting *to* appears in the *numerator* of the conversion factor.

Conversion between Degrees and Radians

Using the basic relationship π radians $= 180°$,

1. To convert degrees to radians, multiply degrees by $\dfrac{\pi \text{ radians}}{180°}$.
2. To convert radians to degrees, multiply radians by $\dfrac{180°}{\pi \text{ radians}}$.

Angles that are fractions of a complete rotation are usually expressed in radian measure as fractional multiples of π, rather than as decimal approximations. For example, we write $\theta = \dfrac{\pi}{2}$ rather than using the decimal approximation $\theta \approx 1.57$.

EXAMPLE 2 Converting from Degrees to Radians

Convert each angle in degrees to radians:

a. 30° **b.** 90° **c.** −135°.

Solution To convert degrees to radians, multiply by $\dfrac{\pi \text{ radians}}{180°}$. Observe how the degree units cancel.

$$\textbf{a. } 30° = 30° \cdot \frac{\pi \text{ radians}}{180°} = \frac{30\pi}{180} \text{radians} = \frac{\pi}{6} \text{radians}$$

$$\textbf{b. } 90° = 90° \cdot \frac{\pi \text{ radians}}{180°} = \frac{90\pi}{180} \text{radians} = \frac{\pi}{2} \text{radians}$$

$$\textbf{c. } -135° = -135° \cdot \frac{\pi \text{ radians}}{180°} = -\frac{135\pi}{180} \text{radians} = -\frac{3\pi}{4} \text{radians}$$

Divide the numerator and denominator by 45.

Check Point 2 Convert each angle in degrees to radians:

a. 60° **b.** 270° **c.** −300°.

EXAMPLE 3 Converting from Radians to Degrees

Convert each angle in radians to degrees:

a. $\dfrac{\pi}{3}$ radians **b.** $-\dfrac{5\pi}{3}$ radians **c.** 1 radian.

Solution To convert radians to degrees, multiply by $\dfrac{180°}{\pi \text{ radians}}$. Observe how the radian units cancel.

$$\textbf{a. } \frac{\pi}{3}\text{radians} = \frac{\pi \text{ radians}}{3} \cdot \frac{180°}{\pi \text{ radians}} = \frac{180°}{3} = 60°$$

$$\textbf{b. } -\frac{5\pi}{3}\text{radians} = -\frac{5\pi \text{ radians}}{3} \cdot \frac{180°}{\pi \text{ radians}} = -\frac{5 \cdot 180°}{3} = -300°$$

$$\textbf{c. } 1 \text{ radian} = 1 \text{ radian} \cdot \frac{180°}{\pi \text{ radians}} = \frac{180°}{\pi} \approx 57.3°$$

Study Tip

In Example 3(c), we see that 1 radian is approximately 57°. Keep in mind that a radian is much larger than a degree.

Check Point 3 Convert each angle in radians to degrees:

a. $\dfrac{\pi}{4}$ radians **b.** $-\dfrac{4\pi}{3}$ radians **c.** 6 radians.

5 Draw angles in standard position.

Drawing Angles in Standard Position

Although we can convert angles in radians to degrees, it is helpful to "think in radians" without having to make this conversion. To become comfortable with radian measure, consider angles in standard position: Each vertex is at the origin and each initial side lies along the positive x-axis. Think of the terminal side of the angle revolving around the origin. Thinking in radians means determining what part of a complete revolution or how many full revolutions will produce an angle whose radian measure is known. And here's the thing: We want to do this without having to convert from radians to degrees.

Figure 4.10 is a starting point for learning to think in radians. The figure illustrates that when the terminal side makes one full revolution, it forms an angle whose radian measure is 2π. The figure shows the quadrantal angles formed by $\frac{3}{4}$ of a revolution, $\frac{1}{2}$ of a revolution, and $\frac{1}{4}$ of a revolution.

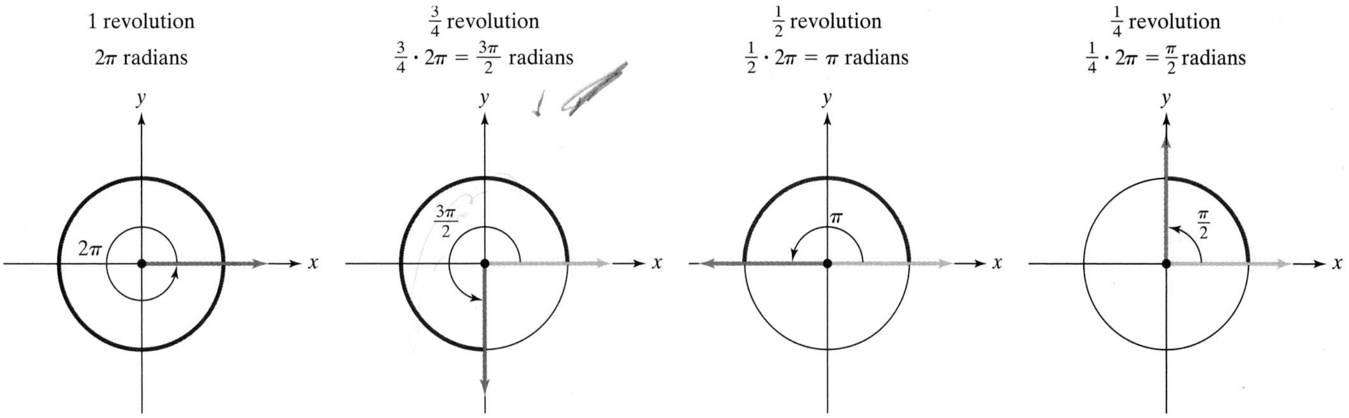

Figure 4.10 Angles formed by revolutions of terminal sides

EXAMPLE 4 Drawing Angles in Standard Position

Draw and label each angle in standard position:

a. $\theta = \frac{\pi}{4}$ (theta) **b.** $\alpha = \frac{5\pi}{4}$ (alpha) **c.** $\beta = -\frac{3\pi}{4}$ (beta) **d.** $\gamma = \frac{9\pi}{4}$. (gamma)

Solution Because we are drawing angles in standard position, each vertex is at the origin and each initial side lies along the positive x-axis.

a. An angle of $\frac{\pi}{4}$ radians is a positive angle. It is obtained by rotating the terminal side counterclockwise. Because 2π is a full-circle revolution, we can express $\frac{\pi}{4}$ as a fractional part of 2π to determine the necessary rotation:

$$\frac{\pi}{4} = \frac{1}{8} \cdot 2\pi$$

$\frac{\pi}{4}$ is $\frac{1}{8}$ of a complete revolution of 2π radians.

We see that $\theta = \frac{\pi}{4}$ is obtained by rotating the terminal side counterclockwise for $\frac{1}{8}$ of a revolution. The angle lies in quadrant I and is shown in Figure 4.11.

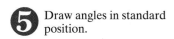

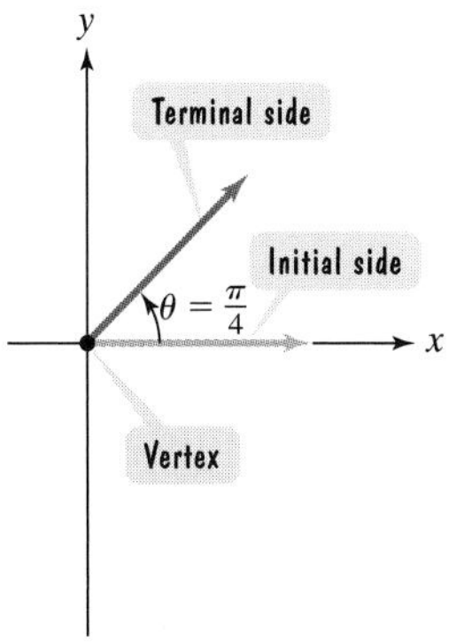

Figure 4.11

b. An angle of $\frac{5\pi}{4}$ radians is a positive angle. It is obtained by rotating the terminal side counterclockwise. Here are two ways to determine the necessary rotation:

Method 1

$$\frac{5\pi}{4} = \frac{5}{8} \cdot 2\pi$$

$\frac{5\pi}{4}$ is $\frac{5}{8}$ of a complete revolution of 2π radians.

Method 2

$$\frac{5\pi}{4} = \pi + \frac{\pi}{4}.$$

π is a half-circle revolution.

$\frac{\pi}{4}$ is $\frac{1}{8}$ of a complete revolution.

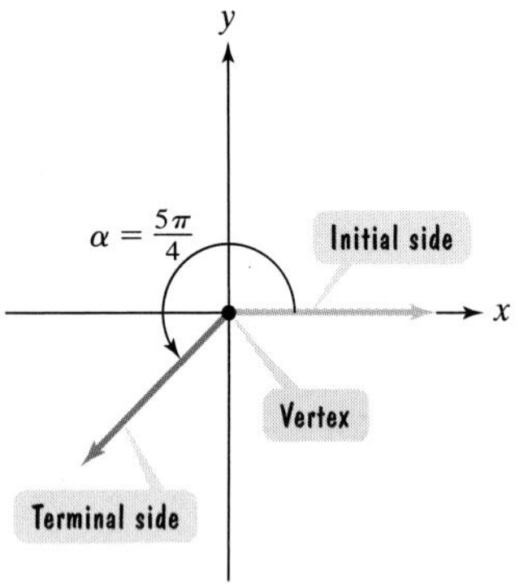

Figure 4.12

Method 1 shows that $\alpha = \frac{5\pi}{4}$ is obtained by rotating the terminal side counterclockwise for $\frac{5}{8}$ of a revolution. Method 2 shows that $\alpha = \frac{5\pi}{4}$ is obtained by rotating the terminal side counterclockwise for half of a revolution followed by a counterclockwise rotation of $\frac{1}{4}$ of a revolution. The angle lies in quadrant III and is shown in Figure 4.12.

c. An angle of $-\frac{3\pi}{4}$ is a negative angle. It is obtained by rotating the terminal side clockwise. We use $\left|-\frac{3\pi}{4}\right|$, or $\frac{3\pi}{4}$, to determine the necessary rotation.

Method 1

$$\frac{3\pi}{4} = \frac{3}{8} \cdot 2\pi$$

$\frac{3\pi}{4}$ is $\frac{3}{8}$ of a complete revolution of 2π radians.

Method 2

$$\frac{3\pi}{4} = \frac{2\pi}{4} + \frac{\pi}{4} = \frac{\pi}{2} + \frac{\pi}{4}$$

$\frac{\pi}{2}$ is a quarter-circle revolution.

$\frac{\pi}{4}$ is $\frac{1}{8}$ of a complete revolution.

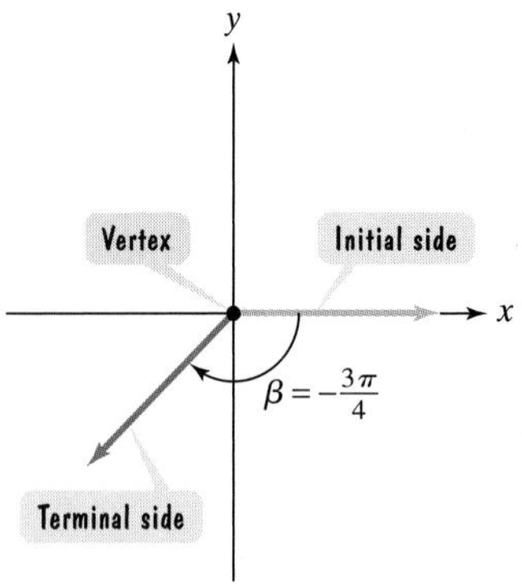

Figure 4.13

Method 1 shows that $\beta = -\frac{3\pi}{4}$ is obtained by rotating the terminal side clockwise for $\frac{3}{8}$ of a revolution. Method 2 shows that $\beta = -\frac{3\pi}{4}$ is obtained by rotating the terminal side clockwise for $\frac{1}{4}$ of a revolution followed by a clockwise rotation of $\frac{1}{8}$ of a revolution. The angle lies in quadrant III and is shown in Figure 4.13.

d. An angle of $\frac{9\pi}{4}$ radians is a positive angle. It is obtained by rotating the terminal side counterclockwise. Here are two methods to determine the necessary rotation:

Method 1

$$\frac{9\pi}{4} = \frac{9}{8} \cdot 2\pi$$

$\frac{9\pi}{4}$ is $\frac{9}{8}$, or $1\frac{1}{8}$, complete revolutions of 2π radians.

Method 2

$$\frac{9\pi}{4} = 2\pi + \frac{\pi}{4}.$$

2π is a full-circle revolution.

$\frac{\pi}{4}$ is $\frac{1}{8}$ of a complete revolution.

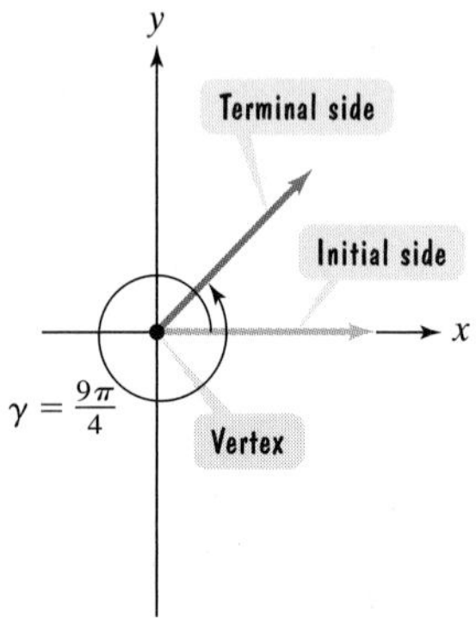

Figure 4.14

Method 1 shows that $\gamma = \frac{9\pi}{4}$ is obtained by rotating the terminal side counterclockwise for $1\frac{1}{8}$ revolutions. Method 2 shows that $\gamma = \frac{9\pi}{4}$ is obtained by rotating the terminal side counterclockwise for a full-circle revolution followed by a counterclockwise rotation of $\frac{1}{8}$ of a revolution. The angle lies in quadrant I and is shown in Figure 4.14.

Check Point 4 Draw and label each angle in standard position:

a. $\theta = -\dfrac{\pi}{4}$ **b.** $\alpha = \dfrac{3\pi}{4}$ **c.** $\beta = -\dfrac{7\pi}{4}$ **d.** $\gamma = \dfrac{13\pi}{4}$.

Figure 4.15 illustrates the degree and radian measures of angles that you will commonly see in trigonometry. Each angle is in standard position, so that the initial side lies along the positive x-axis. We will be using both degree and radian measure for these angles.

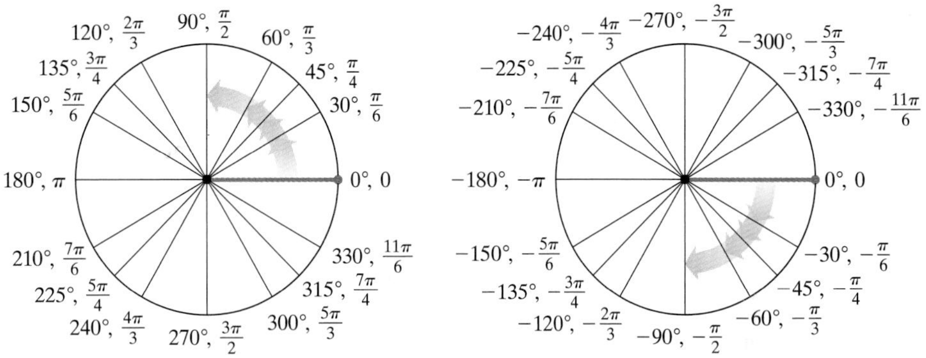

Figure 4.15 Degree and radian measures of selected positive and negative angles

Table 4.1 describes some of the positive angles in Figure 4.15 in terms of revolutions of the angle's terminal side around the origin.

Table 4.1

Terminal Side	Radian Measure of Angle	Degree Measure of Angle
$\dfrac{1}{12}$ revolution	$\dfrac{1}{12} \cdot 2\pi = \dfrac{\pi}{6}$	$\dfrac{1}{12} \cdot 360° = 30°$
$\dfrac{1}{8}$ revolution	$\dfrac{1}{8} \cdot 2\pi = \dfrac{\pi}{4}$	$\dfrac{1}{8} \cdot 360° = 45°$
$\dfrac{1}{6}$ revolution	$\dfrac{1}{6} \cdot 2\pi = \dfrac{\pi}{3}$	$\dfrac{1}{6} \cdot 360° = 60°$
$\dfrac{1}{4}$ revolution	$\dfrac{1}{4} \cdot 2\pi = \dfrac{\pi}{2}$	$\dfrac{1}{4} \cdot 360° = 90°$
$\dfrac{1}{3}$ revolution	$\dfrac{1}{3} \cdot 2\pi = \dfrac{2\pi}{3}$	$\dfrac{1}{3} \cdot 360° = 120°$
$\dfrac{1}{2}$ revolution	$\dfrac{1}{2} \cdot 2\pi = \pi$	$\dfrac{1}{2} \cdot 360° = 180°$
$\dfrac{2}{3}$ revolution	$\dfrac{2}{3} \cdot 2\pi = \dfrac{4\pi}{3}$	$\dfrac{2}{3} \cdot 360° = 240°$
$\dfrac{3}{4}$ revolution	$\dfrac{3}{4} \cdot 2\pi = \dfrac{3\pi}{2}$	$\dfrac{3}{4} \cdot 360° = 270°$
$\dfrac{7}{8}$ revolution	$\dfrac{7}{8} \cdot 2\pi = \dfrac{7\pi}{4}$	$\dfrac{7}{8} \cdot 360° = 315°$
1 revolution	$1 \cdot 2\pi = 2\pi$	$1 \cdot 360° = 360°$

Study Tip

When drawing the angles in Table 4.1 and Figure 4.15, it is helpful to first divide the rectangular coordinate system into eight equal sectors:

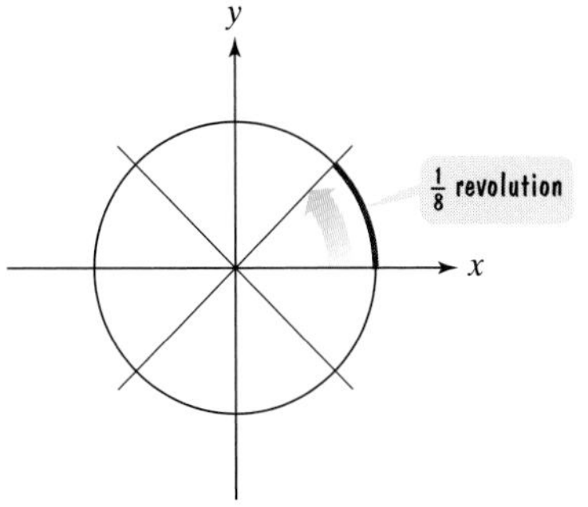

or 12 equal sectors:

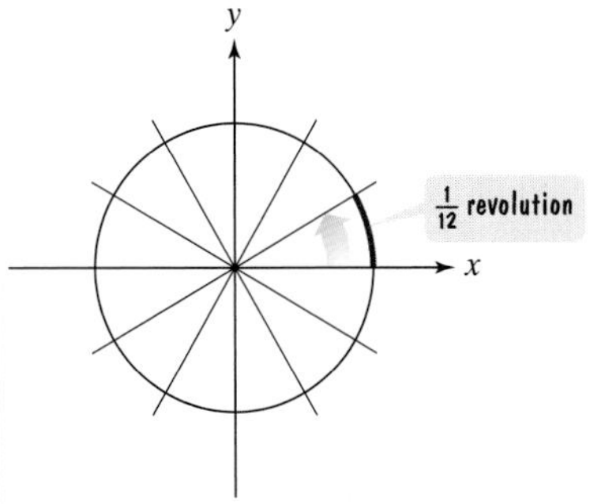

Perhaps we should call this study tip "Making a Clone of Arc."

6 Find coterminal angles.

Coterminal Angles

Two angles with the same initial and terminal sides but possibly different rotations are called **coterminal angles**.

Every angle has infinitely many coterminal angles. Why? Think of an angle in standard position. If the rotation of the angle is extended by one or more complete rotations of 360° or 2π, clockwise or counterclockwise, the result is an angle with the same initial and terminal sides as the original angle.

Coterminal Angles

Increasing or decreasing the degree measure of an angle in standard position by an integer multiple of 360° results in a coterminal angle. Thus, an angle of $\theta°$ is coterminal with angles of $\theta° \pm 360°k$, where k is an integer.

Increasing or decreasing the radian measure of an angle by an integer multiple of 2π results in a coterminal angle. Thus, an angle of θ radians is coterminal with angles of $\theta \pm 2\pi k$, where k is an integer.

Two coterminal angles for an angle of $\theta°$ can be found by adding 360° to $\theta°$ and subtracting 360° from $\theta°$.

EXAMPLE 5 Finding Coterminal Angles

Assume the following angles are in standard position. Find a positive angle less than 360° that is coterminal with each of the following:

a. a 420° angle **b.** a −120° angle.

Solution We obtain the coterminal angle by adding or subtracting 360°. The requirement to obtain a positive angle less than 360° determines whether we should add or subtract.

a. For a 420° angle, subtract 360° to find a positive coterminal angle.

$$420° - 360° = 60°$$

A 60° angle is coterminal with a 420° angle. Figure 4.16(a) illustrates that these angles have the same initial and terminal sides.

b. For a −120° angle, add 360° to find a positive coterminal angle.

$$-120° + 360° = 240°$$

A 240° angle is coterminal with a −120° angle. Figure 4.16(b) illustrates that these angles have the same initial and terminal sides.

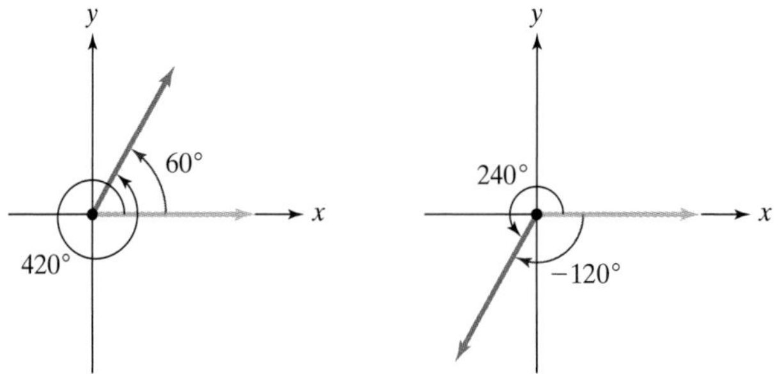

(a) Angles of 420° and 60° are coterminal.

(b) Angles of −120° and 240° are coterminal.

Figure 4.16 Pairs of coterminal angles

Check Point 5 Find a positive angle less than 360° that is coterminal with each of the following:

a. a 400° angle **b.** a −135° angle.

Two coterminal angles for an angle of θ radians can be found by adding 2π to θ and subtracting 2π from θ.

EXAMPLE 6 Finding Coterminal Angles

Assume the following angles are in standard position. Find a positive angle less than 2π that is coterminal with each of the following:

a. a $\frac{17\pi}{6}$ angle **b.** a $-\frac{\pi}{12}$ angle.

Solution We obtain the coterminal angle by adding or subtracting 2π. The requirement to obtain a positive angle less than 2π determines whether we should add or subtract.

a. For a $\frac{17\pi}{6}$, or $2\frac{5}{6}\pi$, angle, subtract 2π to find a positive coterminal angle.

$$\frac{17\pi}{6} - 2\pi = \frac{17\pi}{6} - \frac{12\pi}{6} = \frac{5\pi}{6}$$

A $\frac{5\pi}{6}$ angle is coterminal with a $\frac{17\pi}{6}$ angle. Figure 4.17(a) illustrates that these angles have the same initial and terminal sides.

b. For a $-\frac{\pi}{12}$ angle, add 2π to find a positive coterminal angle.

$$-\frac{\pi}{12} + 2\pi = -\frac{\pi}{12} + \frac{24\pi}{12} = \frac{23\pi}{12}$$

A $\frac{23\pi}{12}$ angle is coterminal with a $-\frac{\pi}{12}$ angle. Figure 4.17(b) illustrates that these angles have the same initial and terminal sides.

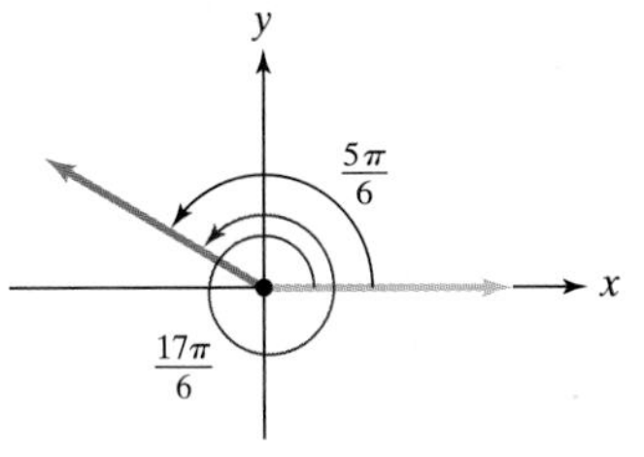

(a) Angles of $\frac{17\pi}{6}$ and $\frac{5\pi}{6}$ are coterminal.

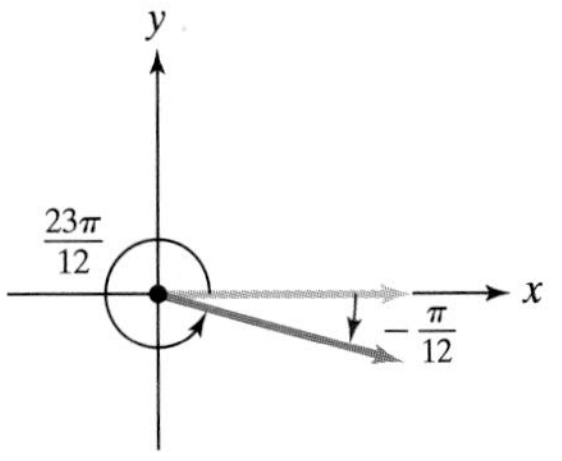

(b) Angles of $-\frac{\pi}{12}$ and $\frac{23\pi}{12}$ are coterminal.

Figure 4.17 Pairs of coterminal angles

Check Point 6 Find a positive angle less than 2π that is coterminal with each of the following:

a. a $\frac{13\pi}{5}$ angle **b.** a $-\frac{\pi}{15}$ angle.

To find a positive coterminal angle less than 360° or 2π, it is sometimes necessary to add or subtract more than one multiple of 360° or 2π.

EXAMPLE 7 Finding Coterminal Angles

Find a positive angle less than 360° or 2π that is coterminal with each of the following:

a. a 750° angle **b.** a $\frac{22\pi}{3}$ angle **c.** a $-\frac{17\pi}{6}$ angle.

Solution

a. For a 750° angle, subtract two multiples of 360°, or 720°, to find a positive coterminal angle less than 360°.

$$750° - 360° \cdot 2 = 750° - 720° = 30°$$

A 30° angle is coterminal with a 750° angle.

Discovery

Make a sketch for each part of Example 7 illustrating that the coterminal angle we found and the given angle have the same initial and terminal sides.

b. For a $\frac{22\pi}{3}$, or $7\frac{1}{3}\pi$, angle, subtract three multiples of 2π, or 6π, to find a positive coterminal angle less than 2π.

$$\frac{22\pi}{3} - 2\pi \cdot 3 = \frac{22\pi}{3} - 6\pi = \frac{22\pi}{3} - \frac{18\pi}{3} = \frac{4\pi}{3}$$

A $\frac{4\pi}{3}$ angle is coterminal with a $\frac{22\pi}{3}$ angle.

c. For a $-\frac{17\pi}{6}$, or $-2\frac{5}{6}\pi$ angle, add two multiples of 2π, or 4π, to find a positive coterminal angle less than 2π.

$$-\frac{17\pi}{6} + 2\pi \cdot 2 = -\frac{17\pi}{6} + 4\pi = -\frac{17\pi}{6} + \frac{24\pi}{6} = \frac{7\pi}{6}$$

A $\frac{7\pi}{6}$ angle is coterminal with a $-\frac{17\pi}{6}$ angle.

Check Point 7 Find a positive angle less than 360° or 2π that is coterminal with each of the following:

a. an 855° angle **b.** a $\frac{17\pi}{3}$ angle **c.** a $-\frac{25\pi}{6}$ angle.

7 Find the length of a circular arc.

The Length of a Circular Arc

We can use the radian measure formula, $\theta = \frac{s}{r}$, to find the length of the arc of a circle. How do we do this? Remember that s represents the length of the arc intercepted by the central angle θ. Thus, by solving the formula for s, we have an equation for arc length.

The Length of a Circular Arc

Let r be the radius of a circle and θ the nonnegative radian measure of a central angle of the circle. The length of the arc intercepted by the central angle is

$$s = r\theta.$$

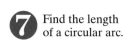

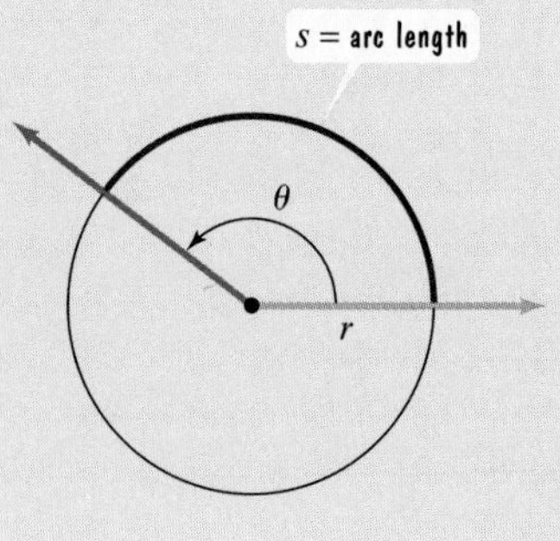

EXAMPLE 8 Finding the Length of a Circular Arc

A circle has a radius of 10 inches. Find the length of the arc intercepted by a central angle of 120°.

Solution The formula $s = r\theta$ can be used only when θ is expressed in radians. Thus, we begin by converting 120° to radians. Multiply by $\frac{\pi \text{ radians}}{180°}$.

$$120° = 120° \cdot \frac{\pi \text{ radians}}{180°} = \frac{120\pi}{180} \text{radians} = \frac{2\pi}{3} \text{radians}$$

Study Tip

The unit used to describe the length of a circular arc is the same unit that is given in the circle's radius.

Now we can use the formula $s = r\theta$ to find the length of the arc. The circle's radius is 10 inches: $r = 10$ inches. The measure of the central angle, in radians, is $\frac{2\pi}{3}$: $\theta = \frac{2\pi}{3}$. The length of the arc intercepted by this central angle is

$$s = r\theta = (10 \text{ inches})\left(\frac{2\pi}{3}\right) = \frac{20\pi}{3} \text{ inches} \approx 20.94 \text{ inches}.$$

Check Point 8 A circle has a radius of 6 inches. Find the length of the arc intercepted by a central angle of 45°. Express arc length in terms of π. Then round your answer to two decimal places.

8 Use linear and angular speed to describe motion on a circular path.

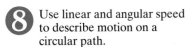

Linear and Angular Speed

A carousel contains four circular rows of animals. As the carousel revolves, the animals in the outer row travel a greater distance per unit of time than those in the inner rows. These animals have a greater *linear speed* than those in the inner rows. By contrast, all animals, regardless of the row, complete the same number of revolutions per unit of time. All animals in the four circular rows travel at the same *angular speed*.

Using v for linear speed and ω (omega) for angular speed, we define these two kinds of speeds along a circular path as follows:

Definitions of Linear and Angular Speed

If a point is in motion on a circle of radius r through an angle of θ radians in time t, then its **linear speed** is

$$v = \frac{s}{t},$$

where s is the arc length given by $s = r\theta$, and its **angular speed** is

$$\omega = \frac{\theta}{t}.$$

The hard drive in a computer rotates at 3600 revolutions per minute. This angular speed, expressed in revolutions per minute, can also be expressed in revolutions per second, radians per minute, and radians per second. Using 2π radians $= 1$ revolution, we express the angular speed of a hard drive in radians per minute as follows:

$$3600 \text{ revolutions per minute}$$
$$= \frac{3600 \text{ revolutions}}{1 \text{ minute}} \cdot \frac{2\pi \text{ radians}}{1 \text{ revolution}} = \frac{7200\pi \text{ radians}}{1 \text{ minute}}$$
$$= 7200\pi \text{ radians per minute.}$$

We can establish a relationship between the two kinds of speed by dividing both sides of the arc length formula, $s = r\theta$, by t:

$$\frac{s}{t} = \frac{r\theta}{t} = r\frac{\theta}{t}.$$

This expression defines linear speed. ($\frac{s}{t}$)

This expression defines angular speed. ($\frac{\theta}{t}$)

Thus, linear speed is the product of the radius and the angular speed.

Linear Speed in Terms of Angular Speed

The linear speed, v, of a point a distance r from the center of rotation is given by

$$v = r\omega,$$

where ω is the angular speed in radians per unit of time.

EXAMPLE 9 Finding Linear Speed

A wind machine used to generate electricity has blades that are 10 feet in length (see Figure 4.18). The propeller is rotating at four revolutions per second. Find the linear speed, in feet per second, of the tips of the blades.

Figure 4.18

Solution We are given ω, the angular speed.

$$\omega = 4 \text{ revolutions per second}$$

We use the formula $v = r\omega$ to find v, the linear speed. Before applying the formula, we must express ω in radians per second.

$$\omega = \frac{4 \text{ ~~revolutions~~}}{1 \text{ second}} \cdot \frac{2\pi \text{ radians}}{1 \text{ ~~revolution~~}} = \frac{8\pi \text{ radians}}{1 \text{ second}} \text{ or } \frac{8\pi}{1 \text{ second}}$$

The angular speed of the propeller is 8π radians per second. The linear speed is

$$v = r\omega = 10 \text{ feet} \cdot \frac{8\pi}{1 \text{ second}} = \frac{80\pi \text{ feet}}{\text{second}}.$$

The linear speed of the tips of the blades is 80π feet per second, which is approximately 251 feet per second.

Check Point 9 Long before iPods that hold thousands of songs and play them with superb audio quality, individual songs were delivered on 75-rpm and 45-rpm circular records. A 45-rpm record has an angular speed of 45 revolutions per minute. Find the linear speed, in inches per minute, at the point where the needle is 1.5 inches from the record's center.

EXERCISE SET 4.1

Practice Exercises

In Exercises 1–6, the measure of an angle is given. Classify the angle as acute, right, obtuse, or straight.

1. 135° **2.** 177° **3.** 83.135°

4. 87.177° **5.** π **6.** $\frac{\pi}{2}$

In Exercises 7–12, find the radian measure of the central angle of a circle of radius r that intercepts an arc of length s.

	Radius, r	**Arc length, s**
7.	10 inches	40 inches
8.	5 feet	30 feet
9.	6 yards	8 yards
10.	8 yards	18 yards
11.	1 meter	400 centimeters
12.	1 meter	600 centimeters

In Exercises 13–20, convert each angle in degrees to radians. Express your answer as a multiple of π.

13. 45° **14.** 18° **15.** 135°

16. 150° **17.** 300° **18.** 330°

19. −225° **20.** −270°

In Exercises 21–28, convert each angle in radians to degrees.

21. $\frac{\pi}{2}$ **22.** $\frac{\pi}{9}$ **23.** $\frac{2\pi}{3}$

24. $\frac{3\pi}{4}$ **25.** $\frac{7\pi}{6}$ **26.** $\frac{11\pi}{6}$

27. -3π **28.** -4π

In Exercises 29–34, convert each angle in degrees to radians. Round to two decimal places.

29. 18° **30.** 76° **31.** −40°

32. −50° **33.** 200° **34.** 250°

In Exercises 35–40, convert each angle in radians to degrees. Round to two decimal places.

35. 2 radians **36.** 3 radians

37. $\frac{\pi}{13}$ radians **38.** $\frac{\pi}{17}$ radians

39. −4.8 radians **40.** −5.2 radians

In Exercises 41–56, use the circle shown in the rectangular coordinate system to draw each angle in standard position. State the quadrant in which the angle lies. When an angle's measure is given in radians, work the exercise without converting to degrees.

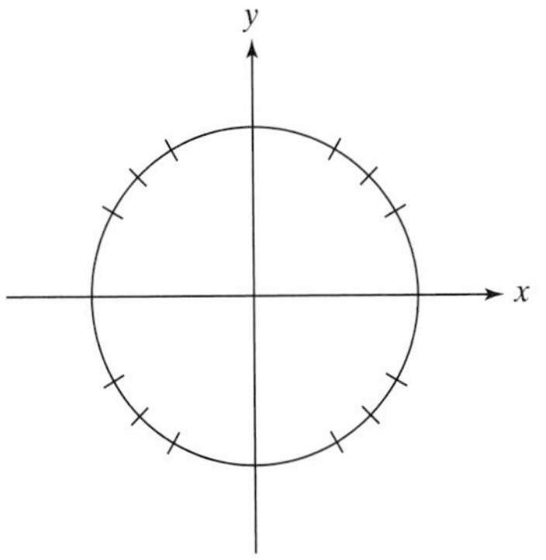

41. $\frac{7\pi}{6}$ **42.** $\frac{4\pi}{3}$ **43.** $\frac{3\pi}{4}$

44. $\frac{7\pi}{4}$ **45.** $-\frac{2\pi}{3}$ **46.** $-\frac{5\pi}{6}$

47. $-\frac{5\pi}{4}$ **48.** $-\frac{7\pi}{4}$ **49.** $\frac{16\pi}{3}$

50. $\frac{14\pi}{3}$ **51.** 120° **52.** 150°

53. −210° **54.** −240° **55.** 420°

56. 405°

In Exercises 57–70, find a positive angle less than 360° or 2π that is coterminal with the given angle.

57. 395° **58.** 415° **59.** −150°

60. −160° **61.** −765° **62.** −760°

63. $\frac{19\pi}{6}$ **64.** $\frac{17\pi}{5}$ **65.** $\frac{23\pi}{5}$

66. $\frac{25\pi}{6}$ **67.** $-\frac{\pi}{50}$ **68.** $-\frac{\pi}{40}$

69. $-\frac{31\pi}{7}$ **70.** $-\frac{38\pi}{9}$

In Exercises 71–74, find the length of the arc on a circle of radius r intercepted by a central angle θ. Express arc length in terms of π. Then round your answer to two decimal places.

Radius, *r*	Central angle, θ
71. 12 inches	$\theta = 45°$
72. 16 inches	$\theta = 60°$
73. 8 feet	$\theta = 225°$
74. 9 yards	$\theta = 315°$

In Exercises 75–76, express each angular speed in radians per second.

75. 6 revolutions per second **76.** 20 revolutions per second

Practice Plus

Use the circle shown in the rectangular coordinate system to solve Exercises 77–82. Find two angles, in radians, between -2π and 2π such that each angle's terminal side passes through the origin and the given point.

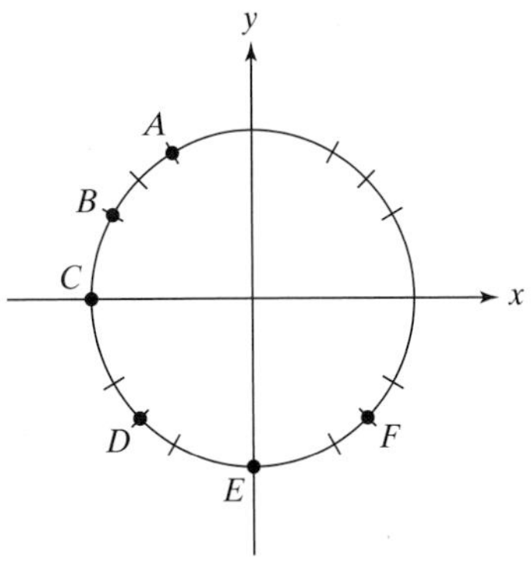

77. *A* **78.** *B*

79. *D* **80.** *F*

81. *E* **82.** *C*

In Exercises 83–86, find the positive radian measure of the angle that the second hand of a clock moves through in the given time.

83. 55 seconds **84.** 35 seconds

85. 3 minutes and 40 seconds

86. 4 minutes and 25 seconds

Application Exercises

87. The minute hand of a clock moves from 12 to 2 o'clock, or $\frac{1}{6}$ of a complete revolution. Through how many degrees does it move? Through how many radians does it move?

88. The minute hand of a clock moves from 12 to 4 o'clock, or $\frac{1}{3}$ of a complete revolution. Through how many degrees does it move? Through how many radians does it move?

89. The minute hand of a clock is 8 inches long and moves from 12 to 2 o'clock. How far does the tip of the minute hand move? Express your answer in terms of π and then round to two decimal places.

90. The minute hand of a clock is 6 inches long and moves from 12 to 4 o'clock. How far does the tip of the minute hand move? Express your answer in terms of π and then round to two decimal places.

91. The figure shows a highway sign that warns of a railway crossing. The lines that form the cross pass through the circle's center and intersect at right angles. If the radius of the circle is 24 inches, find the length of each of the four arcs formed by the cross. Express your answer in terms of π and then round to two decimal places.

92. The radius of a wheel rolling on the ground is 80 centimeters. If the wheel rotates through an angle of 60°, how many centimeters does it move? Express your answer in terms of π and then round to two decimal places.

How do we measure the distance between two points, A and B, on Earth? We measure along a circle with a center, C, at the center of Earth. The radius of the circle is equal to the distance from C to the surface. Use the fact that Earth is a sphere of radius equal to approximately 4000 miles to solve Exercises 93–96.

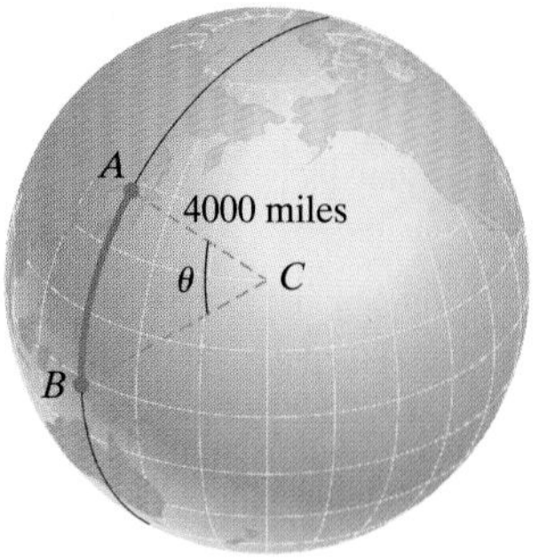

93. If two points, A and B, are 8000 miles apart, express angle θ in radians and in degrees.

94. If two points, A and B, are 10,000 miles apart, express angle θ in radians and in degrees.

95. If $\theta = 30°$, find the distance between A and B to the nearest mile.

96. If $\theta = 10°$, find the distance between A and B to the nearest mile.

97. The angular speed of a point on Earth is $\frac{\pi}{12}$ radians per hour. The Equator lies on a circle of radius approximately 4000 miles. Find the linear velocity, in miles per hour, of a point on the Equator.

98. A Ferris wheel has a radius of 25 feet. The wheel is rotating at two revolutions per minute. Find the linear speed, in feet per minute, of a seat on this Ferris wheel.

99. A water wheel has a radius of 12 feet. The wheel is rotating at 20 revolutions per minute. Find the linear speed, in feet per minute, of the water.

100. On a carousel, the outer row of animals is 20 feet from the center. The inner row of animals is 10 feet from the center. The carousel is rotating at 2.5 revolutions per minute. What is the difference, in feet per minute, in the linear speeds of the animals in the outer and inner rows? Round to the nearest foot per minute.

Writing in Mathematics

101. What is an angle?

102. What determines the size of an angle?

103. Describe an angle in standard position.

104. Explain the difference between positive and negative angles. What are coterminal angles?

105. Explain what is meant by one radian.

106. Explain how to find the radian measure of a central angle.

107. Describe how to convert an angle in degrees to radians.

108. Explain how to convert an angle in radians to degrees.

109. Explain how to find the length of a circular arc.

110. If a carousel is rotating at 2.5 revolutions per minute, explain how to find the linear speed of a child seated on one of the animals.

111. The angular velocity of a point on Earth is $\frac{\pi}{12}$ radians per hour. Describe what happens every 24 hours.

112. Have you ever noticed that we use the vocabulary of angles in everyday speech? Here is an example:

> My opinion about art museums took a 180° turn after visiting the San Francisco Museum of Modern Art.

Explain what this means. Then give another example of the vocabulary of angles in everyday use.

Technology Exercises

In Exercises 113–116, use the keys on your calculator or graphing utility for converting an angle in degrees, minutes, and seconds ($D°M'S''$) into decimal form, and vice versa.

In Exercises 113–114, convert each angle to a decimal in degrees. Round your answer to two decimal places.

113. $30°15'10''$ **114.** $65°45'20''$

In Exercises 115–116, convert each angle to $D°M'S''$ form. Round your answer to the nearest second.

115. 30.42° **116.** 50.42°

Critical Thinking Exercises

117. If $\theta = \frac{3}{2}$, is this angle larger or smaller than a right angle?

118. A railroad curve is laid out on a circle. What radius should be used if the track is to change direction by 20° in a distance of 100 miles? Round your answer to the nearest mile.

119. Assuming Earth to be a sphere of radius 4000 miles, how many miles north of the Equator is Miami, Florida, if it is 26° north from the Equator? Round your answer to the nearest mile.

SECTION 4.2 Right Triangle Trigonometry

Objectives

1. Use right triangles to evaluate trigonometric functions.
2. Find function values for $30°\left(\frac{\pi}{6}\right)$, $45°\left(\frac{\pi}{4}\right)$, and $60°\left(\frac{\pi}{3}\right)$.
3. Recognize and use fundamental identities.
4. Use equal cofunctions of complements.
5. Evaluate trigonometric functions with a calculator.
6. Use right triangle trigonometry to solve applied problems.

In the last century, Ang Rita Sherpa climbed Mount Everest ten times, all without the use of bottled oxygen.

Mountain climbers have forever been fascinated by reaching the top of Mount Everest, sometimes with tragic results. The mountain, on Asia's Tibet-Nepal border, is Earth's highest, peaking at an incredible 29,035 feet. The heights of mountains can be found using **trigonometry**. The word *trigonometry* means *measurement of triangles*. Trigonometry is used in navigation, building, and engineering. For centuries, Muslims used trigonometry and the stars to navigate across the Arabian desert to Mecca, the birthplace of the prophet Muhammad, the founder of Islam. The ancient Greeks used trigonometry to record the locations of thousands of stars and worked out the motion of the Moon relative to Earth. Today, trigonometry is used to study the structure of DNA, the master molecule that determines how we grow from a single cell to a complex, fully developed adult.

The Six Trigonometric Functions

1 Use right triangles to evaluate trigonometric functions.

We begin the study of trigonometry by defining six functions, the six *trigonometric functions*. The inputs for these functions are measures of acute angles in right triangles. The outputs are the ratios of the lengths of the sides of right triangles.

Figure 4.19 shows a right triangle with one of its acute angles labeled θ. The side opposite the right angle is known as the **hypotenuse**. The other sides of the triangle are described by their position relative to the acute angle θ. One side is opposite θ and one is adjacent to θ.

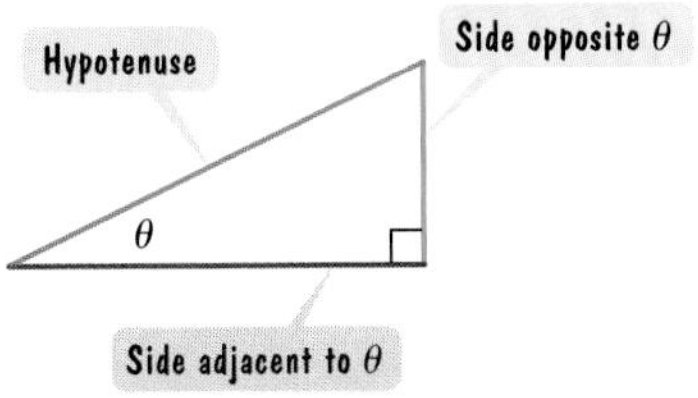

Figure 4.19 Naming a right triangle's sides from the point of view of an acute angle u

The trigonometric functions have names that are words, rather than single letters such as f, g, and h. For example, the **sine of θ** is the length of the side opposite θ divided by the length of the hypotenuse:

$$\sin\theta = \frac{\text{length of side opposite } \theta}{\text{length of hypotenuse}}.$$

Input is the measure of an acute angle.

Output is the ratio of the lengths of the sides.

The ratio of lengths depends on angle θ and thus is a function of θ. The expression $\sin\theta$ really means $\sin(\theta)$, where sine is the name of the function and θ, the measure of an acute angle, is the input.

Here are the names of the six trigonometric functions, along with their abbreviations:

Name	Abbreviation	Name	Abbreviation
sine	sin	cosecant	csc
cosine	cos	secant	sec
tangent	tan	cotangent	cot

Now, let θ be an acute angle in a right triangle, as shown in Figure 4.20. The length of the side opposite θ is a, the length of the side adjacent to θ is b, and the length of the hypotenuse is c.

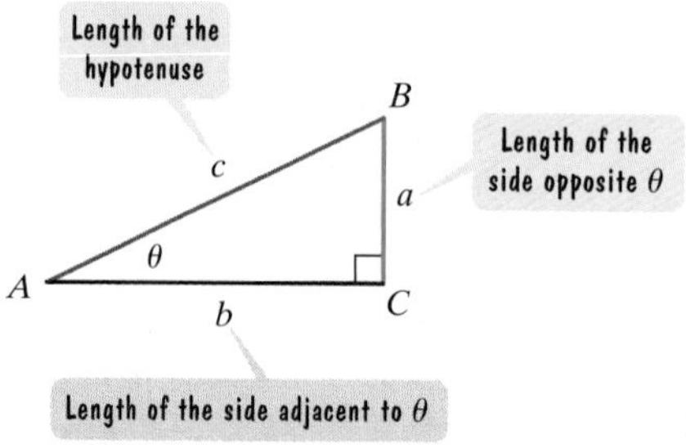

Figure 4.20

Right Triangle Definitions of Trigonometric Functions

See Figure 4.20. The six **trigonometric functions of the acute angle θ** are defined as follows:

$$\sin \theta = \frac{\text{length of side opposite angle } \theta}{\text{length of hypotenuse}} = \frac{a}{c}$$

$$\csc \theta = \frac{\text{length of hypotenuse}}{\text{length of side opposite angle } \theta} = \frac{c}{a}$$

$$\cos \theta = \frac{\text{length of side adjacent to angle } \theta}{\text{length of hypotenuse}} = \frac{b}{c}$$

$$\sec \theta = \frac{\text{length of hypotenuse}}{\text{length of side adjacent to angle } \theta} = \frac{c}{b}$$

$$\tan \theta = \frac{\text{length of side opposite angle } \theta}{\text{length of side adjacent to angle } \theta} = \frac{a}{b}$$

$$\cot \theta = \frac{\text{length of side adjacent to angle } \theta}{\text{length of side opposite angle } \theta} = \frac{b}{a}$$

Each of the trigonometric functions of the acute angle θ is positive. Observe that the ratios in the second column in the box are the reciprocals of the corresponding ratios in the first column.

Study Tip

The word

SOHCAHTOA (pronounced: so-cah-tow-ah)

is a way to remember the right triangle definitions of the three basic trigonometric functions, sine, cosine, and tangent.

"Some Old Hog Came Around Here and Took Our Apples."

Figure 4.21 shows four right triangles of varying sizes. In each of the triangles, θ is the same acute angle, measuring approximately 56.3°. All four of these similar triangles have the same shape and the lengths of corresponding sides are in the same ratio. In each triangle, the tangent function has the same value for the angle θ: $\tan \theta = \frac{3}{2}$.

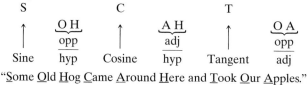

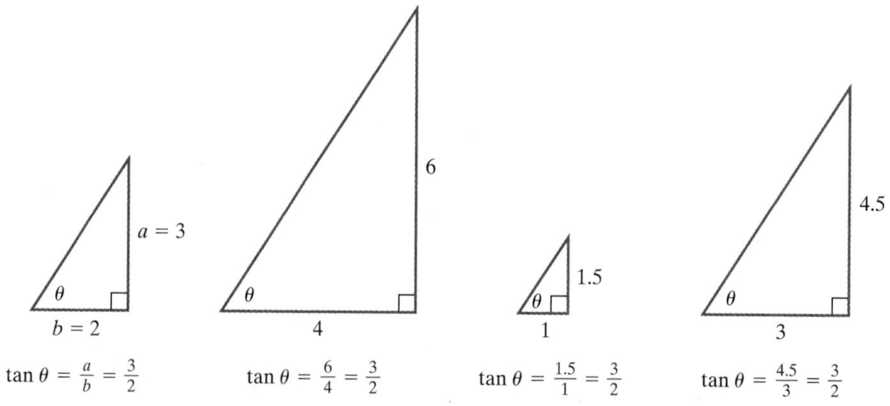

Figure 4.21 A particular acute angle always gives the same ratio of opposite to adjacent sides.

$$\tan \theta = \frac{a}{b} = \frac{3}{2}$$
$$\tan \theta = \frac{6}{4} = \frac{3}{2}$$
$$\tan \theta = \frac{1.5}{1} = \frac{3}{2}$$
$$\tan \theta = \frac{4.5}{3} = \frac{3}{2}$$

In general, **the trigonometric function values of θ depend only on the size of angle θ and not on the size of the triangle.**

EXAMPLE 1 Evaluating Trigonometric Functions

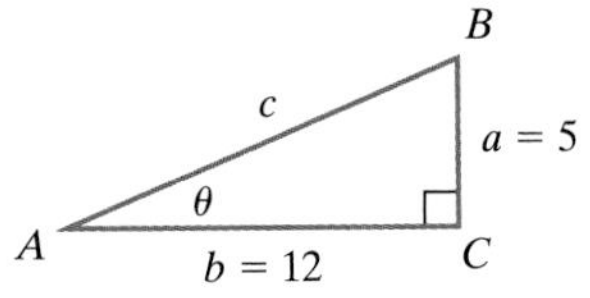

Figure 4.22

Find the value of each of the six trigonometric functions of θ in Figure 4.22.

Solution We need to find the values of the six trigonometric functions of θ. However, we must know the lengths of all three sides of the triangle (a, b, and c) to evaluate all six functions. The values of a and b are given. We can use the Pythagorean Theorem, $c^2 = a^2 + b^2$, to find c.

$a = 5$ $b = 12$

$$c^2 = a^2 + b^2 = 5^2 + 12^2 = 25 + 144 = 169$$

$$c = \sqrt{169} = 13$$

Now that we know the lengths of the three sides of the triangle, we apply the definitions of the six trigonometric functions of θ. Referring to these lengths as opposite, adjacent, and hypotenuse, we have

$$\sin\theta = \frac{\text{opposite}}{\text{hypotenuse}} = \frac{5}{13} \qquad \csc\theta = \frac{\text{hypotenuse}}{\text{opposite}} = \frac{13}{5}$$

$$\cos\theta = \frac{\text{adjacent}}{\text{hypotenuse}} = \frac{12}{13} \qquad \sec\theta = \frac{\text{hypotenuse}}{\text{adjacent}} = \frac{13}{12}$$

$$\tan\theta = \frac{\text{opposite}}{\text{adjacent}} = \frac{5}{12} \qquad \cot\theta = \frac{\text{adjacent}}{\text{opposite}} = \frac{12}{5}.$$

Study Tip

The function values in the second column are reciprocals of those in the first column. You can obtain these values by exchanging the numerator and denominator of the corresponding ratios in the first column.

Check Point 1 Find the value of each of the six trigonometric functions of θ in the figure.

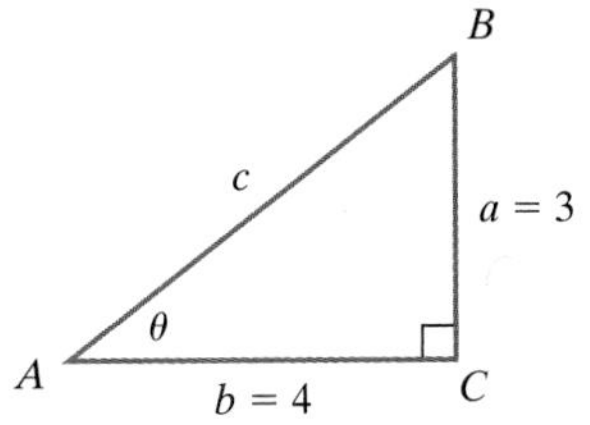

EXAMPLE 2 Evaluating Trigonometric Functions

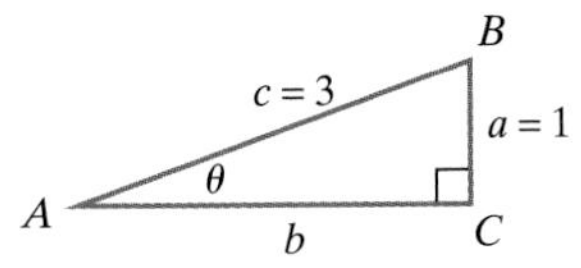

Figure 4.23

Find the value of each of the six trigonometric functions of θ in Figure 4.23.

Solution We begin by finding b.

$a^2 + b^2 = c^2$ — Use the Pythagorean Theorem.

$1^2 + b^2 = 3^2$ — Figure 4.23 shows that $a = 1$ and $c = 3$.

$1 + b^2 = 9$ — $1^2 = 1$ and $3^2 = 9$.

$b^2 = 8$ — Subtract 1 from both sides.

$b = \sqrt{8} = 2\sqrt{2}$ — Take the principal square root and simplify: $\sqrt{8} = \sqrt{4 \cdot 2} = \sqrt{4}\sqrt{2} = 2\sqrt{2}$.

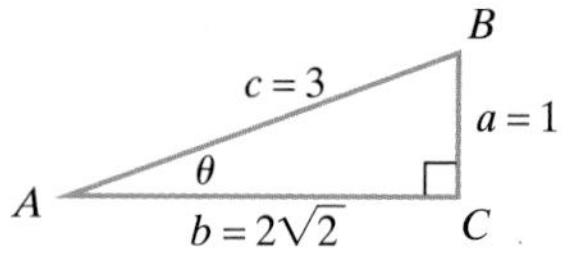

Figure 4.23 (repeated, showing $b = 2\sqrt{2}$)

Now that we know the lengths of the three sides of the triangle, we apply the definitions of the six trigonometric functions of θ.

$$\sin\theta = \frac{\text{opposite}}{\text{hypotenuse}} = \frac{1}{3} \qquad \csc\theta = \frac{\text{hypotenuse}}{\text{opposite}} = \frac{3}{1} = 3$$

$$\cos\theta = \frac{\text{adjacent}}{\text{hypotenuse}} = \frac{2\sqrt{2}}{3} \qquad \sec\theta = \frac{\text{hypotenuse}}{\text{adjacent}} = \frac{3}{2\sqrt{2}}$$

$$\tan\theta = \frac{\text{opposite}}{\text{adjacent}} = \frac{1}{2\sqrt{2}} \qquad \cot\theta = \frac{\text{adjacent}}{\text{opposite}} = \frac{2\sqrt{2}}{1} = 2\sqrt{2}$$

Because radical expressions are usually written without radicals in the denominators, we simplify the values of $\tan\theta$ and $\sec\theta$ by rationalizing the denominators:

$$\tan\theta = \frac{1}{2\sqrt{2}} = \frac{1}{2\sqrt{2}} \cdot \frac{\sqrt{2}}{\sqrt{2}} = \frac{\sqrt{2}}{2 \cdot 2} = \frac{\sqrt{2}}{4} \qquad \sec\theta = \frac{3}{2\sqrt{2}} = \frac{3}{2\sqrt{2}} \cdot \frac{\sqrt{2}}{\sqrt{2}} = \frac{3\sqrt{2}}{2 \cdot 2} = \frac{3\sqrt{2}}{4}.$$

We are multiplying by 1 and not changing the value of $\frac{1}{2\sqrt{2}}$.

We are multiplying by 1 and not changing the value of $\frac{3}{2\sqrt{2}}$.

Check Point 2 Find the value of each of the six trigonometric functions of θ in the figure. Express each value in simplified form.

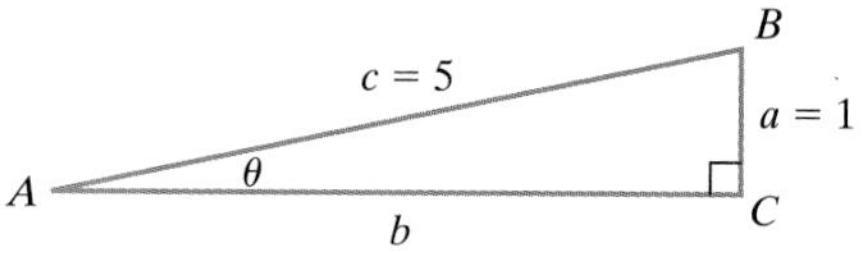

2 Find function values for $30°\left(\frac{\pi}{6}\right)$, $45°\left(\frac{\pi}{4}\right)$, and $60°\left(\frac{\pi}{3}\right)$.

Function Values for Some Special Angles

A 45°, or $\frac{\pi}{4}$ radian, angle occurs frequently in trigonometry. How do we find the values of the trigonometric functions of 45°? We construct a right triangle with a 45° angle, as shown in Figure 4.24. The triangle actually has two 45° angles. Thus, the triangle is isosceles—that is, it has two sides of the same length. Assume that each leg of the triangle has a length equal to 1. We can find the length of the hypotenuse using the Pythagorean Theorem.

$$(\text{length of hypotenuse})^2 = 1^2 + 1^2 = 2$$

$$\text{length of hypotenuse} = \sqrt{2}$$

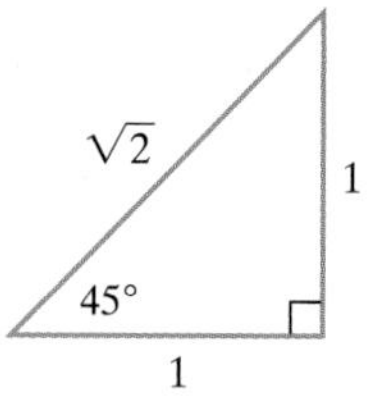

Figure 4.24 An isosceles right triangle

With Figure 4.24, we can determine the trigonometric function values for 45°.

EXAMPLE 3 Evaluating Trigonometric Functions of 45°

Use Figure 4.24 to find sin 45°, cos 45°, and tan 45°.

Solution We apply the definitions of these three trigonometric functions. Where appropriate, we simplify by rationalizing denominators.

$$\sin 45° = \frac{\text{length of side opposite } 45°}{\text{length of hypotenuse}} = \frac{1}{\sqrt{2}} = \frac{1}{\sqrt{2}} \cdot \frac{\sqrt{2}}{\sqrt{2}} = \frac{\sqrt{2}}{2}$$

Rationalize denominators

$$\cos 45° = \frac{\text{length of side adjacent to } 45°}{\text{length of hypotenuse}} = \frac{1}{\sqrt{2}} = \frac{1}{\sqrt{2}} \cdot \frac{\sqrt{2}}{\sqrt{2}} = \frac{\sqrt{2}}{2}$$

$$\tan 45° = \frac{\text{length of side opposite } 45°}{\text{length of side adjacent to } 45°} = \frac{1}{1} = 1$$

Check Point 3 Use Figure 4.24 to find csc 45°, sec 45°, and cot 45°.

When you worked Check Point 3, did you actually use Figure 4.24 or did you use reciprocals to find the values?

$$\csc 45^\circ = \sqrt{2} \qquad \sec 45^\circ = \sqrt{2} \qquad \cot 45^\circ = 1$$

Take the reciprocal of $\sin 45^\circ = \frac{1}{\sqrt{2}}$.

Take the reciprocal of $\cos 45^\circ = \frac{1}{\sqrt{2}}$.

Take the reciprocal of $\tan 45^\circ = \frac{1}{1}$.

Notice that if you use reciprocals, you should take the reciprocal of a function value before the denominator is rationalized. In this way, the reciprocal value will not contain a radical in the denominator.

Two other angles that occur frequently in trigonometry are 30°, or $\frac{\pi}{6}$ radian, and 60°, or $\frac{\pi}{3}$ radian, angles. We can find the values of the trigonometric functions of 30° and 60° by using a right triangle. To form this right triangle, draw an equilateral triangle—that is a triangle with all sides the same length. Assume that each side has a length equal to 2. Now take half of the equilateral triangle. We obtain the right triangle in Figure 4.25. This right triangle has a hypotenuse of length 2 and a leg of length 1. The other leg has length a, which can be found using the Pythagorean Theorem.

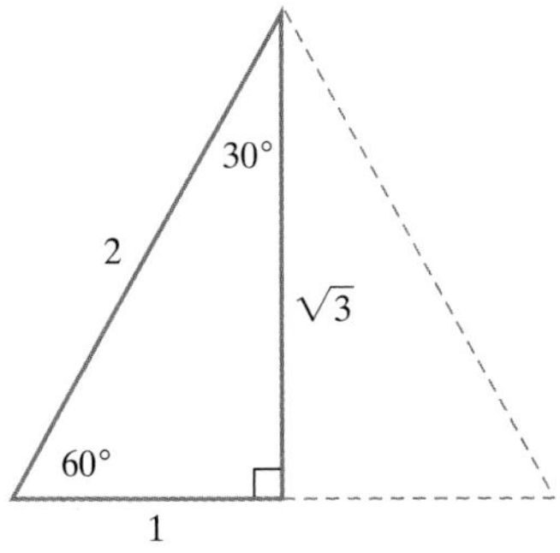

Figure 4.25 30°–60°–90° triangle

$$a^2 + 1^2 = 2^2$$
$$a^2 + 1 = 4$$
$$a^2 = 3$$
$$a = \sqrt{3}$$

With the right triangle in Figure 4.25, we can determine the trigonometric functions for 30° and 60°.

EXAMPLE 4 Evaluating Trigonometric Functions of 30° and 60°

Use Figure 4.25 to find sin 60°, cos 60°, sin 30°, and cos 30°.

Solution We begin with 60°. Use the angle on the lower left in Figure 4.25.

$$\sin 60^\circ = \frac{\text{length of side opposite } 60^\circ}{\text{length of hypotenuse}} = \frac{\sqrt{3}}{2}$$

$$\cos 60^\circ = \frac{\text{length of side adjacent to } 60^\circ}{\text{length of hypotenuse}} = \frac{1}{2}$$

To find sin 30° and cos 30°, use the angle on the upper right in Figure 4.25.

$$\sin 30^\circ = \frac{\text{length of side opposite } 30^\circ}{\text{length of hypotenuse}} = \frac{1}{2}$$

$$\cos 30^\circ = \frac{\text{length of side adjacent to } 30^\circ}{\text{length of hypotenuse}} = \frac{\sqrt{3}}{2}$$

Check Point 4 Use Figure 4.25 to find tan 60° and tan 30°. If a radical appears in a denominator, rationalize the denominator.

Because we will often use the function values of 30°, 45°, and 60°, you should learn to construct the right triangles shown in Figures 4.24 and 5.25. With sufficient practice, you will memorize the values in Table 4.2.

Table 4.2 Trigonometric Functions of Special Angles

θ	$30° = \frac{\pi}{6}$	$45° = \frac{\pi}{4}$	$60° = \frac{\pi}{3}$
$\sin\theta$	$\frac{1}{2}$	$\frac{\sqrt{2}}{2}$	$\frac{\sqrt{3}}{2}$
$\cos\theta$	$\frac{\sqrt{3}}{2}$	$\frac{\sqrt{2}}{2}$	$\frac{1}{2}$
$\tan\theta$	$\frac{\sqrt{3}}{3}$	1	$\sqrt{3}$

3 Recognize and use fundamental identities.

Fundamental Identities

Many relationships exist among the six trigonometric functions. These relationships are described using **trigonometric identities**. For example, $\csc\theta$ is defined as the reciprocal of $\sin\theta$. This relationship can be expressed by the identity

$$\csc\theta = \frac{1}{\sin\theta}.$$

This identity is one of six **reciprocal identities**.

Reciprocal Identities

$$\sin\theta = \frac{1}{\csc\theta} \qquad \csc\theta = \frac{1}{\sin\theta}$$

$$\cos\theta = \frac{1}{\sec\theta} \qquad \sec\theta = \frac{1}{\cos\theta}$$

$$\tan\theta = \frac{1}{\cot\theta} \qquad \cot\theta = \frac{1}{\tan\theta}$$

Two other relationships that follow from the definitions of the trigonometric functions are called the **quotient identities**.

Quotient Identities

$$\tan\theta = \frac{\sin\theta}{\cos\theta} \qquad \cot\theta = \frac{\cos\theta}{\sin\theta}$$

If $\sin\theta$ and $\cos\theta$ are known, a quotient identity and three reciprocal identities make it possible to find the value of each of the four remaining trigonometric functions.

EXAMPLE 5 Using Quotient and Reciprocal Identities

Given $\sin\theta = \frac{2}{5}$ and $\cos\theta = \frac{\sqrt{21}}{5}$, find the value of each of the four remaining trigonometric functions.

Solution We can find $\tan\theta$ by using the quotient identity that describes $\tan\theta$ as the quotient of $\sin\theta$ and $\cos\theta$.

$$\tan\theta = \frac{\sin\theta}{\cos\theta} = \frac{\frac{2}{5}}{\frac{\sqrt{21}}{5}} = \frac{2}{5}\cdot\frac{5}{\sqrt{21}} = \frac{2}{\sqrt{21}} = \frac{2}{\sqrt{21}}\cdot\frac{\sqrt{21}}{\sqrt{21}} = \frac{2\sqrt{21}}{21}$$

Rationalize the denominator.

We use the reciprocal identities to find the value of each of the remaining three functions.

$$\csc\theta = \frac{1}{\sin\theta} = \frac{1}{\frac{2}{5}} = \frac{5}{2}$$

$$\sec\theta = \frac{1}{\cos\theta} = \frac{1}{\frac{\sqrt{21}}{5}} = \frac{5}{\sqrt{21}} = \frac{5}{\sqrt{21}}\cdot\frac{\sqrt{21}}{\sqrt{21}} = \frac{5\sqrt{21}}{21}$$

Rationalize the denominator.

$$\cot\theta = \frac{1}{\tan\theta} = \frac{1}{\frac{2}{\sqrt{21}}} = \frac{\sqrt{21}}{2}$$

We found $\tan\theta = \frac{2}{\sqrt{21}}$. We could use $\tan\theta = \frac{2\sqrt{21}}{21}$, but then we would have to rationalize the denominator.

Check Point 5 Given $\sin\theta = \frac{2}{3}$ and $\cos\theta = \frac{\sqrt{5}}{3}$, find the value of each of the four remaining trigonometric functions.

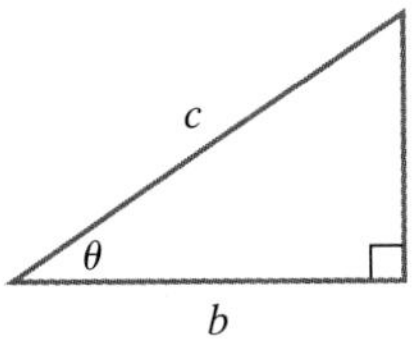

Figure 4.26

Other relationships among trigonometric functions follow from the Pythagorean Theorem. Using Figure 4.26, the Pythagorean Theorem states that

$$a^2 + b^2 = c^2.$$

To obtain ratios that correspond to trigonometric functions, divide both sides of this equation by c^2.

$$\frac{a^2}{c^2} + \frac{b^2}{c^2} = 1 \quad \text{or} \quad \left(\frac{a}{c}\right)^2 + \left(\frac{b}{c}\right)^2 = 1$$

In Figure 5.26, $\sin\theta = \frac{a}{c}$, so this is $(\sin\theta)^2$.

In Figure 5.26, $\cos\theta = \frac{b}{c}$, so this is $(\cos\theta)^2$.

Based on the observations in the voice balloons, we see that

$$(\sin\theta)^2 + (\cos\theta)^2 = 1.$$

We will use the notation $\sin^2\theta$ for $(\sin\theta)^2$ and $\cos^2\theta$ for $(\cos\theta)^2$. With this notation, we can write the identity as

$$\sin^2\theta + \cos^2\theta = 1.$$

Two additional identities can be obtained from $a^2 + b^2 = c^2$ by dividing both sides by b^2 and a^2, respectively. The three identities are called the **Pythagorean identities**.

Pythagorean Identities

$$\sin^2\theta + \cos^2\theta = 1 \qquad 1 + \tan^2\theta = \sec^2\theta \qquad 1 + \cot^2\theta = \csc^2\theta$$

EXAMPLE 6 Using a Pythagorean Identity

Given that $\sin\theta = \frac{3}{5}$ and θ is an acute angle, find the value of $\cos\theta$ using a trigonometric identity.

Solution We can find the value of $\cos\theta$ by using the Pythagorean identity

$$\sin^2\theta + \cos^2\theta = 1.$$

$$\left(\frac{3}{5}\right)^2 + \cos^2\theta = 1 \qquad \text{We are given that } \sin\theta = \frac{3}{5}.$$

$$\frac{9}{25} + \cos^2\theta = 1 \qquad \text{Square } \frac{3}{5}: \left(\frac{3}{5}\right)^2 = \frac{3^2}{5^2} = \frac{9}{25}.$$

$$\cos^2\theta = 1 - \frac{9}{25} \qquad \text{Subtract } \frac{9}{25} \text{ from both sides.}$$

$$\cos^2\theta = \frac{16}{25} \qquad \text{Simplify: } 1 - \frac{9}{25} = \frac{25}{25} - \frac{9}{25} = \frac{16}{25}.$$

$$\cos\theta = \sqrt{\frac{16}{25}} = \frac{4}{5} \qquad \text{Because } \theta \text{ is an acute angle, } \cos\theta \text{ is positive.}$$

Thus, $\cos\theta = \frac{4}{5}$.

Check Point 6 Given that $\sin\theta = \frac{1}{2}$ and θ is an acute angle, find the value of $\cos\theta$ using a trigonometric identity.

4 Use equal cofunctions of complements.

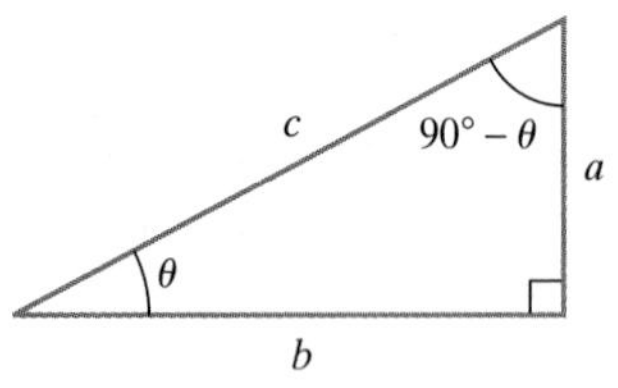

Figure 4.27

Trigonometric Functions and Complements

Two positive angles are **complements** if their sum is $90°$ or $\frac{\pi}{2}$. For example, angles of $70°$ and $20°$ are complements because $70° + 20° = 90°$.

Another relationship among trigonometric functions is based on angles that are complements. Refer to Figure 4.27. Because the sum of the angles of any triangle is $180°$, in a right triangle the sum of the acute angles is $90°$. Thus, the acute angles are complements. If the degree measure of one acute angle is θ, then the degree measure of the other acute angle is $(90° - \theta)$. This angle is shown on the upper right in Figure 4.27.

Let's use Figure 4.27 to compare $\sin\theta$ and $\cos(90° - \theta)$.

$$\sin\theta = \frac{\text{length of side opposite } \theta}{\text{length of hypotenuse}} = \frac{a}{c}$$

$$\cos(90° - \theta) = \frac{\text{length of side adjacent to } (90° - \theta)}{\text{length of hypotenuse}} = \frac{a}{c}$$

Thus, $\sin\theta = \cos(90° - \theta)$. If two angles are complements, the sine of one equals the cosine of the other. Because of this relationship, the sine and cosine are called *cofunctions* of each other. The name *cosine* is a shortened form of the phrase *complement's sine*.

Any pair of trigonometric functions f and g for which

$$f(\theta) = g(90° - \theta) \quad \text{and} \quad g(\theta) = f(90° - \theta)$$

are called **cofunctions**. Using Figure 4.27, we can show that the tangent and cotangent are also cofunctions of each other. So are the secant and cosecant.

Cofunction Identities

The value of a trigonometric function of θ is equal to the cofunction of the complement of θ. Cofunctions of complementary angles are equal.

$$\sin\theta = \cos(90° - \theta) \qquad \cos\theta = \sin(90° - \theta)$$

$$\tan\theta = \cot(90° - \theta) \qquad \cot\theta = \tan(90° - \theta)$$

$$\sec\theta = \csc(90° - \theta) \qquad \csc\theta = \sec(90° - \theta)$$

If θ is in radians, replace $90°$ with $\frac{\pi}{2}$.

EXAMPLE 7 Using Confuction Identities

Find a cofunction with the same value as the given expression:

a. $\sin 72°$ **b.** $\csc \frac{\pi}{3}$.

Solution Because the value of a trigonometric function of θ is equal to the cofunction of the complement of θ, we need to find the complement of each angle. We do this by subtracting the angle's measure from 90° or its radian equivalent, $\frac{\pi}{2}$.

a. $\sin 72° = \cos(90° - 72°) = \cos 18°$

We have a function and its cofunction.

b. $\csc \frac{\pi}{3} = \sec\left(\frac{\pi}{2} - \frac{\pi}{3}\right) = \sec\left(\frac{3\pi}{6} - \frac{2\pi}{6}\right) = \sec \frac{\pi}{6}$

We have a cofunction and its function.

Perform the subtraction using the least common denominator, 6.

Check Point 7 Find a cofunction with the same value as the given expression:

a. $\sin 46°$ **b.** $\cot \frac{\pi}{12}$.

5 Evaluate trigonometric functions with a calculator.

Using a Calculator to Evaluate Trigonometric Functions

The values of the trigonometric functions obtained with the special triangles are exact values. For most acute angles other than 30°, 45°, and 60°, we approximate the value of each of the trigonometric functions using a calculator. The first step is to set the calculator to the correct *mode*, degrees or radians, depending on how the acute angle is measured.

Most calculators have keys marked [SIN], [COS], and [TAN]. For example, to find the value of sin 30°, set the calculator to the degree mode and enter 30 [SIN] on most scientific calculators and [SIN] 30 [ENTER] on most graphing calculators. Consult the manual for your calculator.

To evaluate the cosecant, secant, and cotangent functions, use the key for the respective reciprocal function, [SIN], [COS], or [TAN], and then use the reciprocal key. The reciprocal key is [$1/x$] on many scientific calculators and [x^{-1}] on many graphing calculators. For example, we can evaluate $\sec \frac{\pi}{12}$ using the following reciprocal relationship:

$$\sec \frac{\pi}{12} = \frac{1}{\cos \frac{\pi}{12}}.$$

Using the radian mode, enter one of the following keystroke sequences:

Many Scientific Calculators

[π] [÷] 12 [=] [COS] [$1/x$]

Many Graphing Calculators

[(] [COS] [(] [π] [÷] 12 [)] [)] [x^{-1}] [ENTER].

Rounding the display to four decimal places, we obtain $\sec \frac{\pi}{12} \approx 1.0353$.

EXAMPLE 8 Evaluating Trigonometric Functions with a Calculator

Use a calculator to find the value to four decimal places:

a. cos 48.2° **b.** cot 1.2.

Solution

Scientific Calculator Solution

Function	**Mode**	**Keystrokes**	**Display, rounded to four decimal places**
a. cos 48.2°	Degree	48.2 [COS]	0.6665
b. cot 1.2	Radian	1.2 [TAN] [1/x]	0.3888

Graphing Calculator Solution

Function	**Mode**	**Keystrokes**	**Display, rounded to four decimal places**
a. cos 48.2°	Degree	[COS] 48.2 [ENTER]	0.6665
b. cot 1.2	Radian	[(] [TAN] 1.2 [)] [x^{-1}] [ENTER]	0.3888

Check Point 8 Use a calculator to find the value to four decimal places:

a. sin 72.8° **b.** csc 1.5.

6 Use right triangle trigonometry to solve applied problems.

Applications

Many applications of right triangle trigonometry involve the angle made with an imaginary horizontal line. As shown in Figure 4.28, an angle formed by a horizontal line and the line of sight to an object that is above the horizontal line is called the **angle of elevation**. The angle formed by a horizontal line and the line of sight to an object that is below the horizontal line is called the **angle of depression**. Transits and sextants are instruments used to measure such angles.

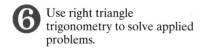

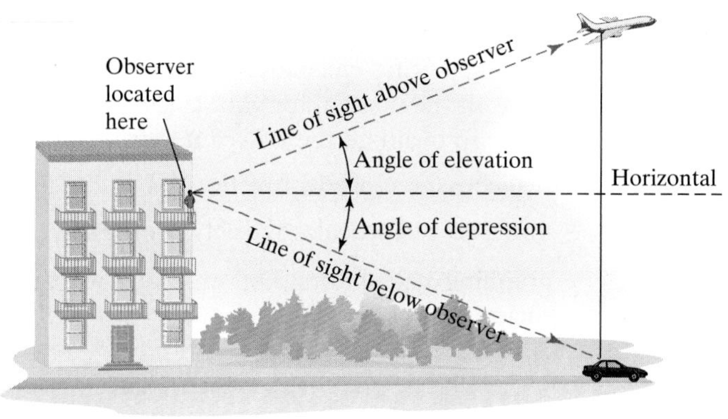

Figure 4.28

EXAMPLE 9 Problem Solving Using an Angle of Elevation

Sighting the top of a building, a surveyor measured the angle of elevation to be 22°. The transit is 5 feet above the ground and 300 feet from the building. Find the building's height.

Solution The situation is illustrated in Figure 4.29. Let a be the height of the portion of the building that lies above the transit. The height of the building is the transit's height, 5 feet, plus a. Thus, we need to identify a trigonometric function that will make it possible to find a. In terms of the 22° angle, we are looking for the side

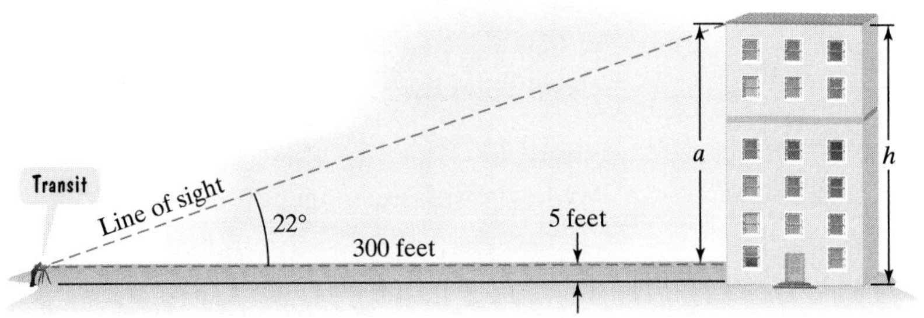

Figure 4.29

opposite the angle. The transit is 300 feet from the building, so the side adjacent to the 22° angle is 300 feet. Because we have a known angle, an unknown opposite side, and a known adjacent side, we select the tangent function.

$$\tan 22^\circ = \frac{a}{300}$$

Length of side opposite the 22° angle

Length of side adjacent to the 22° angle

$$a = 300 \tan 22^\circ$$ Multiply both sides of the equation by 300.

$$a \approx 121$$ Use a calculator in the degree mode.

The height of the part of the building above the transit is approximately 121 feet. Thus, the height of the building is determined by adding the transit's height, 5 feet, to 121 feet.

$$h \approx 5 + 121 = 126$$

The building's height is approximately 126 feet.

Check Point 9 The irregular blue shape in Figure 4.30 represents a lake. The distance across the lake, a, is unknown. To find this distance, a surveyor took the measurements shown in the figure. What is the distance across the lake?

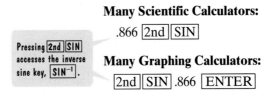

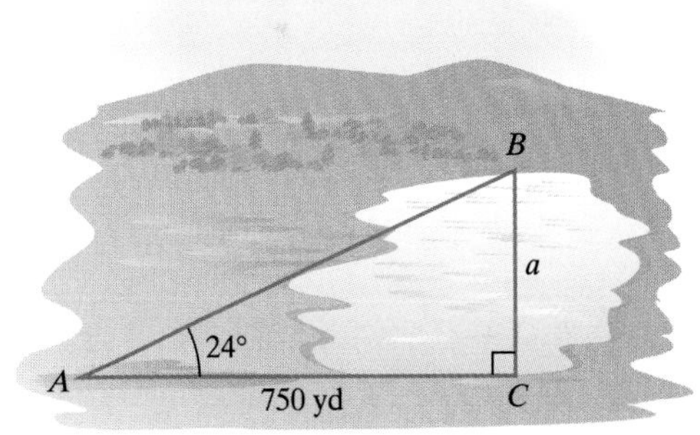

Figure 4.30

If two sides of a right triangle are known, an appropriate trigonometric function can be used to find an acute angle θ in the triangle. You will also need to use an inverse trigonometric key on a calculator. These keys use a function value to display the acute angle θ. For example, suppose that $\sin \theta = 0.866$. We can find θ in the degree mode by using the secondary *inverse sine* key, usually labeled $\boxed{\text{SIN}^{-1}}$. The key $\boxed{\text{SIN}^{-1}}$ is not a button you will actually press. It is the secondary function for the button labeled $\boxed{\text{SIN}}$.

Many Scientific Calculators:

.866 $\boxed{\text{2nd}}\boxed{\text{SIN}}$

Pressing $\boxed{\text{2nd}}\boxed{\text{SIN}}$ accesses the inverse sine key, $\boxed{\text{SIN}^{-1}}$.

Many Graphing Calculators:

$\boxed{\text{2nd}}\boxed{\text{SIN}}$ .866 $\boxed{\text{ENTER}}$

The display should show approximately 59.99, which can be rounded to 60. Thus, if $\sin \theta = 0.866$, then $\theta \approx 60^\circ$.

EXAMPLE 10 Determining the Angle of Elevation

A building that is 21 meters tall casts a shadow 25 meters long. Find the angle of elevation of the sun to the nearest degree.

Solution The situation is illustrated in Figure 4.31. We are asked to find θ. We begin with the tangent function.

$$\tan\theta = \frac{\text{side opposite }\theta}{\text{side adjacent to }\theta} = \frac{21}{25}$$

We use a calculator in the degree mode to find θ.

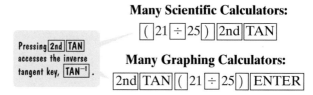

Many Scientific Calculators:

[(] 21 [÷] 25 [)] [2nd] [TAN]

Pressing [2nd] [TAN] accesses the inverse tangent key, [TAN^{-1}].

Many Graphing Calculators:

[2nd] [TAN] [(] 21 [÷] 25 [)] [ENTER]

The display should show approximately 40. Thus, the angle of elevation of the sun is approximately 40°.

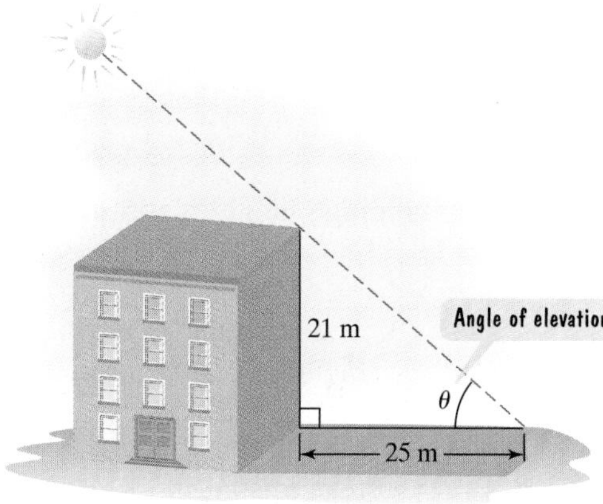

Figure 4.31

Check Point 10 A flagpole that is 14 meters tall casts a shadow 10 meters long. Find the angle of elevation of the sun to the nearest degree.

The Mountain Man

In the 1930s, a *National Geographic* team headed by Brad Washburn used trigonometry to create a map of the 5000-square-mile region of the Yukon, near the Canadian border. The team started with aerial photography. By drawing a network of angles on the photographs, the approximate locations of the major mountains and their rough heights were determined. The expedition then spent three months on foot to find the exact heights. Team members established two base points a known distance apart, one directly under the mountain's peak. By measuring the angle of elevation from one of the base points to the peak, the tangent function was used to determine the peak's height. The Yukon expedition was a major advance in the way maps are made.

EXERCISE SET 4.2

Practice Exercises

In Exercises 1–8, use the Pythagorean Theorem to find the length of the missing side of each right triangle. Then find the value of each of the six trigonometric functions of θ.

1.

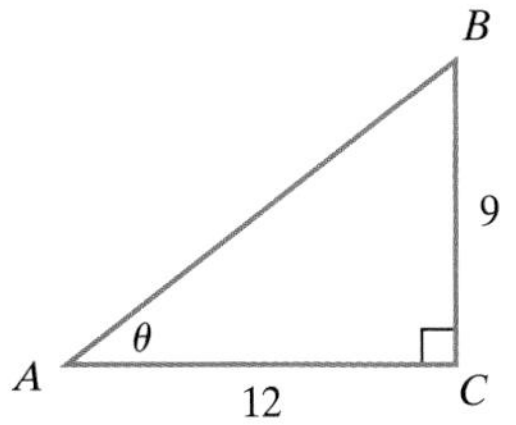

2.

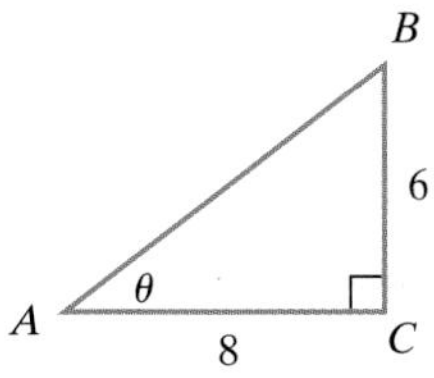

3.

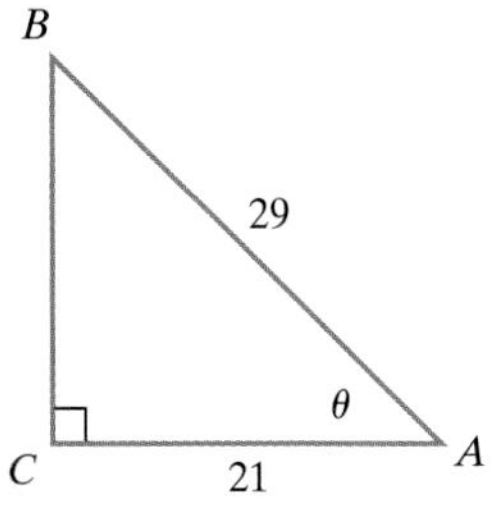

4.

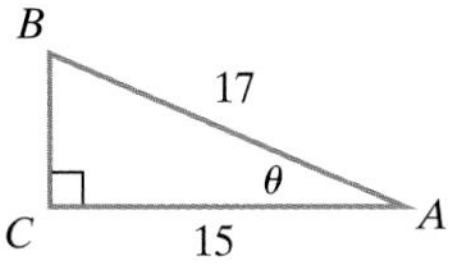

5.

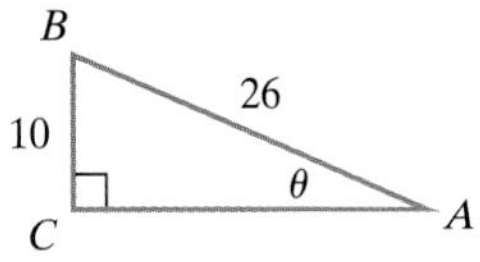

6.

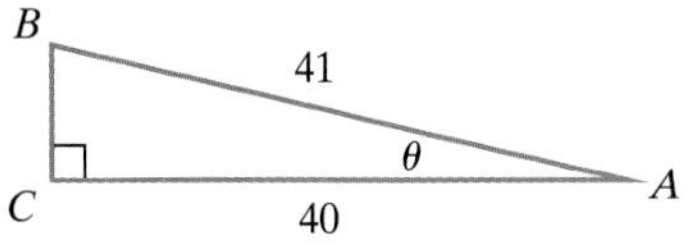

7.

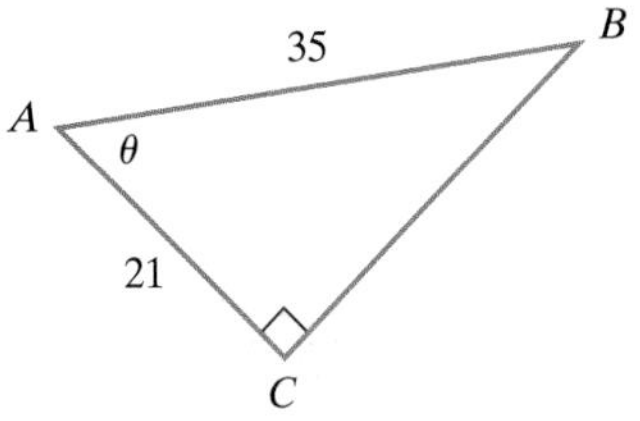

8.

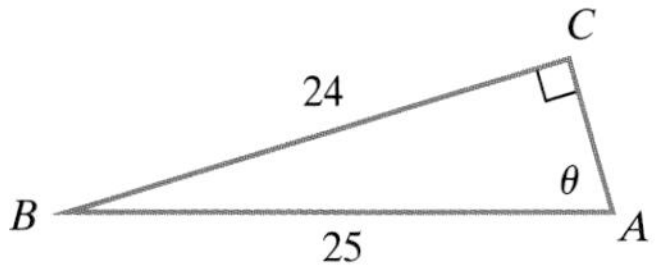

In Exercises 9–16, use the given triangles to evaluate each expression. If necessary, express the value without a square root in the denominator by rationalizing the denominator.

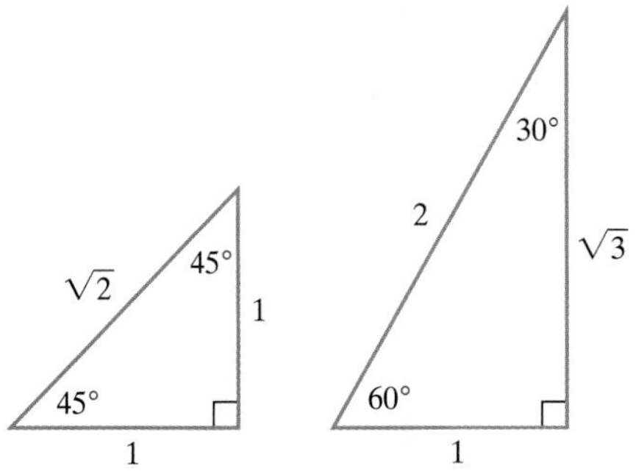

9. $\cos 30°$

10. $\tan 30°$

11. $\sec 45°$

12. $\csc 45°$

13. $\tan \dfrac{\pi}{3}$

14. $\cot \dfrac{\pi}{3}$

15. $\sin \dfrac{\pi}{4} - \cos \dfrac{\pi}{4}$

16. $\tan \dfrac{\pi}{4} + \csc \dfrac{\pi}{6}$

In Exercises 17–20, θ is an acute angle and sin θ and cos θ are given. Use identities to find tan θ, csc θ, sec θ, and cot θ. Where necessary, rationalize denominators.

17. $\sin \theta = \dfrac{8}{17}, \quad \cos \theta = \dfrac{15}{17}$

18. $\sin \theta = \dfrac{3}{5}, \quad \cos \theta = \dfrac{4}{5}$

19. $\sin \theta = \dfrac{1}{3}, \quad \cos \theta = \dfrac{2\sqrt{2}}{3}$

20. $\sin \theta = \dfrac{2}{3}, \quad \cos \theta = \dfrac{\sqrt{5}}{3}$

In Exercises 21–24, θ is an acute angle and sin θ is given. Use the Pythagorean identity $\sin^2 \theta + \cos^2 \theta = 1$ to find cos θ.

21. $\sin \theta = \dfrac{6}{7}$

22. $\sin \theta = \dfrac{7}{8}$

23. $\sin \theta = \dfrac{\sqrt{39}}{8}$

24. $\sin \theta = \dfrac{\sqrt{21}}{5}$

In Exercises 25–30, use an identity to find the value of each expression. Do not use a calculator.

25. $\sin 37° \csc 37°$

26. $\cos 53° \sec 53°$

27. $\sin^2 \dfrac{\pi}{9} + \cos^2 \dfrac{\pi}{9}$

28. $\sin^2 \dfrac{\pi}{10} + \cos^2 \dfrac{\pi}{10}$

29. $\sec^2 23° - \tan^2 23°$

30. $\csc^2 63° - \cot^2 63°$

In Exercises 31–38, find a cofunction with the same value as the given expression.

31. $\sin 7°$

32. $\sin 19°$

33. $\csc 25°$

34. $\csc 35°$

35. $\tan \dfrac{\pi}{9}$

36. $\tan \dfrac{\pi}{7}$

37. $\cos \dfrac{2\pi}{5}$

38. $\cos \dfrac{3\pi}{8}$

In Exercises 39–48, use a calculator to find the value of the trigonometric function to four decimal places.

39. $\sin 38°$

40. $\cos 21°$

41. $\tan 32.7°$

42. $\tan 52.6°$

43. $\csc 17°$

44. $\sec 55°$

45. $\cos \dfrac{\pi}{10}$

46. $\sin \dfrac{3\pi}{10}$

47. $\cot \dfrac{\pi}{12}$

In Exercises 49–54, find the measure of the side of the right triangle whose length is designated by a lowercase letter. Round answers to the nearest whole number.

49.

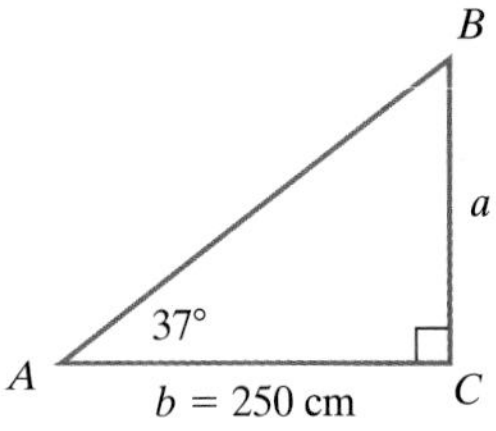

50.

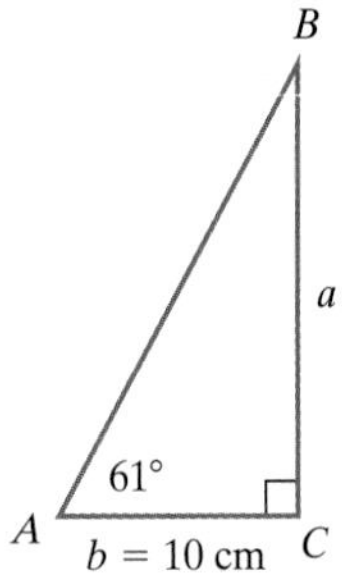

51.

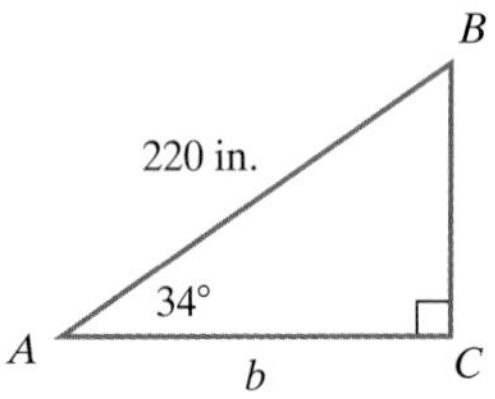

52.

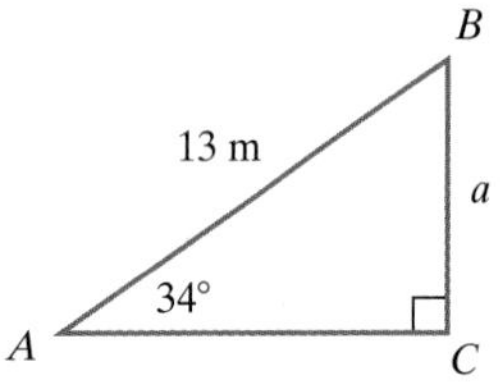

53.

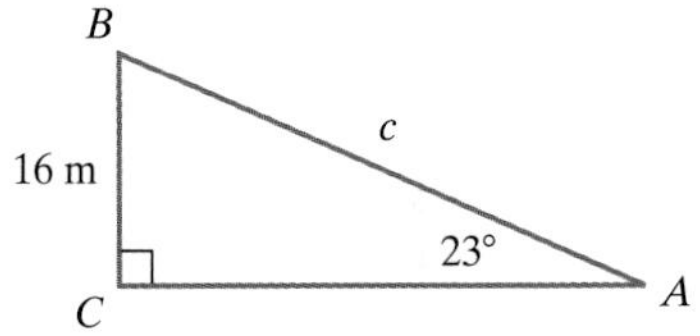

54.

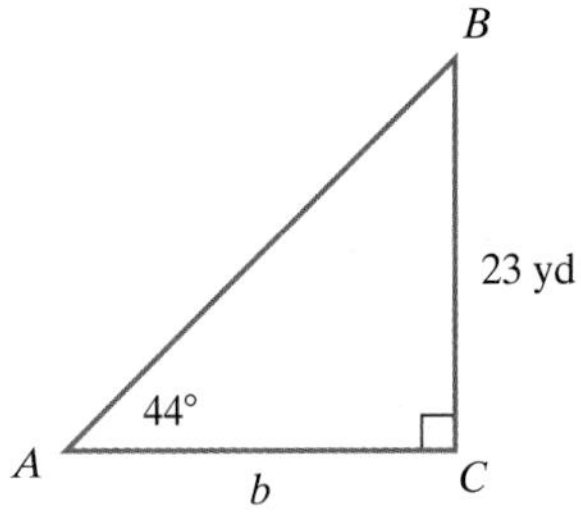

In Exercises 55–58, use a calculator to find the value of the acute angle θ to the nearest degree.

55. $\sin\theta = 0.2974$ **56.** $\cos\theta = 0.8771$

57. $\tan\theta = 4.6252$ **58.** $\tan\theta = 26.0307$

In Exercises 59–62, use a calculator to find the value of the acute angle θ in radians, rounded to three decimal places.

59. $\cos\theta = 0.4112$ **60.** $\sin\theta = 0.9499$

61. $\tan\theta = 0.4169$ **62.** $\tan\theta = 0.5117$

Practice Plus

In Exercises 63–68, find the exact value of each expression. Do not use a calculator.

63. $\dfrac{\tan\frac{\pi}{3}}{2} - \dfrac{1}{\sec\frac{\pi}{6}}$ **64.** $\dfrac{1}{\cot\frac{\pi}{4}} - \dfrac{2}{\csc\frac{\pi}{6}}$

65. $1 + \sin^2 40° + \sin^2 50°$ **66.** $1 - \tan^2 10° + \csc^2 80°$

67. $\csc 37° \sec 53° - \tan 53° \cot 37°$

68. $\cos 12° \sin 78° + \cos 78° \sin 12°$

In Exercises 69–70, express each exact value as a single fraction. Do not use a calculator.

69. If $f(\theta) = 2\cos\theta - \cos 2\theta$, find $f\left(\frac{\pi}{6}\right)$.

70. If $f(\theta) = 2\sin\theta - \sin\frac{\theta}{2}$, find $f\left(\frac{\pi}{3}\right)$.

71. If θ is an acute angle and $\cot\theta = \frac{1}{4}$, find $\tan\left(\frac{\pi}{2} - \theta\right)$.

72. If θ is an acute angle and $\cos\theta = \frac{1}{3}$, find $\csc\left(\frac{\pi}{2} - \theta\right)$.

Application Exercises

73. To find the distance across a lake, a surveyor took the measurements shown in the figure. Use these measurements to determine how far it is across the lake. Round to the nearest yard.

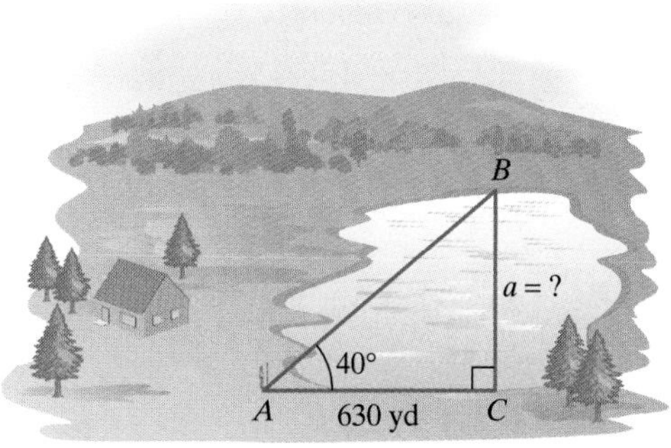

74. At a certain time of day, the angle of elevation of the sun is 40°. To the nearest foot, find the height of a tree whose shadow is 35 feet long.

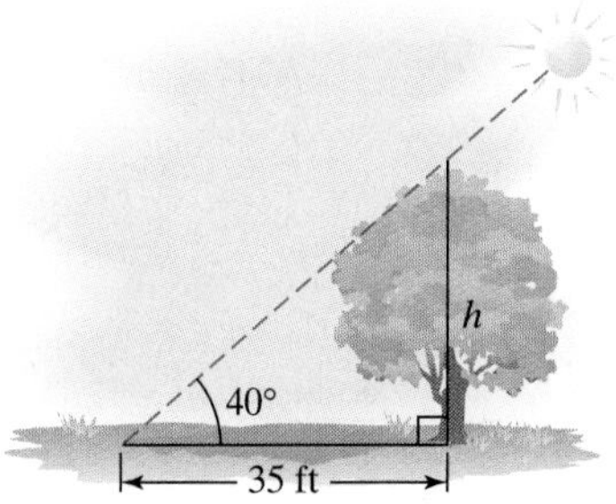

75. A tower that is 125 feet tall casts a shadow 172 feet long. Find the angle of elevation of the sun to the nearest degree.

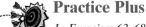

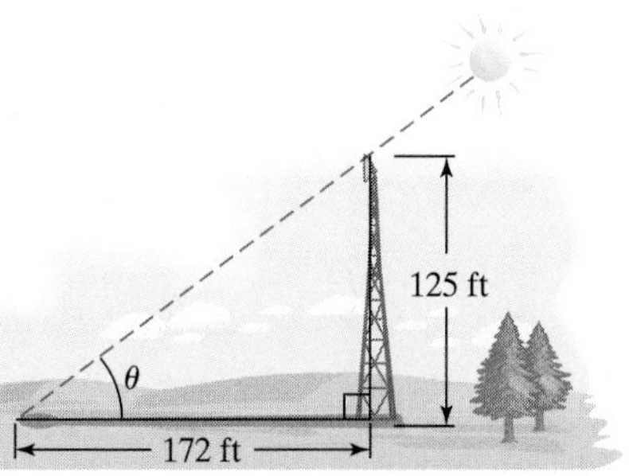

76. The Washington Monument is 555 feet high. If you stand one quarter of a mile, or 1320 feet, from the base of the monument and look to the top, find the angle of elevation to the nearest degree.

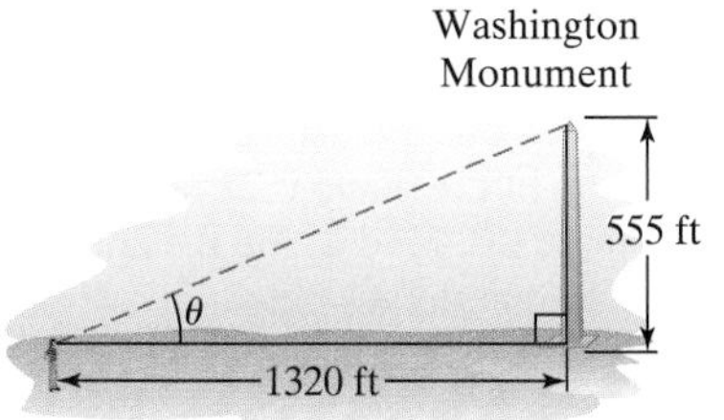

77. A plane rises from take-off and flies at an angle of 10° with the horizontal runway. When it has gained 500 feet, find the distance, to the nearest foot, the plane has flown.

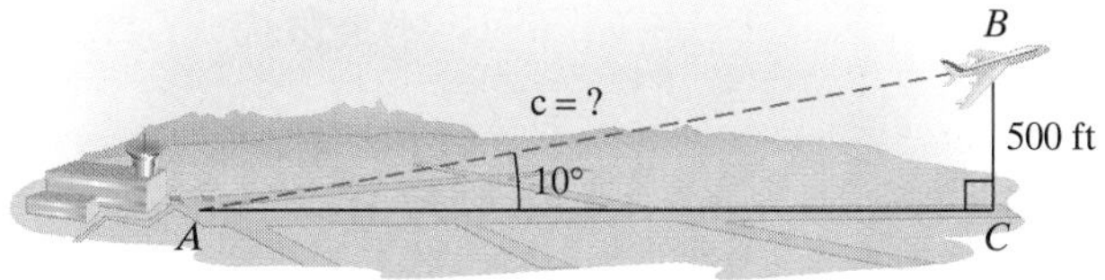

78. A road is inclined at an angle of 5°. After driving 5000 feet along this road, find the driver's increase in altitude. Round to the nearest foot.

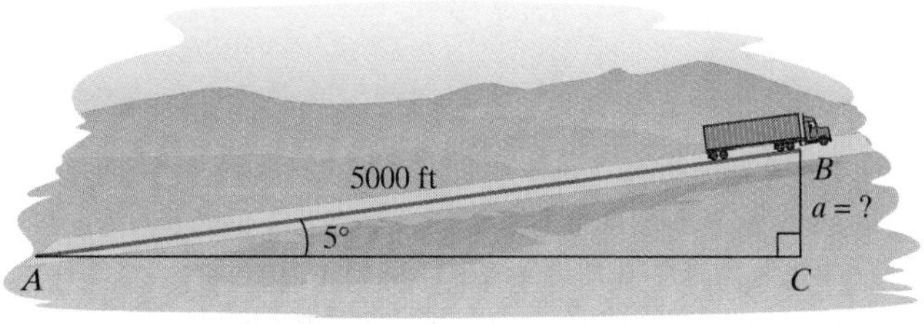

79. A telephone pole is 60 feet tall. A guy wire 75 feet long is attached from the ground to the top of the pole. Find the angle between the wire and the pole to the nearest degree.

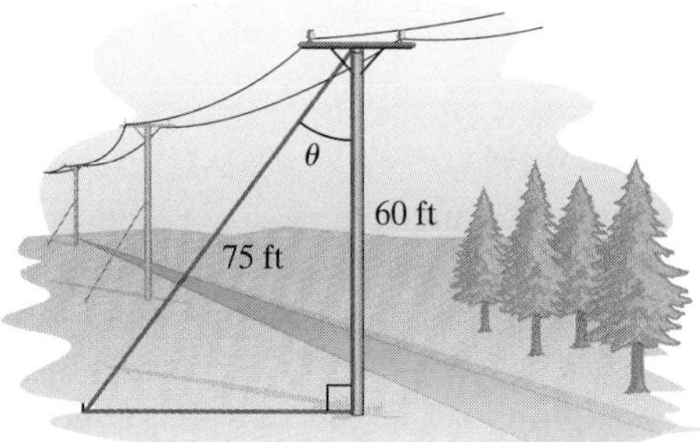

80. A telephone pole is 55 feet tall. A guy wire 80 feet long is attached from the ground to the top of the pole. Find the angle between the wire and the pole to the nearest degree.

Writing in Mathematics

81. If you are given the lengths of the sides of a right triangle, describe how to find the sine of either acute angle.

82. Describe one similarity and one difference between the definitions of $\sin\theta$ and $\cos\theta$, where θ is an acute angle of a right triangle.

83. Describe the triangle used to find the trigonometric functions of 45°.

84. Describe the triangle used to find the trigonometric functions of 30° and 60°.

85. What is a trigonometric identity?

86. Use words (not an equation) to describe one of the reciprocal identities.

87. Use words (not an equation) to describe one of the quotient identities.

88. Use words (not an equation) to describe one of the Pythagorean identities.

89. Describe a relationship among trigonometric functions that is based on angles that are complements.

90. Describe what is meant by an angle of elevation and an angle of depression.

91. Stonehenge, the famous "stone circle" in England, was built between 2750 B.C. and 1300 B.C. using solid stone blocks weighing over 99,000 pounds each. It required 550 people to pull a single stone up a ramp inclined at a 9° angle. Describe how right triangle trigonometry can be used to determine the distance the 550 workers had to drag a stone in order to raise it to a height of 30 feet.

Technology Exercises

92. Use a calculator in the radian mode to fill in the values in the following table. Then draw a conclusion about $\frac{\sin\theta}{\theta}$ as θ approaches 0.

θ	0.4	0.3	0.2	0.1	0.01	0.001	0.0001	0.00001
$\sin\theta$								
$\frac{\sin\theta}{\theta}$								

93. Use a calculator in the radian mode to fill in the values in the following table. Then draw a conclusion about $\frac{\cos\theta - 1}{\theta}$ as θ approaches 0.

θ	0.4	0.3	0.2	0.1	0.01	0.001	0.0001	0.00001
$\cos\theta$								
$\frac{\cos\theta - 1}{\theta}$								

Critical Thinking Exercises

94. Which one of the following is true?

a. $\dfrac{\tan 45°}{\tan 15°} = \tan 3°$

b. $\tan^2 15° - \sec^2 15° = -1$

c. $\sin 45° + \cos 45° = 1$

d. $\tan^2 5° = \tan 25°$

95. Explain why the sine or cosine of an acute angle cannot be greater than or equal to 1.

96. Describe what happens to the tangent of an acute angle as the angle gets close to 90°. What happens at 90°?

97. From the top of a 250-foot lighthouse, a plane is sighted overhead and a ship is observed directly below the plane. The angle of elevation of the plane is 22° and the angle of depression of the ship is 35°. Find **a.** the distance of the ship from the lighthouse; **b.** the plane's height above the water. Round to the nearest foot.

SECTION 4.3 Trigonometric Functions of Any Angle

Objectives

1. Use the definitions of trigonometric functions of any angle.
2. Use the signs of the trigonometric functions.
3. Find reference angles.
4. Use reference angles to evaluate trigonometric functions.

There is something comforting in the repetition of some of nature's patterns. The ocean level at a beach varies between high and low tide approximately every 12 hours. The number of hours of daylight oscillates from a maximum on the summer solstice, June 21, to a minimum on the winter solstice, December 21. Then it increases to the same maximum the following June 21. Some believe that cycles, called biorhythms, represent physical, emotional, and intellectual aspects of our lives. Throughout the remainder of this chapter, we will see how the trigonometric functions are used to model phenomena that occur again and again. To do this, we need to move beyond right triangles.

1 Use the definitions of trigonometric functions of any angle.

Trigonometric Functions of Any Angle

In the last section, we evaluated trigonometric functions of acute angles, such as that shown in Figure 4.32(a). Note that this angle is in standard position. The point $P = (x, y)$ is a point r units from the origin on the terminal side of θ. A right triangle is formed by drawing a line segment from $P = (x, y)$ perpendicular to the x-axis. Note that y is the length of the side opposite θ and x is the length of the side adjacent to θ.

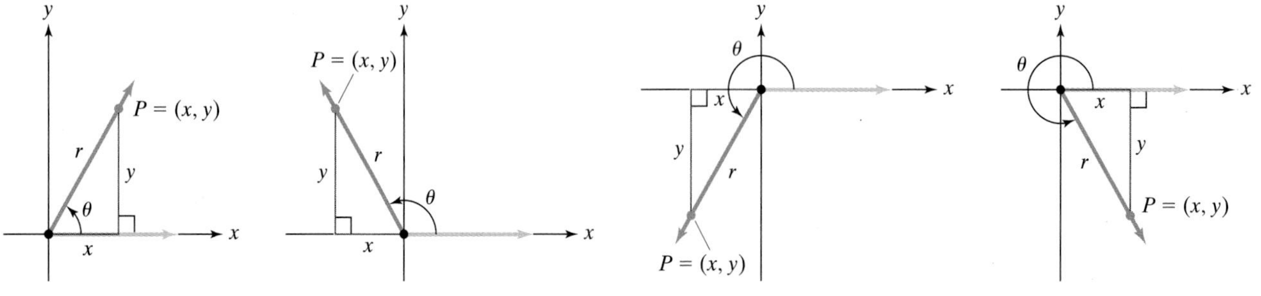

Figure 4.32 (a) θ lies in quadrant I. (b) θ lies in quadrant II. (c) θ lies in quadrant III. (d) θ lies in quadrant IV.

Figures 4.32(b), (c), and (d) show angles in standard position, but they are not acute. We can extend our definitions of the six trigonometric functions to include such angles, as well as quadrantal angles. (Recall that a quadrantal angle has its terminal side on the x-axis or y-axis; such angles are *not* shown in Figure 4.32.) The point $P = (x, y)$ may be any point on the terminal side of the angle θ other than the origin, $(0, 0)$.

Study Tip

If u is acute, we have the right triangle shown in Figure 4.32(a). In this situation, the definitions in the box are the right triangle definitions of the trigonometric functions. This should make it easier for you to remember the six definitions.

Definitions of Trigonometric Functions of Any Angle

Let θ be any angle in standard position and let $P = (x, y)$ be a point on the terminal side of θ. If $r = \sqrt{x^2 + y^2}$ is the distance from $(0, 0)$ to (x, y), as shown in Figure 4.32, the **six trigonometric functions of θ** are defined by the following ratios:

$$\sin\theta = \frac{y}{r} \qquad \csc\theta = \frac{r}{y},\ y \neq 0$$

$$\cos\theta = \frac{x}{r} \qquad \sec\theta = \frac{r}{x},\ x \neq 0$$

$$\tan\theta = \frac{y}{x},\ x \neq 0 \qquad \cot\theta = \frac{x}{y},\ y \neq 0.$$

The ratios in the second column are the reciprocals of the corresponding ratios in the first column.

Because the point $P = (x, y)$ is any point on the terminal side of θ other than the origin, $(0, 0)$, $r = \sqrt{x^2 + y^2}$ cannot be zero. Examine the six trigonometric functions defined above. Note that the denominator of the sine and cosine functions is r. Because $r \neq 0$, the sine and cosine functions are defined for any real value of the angle θ. This is not true for the other four trigonometric functions. Note that the denominator of the tangent and secant functions is x: $\tan\theta = \frac{y}{x}$ and $\sec\theta = \frac{r}{x}$. These functions are not defined if $x = 0$. If the point $P = (x, y)$ is on the y-axis, then $x = 0$. Thus, the tangent and secant functions are undefined for all quadrantal angles with terminal sides on the positive or negative y-axis. Likewise, if $P = (x, y)$ is on the x-axis, then $y = 0$, and the cotangent and cosecant functions are undefined: $\cot\theta = \frac{x}{y}$ and $\csc\theta = \frac{r}{y}$. The cotangent and cosecant functions are undefined for all quadrantal angles with terminal sides on the positive or negative x-axis.

EXAMPLE 1 Evaluating Trigonometric Functions

Let $P = (-3, -5)$ be a point on the terminal side of θ. Find each of the six trigonometric functions of θ.

Solution The situation is shown in Figure 4.33. We need values for x, y, and r to evaluate all six trigonometric functions. We are given the values of x and y. Because $P = (-3, -5)$ is a point on the terminal side of θ, $x = -3$ and $y = -5$. Furthermore,

$$r = \sqrt{x^2 + y^2} = \sqrt{(-3)^2 + (-5)^2} = \sqrt{9 + 25} = \sqrt{34}.$$

Now that we know x, y, and r, we can find the six trigonometric functions of θ. Where appropriate, we will rationalize denominators.

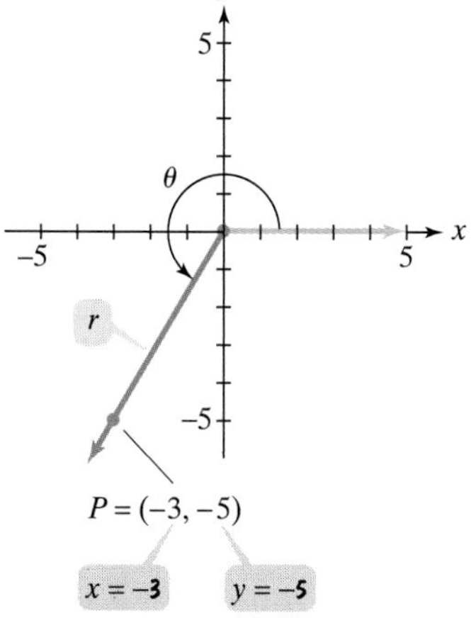

Figure 4.33

$$\sin\theta = \frac{y}{r} = \frac{-5}{\sqrt{34}} = -\frac{5}{\sqrt{34}}\cdot\frac{\sqrt{34}}{\sqrt{34}} = -\frac{5\sqrt{34}}{34} \qquad \csc\theta = \frac{r}{y} = \frac{\sqrt{34}}{-5} = -\frac{\sqrt{34}}{5}$$

$$\cos\theta = \frac{x}{r} = \frac{-3}{\sqrt{34}} = -\frac{3}{\sqrt{34}}\cdot\frac{\sqrt{34}}{\sqrt{34}} = -\frac{3\sqrt{34}}{34} \qquad \sec\theta = \frac{r}{x} = \frac{\sqrt{34}}{-3} = -\frac{\sqrt{34}}{3}$$

$$\tan\theta = \frac{y}{x} = \frac{-5}{-3} = \frac{5}{3} \qquad \cot\theta = \frac{x}{y} = \frac{-3}{-5} = \frac{3}{5}$$

Check Point 1 Let $P = (1, -3)$ be a point on the terminal side of θ. Find each of the six trigonometric functions of θ.

How do we find the values of the trigonometric functions for a quadrantal angle? First, draw the angle in standard position. Second, choose a point P on the angle's terminal side. The trigonometric function values of θ depend only on the size of θ and not on the distance of point P from the origin. Thus, we will choose a point that is 1 unit from the origin. Finally, apply the definitions of the appropriate trigonometric functions.

EXAMPLE 2 Trigonometric Functions of Quadrantal Angles

Evaluate, if possible, the sine function and the tangent function at the following four quadrantal angles:

a. $\theta = 0° = 0$ **b.** $\theta = 90° = \frac{\pi}{2}$ **c.** $\theta = 180° = \pi$ **d.** $\theta = 270° = \frac{3\pi}{2}$.

Solution

a. If $\theta = 0° = 0$ radians, then the terminal side of the angle is on the positive x-axis. Let us select the point $P = (1, 0)$ with $x = 1$ and $y = 0$. This point is 1 unit from the origin, so $r = 1$. Figure 4.34 shows values of x, y, and r corresponding to $\theta = 0°$ or 0 radians. Now that we know x, y, and r, we can apply the definitions of the sine and tangent functions.

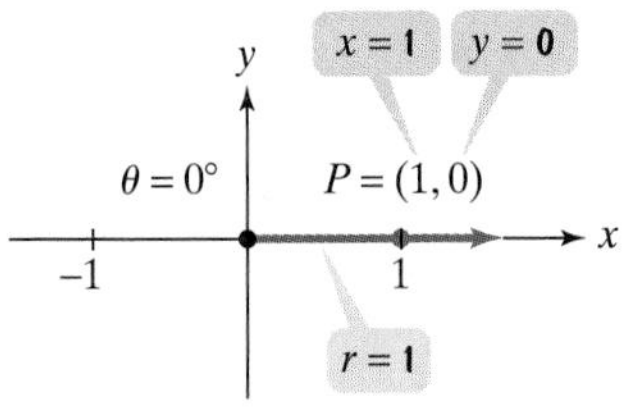

Figure 4.34

$$\sin 0° = \sin 0 = \frac{y}{r} = \frac{0}{1} = 0$$

$$\tan 0° = \tan 0 = \frac{y}{x} = \frac{0}{1} = 0$$

b. If $\theta = 90° = \frac{\pi}{2}$ radians, then the terminal side of the angle is on the positive y-axis. Let us select the point $P = (0, 1)$ with $x = 0$ and $y = 1$. This point is 1 unit from the origin, so $r = 1$. Figure 4.35 shows values of x, y, and r corresponding to $\theta = 90°$ or $\frac{\pi}{2}$. Now that we know x, y, and r, we can apply the definitions of the sine and tangent functions.

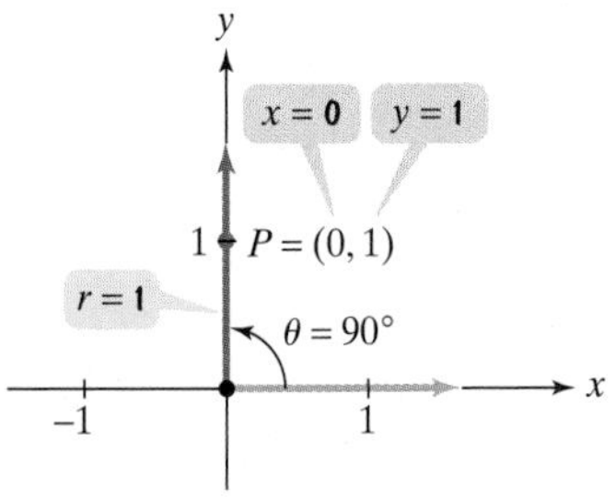

Figure 4.35

$$\sin 90° = \sin \frac{\pi}{2} = \frac{y}{r} = \frac{1}{1} = 1$$

$$\tan 90° = \tan \frac{\pi}{2} = \frac{y}{x} = \frac{1}{0}$$

Because division by 0 is undefined, tan 90° is undefined.

c. If $\theta = 180° = \pi$ radians, then the terminal side of the angle is on the negative x-axis. Let us select the point $P = (-1, 0)$ with $x = -1$ and $y = 0$. This point is 1 unit from the origin, so $r = 1$. Figure 4.36 shows values of x, y, and r corresponding to $\theta = 180°$ or π. Now that we know x, y, and r, we can apply the definitions of the sine and tangent functions.

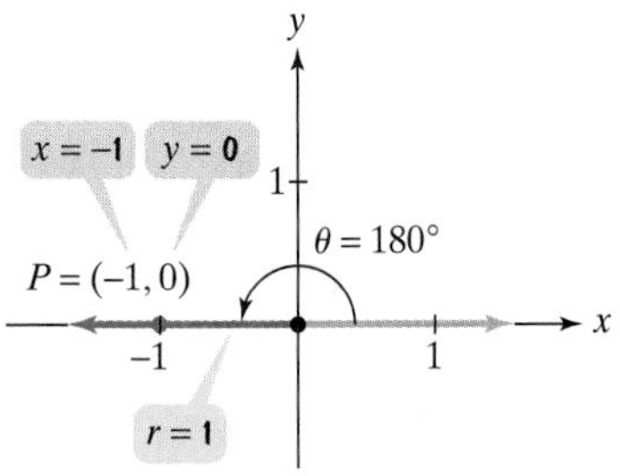

Figure 4.36

$$\sin 180° = \sin \pi = \frac{y}{r} = \frac{0}{1} = 0$$

$$\tan 180° = \tan \pi = \frac{y}{x} = \frac{0}{-1} = 0$$

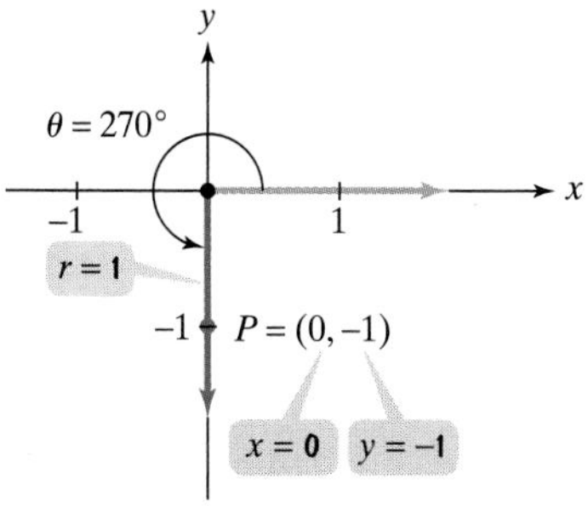

Figure 4.37

Discovery

Try finding tan 90° and tan 270° with your calculator. Describe what occurs.

d. If $\theta = 270° = \frac{3\pi}{2}$ radians, then the terminal side of the angle is on the negative y-axis. Let us select the point $P = (0, -1)$ with $x = 0$ and $y = -1$. This point is 1 unit from the origin, so $r = 1$. Figure 4.37 shows values of x, y, and r corresponding to $\theta = 270°$ or $\frac{3\pi}{2}$. Now that we know x, y, and r, we can apply the definitions of the sine and tangent functions.

$$\sin 270° = \sin\frac{3\pi}{2} = \frac{y}{r} = \frac{-1}{1} = -1$$

$$\tan 270° = \tan\frac{3\pi}{2} = \frac{y}{x} = \frac{-1}{0}$$

Because division by 0 is undefined, tan 270° is undefined.

Check Point 2 Evaluate, if possible, the cosine function and the cosecant function at the following four quadrantal angles:

a. $\theta = 0° = 0$ **b.** $\theta = 90° = \frac{\pi}{2}$

c. $\theta = 180° = \pi$ **d.** $\theta = 270° = \frac{3\pi}{2}$.

2 Use the signs of the trigonometric functions.

The Signs of the Trigonometric Functions

In Example 2, we evaluated trigonometric functions of quadrantal angles. However, we will now return to the trigonometric functions of nonquadrantal angles. **If θ is not a quadrantal angle, the sign of a trigonometric function depends on the quadrant in which θ lies.** In all four quadrants, r is positive. However, x and y can be positive or negative. For example, if θ lies in quadrant II, x is negative and y is positive. Thus, the only positive ratios in this quadrant are $\frac{y}{r}$ and its reciprocal, $\frac{r}{y}$. These ratios are the function values for the sine and cosecant, respectively. In short, if θ lies in quadrant II, $\sin\theta$ and $\csc\theta$ are positive. The other four trigonometric functions are negative.

Figure 4.38 summarizes the signs of the trigonometric functions. If θ lies in quadrant I, all six functions are positive. If θ lies in quadrant II, only $\sin\theta$ and $\csc\theta$ are positive. If θ lies in quadrant III, only $\tan\theta$ and $\cot\theta$ are positive. Finally, if θ lies in quadrant IV, only $\cos\theta$ and $\sec\theta$ are positive. Observe that the positive functions in each quadrant occur in reciprocal pairs.

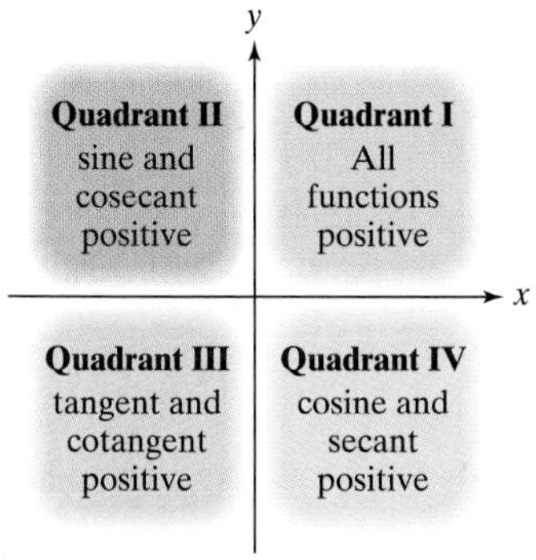

Figure 4.38 The signs of the trigonometric functions

Study Tip

Your author's high school trig teacher showed him this sentence to remember the signs of the trig functions:

All	Students	Take	Calculus.
All trig functions are positive in QI.	Sine and its reciprocal, cosecant, are positive in QII.	Tangent and its reciprocal, cotangent, are positive in QIII.	Cosine and its reciprocal, secant, are positive in QIV.

The sentence isn't true anymore, so you may prefer these memory devices:

All **S**nakes **T**ease **C**hickens.
A **S**mart **T**rig **C**lass.

EXAMPLE 3 Finding the Quadrant in Which an Angle Lies

If $\tan\theta < 0$ and $\cos\theta > 0$, name the quadrant in which angle θ lies.

Solution When $\tan\theta < 0$, θ lies in quadrant II or IV. When $\cos\theta > 0$, θ lies in quadrant I or IV. When both conditions are met ($\tan\theta < 0$ and $\cos\theta > 0$), θ must lie in quadrant IV.

Check Point 3 If $\sin\theta < 0$ and $\cos\theta < 0$, name the quadrant in which angle θ lies.

EXAMPLE 4 Evaluating Trigonometric Functions

Given $\tan\theta = -\frac{2}{3}$ and $\cos\theta > 0$, find $\cos\theta$ and $\csc\theta$.

Solution Because the tangent is negative and the cosine is positive, θ lies in quadrant IV. This will help us to determine whether the negative sign in $\tan\theta = -\frac{2}{3}$ should be associated with the numerator or the denominator. Keep in mind that in quadrant IV, x is positive and y is negative. Thus,

In quadrant IV, y is negative.

$$\tan\theta = -\frac{2}{3} = \frac{y}{x} = \frac{-2}{3}.$$

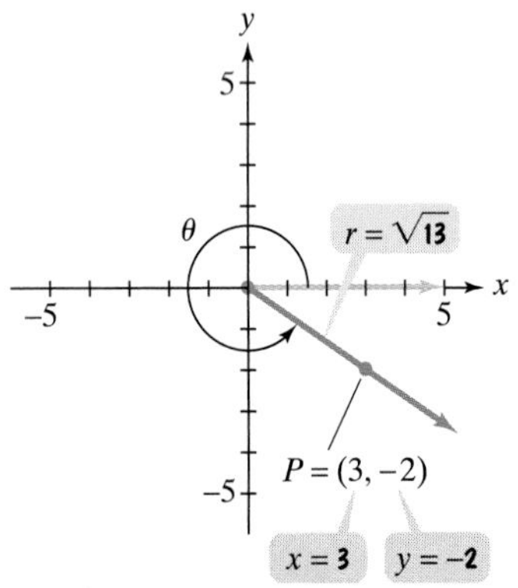

Figure 4.39 $\tan\theta = -\frac{2}{3}$ and $\cos\theta > 0$

(See Figure 4.39.) Thus, $x = 3$ and $y = -2$. Furthermore,

$$r = \sqrt{x^2 + y^2} = \sqrt{3^2 + (-2)^2} = \sqrt{9+4} = \sqrt{13}.$$

Now that we know x, y, and r, we can find $\cos\theta$ and $\csc\theta$.

$$\cos\theta = \frac{x}{r} = \frac{3}{\sqrt{13}} = \frac{3}{\sqrt{13}}\cdot\frac{\sqrt{13}}{\sqrt{13}} = \frac{3\sqrt{13}}{13} \qquad \csc\theta = \frac{r}{y} = \frac{\sqrt{13}}{-2} = -\frac{\sqrt{13}}{2}$$

Check Point 4 Given $\tan\theta = -\frac{1}{3}$ and $\cos\theta < 0$, find $\sin\theta$ and $\sec\theta$.

In Example 4, we used the quadrant in which θ lies to determine whether a negative sign should be associated with the numerator or the denominator. Here's a situation, similar to Example 4, where negative signs should be associated with *both* the numerator and the denominator:

$$\tan\theta = \frac{3}{5} \quad \text{and} \quad \cos\theta < 0.$$

Because the tangent is positive and the cosine is negative, θ lies in quadrant III. In quadrant III, x is negative and y is negative. Thus,

$$\tan\theta = \frac{3}{5} = \frac{y}{x} = \frac{-3}{-5}.$$

We see that $x = -5$ and $y = -3$.

3 Find reference angles.

Reference Angles

We will often evaluate trigonometric functions of positive angles greater than 90° and all negative angles by making use of a positive acute angle. This positive acute angle is called a *reference angle*.

Definition of a Reference Angle

Let θ be a nonacute angle in standard position that lies in a quadrant. Its **reference angle** is the positive acute angle θ' formed by the terminal side of θ and the x-axis.

Figure 4.40 shows the reference angle for θ lying in quadrants II, III, and IV. Notice that the formula used to find θ', the reference angle, varies according to the quadrant in which θ lies. You may find it easier to find the reference angle for a given angle by making a figure that shows the angle in standard position. The acute angle formed by the terminal side of this angle and the x-axis is the reference angle.

Figure 4.40 Reference angles, θ', for positive angles, θ, in quadrants II, III, and IV

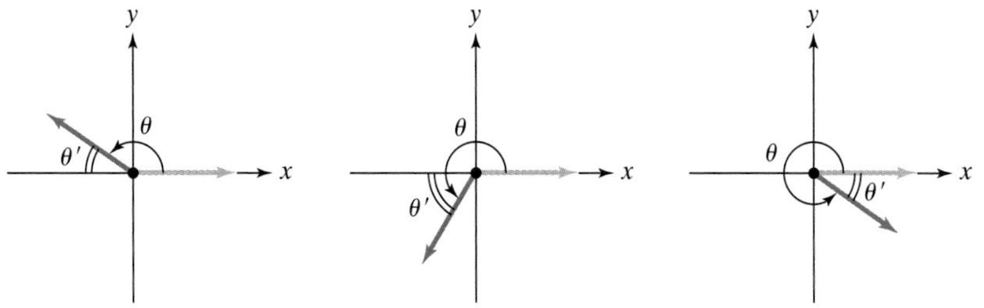

If $90° < \theta < 180°$, then $\theta' = 180° - \theta$.

If $180° < \theta < 270°$, then $\theta' = \theta - 180°$.

If $270° < \theta < 360°$, then $\theta' = 360° - \theta$.

EXAMPLE 5 Finding Reference Angles

Find the reference angle, θ', for each of the following angles:

a. $\theta = 345°$ **b.** $\theta = \dfrac{5\pi}{6}$ **c.** $\theta = -135°$ **d.** $\theta = 2.5$.

Solution

a. A 345° angle in standard position is shown in Figure 4.41. Because 345° lies in quadrant IV, the reference angle is

$$\theta' = 360° - 345° = 15°.$$

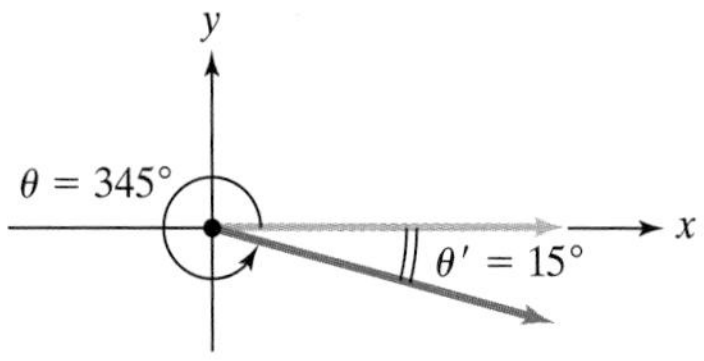

Figure 4.41

b. Because $\dfrac{5\pi}{6}$ lies between $\dfrac{\pi}{2} = \dfrac{3\pi}{6}$ and $\pi = \dfrac{6\pi}{6}$, $\theta = \dfrac{5\pi}{6}$ lies in quadrant II. The angle is shown in Figure 4.42. The reference angle is

$$\theta' = \pi - \frac{5\pi}{6} = \frac{6\pi}{6} - \frac{5\pi}{6} = \frac{\pi}{6}.$$

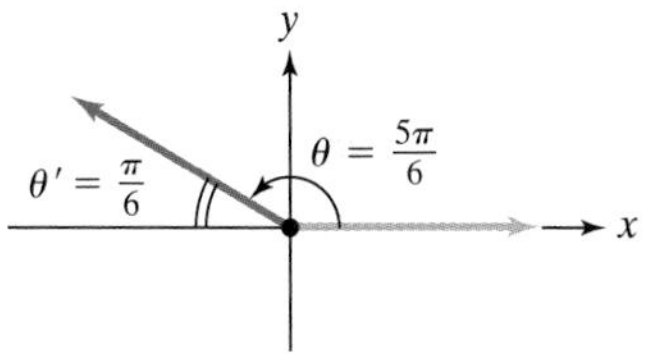

Figure 4.42

Discovery

Solve part (c) by first finding a positive coterminal angle for $-135°$ less than 360°. Use the positive coterminal angle to find the reference angle.

c. A $-135°$ angle in standard position is shown in Figure 4.43. The figure indicates that the positive acute angle formed by the terminal side of θ and the x-axis is 45°. The reference angle is

$$\theta' = 45°.$$

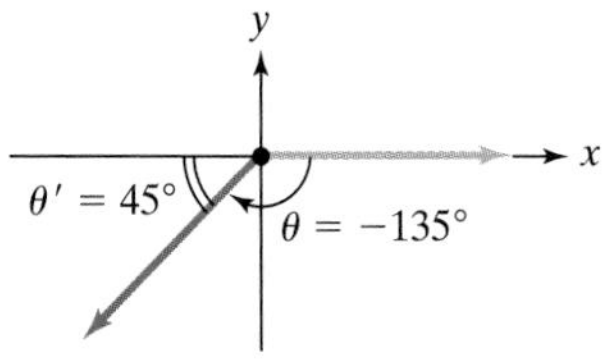

Figure 4.43

d. The angle $\theta = 2.5$ lies between $\dfrac{\pi}{2} \approx 1.57$ and $\pi \approx 3.14$. This means that $\theta = 2.5$ is in quadrant II, shown in Figure 4.44. The reference angle is

$$\theta' = \pi - 2.5 \approx 0.64.$$

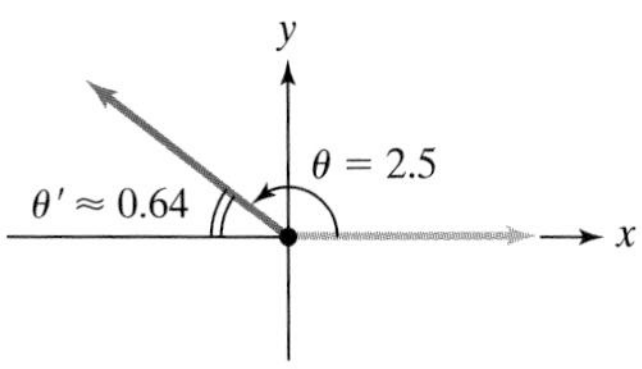

Figure 4.44

Check Point 5 Find the reference angle, θ', for each of the following angles:

a. $\theta = 210°$ **b.** $\theta = \frac{7\pi}{4}$ **c.** $\theta = -240°$ **d.** $\theta = 3.6$.

Finding reference angles for angles that are greater than 360° (2π) or less than $-360°$ (-2π) involves using coterminal angles. We have seen that coterminal angles have the same initial and terminal sides. Recall that coterminal angles can be obtained by increasing or decreasing an angle's measure by an integer multiple of 360° or 2π.

Finding Reference Angles for Angles Greater Than 360° (2π) or Less Than $-360°$ (-2π)

1. Find a positive angle α less than 360° or 2π that is coterminal with the given angle.
2. Draw α in standard position.
3. Use the drawing to find the reference angle for the given angle. The positive acute angle formed by the terminal side of α and the x-axis is the reference angle.

EXAMPLE 6 Finding Reference Angles

Find the reference angle for each of the following angles:

a. $\theta = 580°$ **b.** $\theta = \frac{8\pi}{3}$ **c.** $\theta = -\frac{13\pi}{6}$.

Solution

a. For a 580° angle, subtract 360° to find a positive coterminal angle less than 360°.

$$580° - 360° = 220°$$

Figure 4.45 shows $\alpha = 220°$ in standard position. Because 220° lies in quadrant III, the reference angle is

$$\alpha' = 220° - 180° = 40°.$$

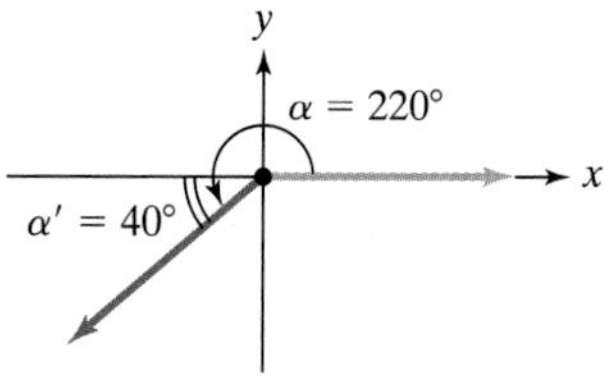

Figure 4.45

b. For an $\frac{8\pi}{3}$, or $2\frac{2}{3}\pi$ angle, subtract 2π to find a positive coterminal angle less than 2π.

$$\frac{8\pi}{3} - 2\pi = \frac{8\pi}{3} - \frac{6\pi}{3} = \frac{2\pi}{3}$$

Figure 4.46 shows $\alpha = \frac{2\pi}{3}$ in standard position.

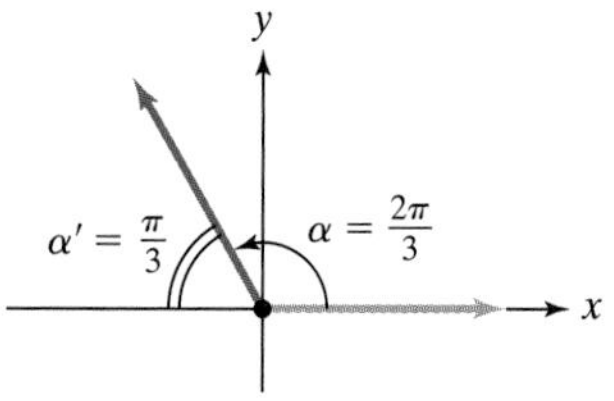

Figure 4.46

Because $\frac{2\pi}{3}$ lies in quadrant II, the reference angle is

$$\alpha' = \pi - \frac{2\pi}{3} = \frac{3\pi}{3} - \frac{2\pi}{3} = \frac{\pi}{3}.$$

c. For a $-\frac{13\pi}{6}$, or $-2\frac{1}{6}\pi$ angle, add 4π to find a positive coterminal angle less than 2π.

$$-\frac{13\pi}{6} + 4\pi = -\frac{13\pi}{6} + \frac{24\pi}{6} = \frac{11\pi}{6}$$

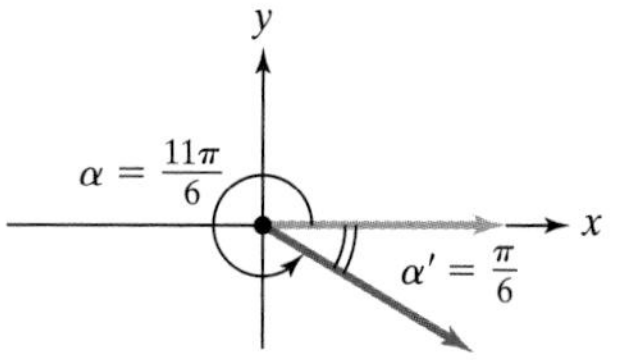

Figure 4.47

Figure 4.47 shows $\alpha = \frac{11\pi}{6}$ in standard position.

Because $\frac{11\pi}{6}$ lies in quadrant IV, the reference angle is

$$\alpha' = 2\pi - \frac{11\pi}{6} = \frac{12\pi}{6} - \frac{11\pi}{6} = \frac{\pi}{6}.$$

Discovery

Solve part (c) using the coterminal angle formed by adding 2π, rather than 4π, to the given angle.

Check Point 6 Find the reference angle for each of the following angles:

a. $\theta = 665°$ **b.** $\theta = \frac{15\pi}{4}$ **c.** $\theta = -\frac{11\pi}{3}$.

4 Use reference angles to evaluate trigonometric functions.

Evaluating Trigonometric Functions Using Reference Angles

The way that reference angles are defined makes them useful in evaluating trigonometric functions.

Using Reference Angles to Evaluate Trigonometric Functions

The values of the trigonometric functions of a given angle, θ, are the same as the values of the trigonometric functions of the reference angle, θ', except possibly for the sign. A function value of the acute reference angle, θ', is always positive. However, the same function value for θ may be positive or negative.

For example, we can use a reference angle, θ', to obtain an exact value for tan 120°. The reference angle for $\theta = 120°$ is $\theta' = 180° - 120° = 60°$. We know the exact value of the tangent function of the reference angle: $\tan 60° = \sqrt{3}$. We also know that the value of a trigonometric function of a given angle, θ, is the same as that of its reference angle, θ', except possibly for the sign. Thus, we can conclude that tan 120° equals $-\sqrt{3}$ or $\sqrt{3}$.

What sign should we attach to $\sqrt{3}$? A 120° angle lies in quadrant II, where only the sine and cosecant are positive. Thus, the tangent function is negative for a 120° angle. Therefore,

Prefix by a negative sign to show tangent is negative in quadrant II.

$$\tan 120° = -\tan 60° = -\sqrt{3}.$$

The reference angle for 120° is 60°.

In the previous section, we used two right triangles to find exact trigonometric values of 30°, 45°, and 60°. Using a procedure similar to finding tan 120°, we can now find the exact function values of all angles for which 30°, 45°, or 60° are reference angles.

A Procedure for Using Reference Angles to Evaluate Trigonometric Functions

The value of a trigonometric function of any angle θ is found as follows:

1. Find the associated reference angle, θ', and the function value for θ'.
2. Use the quadrant in which θ lies to prefix the appropriate sign to the function value in step 1.

Discovery

Draw the two right triangles involving 30°, 45°, and 60°. Indicate the length of each side. Use these lengths to verify the function values for the reference angles in the solution to Example 7.

EXAMPLE 7 Using Reference Angles to Evaluate Trigonometric Functions

Use reference angles to find the exact value of each of the following trigonometric functions:

a. $\sin 135°$ **b.** $\cos \frac{4\pi}{3}$ **c.** $\cot\left(-\frac{\pi}{3}\right)$.

Solution

a. We use our two-step procedure to find sin 135°.

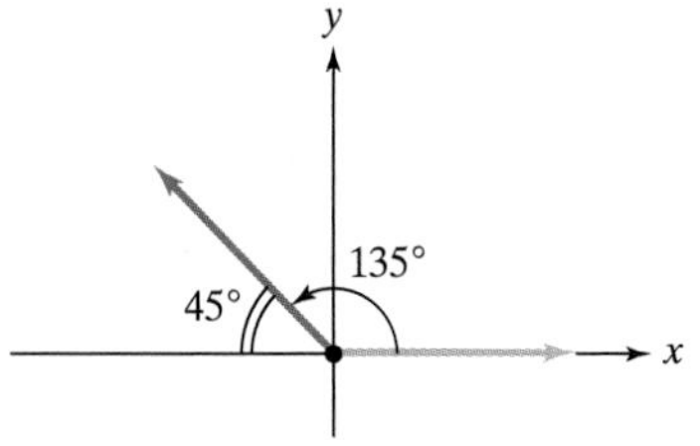

Figure 4.48 Reference angle for 135°

Step 1 Find the reference angle, θ', and sin θ'. Figure 4.48 shows 135° lies in quadrant II. The reference angle is

$$\theta' = 180° - 135° = 45°.$$

The function value for the reference angle is $\sin 45° = \frac{\sqrt{2}}{2}$.

Step 2 Use the quadrant in which θ lies to prefix the appropriate sign to the function value in step 1. The angle $\theta = 135°$ lies in quadrant II. Because the sine is positive in quadrant II, we put a + sign before the function value of the reference angle. Thus,

The sine is positive in quadrant II.

$$\sin 135° = +\sin 45° = \frac{\sqrt{2}}{2}.$$

The reference angle for 135° is 45°.

b. We use our two-step procedure to find $\cos \frac{4\pi}{3}$.

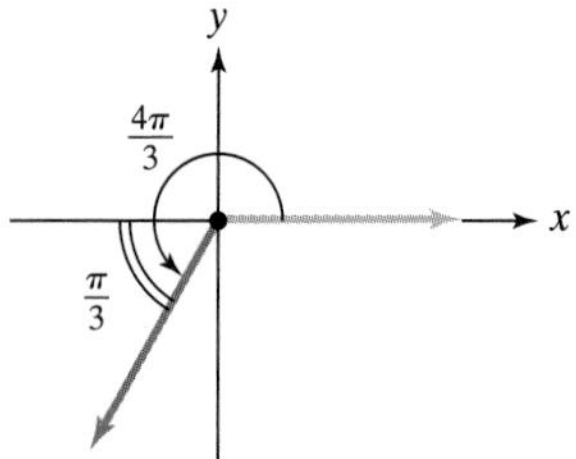

Figure 4.49 Reference angle for $\frac{4\pi}{3}$

Step 1 Find the reference angle, θ', and cos θ'. Figure 4.49 shows that $\theta = \frac{4\pi}{3}$ lies in quadrant III. The reference angle is

$$\theta' = \frac{4\pi}{3} - \pi = \frac{4\pi}{3} - \frac{3\pi}{3} = \frac{\pi}{3}.$$

The function value for the reference angle is

$$\cos\frac{\pi}{3} = \frac{1}{2}.$$

Step 2 Use the quadrant in which θ lies to prefix the appropriate sign to the function value in step 1. The angle $\theta = \frac{4\pi}{3}$ lies in quadrant III. Because only the tangent and cotangent are positive in quadrant III, the cosine is negative in this quadrant. We put a − sign before the function value of the reference angle. Thus,

The cosine is negative in quadrant III.

$$\cos\frac{4\pi}{3} = -\cos\frac{\pi}{3} = -\frac{1}{2}.$$

The reference angle for $\frac{4\pi}{3}$ is $\frac{\pi}{3}$.

c. We use our two-step procedure to find $\cot\left(-\frac{\pi}{3}\right)$.

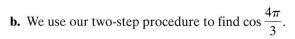

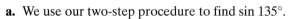

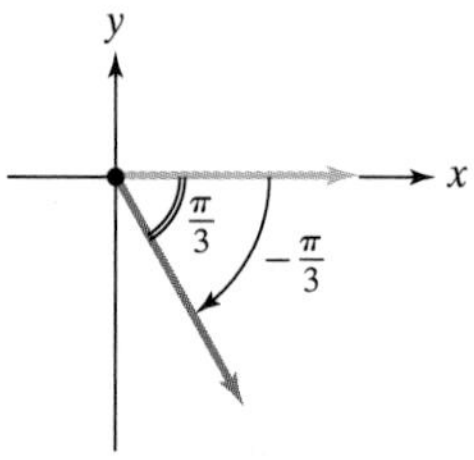

Figure 4.50 Reference angle for $-\frac{\pi}{3}$

Step 1 Find the reference angle, θ', and cot θ'. Figure 4.50 shows that $\theta = -\frac{\pi}{3}$ lies in quadrant IV. The reference angle is $\theta' = \frac{\pi}{3}$. The function value for the reference angle is $\cot\frac{\pi}{3} = \frac{\sqrt{3}}{3}$.

Step 2 Use the quadrant in which θ lies to prefix the appropriate sign to the function value in step 1. The angle $\theta = -\frac{\pi}{3}$ lies in quadrant IV. Because only the cosine and secant are positive in quadrant IV, the cotangent is negative in this quadrant. We put a − sign before the function value of the reference angle. Thus,

The cotangent is negative in quadrant IV.

$$\cot\left(-\frac{\pi}{3}\right) = -\cot\frac{\pi}{3} = -\frac{\sqrt{3}}{3}.$$

The reference angle for $-\frac{\pi}{3}$ is $\frac{\pi}{3}$.

Check Point 7 Use reference angles to find the exact value of the following trigonometric functions:

a. $\sin 300°$ **b.** $\tan\frac{5\pi}{4}$ **c.** $\sec\left(-\frac{\pi}{6}\right)$.

In our final example, we use positive coterminal angles less than 2π to find the reference angles.

EXAMPLE 8 Using Reference Angles to Evaluate Trigonometric Functions

Use reference angles to find the exact value of each of the following trigonometric functions:

a. $\tan\frac{14\pi}{3}$ **b.** $\sec\left(-\frac{17\pi}{4}\right)$.

Solution

a. We use our two-step procedure to find $\tan\frac{14\pi}{3}$.

Step 1 Find the reference angle, θ', and $\tan\theta'$. Because the given angle, $\frac{14\pi}{3}$ or $4\frac{2}{3}\pi$, exceeds 2π, subtract 4π to find a positive coterminal angle less than 2π.

$$\theta = \frac{14\pi}{3} - 4\pi = \frac{14\pi}{3} - \frac{12\pi}{3} = \frac{2\pi}{3}$$

Figure 4.51 shows $\theta = \frac{2\pi}{3}$ in standard position. The angle lies in quadrant II. The reference angle is

$$\theta' = \pi - \frac{2\pi}{3} = \frac{3\pi}{3} - \frac{2\pi}{3} = \frac{\pi}{3}.$$

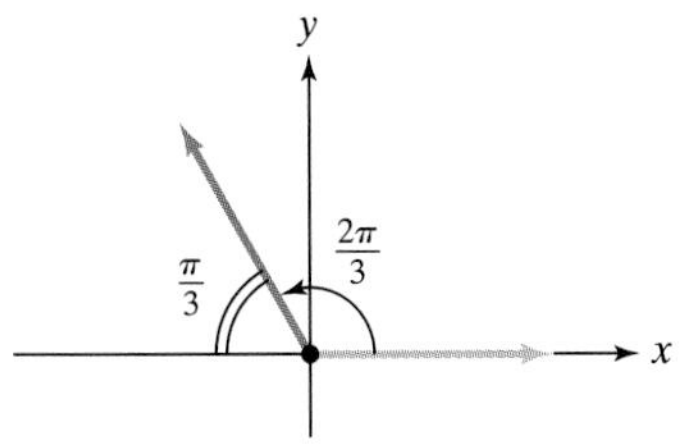

Figure 4.51 Reference angle for $\frac{2\pi}{3}$

The function value for the reference angle is $\tan\frac{\pi}{3} = \sqrt{3}$.

Step 2 Use the quadrant in which θ lies to prefix the appropriate sign to the function value in step 1. The coterminal angle $\theta = \frac{2\pi}{3}$ lies in quadrant II.

Because the tangent is negative in quadrant II, we put a $-$ sign before the function value of the reference angle. Thus,

The tangent is negative in quadrant II.

$$\tan\frac{14\pi}{3} = \tan\frac{2\pi}{3} = -\tan\frac{\pi}{3} = -\sqrt{3}.$$

The reference angle for $\frac{2\pi}{3}$ is $\frac{\pi}{3}$.

b. We use our two-step procedure to find $\sec\left(-\frac{17\pi}{4}\right)$.

Step 1 Find the reference angle, θ', and $\sec\theta'$. Because the given angle, $-\frac{17\pi}{4}$ or $-4\frac{1}{4}\pi$, is less than -2π, add 6π (three multiples of 2π) to find a positive coterminal angle less than 2π.

$$\theta = -\frac{17\pi}{4} + 6\pi = -\frac{17\pi}{4} + \frac{24\pi}{4} = \frac{7\pi}{4}$$

Figure 4.52 shows $\theta = \frac{7\pi}{4}$ in standard position. The angle lies in quadrant IV. The reference angle is

$$\theta' = 2\pi - \frac{7\pi}{4} = \frac{8\pi}{4} - \frac{7\pi}{4} = \frac{\pi}{4}.$$

The function value for the reference angle is $\sec\frac{\pi}{4} = \sqrt{2}$.

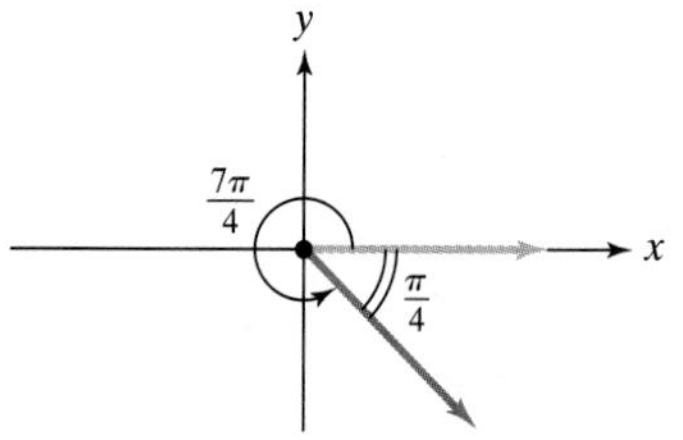

Figure 4.52 Reference angle for $\frac{7\pi}{4}$

Step 2 Use the quadrant in which θ lies to prefix the appropriate sign to the function value in step 1. The coterminal angle $\theta = \frac{7\pi}{4}$ lies in quadrant IV. Because the secant is positive in quadrant IV, we put a + sign before the function value of the reference angle. Thus,

The secant is positive in quadrant IV.

$$\sec\left(-\frac{17\pi}{4}\right) = \sec\frac{7\pi}{4} = +\sec\frac{\pi}{4} = \sqrt{2}.$$

The reference angle for $\frac{7\pi}{4}$ is $\frac{\pi}{4}$.

Check Point 8 Use reference angles to find the exact value of each of the following trigonometric functions:

a. $\cos\frac{17\pi}{6}$ **b.** $\sin\left(-\frac{22\pi}{3}\right)$.

Study Tip

Evaluating trigonometric functions like those in Example 8 and Check Point 8 involves using a number of concepts, including finding coterminal angles and reference angles, locating special angles, determining the signs of trigonometric functions in specific quadrants, and finding the trigonometric functions of special angles $\left(30° = \frac{\pi}{6}, 45° = \frac{\pi}{4}, \text{ and } 60° = \frac{\pi}{3}\right)$. To be successful in trigonometry, it is often necessary to connect concepts. Here's an early reference sheet showing some of the concepts you should have at your fingertips (or memorized).

Degree and Radian Measures of Special and Quadrantal Angles

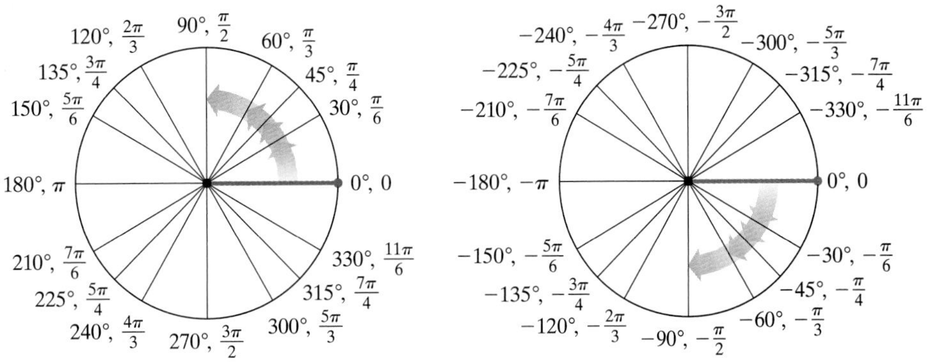

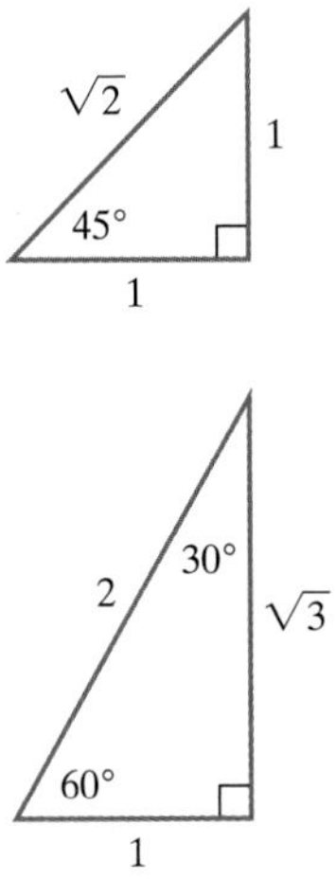

Special Right Triangles and Trigonometric Functions of Special Angles

θ	$30° = \frac{\pi}{6}$	$45° = \frac{\pi}{4}$	$60° = \frac{\pi}{3}$
$\sin\theta$	$\frac{1}{2}$	$\frac{\sqrt{2}}{2}$	$\frac{\sqrt{3}}{2}$
$\cos\theta$	$\frac{\sqrt{3}}{2}$	$\frac{\sqrt{2}}{2}$	$\frac{1}{2}$
$\tan\theta$	$\frac{\sqrt{3}}{3}$	1	$\sqrt{3}$

Signs of the Trigonometric Functions

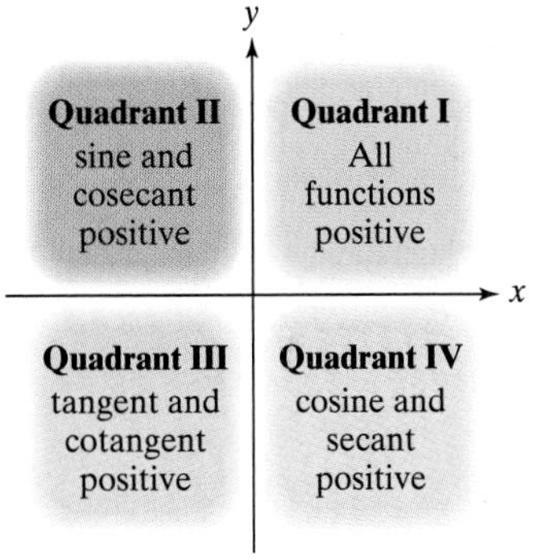
y
Quadrant II
sine and cosecant positive
Quadrant I
All functions positive
x
Quadrant III
tangent and cotangent positive
Quadrant IV
cosine and secant positive

Trigonometric Functions of Quadrantal Angles

θ	$0° = 0$	$90° = \frac{\pi}{2}$	$180° = \pi$	$270° = \frac{3\pi}{2}$
$\sin\theta$	0	1	0	−1
$\cos\theta$	1	0	−1	0
$\tan\theta$	0	undefined	0	undefined

Using Reference Angles to Evaluate Trigonometric Functions

$\sin\theta = \square \sin\theta'$

$\cos\theta = \square \cos\theta'$

$\tan\theta = \square \tan\theta'$

+ or − in $\square$ determined by the quadrant in which θ lies and the sign of the function in that quadrant.

EXERCISE SET 4.3

Practice Exercises

In Exercises 1–8, a point on the terminal side of angle θ is given. Find the exact value of each of the six trigonometric functions of θ.

1. $(-4, 3)$ **2.** $(-12, 5)$ **3.** $(2, 3)$
4. $(3, 7)$ **5.** $(3, -3)$ **6.** $(5, -5)$
7. $(-2, -5)$ **8.** $(-1, -3)$

In Exercises 9–16, evaluate the trigonometric function at the quadrantal angle, or state that the expression is undefined.

9. $\cos \pi$ **10.** $\tan \pi$ **11.** $\sec \pi$
12. $\csc \pi$ **13.** $\tan \frac{3\pi}{2}$ **14.** $\cos \frac{3\pi}{2}$
15. $\cot \frac{\pi}{2}$ **16.** $\tan \frac{\pi}{2}$

In Exercises 17–22, let θ be an angle in standard position. Name the quadrant in which θ lies.

17. $\sin \theta > 0$, $\cos \theta > 0$ **18.** $\sin \theta < 0$, $\cos \theta > 0$
19. $\sin \theta < 0$, $\cos \theta < 0$ **20.** $\tan \theta < 0$, $\sin \theta < 0$
21. $\tan \theta < 0$, $\cos \theta < 0$ **22.** $\cot \theta > 0$, $\sec \theta < 0$

In Exercises 23–34, find the exact value of each of the remaining trigonometric functions of θ.

23. $\cos \theta = -\frac{3}{5}$, θ in quadrant III
24. $\sin \theta = -\frac{12}{13}$, θ in quadrant III
25. $\sin \theta = \frac{5}{13}$, θ in quadrant II
26. $\cos \theta = \frac{4}{5}$, θ in quadrant IV
27. $\cos \theta = \frac{8}{17}$, $270° < \theta < 360°$
28. $\cos \theta = \frac{1}{3}$, $270° < \theta < 360°$
29. $\tan \theta = -\frac{2}{3}$, $\sin \theta > 0$ **30.** $\tan \theta = -\frac{1}{3}$, $\sin \theta > 0$
31. $\tan \theta = \frac{4}{3}$, $\cos \theta < 0$ **32.** $\tan \theta = \frac{5}{12}$, $\cos \theta < 0$
33. $\sec \theta = -3$, $\tan \theta > 0$ **34.** $\csc \theta = -4$, $\tan \theta > 0$

In Exercises 35–60, find the reference angle for each angle.

35. $160°$ **36.** $170°$ **37.** $205°$
38. $210°$ **39.** $355°$ **40.** $351°$
41. $\frac{7\pi}{4}$ **42.** $\frac{5\pi}{4}$ **43.** $\frac{5\pi}{6}$
44. $\frac{5\pi}{7}$ **45.** $-150°$ **46.** $-250°$
47. $-335°$ **48.** $-359°$ **49.** 4.7
50. 5.5 **51.** $565°$ **52.** $553°$
53. $\frac{17\pi}{6}$ **54.** $\frac{11\pi}{4}$ **55.** $\frac{23\pi}{4}$
56. $\frac{17\pi}{3}$ **57.** $-\frac{11\pi}{4}$ **58.** $-\frac{17\pi}{6}$
59. $-\frac{25\pi}{6}$ **60.** $-\frac{13\pi}{3}$

In Exercises 61–86, use reference angles to find the exact value of each expression. Do not use a calculator.

61. $\cos 225°$ **62.** $\sin 300°$ **63.** $\tan 210°$
64. $\sec 240°$ **65.** $\tan 420°$ **66.** $\tan 405°$
67. $\sin \frac{2\pi}{3}$ **68.** $\cos \frac{3\pi}{4}$ **69.** $\csc \frac{7\pi}{6}$
70. $\cot \frac{7\pi}{4}$ **71.** $\tan \frac{9\pi}{4}$ **72.** $\tan \frac{9\pi}{2}$
73. $\sin(-240°)$ **74.** $\sin(-225°)$ **75.** $\tan\left(-\frac{\pi}{4}\right)$
76. $\tan\left(-\frac{\pi}{6}\right)$ **77.** $\sec 495°$ **78.** $\sec 510°$
79. $\cot \frac{19\pi}{6}$ **80.** $\cot \frac{13\pi}{3}$ **81.** $\cos \frac{23\pi}{4}$
82. $\cos \frac{35\pi}{6}$ **83.** $\tan\left(-\frac{17\pi}{6}\right)$ **84.** $\tan\left(-\frac{11\pi}{4}\right)$
85. $\sin\left(-\frac{17\pi}{3}\right)$ **86.** $\sin\left(-\frac{35\pi}{6}\right)$

Practice Plus

In Exercises 87–92, find the exact value of each expression. Write the answer as a single fraction. Do not use a calculator.

87. $\sin \frac{\pi}{3} \cos \pi - \cos \frac{\pi}{3} \sin \frac{3\pi}{2}$

88. $\sin \frac{\pi}{4} \cos 0 - \sin \frac{\pi}{6} \cos \pi$

89. $\sin \frac{11\pi}{4} \cos \frac{5\pi}{6} + \cos \frac{11\pi}{4} \sin \frac{5\pi}{6}$

90. $\sin \frac{17\pi}{3} \cos \frac{5\pi}{4} + \cos \frac{17\pi}{3} \sin \frac{5\pi}{4}$

91. $\sin \frac{3\pi}{2} \tan\left(-\frac{15\pi}{4}\right) - \cos\left(-\frac{5\pi}{3}\right)$

92. $\sin \frac{3\pi}{2} \tan\left(-\frac{8\pi}{3}\right) + \cos\left(-\frac{5\pi}{6}\right)$

In Exercises 93–98, let

$$f(x) = \sin x,\ g(x) = \cos x, \text{ and } h(x) = 2x.$$

Find the exact value of each expression. Do not use a calculator.

93. $f\left(\frac{4\pi}{3} + \frac{\pi}{6}\right) + f\left(\frac{4\pi}{3}\right) + f\left(\frac{\pi}{6}\right)$

94. $g\left(\frac{5\pi}{6} + \frac{\pi}{6}\right) + g\left(\frac{5\pi}{6}\right) + g\left(\frac{\pi}{6}\right)$

95. $(h \circ g)\left(\frac{17\pi}{3}\right)$ **96.** $(h \circ f)\left(\frac{11\pi}{4}\right)$

97. the average rate of change of f from $x_1 = \frac{5\pi}{4}$ to $x_2 = \frac{3\pi}{2}$

98. the average rate of change of g from $x_1 = \frac{3\pi}{4}$ to $x_2 = \pi$

In Exercises 99–104, find two values of θ, $0 \le \theta < 2\pi$, that satisfy each equation.

99. $\sin \theta = \frac{\sqrt{2}}{2}$ **100.** $\cos \theta = \frac{1}{2}$

101. $\sin \theta = -\frac{\sqrt{2}}{2}$ **102.** $\cos \theta = -\frac{1}{2}$

103. $\tan \theta = -\sqrt{3}$ **104.** $\tan \theta = -\frac{\sqrt{3}}{3}$

Writing in Mathematics

105. If you are given a point on the terminal side of angle θ, explain how to find $\sin\theta$.

106. Explain why $\tan 90°$ is undefined.

107. If $\cos\theta > 0$ and $\tan\theta < 0$, explain how to find the quadrant in which θ lies.

108. What is a reference angle? Give an example with your description.

109. Explain how reference angles are used to evaluate trigonometric functions. Give an example with your description.

SECTION 4.4 Trigonometric Functions of Real Numbers; Periodic Functions

Objectives

1. Use a unit circle to define trigonometric functions of real numbers.
2. Recognize the domain and range of sine and cosine functions.
3. Use even and odd trigonometric functions.
4. Use periodic properties.

1 Use a unit circle to define trigonometric functions of real numbers.

Cycles govern many aspects of life—heartbeats, sleep patterns, seasons, and tides all follow regular, predictable cycles. In this section, we will see why trigonometric functions are used to model phenomena that occur in cycles. To do this, we need to move beyond angles and consider trigonometric functions of real numbers.

Trigonometric Functions of Real Numbers

Thus far, we have considered trigonometric functions of angles measured in degrees or radians. To define trigonometric functions of real numbers, rather than angles, we use a unit circle. A **unit circle** is a circle of radius 1, with its center at the origin of a rectangular coordinate system. The equation of this unit circle is $x^2 + y^2 = 1$. Figure 4.53 shows a unit circle in which the central angle measures t radians. We can use the formula for the length of a circular arc, $s = r\theta$, to find the length of the intercepted arc.

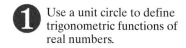

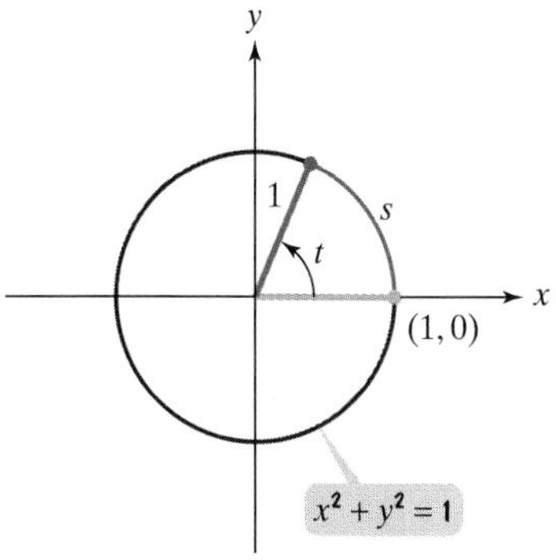

Figure 4.53 Unit circle with a central angle measuring t radians

$$s = r\theta = 1 \cdot t = t$$

The radius of a unit circle is 1. The radian measure of the central angle is t.

Thus, the length of the intercepted arc is t. This is also the radian measure of the central angle. Thus, **in a unit circle, the radian measure of the central angle is equal to the length of the intercepted arc.** Both are given by the same *real number t.*

In Figure 4.54, the radian measure of the angle and the length of the intercepted arc are both shown by t. Let $P = (x, y)$ denote the point on the unit circle that has arc length t from $(1, 0)$. Figure 4.54(a) shows that if t is positive, point P is reached by moving counterclockwise along the unit circle from $(1, 0)$. Figure 4.54(b) shows that if t is negative, point P is reached by moving clockwise along the unit circle from $(1, 0)$. For each real number t, there corresponds a point $P = (x, y)$ on the unit circle.

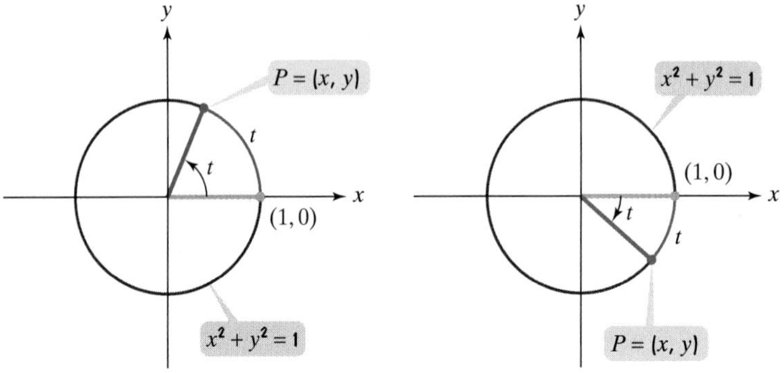

(a) t is positive. (b) t is negative.

Figure 4.54

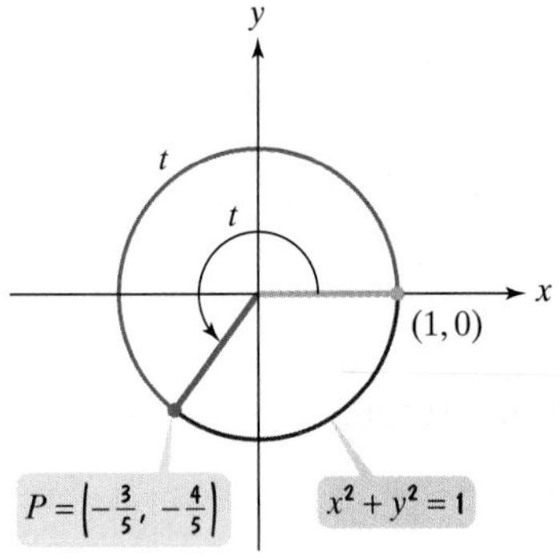

Figure 4.55

Using Figure 4.54, we define the cosine function at t as the x-coordinate of P and the sine function at t as the y-coordinate of P. Thus,

$$x = \cos t \quad \text{and} \quad y = \sin t.$$

For example, a point $P = (x, y)$ on the unit circle corresponding to a real number t is shown in Figure 4.55 for $\pi < t < \frac{3\pi}{2}$. We see that the coordinates of $P = (x, y)$ are $x = -\frac{3}{5}$ and $y = -\frac{4}{5}$. Because the cosine function is the x-coordinate of P and the sine function is the y-coordinate of P, the values of these trigonometric functions at the real number t are

$$\cos t = -\frac{3}{5} \quad \text{and} \quad \sin t = -\frac{4}{5}.$$

Definitions of the Trigonometric Functions in Terms of a Unit Circle

If t is a real number and $P = (x, y)$ is a point on the unit circle that corresponds to t, then

$$\sin t = y \qquad \csc t = \frac{1}{y}, y \neq 0$$

$$\cos t = x \qquad \sec t = \frac{1}{x}, x \neq 0$$

$$\tan t = \frac{y}{x}, x \neq 0 \qquad \cot t = \frac{x}{y}, y \neq 0.$$

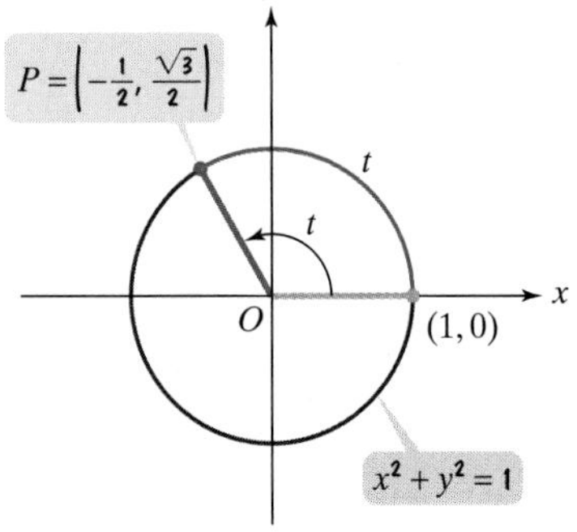

Figure 4.56

Because this definition expresses function values in terms of coordinates of a point on a unit circle, the trigonometric functions are sometimes called the **circular functions**.

EXAMPLE 1 Finding Values of the Trigonometric Functions

In Figure 4.56, t is a real number equal to the length of the intercepted arc of an angle that measures t radians and $P = \left(-\frac{1}{2}, \frac{\sqrt{3}}{2}\right)$ is a point on the unit circle that corresponds to t. Use the figure to find the values of the trigonometric functions at t.

Solution The point P on the unit circle that corresponds to t has coordinates $\left(-\frac{1}{2}, \frac{\sqrt{3}}{2}\right)$. We use $x = -\frac{1}{2}$ and $y = \frac{\sqrt{3}}{2}$ to find the values of the trigonometric functions.

$$\sin t = y = \frac{\sqrt{3}}{2} \qquad \csc t = \frac{1}{y} = \frac{1}{\frac{\sqrt{3}}{2}} = \frac{2}{\sqrt{3}} = \frac{2}{\sqrt{3}}\cdot\frac{\sqrt{3}}{\sqrt{3}} = \frac{2\sqrt{3}}{3}$$

$$\cos t = x = -\frac{1}{2} \qquad \sec t = \frac{1}{x} = \frac{1}{-\frac{1}{2}} = -2$$

$$\tan t = \frac{y}{x} = \frac{\frac{\sqrt{3}}{2}}{-\frac{1}{2}} = -\sqrt{3} \qquad \cot t = \frac{x}{y} = \frac{-\frac{1}{2}}{\frac{\sqrt{3}}{2}} = -\frac{1}{\sqrt{3}} = -\frac{1}{\sqrt{3}}\cdot\frac{\sqrt{3}}{\sqrt{3}} = -\frac{\sqrt{3}}{3}$$

Check Point 1 Use the figure on the right to find the values of the trigonometric functions at t.

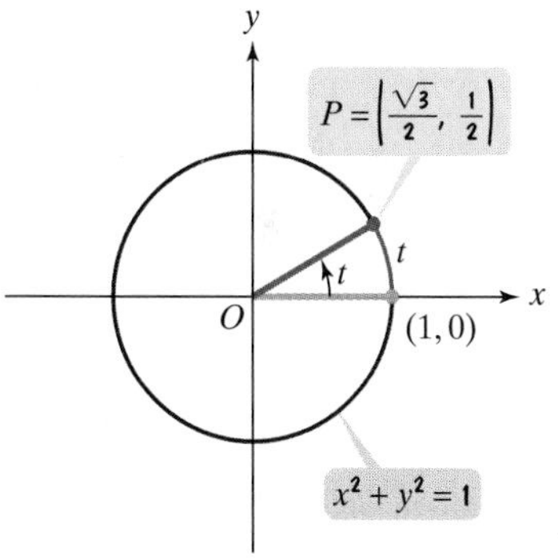

EXAMPLE 2 Finding Values of the Trigonometric Functions

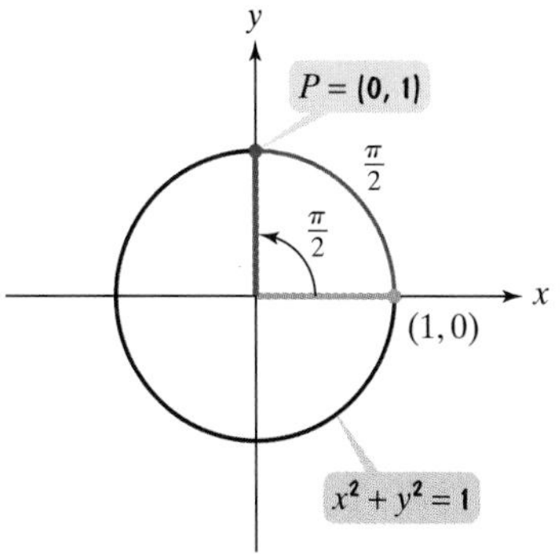

Figure 4.57

Use Figure 4.57 to find the values of the trigonometric functions at $t = \frac{\pi}{2}$.

Solution The point P on the unit circle that corresponds to $t = \frac{\pi}{2}$ has coordinates $(0, 1)$. We use $x = 0$ and $y = 1$ to find the values of the trigonometric functions at $\frac{\pi}{2}$.

$$\sin\frac{\pi}{2} = y = 1 \qquad \csc\frac{\pi}{2} = \frac{1}{y} = \frac{1}{1} = 1$$

$$\cos\frac{\pi}{2} = x = 0 \qquad \sec\frac{\pi}{2} = \frac{1}{x} = \cancel{\frac{1}{0}}$$

$$\tan\frac{\pi}{2} = \frac{y}{x} = \cancel{\frac{1}{0}} \qquad \cot\frac{\pi}{2} = \frac{x}{y} = \frac{0}{1} = 0$$

$\sec\frac{\pi}{2}$ and $\tan\frac{\pi}{2}$ are undefined.

Check Point 2 Use the figure on the right to find the values of the trigonometric functions at $t = \pi$.

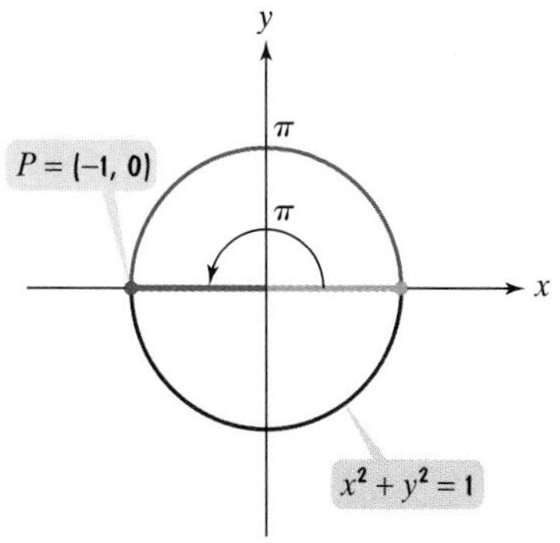

2 Recognize the domain and range of sine and cosine functions.

Domain and Range of Sine and Cosine Functions

The value of a trigonometric function at the real number t is its value at an angle of t radians. However, using real number domains, we can observe properties of trigonometric functions that are not as apparent using the angle approach. For example, the domain and range of each trigonometric function can be found from the unit circle definition. At this point, let's look only at the sine and cosine functions,

$$\sin t = y \quad \text{and} \quad \cos t = x.$$

Figure 4.58 shows the sine function at t as the y-coordinate of a point along the unit circle:

$$y = \sin t.$$

The domain is associated with t, the angle's radian measure and the intercepted arc's length.

The range is associated with y, the point's second coordinate.

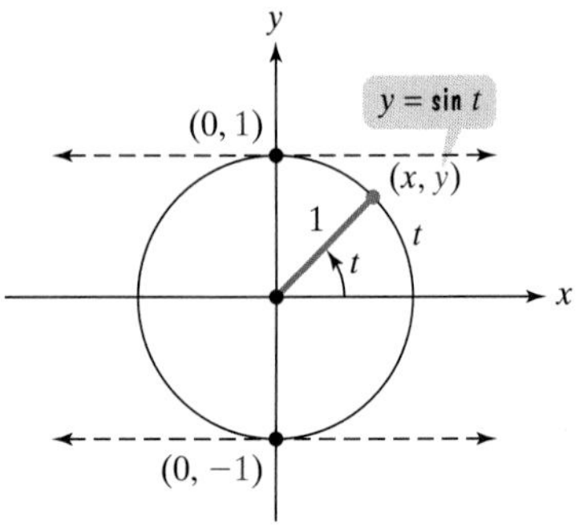

Figure 4.58

Because t can be any real number, the domain of the sine function is $(-\infty, \infty)$, the set of all real numbers. The radius of the unit circle is 1 and the dashed horizontal lines in Figure 4.58 show that y cannot be less than -1 or greater than 1. Thus, the range of the sine function is $[-1, 1]$, the set of all real numbers from -1 to 1, inclusive.

Figure 4.59 shows the cosine function at t as the x-coordinate of a point along the unit circle:

$$x = \cos t.$$

The domain is associated with t, the angle's radian measure and the intercepted arc's length.

The range is associated with x, the point's first coordinate.

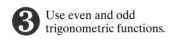

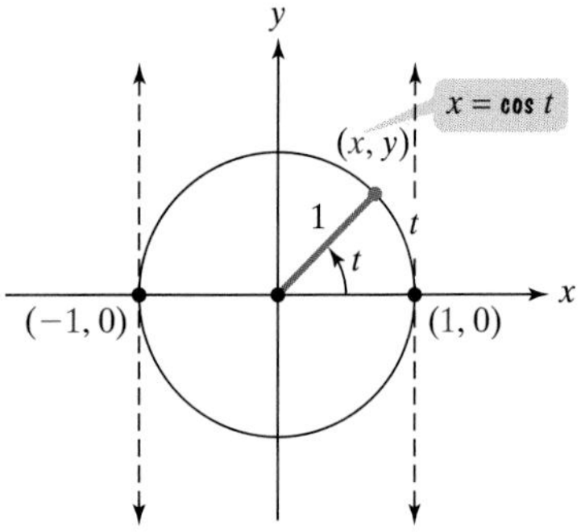

Figure 4.59

Because t can be any real number, the domain of the cosine function is $(-\infty, \infty)$. The radius of the unit circle is 1 and the dashed vertical lines in Figure 4.59 show that x cannot be less than -1 or greater than 1. Thus, the range of the cosine function is $[-1, 1]$.

The Domain and Range of the Sine and Cosine Functions

The domain of the sine function and the cosine function is $(-\infty, \infty)$, the set of all real numbers. The range of these functions is $[-1, 1]$, the set of all real numbers from -1 to 1, inclusive.

3 Use even and odd trigonometric functions.

Even and Odd Trigonometric Functions

We have seen that a function is even if $f(-t) = f(t)$ and odd if $f(-t) = -f(t)$. We can use Figure 4.60 at the top of the next page to show that the cosine function is an even function and the sine function is an odd function. By definition, the coordinates of the points P and Q in Figure 4.60 are as follows:

$$P: \ (\cos t, \sin t)$$
$$Q: \ (\cos(-t), \sin(-t)).$$

In Figure 4.60, the x-coordinates of P and Q are the same. Thus,

$$\cos(-t) = \cos t.$$

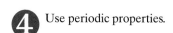

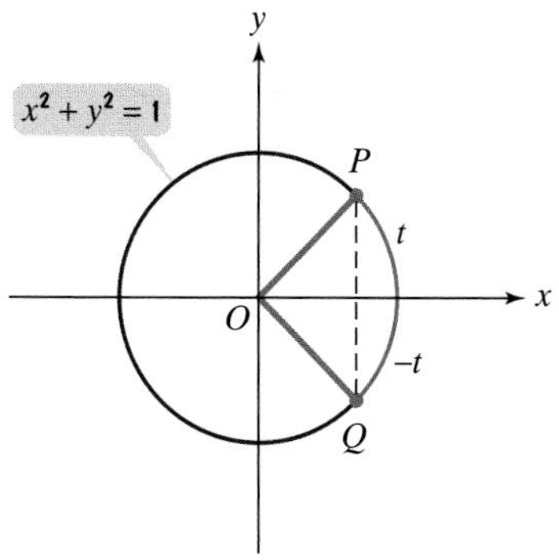

Figure 4.60

This shows that the cosine function is an even function. By contrast, the y-coordinates of P and Q are negatives of each other. Thus,

$$\sin(-t) = -\sin t.$$

This shows that the sine function is an odd function.

This argument is valid regardless of the length of t. Thus, the arc may terminate in any of the four quadrants or on any axis. Using the unit circle definition of the trigonometric functions, we obtain the following results:

Even and Odd Trigonometric Functions

The cosine and secant functions are *even.*

$$\cos(-t) = \cos t \qquad \sec(-t) = \sec t$$

The sine, cosecant, tangent, and cotangent functions are *odd.*

$$\sin(-t) = -\sin t \qquad \csc(-t) = -\csc t$$
$$\tan(-t) = -\tan t \qquad \cot(-t) = -\cot t$$

EXAMPLE 3 Using Even and Odd Functions to Find Exact Values

Find the exact value of each trigonometric function:

a. $\cos(-45°)$ **b.** $\tan\left(-\frac{\pi}{3}\right)$.

Solution

a. $\cos(-45°) = \cos 45° = \frac{\sqrt{2}}{2}$ **b.** $\tan\left(-\frac{\pi}{3}\right) = -\tan\frac{\pi}{3} = -\sqrt{3}$

Check Point 3 Find the exact value of each trigonometric function:

a. $\cos(-60°)$ **b.** $\tan\left(-\frac{\pi}{6}\right)$.

4 Use periodic properties.

Periodic Functions

Certain patterns in nature repeat again and again. For example, the ocean level at a beach varies from low tide to high tide and then back to low tide approximately every 12 hours. If low tide occurs at noon, then high tide will be around 6 P.M. and low tide will occur again around midnight, and so on infinitely. If $f(t)$ represents the ocean level at the beach at any time t, then the level is the same 12 hours later. Thus,

$$f(t + 12) = f(t).$$

The word *periodic* means that this tidal behavior repeats infinitely. The *period*, 12 hours, is the time it takes to complete one full cycle.

Definition of a Periodic Function

A function f is **periodic** if there exists a positive number p such that

$$f(t + p) = f(t)$$

for all t in the domain of f. The smallest positive number p for which f is periodic is called the **period** of f.

The trigonometric functions are used to model periodic phenomena. Why? If we begin at any point P on the unit circle and travel a distance of 2π units along the perimeter, we will return to the same point P. Because the trigonometric functions are defined in terms of the coordinates of that point P, we obtain the following results:

Periodic Properties of the Sine and Cosine Functions

$$\sin(t + 2\pi) = \sin t \quad \text{and} \quad \cos(t + 2\pi) = \cos t$$

The sine and cosine functions are periodic functions and have period 2π.

EXAMPLE 4 Using Periodic Properties to Find Exact Values

Find the exact value of each trigonometric function:

a. $\cos 420°$ **b.** $\sin \frac{9\pi}{4}$.

Solution

a. $\cos 420° = \cos(60° + 360°) = \cos 60° = \frac{1}{2}$

b. $\sin \frac{9\pi}{4} = \sin\left(\frac{\pi}{4} + 2\pi\right) = \sin \frac{\pi}{4} = \frac{\sqrt{2}}{2}$

Check Point 4 Find the exact value of each trigonometric function:

a. $\cos 405°$ **b.** $\sin \frac{7\pi}{3}$.

Like the sine and cosine functions, the secant and cosecant functions have period 2π. However, the tangent and cotangent functions have a smaller period. Figure 4.61 shows that if we begin at any point $P(x, y)$ on the unit circle and travel a distance of π units along the perimeter, we arrive at the point $Q(-x, -y)$. The tangent function, defined in terms of the coordinates of a point, is the same at (x, y) and $(-x, -y)$.

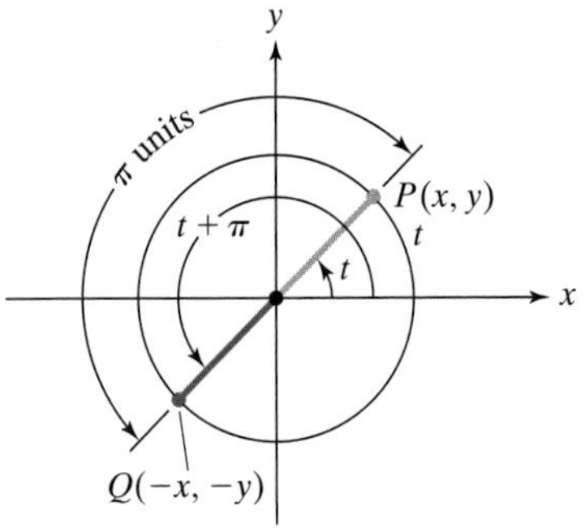

Figure 4.61 tan at P = tan at Q

Tangent function at (x, y) $\quad \frac{y}{x} = \frac{-y}{-x} \quad$ Tangent function π radians later

We see that $\tan(t + \pi) = \tan t$. The same observations apply to the cotangent function.

Periodic Properties of the Tangent and Cotangent Functions

$$\tan(t + \pi) = \tan t \quad \text{and} \quad \cot(t + \pi) = \cot t$$

The tangent and cotangent functions are periodic functions and have period π.

Why do the trigonometric functions model phenomena that repeat *indefinitely*? By starting at point P on the unit circle and traveling a distance of 2π units, 4π units, 6π units, and so on, we return to the starting point P. Because the trigonometric functions are defined in terms of the coordinates of that point P, if we add (or subtract) multiples of 2π to t, the values of the trigonometric functions of t do not change. Furthermore, the values for the tangent and cotangent functions of t do not change if we add (or subtract) multiples of π to t.

Repetitive Behavior of the Sine, Cosine, and Tangent Functions

For any integer n and real number t,

$$\sin(t + 2\pi n) = \sin t, \quad \cos(t + 2\pi n) = \cos t, \quad \text{and} \quad \tan(t + \pi n) = \tan t.$$

EXERCISE SET 4.4

Practice Exercises

In Exercises 1–4, a point $P(x, y)$ is shown on the unit circle corresponding to a real number t. Find the values of the trigonometric functions at t.

1.

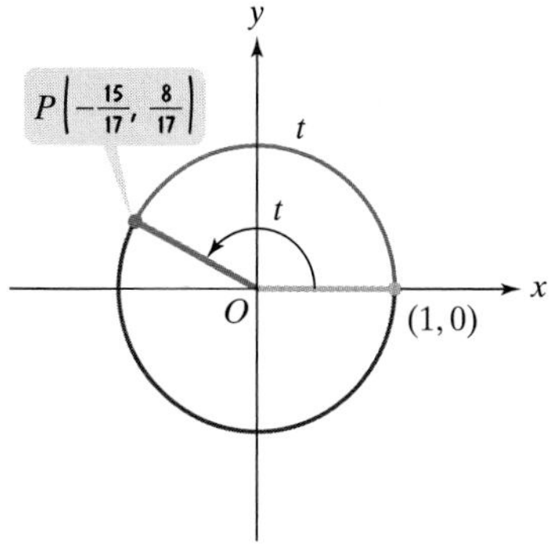

2.

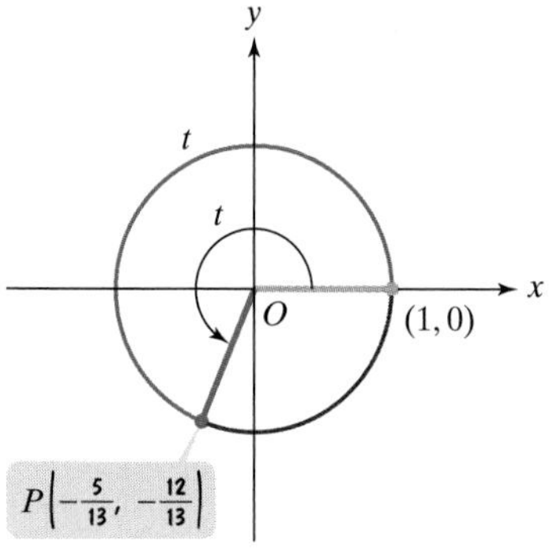

3.

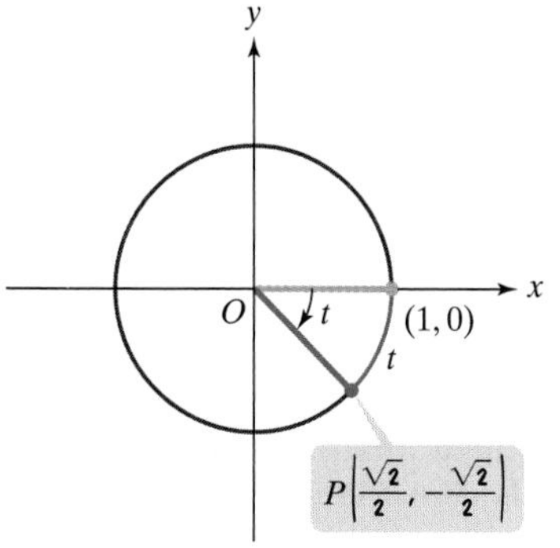

4.

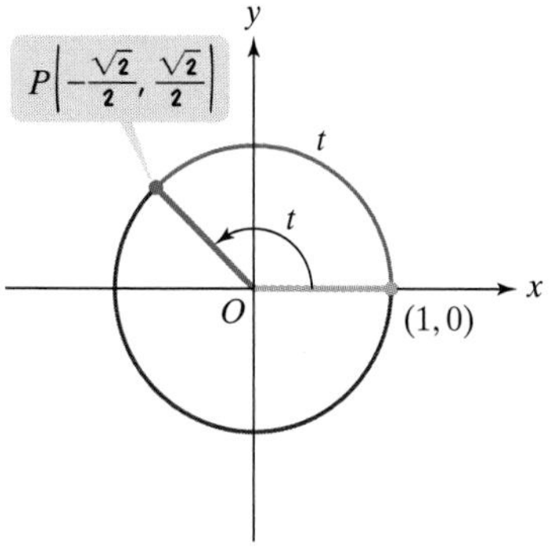

In Exercises 5–18, the unit circle has been divided into twelve equal arcs, corresponding to t-values of

$$0, \frac{\pi}{6}, \frac{\pi}{3}, \frac{\pi}{2}, \frac{2\pi}{3}, \frac{5\pi}{6}, \pi, \frac{7\pi}{6}, \frac{4\pi}{3}, \frac{3\pi}{2}, \frac{5\pi}{3}, \frac{11\pi}{6}, \text{ and } 2\pi.$$

Use the (x, y) coordinates in the figure to find the value of each trigonometric function at the indicated real number, t, or state that the expression is undefined.

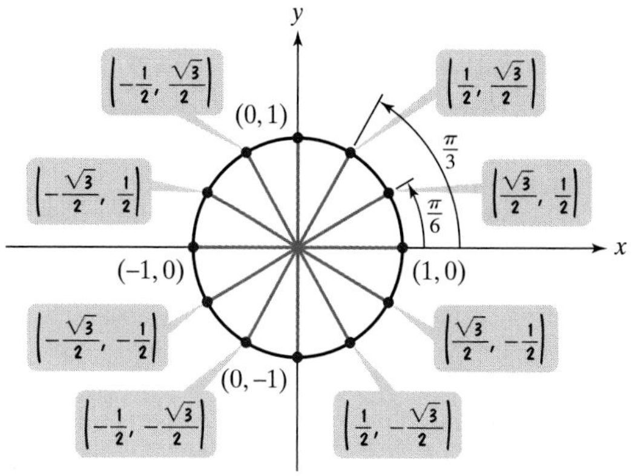

5. $\sin \frac{\pi}{6}$ **6.** $\sin \frac{\pi}{3}$ **7.** $\cos \frac{5\pi}{6}$

8. $\cos \frac{2\pi}{3}$ **9.** $\tan \pi$ **10.** $\tan 0$

11. $\csc \frac{7\pi}{6}$ **12.** $\csc \frac{4\pi}{3}$ **13.** $\sec \frac{11\pi}{6}$

14. $\sec \frac{5\pi}{3}$ **15.** $\sin \frac{3\pi}{2}$ **16.** $\cos \frac{3\pi}{2}$

17. $\sec \frac{3\pi}{2}$ **18.** $\tan \frac{3\pi}{2}$

In Exercises 19–24,

a. *Use the unit circle shown for Exercises 5–18 to find the value of the trigonometric function.*

b. *Use even and odd properties of trigonometric functions and your answer from part (a) to find the value of the same trigonometric function at the indicated real number.*

19. a. $\cos \frac{\pi}{6}$
b. $\cos\left(-\frac{\pi}{6}\right)$

20. a. $\cos \frac{\pi}{3}$
b. $\cos\left(-\frac{\pi}{3}\right)$

21. a. $\sin \frac{5\pi}{6}$
b. $\sin\left(-\frac{5\pi}{6}\right)$

22. a. $\sin \frac{2\pi}{3}$
b. $\sin\left(-\frac{2\pi}{3}\right)$

23. a. $\tan \frac{5\pi}{3}$
b. $\tan\left(-\frac{5\pi}{3}\right)$

24. a. $\tan \frac{11\pi}{6}$
b. $\tan\left(-\frac{11\pi}{6}\right)$

In Exercises 25–32, the unit circle has been divided into eight equal arcs, corresponding to t-values of

$$0, \frac{\pi}{4}, \frac{\pi}{2}, \frac{3\pi}{4}, \pi, \frac{5\pi}{4}, \frac{3\pi}{2}, \frac{7\pi}{4}, \text{ and } 2\pi.$$

a. *Use the (x, y) coordinates in the figure to find the value of the trigonometric function.*

b. *Use periodic properties and your answer from part (a) to find the value of the same trigonometric function at the indicated real number.*

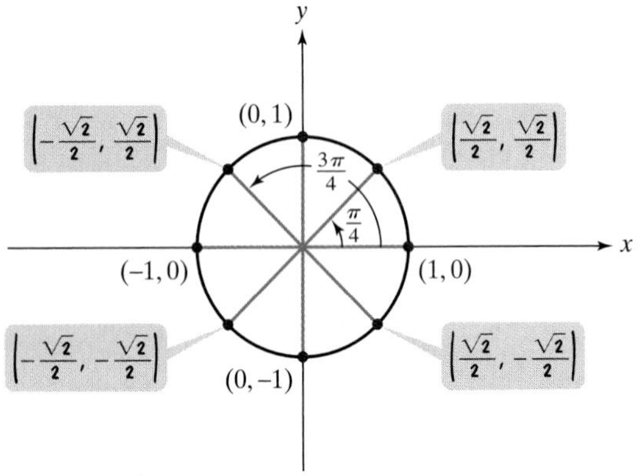

25. a. $\sin \frac{3\pi}{4}$ **b.** $\sin \frac{11\pi}{4}$

26. a. $\cos \frac{3\pi}{4}$ **b.** $\cos \frac{11\pi}{4}$

27. a. $\cos \frac{\pi}{2}$ **b.** $\cos \frac{9\pi}{2}$

28. a. $\sin \frac{\pi}{2}$ **b.** $\sin \frac{9\pi}{2}$

29. a. $\tan \pi$ **b.** $\tan 17\pi$

30. a. $\cot \frac{\pi}{2}$ **b.** $\cot \frac{15\pi}{2}$

31. a. $\sin \frac{7\pi}{4}$ **b.** $\sin \frac{47\pi}{4}$

32. a. $\cos \frac{7\pi}{4}$ **b.** $\cos \frac{47\pi}{4}$

Practice Plus

In Exercises 33–42, let

$$\sin t = a, \ \cos t = b, \text{ and } \tan t = c.$$

Write each expression in terms of a, b, and c.

33. $\sin(-t) - \sin t$

34. $\tan(-t) - \tan t$

35. $4\cos(-t) - \cos t$

36. $3\cos(-t) - \cos t$

37. $\sin(t + 2\pi) - \cos(t + 4\pi) + \tan(t + \pi)$

38. $\sin(t + 2\pi) + \cos(t + 4\pi) - \tan(t + \pi)$

39. $\sin(-t - 2\pi) - \cos(-t - 4\pi) - \tan(-t - \pi)$

40. $\sin(-t - 2\pi) + \cos(-t - 4\pi) - \tan(-t - \pi)$

41. $\cos t + \cos(t + 1000\pi) - \tan t - \tan(t + 999\pi) - \sin t + 4\sin(t - 1000\pi)$

42. $-\cos t + 7\cos(t + 1000\pi) + \tan t + \tan(t + 999\pi) + \sin t + \sin(t - 1000\pi)$

Application Exercises

43. The number of hours of daylight, H, on day t of any given year (on January 1, $t = 1$) in Fairbanks, Alaska, can be modeled by the function

$$H(t) = 12 + 8.3 \sin\left[\frac{2\pi}{365}(t - 80)\right].$$

a. March 21, the 80th day of the year, is the spring equinox. Find the number of hours of daylight in Fairbanks on this day.

b. June 21, the 172nd day of the year, is the summer solstice, the day with the maximum number of hours of daylight. To the nearest tenth of an hour, find the number of hours of daylight in Fairbanks on this day.

c. December 21, the 355th day of the year, is the winter solstice, the day with the minimum number of hours of daylight. Find, to the nearest tenth of an hour, the number of hours of daylight in Fairbanks on this day.

44. The number of hours of daylight, H, on day t of any given year (on January 1, $t = 1$) in San Diego, California, can be modeled by the function

$$H(t) = 12 + 2.4 \sin\left[\frac{2\pi}{365}(t - 80)\right].$$

a. March 21, the 80th day of the year, is the spring equinox. Find the number of hours of daylight in San Diego on this day.

b. June 21, the 172nd day of the year, is the summer solstice, the day with the maximum number of hours of daylight. Find, to the nearest tenth of an hour, the number of hours of daylight in San Diego on this day.

c. December 21, the 355th day of the year, is the winter solstice, the day with the minimum number of hours of daylight. To the nearest tenth of an hour, find the number of hours of daylight in San Diego on this day.

45. People who believe in biorhythms claim that there are three cycles that rule our behavior—the physical, emotional, and mental. Each is a sine function of a certain period. The function for our emotional fluctuations is

$$E = \sin \frac{\pi}{14} t,$$

where t is measured in days starting at birth. Emotional fluctuations, E, are measured from -1 to 1, inclusive, with 1 representing peak emotional well-being, -1 representing the low for emotional well-being, and 0 representing feeling neither emotionally high nor low.

a. Find E corresponding to $t = 7, 14, 21, 28$, and 35. Describe what you observe.

b. What is the period of the emotional cycle?

46. The height of the water, H, in feet, at a boat dock t hours after 6 A.M. is given by

$$H = 10 + 4 \sin \frac{\pi}{6} t.$$

a. Find the height of the water at the dock at 6 A.M., 9 A.M., noon, 6 P.M., midnight, and 3 A.M.

b. When is low tide and when is high tide?

c. What is the period of this function and what does this mean about the tides?

Writing in Mathematics

47. Why are the trigonometric functions sometimes called circular functions?
48. What is the range of the sine function? Use the unit circle to explain where this range comes from.
49. What do we mean by even trigonometric functions? Which of the six functions fall into this category?
50. What is a periodic function? Why are the sine and cosine functions periodic?
51. Explain how you can use the function for emotional fluctuations in Exercise 45 to determine good days for having dinner with your moody boss.
52. Describe a phenomenon that repeats infinitely. What is its period?

Critical Thinking Exercises

53. Find the exact value of
$\cos 0° + \cos 1° + \cos 2° + \cos 3° + \cdots + \cos 179° + \cos 180°$.
54. If $f(x) = \sin x$ and $f(a) = \frac{1}{4}$, find the value of

$$f(a) + f(a + 2\pi) + f(a + 4\pi) + f(a + 6\pi).$$

55. If $f(x) = \sin x$ and $f(a) = \frac{1}{4}$, find the value of $f(a) + 2f(-a)$.
56. The seats of a Ferris wheel are 40 feet from the wheel's center. When you get on the ride, your seat is 5 feet above the ground. How far above the ground are you after rotating through an angle of 765°? Round to the nearest foot.

CHAPTER 4 CHECK POINT

What You Know: We learned to use radians to measure angles: One radian (approximately 57°) is the measure of the central angle that intercepts an arc equal in length to the radius of the circle. Using $180° = \pi$ radians, we converted degrees to radians (multiply by $\frac{\pi}{180°}$) and radians to degrees (multiply by $\frac{180°}{\pi}$). We defined the six trigonometric functions using right triangles, angles in standard position, and coordinates of points along the unit circle. Evaluating trigonometric functions using reference angles involved connecting a number of concepts, including finding coterminal and reference angles, locating special angles, determining the signs of the trigonometric functions in specific quadrants, and finding the function values at special angles. Use the important Study Tip on page 381 as a reference sheet to help connect these concepts.

In Exercises 1–2, convert each angle in degrees to radians. Express your answer as a multiple of π.

1. 10°
2. −105°

In Exercises 3–4, convert each angle in radians to degrees.

3. $\frac{5\pi}{12}$
4. $-\frac{13\pi}{20}$

In Exercises 5–7,

a. *Find a positive angle less than 360° or 2π that is coterminal with the given angle.*

b. *Draw the given angle in standard position.*

c. *Find the reference angle for the given angle.*

5. $\frac{11\pi}{3}$
6. $-\frac{19\pi}{4}$
7. 510°

8. Use the triangle to find each of the six trigonometric functions of θ.

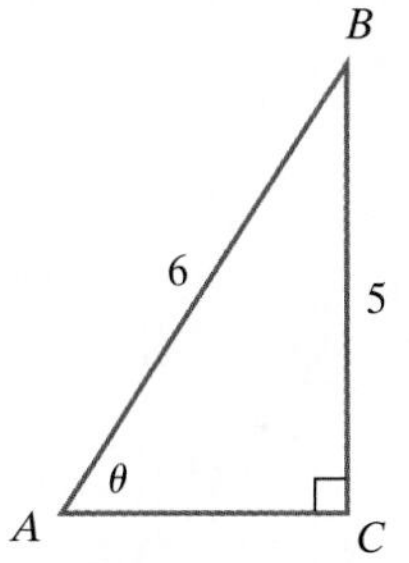

9. Use the point on the terminal side of θ to find each of the six trigonometric functions of θ.

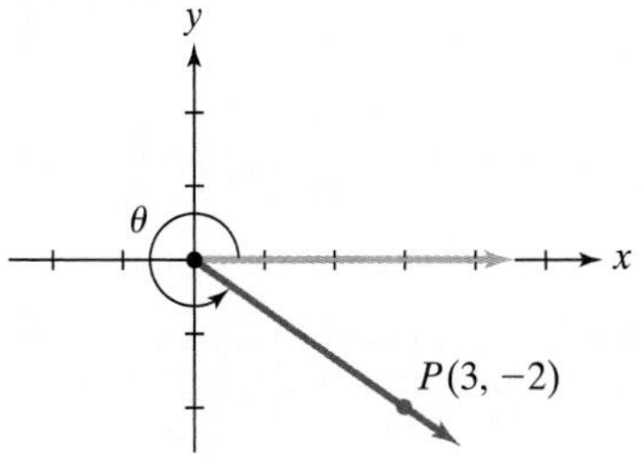

10. Use the point shown on the unit circle to find each of the six trigonometric functions at t.

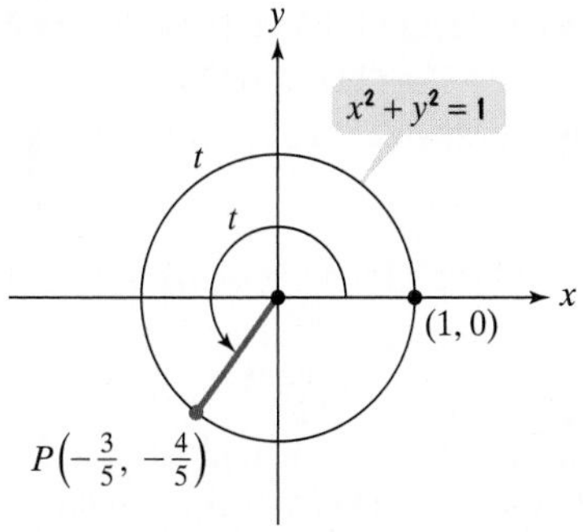

In Exercises 11–12, find the exact value of the remaining trigonometric functions of θ.

11. $\tan\theta = -\frac{3}{4}$, $\cos\theta < 0$ **12.** $\cos\theta = \frac{3}{7}$, $\sin\theta < 0$

In Exercises 13–14, find the measure of the side of the right triangle whose length is designated by a lowercase letter. Round the answer to the nearest whole number.

13.

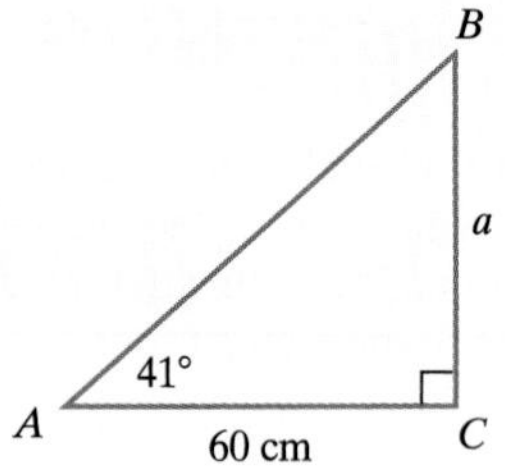

14.

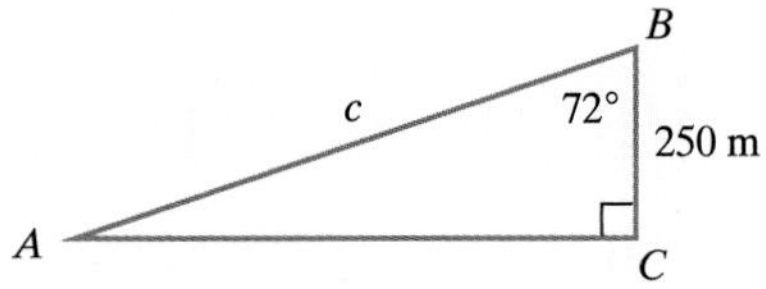

15. If $\cos\theta = \frac{1}{6}$ and θ is acute, find $\cot\left(\frac{\pi}{2} - \theta\right)$.

In Exercises 16–26, find the exact value of each expression. Do not use a calculator.

16. $\tan 30°$

17. $\cot 120°$

18. $\cos 240°$

19. $\sec\frac{11\pi}{6}$

20. $\sin^2\frac{\pi}{7} + \cos^2\frac{\pi}{7}$

21. $\sin\left(-\frac{2\pi}{3}\right)$

22. $\csc\left(\frac{22\pi}{3}\right)$

23. $\cos 495°$

24. $\tan\left(-\frac{17\pi}{6}\right)$

25. $\sin^2\frac{\pi}{2} - \cos\pi$

26. $\cos\left(\frac{5\pi}{6} + 2\pi n\right) + \tan\left(\frac{5\pi}{6} + n\pi\right)$, n is an integer.

27. A circle has a radius of 40 centimeters. Find the length of the arc intercepted by a central angle of 36°. Express the answer in terms of π. Then round to two decimal places.

28. A merry-go-round makes 8 revolutions per minute. Find the linear speed, in feet per minute, of a horse 10 feet from the center. Express the answer in terms of π. Then round to one decimal place.

29. A plane takes off at an angle of 6°. After traveling for one mile, or 5280 feet, along this flight path, find the plane's height, to the nearest tenth of a foot, above the ground.

30. A tree that is 50 feet tall casts a shadow that is 60 feet long. Find the angle of elevation, to the nearest degree, of the sun.

Chapter 4 Summary, Review, and Test

Summary

DEFINITIONS AND CONCEPTS	EXAMPLES
4.1 *Angles and Radian Measure*	
a. An angle consists of two rays with a common endpoint, the vertex.	
b. An angle is in standard position if its vertex is at the origin and its initial side lies along the positive x-axis. Figure 4.3 on page 341 shows positive and negative angles in standard position.	
c. A quadrantal angle is an angle with its terminal side on the x-axis or the y-axis.	
d. Angles can be measured in degrees. 1° is $\frac{1}{360}$ of a complete rotation.	
e. Acute angles measure more than 0° but less than 90°, right angles 90°, obtuse angles more than 90° but less than 180°, and straight angles 180°.	Figure 4.5, p. 341
f. Angles can be measured in radians. One radian is the measure of the central angle when the intercepted arc and radius have the same length. In general, the radian measure of a central angle is the length of the intercepted arc divided by the circle's radius: $\theta = \frac{s}{r}$.	Ex. 1, p. 343
g. To convert from degrees to radians, multiply degrees by $\frac{\pi \text{ radians}}{180°}$. To convert from radians to degrees, multiply radians by $\frac{180°}{\pi \text{ radians}}$.	Ex. 2, p. 344; Ex. 3, p. 344
h. To draw angles measured in radians in standard position, it is helpful to "think in radians" without having to convert to degrees. See Figure 4.15 on page 347.	Ex. 4, p. 345

DEFINITIONS AND CONCEPTS | **EXAMPLES**

i. Two angles with the same initial and terminal sides are called coterminal angles. Increasing or decreasing an angle's measure by integer multiples of 360° or 2π produces coterminal angles. — Ex. 5, p. 348; Ex. 6, p. 349; Ex. 7, p. 349

j. The arc length formula, $s = r\theta$, is described in the box on page 350. — Ex. 8, p. 350

k. The definitions of linear speed, $v = \frac{s}{t}$, and angular speed, $\omega = \frac{\theta}{t}$, are given in the box on page 351.

l. Linear speed is expressed in terms of angular speed by $v = r\omega$, where v is the linear speed of a point a distance r from the center of rotation and ω is the angular speed in radians per unit of time. — Ex. 9, p. 352

4.2 Right Triangle Trigonometry

a. The right triangle definitions of the six trigonometric functions are given in the box on page 356. — Ex. 1, p. 357; Ex. 2, p. 357

b. Function values for 30°, 45°, and 60° can be obtained using these special triangles. — Ex. 3, p. 358; Ex. 4, p. 359

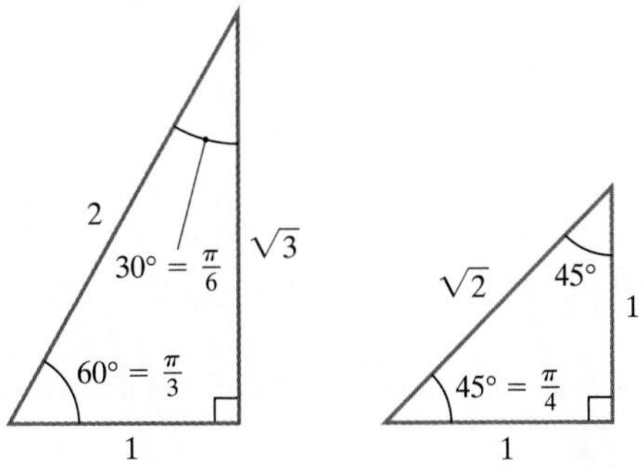

c. Fundamental Identities — Ex. 5, p. 360; Ex. 6, p. 362

1. Reciprocal Identities

$$\sin\theta = \frac{1}{\csc\theta} \text{ and } \csc\theta = \frac{1}{\sin\theta};\ \cos\theta = \frac{1}{\sec\theta} \text{ and } \sec\theta = \frac{1}{\cos\theta};\ \tan\theta = \frac{1}{\cot\theta} \text{ and } \cot\theta = \frac{1}{\tan\theta}$$

2. Quotient Identities

$$\tan\theta = \frac{\sin\theta}{\cos\theta};\ \cot\theta = \frac{\cos\theta}{\sin\theta}$$

3. Pythagorean Identities

$$\sin^2\theta + \cos^2\theta = 1;\ 1 + \tan^2\theta = \sec^2\theta;\ 1 + \cot^2\theta = \csc^2\theta$$

d. Two angles are complements if their sum is 90° or $\frac{\pi}{2}$. The value of a trigonometric function of θ is equal to the cofunction of the complement of θ. Cofunction identities are listed in the box on page 362. — Ex. 7, p. 363

4.3 Trigonometric Functions of Any Angle

a. Definitions of the trigonometric functions of any angle are given in the box on page 371. — Ex. 1, p. 371; Ex. 2, p. 372

b. Signs of the trigonometric functions: All functions are positive in quadrant I. If θ lies in quadrant II, $\sin\theta$ and $\csc\theta$ are positive. If θ lies in quadrant III, $\tan\theta$ and $\cot\theta$ are positive. If θ lies in quadrant IV, $\cos\theta$ and $\sec\theta$ are positive. — Ex. 3, p. 374; Ex. 4, p. 374

c. If θ is a nonacute angle in standard position that lies in a quadrant, its reference angle is the positive acute angle θ' formed by the terminal side of θ and the x-axis. The reference angle for a given angle can be found by making a sketch that shows the angle in standard position. Figure 4.40 on page 375 shows reference angles for θ in quadrants II, III, and IV. — Ex. 5, p. 375; Ex. 6, p. 376

DEFINITIONS AND CONCEPTS	EXAMPLES
d. The values of the trigonometric functions of a given angle are the same as the values of the functions of the reference angle, except possibly for the sign. A procedure for using reference angles to evaluate trigonometric functions is given in the lower box on page 377.	Ex. 7, p. 377; Ex. 8, p. 379

4.4 Trigonometric Functions of Real Numbers; Periodic Functions

a. Definitions of the trigonometric functions in terms of a unit circle are given in the box on page 384.	Ex. 1, p. 384; Ex. 2, p. 385
b. The cosine and secant functions are even: $\cos(-t) = \cos t,\quad \sec(-t) = \sec t.$ The other trigonometric functions are odd: $\sin(-t) = -\sin t,\quad \csc(-t) = -\csc t,$ $\tan(-t) = -\tan t,\quad \cot(-t) = -\cot t.$	Ex. 3, p. 387
c. If $f(t + p) = f(t)$, the function f is periodic. The smallest p for which $f(t + p) = f(t)$ is the period of f. The tangent and cotangent functions have period π. The other four trigonometric functions have period 2π.	Ex. 4, p. 388

Study Tip

- Study Tip on page 381, showing special angles and how to obtain exact values of trigonometric functions at these angles

Review Exercises

4.1

1. Find the radian measure of the central angle of a circle of radius 6 centimeters that intercepts an arc of length 27 centimeters.

In Exercises 2–4, convert each angle in degrees to radians. Express your answer as a multiple of π.

2. $15°$ **3.** $120°$ **4.** $315°$

In Exercises 5–7, convert each angle in radians to degrees.

5. $\frac{5\pi}{3}$ **6.** $\frac{7\pi}{5}$ **7.** $-\frac{5\pi}{6}$

In Exercises 8–12, draw each angle in standard position.

8. $\frac{5\pi}{6}$ **9.** $-\frac{2\pi}{3}$ **10.** $\frac{8\pi}{3}$

11. $190°$ **12.** $-135°$

In Exercises 13–17, find a positive angle less than $360°$ or 2π that is coterminal with the given angle.

13. $400°$ **14.** $-445°$ **15.** $\frac{13\pi}{4}$

16. $\frac{31\pi}{6}$ **17.** $-\frac{8\pi}{3}$

18. Find the length of the arc on a circle of radius 10 feet intercepted by a $135°$ central angle. Express arc length in terms of π. Then round your answer to two decimal places.

19. The angular speed of a propeller on a wind generator is 10.3 revolutions per minute. Express this angular speed in radians per minute.

20. The propeller of an airplane has a radius of 3 feet. The propeller is rotating at 2250 revolutions per minute. Find the linear speed, in feet per minute, of the tip of the propeller.

4.2

21. Use the triangle to find each of the six trigonometric functions of θ.

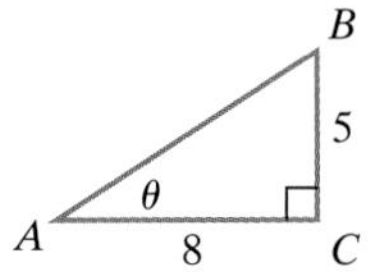

In Exercises 22–25, find the exact value of each expression. Do not use a calculator.

22. $\sin\frac{\pi}{6} + \tan^2\frac{\pi}{3}$ **23.** $\cos^2\frac{\pi}{4} - \tan^2\frac{\pi}{4}$

24. $\sec^2\frac{\pi}{5} - \tan^2\frac{\pi}{5}$ **25.** $\cos\frac{2\pi}{9}\sec\frac{2\pi}{9}$

26. If θ is an acute angle and $\sin\theta = \frac{2\sqrt{7}}{7}$, use the identity $\sin^2\theta + \cos^2\theta = 1$ to find $\cos\theta$.

In Exercises 27–28, find a cofunction with the same value as the given expression.

27. $\sin 70°$ **28.** $\cos\frac{\pi}{2}$

In Exercises 29–31, find the measure of the side of the right triangle whose length is designated by a lowercase letter. Round answers to the nearest whole number.

29.

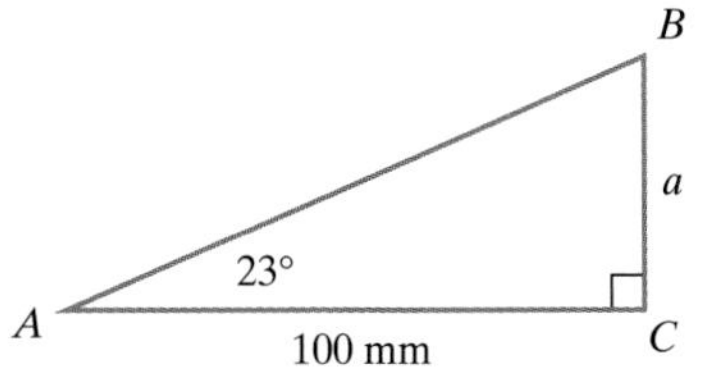

30.

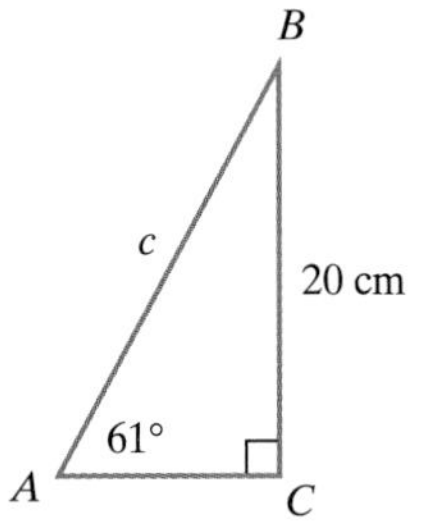

31.

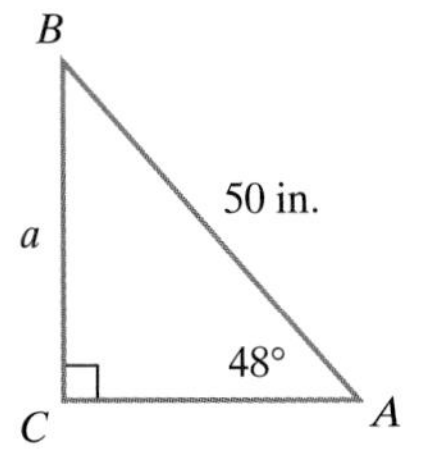

32. If $\sin\theta = \frac{1}{4}$ and θ is acute, find $\tan\left(\frac{\pi}{2} - \theta\right)$.

33. A hiker climbs for a half mile up a slope whose inclination is 17°. How many feet of altitude, to the nearest foot, does the hiker gain?

34. To find the distance across a lake, a surveyor took the measurements in the figure shown. What is the distance across the lake? Round to the nearest meter.

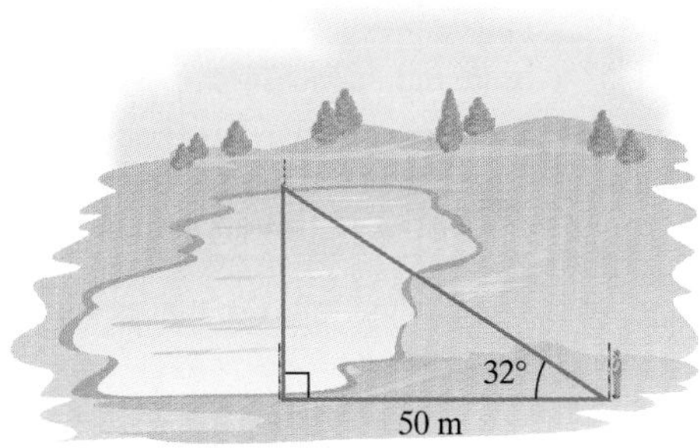

35. When a six-foot pole casts a four-foot shadow, what is the angle of elevation of the sun? Round to the nearest whole degree.

4.3 and 4.4

In Exercises 36–37, a point on the terminal side of angle θ is given. Find the exact value of each of the six trigonometric functions of θ, or state that the function is undefined.

36. $(-1, -5)$ **37.** $(0, -1)$

In Exercises 38–39, let θ be an angle in standard position. Name the quadrant in which θ lies.

38. $\tan\theta > 0$ and $\sec\theta > 0$

39. $\tan\theta > 0$ and $\cos\theta < 0$

In Exercises 40–42, find the exact value of each of the remaining trigonometric functions of θ.

40. $\cos\theta = \frac{2}{5}$, $\sin\theta < 0$ **41.** $\tan\theta = -\frac{1}{3}$, $\sin\theta > 0$

42. $\cot\theta = 3$, $\cos\theta < 0$

In Exercises 43–47, find the reference angle for each angle.

43. $265°$ **44.** $\frac{5\pi}{8}$ **45.** $-410°$

46. $\frac{17\pi}{6}$ **47.** $-\frac{11\pi}{3}$

In Exercises 48–58, find the exact value of each expression. Do not use a calculator.

48. $\sin 240°$ **49.** $\tan 120°$ **50.** $\sec\frac{7\pi}{4}$

51. $\cos\frac{11\pi}{6}$ **52.** $\cot(-210°)$ **53.** $\csc\left(-\frac{2\pi}{3}\right)$

54. $\sin\left(-\frac{\pi}{3}\right)$ **55.** $\sin 495°$ **56.** $\tan\frac{13\pi}{4}$

57. $\sin\frac{22\pi}{3}$ **58.** $\cos\left(-\frac{35\pi}{6}\right)$

Chapter 4 Test

1. Convert 135° to exact radian measure.
2. Find the length of the arc on a circle of radius 20 feet intercepted by a 75° central angle. Express arc length in terms of π. Then round your answer to two decimal places.
3. **a.** Find a positive angle less than 2π that is coterminal with $\frac{16\pi}{3}$.
   b. Find the reference angle for $\frac{16\pi}{3}$.
4. If $(-2, 5)$ is a point on the terminal side of angle θ, find the exact value of each of the six trigonometric functions of θ.
5. Determine the quadrant in which θ lies if $\cos\theta < 0$ and $\cot\theta > 0$.
6. If $\cos\theta = \frac{1}{3}$ and $\tan\theta < 0$, find the exact value of each of the remaining trigonometric functions of θ.

In Exercises 7–12, find the exact value of each expression. Do not use a calculator.

7. $\tan\frac{\pi}{6}\cos\frac{\pi}{3} - \cos\frac{\pi}{2}$
8. $\tan 300°$
9. $\sin\frac{7\pi}{4}$
10. $\sec\frac{22\pi}{3}$
11. $\cot\left(-\frac{8\pi}{3}\right)$
12. $\tan\left(\frac{7\pi}{3} + n\pi\right)$, n is an integer.
13. If $\sin\theta = a$ and $\cos\theta = b$, represent each of the following in terms of a and b.
    a. $\sin(-\theta) + \cos(-\theta)$ **b.** $\tan\theta - \sec\theta$

Cumulative Review Exercises (Chapters 1–4)

Solve each equation or inequality in Exercises 1–5.

1. $x^2 = 18 + 3x$
2. $x^3 + 5x^2 - 4x - 20 = 0$
3. $\sqrt{x - 3} + 5 = x$
4. $|2x - 5| \leq 11$
5. Convert $\frac{14\pi}{9}$ radians to degrees.

In Exercise 6, graph the equation.

6. $(x - 2)^2 + y^2 = 1$
7. You invest in a new play. The cost includes an overhead of \$30,000, plus production costs of \$2500 per performance. A sold-out performance brings you \$3125. How many sold-out performances must be played in order for you to break even?

Answers to Selected Exercises

CHAPTER P

Section P.1

Check Point Exercises

1. 608 **2.** 2311; The formula models the data quite well. **3.** $\{3, 7\}$ **4.** $\{3, 4, 5, 6, 7, 8, 9\}$ **5. a.** $\sqrt{9}$ **b.** $0, \sqrt{9}$ **c.** $-9, 0, \sqrt{9}$ **d.** $-9, -1.3, 0, 0.\overline{3}, \sqrt{9}$ **e.** $\frac{\pi}{2}, \sqrt{10}$ **f.** $-9, -1.3, 0, 0.\overline{3}, \frac{\pi}{2}, \sqrt{9}, \sqrt{10}$ **6. a.** $\sqrt{2} - 1$ **b.** $\pi - 3$ **c.** 1 **7.** 9 **8.** $38x^2 + 23x$ **9.** $42 - 4x$

Exercise Set P.1

1. 57 **3.** 10 **5.** 88 **7.** 10 **9.** 44 **11.** 46 **13.** 10 **15.** -8 **17.** 10°C **19.** 60 ft **21.** $\{2, 4\}$ **23.** $\{s, e, t\}$ **25.** $\varnothing$ **27.** $\varnothing$ **29.** $\{1, 2, 3, 4, 5\}$ **31.** $\{1, 2, 3, 4, 5, 6, 7, 8, 10\}$ **33.** $\{a, e, i, o, u\}$ **35. a.** $\sqrt{100}$ **b.** $0, \sqrt{100}$ **c.** $-9, 0, \sqrt{100}$ **d.** $-9, -\frac{4}{5}, 0, 0.25, 9.2, \sqrt{100}$ **e.** $\sqrt{3}$ **f.** $-9, -\frac{4}{5}, 0, 0.25, \sqrt{3}, 9.2, \sqrt{100}$ **37. a.** $\sqrt{64}$ **b.** $0, \sqrt{64}$ **c.** $-11, 0, \sqrt{64}$ **d.** $-11, -\frac{5}{6}, 0, 0.75, \sqrt{64}$ **e.** $\sqrt{5}, \pi$ **f.** $-11, -\frac{5}{6}, 0, 0.75, \sqrt{5}, \pi, \sqrt{64}$ **39.** 0 **41.** Answers may vary. **43.** true **45.** true **47.** true **49.** true **51.** 300 **53.** $12 - \pi$ **55.** $5 - \sqrt{2}$ **57.** -1 **59.** 4 **61.** 3 **63.** 7 **65.** -1 **67.** $|17 - 2|; 15$ **69.** $|5 - (-2)|; 7$ **71.** $|-4 - (-19)|; 15$ **73.** $|-1.4 - (-3.6)|; 2.2$ **75.** commutative property of addition **77.** associative property of addition **79.** commutative property of addition **81.** distributive property of multiplication over addition **83.** inverse property of multiplication **85.** $15x + 16$ **87.** $27x - 10$ **89.** $29y - 29$ **91.** $8y - 12$ **93.** $16y - 25$ **95.** $12x^2 + 11$ **97.** $14x$ **99.** $-2x + 3y + 6$ **101.** x **103.** $>$ **105.** $=$ **107.** $<$ **109.** $=$ **111.** $x - (x + 4); -4$ **113.** $6(-5x); -30x$ **115.** $5x - 2x; 3x$ **117.** $8x - (3x + 6); 5x - 6$ **119.** 313; very well **121.** 522 **123.** Model 3 **125.** Model 3 **127. a.** $1200 - 0.07x$ **b.** \$780 **141.** d **143.** $>$ **145. a.** \$50.50, \$5.50, \$1.00 **b.** no

Section P.2

Check Point Exercises

1. a. 3^5 or 243 **b.** $40x^5y^{10}$ **2. a.** $(-3)^3$ or -27 **b.** $9x^{11}y^3$ **3. a.** $\frac{1}{25}$ **b.** $-\frac{1}{27}$ **c.** 16 **d.** $\frac{3y^4}{x^6}$ **4. a.** 3^6 or 729 **b.** $\frac{1}{y^{14}}$ **c.** b^{12} **5.** $-64x^3$ **6. a.** $-\frac{32}{y^5}$ **b.** $\frac{x^{15}}{27}$ **7. a.** $16x^{12}y^{24}$ **b.** $-18x^3y^8$ **c.** $\frac{5y^6}{x^4}$ **d.** $\frac{y^8}{25x^2}$ **8. a.** $-2{,}600{,}000{,}000$ **b.** 0.000003017 **9. a.** 5.21×10^9 **b.** -6.893×10^{-8} **10.** 4.1×10^9 **11.** a. 3.55×10^{-1} **b.** 4×10^8 **12.** \$7,014

Exercise Set P.2

1. 50 **3.** 64 **5.** -64 **7.** 1 **9.** -1 **11.** $\frac{1}{64}$ **13.** 32 **15.** 64 **17.** 16 **19.** $\frac{1}{9}$ **21.** $\frac{1}{16}$ **23.** $\frac{y}{x^2}$ **25.** y^5 **27.** x^{10} **29.** x^5 **31.** x^{21} **33.** $\frac{1}{x^{15}}$ **35.** x^7 **37.** x^{21} **39.** $64x^6$ **41.** $-\frac{64}{x^3}$ **43.** $9x^4y^{10}$ **45.** $6x^{11}$ **47.** $18x^9y^5$ **49.** $4x^{16}$ **51.** $-5a^{11}b$ **53.** $\frac{2}{b^7}$ **55.** $\frac{1}{16x^6}$ **57.** $\frac{3y^{14}}{4x^4}$ **59.** $\frac{y^2}{25x^6}$ **61.** $-\frac{27b^{15}}{a^{18}}$ **63.** 1 **65.** 380 **67.** 0.0006 **69.** $-7{,}160{,}000$ **71.** 0.79 **73.** -0.00415 **75.** $-60{,}000{,}100{,}000$ **77.** 3.2×10^4 **79.** 6.38×10^{17} **81.** -5.716×10^3 **83.** 2.7×10^{-3} **85.** -5.04×10^{-9} **87.** 6.3×10^7 **89.** 6.4×10^4 **91.** 1.22×10^{-11} **93.** 2.67×10^{13} **95.** 2.1×10^3 **97.** 4×10^5 **99.** 2×10^{-8} **101.** 5×10^3 **103.** 4×10^{15} **105.** 9×10^{-3} **107.** 1 **109.** $\frac{y}{16x^8z^6}$ **111.** $\frac{1}{x^{12}y^{16}z^{20}}$ **113.** $\frac{x^{18}y^6}{4}$ **115.** 6.26×10^7 people **117.** 9.63×10^7 people **119.** approximately 68 hot dogs per person **121.** $2.5 \times 10^2 = 250$ chickens **123.** approximately \$23,448 **133.** b **135.** $A = C + D$

Section P.3

Check Point Exercises

1. a. 9 **b.** -3 **c.** $\frac{1}{5}$ **d.** 10 **e.** 14 **2. a.** $5\sqrt{3}$ **b.** $5x\sqrt{2}$ **3. a.** $\frac{5}{4}$ **b.** $5x\sqrt{3}$ **4. a.** $17\sqrt{13}$ **b.** $-19\sqrt{17x}$ **5. a.** $17\sqrt{3}$ **b.** $10\sqrt{2x}$ **6. a.** $\frac{5\sqrt{3}}{3}$ **b.** $\sqrt{3}$ **7.** $\frac{32 - 8\sqrt{5}}{11}$ **8. a.** $2\sqrt[3]{5}$ **b.** $2\sqrt[5]{2}$ **c.** $\frac{5}{3}$ **9.** $5\sqrt[3]{3}$ **10. a.** 5 **b.** 2 **c.** -3 **d.** -2 **e.** $\frac{1}{3}$ **11. a.** 81 **b.** 8 **c.** $\frac{1}{4}$ **12. a.** $10x^4$ **b.** $4x^{5/2}$ **13.** $\sqrt{x}$

Exercise Set P.3

1. 6 **3.** -6 **5.** not a real number **7.** 3 **9.** 1 **11.** 13 **13.** $5\sqrt{2}$ **15.** $3|x|\sqrt{5}$ **17.** $2x\sqrt{3}$ **19.** $x\sqrt{x}$ **21.** $2x\sqrt{3x}$ **23.** $\frac{1}{9}$ **25.** $\frac{7}{4}$ **27.** $4x$ **29.** $5x\sqrt{2x}$ **31.** $2x^2\sqrt{5}$ **33.** $13\sqrt{3}$ **35.** $-2\sqrt{17x}$ **37.** $5\sqrt{2}$ **39.** $3\sqrt{2x}$ **41.** $34\sqrt{2}$ **43.** $20\sqrt{2} - 5\sqrt{3}$ **45.** $\frac{\sqrt{7}}{7}$ **47.** $\frac{\sqrt{10}}{5}$ **49.** $\frac{13(3 - \sqrt{11})}{-2}$ **51.** $7(\sqrt{5} + 2)$ **53.** $3(\sqrt{5} - \sqrt{3})$ **55.** 5 **57.** -2 **59.** not a real number **61.** 3

63. -3 **65.** $-\frac{1}{2}$ **67.** $2\sqrt[3]{4}$ **69.** $x\sqrt[3]{x}$ **71.** $3\sqrt[3]{2}$ **73.** $2x$ **75.** $7\sqrt[5]{2}$ **77.** $13\sqrt[3]{2}$ **79.** $-y\sqrt[3]{2x}$ **81.** $\sqrt{2}+2$ **83.** 6
85. 2 **87.** 25 **89.** $\frac{1}{16}$ **91.** $14x^{7/12}$ **93.** $4x^{1/4}$ **95.** x^2 **97.** $5x^2|y|^3$ **99.** $27y^{2/3}$ **101.** $\sqrt{5}$ **103.** x^2 **105.** $\sqrt[3]{x^2}$
107. $\sqrt[3]{x^2y}$ **109.** 3 **111.** $\frac{x^2}{7y^{3/2}}$ **113.** $\frac{x^3}{y^2}$ **115.** $6\sqrt{3}$ miles; 10.4 miles **117.** 70 mph; He was speeding.
119. $\frac{7\sqrt{2\cdot 2\cdot 3}}{6}=\frac{7\cdot 2\sqrt{3}}{6}=\frac{14\sqrt{3}}{6}=\frac{7\sqrt{3}}{3}=\frac{7}{3}\sqrt{3}$ **121. a.** $C=35.74+0.6215t-35.74v^{4/25}+0.4275tv^{4/25}$ **b.** 8°F
123. $P=18\sqrt{5}$ ft; $A=100$ sq ft **133.** d **135.** Let □ = 25 and □ = 14. **137. a.** $>$ **b.** $>$

Section P.4

Check Point Exercises

1. a. $-x^3+x^2-8x-20$ **b.** $20x^3-11x^2-2x-8$ **2.** $15x^3-31x^2+30x-8$ **3.** $28x^2-41x+15$ **4. a.** $49x^2-64$ **b.** $4y^6-25$
5. a. $x^2+20x+100$ **b.** $25x^2+40x+16$ **6. a.** $x^2-18x+81$ **b.** $49x^2-42x+9$ **7.** $2x^2y+5xy^2-2y^3$ **8. a.** $21x^2-25xy+6y^2$
b. $4x^2+16xy+16y^2$

Exercise Set P.4

1. yes; $3x^2+2x-5$ **3.** no **5.** 2 **7.** 4 **9.** $11x^3+7x^2-12x-4$; 3 **11.** $12x^3+4x^2+12x-14$; 3 **13.** $6x^2-6x+2$; 2
15. x^3+1 **17.** $2x^3-9x^2+19x-15$ **19.** $x^2+10x+21$ **21.** $x^2-2x-15$ **23.** $6x^2+13x+5$ **25.** $10x^2-9x-9$
27. $15x^4-47x^2+28$ **29.** $8x^5-40x^3+3x^2-15$ **31.** x^2-9 **33.** $9x^2-4$ **35.** $25-49x^2$ **37.** $16x^4-25x^2$ **39.** $1-y^{10}$
41. x^2+4x+4 **43.** $4x^2+12x+9$ **45.** x^2-6x+9 **47.** $16x^4-8x^2+1$ **49.** $4x^2-28x+49$ **51.** x^3+3x^2+3x+1
53. $8x^3+36x^2+54x+27$ **55.** $x^3-9x^2+27x-27$ **57.** $27x^3-108x^2+144x-64$ **59.** $7x^2y-4xy$ is of degree 3
61. $2x^2y+13xy+13$ is of degree 3 **63.** $-5x^3+8xy-9y^2$ is of degree 3 **65.** $x^4y^2+8x^3y+y-6x$ is of degree 6
67. $7x^2+38xy+15y^2$ **69.** $2x^2+xy-21y^2$ **71.** $15x^2y^2+xy-2$ **73.** $49x^2+70xy+25y^2$ **75.** $x^4y^4-6x^2y^2+9$
77. x^3-y^3 **79.** $9x^2-25y^2$ **81.** $49x^2y^4-100y^2$ **83.** $48xy$ **85.** $-9x^2+3x+9$ **87.** $16x^4-625$ **89.** $4x^2-28x+49$
91. Model 4; $0.01x^3+0.09x^2+1.1x+5.64$ **93.** Model 1 **95.** very well **97.** $4x^3-36x^2+80x$ **99.** $6x+22$
109. $49x^2+70x+25-16y^2$ **111.** $6x^n-13$

Mid-Chapter P Check Point

1. $12x^2-x-35$ **2.** $-x+12$ **3.** $10\sqrt{6}$ **4.** $3\sqrt{3}$ **5.** $x+45$ **6.** $6x^2-48x+9$ **7.** $\frac{x^2}{y^3}$ **8.** $\frac{3}{4}$ **9.** $-x^2+5x-6$
10. $2x^3-11x^2+17x-5$ **11.** $-x^6+2x^3$ **12.** $18a^2-11ab-10b^2$ **13.** $\{a, c, d, e, f, h\}$ **14.** $\{c, d\}$ **15.** $5x^2y^3+2xy-y^2$
16. $-\frac{12y^{15}}{x^3}$ **17.** $\frac{6y^3}{x^7}$ **18.** $|\sqrt[3]{x}|$ **19.** 1.2×10^{-2} **20.** $2\sqrt[3]{2}$ **21.** x^6-4 **22.** x^4+4x^2+4 **23.** $10\sqrt{3}$
24. $\frac{77+11\sqrt{3}}{46}$ **25.** $\frac{11\sqrt{3}}{3}$ **26.** $-11, -\frac{3}{7}, 0, 0.45, \sqrt{25}$ **27.** $\sqrt{13}-2$ **28.** $-x^3$ **29.** $\$3.48\times10^{10}$ **30.** 4 times
31. a. Model 3 **b.** \$1001 million, or \$1,001,000,000

Section P.5

Check Point Exercises

1. a. $2x^2(5x-2)$ **b.** $(x-7)(2x+3)$ **2.** $(x+5)(x^2-2)$ **3. a.** $(x+8)(x+5)$ **b.** $(x-7)(x+2)$ **4.** $(3x-1)(2x+7)$
5. $(3x-y)(x-4y)$ **6. a.** $(x+9)(x-9)$ **b.** $(6x+5)(6x-5)$ **7.** $(9x^2+4)(3x+2)(3x-2)$ **8. a.** $(x+7)^2$ **b.** $(4x-7)^2$
9. a. $(x+1)(x^2-x+1)$ **b.** $(5x-2)(25x^2+10x+4)$ **10.** $3x(x-5)^2$ **11.** $(x+10+6a)(x+10-6a)$ **12.** $\frac{2x-1}{(x-1)^{1/2}}$

Exercise Set P.5

1. $9(2x+3)$ **3.** $3x(x+2)$ **5.** $9x^2(x^2-2x+3)$ **7.** $(x+5)(x+3)$ **9.** $(x-3)(x^2+12)$ **11.** $(x-2)(x^2+5)$
13. $(x-1)(x^2+2)$ **15.** $(3x-2)(x^2-2)$ **17.** $(x+2)(x+3)$ **19.** $(x-5)(x+3)$ **21.** $(x-5)(x-3)$ **23.** $(3x+2)(x-1)$
25. $(3x-28)(x+1)$ **27.** $(2x-1)(3x-4)$ **29.** $(2x+3)(2x+5)$ **31.** $(3x-2)(3x-1)$ **33.** $(5x+8)(4x-1)$
35. $(2x+y)(x+y)$ **37.** $(3x+2y)(2x-3y)$ **39.** $(x+10)(x-10)$ **41.** $(6x+7)(6x-7)$ **43.** $(3x+5y)(3x-5y)$
45. $(x^2+4)(x+2)(x-2)$ **47.** $(4x^2+9)(2x+3)(2x-3)$ **49.** $(x+1)^2$ **51.** $(x-7)^2$ **53.** $(2x+1)^2$ **55.** $(3x-1)^2$
57. $(x+3)(x^2-3x+9)$ **59.** $(x-4)(x^2+4x+16)$ **61.** $(2x-1)(4x^2+2x+1)$ **63.** $(4x+3)(16x^2-12x+9)$
65. $3x(x+1)(x-1)$ **67.** $4(x+2)(x-3)$ **69.** $2(x^2+9)(x+3)(x-3)$ **71.** $(x-3)(x+3)(x+2)$ **73.** $2(x-8)(x+7)$
75. $x(x-2)(x+2)$ **77.** prime **79.** $(x-2)(x+2)^2$ **81.** $y(y^2+9)(y+3)(y-3)$ **83.** $5y^2(2y+3)(2y-3)$
85. $(x-6+7y)(x-6-7y)$ **87.** $(x+y)(3b+4)(3b-4)$ **89.** $(y-2)(x+4)(x-4)$ **91.** $2x(x+6+2a)(x+6-2a)$
93. $x^{1/2}(x-1)$ **95.** $\frac{4(1+2x)}{x^{2/3}}$ **97.** $-(x+3)^{1/2}(x+2)$ **99.** $\frac{x+4}{(x+5)^{3/2}}$ **101.** $-\frac{4(4x-1)^{1/2}(x-1)}{3}$ **103.** $(x+1)(5x-6)(2x+1)$
105. $(x^2+6)(6x^2-1)$ **107.** $y(y^2+1)(y^4-y^2+1)$ **109.** $(x+2y)(x-2y)(x+y)(x-y)$ **111.** $(x-y)^2(x-y+2)(x-y-2)$
113. $(2x-y^2)(x-3y^2)$ **115. a.** $(x-0.4x)(1-0.4)=(0.6x)(0.6)=0.36x$ **b.** no; 36% **117. a.** $9x^2-16$ **b.** $(3x+4)(3x-4)$
119. a. $x(x+y)-y(x+y)$ **b.** $(x+y)(x-y)$ **121.** $4a^3-4ab^2=4a(a+b)(a-b)$ **131.** $(x^n+4)(x^n+2)$ **133.** $(x-y)^3(x+y)$
135. $b=8, -8, 16, -16$

Section P.6

Check Point Exercises

1. a. -5 **b.** $6, -6$ **2. a.** $x^2, x\neq-3$ **b.** $\frac{x-1}{x+1}, x\neq-1$ **3.** $\frac{x-3}{(x-2)(x+3)}, x\neq2, x\neq-2, x\neq-3$

4. $\frac{3(x-1)}{x(x+2)}, x \neq 1, x \neq 0, x \neq -2$ **5.** $-2, x \neq -1$ **6.** $\frac{2(4x+1)}{(x+1)(x-1)}, x \neq 1, x \neq -1$ **7.** $(x-3)(x-3)(x+3)$
8. $\frac{-x^2+11x-20}{2(x-5)^2}, x \neq 5$ **9.** $\frac{2(2-3x)}{4+3x}, x \neq 0, x \neq -\frac{4}{3}$ **10.** $-\frac{1}{x(x+7)}, x \neq 0, x \neq -7$

Exercise Set P.6

1. 3 **3.** 5, −5 **5.** −1, −10 **7.** $\frac{3}{x-3}, x \neq 3$ **9.** $\frac{x-6}{4}, x \neq 6$ **11.** $\frac{y+9}{y-1}, y \neq 1, 2$ **13.** $\frac{x+6}{x-6}, x \neq 6, -6$ **15.** $\frac{1}{3}, x \neq 2, -3$
17. $\frac{(x-3)(x+3)}{x(x+4)}, x \neq 0, -4, 3$ **19.** $\frac{x-1}{x+2}, x \neq -2, -1, 2, 3$ **21.** $\frac{x^2+2x+4}{3x}, x \neq -2, 0, 2$ **23.** $\frac{7}{9}, x \neq -1$ **25.** $\frac{(x-2)^2}{x}, x \neq 0, -2, 2$
27. $\frac{2(x+3)}{3}, x \neq 3, -3$ **29.** $\frac{x-5}{2}, x \neq 1, -5$ **31.** $\frac{(x+2)(x+4)}{x-5}, x \neq -6, -3, -1, 3, 5$ **33.** $2, x \neq -\frac{5}{6}$ **35.** $\frac{2x-1}{x+3}, x \neq 0, -3$
37. $3, x \neq 2$ **39.** $\frac{3}{x-3}, x \neq 3, -4$ **41.** $\frac{9x+39}{(x+4)(x+5)}, x \neq -4, -5$ **43.** $-\frac{3}{x(x+1)}, x \neq -1, 0$ **45.** $\frac{3x^2+4}{(x+2)(x-2)}, x \neq -2, 2$
47. $\frac{2x^2+50}{(x-5)(x+5)}, x \neq -5, 5$ **49.** $\frac{4x+16}{(x+3)^2}, x \neq -3$ **51.** $\frac{x^2-x}{(x+5)(x-2)(x+3)}, x \neq -5, 2, -3$ **53.** $\frac{x-1}{x+2}, x \neq -2, -1$ **55.** $\frac{1}{3}, x \neq 3$
57. $\frac{x+1}{3x-1}, x \neq 0, \frac{1}{3}$ **59.** $\frac{1}{xy}, x \neq 0, y \neq 0, x \neq -y$ **61.** $\frac{x}{x+3}, x \neq -2, -3$ **63.** $-\frac{x-14}{7}, x \neq -2, 2$ **65.** $\frac{x-3}{x+2}, x \neq -2, -1, 3$
67. $-\frac{2x+h}{x^2(x+h)^2}, x \neq 0, h \neq 0, x \neq -h$ **69.** $\frac{x^2+5x+8}{(x+2)(x+1)}$ **71.** 2 **73.** $\frac{1}{y(y+5)}$ **75.** $\frac{2d}{a^2+ab+b^2}$
77. a. 86.67, 520, 1170; It costs \$86,670,000 to inoculate 40% of the population against this strain of flu, \$520,000,000 to inoculate 80% of the population, and \$1,170,000,000 to inoculate 90% of the population. **b.** $x = 100$ **c.** increases rapidly; impossible to inoculate 100% of the population.
79. a. $\frac{-0.3t+14}{3.6t+260}$ **b.** 0.04; 4000 **c.** fairly well **81.** $\frac{4x^2+14x}{(x+3)(x+4)}$ **97.** $\frac{1}{x^{2n}-1}$ **99.** $\frac{x-y+1}{(x-y)(x-y)}$

Chapter P Review Exercises

1. 51 **2.** 16 **3.** 124 ft **4.** $\{a, c\}$ **5.** $\{a, b, c, d, e\}$ **6.** $\{a, b, c, d, f, g\}$ **7.** $\{a\}$ **8. a.** $\sqrt{81}$ **b.** $0, \sqrt{81}$
c. $-17, 0, \sqrt{81}$ **d.** $-17, -\frac{9}{13}, 0, 0.75, \sqrt{81}$ **e.** $\sqrt{2}, \pi$ **f.** $-17, -\frac{9}{13}, 0, 0.75, \sqrt{2}, \pi, \sqrt{81}$ **9.** 103 **10.** $\sqrt{2}-1$
11. $\sqrt{17}-3$ **12.** $|4-(-17)|$; 21 **13.** commutative property of addition **14.** associative property of multiplication
15. distributive property of multiplication over addition **16.** commutative property of multiplication **17.** commutative property of multiplication **18.** commutative property of addition **19.** $17x-15$ **20.** $2x$ **21.** $5y-17$ **22.** $10x$
23. $E = 0.04x^2 + 9.2x + 169$ **24.** −108 **25.** $\frac{5}{16}$ **26.** $\frac{1}{25}$ **27.** $\frac{1}{27}$ **28.** $-8x^{12}y^9$ **29.** $\frac{10}{x^8}$ **30.** $\frac{1}{16x^{12}}$ **31.** $\frac{y^8}{4x^{10}}$ **32.** 37,400
33. 0.0000745 **34.** 3.59×10^6 **35.** 7.25×10^{-3} **36.** 390,000 **37.** 0.023 **38.** 10^3 or 1000 yr **39.** $\$4.35 \times 10^{10}$ **40.** $10\sqrt{3}$
41. $2|x|\sqrt{3}$ **42.** $2x\sqrt{5}$ **43.** $r\sqrt{r}$ **44.** $\frac{11}{2}$ **45.** $4x\sqrt{3}$ **46.** $20\sqrt{5}$ **47.** $16\sqrt{2}$ **48.** $24\sqrt{2}-8\sqrt{3}$ **49.** $6\sqrt{5}$ **50.** $\frac{\sqrt{6}}{3}$
51. $\frac{5(6-\sqrt{3})}{33}$ **52.** $7(\sqrt{7}+\sqrt{5})$ **53.** 5 **54.** −2 **55.** not a real number **56.** 5 **57.** $3\sqrt[3]{3}$ **58.** $y\sqrt[3]{y^2}$ **59.** $2\sqrt[4]{5}$
60. $13\sqrt[3]{2}$ **61.** $x\sqrt[4]{2}$ **62.** 4 **63.** $\frac{1}{5}$ **64.** 5 **65.** $\frac{1}{3}$ **66.** 16 **67.** $\frac{1}{81}$ **68.** $20x^{11/12}$ **69.** $3x^{1/4}$ **70.** $25x^4$ **71.** $\sqrt{y}$
72. $8x^3+10x^2-20x-4$; degree 3 **73.** $8x^4-5x^3+6$; degree 4 **74.** $12x^3+x^2-21x+10$ **75.** $6x^2-7x-5$ **76.** $16x^2-25$
77. $4x^2+20x+25$ **78.** $9x^2-24x+16$ **79.** $8x^3+12x^2+6x+1$ **80.** $125x^3-150x^2+60x-8$ **81.** $-x^2-17xy-3y^2$; degree 2
82. $24x^3y^2+x^2y-12x^2+4$; degree 5 **83.** $3x^2+16xy-35y^2$ **84.** $9x^2-30xy+25y^2$ **85.** $9x^4+12x^2y+4y^2$ **86.** $49x^2-16y^2$
87. a^3-b^3 **88.** $3x^2(5x+1)$ **89.** $(x-4)(x-7)$ **90.** $(3x+1)(5x-2)$ **91.** $(8-x)(8+x)$ **92.** prime **93.** $3x^2(x-5)(x+2)$
94. $4x^3(5x^4-9)$ **95.** $(x+3)(x-3)^2$ **96.** $(4x-5)^2$ **97.** $(x^2+4)(x+2)(x-2)$ **98.** $(y-2)(y^2+2y+4)$
99. $(x+4)(x^2-4x+16)$ **100.** $3x^2(x-2)(x+2)$ **101.** $(3x-5)(9x^2+15x+25)$ **102.** $x(x-1)(x+1)(x^2+1)$
103. $(x^2-2)(x+5)$ **104.** $(x+9+y)(x+9-y)$ **105.** $\frac{16(1+2x)}{x^{3/4}}$ **106.** $(x+2)(x-2)(x^2+3)^{1/2}(-x^4+x^2+13)$ **107.** $\frac{6(2x+1)}{x^{3/2}}$
108. $x^2, x \neq -2$ **109.** $\frac{x-3}{x-6}, x \neq -6, 6$ **110.** $\frac{x}{x+2}, x \neq -2$ **111.** $\frac{(x+3)^3}{(x-2)^2(x+2)}, x \neq 2, -2$ **112.** $\frac{2}{x(x+1)}, x \neq 0, 1, -1, -\frac{1}{3}$
113. $\frac{x+3}{x-4}, x \neq -3, 4, 2, 8$ **114.** $\frac{1}{x-3}, x \neq 3, -3$ **115.** $\frac{4x(x-1)}{(x+2)(x-2)}, x \neq 2, -2$ **116.** $\frac{2x^2-3}{(x-3)(x+3)(x-2)}, x \neq 3, -3, 2$
117. $\frac{11x^2-x-11}{(2x-1)(x+3)(3x+2)}, x \neq \frac{1}{2}, -3, -\frac{2}{3}$ **118.** $\frac{3}{x}, x \neq 0, 2$ **119.** $\frac{3x}{x-4}, x \neq 0, 4, -4$ **120.** $\frac{3x+8}{3x+10}, x \neq -3, -\frac{10}{3}$

Chapter P Test

1. $6x^2-27x$ **2.** $-6x+17$ **3.** $\{5\}$ **4.** $\{1, 2, 5, a\}$ **5.** $6x^2y^3+4xy+2y^2$ **6.** $\frac{5y^8}{x^6}$ **7.** $3r\sqrt{2}$ **8.** $11\sqrt{2}$ **9.** $\frac{3(5-\sqrt{2})}{23}$
10. $2x\sqrt[3]{2x}$ **11.** $\frac{x+3}{x-2}, x \neq 2, 1$ **12.** 2.5×10^1 **13.** $2x^3-13x^2+26x-15$ **14.** $25x^2+30xy+9y^2$ **15.** $\frac{2(x+3)}{x+1}, x \neq 3, -1, -4, -3$
16. $\frac{x^2+2x+15}{(x+3)(x-3)}, x \neq 3, -3$ **17.** $\frac{11}{(x-3)(x-4)}, x \neq 3, 4$ **18.** $\frac{3-x}{3}, x \neq 0$ **19.** $(x-3)(x-6)$ **20.** $(x^2+3)(x+2)$
21. $(5x-3)(5x+3)$ **22.** $(6x-7)^2$ **23.** $(y-5)(y^2+5y+25)$ **24.** $(x+5+3y)(x+5-3y)$ **25.** $\frac{2x+3}{(x+3)^{3/5}}$
26. $-7, -\frac{4}{5}, 0, 0.25, \sqrt{4}, \frac{22}{7}$ **27.** commutative property of addition **28.** distributive property of multiplication over addition **29.** 7.6×10^{-4}
30. $\frac{1}{243}$ **31.** 1.26×10^{10} **32. a.** men: Model 2; women: Model 1 **b.** 74; fairly well

CHAPTER 1

Section 1.1

Check Point Exercises

1.

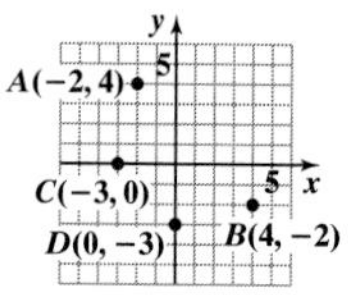

2.

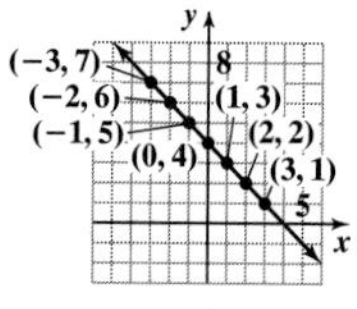

$y = 4 - x$

3.

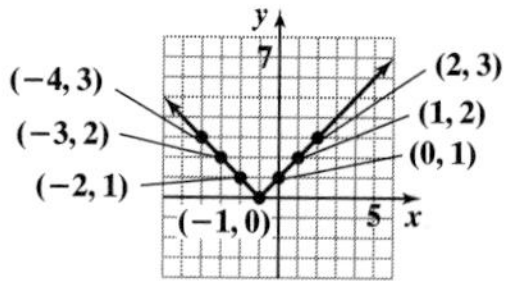

$y = |x + 1|$

4. minimum x-value: -100; maximum x-value: 100; distance between tick marks on x-axis: 50; minimum y-value: -100; maximum y-value: 100; distance between tick marks on y-axis: 10

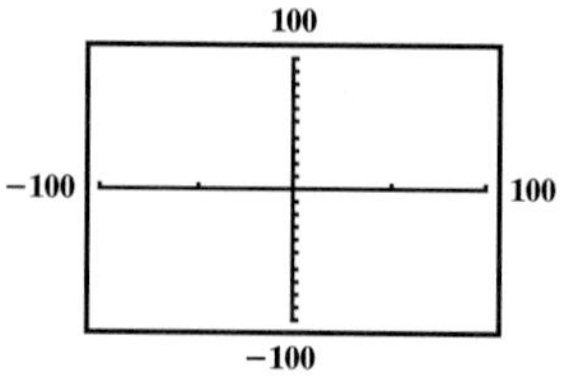

5. a. x-intercept: -3; y-intercept: 5 **b.** no x-intercept; y-intercept: 4 **c.** x-intercept: 0; y-intercept: 0

6. approximately 96,000

Exercise Set 1.1

1.

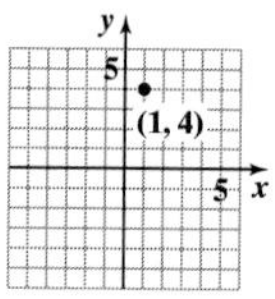

3.

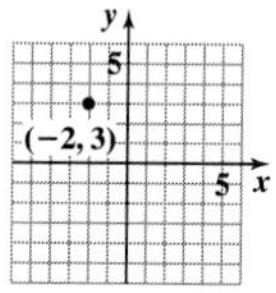

5.

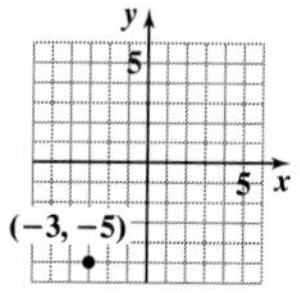

7.

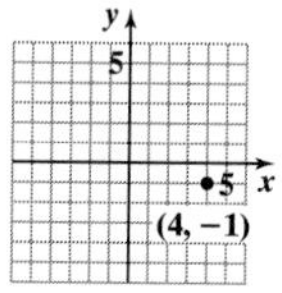

9.

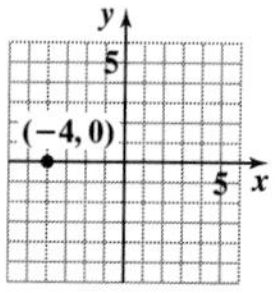

11.

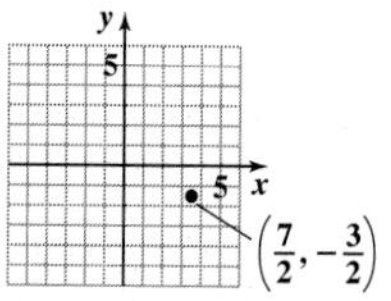

13.

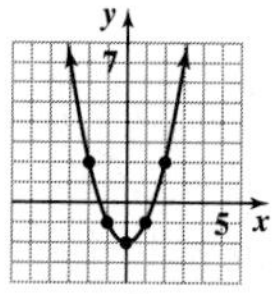

$y = x^2 - 2$

15.

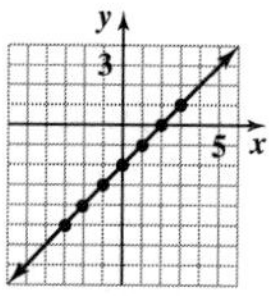

$y = x - 2$

17.

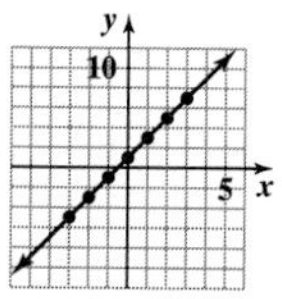

$y = 2x + 1$

19.

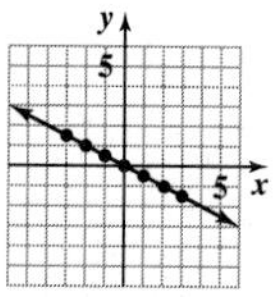

$y = -\frac{1}{2}x$

21.

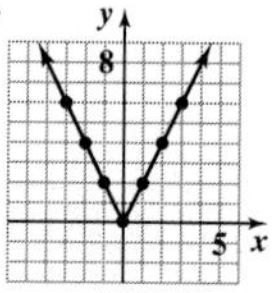

$y = 2|x|$

23.

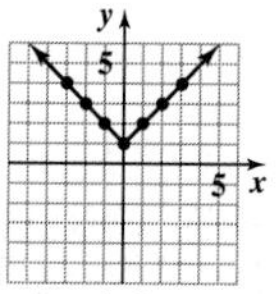

$y = |x| + 1$

25.

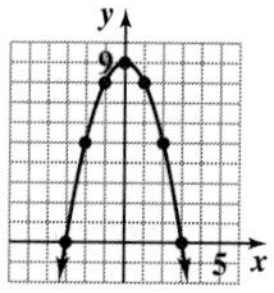

$y = 9 - x^2$

27.

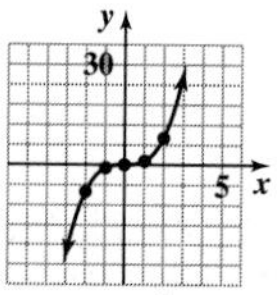

$y = x^3$

29. (c) **31.** (b) **33.** c **35.** no **37.** (2, 0) **39.** (−2, 4) and (1, 1) **41. a.** 2 **b.** −4 **43. a.** 1, −2 **b.** 2 **45. a.** −1 **b.** none

47. $y = 2x + 4$

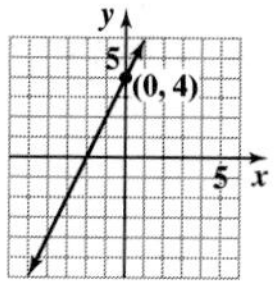

49. $y = 3 - x^2$

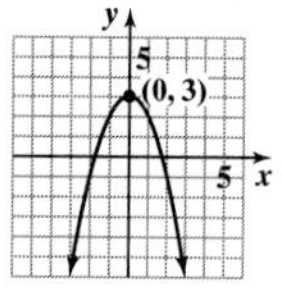

51.

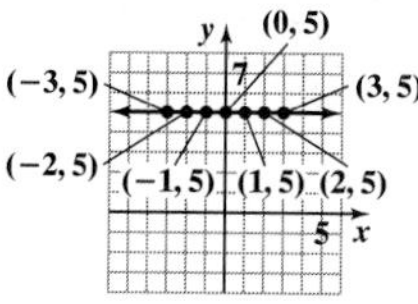

53.

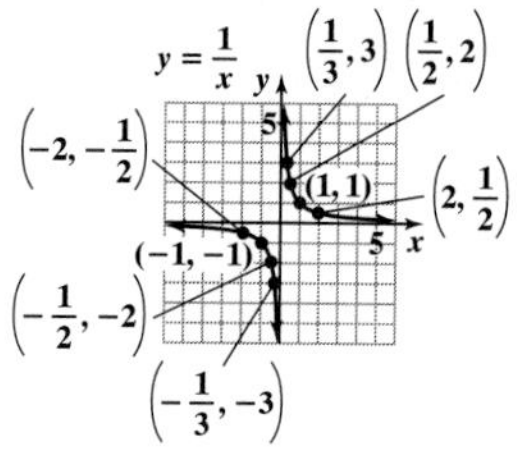

55. 65 **57.** 1989–1993 **59.** 1977 **61.** 135 beats/min; (40, 135) on blue graph **63. a.** 36 cm **b.** 44.7 cm **c.** 46.9 cm **d.** describes healthy children **71.**

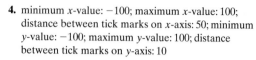

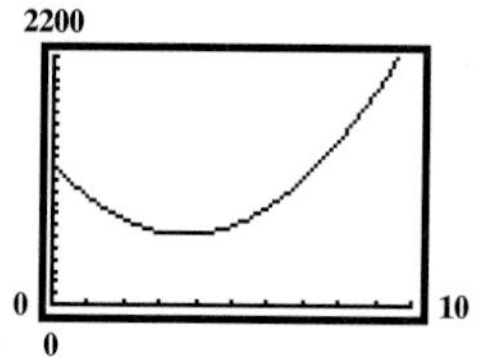

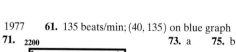

73. a **75.** b **77.** b

Section 1.2

Check Point Exercises

1. {6} **2.** {5} **3.** {1} **4.** {3} **5.** ∅ **6.** 11 **7.** ∅; inconsistent equation

Exercise Set 1.2

1. {11} **3.** {7} **5.** {13} **7.** {2} **9.** {9} **11.** {−5} **13.** {6} **15.** {−2} **17.** {12} **19.** {24} **21.** {−15} **23.** {5} **25.** $\left\{\frac{33}{2}\right\}$ **27.** {−12} **29.** $\left\{\frac{46}{5}\right\}$ **31. a.** 0 **b.** $\left\{\frac{1}{2}\right\}$ **33. a.** 0 **b.** {−2} **35. a.** 0 **b.** {2} **37. a.** 0 **b.** {4}

39. a. 1 **b.** {3} **41. a.** -1 **b.** $\varnothing$ **43. a.** 1 **b.** {2} **45. a.** $-2, 2$ **b.** $\varnothing$ **47. a.** $-1, 1$ **b.** {-3} **49. a.** $-2, 4$ **b.** $\varnothing$
51. 6 **53.** -7 **55.** 2 **57.** 19 **59.** -1 **61.** identity **63.** inconsistent equation **65.** conditional equation
67. inconsistent equation **69.** {-7}; conditional equation **71.** $\varnothing$; inconsistent equation **73.** {-4}; conditional equation
75. {8}; conditional equation **77.** {-1}; conditional equation **79.** $\varnothing$; inconsistent equation **81.** $3(x-4) = 3(2-2x)$; {2}
83. $-3(x-3) = 5(2-x)$; {0.5} **85.** 2 **87.** -7 **89.** {-2} **91.** $\varnothing$ or no solution **93.** {10} **95.** {-2} **97.** 2006
99. 5.5; point (5.5, 3.5) on high-humor graph **101.** 12 years old **103.** (12, 500) on blue graph **105.** no **107.** 11 learning trials; (11, 0.95)
109. 125 liters

121. {5} $y_2 = 4x - 7$ **123.** {-5} $y_1 = \dfrac{2x-1}{3} - \dfrac{x-5}{6}$ **127.** 20

$y_1 = 2x + 3(x-4)$

$y_2 = \dfrac{x-3}{4}$

Section 1.3

Check Point Exercises

1. basketball: 1.6 million; bicycle riding: 1.3 million; football: 1 million **2.** 2011 **3.** 300 min **4.** $1200 **5.** $3150 at 9%; $1850 at 11%
6. 50 ft by 94 ft **7.** $w = \dfrac{P - 2l}{2}$ **8.** $C = \dfrac{P}{1 + M}$

Exercise Set 1.3

1. 6 **3.** 25 **5.** 120 **7.** 320 **9.** 19 and 45 **11.** 2 **13.** 8 **15.** all real numbers **17.** 5 **19.** births: 375 thousand; deaths:
146 thousand **21.** U.S.: 169 million; Japan: 56 million; China: 46 million **23.** liberals: 39.6%; conservatives: 17.6% **25.** 2050
27. a. $y = 1.7x + 39.8$ **b.** 2008 **29.** after 7 years **31.** after 5 months; $165 **33.** 30 times

c.

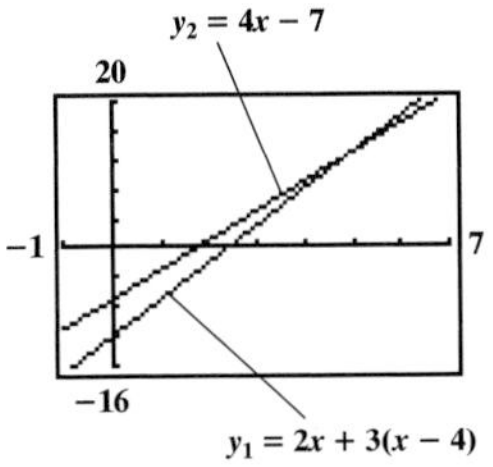

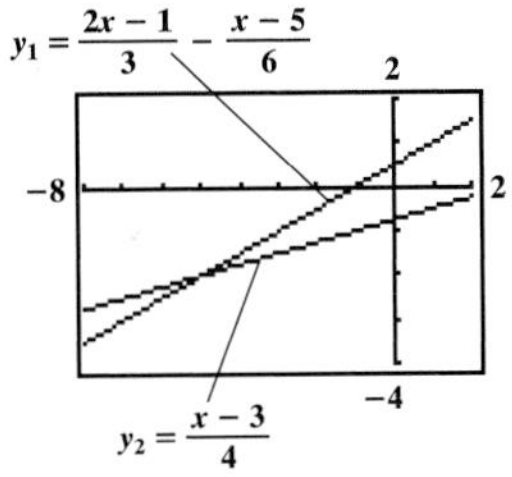

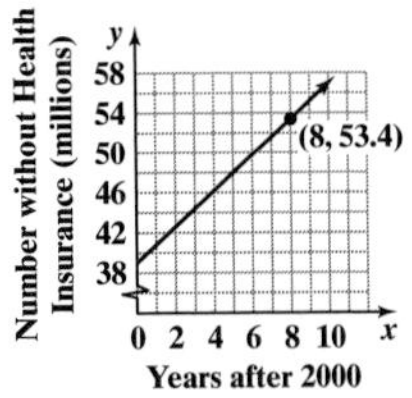

$y = 1.7x + 39.8$

35. a. 2014; 22,300 students **b.** $y_1 = 13{,}300 + 1000x$; $y_2 = 26{,}800 - 500x$ **37.** $420 **39.** $150 **41.** $36,000 **43.** $467.20
45. $2000 at 6%; $5000 at 8% **47.** $6000 at 12%; $2000 at a 5% loss **49.** 50 yd by 100 yd **51.** 36 ft by 78 ft **53.** 2 in.
55. 11 hr **57.** 5 ft 7 in. **59.** 7 oz **61.** $\omega = \dfrac{A}{l}$ **63.** $b = \dfrac{2A}{h}$ **65.** $p = \dfrac{I}{rt}$ **67.** $m = \dfrac{E}{c^2}$ **69.** $p = \dfrac{T - D}{m}$ **71.** $a = \dfrac{2A}{h} - b$
73. $r = \dfrac{S - P}{Pt}$ **75.** $S = \dfrac{F}{B} + V$ **77.** $I = \dfrac{E}{R + r}$ **79.** $f = \dfrac{pq}{p + q}$

89. a. $F = 30 + 5x$; $F = 7.5x$ **91.** $200
b. 120 **93.** 10 correct answers
 95. 36 plants

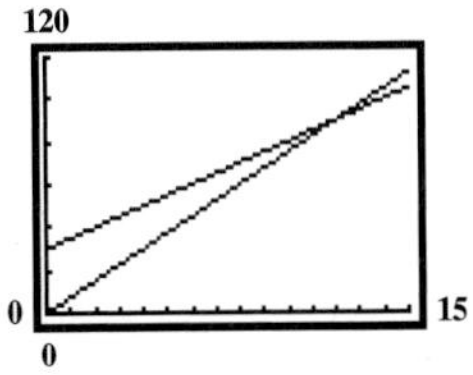

c. (12, 90); For 12 hours, both options
cost the same, $90.

Section 1.4

Check Point Exercises

1. a. $8 + i$ **b.** $-10 + 7i$ **2. a.** $63 + 14i$ **b.** $58 - 11i$ **3.** $\dfrac{16}{17} + \dfrac{21}{17}i$ **4. a.** $7i\sqrt{3}$ **b.** $1 - 4i\sqrt{3}$ **c.** $-7 + i\sqrt{3}$

Exercise Set 1.4

1. $8 - 2i$ **3.** $-2 + 9i$ **5.** $24 - 3i$ **7.** $-14 + 17i$ **9.** $21 + 15i$ **11.** $-19 + 7i$ **13.** $-29 - 11i$ **15.** 34 **17.** 26
19. $-5 + 12i$ **21.** $\dfrac{3}{5} + \dfrac{1}{5}i$ **23.** $1 + i$ **25.** $-\dfrac{24}{25} + \dfrac{32}{25}i$ **27.** $\dfrac{7}{5} + \dfrac{4}{5}i$ **29.** $3i$ **31.** $47i$ **33.** $-8i$ **35.** $2 + 6i\sqrt{7}$
37. $-\dfrac{1}{3} + \dfrac{\sqrt{2}}{6}i$ **39.** $-\dfrac{1}{8} - \dfrac{\sqrt{3}}{24}i$ **41.** $-2\sqrt{6} - 2i\sqrt{10}$ **43.** $24\sqrt{15}$ **45.** $-11 - 5i$ **47.** $-5 + 10i$ **49.** $0 + 47i$ or $47i$
51. 0 **53.** $\dfrac{20}{13} + \dfrac{30}{13}i$ **55.** $(47 + 13i)$ volts **57.** $(5 + i\sqrt{15}) + (5 - i\sqrt{15}) = 10$; $(5 + i\sqrt{15})(5 - i\sqrt{15}) = 25 - 15i^2 = 25 + 15 = 40$

67. d **69.** $\frac{6}{5} + 0i$ or $\frac{6}{5}$

Section 1.5

Check Point Exercises

1. a. $\{0, 3\}$ **b.** $\left\{-1, \frac{1}{2}\right\}$ **2. a.** $\{-\sqrt{7}, \sqrt{7}\}$ **b.** $\pm 3i$ **c.** $\{-5 + \sqrt{11}, -5 - \sqrt{11}\}$ **3. a.** 9; $x^2 + 6x + 9 = (x + 3)^2$ **b.** $\frac{25}{4}$; $x^2 - 5x + \frac{25}{4} = \left(x - \frac{5}{2}\right)^2$ **c.** $\frac{1}{9}$; $x^2 + \frac{2}{3}x + \frac{1}{9} = \left(x + \frac{1}{3}\right)^2$ **4.** $\{-2 \pm \sqrt{5}\}$ **5.** $\left\{\frac{-3 \pm \sqrt{41}}{4}\right\}$ **6.** $\left\{\frac{-1 + \sqrt{3}}{2}, \frac{-1 - \sqrt{3}}{2}\right\}$ **7.** $\{1 + i, 1 - i\}$ **8. a.** 0; one real solution **b.** 81; two rational solutions **c.** -44; two imaginary solutions that are complex conjugates **9.** approximately 26 years old **10.** 12 in.

Exercise Set 1.5

1. $\{-2, 5\}$ **3.** $\{3, 5\}$ **5.** $\left\{-\frac{5}{2}, \frac{2}{3}\right\}$ **7.** $\left\{-\frac{4}{3}, 2\right\}$ **9.** $\{-4, 0\}$ **11.** $\left\{0, \frac{1}{3}\right\}$ **13.** $\{-3, 1\}$ **15.** $\{-3, 3\}$ **17.** $\{-\sqrt{10}, \sqrt{10}\}$ **19.** $\{\pm 5i\}$ **21.** $\{-7, 3\}$ **23.** $\{4 \pm \sqrt{5}\}$ **25.** $\{-3 \pm 4i\}$ **27.** $\{3 \pm i\sqrt{5}\}$ **29.** $\left\{-\frac{5}{3}, \frac{1}{3}\right\}$ **31.** $\left\{\frac{1 - \sqrt{7}}{5}, \frac{1 + \sqrt{7}}{5}\right\}$ **33.** $\left\{\frac{4 - 2\sqrt{2}}{3}, \frac{4 + 2\sqrt{2}}{3}\right\}$ **35.** 36; $x^2 + 12x + 36 = (x + 6)^2$ **37.** 25; $x^2 - 10x + 25 = (x - 5)^2$ **39.** $\frac{9}{4}$; $x^2 + 3x + \frac{9}{4} = \left(x + \frac{3}{2}\right)^2$ **41.** $\frac{49}{4}$; $x^2 - 7x + \frac{49}{4} = \left(x - \frac{7}{2}\right)^2$ **43.** $\frac{1}{9}$; $x^2 - \frac{2}{3}x + \frac{1}{9} = \left(x - \frac{1}{3}\right)^2$ **45.** $\frac{1}{36}$; $x^2 - \frac{1}{3}x + \frac{1}{36} = \left(x - \frac{1}{6}\right)^2$ **47.** $\{-7, 1\}$ **49.** $\{1 + \sqrt{3}, 1 - \sqrt{3}\}$ **51.** $\{3 + 2\sqrt{5}, 3 - 2\sqrt{5}\}$ **53.** $\{-2 + \sqrt{3}, -2 - \sqrt{3}\}$ **55.** $\{2, 3\}$ **57.** $\left\{\frac{-3 + \sqrt{13}}{2}, \frac{-3 - \sqrt{13}}{2}\right\}$ **59.** $\left\{\frac{1}{2}, 3\right\}$ **61.** $\left\{\frac{1 + \sqrt{2}}{2}, \frac{1 - \sqrt{2}}{2}\right\}$ **63.** $\left\{\frac{1 + \sqrt{7}}{3}, \frac{1 - \sqrt{7}}{3}\right\}$ **65.** $\{-5, -3\}$ **67.** $\left\{\frac{-5 + \sqrt{13}}{2}, \frac{-5 - \sqrt{13}}{2}\right\}$ **69.** $\left\{\frac{3 + \sqrt{57}}{6}, \frac{3 - \sqrt{57}}{6}\right\}$ **71.** $\left\{\frac{1 + \sqrt{29}}{4}, \frac{1 - \sqrt{29}}{4}\right\}$ **73.** $\{3 + i, 3 - i\}$ **75.** 36; 2 unequal real solutions **77.** 97; 2 unequal real solutions **79.** 0; 1 real solution **81.** 37; 2 unequal real solutions **83.** $\left\{-\frac{1}{2}, 1\right\}$ **85.** $\left\{\frac{1}{5}, 2\right\}$ **87.** $\{-2\sqrt{5}, 2\sqrt{5}\}$ **89.** $\{1 + \sqrt{2}, 1 - \sqrt{2}\}$ **91.** $\left\{\frac{-11 + \sqrt{33}}{4}, \frac{-11 - \sqrt{33}}{4}\right\}$ **93.** $\left\{0, \frac{8}{3}\right\}$ **95.** $\{2\}$ **97.** $\{-2, 2\}$ **99.** $\{3 + 2i, 3 - 2i\}$ **101.** $\{2 + i\sqrt{3}, 2 - i\sqrt{3}\}$ **103.** $\left\{0, \frac{7}{2}\right\}$ **105.** $\{2 + \sqrt{10}, 2 - \sqrt{10}\}$ **107.** $\{-5, -1\}$ **109.** -1 and 5; d **111.** -3 and 1; f **113.** no x-intercepts; b **115.** $-\frac{1}{2}$ and 2 **117.** -6 and 3 **119.** $\frac{-5 - \sqrt{33}}{2}$ and $\frac{-5 + \sqrt{33}}{2}$ **121.** $\frac{5 - \sqrt{7}}{3}$ and $\frac{5 + \sqrt{7}}{3}$ **123.** $\frac{-2 - \sqrt{22}}{2}$ and $\frac{-2 + \sqrt{22}}{2}$ **125.** $1 + \sqrt{7}$ **127.** $\left\{\frac{-1 \pm \sqrt{21}}{2}\right\}$ **129.** $\left\{-2\sqrt{2}, \frac{\sqrt{2}}{2}\right\}$ **131.** 33-year-olds and 58-year-olds; The formula models the actual data well. **133.** 77.8 ft; (b) **135.** $4\sqrt{5}$ ft or 8.9 ft **137.** 13.23 ft **139.** length: 9 ft; width: 6 ft **141.** 5 in. **143.** 5 m **145.** 10 in. **147.** 9.3 in. and 0.7 in. **161.** $x^2 - 2x - 15 = 0$ **163.** 2.4 m; yes

Mid-Chapter 1 Check Point

1. $\{6\}$ **2.** $\left\{-1, \frac{7}{5}\right\}$ **3.** $\{-7\}$ **4.** $\left\{\frac{3 \pm \sqrt{15}}{3}\right\}$ **5.** all real numbers **6.** $\left\{\pm \frac{6\sqrt{5}}{5}\right\}$ **7.** $\left\{\frac{3}{4} \pm \frac{\sqrt{23}}{4}i\right\}$ **8.** $\{3\}$ **9.** $\{-3 \pm 2\sqrt{6}\}$ **10.** $\{2 \pm \sqrt{3}\}$ **11.** $\varnothing$ **12.** $\{4\}$ **13.** $-3 - \sqrt{7}$ and $-3 + \sqrt{7}$ **14.** 1 **15.** no x-intercepts **16.** $\frac{-3 - \sqrt{41}}{4}$ and $\frac{-3 + \sqrt{41}}{4}$ **17.** no x-intercepts **18.** 0 **19.** -4 and $\frac{1}{2}$ **20.** $\{-5 \pm 2\sqrt{7}\}$ **21.** two imaginary solutions **22.** two rational solutions

23.

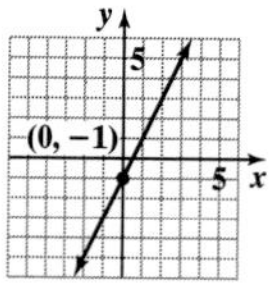

$y = 2x - 1$

24.

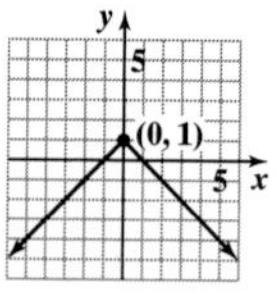

$y = 1 - |x|$

25.

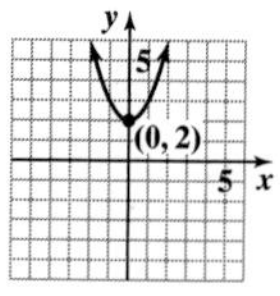

$y = x^2 + 2$

26. $n = \frac{L - a}{d} + 1$ **27.** $l = \frac{A - 2wh}{2w + 2h}$ **28.** $f_1 = -\frac{ff_2}{f - f_2}$ or $f_1 = -\frac{ff_2}{f_2 - f}$ **29.** U.S.: \$291 billion; Russia: \$44 billion; Japan: \$40 billion **30.** 6 months **31.** \$11,500 at 8%; \$13,500 at 9% **32.** 20 prints; \$3.80 **33.** 129 pounds **34.** \$2500 at 4%; \$1500 at 3% loss **35.** length: 17 ft; width: 6 ft **36.** length: 7 ft; width: 4 ft **37.** 12 yd **38.** 1995; quite well **39.** 2011 **40.** $-1 - i$ **41.** $-3 + 6i$ **42.** $7 + i$ **43.** i **44.** $3i\sqrt{3}$ **45.** $1 - 4i\sqrt{3}$

Section 1.6

Check Point Exercises

1. $\{-\sqrt{3}, 0, \sqrt{3}\}$ **2.** $\left\{-2, -\frac{3}{2}, 2\right\}$ **3.** $\{6\}$ **4.** $\{4\}$ **5. a.** $\{\sqrt[3]{25}\}$ or $\{5^{2/3}\}$ **b.** $\{-8, 8\}$ **6.** $\{-\sqrt{3}, -\sqrt{2}, \sqrt{2}, \sqrt{3}\}$ **7.** $\left\{-\frac{1}{27}, 64\right\}$ **8.** $\{-2, 3\}$ **9.** $\{-2, 3\}$

Exercise Set 1.6

1. $\{-4, 0, 4\}$ **3.** $\left\{-2, -\frac{2}{3}, 2\right\}$ **5.** $\left\{-\frac{1}{2}, \frac{1}{2}, \frac{3}{2}\right\}$ **7.** $\left\{-2, -\frac{1}{2}, \frac{1}{2}\right\}$ **9.** $\{0, 2, -1 + i\sqrt{3}, -1 - i\sqrt{3}\}$ **11.** $\{6\}$ **13.** $\{6\}$

15. $\{-6\}$ **17.** $\{10\}$ **19.** $\{-5\}$ **21.** $\{12\}$ **23.** $\{8\}$ **25.** $\varnothing$ **27.** $\varnothing$ **29.** $\left\{\frac{13+\sqrt{105}}{6}\right\}$ **31.** $\{4\}$ **33.** $\{13\}$ **35.** $\{\sqrt[5]{4}\}$
37. $\{-60, 68\}$ **39.** $\{-4, 5\}$ **41.** $\{-2, -1, 1, 2\}$ **43.** $\left\{-\frac{4}{3}, -1, 1, \frac{4}{3}\right\}$ **45.** $\{25, 64\}$ **47.** $\left\{-\frac{1}{4}, \frac{1}{5}\right\}$ **49.** $\{-8, 27\}$ **51.** $\{1\}$
53. $\left\{\frac{1}{4}, 1\right\}$ **55.** $\{2, 12\}$ **57.** $\{-3, -1, 2, 4\}$ **59.** $\{-8, -2, 1, 4\}$ **61.** $\{-8, 8\}$ **63.** $\{-5, 9\}$ **65.** $\{-2, 3\}$ **67.** $\left\{-\frac{5}{3}, 3\right\}$
69. $\left\{-\frac{2}{5}, \frac{2}{5}\right\}$ **71.** $\left\{-\frac{4}{5}, 4\right\}$ **73.** $\varnothing$ **75.** $\left\{\frac{1}{2}\right\}$ **77.** $\{-1, 3\}$ **79.** 2; c **81.** 1; e **83.** 2 and 3; f **85.** $\left\{-\frac{3}{2}, 4\right\}$ **87.** $\{4\}$
89. $\left\{-2, -\frac{1}{2}, 2\right\}$ **91.** $\{0\}$ **93.** $\{-2, 0, 2\}$ **95.** $\{-8, -6, 4, 6\}$ **97.** $\{-7, -1, 6\}$ **99.** 8 **101.** $V = \frac{\pi r^2 h}{3}$ or $\frac{1}{3}\pi r^2 h$ **103.** -16 and 12
105. 16 years after 1996, or 2012 **107.** High: 66.0°; Low: 61.5° **109.** Using H: 2014; Using L: 2010 **111.** 36 years old; (36, 40,000)
113. 149 million km **115.** either 1.2 feet or 7.5 feet from the base of the 6 foot pole **125.** $\{-3, -1, 1\}$ **127.** $\{-2\}$
129. d **131.** $\left\{\frac{2}{5}, \frac{1}{2}\right\}$ **133.** $\{0, 1\}$

Section 1.7

Check Point Exercises

1. a. $\{x \mid -2 \le x < 5\}$

b. $\{x \mid 1 \le x \le 3.5\}$

c. $\{x \mid x < -1\}$

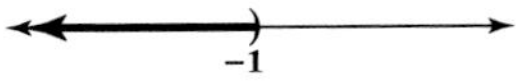

2. a. $(2, 3]$ **b.** $[1, 6)$

3. $[-1, \infty)$ or $\{x \mid x \ge -1\}$

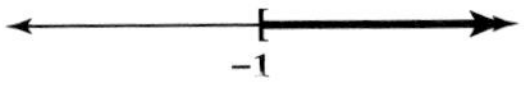

4. $\{x \mid x < 4\}$ or $(-\infty, 4)$

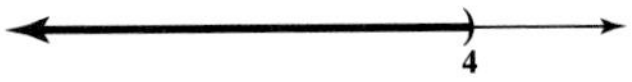

5. a. $\{x \mid x$ is a real number$\}$ or $\mathbb{R}$ or $(-\infty, \infty)$ **b.** $\varnothing$

6. $[-1, 4)$ or $\{x \mid -1 \le x < 4\}$

7. $(-3, 7)$ or $\{x \mid -3 < x < 7\}$

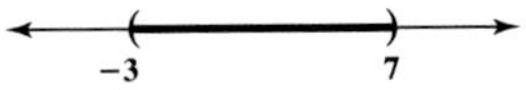

8. $\left\{x \mid -\frac{11}{5} \le x \le 3\right\}$ or $\left[-\frac{11}{5}, 3\right]$

9. $\{x \mid x < -4$ or $x > 8\}$ or $(-\infty, -4) \cup (8, \infty)$

10. more than 720 mi per week

Exercise Set 1.7

1. $1 < x \le 6$

3. $-5 \le x < 2$

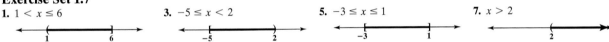

5. $-3 \le x \le 1$

7. $x > 2$

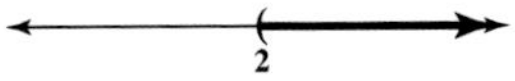

9. $x \ge -3$

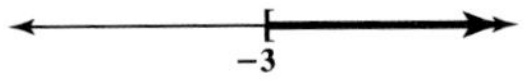

11. $x < 3$

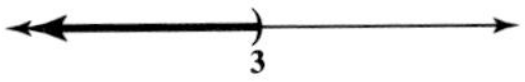

13. $x < 5.5$

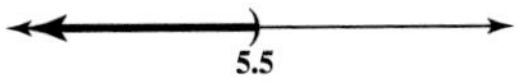

15. $[-1, 0)$ **17.** $(-3, 2]$ **19.** $[1, 5)$ **21.** $(-\infty, 8)$ **23.** $(6, \infty)$ **25.** $[3, \infty)$

27. $(-\infty, 3)$

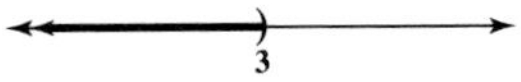

29. $\left[\frac{20}{3}, \infty\right)$

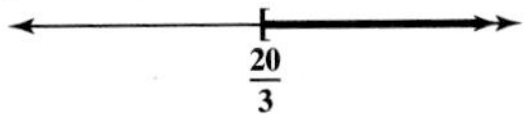

31. $(-\infty, -4]$

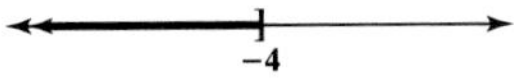

33. $\left(-\infty, -\frac{2}{5}\right]$

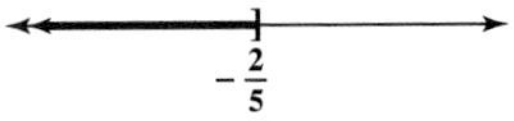

35. $[0, \infty)$

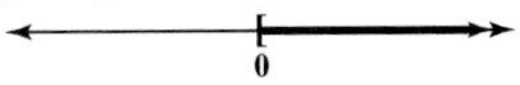

37. $(-\infty, 1)$

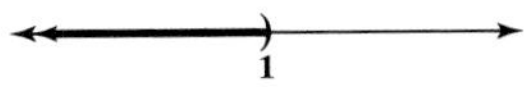

39. $[6, \infty)$

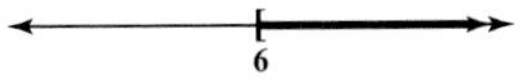

41. $[-10, \infty)$

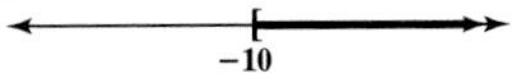

43. $(-\infty, -6)$

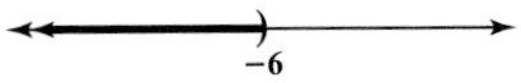

45. $[13, \infty)$

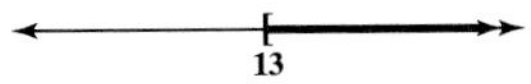

47. $(-\infty, \infty)$

49. $\varnothing$

51. $(3, 5)$ **53.** $[-1, 3)$ **55.** $(-5, -2]$ **57.** $[3, 6)$ **59.** $(-3, 3)$ **61.** $[-1, 3]$ **63.** $(-1, 7)$ **65.** $[-5, 3]$ **67.** $(-6, 0)$
69. $(-\infty, -3)$ or $(3, \infty)$ **71.** $(-\infty, -1]$ or $[3, \infty)$ **73.** $\left(-\infty, \frac{1}{3}\right)$ or $(5, \infty)$ **75.** $(-\infty, -5]$ or $[3, \infty)$ **77.** $(-\infty, -3)$ or $(12, \infty)$
79. $(-\infty, -1]$ or $[3, \infty)$ **81.** $[2, 6]$ **83.** $(-\infty, -3) \cup (5, \infty)$ **85.** $(-\infty, 1] \cup [2, \infty)$ **87.** $(-1, 9)$ **89.** $\left(-\infty, \frac{1}{3}\right) \cup (1, \infty)$
91. $\left(-\infty, -\frac{75}{14}\right) \cup \left(\frac{87}{14}, \infty\right)$ **93.** $(-\infty, -6]$ or $[24, \infty)$ **95.** $(-\infty, -3]$ **97.** $[6, \infty)$ **99.** $\left(-\frac{2}{3}, \frac{10}{3}\right)$ **101.** $(-\infty, -10] \cup [2, \infty)$
103. $(-1, 9)$ **105.** $[-1, 2)$ **107.** $\left(-\infty, -\frac{1}{3}\right] \cup [3, \infty)$ **109.** $(0, 4)$ **111.** intimacy $\ge$ passion or passion $\le$ intimacy
113. commitment $>$ passion or passion $<$ commitment **115.** 9; after 3 years **117.** voting years after 2006 **119.** between 80 and 110 minutes, inclusive **121.** $h \le 41$ or $h \ge 59$ **123.** $15 + 0.08x < 3 + 0.12x$; more than 300 min **125.** $2 + 0.08x < 8 + 0.05x$; 199 checks or less **127.** $5.50x > 3000 + 3x$; more than 1200 packages **129.** $245 + 95x \le 3000$; at most 29 bags

131. a. $\frac{86 + 88 + x}{3} \geq 90$; at least a 96 **b.** $\frac{86 + 88 + x}{3} < 80$; a grade less than 66

133. more than 3 and less than 15 crossings per three-month period

143.

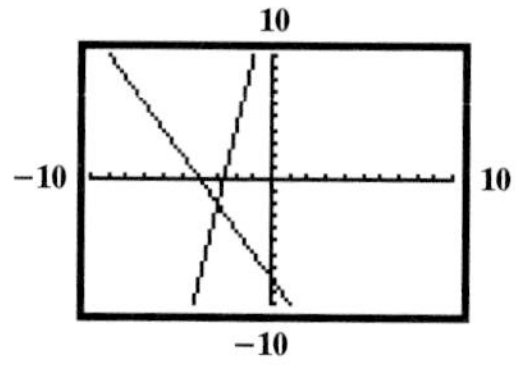

$x < -3$

145. a. $C = 4 + 0.10x$; $C = 2 + 0.15x$

b.

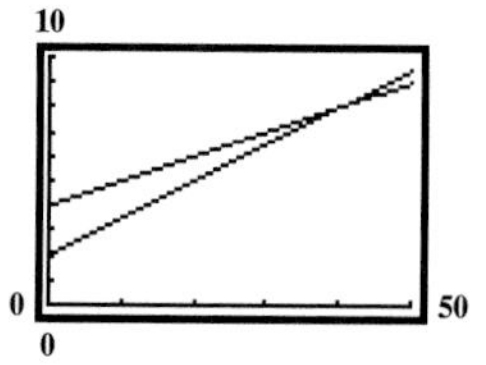

c. 41 or more checks

d. $x > 40$

147. Because $x > y$, $y - x$ represents a negative number, so when both sides are multiplied by $(y - x)$, the inequality must be reversed.

149. Albany: Model 2; San Francisco: Model 1

Chapter 1 Review Exercises

1.

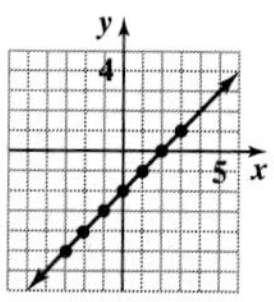

$y = 2x - 2$

2.

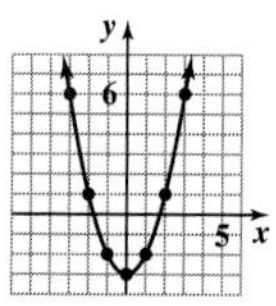

$y = x^2 - 3$

3.

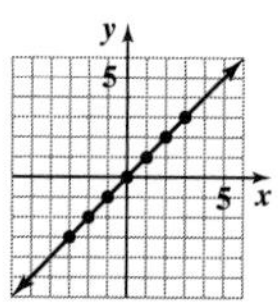

$y = x$

4.

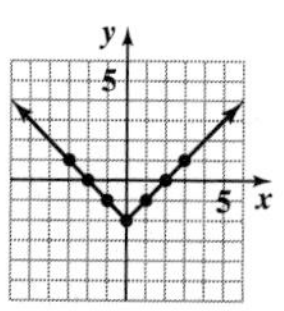

$y = |x| - 2$

5.

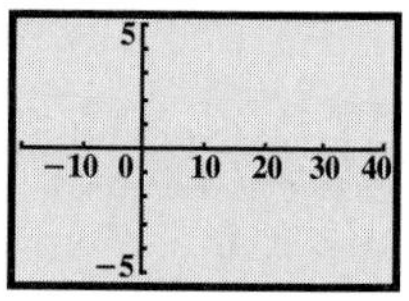

6. x-intercept: −2; y-intercept: 2 **7.** x-intercepts: −2, 2; y-intercept: −4 **8.** x-intercept: 5; no y-intercept
9. (91, 125); In 1991, 125 thousand acres were used for cultivation. **10.** 1997 **11.** 2001; 25 thousand acres
12. 2004; 300 thousand acres **13.** 1991 and 1992 **14.** 2001 and 2002; 155 thousand acres **15.** {6}; conditional equation
16. {−10}; conditional equation **17.** {5}; conditional equation **18.** {−13}; conditional equation **19.** {−3}; conditional equation
20. {−1}; conditional equation **21.** ∅; inconsistent equation **22.** all real numbers; identity **23.** {2}; conditional equation
24. {2}; conditional equation **25.** $\left\{\frac{72}{11}\right\}$; conditional equation **26.** $\left\{\frac{36}{7}\right\}$; conditional equation **27.** $\left\{\frac{77}{15}\right\}$; conditional equation
28. {2}; conditional equation **29.** ∅; inconsistent equation **30.** all real numbers except −1 and 1; conditional equation
31. $\left\{\frac{5}{2}\right\}$; conditional equation **32.** ∅; inconsistent equation **33.** $\left\{\frac{4}{7}\right\}$; conditional equation **34.** $\left\{\frac{1}{2}\right\}$; conditional equation
35. {2}; conditional equation **36.** Chicken Caesar: 495; Express Taco: 620; Mandarin Chicken: 590 **37.** 2008 **38.** 500 min
39. \$60 **40.** \$10,000 in sales **41.** \$2500 at 4%; \$6500 at 7% **42.** \$4500 at 2%; \$3500 at 5% **43.** 44 yd by 126 yd
44. a. $14{,}100 + 1500x = 41{,}700 - 800x$ **b.** 2019; 32,100 **45.** $g = \frac{s - vt}{t^2}$ **46.** $g = \frac{T}{r + vt}$ **47.** $P = \frac{A}{1 + rt}$ **48.** $-9 + 4i$
49. $-12 - 8i$ **50.** $17 + 19i$ **51.** $-7 - 24i$ **52.** 113 **53.** $\frac{15}{13} - \frac{3}{13}i$ **54.** $\frac{1}{5} + \frac{11}{10}i$ **55.** $i\sqrt{2}$ **56.** $-96 - 40i$
57. $2 + i\sqrt{2}$ **58.** $\left\{-8, \frac{1}{2}\right\}$ **59.** {−4, 0} **60.** {−8, 8} **61.** $\{-4i, 4i\}$ **62.** $\{-3 - i\sqrt{10}, -3 + i\sqrt{10}\}$ **63.** $\left\{\frac{4 - 3\sqrt{2}}{3}, \frac{4 + 3\sqrt{2}}{3}\right\}$
64. 100; $(x + 10)^2$ **65.** $\frac{9}{4}$; $\left(x - \frac{3}{2}\right)^2$ **66.** {3, 9} **67.** $\left\{2 + \frac{\sqrt{3}}{3}, 2 - \frac{\sqrt{3}}{3}\right\}$ **68.** $\{1 + \sqrt{5}, 1 - \sqrt{5}\}$ **69.** $\{1 + 3i\sqrt{2}, 1 - 3i\sqrt{2}\}$
70. $\left\{\frac{-2 + \sqrt{10}}{2}, \frac{-2 - \sqrt{10}}{2}\right\}$ **71.** −36; 2 complex imaginary solutions **72.** 81; 2 unequal real solutions **73.** $\left\{\frac{1}{2}, 5\right\}$ **74.** $\left\{-2, \frac{10}{3}\right\}$
75. $\left\{\frac{7 + \sqrt{37}}{6}, \frac{7 - \sqrt{37}}{6}\right\}$ **76.** {−3, 3} **77.** {−2, 8} **78.** $\left\{\frac{1}{6} + i\frac{\sqrt{23}}{6}, \frac{1}{6} - i\frac{\sqrt{23}}{6}\right\}$ **79.** $\left\{-\frac{2}{3}, 4\right\}$ **80.** $\{-2 - 2i, -2 + 2i\}$
81. $\{4 + \sqrt{5}, 4 - \sqrt{5}\}$ **82.** 14 weeks **83.** 2012 **84.** length = 5 yd; width = 3 yd **85.** approximately 134 m **86.** {−5, 0, 5}
87. $\left\{-3, \frac{1}{2}, 3\right\}$ **88.** {2} **89.** {8} **90.** {16} **91.** {132} **92.** {−2, −1, 1, 2} **93.** {16} **94.** {−4, 3} **95.** {−5, 11}
96. $\left\{-1, -\frac{2\sqrt{6}}{9}, \frac{2\sqrt{6}}{9}, 1\right\}$ **97.** {2} **98.** {1, 4} **99.** {−3, −2, 3} **100.** {2} **101.** $\{-3, -\sqrt{2}, \sqrt{2}\}$ **102.** {−4, 2} **103.** 2007

104. $\{x \mid -3 \leq x < 5\}$

105. $\{x \mid x > -2\}$

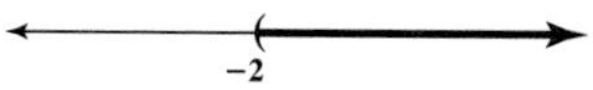

106. $\{x \mid x \leq 0\}$

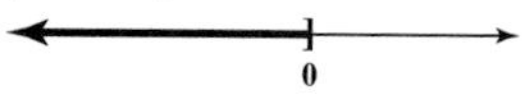

107. [−1, 1] **108.** (−2, 3)
109. [1, 3) **110.** (0, 4)

111. $[-2, \infty)$
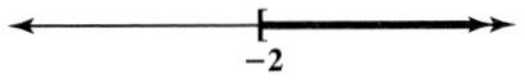

112. $\left[\frac{3}{5}, \infty\right)$
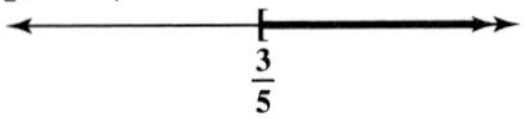

113. $\left(-\infty, -\frac{21}{2}\right)$
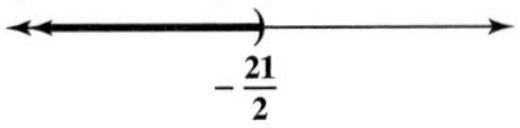

114. $(-3, \infty)$
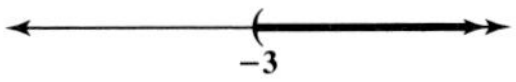

115. $(-\infty, -2]$
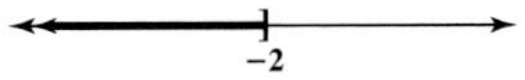

116. $\varnothing$

117. $(2, 3]$

118. $[-9, 6]$

119. $(-\infty, -6)$ or $(0, \infty)$
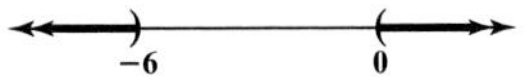

120. $(-\infty, -3]$ or $[-2, \infty)$

121. $(-\infty, -5] \cup [1, \infty)$;

122. $(-\infty, -1)$ **123.** $[-2, 7]$ **124.** no more than 80 miles per day **125.** $[49\%, 99\%)$ **126.** at least \$120,000

Chapter 1 Test

1. $\{-1\}$ **2.** $\{-1\}$ **3.** $\{-6\}$ **4.** $\{5\}$ **5.** $\left\{-\frac{1}{2}, 2\right\}$ **6.** $\left\{\frac{1-5\sqrt{3}}{3}, \frac{1+5\sqrt{3}}{3}\right\}$ **7.** $\{-3-5i, -3+5i\}$

8. $\{1-\sqrt{5}, 1+\sqrt{5}\}$ **9.** $\left\{1+\frac{1}{2}i, 1-\frac{1}{2}i\right\}$ **10.** $\{-1, 1, 4\}$ **11.** $\{7\}$ **12.** $\{2\}$ **13.** $\{5\}$ **14.** $\{\sqrt[3]{4}\}$ **15.** $\{1, 512\}$

16. $\{6, 12\}$ **17.** $\left\{\frac{1}{2}, 3\right\}$ **18.** $\{2-\sqrt{3}, 2+\sqrt{3}\}$ **19.** $\{4\}$

20. $(-\infty, 12]$
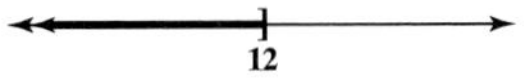

21. $\left[\frac{21}{8}, \infty\right)$
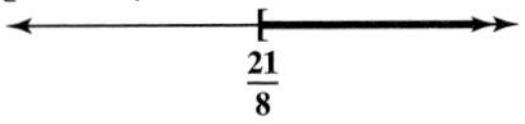

22. $\left[-7, \frac{13}{2}\right)$
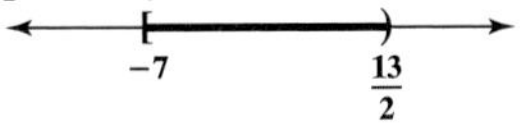

23. $\left(-\infty, -\frac{5}{3}\right]$ or $\left[\frac{1}{3}, \infty\right)$
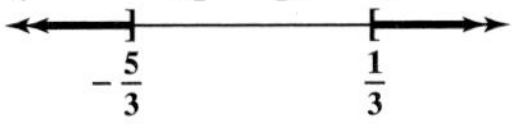

24. $[1, 6]$ **25.** $(-\infty, -2] \cup [6, \infty)$ **26.** $[-1, 5]$ **27.** $(0, 2)$ **28.** $h = \frac{3V}{lw}$ **29.** $x = \frac{y - y_1}{m} + x_1$

30.
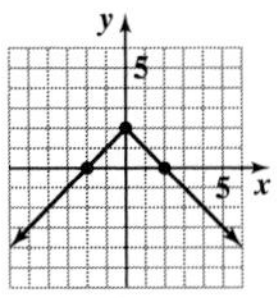

$y = 2 - |x|$

31.
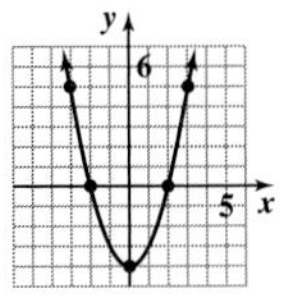

$y = x^2 - 4$

32. $47 + 16i$ **33.** $2 + i$ **34.** $38i$ **35.** 2018 **36.** 2018
37. quite well **38.** 2002: 782 books; 2003: 844 books; 2003: 972 books
39. 26 yr; \$33,600 **40.** \$3000 at 8%; \$7000 at 10%
41. length = 12 ft; width = 4 ft **42.** 10 ft **43.** \$50
44. more than 200 calls

CHAPTER 2

Section 2.1

Check Point Exercises

1. domain: $\{5, 10, 15, 20, 25\}$; range: $\{12.8, 16.2, 18.9, 20.7, 21.8\}$ **2. a.** not a function **b.** function **3. a.** $y = 6 - 2x$; function
b. $y = \pm\sqrt{1 - x^2}$; not a function **4. a.** 42 **b.** $x^2 + 6x + 15$ **c.** $x^2 + 2x + 7$

5.
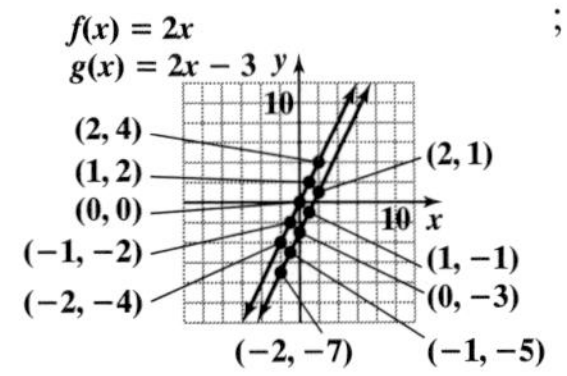

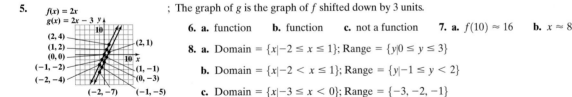

; The graph of g is the graph of f shifted down by 3 units.

6. a. function **b.** function **c.** not a function **7. a.** $f(10) \approx 16$ **b.** $x \approx 8$

8. a. Domain = $\{x|-2 \le x \le 1\}$; Range = $\{y|0 \le y \le 3\}$

b. Domain = $\{x|-2 < x \le 1\}$; Range = $\{y|-1 \le y < 2\}$

c. Domain = $\{x|-3 \le x < 0\}$; Range = $\{-3, -2, -1\}$

Exercise Set 2.1

1. function; $\{1, 3, 5\}$; $\{2, 4, 5\}$ **3.** not a function; $\{3, 4\}$; $\{4, 5\}$ **5.** function; $\{3, 4, 5, 7\}$; $\{-2, 1, 9\}$ **7.** function; $\{-3, -2, -1, 0\}$; $\{-3, -2, -1, 0\}$
9. not a function; $\{1\}$; $\{4, 5, 6\}$ **11.** y is a function of x. **13.** y is a function of x. **15.** y is not a function of x.
17. y is not a function of x. **19.** y is a function of x. **21.** y is a function of x. **23.** y is a function of x. **25.** y is a function of x.
27. a. 29 **b.** $4x + 9$ **c.** $-4x + 5$ **29. a.** 2 **b.** $x^2 + 12x + 38$ **c.** $x^2 - 2x + 3$ **31. a.** 13 **b.** 1 **c.** $x^4 - x^2 + 1$
d. $81a^4 - 9a^2 + 1$ **33. a.** 3 **b.** 7 **c.** $\sqrt{x} + 3$ **35. a.** $\frac{15}{4}$ **b.** $\frac{15}{4}$ **c.** $\frac{4x^2 - 1}{x^2}$ **37. a.** 1 **b.** -1 **c.** 1

39.

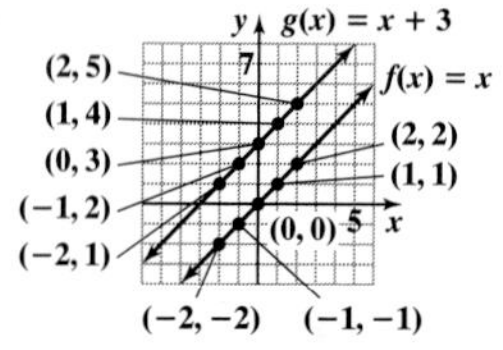

The graph of g is the graph of f shifted up by 3 units.

41.

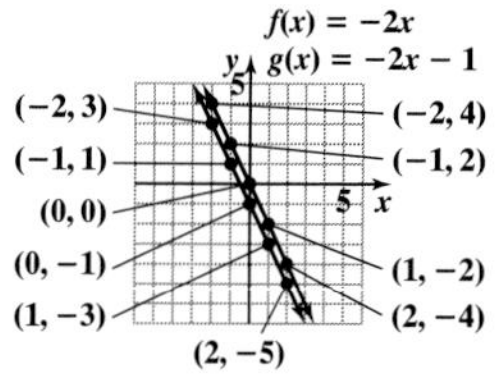

The graph of g is the graph of f shifted down by 1 unit.

43.

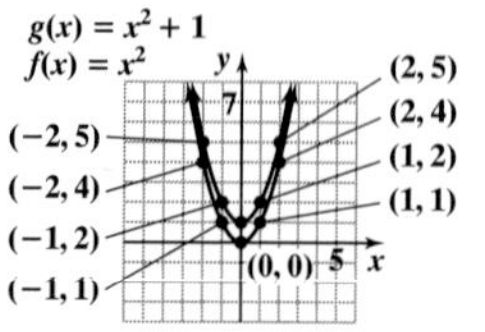

The graph of g is the graph of f shifted up by 1 unit.

45.

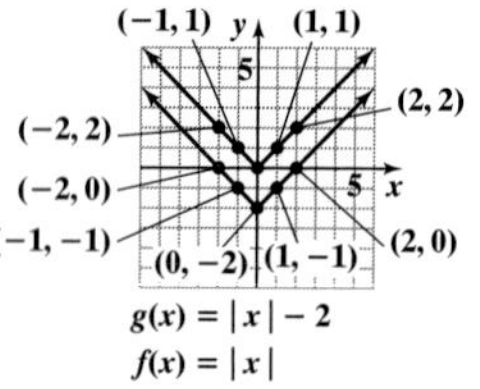

The graph of g is the graph of f shifted down by 2 units.

47.

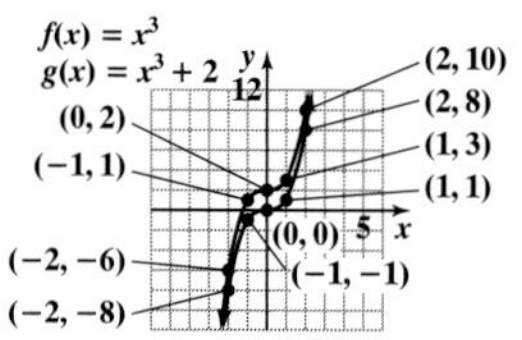

The graph of g is the graph of f shifted up by 2 units.

49.

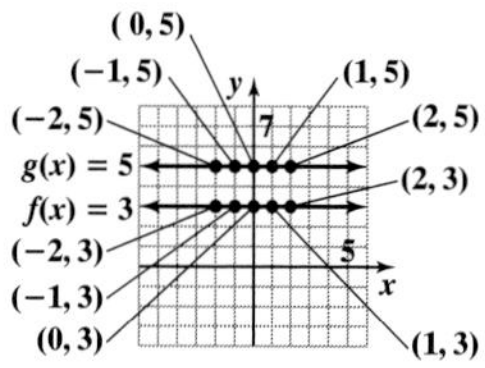

The graph of g is the graph of f shifted up by 2 units.

51.

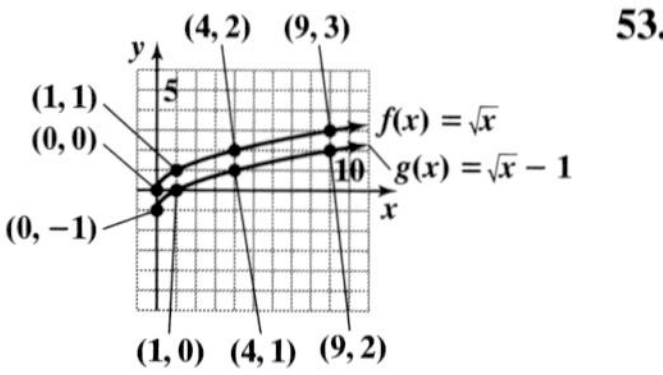

The graph of g is the graph of f shifted down by 1 unit.

53.

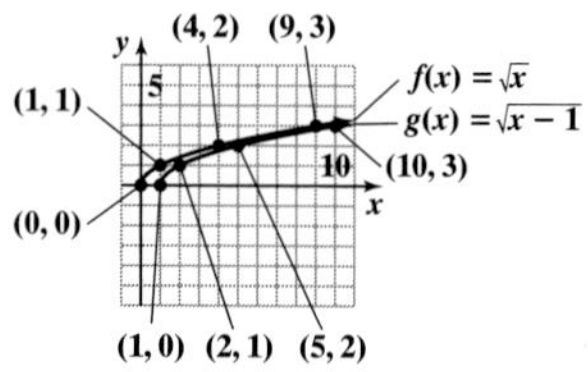

The graph of g is the graph of f shifted to the right by 1 unit.

55. function **57.** function **59.** not a function **61.** function **63.** function **65.** -4 **67.** 4 **69.** 0 **71.** 2 **73.** 2 **75.** -2 **77. a.** $(-\infty, \infty)$ **b.** $[-4, \infty)$ **c.** -3 and 1 **d.** -3 **e.** $f(-2) = -3$ and $f(2) = 5$ **79. a.** $(-\infty, \infty)$ **b.** $[1, \infty)$ **c.** none **d.** 1 **e.** $f(-1) = 2$ and $f(3) = 4$ **81. a.** $[0, 5)$ **b.** $[-1, 5)$ **c.** 2 **d.** -1 **e.** $f(3) = 1$ **83. a.** $[0, \infty)$ **b.** $[1, \infty)$ **c.** none **d.** 1 **e.** $f(4) = 3$ **85. a.** $[-2, 6]$ **b.** $[-2, 6]$ **c.** 4 **d.** 4 **e.** $f(-1) = 5$ **87. a.** $(-\infty, \infty)$ **b.** $(-\infty, -2]$ **c.** none **d.** -2 **e.** $f(-4) = -5$ and $f(4) = -2$ **89. a.** $(-\infty, \infty)$ **b.** $(0, \infty)$ **c.** none **d.** 1.5 **e.** $f(4) = 6$ **91. a.** $\{-5, -2, 0, 1, 3\}$ **b.** $\{2\}$ **c.** none **d.** 2 **e.** $f(-5) + f(3) = 4$ **93.** -2; 10 **95.** -38 **97.** $-2x^3 - 2x$ **99. a.** {(U.S., 80%), (Japan, 64%), (France, 64%), (Germany, 61%), (England, 59%), (China, 47%)} **b.** Yes; Each country corresponds to a unique percent. **c.** {(80%, U.S.), (64%, Japan), (64%, France), (61%, Germany), (59% England), (47%, China)} **d.** No; 64% in the domain corresponds to two members of the range, Japan and France. **101.** 5.22; In 2000, there were 5.22 million women enrolled in U.S. colleges; (2000, 5.22). **103.** 1.4; In 2004, there were 1.4 million more women than men enrolled in U.S. colleges. **105. a.** 73% **b.** 72.8% **c.** 73.3% **107.** $C = 100{,}000 + 100x$, where x is the number of bicycles produced; $C(90) = 109{,}000$; It cost \$109,000 to produce 90 bicycles. **109.** $T = \frac{40}{x} + \frac{40}{x + 30}$, where x is the rate on the outgoing trip; $T(30) = 2$; It takes 2 hours, traveling 30 mph outgoing and 60 mph returning. **121.** c **123.** Answers will vary; an example is $\{(1, 1), (2, 1)\}$.

Section 2.2

Check Point Exercises

1. a. $-2x^2 - 4xh - 2h^2 + x + h + 5$ **b.** $-4x - 2h + 1$ **2. a.** 20; With 40 calling minutes, the cost is \$20; (40, 20). **b.** 28; With 80 calling minutes, the cost is \$28; (80, 28). **3.** increasing on $(-\infty, -1)$, decreasing on $(-1, 1)$, increasing on $(1, \infty)$ **4. a.** even **b.** odd **c.** neither

Exercise Set 2.2

1. $4, h \neq 0$ **3.** $3, h \neq 0$ **5.** $2x + h, h \neq 0$ **7.** $2x + h - 4, h \neq 0$ **9.** $4x + 2h + 1, h \neq 0$ **11.** $-2x - h + 2, h \neq 0$ **13.** $-4x - 2h + 5, h \neq 0$ **15.** $-4x - 2h - 1, h \neq 0$ **17.** $0, h \neq 0$ **19.** $-\frac{1}{x(x + h)}, h \neq 0$ **21.** $\frac{1}{\sqrt{x + h} + \sqrt{x}}, h \neq 0$ **23. a.** -1 **b.** 7 **c.** 19 **25. a.** 3 **b.** 3 **c.** 0 **27. a.** 8 **b.** 3 **c.** 6 **29. a.** increasing: $(-1, \infty)$ **b.** decreasing: $(-\infty, -1)$ **c.** constant: none **31. a.** increasing: $(0, \infty)$ **b.** decreasing: none **c.** constant: none **33. a.** increasing: none **b.** decreasing: $(-2, 6)$ **c.** constant: none **35. a.** increasing: $(-\infty, -1)$ **b.** decreasing: none **c.** constant: $(-1, \infty)$ **37. a.** increasing: $(-\infty, 0)$ or $(1.5, 3)$ **b.** decreasing: $(0, 1.5)$ or $(3, \infty)$ **c.** constant: none **39. a.** increasing: $(-2, 4)$ **b.** decreasing: none **c.** constant: $(-\infty, -2)$ or $(4, \infty)$ **41. a.** $0; f(0) = 4$ **b.** $-3, 3; f(-3) = f(3) = 0$ **43. a.** $-2; f(-2) = 21$ **b.** $1; f(1) = -6$ **45.** odd **47.** neither **49.** even **51.** even **53.** even **55.** odd **57.** even **59.** odd **61. a.** $(-\infty, \infty)$ **b.** $[-4, \infty)$ **c.** 1 and 7 **d.** 4 **e.** $(4, \infty)$ **f.** $(0, 4)$ **g.** $(-\infty, 0)$ **h.** 4 **i.** -4 **j.** 4 **k.** 2 and 6 **l.** neither **63. a.** $(-\infty, 3]$ **b.** $(-\infty, 4]$ **c.** -3 and 3 **d.** 3 **e.** $(-\infty, 1)$ **f.** $(1, 3)$ **g.** $(-\infty, -3]$ **h.** A relative maximum of 4 occurs at 1. **i.** 1 **j.** positive

65. $f(1.06) = 1$ **67.** $f\left(\frac{1}{3}\right) = 0$ **69.** $f(-2.3) = -3$ **71.** -18

73. $0.30t - 6$

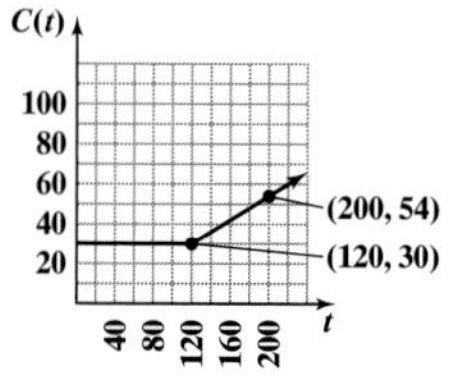

75. $C(t) = \begin{cases} 50 & \text{if } 0 \leq t \leq 400 \\ 50 + 0.30(t - 400) & \text{if } t > 400 \end{cases}$

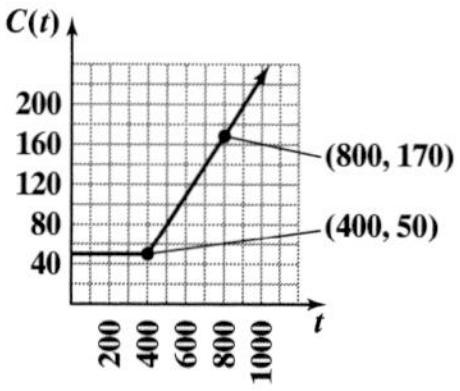

77. $f(60) \approx 3.1$; In 1960, Jewish Americans made up about 3.1% of the U.S. population. **79.** $x \approx 19$ and $x \approx 64$; In 1919 and 1964, Jewish Americans made up about 3% of the U.S. population. **81.** 1940; 3.7% **83.** Each year corresponds to only one percentage. **85.** increasing: (45, 74); decreasing: (16, 45); The number of accidents occurring per 50,000 miles driven increases with age starting at age 45, while it decreases with age starting at age 16. **87.** Answers will vary; an example is 16 and 74 years old. For those ages, the number of accidents is 526.4 per 50 million miles. **89.** 1989 cigarettes per adult; quite well **91.** 1960; 4100 cigarettes per adult; The function estimates 3797 cigarettes per adult, which models the graph reasonably well.

93.

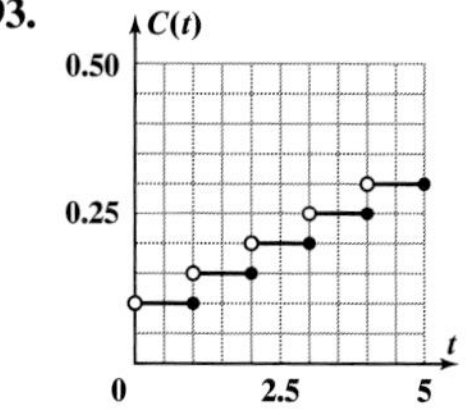

103. a.

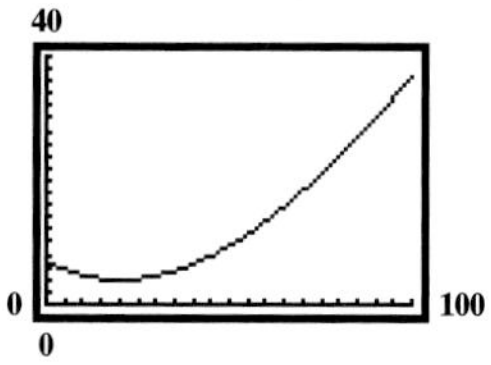

The number of doctor visits decreases during childhood and then increases as you get older. The minimum is (20.29, 3.99), which means that the minimum number of annual doctor visits, about 4, occurs at around age 20.

105.

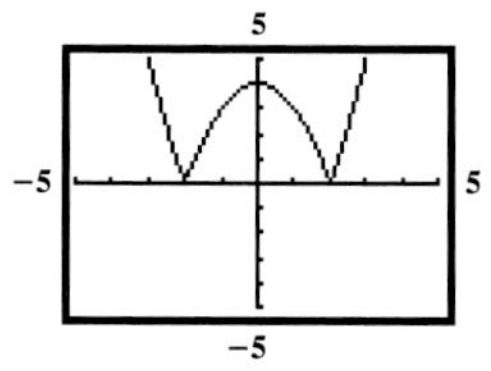

Increasing: $(-2, 0)$ or $(2, \infty)$
Decreasing: $(-\infty, -2)$ or $(0, 2)$

107.

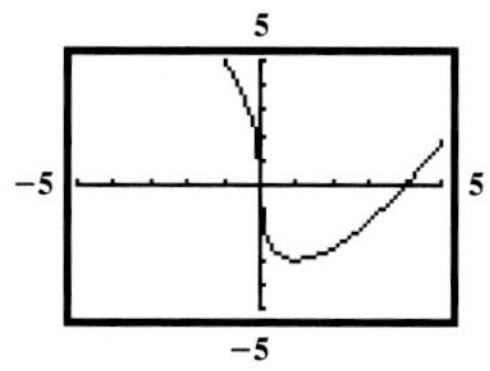

Increasing: $(1, \infty)$
Decreasing: $(-\infty, 1)$

109.

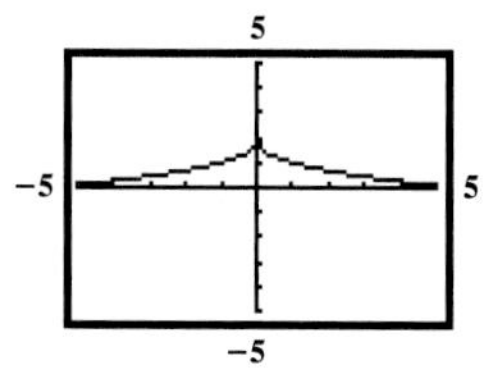

Increasing: $(-\infty, 0)$
Decreasing: $(0, \infty)$

113. a. h is even if both f and g are even or if both f and g are odd.
b. h is odd if f is odd and g is even or if f is even and g is odd.

Section 2.3

Check Point Exercises

1. a. 6 **b.** $-\frac{7}{5}$ **2.** $y + 5 = 6(x - 2)$; $y = 6x - 17$ **3.** $y + 1 = -5(x + 2)$; $y = -5x - 11$

4.

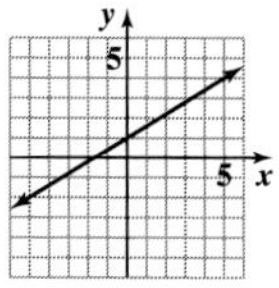

$f(x) = \frac{3}{5}x + 1$

5. $x = -3$

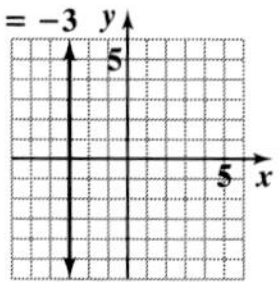

6. slope: $-\frac{1}{2}$; y-intercept: 2

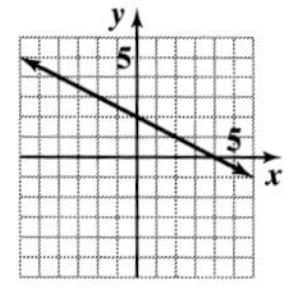

$3x + 6y - 12 = 0$

7.

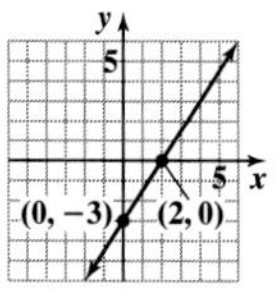

$3x - 2y = 6$

8. $y = 0.28x + 27.2$; 41.2

Exercise Set 2.3

1. $\frac{3}{4}$; rises **3.** $\frac{1}{4}$; rises **5.** 0; horizontal **7.** -5; falls **9.** undefined; vertical **11.** $y - 5 = 2(x - 3)$; $y = 2x - 1$
13. $y - 5 = 6(x + 2)$; $y = 6x + 17$ **15.** $y + 3 = -3(x + 2)$; $y = -3x - 9$ **17.** $y - 0 = -4(x + 4)$; $y = -4x - 16$
19. $y + 2 = -1\left(x + \frac{1}{2}\right)$; $y = -x - \frac{5}{2}$ **21.** $y - 0 = \frac{1}{2}(x - 0)$; $y = \frac{1}{2}x$ **23.** $y + 2 = -\frac{2}{3}(x - 6)$; $y = -\frac{2}{3}x + 2$
25. using $(1, 2)$, $y - 2 = 2(x - 1)$; $y = 2x$ **27.** using $(-3, 0)$, $y - 0 = 1(x + 3)$; $y = x + 3$ **29.** using $(-3, -1)$, $y + 1 = 1(x + 3)$; $y = x + 2$
31. using $(-3, -2)$, $y + 2 = \frac{4}{3}(x + 3)$; $y = \frac{4}{3}x + 2$ **33.** using $(-3, -1)$, $y + 1 = 0(x + 3)$; $y = -1$ **35.** using $(2, 4)$, $y - 4 = 1(x - 2)$; $y = x + 2$
37. using $(0, 4)$, $y - 4 = 8(x - 0)$; $y = 8x + 4$

39. $m = 2$; $b = 1$

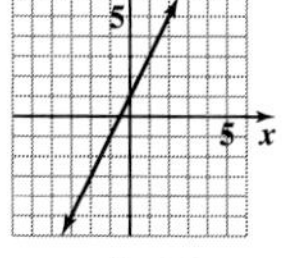

$y = 2x + 1$

41. $m = -2$; $b = 1$

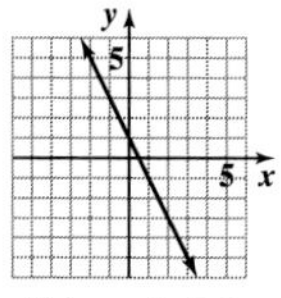

$f(x) = -2x + 1$

43. $m = \frac{3}{4}$; $b = -2$

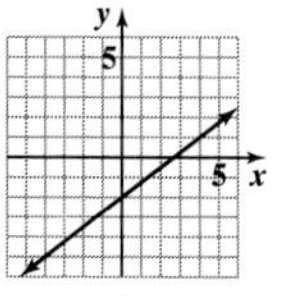

$f(x) = \frac{3}{4}x - 2$

45. $m = -\frac{3}{5}$; $b = 7$

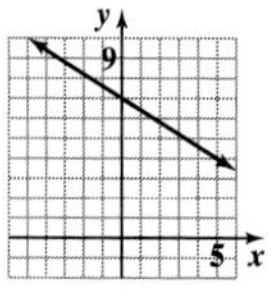

$y = -\frac{3}{5}x + 7$

47. $m = -\frac{1}{2}$; $b = 0$

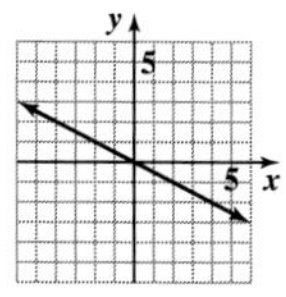

$g(x) = -\frac{1}{2}x$

49. $y = -2$

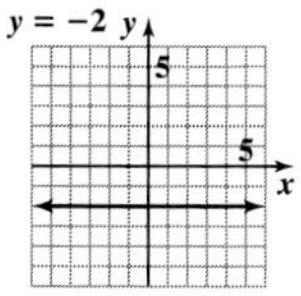

51. $x = -3$

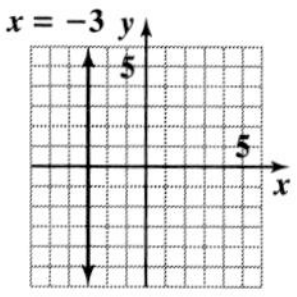

53. $y = 0$

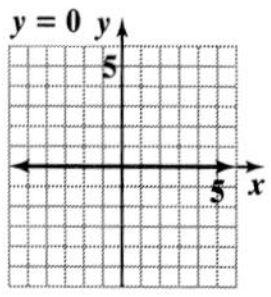

55.

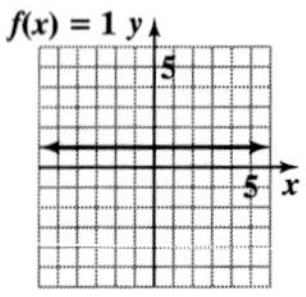

57.

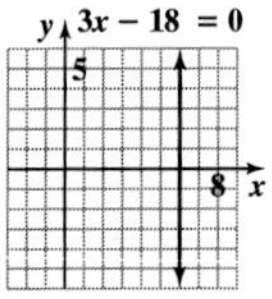
$3x - 18 = 0$
y
5
8
x

59. a. $y = -3x + 5$

b. $m = -3; b = 5$

c.

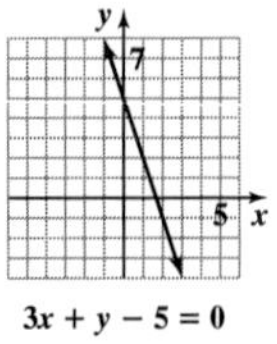
y
7
5
x
$3x + y - 5 = 0$

61. a. $y = -\frac{2}{3}x + 6$

b. $m = -\frac{2}{3}; b = 6$

c.

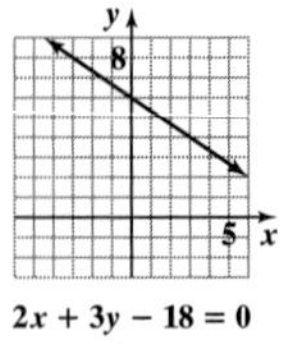

63. a. $y = 2x - 3$
b. $m = 2; b = -3$
c.

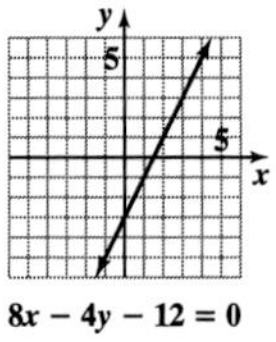
y
5
5
x
$8x - 4y - 12 = 0$

65. a. $y = 3$
b. $m = 0; b = 3$
c.

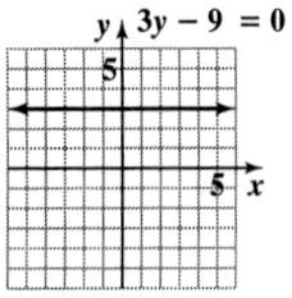
$3y - 9 = 0$
y
5
5
x

67.

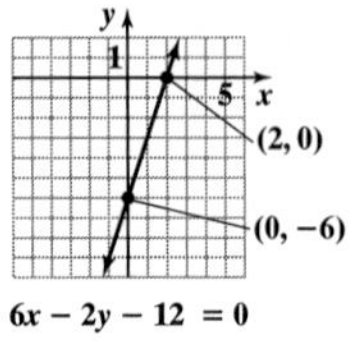
y
1
5
x
(2, 0)
(0, −6)
$6x - 2y - 12 = 0$

69.

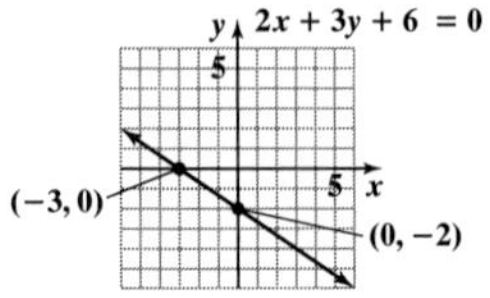
$2x + 3y + 6 = 0$
y
5
(−3, 0)
5
x
(0, −2)

71.

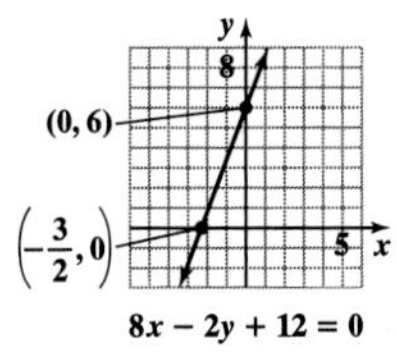
y
8
(0, 6)
$\left(-\frac{3}{2}, 0\right)$
5
x
$8x - 2y + 12 = 0$

73. $m = -\frac{a}{b}$; falls **75.** undefined slope; vertical **77.** $m = -\frac{A}{B}; b = \frac{C}{B}$ **79.** −2

81.

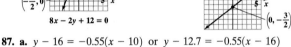

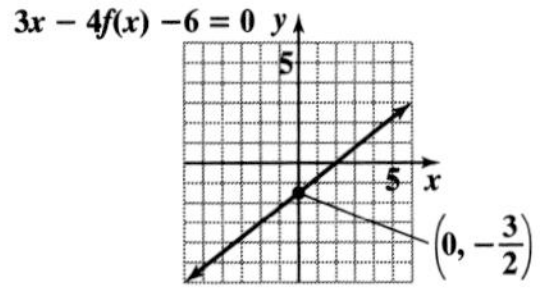

83. 5 **85.** m_1, m_3, m_2, m_4

87. a. $y - 16 = -0.55(x - 10)$ or $y - 12.7 = -0.55(x - 16)$ **b.** $f(x) = -0.55x + 21.5$ **c.** 10.5%

89. a.

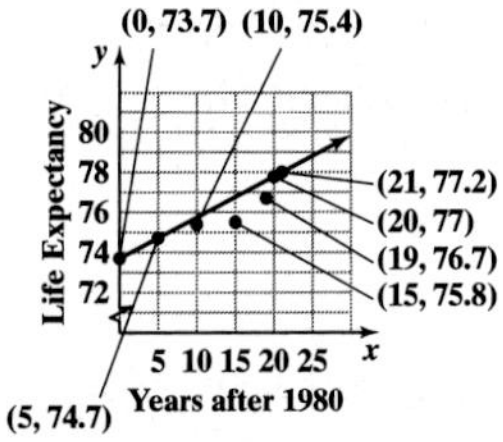
(0, 73.7) (10, 75.4)
y
Life Expectancy
80
78
76
74
72
(21, 77.2)
(20, 77)
(19, 76.7)
(15, 75.8)
5 10 15 20 25
x
(5, 74.7)
Years after 1980

b. $y - 74.7 = 0.15(x - 5)$ or $y - 77.0 = 0.15(x - 20)$;
$y = 0.15x + 73.95$ or $y = 0.15x + 74$

c. $E(x) = 0.15x + 73.95$ or $E(x) = 0.15x + 74$; 80 years

91. $y = -2.3x + 255$, where x is the percentage of adult females who are literate and y is under-five mortality per thousand; For each percent increase in adult female literacy, under-five mortality decreases by 2.3 per thousand.

101. $m = -3$

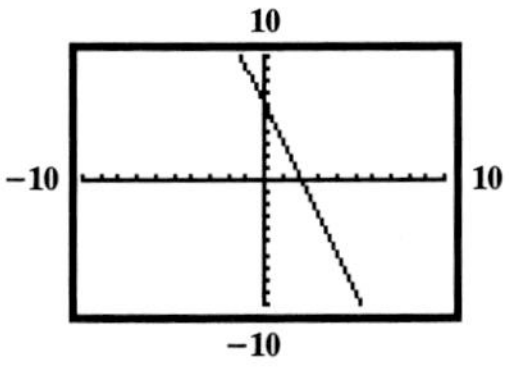

103. $m = \frac{3}{4}$

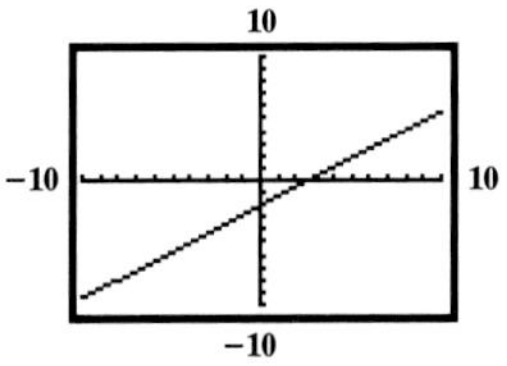

105. c **107.** coefficient of x: 1; coefficient of y: −2 **109.** $E = 2.4M - 20$

Section 2.4

Check Point Exercises

1. $y - 5 = 3(x + 2)$; $y = 3x + 11$ or $f(x) = 3x + 11$ **2. a.** 3 **b.** $3x - y = 0$ **3.** $\frac{2}{15} \approx 0.13$; The number of U.S. men living alone is projected to increase by 0.13 million each year. **4. a.** 1 **b.** 7 **c.** 4 **5.** 0.01 mg per 100 ml per hr

Exercise Set 2.4

1. $y - 2 = 2(x - 4)$; $y = 2x - 6$ or $f(x) = 2x - 6$ **3.** $y - 4 = -\frac{1}{2}(x - 2)$; $y = -\frac{1}{2}x + 5$ or $f(x) = -\frac{1}{2}x + 5$ **5.** $y + 10 = -4(x + 8)$; $y = -4x - 42$ **7.** $y + 3 = -5(x - 2)$; $y = -5x + 7$ **9.** $y - 2 = \frac{2}{3}(x + 2)$; $2x - 3y + 10 = 0$ **11.** $y + 7 = -2(x - 4)$; $2x + y - 1 = 0$ **13.** 3 **15.** 10 **17.** $\frac{1}{5}$ **19.** $f(x) = 5$ **21.** $f(x) = -\frac{1}{2}x + 1$ **23.** $f(x) = -\frac{2}{3}x - 2$

25. $m = 0.01$; The temperature of Earth is increasing by 0.01°F per year. **27.** $m = -0.52$; The percentage of U.S. adults who smoke cigarettes is decreasing by 0.52% each year. **29.** $f(x) = 13x + 222$ **31.** $f(x) = -2.40x + 52.40$ **33.** $m = -1.22$; average decrease of 1.22% of total sales per year

41. a. The product of their slopes is -1.

b.

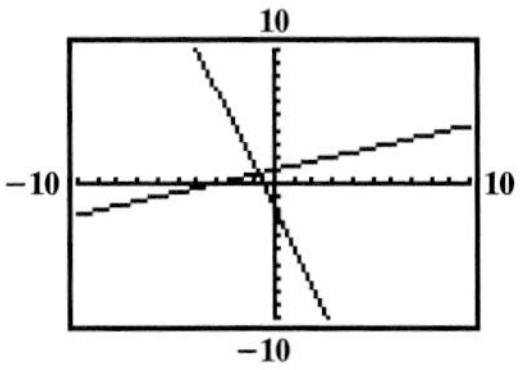

c.

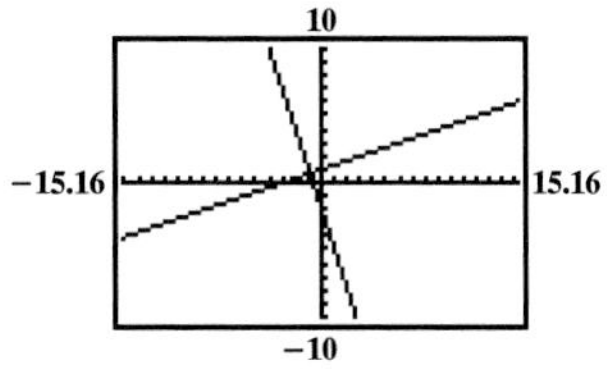

43.

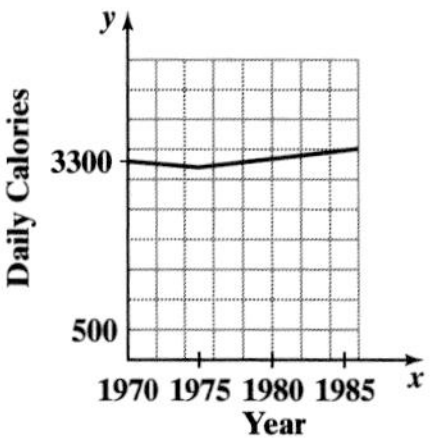

45. $-\frac{3}{7}$

Mid-Chapter 2 Check Point

1. not a function; Domain: $\{1, 2\}$; Range: $\{-6, 4, 6\}$ **2.** function; Domain: $\{0, 2, 3\}$; Range: $\{1, 4\}$ **3.** function; Domain: $\{x \mid -2 \le x < 2\}$; Range: $\{y \mid 0 \le y \le 3\}$ **4.** not a function; Domain: $\{x \mid -3 < x \le 4\}$; Range: $\{y \mid -1 \le y \le 2\}$ **5.** not a function; Domain: $\{-2, -1, 0, 1, 2\}$; Range: $\{-2, -1, 1, 3\}$ **6.** function; Domain: $\{x \mid x \le 1\}$; Range: $\{y \mid y \ge -1\}$ **7.** y is a function of x **8.** y is not a function of x **9.** No vertical line intersects the graph in more than one point. **10.** $(-\infty, \infty)$ **11.** $(-\infty, 4]$ **12.** -6 and 2 **13.** 3 **14.** $(-\infty, -2)$ **15.** $(-2, \infty)$ **16.** -2 **17.** 4 **18.** 3 **19.** -7 and 3 **20.** -6 and 2 **21.** $(-6, 2)$ **22.** negative **23.** neither **24.** -1

25. $y = -2x$

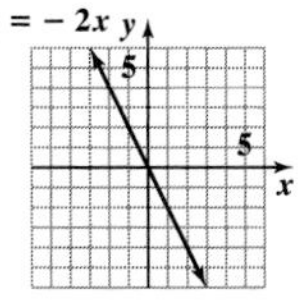

26. $y = -2$

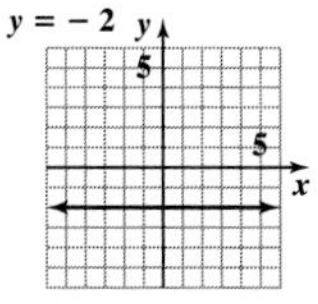

27. $x + y = -2$

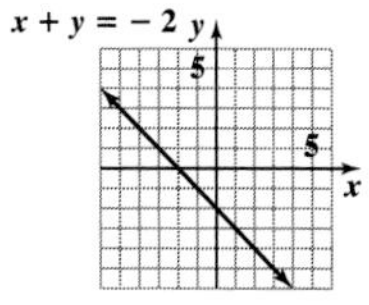

28. $y = \frac{1}{3}x - 2$

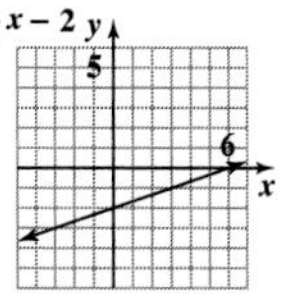

29. $x = 3.5$

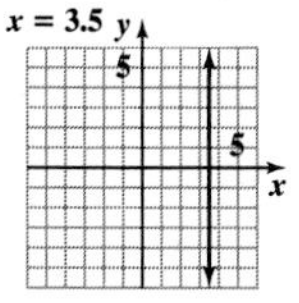

30.

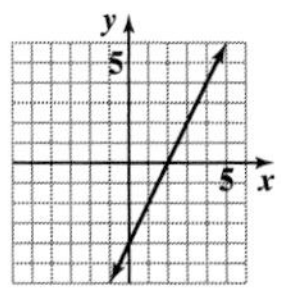

$4x - 2y = 8$

31.

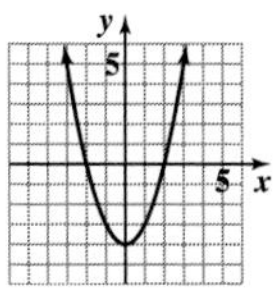

$f(x) = x^2 - 4$

32.

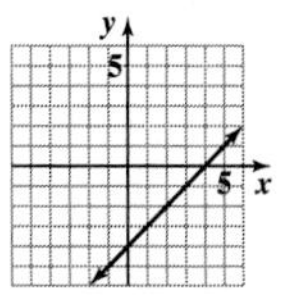

$f(x) = x - 4$

33.

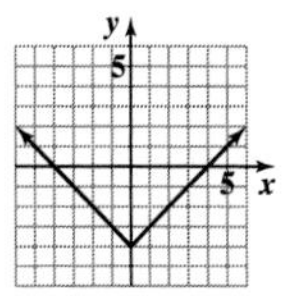

$f(x) = |x| - 4$

34.

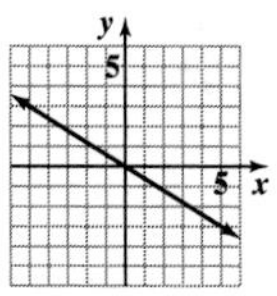

$5y = -3x$

35.

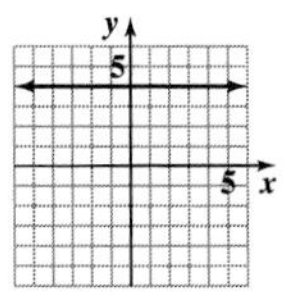

$5y = 20$

36.

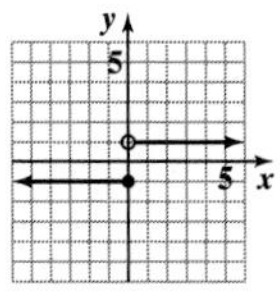

$f(x) = \begin{cases} -1 & \text{if } x \le 0 \\ 1 & \text{if } x > 0 \end{cases}$

37. a. $f(x) = -2x^2 - x - 5$; neither **b.** $-4x - 2h + 1$ **38. a.** 30 **b.** 50 **39.** $f(x) = -2x - 5$ **40.** $f(x) = 2x - 3$ **41.** $f(x) = 3x - 13$ **42.** $f(x) = -\frac{5}{2}x - 13$ **43.** The lines are parallel. **44.** $m = 7.8$; The percentage of U.S. colleges offering distance learning is increasing by 7.8% each year. **45.** 2

Section 2.5

Check Point Exercises

1.

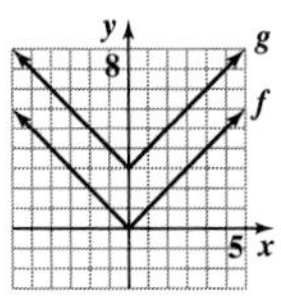

2.

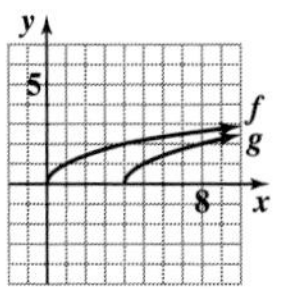

3.

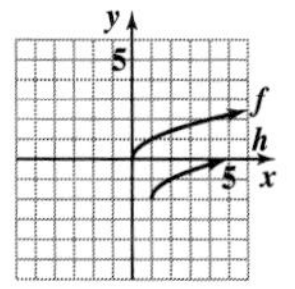

4.

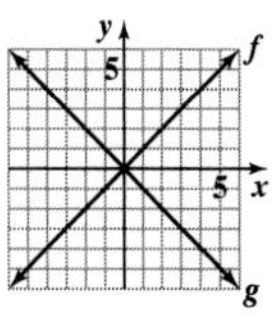

5.

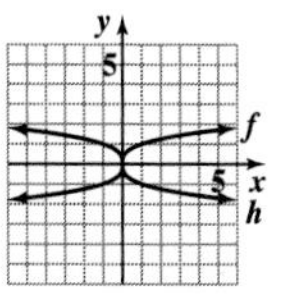

6.

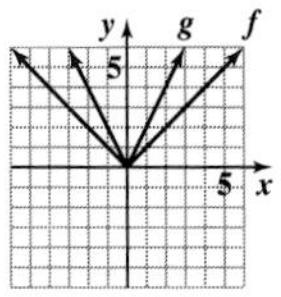

7. a.

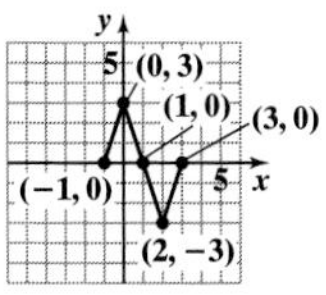

$g(x) = f(2x)$

b.

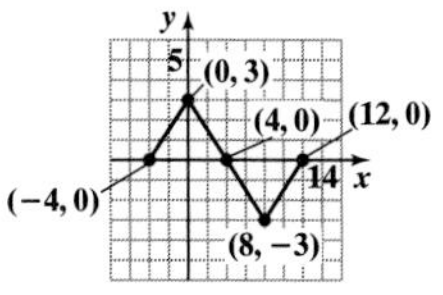

$h(x) = f\left(\frac{1}{2}x\right)$

8.

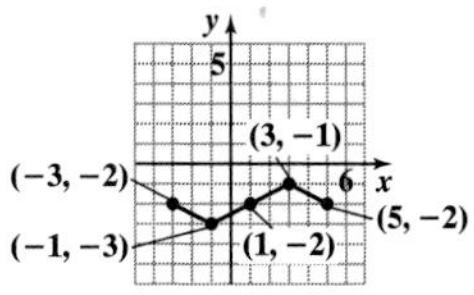

$y = -\frac{1}{3}f(x + 1) - 2$

9.

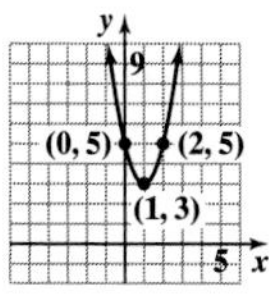

$g(x) = 2(x - 1)^2 + 3$

Exercise Set 2.5

1.

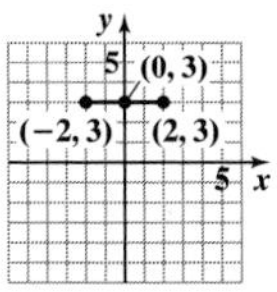

$g(x) = f(x) + 1$

3.

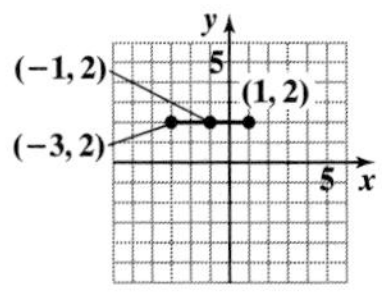

$g(x) = f(x + 1)$

5.

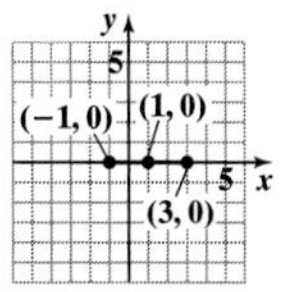

$g(x) = f(x - 1) - 2$

7.

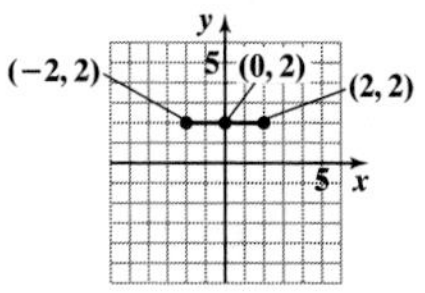

$g(x) = f(-x)$

9.

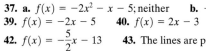

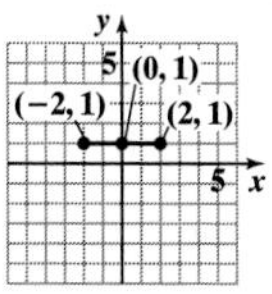

$g(x) = -f(x) + 3$

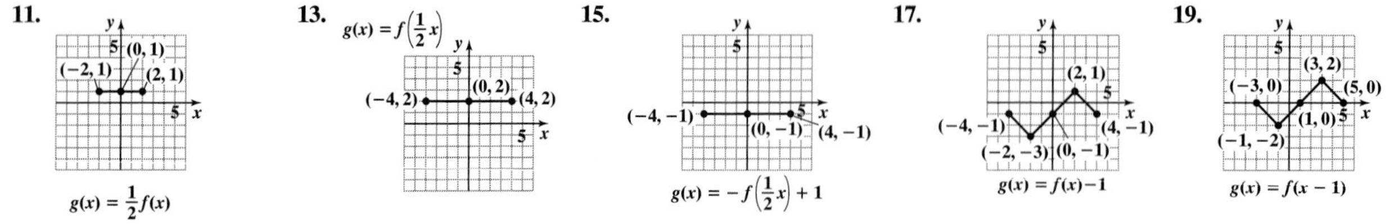

11. $g(x) = \frac{1}{2}f(x)$ 13. $g(x) = f\left(\frac{1}{2}x\right)$ 15. $g(x) = -f\left(\frac{1}{2}x\right) + 1$ 17. $g(x) = f(x) - 1$ 19. $g(x) = f(x - 1)$

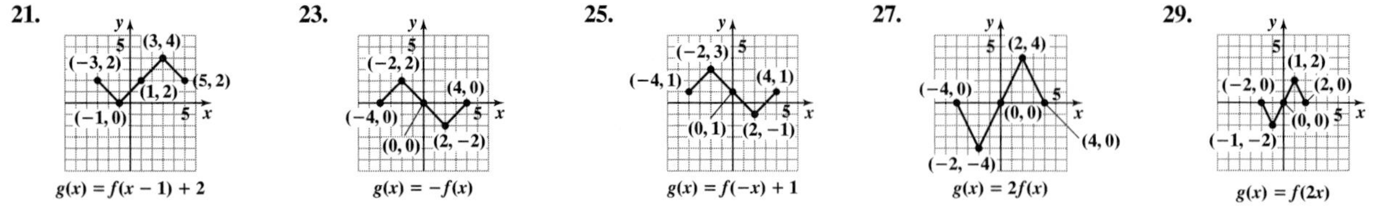

21. $g(x) = f(x - 1) + 2$ 23. $g(x) = -f(x)$ 25. $g(x) = f(-x) + 1$ 27. $g(x) = 2f(x)$ 29. $g(x) = f(2x)$

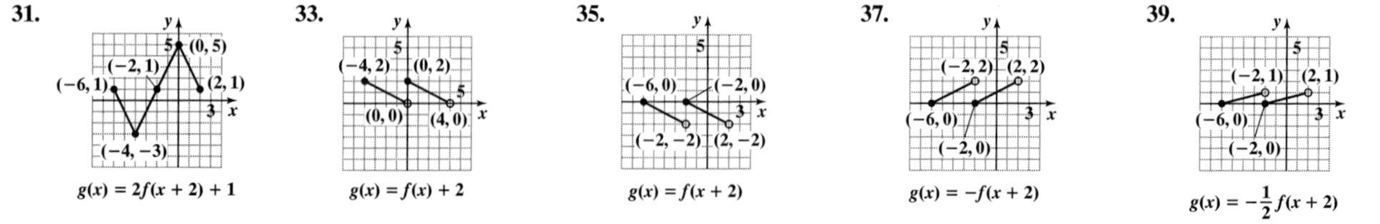

31. $g(x) = 2f(x + 2) + 1$ 33. $g(x) = f(x) + 2$ 35. $g(x) = f(x + 2)$ 37. $g(x) = -f(x + 2)$ 39. $g(x) = -\frac{1}{2}f(x + 2)$

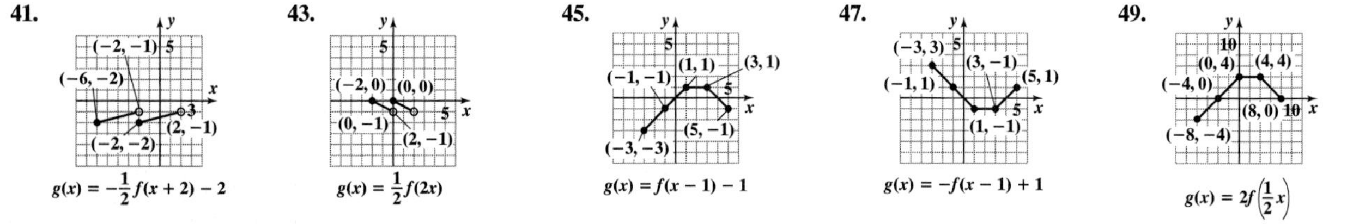

41. $g(x) = -\frac{1}{2}f(x + 2) - 2$ 43. $g(x) = \frac{1}{2}f(2x)$ 45. $g(x) = f(x - 1) - 1$ 47. $g(x) = -f(x - 1) + 1$ 49. $g(x) = 2f\left(\frac{1}{2}x\right)$

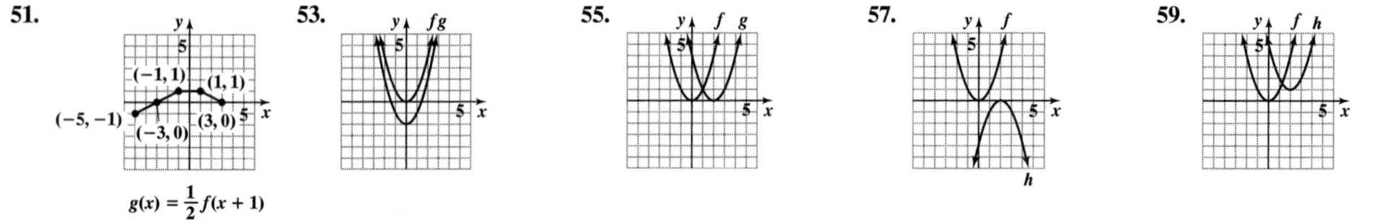
51.
(−1, 1)
(1, 1)
(−5, −1)
(3, 0)
(−3, 0)
53.
55.
57.
59.

51. $g(x) = \frac{1}{2}f(x + 1)$

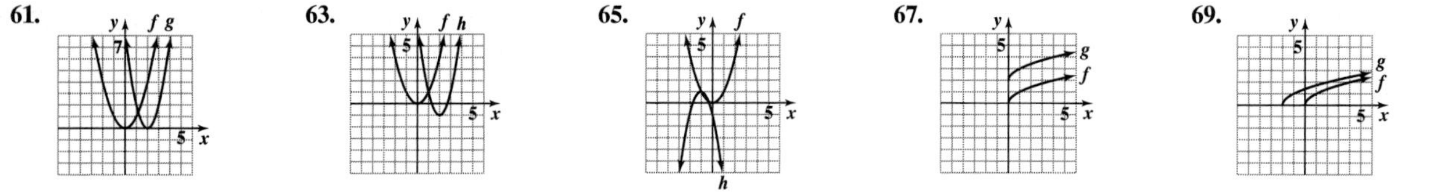
61.
63.
65.
67.
69.

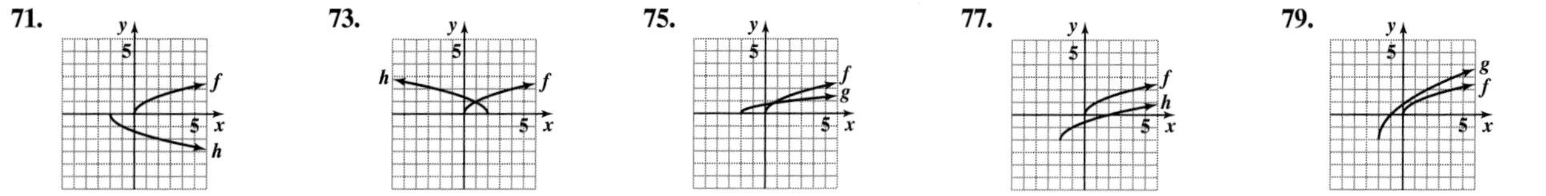
71.
73.
75.
77.
79.

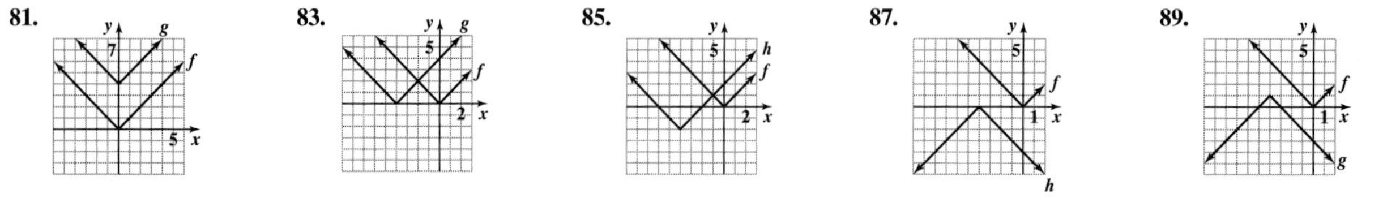
81.
83.
85.
87.
89.

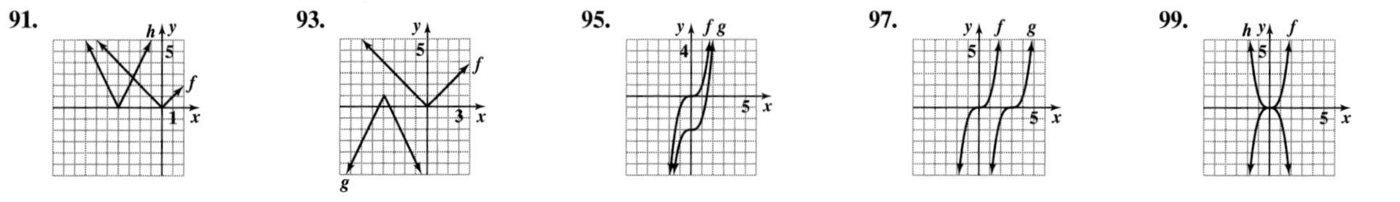
91.
93.
95.
97.
99.

101. 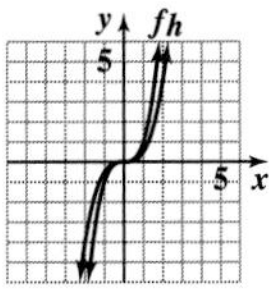

103. 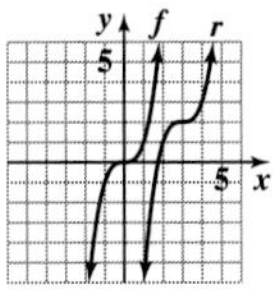

105. 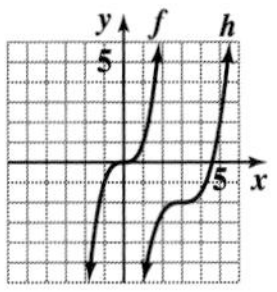

107. 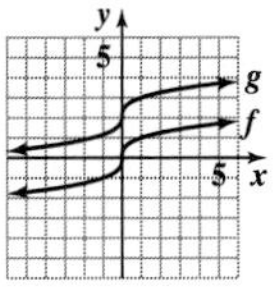

109. 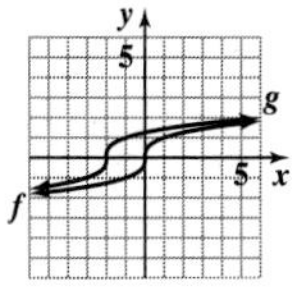

111. 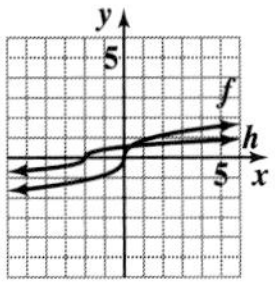

113. 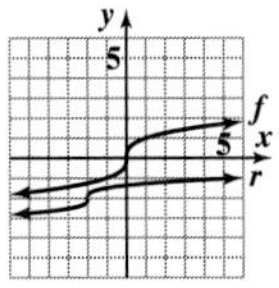

115. 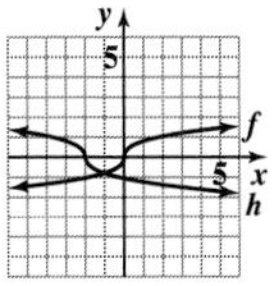

117. 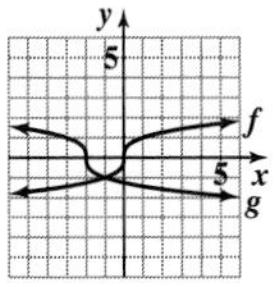

119. 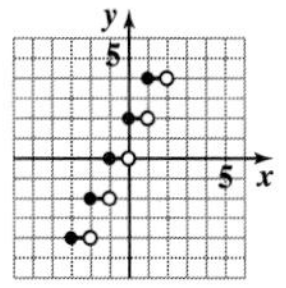

$g(x) = 2 \text{ int } (x + 1)$

121. 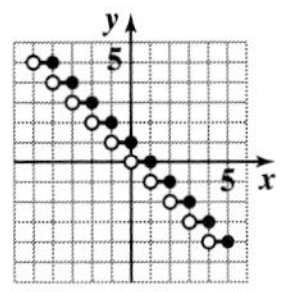

$h(x) = \text{int } (-x) + 1$

123. $y = \sqrt{x - 2}$ **125.** $y = (x + 1)^2 - 4$

127. a. First, vertically stretch the graph of $f(x) = \sqrt{x}$ by the factor 2.9; then, shift the result up 20.1 units. **b.** 40.2 in.; very well **c.** 0.9 in. per month **d.** 0.2 in. per month; This is a much smaller rate of change; The graph is not as steep between 50 and 60 as it is between 0 and 10.

135. a. 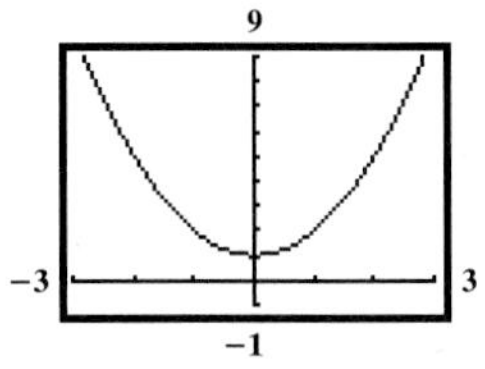

b. 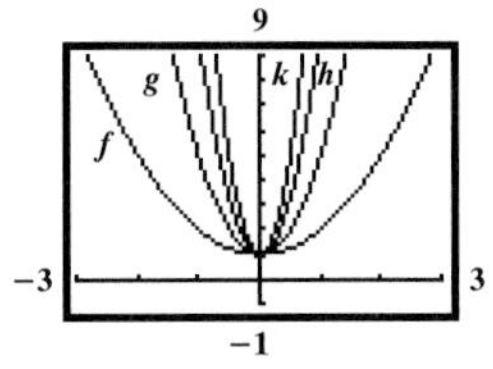

137. d **139.** $g(x) = -|x - 5| + 1$ **141.** $g(x) = -\frac{1}{4}\sqrt{16 - x^2} - 1$ **143.** $(a, 2b)$ **145.** $(a, b - 3)$

Section 2.6

Check Point Exercises

1. a. $(-\infty, \infty)$ **b.** $(-\infty, -7)\cup(-7, 7)\cup(7, \infty)$ **c.** $[3, \infty)$ **2. a.** $(f + g)(x) = x^2 + x - 6$ **b.** $(f - g)(x) = -x^2 + x - 4$ **c.** $(fg)(x) = x^3 - 5x^2 - x + 5$ **d.** $\left(\frac{f}{g}\right)(x) = \frac{x - 5}{x^2 - 1}, x \neq \pm 1$ **3. a.** $(f + g)(x) = \sqrt{x - 3} + \sqrt{x + 1}$ **b.** $[3, \infty)$ **4. a.** $(f \circ g)(x) = 10x^2 - 5x + 1$ **b.** $(g \circ f)(x) = 50x^2 + 115x + 65$ **5. a.** $(f \circ g)(x) = \frac{4x}{1 + 2x}$ **b.** $\left(-\infty, -\frac{1}{2}\right)\cup\left(-\frac{1}{2}, 0\right)\cup(0, \infty)$ **6.** if $f(x) = \sqrt{x}$ and $g(x) = x^2 + 5$, then $h(x) = (f \circ g)(x)$

Exercise Set 2.6

1. $(-\infty, \infty)$ **3.** $(-\infty, 4)\cup(4, \infty)$ **5.** $(-\infty, \infty)$ **7.** $(-\infty, -3)\cup(-3, 5)\cup(5, \infty)$ **9.** $(-\infty, -7)\cup(-7, 9)\cup(9, \infty)$ **11.** $(-\infty, -1)\cup(-1, 1)\cup(1, \infty)$ **13.** $(-\infty, 0)\cup(0, 3)\cup(3, \infty)$ **15.** $(-\infty, 1)\cup(1, 3)\cup(3, \infty)$ **17.** $[3, \infty)$ **19.** $(3, \infty)$ **21.** $[-7, \infty)$ **23.** $(-\infty, 12]$ **25.** $[2, \infty)$ **27.** $[2, 5)\cup(5, \infty)$ **29.** $(-\infty, -2)\cup(-2, 2)\cup(2, 5)\cup(5, \infty)$

31. $(f + g)(x) = 3x + 2$; Domain: $(-\infty, \infty)$; $(f - g)(x) = x + 4$; Domain: $(-\infty, \infty)$; $(fg)(x) = 2x^2 + x - 3$; Domain: $(-\infty, \infty)$; $\left(\frac{f}{g}\right)(x) = \frac{2x + 3}{x - 1}$; Domain: $(-\infty, 1)\cup(1, \infty)$ **33.** $(f + g)(x) = 3x^2 + x - 5$; Domain: $(-\infty, \infty)$; $(f - g)(x) = -3x^2 + x - 5$; Domain: $(-\infty, \infty)$; $(fg)(x) = 3x^3 - 15x^2$; Domain: $(-\infty, \infty)$; $\left(\frac{f}{g}\right)(x) = \frac{x - 5}{3x^2}$; Domain: $(-\infty, 0)\cup(0, \infty)$ **35.** $(f + g)(x) = 2x^2 - 2$; Domain: $(-\infty, \infty)$; $(f - g)(x) = 2x^2 - 2x - 4$; Domain: $(-\infty, \infty)$; $(fg)(x) = 2x^3 + x^2 - 4x - 3$; Domain: $(-\infty, \infty)$; $\left(\frac{f}{g}\right)(x) = 2x - 3$; Domain: $(-\infty, -1)\cup(-1, \infty)$

37. $(f + g)(x) = 2x - 12$; Domain: $(-\infty, \infty)$; $(f - g)(x) = -2x^2 - 2x + 18$; Domain: $(-\infty, \infty)$; $(fg)(x) = -x^4 - 2x^3 + 18x^2 + 6x - 45$; Domain: $(-\infty, \infty)$; $\left(\frac{f}{g}\right)(x) = \frac{3 - x^2}{x^2 + 2x - 15}$; Domain: $(-\infty, -5) \cup (-5, 3)\cup(3, \infty)$ **39.** $(f + g)(x) = \sqrt{x} + x - 4$; Domain: $[0, \infty)$; $(f - g)(x) = \sqrt{x} - x + 4$; Domain: $[0, \infty)$; $(fg)(x) = \sqrt{x}(x - 4)$; Domain: $[0, \infty)$; $\left(\frac{f}{g}\right)(x) = \frac{\sqrt{x}}{x - 4}$; Domain: $[0, 4)\cup(4, \infty)$

41. $(f + g)(x) = \frac{2x + 2}{x}$; Domain: $(-\infty, 0)\cup(0, \infty)$; $(f - g)(x) = 2$; Domain: $(-\infty, 0)\cup(0, \infty)$; $(fg)(x) = \frac{2x + 1}{x^2}$; Domain: $(-\infty, 0)\cup(0, \infty)$; $\left(\frac{f}{g}\right)(x) = 2x + 1$; Domain: $(-\infty, 0)\cup(0, \infty)$ **43.** $(f + g)(x) = \frac{9x - 1}{x^2 - 9}$; Domain: $(-\infty, -3)\cup(-3, 3)\cup(3, \infty)$; $(f - g)(x) = \frac{x + 3}{x^2 - 9} = \frac{1}{x - 3}$; Domain: $(-\infty, -3)\cup(-3, 3)\cup(3, \infty)$; $(fg)(x) = \frac{20x^2 - 6x - 2}{(x^2 - 9)^2}$;

Domain: $(-\infty, -3)\cup(-3, 3)\cup(3, \infty)$; $\left(\frac{f}{g}\right)(x) = \frac{5x + 1}{4x - 2}$; Domain: $(-\infty, -3)\cup\left(-3, \frac{1}{2}\right)\cup\left(\frac{1}{2}, 3\right)\cup(3, \infty)$

45. $(f + g)(x) = \sqrt{x + 4} + \sqrt{x - 1}$; Domain: $[1, \infty)$; $(f - g)(x) = \sqrt{x + 4} - \sqrt{x - 1}$; Domain: $[1, \infty)$; $(fg)(x) = \sqrt{x^2 + 3x - 4}$; Domain: $[1, \infty)$; $\left(\frac{f}{g}\right)(x) = \frac{\sqrt{x + 4}}{\sqrt{x - 1}}$; Domain: $(1, \infty)$ **47.** $(f + g)(x) = \sqrt{x - 2} + \sqrt{2 - x}$; Domain: $\{2\}$; $(f - g)(x) = \sqrt{x - 2} - \sqrt{2 - x}$; Domain: $\{2\}$; $(fg)(x) = \sqrt{x - 2} \cdot \sqrt{2 - x}$; Domain: $\{2\}$; $\left(\frac{f}{g}\right)(x) = \frac{\sqrt{x - 2}}{\sqrt{2 - x}}$; Domain: $\varnothing$ **49. a.** $(f \circ g)(x) = 2x + 14$ **b.** $(g \circ f)(x) = 2x + 7$ **c.** $(f \circ g)(2) = 18$ **51. a.** $(f \circ g)(x) = 2x + 5$ **b.** $(g \circ f)(x) = 2x + 9$ **c.** $(f \circ g)(2) = 9$ **53. a.** $(f \circ g)(x) = 20x^2 - 11$ **b.** $(g \circ f)(x) = 80x^2 - 120x + 43$ **c.** $(f \circ g)(2) = 69$ **55. a.** $(f \circ g)(x) = x^4 - 4x^2 + 6$ **b.** $(g \circ f)(x) = x^4 + 4x^2 + 2$ **c.** $(f \circ g)(2) = 6$ **57. a.** $(f \circ g)(x) = -2x^2 - x - 1$ **b.** $(g \circ f)(x) = 2x^2 - 17x + 41$ **c.** -11 **59. a.** $(f \circ g)(x) = \sqrt{x - 1}$ **b.** $(g \circ f)(x) = \sqrt{x} - 1$ **c.** $(f \circ g)(2) = 1$ **61. a.** $(f \circ g)(x) = x$ **b.** $(g \circ f)(x) = x$ **c.** $(f \circ g)(2) = 2$ **63. a.** $(f \circ g)(x) = x$ **b.** $(g \circ f)(x) = x$ **c.** 2 **65. a.** $(f \circ g)(x) = \frac{2x}{1 + 3x}$ **b.** $\left(-\infty, -\frac{1}{3}\right)\cup\left(-\frac{1}{3}, 0\right)\cup(0, \infty)$ **67. a.** $(f \circ g)(x) = \frac{4}{4 + x}$ **b.** $(-\infty, -4)\cup(-4, 0)\cup(0, \infty)$ **69. a.** $(f \circ g)(x) = \sqrt{x - 2}$ **b.** $[2, \infty)$ **71. a.** $(f \circ g)(x) = 5 - x$ **b.** $(-\infty, 1]$ **73.** $f(x) = x^4$, $g(x) = 3x - 1$ **75.** $f(x) = \sqrt[3]{x}$, $g(x) = x^2 - 9$ **77.** $f(x) = |x|$, $g(x) = 2x - 5$ **79.** $f(x) = \frac{1}{x}$, $g(x) = 2x - 3$ **81.** 5 **83.** -1 **85.** $\{x|-4 \le x \le 3\}$

87.

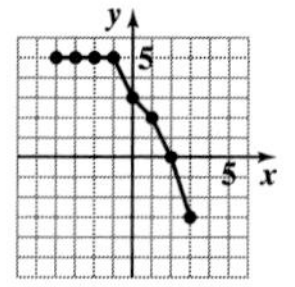

89. 1 **91.** -6 **93.** 1 and 2 **95.** $\{x|x = 0, 1, 2, \ldots, 8\}$ **97. a.** $(B - D)(x) = 8244x + 1{,}569{,}712$; change in U.S. population **b.** 1,635,664; In 2003, the U.S. population increased by 1,635,664. **c.** 1,670,000; fairly well **99.** $f + g$ represents the total world population in year x. **101.** $(f + g)(2000) \approx 6$ billion people **103.** $(R - C)(20{,}000) = -200{,}000$; The company lost \$200,000 since costs exceeded revenues; $(R - C)(30{,}000) = 0$; The company broke even since revenues equaled cost; $(R - C)(40{,}000) = 200{,}000$; The company made a profit of \$200,000. **105. a.** f gives the price of the computer after a \$400 discount. g gives the price of the computer after a 25% discount. **b.** $(f \circ g)(x) = 0.75x - 400$; This models the price of a computer after first a 25% discount and then a \$400 discount. **c.** $(g \circ f)(x) = 0.75(x - 400)$; This models the price of a computer after first a \$400 discount and then a 25% discount. **d.** The function $f \circ g$ models the greater discount, since the 25% discount is taken on the regular price first.

113.

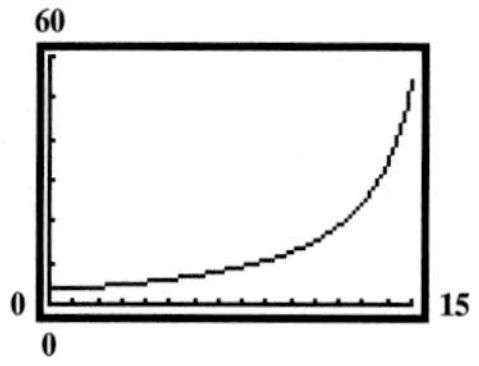

The per capita costs are increasing over time.

115.

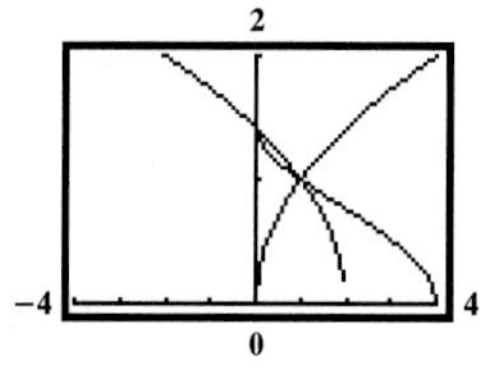

Domain: $[0, 4]$

117. Assume f and g are even; then $f(-x) = f(x)$ and $g(-x) = g(x)$. $(fg)(-x) = f(-x)g(-x) = f(x)g(x) = (fg)(x)$, so fg is even.

119.

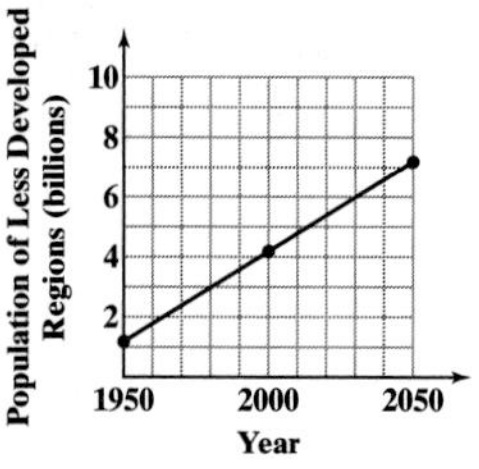

Section 2.7

Check Point Exercises

1. 13 **2.** $\left(4, -\frac{1}{2}\right)$ **3.** $x^2 + y^2 = 16$ **4.** $(x - 5)^2 + (y + 6)^2 = 100$

5. a. center: $(-3, 1)$; radius: 2

b.

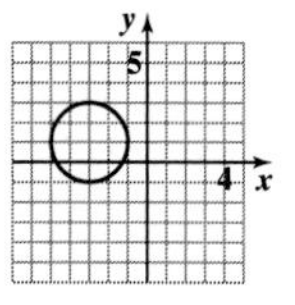

$(x + 3)^2 + (y - 1)^2 = 4$

c. Domain: $[-5, -1]$; Range: $[-1, 3]$

6. $(x + 2)^2 + (y - 2)^2 = 9$

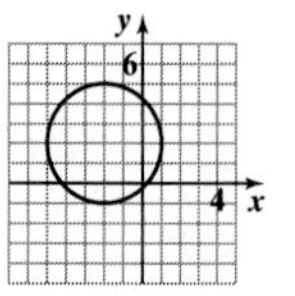

$x^2 + y^2 + 4x - 4y - 1 = 0$

Exercise Set 2.7

1. 13 **3.** $2\sqrt{29} \approx 10.77$ **5.** 5 **7.** $\sqrt{29} \approx 5.39$ **9.** $4\sqrt{2} \approx 5.66$ **11.** $2\sqrt{5} \approx 4.47$ **13.** $2\sqrt{2} \approx 2.83$ **15.** $\sqrt{93} \approx 9.64$ **17.** $\sqrt{5} \approx 2.24$ **19.** $(4, 6)$ **21.** $(-4, -5)$ **23.** $\left(\frac{3}{2}, -6\right)$ **25.** $(-3, -2)$ **27.** $(1, 5\sqrt{5})$ **29.** $(2\sqrt{2}, 0)$ **31.** $x^2 + y^2 = 49$ **33.** $(x - 3)^2 + (y - 2)^2 = 25$ **35.** $(x + 1)^2 + (y - 4)^2 = 4$ **37.** $(x + 3)^2 + (y + 1)^2 = 3$ **39.** $(x + 4)^2 + (y - 0)^2 = 100$

41. center: $(0, 0)$
radius: 4
Domain: $[-4, 4]$;
Range: $[-4, 4]$

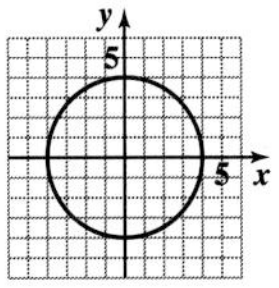

$x^2 + y^2 = 16$

43. center: $(3, 1)$
radius: 6
Domain: $[-3, 9]$;
Range: $[-5, 7]$

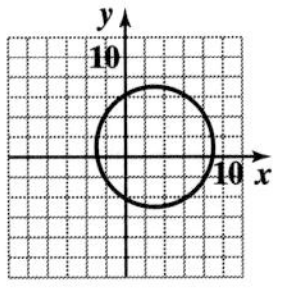

$(x - 3)^2 + (y - 1)^2 = 36$

45. center: $(-3, 2)$
radius: 2
Domain: $[-5, -1]$;
Range: $[0, 4]$

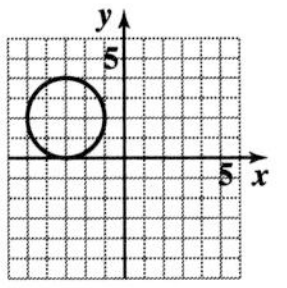

$(x + 3)^2 + (y - 2)^2 = 4$

47. center: $(-2, -2)$
radius: 2
Domain: $[-4, 0]$;
Range: $[-4, 0]$

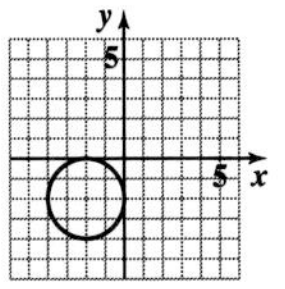

$(x + 2)^2 + (y + 2)^2 = 4$

49. $(x + 3)^2 + (y + 1)^2 = 4$
center: $(-3, -1)$
radius: 2

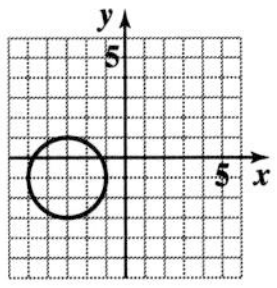

$x^2 + y^2 + 6x + 2y + 6 = 0$

51. $(x - 5)^2 + (y - 3)^2 = 64$
center: $(5, 3)$
radius: 8

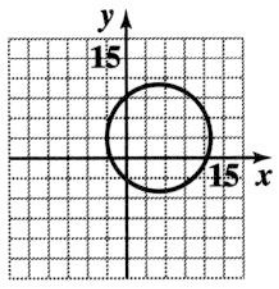

$x^2 + y^2 - 10x - 6y - 30 = 0$

53. $(x + 4)^2 + (y - 1)^2 = 25$
center: $(-4, 1)$
radius: 5

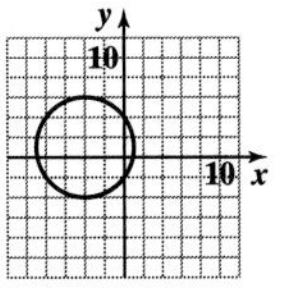

$x^2 + y^2 + 8x - 2y - 8 = 0$

55. $(x - 1)^2 + (y - 0)^2 = 16$
center: $(1, 0)$
radius: 4

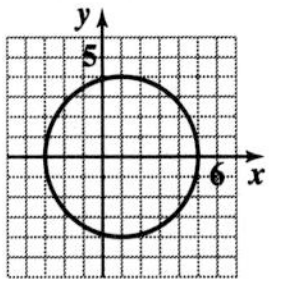

$x^2 - 2x + y^2 - 15 = 0$

57. $\left(x - \frac{1}{2}\right)^2 + (y + 1)^2 = \frac{1}{4}$
center: $\left(\frac{1}{2}, -1\right)$
radius: $\frac{1}{2}$

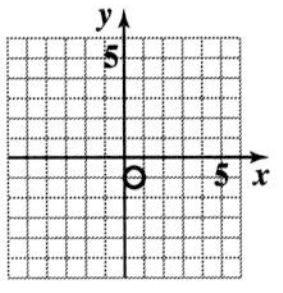

$x^2 + y^2 - x + 2y + 1 = 0$

59. $\left(x + \frac{3}{2}\right)^2 + (y - 1)^2 = \frac{17}{4}$
center: $\left(-\frac{1}{2}, -\frac{1}{2}\right)$
radius: $\frac{\sqrt{17}}{2}$

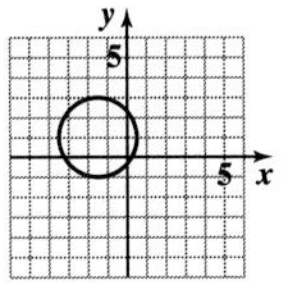

$x^2 + y^2 + 3x - 2y - 1 = 0$

61. a. $(5, 10)$ **b.** $\sqrt{5}$ **c.** $(x - 5)^2 + (y - 10)^2 = 5$

63. $\{(0, -4), (4, 0)\}$

$x^2 + y^2 = 16$
$x - y = 4$

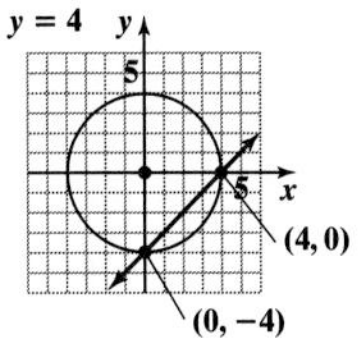

65. $\{(0, -3), (2, -1)\}$

$(x - 2)^2 + (y + 3)^2 = 4$
$y = x - 3$

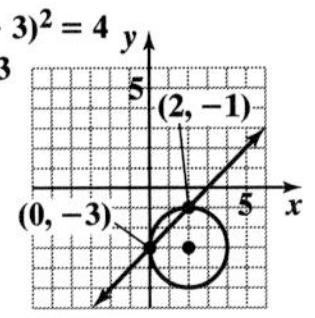

67. 0.5hr; 30 min **69.** $(x + 2.4)^2 + (y + 2.7)^2 = 900$

77.

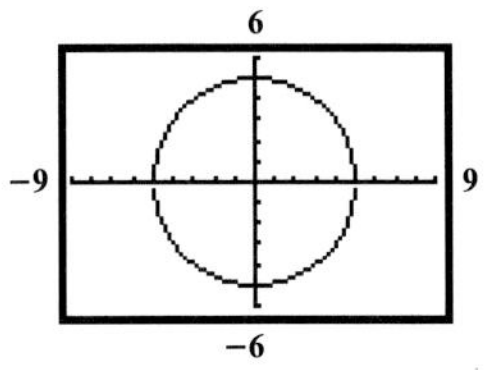

79.

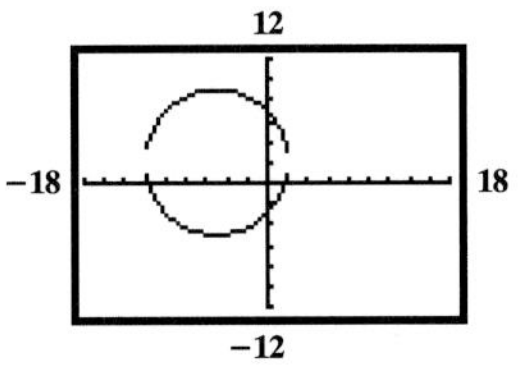

81. $2\sqrt{2} + 3\sqrt{2} = 5\sqrt{2}$

83. 11π

Chapter 2 Review Exercises

1. Function; Domain: $\{2, 3, 5\}$; Range: $\{7\}$ **2.** Function; Domain: $\{1, 2, 13\}$; Range: $\{10, 500, \pi\}$ **3.** Not a function; Domain: $\{12, 14\}$; Range: $\{13, 15, 19\}$ **4.** y is a function of x. **5.** y is a function of x. **6.** y is not a function of x. **7. a.** $f(4) = -23$ **b.** $f(x + 3) = -7x - 16$ **c.** $f(-x) = 5 + 7x$ **8. a.** $g(0) = 2$ **b.** $g(-2) = 24$ **c.** $g(x - 1) = 3x^2 - 11x + 10$ **d.** $g(-x) = 3x^2 + 5x + 2$ **9. a.** $g(13) = 3$ **b.** $g(0) = 4$ **c.** $g(-3) = 7$ **10. a.** -1 **b.** 12 **c.** 3 **11.** not a function **12.** function **13.** function **14.** not a function **15.** not a function **16.** function **17.** 8 **18.** $-4x - 2h + 1$ **19. a.** Domain: $[-3, 5)$ **b.** Range: $[-5, 0]$ **c.** x-intercept: -3 **d.** y-intercept: -2 **e.** increasing: $(-2, 0)$; or $(3, 5)$ decreasing: $(-3, -2)$ or $(0, 3)$ **f.** $f(-2) = -3$ and $f(3) = -5$ **20. a.** Domain: $(-\infty, \infty)$ **b.** Range: $(-\infty, \infty)$ **c.** x-intercepts: -2 and 3 **d.** y-intercept: 3 **e.** increasing: $(-5, 0)$; decreasing: $(-\infty, -5)$ or $(0, \infty)$ **f.** $f(-2) = 0$ and $f(6) = -3$ **21. a.** Domain: $(-\infty, \infty)$ **b.** Range: $[-2, 2]$ **c.** x-intercept: 0 **d.** y-intercept: 0 **e.** increasing: $(-2, 2)$; constant: $(-\infty, -2)$ or $(2, \infty)$ **f.** $f(-9) = -2$ and $f(14) = 2$ **22. a.** 0; $f(0) = -2$ **b.** $-2, 3$; $f(-2) = -3, f(3) = -5$ **23. a.** 0; $f(0) = 3$ **b.** -5; $f(-5) = -6$ **24.** odd; symmetric with respect to the origin **25.** even; symmetric with respect to the y-axis **26.** odd; symmetric with respect to the origin **27. a.** yes; The graph passes the vertical line test. **b.** Decreasing: (3, 12); The eagle descended. **c.** Constant: (0, 3) and (12, 17); The eagle's height held steady during the first 3 seconds and the eagle was on the ground for 5 seconds. **d.** Increasing: (17, 30); The eagle was ascending.

28.

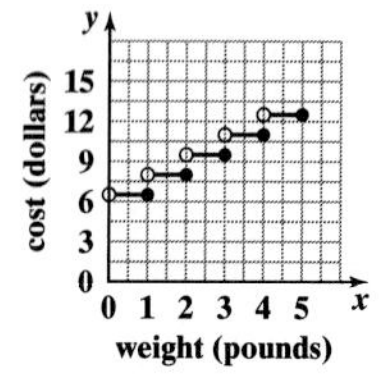

29. $m = -\dfrac{1}{2}$; falls **30.** $m = 1$; rises **31.** $m = 0$; horizontal **32.** $m =$ undefined; vertical

33. $y - 2 = -6(x + 3)$; $y = -6x - 16$ **34.** using $(1, 6)$, $y - 6 = 2(x - 1)$; $y = 2x + 4$

35. $y + 7 = -3(x - 4)$; $y = -3x + 5$ **36.** $y - 6 = -3(x + 3)$; $y = -3x - 3$ **37.** $x + 6y + 18 = 0$

38. Slope: $\dfrac{2}{5}$; y-intercept: -1 **39.** Slope: -4; y-intercept: 5 **40.** Slope: $-\dfrac{2}{3}$; y-intercept: -2 **41.** Slope: 0; y-intercept: 4

$y = \dfrac{2}{5}x - 1$

$f(x) = -4x + 5$

$2x + 3y + 6 = 0$

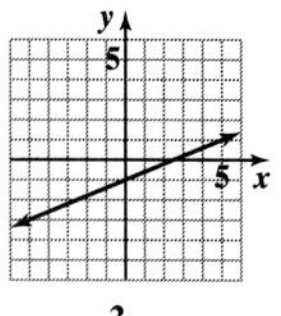

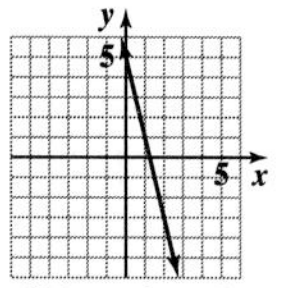

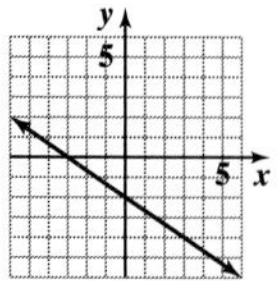

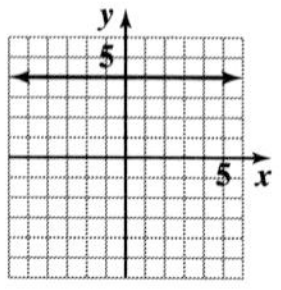

$2y - 8 = 0$

42. $2x - 5y - 10 = 0$

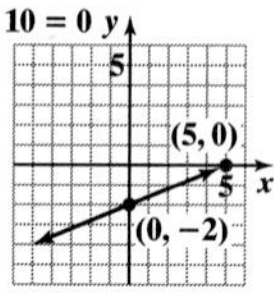

43. $2x - 10 = 0$

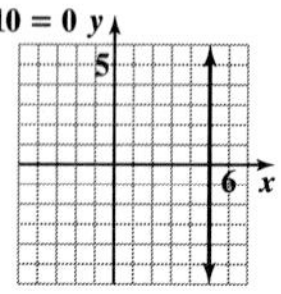

44. a. $y - 1.5 = 0.95(x - 1)$, or $y - 3.4 = 0.95(x - 3)$ **b.** $y = 0.95x + 0.55$
c. \$10.05 billion **45. a.** $m = -44$; The number of new AIDS diagnoses decreased at a rate of 44 each year from 1999 to 2001. **b.** $m = 909$; The number of new AIDS diagnoses increased at a rate of 909 each year from 2001 to 2003. **c.** $m = 432.5$; yes; Answers will vary. **46.** 10

47. $y = g(x)$

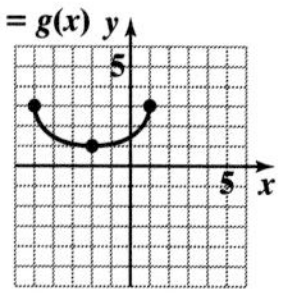

48. $y = g(x)$

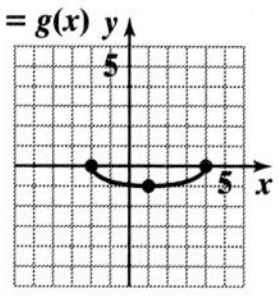

49.

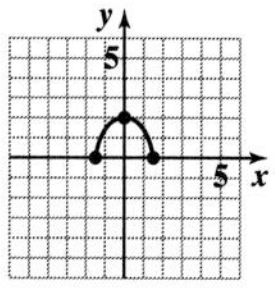

$y = g(x)$

50.

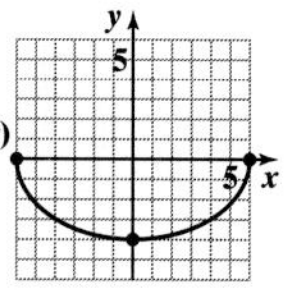

$y = g(x)$

51.

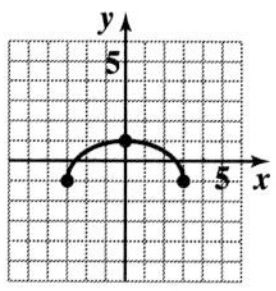

$y = g(x)$

52.

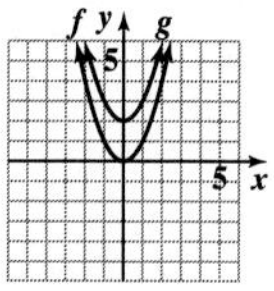

53.

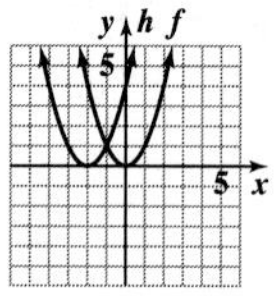

54.

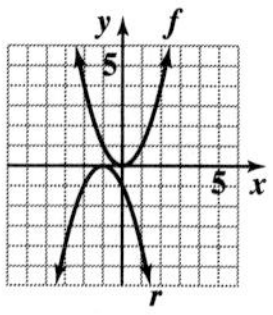

55.

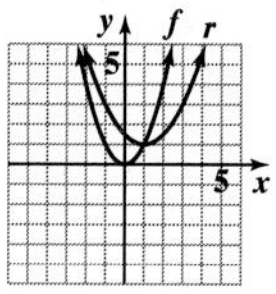

56.

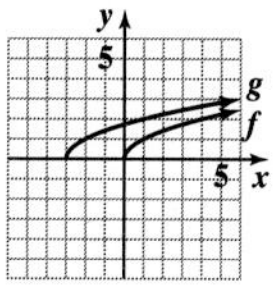

57.

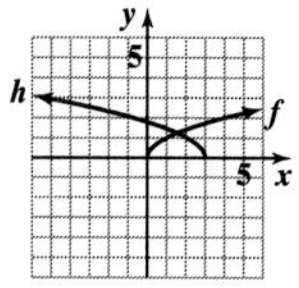

58.

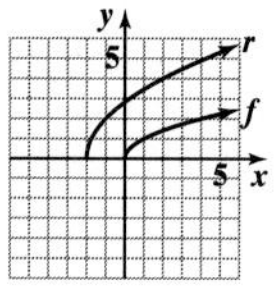

59.

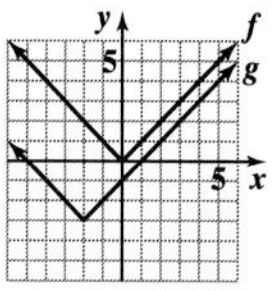

60.

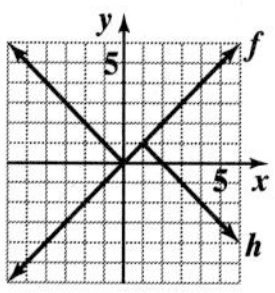

61.

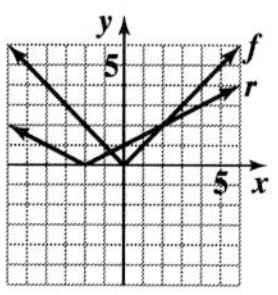

62.

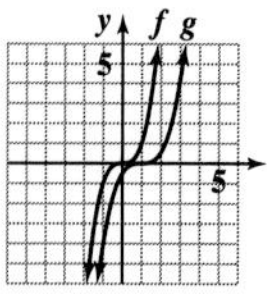

63.

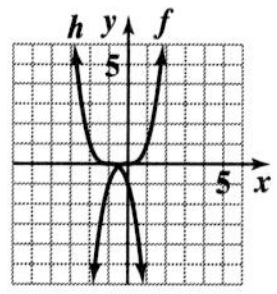

64.

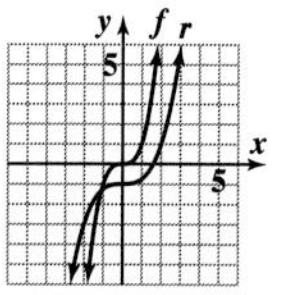

65.

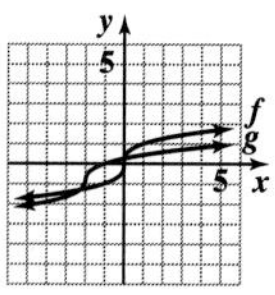

66.

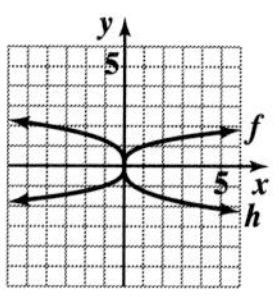

67.

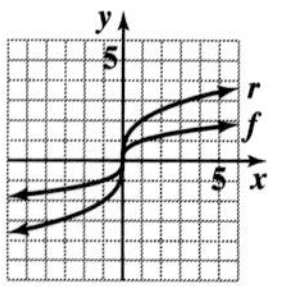

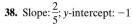

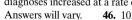

68. $(-\infty, \infty)$ **69.** $(-\infty, 7)\cup(7, \infty)$ **70.** $(-\infty, 4]$ **71.** $(-\infty, -7)\cup(-7, 3)\cup(3, \infty)$
72. $[2, 5)\cup(5, \infty)$ **73.** $[1, \infty)$ **74.** $(f + g)(x) = 4x - 6$; Domain: $(-\infty, \infty)$; $(f - g)(x) = 2x + 4$; Domain: $(-\infty, \infty)$; $(fg)(x) = 3x^2 - 16x + 5$; Domain: $(-\infty, \infty)$; $\left(\dfrac{f}{g}\right)(x) = \dfrac{3x - 1}{x - 5}$; Domain: $(-\infty, 5)\cup(5, \infty)$

75. $(f + g)(x) = 2x^2 + x$; Domain: $(-\infty, \infty)$; $(f - g)(x) = x + 2$; Domain: $(-\infty, \infty)$; $(fg)(x) = x^4 + x^3 - x - 1$; Domain: $(-\infty, \infty)$; $\left(\dfrac{f}{g}\right)(x) = \dfrac{x^2 + x + 1}{x^2 - 1}$; Domain: $(-\infty, -1)\cup(-1, 1)\cup(1, \infty)$

76. $(f + g)(x) = \sqrt{x + 7} + \sqrt{x - 2}$; Domain: $[2, \infty)$; $(f - g)(x) = \sqrt{x + 7} - \sqrt{x - 2}$; Domain: $[2, \infty)$; $(fg)(x) = \sqrt{x^2 + 5x - 14}$; Domain: $[2, \infty)$; $\left(\dfrac{f}{g}\right)(x) = \dfrac{\sqrt{x + 7}}{\sqrt{x - 2}}$; Domain: $(2, \infty)$ **77. a.** $(f \circ g)(x) = 16x^2 - 8x + 4$ **b.** $(g \circ f)(x) = 4x^2 + 11$ **c.** $(f \circ g)(3) = 124$

78. a. $(f \circ g)(x) = \sqrt{x + 1}$ **b.** $(g \circ f)(x) = \sqrt{x} + 1$ **c.** $(f \circ g)(3) = 2$ **79. a.** $(f \circ g)(x) = \dfrac{1 + x}{1 - 2x}$ **b.** $\left\{x \,\middle|\, x \neq 0 \text{ and } x \neq \dfrac{1}{2}\right\}$

80. a. $(f \circ g)(x) = \sqrt{x + 2}$ **b.** $\{x | x \geq -2\}$ **81.** $f(x) = x^4, g(x) = x^2 + 2x - 1$ **82.** $f(x) = \sqrt[3]{x}, g(x) = 7x + 4$ **83.** 13

84. $2\sqrt{2} \approx 2.83$ **85.** $(-5, 5)$ **86.** $\left(-\dfrac{11}{2}, -2\right)$ **87.** $x^2 + y^2 = 9$ **88.** $(x + 2)^2 + (y - 4)^2 = 36$

89. Center: (0, 0); radius: 1
Domain: $[-1, 1]$; Range: $[-1, 1]$

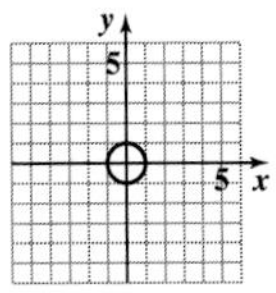

$x^2 + y^2 = 1$

90. Center: $(-2, 3)$; radius: 3
Domain: $[-5, 1]$; Range: $[0, 6]$

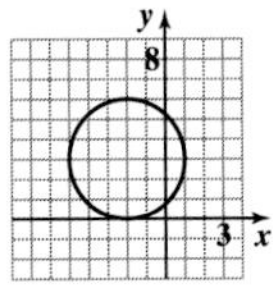

$(x + 2)^2 + (y - 3)^2 = 9$

91. Center: $(2, -1)$; radius: 3
Domain: $[-1, 5]$; Range: $[-4, 2]$

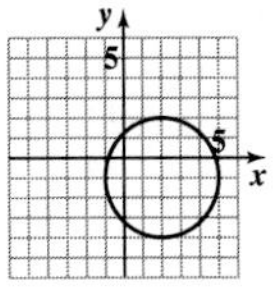

$x^2 + y^2 - 4x + 2y - 4 = 0$

Chapter 2 Test

1. b, c, d **2. a.** $f(4) - f(-3) = 5$ **b.** Domain: $(-5, 6]$ **c.** Range: $[-4, 5]$ **d.** Increasing: $(-1, 2)$ **e.** Decreasing: $(-5, -1)$ or $(2, 6)$ **f.** 2; $f(2) = 5$ **g.** -1; $f(-1) = -4$ **h.** -4, 1, and 5 **i.** -3 **3. a.** -2 and 2 **b.** -1 and 1 **c.** 0 **d.** even **e.** relative minimum

f.

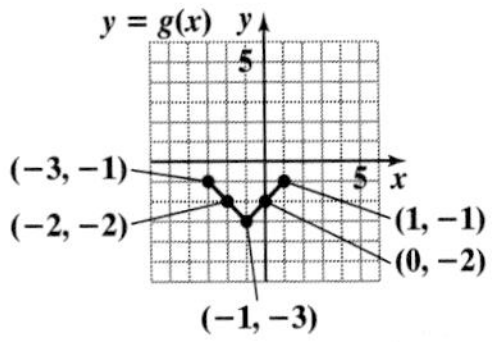

g.

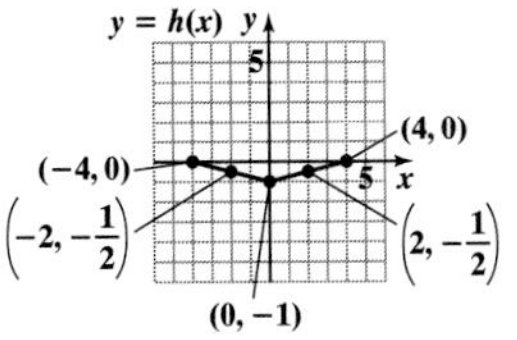

h.

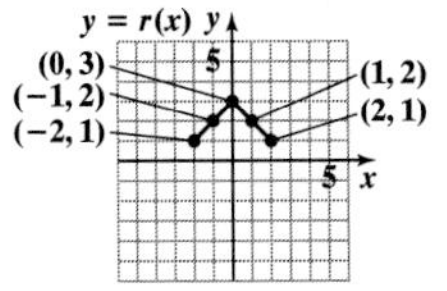

i. $-\frac{1}{3}$

4.

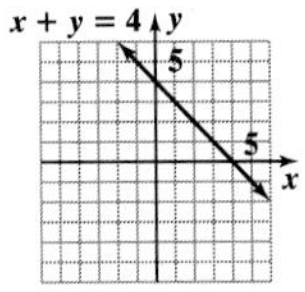

Domain: $(-\infty, \infty)$;
Range: $(-\infty, \infty)$

5.

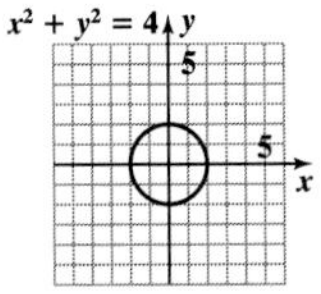

Domain: $[-2, 2]$;
Range: $[-2, 2]$

6.

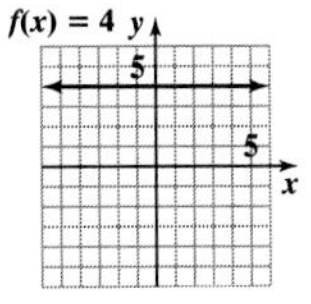

Domain: $(-\infty, \infty)$;
Range: $\{4\}$

7.

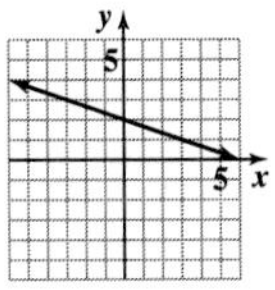

$f(x) = -\frac{1}{3}x + 2$

Domain: $(-\infty, \infty)$;
Range: $(-\infty, \infty)$

8.

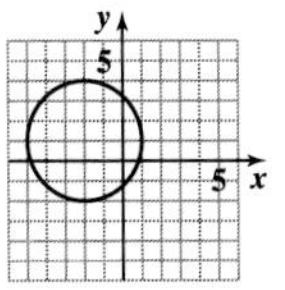

$(x + 2)^2 + (y - 1)^2 = 9$

Domain: $[-5, 1]$;
Range: $[-2, 4]$

9.

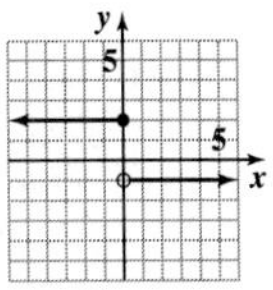

$f(x) = \begin{cases} 2 \text{ if } x \le 0 \\ -1 \text{ if } x > 0 \end{cases}$

Domain: $(-\infty, \infty)$;
Range: $\{-1, 2\}$

10.

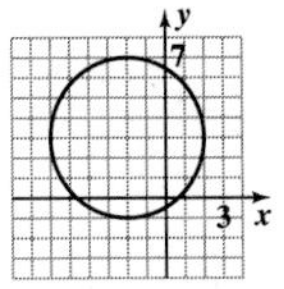

$x^2 + y^2 + 4x - 6y - 3 = 0$

Domain: $[-6, 2]$;
Range: $[-1, 7]$

11.

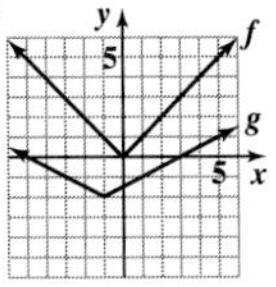

Domain of f = Domain of g = $(-\infty, \infty)$;
Range of f = $[0, \infty)$; Range of g = $[-2, \infty)$

12.

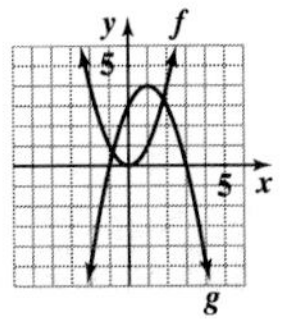

Domain of f = Domain of g = $(-\infty, \infty)$;
Range of f = $[0, \infty)$; Range of g = $(-\infty, 4]$

13. $f(x - 1) = x^2 - 3x - 2$ **14.** $2x + h - 1$ **15.** $(g - f)(x) = -x^2 + 3x - 2$ **16.** $\left(\frac{f}{g}\right)(x) = \frac{x^2 - x - 4}{2x - 6}$; $(-\infty, 3)\cup(3, \infty)$

17. $(f \circ g)(x) = 4x^2 - 26x + 38$ **18.** $(g \circ f)(x) = 2x^2 - 2x - 14$ **19.** -10 **20.** $f(-x) = x^2 + x - 4$; neither

21. using (2, 1), $y - 1 = 3(x - 2)$; $y = 3x - 5$ **22.** $y - 6 = 4(x + 4)$; $y = 4x + 22$ **23.** $2x + y + 24 = 0$

24. a. $y - 4.85 = -0.12(x - 2)$ or $y - 4.49 = -0.12(x - 5)$ **b.** $f(x) = -0.12x + 5.09$ **c.** \$3.89 **25.** 48 **26.** $g(-1) = 4$; $g(7) = 2$

27. $(-\infty, -5)\cup(-5, 1)\cup(1, \infty)$ **28.** $[1, \infty)$ **29.** $\frac{7x}{2 - 4x}$; $\left\{x \mid x \neq 0 \text{ or } x \neq \frac{1}{2}\right\}$ **30.** $f(x) = x^7$, $g(x) = 2x + 13$ **31.** 5; (3.5, 0)

Cumulative Review Exercises (Chapters 1–2)

1. Domain: $[0, 2)$; Range: $[0, 2]$ **2.** $\frac{1}{2}$ and $\frac{3}{2}$ **3.** 2

4.

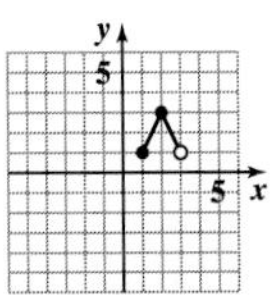

$g(x) = f(x - 1) + 1$

5.

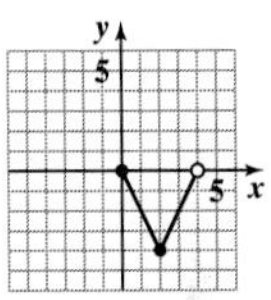

6. $\{-4, 5\}$
7. $\left\{\frac{25}{18}\right\}$
8. $\{4\}$
9. $\{-8, 27\}$
10. $(-\infty, 20)$

11.

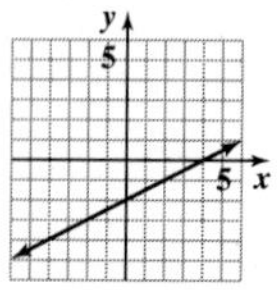

$3x - 6y - 12 = 0$

Domain: $(-\infty, \infty)$;
Range: $(-\infty, \infty)$

12.

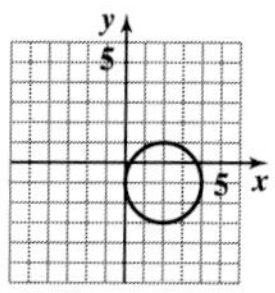

$(x-2)^2 + (y+1)^2 = 4$

Domain: $[0, 4]$;
Range: $[-3, 1]$

13.

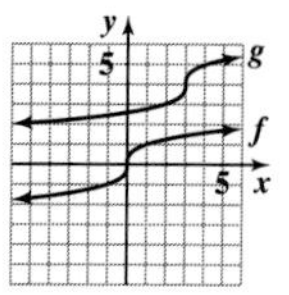

Domain of f = Domain of $g = (-\infty, \infty)$;
Range of f = Range of $g = (-\infty, \infty)$

14. $-2x - h$ **15.** -7 and -3 **16.** $y - 5 = 4(x+2)$; $y = 4x + 13$; $4x - y = -13$ **17.** \$1500 at 7%; \$4500 at 9% **18.** \$2000 **19.** 3 ft by 8 ft

CHAPTER 3

Section 3.1

Check Point Exercises

1. a. solution **b.** not a solution **2.** $\{(-2, 5)\}$ **3.** $\{(2, -1)\}$ **4.** $\left\{\left(\frac{60}{17}, -\frac{11}{17}\right)\right\}$ **5.** no solution or $\varnothing$ **6.** $\{(x, y) | x = 4y - 8\}$ or $\{(x, y) | 5x - 20y = -40\}$ **7. a.** $C(x) = 300{,}000 + 30x$ **b.** $R(x) = 80x$ **c.** $(6000, 480{,}000)$; The company will break even if it produces and sells 6000 pairs of shoes.

Exercise Set 3.1

1. solution **3.** not a solution **5.** $\{(1, 3)\}$ **7.** $\{(5, 1)\}$ **9.** $\{(-22, -5)\}$ **11.** $\{(0, 0)\}$ **13.** $\{(3, -2)\}$ **15.** $\{(5, 4)\}$ **17.** $\{(7, 3)\}$ **19.** $\{(2, -1)\}$ **21.** $\{(3, 0)\}$ **23.** $\{(-4, 3)\}$ **25.** $\{(3, 1)\}$ **27.** $\{(1, -2)\}$ **29.** $\left\{\left(\frac{7}{25}, -\frac{1}{25}\right)\right\}$ **31.** $\varnothing$ **33.** $\{(x, y) | y = 3x - 5\}$ **35.** $\{(1, 4)\}$ **37.** $\{(x, y) | x + 3y = 2\}$ **39.** $\{(-5, -1)\}$ **41.** $\left\{\left(\frac{29}{22}, -\frac{5}{11}\right)\right\}$ **43.** $x + y = 7$; $x - y = -1$; 3 and 4 **45.** $3x - y = 1$; $x + 2y = 12$; 2 and 5 **47.** $(6, -1)$ **49.** $\left\{\left(\frac{1}{a}, 3\right)\right\}$ **51.** $m = -4, b = 3$ **53.** $y = x - 4$; $y = -\frac{1}{3}x + 4$ **55.** 500 radios **57.** -6000; When the company produces and sells 200 radios, the loss is \$6000. **59. a.** $P(x) = 20x - 10{,}000$ **b.** \$190,000 **61. a.** $C(x) = 18{,}000 + 20x$ **b.** $R(x) = 80x$ **c.** $(300, 24{,}000)$; When 300 canoes are produced and sold, both revenue and cost are \$24,000. **63. a.** $C(x) = 30{,}000 + 2500x$ **b.** $R(x) = 3125x$ **c.** $(48, 150{,}000)$; For 48 sold-out performances, both cost and revenue are \$150,000. **65. a.** 150 sold; 300 supplied **b.** \$100; 250 **67.** 2020; 48% **69. a.** $y = 5.48 + 0.04x$ **b.** $y = 1.84 + 0.17x$ **c.** 2028; 6.6%; Medicare **71. a.** $y = -0.75x + 38$ **b.** $y = -x + 40$ **c.** 1993; 32% **73.** Pan pizza: 1120 calories; beef burrito: 430 calories **75.** Scrambled eggs: 366 mg cholesterol; Double Beef Whopper: 175 mg cholesterol **77.** 50 rooms with kitchen facilities, 150 rooms without kitchen facilities **79.** 100 ft long by 80 ft wide **81.** Rate rowing in still water: 6 mph; rate of the current: 2 mph **83.** 80°, 50°, 50° **97.** the twin who always lies

Section 3.2

Check Point Exercises

1. $(-1) - 2(-4) + 3(5) = 22$; $2(-1) - 3(-4) - 5 = 5$; $3(-1) + (-4) - 5(5) = -32$ **2.** $\{(1, 4, -3)\}$ **3.** $\{(4, 5, 3)\}$ **4.** $y = 3x^2 - 12x + 13$

Exercise Set 3.2

1. solution **3.** solution **5.** $\{(2, 3, 3)\}$ **7.** $\{(2, -1, 1)\}$ **9.** $\{(1, 2, 3)\}$ **11.** $\{(3, 1, 5)\}$ **13.** $\{(1, 0, -3)\}$ **15.** $\{(1, -5, -6)\}$ **17.** $\left\{\left(\frac{1}{2}, \frac{1}{3}, -1\right)\right\}$ **19.** $y = 2x^2 - x + 3$ **21.** $y = 2x^2 + x - 5$ **23.** 7, 4, and 5 **25.** $\{(4, 8, 6)\}$ **27.** $y = -\frac{3}{4}x^2 + 6x - 11$ **29.** $\left\{\left(\frac{8}{a}, -\frac{3}{b}, -\frac{5}{c}\right)\right\}$ **31. a.** $(0, 2.5)$, $(2, 4.1)$, $(3, 3.5)$ **b.** $c = 2.5$; $4a + 2b + c = 4.1$; $9a + 3b + c = 3.5$ **c.** $y = -\frac{7}{15}x^2 + \frac{26}{15}x + \frac{5}{2}$ **33. a.** $y = -16x^2 + 40x + 200$ **b.** $y = 0$ when $x = 5$; The ball hits the ground after 5 seconds **35.** Carnegie: \$100 billion; Vanderbilt: \$96 billion; Gates: \$48 billion **37.** 200 \$8 tickets; 150 \$10 tickets; 50 \$12 tickets **39.** \$1200 at 8%, \$2000 at 10%, and \$3500 at 12% **41.** $x = 60, y = 55, z = 65$ **49.** 13 triangles, 21 rectangles, and 6 pentagons

Section 3.3

Check Point Exercises

1. $\{(4, -3, 1)\}$ **2. a.** $\left[\begin{array}{rrr|r} 1 & 6 & -3 & 7 \\ 4 & 12 & -20 & 8 \\ -3 & -2 & 1 & -9 \end{array}\right]$ **b.** $\left[\begin{array}{rrr|r} 1 & 3 & -5 & 2 \\ 1 & 6 & -3 & 7 \\ -3 & -2 & 1 & -9 \end{array}\right]$ **c.** $\left[\begin{array}{rrr|r} 4 & 12 & -20 & 8 \\ 1 & 6 & -3 & 7 \\ 0 & 16 & -8 & 12 \end{array}\right]$ **3.** $\{(5, 2, 3)\}$ **4.** $\{(1, -1, 2, -3)\}$ **5.** $\{(5, 2, 3)\}$

Exercise Set 3.3

1. $\left[\begin{array}{ccc|c} 2 & 1 & 2 & 2 \\ 3 & -5 & -1 & 4 \\ 1 & -2 & -3 & -6 \end{array}\right]$ **3.** $\left[\begin{array}{ccc|c} 1 & -1 & 1 & 8 \\ 0 & 1 & -12 & -15 \\ 0 & 0 & 1 & 1 \end{array}\right]$ **5.** $\left[\begin{array}{ccc|c} 5 & -2 & -3 & 0 \\ 1 & 1 & 0 & 5 \\ 2 & 0 & -3 & 4 \end{array}\right]$ **7.** $\left[\begin{array}{cccc|c} 2 & 5 & -3 & 1 & 2 \\ 0 & 3 & 1 & 0 & 4 \\ 1 & -1 & 5 & 0 & 9 \\ 5 & -5 & -2 & 0 & 1 \end{array}\right]$ **9.** $5x + 3z = -11$; $y - 4z = 12$; $7x + 2y = 3$

11. $w + x + 4y + z = 3$; $-w + x - y = 7$; $2w + 5z = 11$; $12y + 4z = 5$ **13.** $x - 4z = 5$; $y - 12z = 13$; $z = -\frac{1}{2}$; $\left\{\left(3, 7, -\frac{1}{2}\right)\right\}$ **15.** $x + \frac{1}{2}y + z = \frac{11}{2}$; $y + \frac{3}{2}z = 7$; $z = 4$; $(\{1, 1, 4)\}$ **17.** $w - x + y + z = 3$; $x - 2y - z = 0$; $y + 6z = 17$; $z = 3$; $\{(2, 1, -1, 3)\}$

19. $\left[\begin{array}{ccc|c} 1 & -3 & 2 & 5 \\ 1 & 5 & -5 & 0 \\ 3 & 0 & 4 & 7 \end{array}\right]$ **21.** $\left[\begin{array}{ccc|c} 1 & -3 & 2 & 0 \\ 0 & 10 & -7 & 7 \\ 2 & -2 & 1 & 3 \end{array}\right]$ **23.** $\left[\begin{array}{cccc|c} 1 & -1 & 1 & 1 & 3 \\ 0 & 1 & -2 & -1 & 0 \\ 0 & 2 & 1 & 2 & 5 \\ 0 & 6 & -3 & -1 & -9 \end{array}\right]$ **25.** R_2: $-3, -18$; R_3: $-12, -15$; R_2: $-\frac{3}{5}, -\frac{18}{5}$; R_3: $-12, -15$

27. $\{(1, -1, 2)\}$ **29.** $\{(3, -1, -1)\}$ **31.** $\{2, -1, 1\}$ **33.** $\{(2, 1, 1)\}$ **35.** $\{(2, -1, 1)\}$ **37.** $\{(-1, 2, -2)\}$ **39.** $\{(1, 2, -1)\}$
41. $\{(1, 2, 3, -2)\}$ **43.** $\{(0, -3, 0, -3)\}$ **45.** $f(x) = -x^2 + x + 2$ **47.** $f(x) = x^3 - 2x^2 + 3$ **49.** $\{(e^{-1}, e, e^{-3}, e^{-2})\}$
51. a. $a = -32, v_0 = 56, s_0 = 0$ **b.** 0; The ball hits the ground 3.5 seconds after it it thrown. **c.** 1.75 sec; 49 ft

53. $x + y + z = 100$; $x + z = y - 22$; $2x = y + 7$; yes: 34%; no: 61%; not sure: 5% **55.** $40x + 200y + 400z = 660$; $5x + 2y + 4z = 25$; $30x + 10y + 300z = 425$; 4 oz of Food *A*; $\frac{1}{2}$ oz of Food *B*; 1 oz of Food *C*

65. d

Section 3.4

Check Point Exercises

1. a. -4 **b.** -17 **2.** $\{(4, -2)\}$ **3.** 80 **4.** -24 **5.** $\{(2, -3, 4)\}$ **6.** -250

Exercise Set 3.4

1. 1 **3.** -29 **5.** 0 **7.** 33 **9.** $-\frac{7}{16}$ **11.** $\{(5, 2)\}$ **13.** $\{(2, -3)\}$ **15.** $\{(3, -1)\}$ **17.** The system is dependent. **19.** $\{(4, 2)\}$
21. $\{(7, 4)\}$ **23.** The system is inconsistent. **25.** The system is dependent. **27.** 72 **29.** -75 **31.** 0 **33.** $\{(-5, -2, 7)\}$
35. $\{(2, -3, 4)\}$ **37.** $\{(3, -1, 2)\}$ **39.** $\{(2, 3, 1)\}$ **41.** -200 **43.** 195 **45.** -42 **47.** $2x - 4y = 8$; $3x + 5y = -10$ **49.** -11
51. 4 **53.** 28 sq units **55.** yes **57.** The equation of the line is $y = -\frac{11}{5}x + \frac{8}{5}$. **69.** 13,200 **71. a.** a^2 **b.** a^3 **c.** a^4
d. Each determinant has zeros below the main diagonal and *a*'s everywhere else. **e.** Each determinant equals *a* raised to the power equal to the order of the determinant. **73.** The sign of the value is changed when 2 columns are interchanged in a 2nd order determinant.
75. $\begin{vmatrix} x & y & 1 \\ x_1 & y_1 & 1 \\ x_2 & y_2 & 1 \end{vmatrix} = x(y_1 - y_2) - y(x_1 - x_2) + (x_1y_2 - x_2y_1) = 0$; solving for y, $y = \frac{y_1 - y_2}{x_1 - x_2}x + \frac{x_1y_2 - x_2y_1}{x_1 - x_2}$, and $m = \frac{y_1 - y_2}{x_1 - x_2}$ and $b = \frac{x_1y_2 - x_2y_1}{x_1 - x_2}$.

Chapter 3 Review Exercises

1. $\{(1, 5)\}$ **2.** $\{(2, 3)\}$ **3.** $\{(2, -3)\}$ **4.** $\varnothing$ **5.** $\{(x, y) | 3x - 6y = 12\}$ **6. a.** $C(x) = 60{,}000 + 200x$ **b.** $R(x) = 450x$
c. (240, 108,000); This means the company will break even if it produces and sells 240 desks. **7.** Japan: 73.6 yr; Switzerland: 72.8 yr
8. 12 ft by 5 ft **9.** $80 per day for the room, $60 per day for the car **10.** 3 apples and 2 avocados **11.** $\{(0, 1, 2)\}$ **12.** $\{(2, 1, -1)\}$
13. $y = 3x^2 - 4x + 5$ **14. a.** (0, 3.5), (15, 5.0), (33, 3.8) **b.**
$c = 3.5$; $225a + 15b + c = 5.0$; $1089a + 33b + c = 3.8$

15. Labrador retrievers: 147; Golden retrievers: 53; German shepherds: 46

16. $x + y + 3z = 12$; $y - 2z = -4$; $z = 3$; $\{(1, 2, 3)\}$ **17.** $w - 2y + 2z = 1$; $x + y - z = 0$; $y - \frac{7}{3}z = -\frac{1}{3}$; $z = 1$; $\{(3, -1, 2, 1)\}$ **18.** $\left[\begin{array}{ccc|c} 1 & 2 & 2 & 2 \\ 0 & 1 & -1 & 2 \\ 0 & 0 & 9 & -9 \end{array}\right]$ **19.** $\left[\begin{array}{ccc|c} 1 & -1 & \frac{1}{2} & -\frac{1}{2} \\ 1 & 2 & -1 & 2 \\ 6 & 4 & 3 & 5 \end{array}\right]$

20. $\{(1, 3, -4)\}$ **21.** $\{(-2, -1, 0)\}$ **22.** $\{(2, -2, 3, 4)\}$ **23. a.** $a = -2$; $b = 32$; $c = 42$ **b.** 2:00 p.m.; 170 parts per million

24. 17 **25.** 4 **26.** -86 **27.** -236 **28.** 4 **29.** 16 **30.** $\left\{\left(\frac{7}{4}, -\frac{25}{8}\right)\right\}$ **31.** $\{(2, -7)\}$ **32.** $\{(23, -12, 3)\}$ **33.** $\{(-3, 2, 1)\}$

34. $a = \frac{5}{8}$; $b = -50$; $c = 1150$; 30- and 50-year-olds are involved in an average of 212.5 automobile accidents per day.

Chapter 3 Test

1. $\{(1, -3)\}$ **2.** $\{(4, -2)\}$ **3.** $\{(1, 3, 2)\}$ **4. a.** $C(x) = 360{,}000 + 850x$ **b.** $R(x) = 1150x$
c. (1200, 1,380,000); The company will break even if it produces and sells 1200 computers. **5** $y = x^2 - 3$ **6.** $\left\{\left(-3, \frac{1}{2}, 1\right)\right\}$
7. 18 **8.** $x = 2$

Cumulative Review Exercises (Chapters 1–3)

1. Domain: $(-2, 2)$; Range: $(-\infty, 3]$ **2.** -1 and 1, each of multiplicity 1 **3.** maximum of 3 at $x = 0$ **4.** $(0, 2)$
5. positive **6.** 3 **7.** even

8.

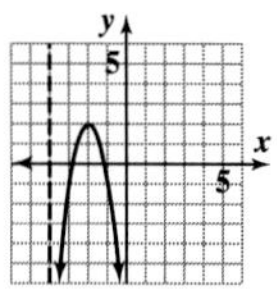

$g(x) = f(x + 2) - 1$

9.

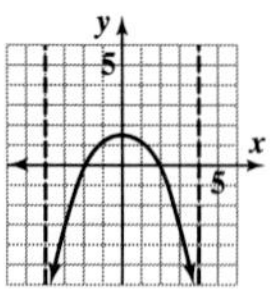

$h(x) = \frac{1}{2} f(\frac{1}{2} x)$

10. $\{3, 4\}$ **11.** $\left\{\frac{2 + i\sqrt{3}}{2}, \frac{2 - i\sqrt{3}}{2}\right\}$
12. $\{(-18, 6)\}$ **13.** $\{-2\}$
14. $\{625\}$ **15.** $\{(8, -2, -2)\}$

16.

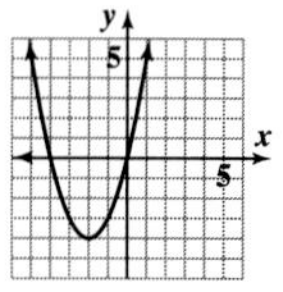

$f(x) = (x + 2)^2 - 4$

17.

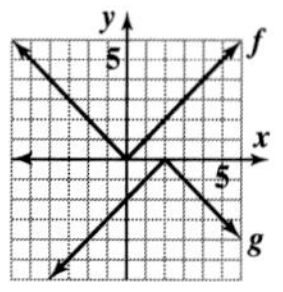

$f(x) = |x|$
$g(x) = -|x - 2|$

18. $(f \circ g)(x) = 2x^2 - 3x$;
$(g \circ f)(x) = -2x^2 + x + 2$
19. $4x + 2h - 1$
20. $y = -3x + 10$
21. $y = 3x + 3$
22. \$2600 at 12%; \$1400 at 14%
23. 4 m by 9 m

24. $\left\{\frac{-1 + \sqrt{33}}{4}, \frac{-1 - \sqrt{33}}{4}\right\}$ **25.** $\left[\frac{1}{2}, \infty\right)$ **26.** $\{6\}$ **27.** $\{(7, -4, 6)\}$ **28.** $y = -1$

29.

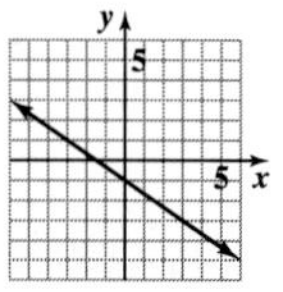

$y = -\frac{2}{3}x - 1$

30.

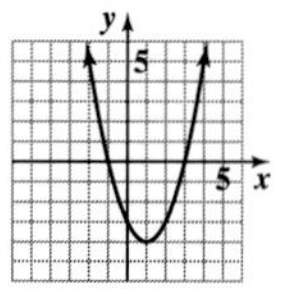

$f(x) = x^2 - 2x - 3$

31.

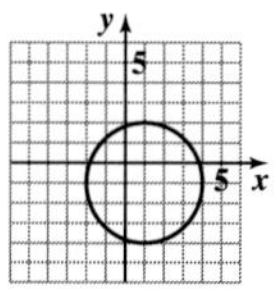

$(x - 1)^2 + (y + 1)^2 = 9$

CHAPTER 4

Section 4.1

Check Point Exercises

1. 3.5 radians **2. a.** $\frac{\pi}{3}$ radians **b.** $\frac{3\pi}{2}$ radians **c.** $-\frac{5\pi}{3}$ radians **3. a.** 45° **b.** −240° **c.** 343.8°

4. a.

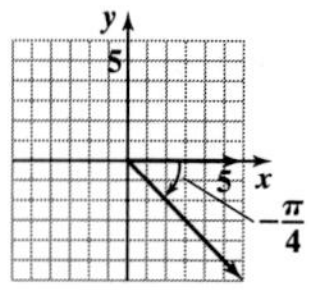

b.

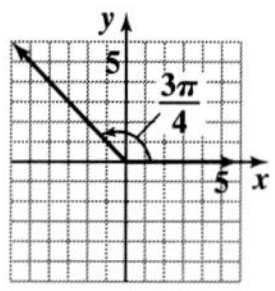

c.

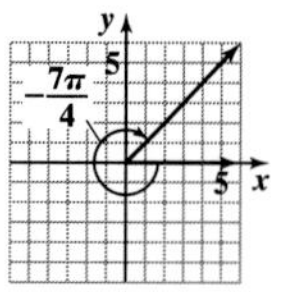

d.

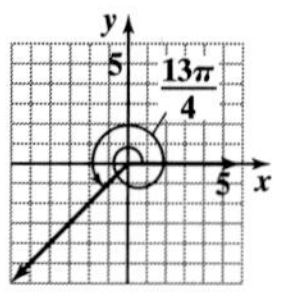

5. a. 40° **b.** 225° **6. a.** $\frac{3\pi}{5}$ **b.** $\frac{29\pi}{15}$ **7. a.** 135° **b.** $\frac{5\pi}{3}$ **c.** $\frac{11\pi}{6}$ **8.** $\frac{3\pi}{2}$ in. ≈ 4.71 in. **9.** 135π in./min ≈ 424 in./min

Exercise Set 4.1

1. obtuse **3.** acute **5.** straight **7.** 4 radians **9.** $\frac{4}{3}$ radians **11.** 4 radians **13.** $\frac{\pi}{4}$ radians **15.** $\frac{3\pi}{4}$ radians **17.** $\frac{5\pi}{3}$ radians **19.** $-\frac{5\pi}{4}$ radians **21.** 90° **23.** 120° **25.** 210° **27.** $-540°$ **29.** 0.31 radians **31.** -0.70 radians **33.** 3.49 radians **35.** 114.59° **37.** 13.85° **39.** $-275.02°$

41. 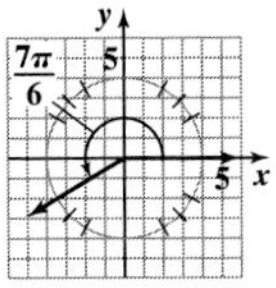

; quadrant III

43. 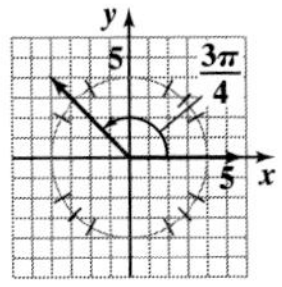

; quadrant II

45. 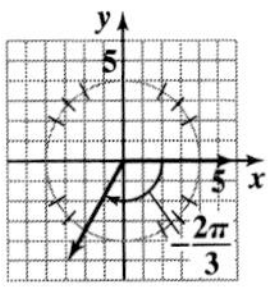

; quadrant III

47. 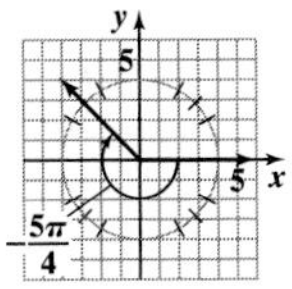

; quadrant II

49. 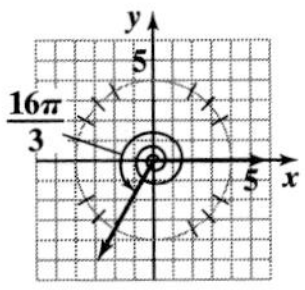

; quadrant III

51. 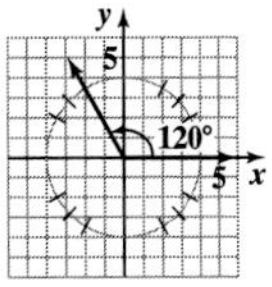

; quadrant II

53. 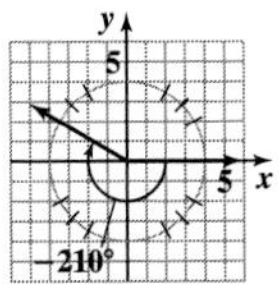

; quadrant II

55. 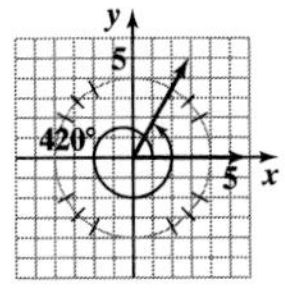

; quadrant I

57. 35° **59.** 210° **61.** 315° **63.** $\frac{7\pi}{6}$ **65.** $\frac{3\pi}{5}$ **67.** $\frac{99\pi}{50}$ **69.** $\frac{11\pi}{7}$ **71.** 3π in. ≈ 9.42 in. **73.** 10π ft ≈ 31.42 ft **75.** $\frac{12\pi \text{ radians}}{\text{second}}$ **77.** $-\frac{4\pi}{3}$ and $\frac{2\pi}{3}$ **79.** $-\frac{3\pi}{4}$ and $\frac{5\pi}{4}$ **81.** $-\frac{\pi}{2}$ and $\frac{3\pi}{2}$ **83.** $\frac{11\pi}{6}$ **85.** $\frac{22\pi}{3}$ **87.** 60°; $\frac{\pi}{3}$ radians **89.** $\frac{8\pi}{3}$ in. ≈ 8.38 in. **91.** 12π in. ≈ 37.70 in. **93.** 2 radians; 114.59° **95.** 2094 mi **97.** 1047 mph **99.** 1508 ft/min **113.** 30.25° **115.** 30°25′12″ **117.** smaller than a right angle **119.** 1815 mi

Section 4.2

Check Point Exercises

1. $\sin\theta = \frac{3}{5}$; $\cos\theta = \frac{4}{5}$; $\tan\theta = \frac{3}{4}$; $\csc\theta = \frac{5}{3}$; $\sec\theta = \frac{5}{4}$; $\cot\theta = \frac{4}{3}$ **2.** $\sin\theta = \frac{1}{5}$; $\cos\theta = \frac{2\sqrt{6}}{5}$; $\tan\theta = \frac{\sqrt{6}}{12}$; $\csc\theta = 5$; $\sec\theta = \frac{5\sqrt{6}}{12}$; $\cot\theta = 2\sqrt{6}$ **3.** $\sqrt{2}$; $\sqrt{2}$; 1 **4.** $\sqrt{3}$; $\frac{\sqrt{3}}{3}$ **5.** $\tan\theta = \frac{2\sqrt{5}}{5}$; $\csc\theta = \frac{3}{2}$; $\sec\theta = \frac{3\sqrt{5}}{5}$; $\cot\theta = \frac{\sqrt{5}}{2}$ **6.** $\frac{\sqrt{3}}{2}$ **7. a.** cos 44° **b.** $\tan\frac{5\pi}{12}$ **8. a.** 0.9553 **b.** 1.0025 **9.** 333.9 yd **10.** 54°

Exercise Set 4.2

1. 15; $\sin\theta = \frac{3}{5}$; $\cos\theta = \frac{4}{5}$; $\tan\theta = \frac{3}{4}$; $\csc\theta = \frac{5}{3}$; $\sec\theta = \frac{5}{4}$; $\cot\theta = \frac{4}{3}$ **3.** 20; $\sin\theta = \frac{20}{29}$; $\cos\theta = \frac{21}{29}$; $\tan\theta = \frac{20}{21}$; $\csc\theta = \frac{29}{20}$; $\sec\theta = \frac{29}{21}$; $\cot\theta = \frac{21}{20}$ **5.** 24; $\sin\theta = \frac{5}{13}$; $\cos\theta = \frac{12}{13}$; $\tan\theta = \frac{5}{12}$; $\csc\theta = \frac{13}{5}$; $\sec\theta = \frac{13}{12}$; $\cot\theta = \frac{12}{5}$ **7.** 28; $\sin\theta = \frac{4}{5}$; $\cos\theta = \frac{3}{5}$; $\tan\theta = \frac{4}{3}$; $\csc\theta = \frac{5}{4}$; $\sec\theta = \frac{5}{3}$; $\cot\theta = \frac{3}{4}$ **9.** $\frac{\sqrt{3}}{2}$ **11.** $\sqrt{2}$ **13.** $\sqrt{3}$ **15.** 0 **17.** $\tan\theta = \frac{8}{15}$; $\csc\theta = \frac{17}{8}$; $\sec\theta = \frac{17}{15}$; $\cot\theta = \frac{15}{8}$ **19.** $\tan\theta = \frac{\sqrt{2}}{4}$; $\csc\theta = 3$; $\sec\theta = \frac{3\sqrt{2}}{4}$; $\cot\theta = 2\sqrt{2}$ **21.** $\frac{\sqrt{13}}{7}$ **23.** $\frac{5}{8}$ **25.** 1 **27.** 1 **29.** 1 **31.** cos 83° **33.** sec 65° **35.** $\cot\frac{7\pi}{18}$ **37.** $\sin\frac{\pi}{10}$ **39.** 0.6157 **41.** 0.6420 **43.** 3.4203 **45.** 0.9511 **47.** 3.7321 **49.** 188 cm **51.** 182 in. **53.** 41 m **55.** 17° **57.** 78° **59.** 1.147 radians **61.** 0.395 radians **63.** 0 **65.** 2 **67.** 1 **69.** $\frac{2\sqrt{3}-1}{2}$ **71.** $\frac{1}{4}$ **73.** 529 yd **75.** 36° **77.** 2879 ft **79.** 37° **93.** 0.92106, -0.19735; 0.95534, -0.148878; 0.98007, -0.099667; 0.99500, -0.04996; 0.99995, -0.005; 0.9999995, -0.0005; 0.999999995, -0.00005; 0.99999999995, -0.000005; $\frac{\cos\theta - 1}{\theta}$ approaches 0 as θ approaches 0. **95.** In a right triangle, the hypotenuse is greater than either other side. Therefore, both $\frac{\text{opposite}}{\text{hypotenuse}}$ and $\frac{\text{adjacent}}{\text{hypotenuse}}$ must be less than 1 for an acute angle in a right triangle. **97. a.** 357 ft **b.** 394 ft

Section 4.3

Check Point Exercises

1. $\sin\theta = -\frac{3\sqrt{10}}{10}$; $\cos\theta = \frac{\sqrt{10}}{10}$; $\tan\theta = -3$; $\csc\theta = -\frac{\sqrt{10}}{3}$; $\sec\theta = \sqrt{10}$; $\cot\theta = -\frac{1}{3}$ **2. a.** 1; undefined **b.** 0; 1 **c.** -1; undefined **d.** 0; -1 **3.** quadrant III **4.** $\frac{\sqrt{10}}{10}$; $-\frac{\sqrt{10}}{3}$ **5. a.** 30° **b.** $\frac{\pi}{4}$ **c.** 60° **d.** 0.46 **6. a.** 55° **b.** $\frac{\pi}{4}$ **c.** $\frac{\pi}{3}$ **7. a.** $-\frac{\sqrt{3}}{2}$ **b.** 1 **c.** $\frac{2\sqrt{3}}{3}$ **8. a.** $-\frac{\sqrt{3}}{2}$ **b.** $\frac{\sqrt{3}}{2}$

Exercise Set 4.3

1. $\sin\theta = \frac{3}{5}$; $\cos\theta = -\frac{4}{5}$; $\tan\theta = -\frac{3}{4}$; $\csc\theta = \frac{5}{3}$; $\sec\theta = -\frac{5}{4}$; $\cot\theta = -\frac{4}{3}$

3. $\sin\theta = \frac{3\sqrt{13}}{13}$; $\cos\theta = \frac{2\sqrt{13}}{13}$; $\tan\theta = \frac{3}{2}$; $\csc\theta = \frac{\sqrt{13}}{3}$; $\sec\theta = \frac{\sqrt{13}}{2}$; $\cot\theta = \frac{2}{3}$

5. $\sin\theta = -\frac{\sqrt{2}}{2}$; $\cos\theta = \frac{\sqrt{2}}{2}$; $\tan\theta = -1$; $\csc\theta = -\sqrt{2}$; $\sec\theta = \sqrt{2}$; $\cot\theta = -1$ **7.** $\sin\theta = -\frac{5\sqrt{29}}{29}$; $\cos\theta = -\frac{2\sqrt{29}}{29}$; $\tan\theta = \frac{5}{2}$; $\csc\theta = -\frac{\sqrt{29}}{5}$; $\sec\theta = -\frac{\sqrt{29}}{2}$; $\cot\theta = \frac{2}{5}$ **9.** -1 **11.** -1 **13.** undefined **15.** 0

17. quadrant I **19.** quadrant III **21.** quadrant II **23.** $\sin\theta = -\frac{4}{5}$; $\tan\theta = \frac{4}{3}$; $\csc\theta = -\frac{5}{4}$; $\sec\theta = -\frac{5}{3}$; $\cot\theta = \frac{3}{4}$

25. $\cos\theta = -\frac{12}{13}$; $\tan\theta = -\frac{5}{12}$; $\csc\theta = \frac{13}{5}$; $\sec\theta = -\frac{13}{12}$; $\cot\theta = -\frac{12}{5}$ **27.** $\sin\theta = -\frac{15}{17}$; $\tan\theta = -\frac{15}{8}$; $\csc\theta = -\frac{17}{15}$; $\sec\theta = \frac{17}{8}$; $\cot\theta = -\frac{8}{15}$

29. $\sin\theta = \frac{2\sqrt{13}}{13}$; $\cos\theta = -\frac{3\sqrt{13}}{13}$; $\csc\theta = \frac{\sqrt{13}}{2}$; $\sec\theta = -\frac{\sqrt{13}}{3}$; $\cot\theta = -\frac{3}{2}$ **31.** $\sin\theta = -\frac{4}{5}$; $\cos\theta = -\frac{3}{5}$; $\csc\theta = -\frac{5}{4}$; $\sec\theta = -\frac{5}{3}$; $\cot\theta = \frac{3}{4}$

33. $\sin\theta = -\frac{2\sqrt{2}}{3}$; $\cos\theta = -\frac{1}{3}$; $\tan\theta = 2\sqrt{2}$; $\csc\theta = -\frac{3\sqrt{2}}{4}$; $\cot\theta = \frac{\sqrt{2}}{4}$ **35.** 20° **37.** 25° **39.** 5° **41.** $\frac{\pi}{4}$ **43.** $\frac{\pi}{6}$ **45.** 30°

47. 25° **49.** 1.56 **51.** 25° **53.** $\frac{\pi}{6}$ **55.** $\frac{\pi}{4}$ **57.** $\frac{\pi}{4}$ **59.** $\frac{\pi}{6}$ **61.** $-\frac{\sqrt{2}}{2}$ **63.** $\frac{\sqrt{3}}{3}$ **65.** $\sqrt{3}$ **67.** $\frac{\sqrt{3}}{2}$ **69.** -2

71. 1 **73.** $\frac{\sqrt{3}}{2}$ **75.** -1 **77.** $-\sqrt{2}$ **79.** $\sqrt{3}$ **81.** $\frac{\sqrt{2}}{2}$ **83.** $\frac{\sqrt{3}}{3}$ **85.** $\frac{\sqrt{3}}{2}$ **87.** $\frac{1-\sqrt{3}}{2}$ **89.** $\frac{-\sqrt{6}-\sqrt{2}}{4}$ or $-\frac{\sqrt{6}+\sqrt{2}}{4}$

91. $-\frac{3}{2}$ **93.** $\frac{-1-\sqrt{3}}{2}$ or $-\frac{1+\sqrt{3}}{2}$ **95.** 1 **97.** $\frac{2\sqrt{2}-4}{\pi}$ **99.** $\frac{\pi}{4}$ and $\frac{3\pi}{4}$ **101.** $\frac{5\pi}{4}$ and $\frac{7\pi}{4}$ **103.** $\frac{2\pi}{3}$ and $\frac{5\pi}{3}$

Section 4.4

Check Point Exercises

1. $\sin t = \frac{1}{2}$; $\cos t = \frac{\sqrt{3}}{2}$; $\tan t = \frac{\sqrt{3}}{3}$; $\csc t = 2$; $\sec t = \frac{2\sqrt{3}}{3}$; $\cot t = \sqrt{3}$ **2.** $\sin\pi = 0$; $\cos\pi = -1$; $\tan\pi = 0$; $\csc\pi$ is undefined; $\sec\pi = -1$; $\cot\pi$ is undefined **3. a.** $\frac{1}{2}$ **b.** $-\frac{\sqrt{3}}{3}$ **4. a.** $\frac{\sqrt{2}}{2}$ **b.** $\frac{\sqrt{3}}{2}$

Exercise Set 4.4

1. $\sin t = \frac{8}{17}$; $\cos t = -\frac{15}{17}$; $\tan t = -\frac{8}{15}$; $\csc t = \frac{17}{8}$; $\sec t = -\frac{17}{15}$; $\cot t = -\frac{15}{8}$

3. $\sin t = -\frac{\sqrt{2}}{2}$; $\cos t = \frac{\sqrt{2}}{2}$; $\tan t = -1$; $\csc t = -\sqrt{2}$; $\sec t = \sqrt{2}$; $\cot t = -1$

5. $\frac{1}{2}$ **7.** $-\frac{\sqrt{3}}{2}$ **9.** 0 **11.** -2 **13.** $\frac{2\sqrt{3}}{3}$ **15.** -1 **17.** undefined **19. a.** $\frac{\sqrt{3}}{2}$ **b.** $\frac{\sqrt{3}}{2}$

21. a. $\frac{1}{2}$ **b.** $-\frac{1}{2}$ **23. a.** $-\sqrt{3}$ **b.** $\sqrt{3}$ **25. a.** $\frac{\sqrt{2}}{2}$ **b.** $\frac{\sqrt{2}}{2}$ **27. a.** 0 **b.** 0 **29. a.** 0 **b.** 0 **31. a.** $-\frac{\sqrt{2}}{2}$ **b.** $-\frac{\sqrt{2}}{2}$ **33.** $-2a$ **35.** $3b$ **37.** $a - b + c$ **39.** $-a - b + c$ **41.** $3a + 2b - 2c$ **43. a.** 12 hr **b.** 20.3 hr **c.** 3.7 hr

45. a. 1; 0; -1; 0; 1 **b.** 28 days **53.** 0 **55.** $-\frac{1}{4}$

Chapter 4 Check Point

1. $\frac{\pi}{18}$ **2.** $-\frac{7\pi}{12}$ **3.** 75° **4.** $-117°$

5. a. $\frac{5\pi}{3}$

b.

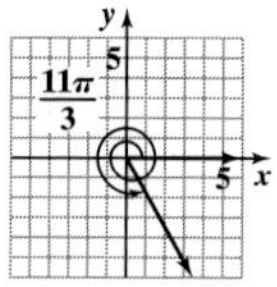

c. $\frac{\pi}{3}$

6. a. $\frac{5\pi}{4}$

b.

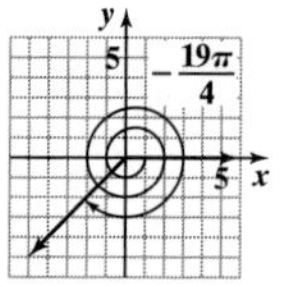

c. $\frac{\pi}{4}$

7. a. 150°

b.

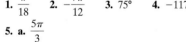

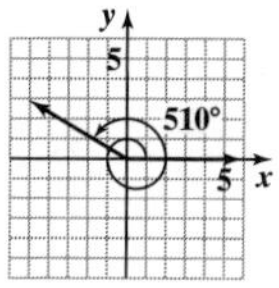

c. 30°

8. $\sin\theta = \frac{5}{6}$; $\cos\theta = \frac{\sqrt{11}}{6}$; $\tan\theta = \frac{5\sqrt{11}}{11}$; $\csc\theta = \frac{6}{5}$; $\sec\theta = \frac{6\sqrt{11}}{11}$; $\cot\theta = \frac{\sqrt{11}}{5}$ **9.** $\sin\theta = -\frac{2\sqrt{13}}{13}$; $\cos\theta = \frac{3\sqrt{13}}{13}$; $\tan\theta = -\frac{2}{3}$; $\csc\theta = -\frac{\sqrt{13}}{2}$; $\sec\theta = \frac{\sqrt{13}}{3}$; $\cot\theta = -\frac{3}{2}$ **10.** $\sin t = -\frac{4}{5}$; $\cos t = -\frac{3}{5}$; $\tan t = \frac{4}{3}$; $\csc t = -\frac{5}{4}$; $\sec t = -\frac{5}{3}$; $\cot t = \frac{3}{4}$ **11.** $\sin\theta = \frac{3}{5}$; $\cos\theta = -\frac{4}{5}$; $\csc\theta = \frac{5}{3}$; $\sec\theta = -\frac{5}{4}$; $\cot\theta = -\frac{4}{3}$ **12.** $\sin\theta = -\frac{2\sqrt{10}}{7}$; $\tan\theta = -\frac{2\sqrt{10}}{3}$; $\csc\theta = -\frac{7\sqrt{10}}{20}$; $\sec\theta = \frac{7}{3}$; $\cot\theta = -\frac{3\sqrt{10}}{20}$ **13.** 52 cm **14.** 809 m

15. $\sqrt{35}$ **16.** $\frac{\sqrt{3}}{3}$ **17.** $-\frac{\sqrt{3}}{3}$ **18.** $-\frac{1}{2}$ **19.** $\frac{2\sqrt{3}}{3}$ **20.** 1 **21.** $-\frac{\sqrt{3}}{2}$ **22.** $-\frac{2\sqrt{3}}{3}$ **23.** $-\frac{\sqrt{2}}{2}$ **24.** $\frac{\sqrt{3}}{3}$ **25.** 2

26. $-\frac{5\sqrt{3}}{6}$ **27.** 8π cm $\approx$ 25.13 cm **28.** 160π ft/min $\approx$ 502 ft/min **29.** 551.9 ft **30.** 40°

Chapter 4 Review Exercises

1. 4.5 radians **2.** $\frac{\pi}{12}$ radians **3.** $\frac{2\pi}{3}$ radians **4.** $\frac{7\pi}{4}$ radians **5.** 300° **6.** 252° **7.** $-150°$

8.

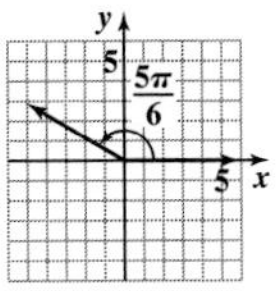

9.

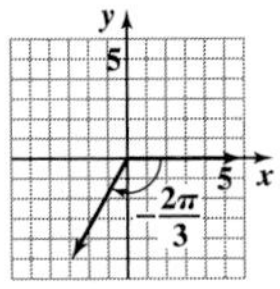

10.

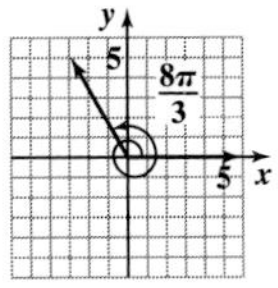

11.

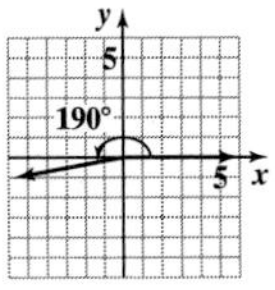

12.

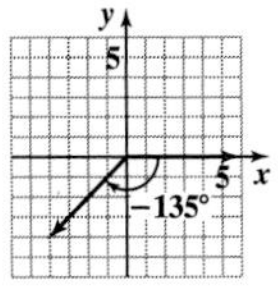

13. 40° **14.** 275° **15.** $\frac{5\pi}{4}$ **16.** $\frac{7\pi}{6}$ **17.** $\frac{4\pi}{3}$ **18.** $\frac{15\pi}{2}$ ft ≈ 23.56 ft **19.** 20.6π radians per min **20.** 42,412 ft per min

21. $\sin\theta = \frac{5\sqrt{89}}{89}$; $\cos\theta = \frac{3\sqrt{89}}{89}$; $\tan\theta = \frac{5}{8}$; $\csc\theta = \frac{\sqrt{89}}{5}$; $\sec\theta = \frac{\sqrt{89}}{8}$; $\cot\theta = \frac{3}{5}$ **22.** $\frac{7}{2}$ **23.** $-\frac{1}{2}$ **24.** 1 **25.** 1 **26.** $\frac{\sqrt{21}}{7}$

27. cos 20° **28.** sin 0 **29.** 42 mm **30.** 23 cm **31.** 37 in. **32.** $\sqrt{15}$ **33.** 772 ft **34.** 31 m **35.** 56°

36. $\sin\theta = -\frac{5\sqrt{26}}{26}$; $\cos\theta = -\frac{\sqrt{26}}{26}$; $\tan\theta = 5$; $\csc\theta = -\frac{\sqrt{26}}{5}$; $\sec\theta = -\sqrt{26}$; $\cot\theta = \frac{1}{5}$

37. $\sin\theta = -1$; $\cos\theta = 0$; $\tan\theta$ is undefined; $\csc\theta = -1$; $\sec\theta$ is undefined; $\cot\theta = 0$ **38.** quadrant I **39.** quadrant III

40. $\sin\theta = -\frac{\sqrt{21}}{5}$; $\tan\theta = -\frac{\sqrt{21}}{2}$; $\csc\theta = -\frac{5\sqrt{21}}{21}$; $\sec\theta = \frac{5}{2}$; $\cot\theta = -\frac{2\sqrt{21}}{21}$

41. $\sin\theta = \frac{\sqrt{10}}{10}$; $\cos\theta = -\frac{3\sqrt{10}}{10}$; $\csc\theta = \sqrt{10}$; $\sec\theta = -\frac{\sqrt{10}}{3}$; $\cot\theta = -3$ **42.** $\sin\theta = -\frac{\sqrt{10}}{10}$; $\cos\theta = -\frac{3\sqrt{10}}{10}$; $\tan\theta = \frac{1}{3}$; $\csc\theta = -\sqrt{10}$; $\sec\theta = -\frac{\sqrt{10}}{3}$ **43.** 85° **44.** $\frac{3\pi}{8}$ **45.** 50° **46.** $\frac{\pi}{6}$ **47.** $\frac{\pi}{3}$ **48.** $-\frac{\sqrt{3}}{2}$ **49.** $-\sqrt{3}$ **50.** $\sqrt{2}$ **51.** $\frac{\sqrt{3}}{2}$ **52.** $-\sqrt{3}$

53. $-\frac{2\sqrt{3}}{3}$ **54.** $-\frac{\sqrt{3}}{2}$ **55.** $\frac{\sqrt{2}}{2}$ **56.** 1 **57.** $-\frac{\sqrt{3}}{2}$ **58.** $\frac{\sqrt{3}}{2}$

Chapter 4 Test

1. $\frac{3\pi}{4}$ radians **2.** $\frac{25\pi}{3}$ ft ≈ 26.18 ft **3. a.** $\frac{4\pi}{3}$ **b.** $\frac{\pi}{3}$

4. $\sin\theta = \frac{5\sqrt{29}}{29}$; $\cos\theta = -\frac{2\sqrt{29}}{29}$; $\tan\theta = -\frac{5}{2}$; $\csc\theta = \frac{\sqrt{29}}{5}$; $\sec\theta = -\frac{\sqrt{29}}{2}$; $\cot\theta = -\frac{2}{5}$ **5.** quadrant III

6. $\sin\theta = -\frac{2\sqrt{2}}{3}$; $\tan\theta = -2\sqrt{2}$; $\csc\theta = -\frac{3\sqrt{2}}{4}$; $\sec\theta = 3$; $\cot\theta = -\frac{\sqrt{2}}{4}$ **7.** $\frac{\sqrt{3}}{6}$ **8.** $-\sqrt{3}$ **9.** $-\frac{\sqrt{2}}{2}$ **10.** -2 **11.** $\frac{\sqrt{3}}{3}$

12. $\sqrt{3}$ **13. a.** $-a + b$ or $b - a$ **b.** $\frac{a}{b} - \frac{1}{b}$ or $\frac{a-1}{b}$

Cumulative Review Exercises (Chapters 1–4)

1. $\{-3, 6\}$ **2.** $\{-5, -2, 2\}$ **3.** $\{7\}$ **4.** $-3 \le x \le 8$ **5.** 280°

6.

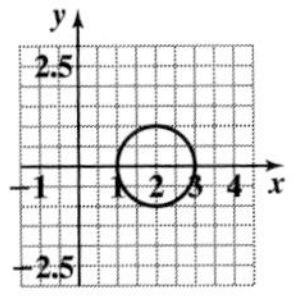

$(x-2)^2 + y^2 = 1$

7. 48 performances

Glossary

Absolute value inequalities Inequalities that contain at least one absolute value expression.

Absolute value of a number The distance between the number and 0 on the number line. The absolute value of a number x is written as $|x|$. The absolute value can be determined by

$$|x| = \begin{cases} x, & \text{if } x \geq 0 \\ -x, & \text{if } x < 0 \end{cases}$$

Algebraic expression A collection of numerical values, variables, and operation symbols. $\sqrt{5xy}$ and $3x - 6y + 3yz$ are algebraic expressions.

Algebraic fraction An expression of the form $\frac{P}{Q}$, where P and Q are polynomials and Q is not zero. Algebraic fractions are also called *rational expressions*. For example, $\frac{x + 3}{x - 4}$ and $\frac{5x^2 + 1}{6x^3 - 5x}$ are algebraic fractions.

Approximate value A value that is not exact. The approximate value of $\sqrt{3}$, correct to the nearest tenth, is 1.7. The symbol $\approx$ is used to indicate "is approximately equal to." We write $\sqrt{3} \approx 1.7$.

Associative property of addition For all real numbers a, b, and c: $a + (b + c) = (a + b) + c$.

Associative property of multiplication For all real numbers a, b, and c: $a(bc) = (ab)c$.

Asymptote A line that a curve continues to approach but never actually touches. Often an asymptote is a helpful reference in making a sketch of a curve, such as a hyperbola.

Augmented matrix A matrix derived from a linear system of equations. It consists of the coefficients of each variable in a linear system and the constants. The augmented matrix of the system $\begin{aligned} -3x + 5y &= -22 \\ 2x - y &= 10 \end{aligned}$ is the matrix $\left[\begin{array}{cc|c} -3 & 5 & -22 \\ 2 & -1 & 10 \end{array}\right]$. Each row of the augmented matrix represents an equation of the system.

Axis of symmetry of a parabola A line passing through the focus and the vertex of a parabola, about which the two sides of the parabola are symmetric. See the sketch.

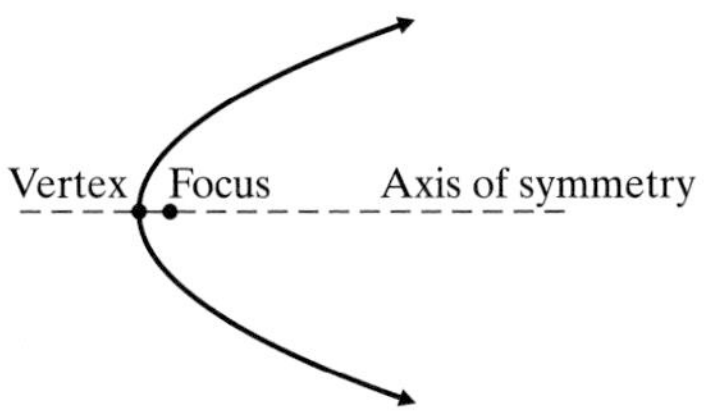

Base The number or variable that is raised to a power. In the expression 2^3, the number 2 is the base.

Base of an exponential function The number b in the function $f(x) = b^x$.

Binomial A polynomial of two terms. For example, $z^2 - 9$ is a binomial.

Cartesian coordinate system Another name for the rectangular coordinate system named after its inventor, René Descartes.

Circle A geometric figure that consists of a collection of points that are of equal distance from a fixed point called the *center*.

Circumference of a circle The distance around a circle. The circumference of a circle is given by the formulas $C = \pi d$ and $C = 2\pi r$, where d is the diameter of the circle and r is the radius of the circle.

Closure property of addition For all real numbers a and b: the sum $a + b$ is a real number.

Closure property of multiplication For all real numbers a and b: the product ab is a real number.

Coefficient Any factor or group of factors in a term. In the term $8xy$, the coefficient of xy is 8. However, the coefficient of x is $8y$. In the term $abcd$, the coefficient of $abcd$ is 1.

Collect like terms The process of adding and subtracting like terms. If we collect like terms in the expression $5x - 8y - 7x - 12y$, we obtain $-2x - 20y$.

Combined variation When y varies directly with x and z and inversely with d^2, written $y = \frac{kxz}{d^2}$, where k is the constant of variation.

Common denominator The same number or polynomial in the denominator of two fractions. The fractions $\frac{4}{13}$ and $\frac{7}{13}$ have a common denominator of 13.

Common logarithm The common logarithm of a number x is given by $\log x = \log_{10} x$ for all $x > 0$. A common logarithm is a logarithm using base 10.

Commutative property of addition For all real numbers a and b: $a + b = b + a$.

Commutative property of multiplication For all real numbers a and b: $ab = ba$.

Complex fraction (also called a Complex rational expression) A fraction made up of polynomials or numerical values in which the numerator or the denominator contains at least one fraction. Examples of complex fractions are

$$\frac{\frac{1}{3} + \frac{1}{5}}{\frac{2}{7}} \quad \text{and} \quad \frac{\frac{1}{x} + 3}{2 + \frac{5}{x}}.$$

Complex number A number that can be written in the form $a + bi$, where a and b are real numbers and $i = \sqrt{-1}$.

Compound inequalities Two inequality statements connected together by the word *and* or by the word *or*.

Conjugate of a binomial with radicals The expressions $a\sqrt{x} + b\sqrt{y}$ and $a\sqrt{x} - b\sqrt{y}$. The conjugate of $2\sqrt{3} + 5\sqrt{2}$ is $2\sqrt{3} - 5\sqrt{2}$. The conjugate of $4 - \sqrt{x}$ is $4 + \sqrt{x}$.

Conjugate of a complex number The expressions $a + bi$ and $a - bi$. The conjugate of $5 + 2i$ is $5 - 2i$. The conjugate of $7 - 3i$ is $7 + 3i$.

Coordinates of a point An ordered pair of numbers (x, y) that specifies the location of a point on a rectangular coordinate system.

Counting numbers The counting numbers are the natural numbers. They are the numbers in the infinite set

$$\{1, 2, 3, 4, 5, 6, 7, \ldots\}.$$

Critical points of a quadratic inequality In a quadratic inequality of the form $ax^2 + bx + c > 0$ or $ax^2 + bx + c < 0$, those points where $ax^2 + bx + c = 0$.

The degree of a polynomial The degree of the highest-degree term in the polynomial. The polynomial $5x^3 + 4x^2 - 3x + 12$ is of degree 3.

The degree of a term The sum of the exponents of the term's variables. The term $5x^2y^2$ is of degree 4.

Denominator The bottom expression in a fraction. The denominator of $\frac{5}{11}$ is 11. The denominator of $\frac{x - 7}{x + 8}$ is $x + 8$.

Descending order for a polynomial A polynomial is written in descending order if the term of the highest degree is first, the term of the next-to-highest degree is second, and so on, with each succeeding term of less degree. The polynomial $5y^4 - 3y^3 + 7y^2 + 8y - 12$ is in descending order.

Determinant A square array of numbers written between vertical lines. For example $\begin{vmatrix} 1 & 5 \\ 2 & 4 \end{vmatrix}$ is a 2×2 determinant. It is also called a *second-order determinant.* $\begin{vmatrix} 1 & 7 & 8 \\ 2 & -5 & -1 \\ -3 & 6 & 9 \end{vmatrix}$ is a 3×3 determinant. It is also called a *third-order determinant.*

Different signs When one number is positive and one number is negative, the two numbers are said to have different signs. The numbers 5 and -9 have different signs.

Direct variation When a variable y varies directly with x, written $y = kx$, where k represents some real number that will stay the same over a range of exercises. This value k is called the *constant of variation*.

Discriminant of a quadratic equation In the equation $ax^2 + bx + c = 0$, where $a \neq 0$, the expression $b^2 - 4ac$. It can be used to determine the nature of the roots of the quadratic equation. If the discriminant is *positive,* there are two rational or irrational roots. The two roots will be rational only if the discriminant is a perfect square. If the discriminant is *zero,* there is only one rational root. If the discriminant is *negative,* there are two complex roots.

Distance between two points The distance between point (x_1, y_1) and point (x_2, y_2) is given by the formula $d = \sqrt{(x_2 - x_1)^2 + (y_2 - y_1)^2}$.

Distributive property of multiplication over addition For any real numbers a, b, and c: $a(b + c) = ab + ac$.

Dividend The expression that is being divided by another. In $12 \div 4 = 3$, the dividend is 12. In $x - 5\overline{)5x^2 + 10x - 3}$, the dividend is $5x^2 + 10x - 3$.

Divisor The expression that is divided into another. In $12 \div 4 = 3$, the divisor is 4. In $x + 3\overline{)2x^2 - 5x - 14}$, the divisor is $x + 3$.

Domain of a relation or a function When the ordered pairs of a relation or a function are listed, all the different first items of each pair.

e An irrational number that can be approximated by the value 2.7183.

Elements The objects that are in a set.

Ellipse The set of points in a plane such that for each point in the set, the sum of its distances to two fixed points is constant. Each of the fixed points is called a *focus*. Each of the following graphs is an ellipse.

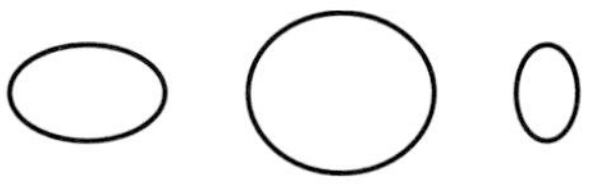

Equation A mathematical statement that two quantities are equal.

Equilateral hyperbola A hyperbola for which $a = b$ in the equation of the hyperbola.

Equivalent equations Equations that have the same solution(s).

Even integers Integers that are exactly divisible by 2, such as $\ldots, -4, -2, 0, 2, 4, 6, \ldots$.

Exponent The number that indicates the power of a base. If the number is a positive integer, it tells us how many factors of the base occur. In the expression 2^3, the exponent is 3. The number 3 tells us that there are 3 factors, each of which is 2 since $2^3 = 2 \cdot 2 \cdot 2$. If an exponent is negative, use the property that $x^{-n} = \frac{1}{x^n}$. If an exponent is zero, use the property that $x^0 = 1$, where $x \neq 0$.

Exponential function $f(x) = b^x$, where $b > 0, b \neq 1$, and x is any real number.

Expression Any combination of mathematical operation symbols with numbers or variables or both. Examples of mathematical expressions are $2x + 3y - 6z$ and $\sqrt{7xyz}$.

Extraneous solution to an equation A correctly obtained potential solution to an equation that when substituted back into the original equation does not yield a true statement. For example, $x = 2$ is an extraneous solution to the equation

$$\frac{x}{x-2} - 4 = \frac{2}{x-2}$$

An extraneous solution is also called an *extraneous root*.

Factor (1.5 and 5.4) Each of the two or more numbers, variables, or algebraic expressions that is multiplied. In the expression $5st$, the factors are 5, s, and t. In the expression $(x - 6)(x + 2)$, the factors are $(x - 6)$ and $(x + 2)$.

First-degree equation A mathematical equation such as $2x - 8 = 4y + 9$ or $7x = 21$ in which each variable has an exponent of 1. It is also called a *linear equation.*

First-degree equation in one unknown An equation such as $x = 5 - 3x$ or $12x - 3(x + 5) = 22$ in which only one kind of variable appears and that variable has an exponent of 1. It is also called a *linear equation in one variable.*

Focus point of a parabola The focus point of a parabola has many properties. For example, the focus point of a parabolic mirror is the point to which all incoming light rays that are parallel to the axis of symmetry will collect. A parabola is a set of points that is the same distance from a fixed line called the *directrix* and a fixed point. This fixed point is the focus.

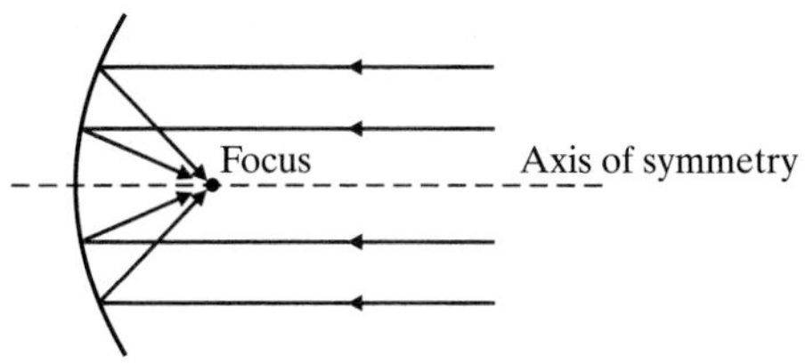

Formula A rule for finding the value of a variable when the values of other variables in the expression are known. For example, the formula for finding the Fahrenheit temperature when the Celsius temperature is known is $F = 1.8C + 32$.

Fractional equation An equation that contains a rational expression. Examples of fractional equations are

$$\frac{x}{3} + \frac{x}{4} = 7 \quad \text{and} \quad \frac{2}{3x-3} + \frac{1}{x-1} = \frac{-5}{12}.$$

Function A relation in which no different ordered pairs have the same first coordinate.

Graph of a function A graph in which a vertical line will never cross in more than one place. The following sketches represent the graphs of functions.

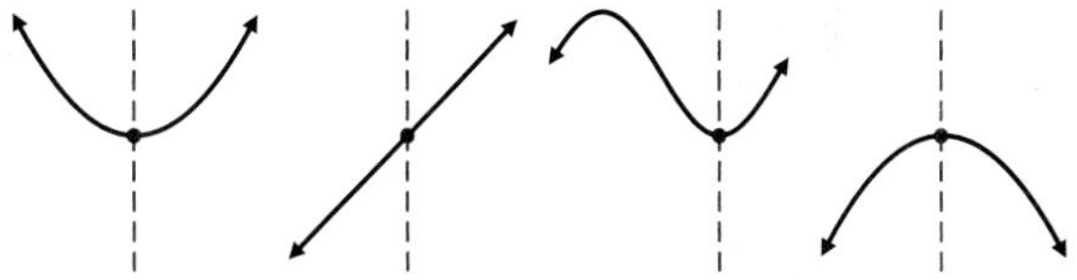

Graph of a linear inequality in two variables A shaded region in two-dimensional space. It may or may not include the boundary line. If the line is included, the sketch shows a solid line. If it is not included, the sketch shows a dashed line. Two sketches follow.

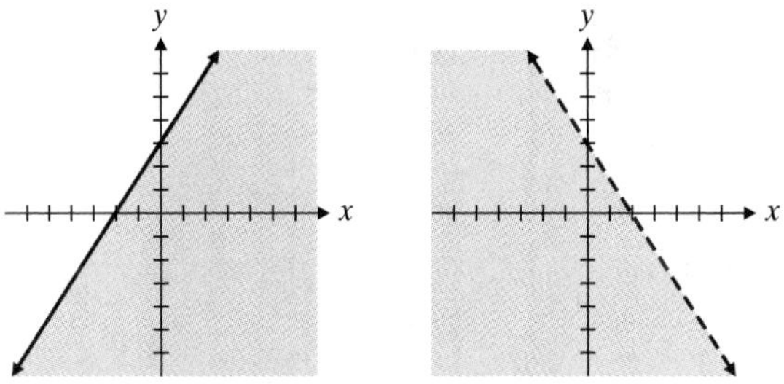

Graph of a one-to-one function A graph of a function with the additional property that a horizontal line will never cross the graph in more than one place. The following sketches represent the graphs of one-to-one functions.

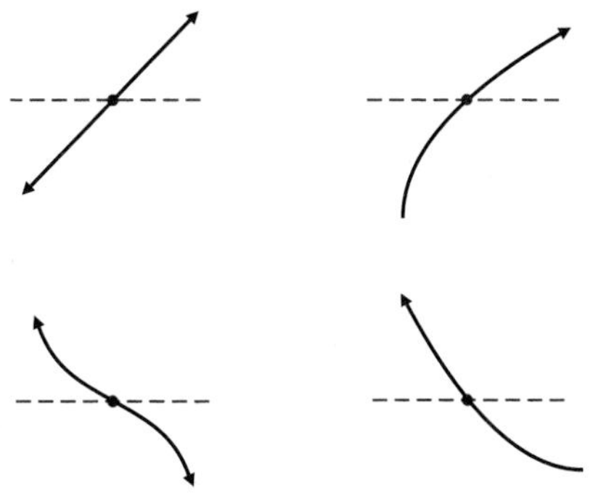

Greater than or equal to symbol The $\geq$ symbol.

Greater than symbol The $>$ symbol. $5 > 3$ is read, "5 is greater than 3."

Greatest common factor of a polynomial A common factor of each term of the polynomial that has the largest possible numerical coefficient and the largest possible exponent for each variable. For example, the greatest common factor of $50x^4y^5 - 25x^3y^4 + 75x^5y^6$ is $25x^3y^4$.

Higher-order equations Equations of degree 3 or higher. Examples of higher-order equations are $x^4 - 29x^2 + 100 = 0$ and $x^3 + 3x^2 - 4x - 12 = 0$.

Higher-order roots Cube roots, fourth roots, and roots with an index greater than 2.

Horizontal line A straight line that is parallel to the x-axis. A horizontal line has a slope of zero. The equation of any horizontal line can be written in the form $y = b$, where b is a constant. A sketch is shown.

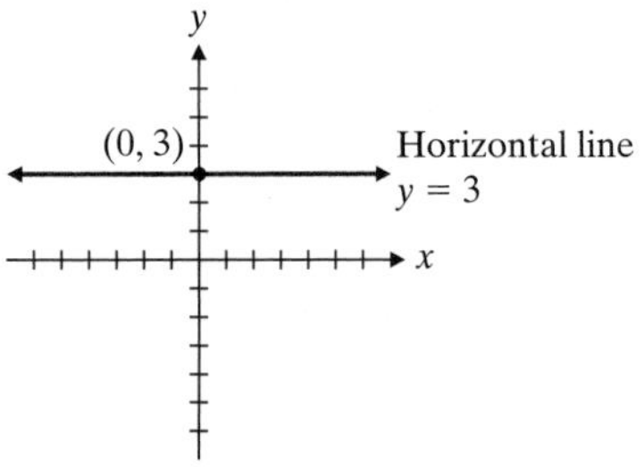

Horizontal parabolas Parabolas that open to the right or to the left. The following graphs represent horizontal parabolas.

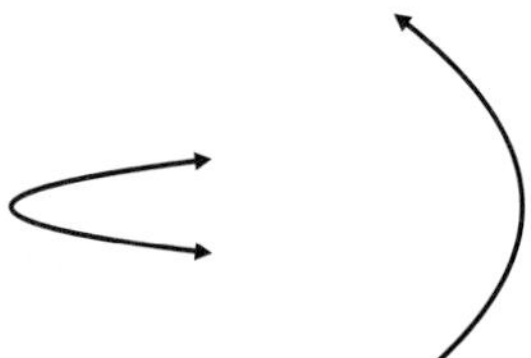

Hyperbola The set of points in a plane such that for each point in the set, the absolute value of the difference of its distances to two fixed points is constant. Each of these fixed points is called a *focus*. The following sketches represent graphs of hyperbolas.

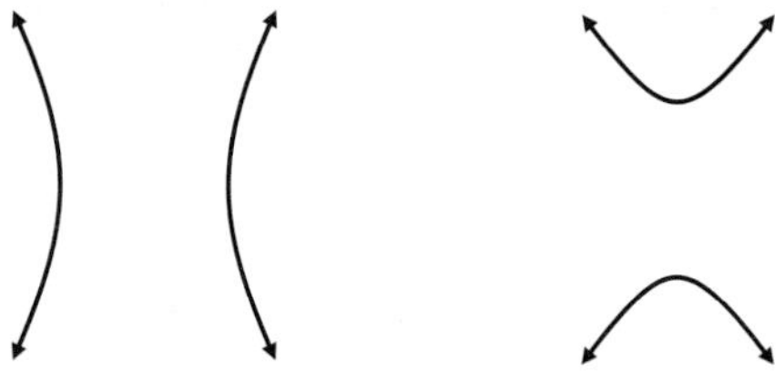

Hypotenuse of a right triangle The side opposite the right angle in any right triangle. The hypotenuse is always the longest side of a right triangle. In the following sketch the hypotenuse is side c.

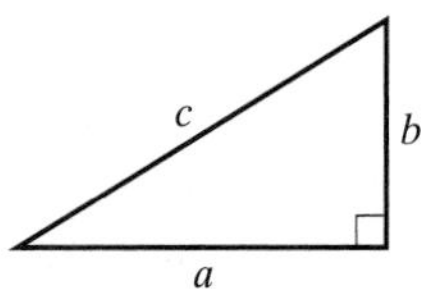

Identity property for addition For any real number a, $a + 0 = a = 0 + a$.

Identity property for multiplication For any real number a, $a(1) = a = 1(a)$.

Imaginary number i, defined as $i = \sqrt{-1}$ and $i^2 = -1$.

Inconsistent system of equations A system of equations for which no solution is possible.

Index of a radical (7.2) Indicates what type of a root is being taken. The index of a cube root is 3. In $\sqrt[3]{x}$, the 3 is the index of the radical. In $\sqrt[4]{y}$, the index is 4. The index of a square root is 2, but the index is not written in the square root symbol, as shown: $\sqrt{x}$.

Inequality A mathematical statement expressing an order relationship. The following are inequalities:

$$x < 3, \quad x \geq 4.5, \quad 2x + 3 \leq 5x - 7,$$
$$x + 2y < 8, \quad 2x^2 - 3x > 0$$

Infinite set A set that has no end to the number of elements that are within it. An infinite set is often indicated by placing an ellipsis (. . .) after listing some of the elements of the set.

Integers The numbers in the infinite set

$$\{\ldots, -3, -2, -1, 0, 1, 2, 3, \ldots\}.$$

Interest The charge made for borrowing money or the income received from investing money. Simple interest is calculated by the formula $I = prt$, where p is the principal that is borrowed, r is the rate of interest, and t is the amount of time the money is borrowed.

Inverse function of a one-to-one function That function obtained by interchanging the first and second coordinates in each ordered pair of the function.

Inverse property of addition For any real number a, $a + (-a) = 0 = (-a) + a$.

Inverse property of multiplication For any real number $a \neq 0$, $a\left(\frac{1}{a}\right) = 1 = \left(\frac{1}{a}\right)a$.

Inverse variation When a variable y varies inversely with x, written $y = \frac{k}{x}$, where k is the constant of variation.

Irrational numbers Numbers whose decimal forms are nonterminating and nonrepeating. The numbers π, e, $\sqrt{2}$, and 1.56832574 . . . are irrational numbers.

Joint variation When a variable y varies jointly with x and z, written $y = kxz$, where k is the constant of variation.

Least common denominator of algebraic fractions A polynomial that is exactly divisible by each denominator. The LCD is the product of all the *different prime factors.* If a factor occurs more than once in a denominator, we must use the highest power of that factor.

For example, the LCD of

$$\frac{5}{2(x+2)(x-3)^2} \quad \text{and} \quad \frac{3}{(x-3)^4}$$

is $2(x+2)(x-3)^4$. The LCD of

$$\frac{5}{(x+2)(x-3)} \quad \text{and} \quad \frac{7}{(x-3)(x+4)}$$

is $(x+2)(x-3)(x+4)$.

Least common denominator of numerical fractions The smallest whole number that is exactly divisible by all the denominators of a group of fractions. The least common denominator (LCD) of $\frac{1}{7}$, $\frac{9}{21}$, and $\frac{3}{14}$ is 42. The number 42 is the smallest number that can be exactly divided by 7, 21, and 14. The least common denominator is sometimes called the *lowest common denominator.*

Leg of a right triangle One of the two shorter sides of a right triangle. In the following sketch, sides a and b are the legs of the right triangle.

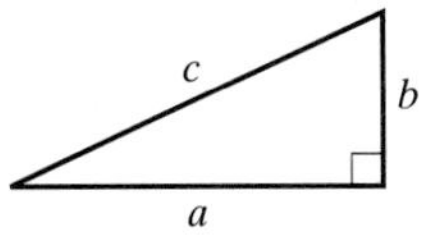

Less than or equal to symbol The $\leq$ symbol.

Less than symbol The $<$ symbol. $2 < 8$ is read, "2 is less than 8."

Like terms Terms that have identical variables and identical exponents. In the mathematical expression $5x - 8syz + 7x + 15syz$, the terms $5x$ and $7x$ are like terms, and the terms $-8syz$ and $15syz$ are like terms.

Linear equation A mathematical equation such as $3x + 7 = 5x - 2$ or $5x + 7y = 9$, in which each variable has an exponent of 1.

Linear inequality An inequality statement in which each variable has an exponent of 1 and no variables are in the denominator. Some examples of linear inequalities are

$$2x + 3 > 5x - 6, \qquad y < 2x + 1, \quad \text{and} \quad x < 8.$$

Literal equation An equation that has other variables in it besides the variable for which we wish to solve. $I = prt$, $7x + 3y - 6z = 12$, and $P = 2w + 2l$ are examples of literal equations.

Logarithm For a positive number x, the power to which the base b must be raised to produce x. That is, $y = \log_b x$ is the same as $x = b^y$, where $b > 0$ and $b \neq 1$. A logarithm is an exponent.

Logarithmic equation An equation that contains at least one logarithm.

Magnitude of an earthquake The magnitude of an earthquake is measured by the formula $M = \log\left(\frac{I}{I_0}\right)$, where I is the intensity of the earthquake and I_0 is the minimum measurable intensity.

Matrix A rectangular array of numbers arranged in rows and columns. We use the symbol [ ] to indicate a matrix. The matrix $\begin{bmatrix} 3 & 4 & 5 \\ 6 & 7 & 8 \end{bmatrix}$ has two rows and three columns and is called a 2×3 *matrix*.

Minor of an element of a third-order determinant The second-order determinant that remains after we delete the row and column in which the element appears. The minor of the element 6 in the determinant $\begin{vmatrix} 1 & 2 & 3 \\ 7 & 6 & 8 \\ -3 & 5 & 9 \end{vmatrix}$ is the second-order determinant $\begin{vmatrix} 1 & 3 \\ -3 & 9 \end{vmatrix}$.

Monomial A polynomial of one term. For example, $3a$ is a monomial.

Natural logarithm For a number x, $\ln x = \log_e x$ for all $x > 0$. A natural logarithm is a logarithm using base e.

Negative integers The numbers in the infinite set

$$\{-1, -2, -3, -4, -5, -6, -7, \ldots\}.$$

Nonlinear system of equations A system of equations in which at least one equation is not a linear equation.

Nonzero A nonzero value is a value other than zero. If we say that the variable x is nonzero, we mean that x cannot have the value of zero.

Numerator The top expression in a fraction. The numerator of $\frac{3}{19}$ is 3. The numerator of $\frac{x+5}{x^2+25}$ is $x + 5$.

Numerical coefficient The numerical value multiplied by the variables in a term. The numerical coefficient of $-8xyw$ is -8. The numerical coefficient of abc is 1.

Odd integer Integers that are not exactly divisible by 2, such as $\ldots, -3, -1, 1, 3, 5, 7, \ldots$.

One-to-one function A function in which no two different ordered pairs have the same second coordinate.

Opposite of a number That number with the same absolute value but a different sign. The opposite of -7 is 7. The opposite of 13 is -13.

Ordered pair A pair of numbers represented in a specified order. An ordered pair is used to identify the location of a point. Every point on a rectangular coordinate system can be represented by an ordered pair (x, y).

Origin The point determined by the intersection of the x-axis and the y-axis. It has the coordinates $(0, 0)$.

Parabola The set of points that is the same distance from some fixed line (called the *directrix*) and some fixed point (called the *focus*) that is not on the line. The graph of any equation of the form $y = ax^2 + bx + c$ or $x = ay^2 + by + c$, where a, b, and c are real numbers and $a \neq 0$, is a parabola. Some examples of the graphs of parabolas are shown.

Parallel lines Two straight lines that never intersect. Parallel lines have the same slope.

Parallelogram A four-sided geometric figure with opposite sides parallel. The opposite sides of a parallelogram are equal.

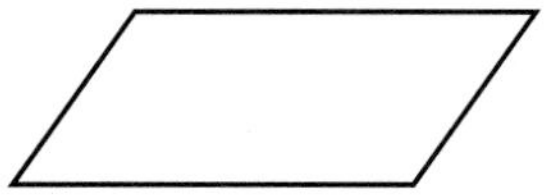

Percent Hundredths or "per one hundred"; indicated by the % symbol. Thirty-seven hundredths means thirty-seven percent: $\frac{37}{100} = 37\%$.

Perfect square If x is an integer and a is a positive real number such that $a = x^2$, then x is a square root of a and a is a perfect square. Some numbers that are perfect squares are 1, 4, 9, 16, 25, 36, 49, 64, 81, and 100.

Perfect square trinomials Trinomials of the form $a^2 + 2ab + b^2$ or $a^2 - 2ab + b^2$.

Perpendicular lines Two straight lines that meet at a 90-degree angle. If two nonvertical lines have slopes m_1 and m_2, and m_1 and $m_2 \neq 0$, then the lines are perpendicular if and only if $m_1 = -\frac{1}{m_2}$.

pH of a solution (11.2) Defined by the equation $\text{pH} = -\log_{10}(H^+)$, where H^+ is the concentration of the hydrogen ion in the solution. The solution is an acid when the pH is less than 7 and a base when the pH is greater than 7.

Pi An irrational number, denoted by the symbol π, which is approximately equal to 3.141592654. In most cases, 3.14 can be used as a sufficiently accurate approximation for π.

Point–slope form of the equation of a straight line For a straight line passing through the point (x_1, y_1) and having slope m, $y - y_1 = m(x - x_1)$.

Polynomials Variable expressions that contain terms with nonnegative integer exponents. A polynomial must contain no division by a variable. Some examples of polynomials are $5y^2 - 8y + 3$, $-12xy$, $12a - 14b$, and $7x$.

Positive integers The numbers in the infinite set $\{1, 2, 3, 4, 5, 6, 7, \ldots\}$. The positive integers are the natural numbers.

Power When a number is raised to a power, the number's exponent is that power. Thus, two to the third power means 2^3. The power is the exponent, which is 3. In the expression x^5, we say, "x is raised to the fifth power."

Prime factors of a number Those factors of a number that are prime. To write the number 40 as a product of prime factors, we would write $40 = 5 \times 2^3$. To write the number 462 as the product of prime factors, we would write $462 = 2 \times 3 \times 7 \times 11$.

Prime factors of a polynomial Those factors of a polynomial that are prime. When a polynomial is completely factored, it is written as a product of prime factors. Thus, the prime factors of $x^4 - 81$ are written as $x^4 - 81 = (x^2 + 9)(x - 3)(x + 3)$.

Prime number A positive integer that is greater than 1 and has no factors other than 1 and itself. The first ten prime numbers are 2, 3, 5, 7, 11, 13, 17, 19, 23, and 29.

Prime polynomial A polynomial that cannot be factored. Examples of prime polynomials are $2x^2 + 100x - 19$, $25x^2 + 9$, and $x^2 - 3x + 5$.

Principal In monetary exercises, the original amount of money invested or borrowed.

Principal square root The positive square root of a number. The symbol indicating the principal square root is $\sqrt{\ }$. Thus, $\sqrt{4}$ means to find the principal square root of 4, which is 2.

Proportion An equation stating that two ratios are equal. For example, $\frac{a}{b} = \frac{c}{d}$ is a proportion.

Pythagorean theorem In any right triangle, if c is the length of the hypotenuse and a and b are the lengths of the two legs, then $c^2 = a^2 + b^2$.

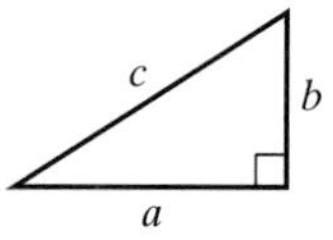

Quadrants The four regions into which the x-axis and the y-axis divide the rectangular coordinate system.

Quadratic equation in standard form An equation of the form $ax^2 + bx + c = 0$, where a, b, and c are real numbers and $a \neq 0$. A quadratic equation is classified as a second-degree equation.

Quadratic formula If $ax^2 + bx + c = 0$ and $a \neq 0$, then the roots to the equation are found by the formula

$$x = \frac{-b \pm \sqrt{b^2 - 4ac}}{2a}.$$

Quadratic inequalities An inequality written in the form $ax^2 + bx + c > 0$, where $a \neq 0$ and a, b, and c are real numbers. The $>$ symbol may be replaced by a $<$, $\geq$, or $\leq$ symbol.

Quotient The result of dividing one number or expression by another. In the equation $12 \div 4 = 3$, the quotient is 3.

Radical equation An equation that contains one or more radicals. The following are examples of radical equations.

$$\sqrt{9x - 20} = x \quad \text{and} \quad 4 = \sqrt{x - 3} + \sqrt{x + 5}$$

Radical sign The symbol $\sqrt{}$, which is used to indicate the root of a number.

Radicand The expression beneath the radical sign. The radicand of $\sqrt{7x}$ is $7x$.

Radius of a circle The distance from any point on the circle to the center of the circle.

Range of a relation or a function When the ordered pairs of a relation or a function are listed, all of the different second items of each pair.

Ratio The ratio of two values is the first value divided by the second. The ratio of a to b, where $b \neq 0$, is written as $\frac{a}{b}$, a/b, $a \div b$, or $a{:}b$.

Rational equation An equation that has at least one variable in a denominator. Examples of rational equations are

$$\frac{x+6}{3x} = \frac{x+8}{5} \quad \text{and} \quad \frac{x+3}{x} - \frac{x+4}{x+5} = \frac{15}{x^2+5x}.$$

Rational exponents When an exponent is a rational number, this is equivalent to a radical expression in the following way: $x^{m/n} = (\sqrt[n]{x})^m = \sqrt[n]{x^m}$. Thus, $x^{3/7} = (\sqrt[7]{x})^3 = \sqrt[7]{x^3}$.

Rational expressions A fraction of the form $\frac{P}{Q}$, where P and Q are polynomials and Q is not zero. Rational expressions are also called *algebraic fractions*. For example, $\frac{7}{x-8}$ and $\frac{3x-5}{2x^2+1}$ are rational expressions.

Rational numbers An infinite set of numbers containing all the integers and all exact quotients of two integers where the denominator is not zero. In set notation, the rational numbers are the set of numbers $\left\{\frac{a}{b} \mid a \text{ and } b \text{ are integers but } b \neq 0\right\}$.

Rationalizing the denominator The process of transforming a fraction that contains one or more radicals in the denominator to an equivalent fraction that does not contain any radicals in the denominator. When we rationalize the denominator of $\frac{5}{\sqrt{3}}$, we obtain $\frac{5\sqrt{3}}{3}$. When we rationalize the denominator of $\frac{-2}{\sqrt{11} - \sqrt{7}}$, we obtain $-\frac{\sqrt{11} + \sqrt{7}}{2}$.

Rationalizing the numerator The process of transforming a fraction that contains one or more radicals in the numerator to an equivalent fraction that does not contain any radicals in the numerator. When we rationalize the numerator of $\frac{\sqrt{5}}{x}$, we obtain $\frac{5}{x\sqrt{5}}$.

Real number line A number line on which all the real numbers are placed. Positive numbers lie to the right of 0 on the number line, and negative numbers lie to the left.

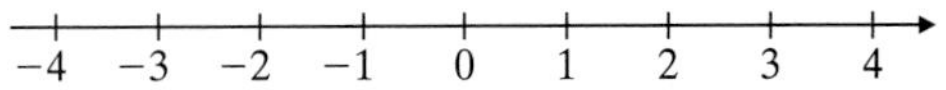

Real Number Line

Real numbers The set of numbers containing the rational and irrational numbers.

Reciprocal The reciprocal of a number is 1 divided by that number. Therefore, the reciprocal of 12 is $\frac{1}{12}$. The reciprocal of $\frac{3}{4}$ is $\frac{4}{3}$. The reciprocal of $-\frac{5}{8}$ is $-\frac{8}{5}$.

Rectangle A four-sided figure with opposite sides parallel and all interior angles measuring 90 degrees. The opposite sides of a rectangle are equal.

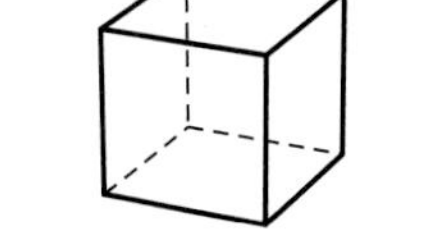

Rectangular solid A three-dimensional object in which each side is a rectangle. A rectangular solid has the shape of a box.

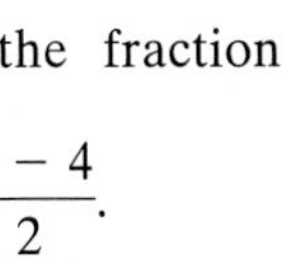

Reducing a fraction Using the basic rule of fractions to simplify a fraction. The basic rule of fractions is: For any polynomials a, b, and c, where $b \neq 0$ and $c \neq 0$, $\frac{ac}{bc} = \frac{a}{b}$. Reducing the fraction $\frac{x^2 - 16}{2x + 8}$, we have $\frac{(x+4)(x-4)}{2(x+4)} = \frac{x-4}{2}$.

Reduced row echelon form In the reduced row echelon form of an augmented matrix, all the numbers to the left of the vertical line are 1s along the diagonal from the top left to the bottom right. If there are elements below or above the 1s, these elements are 0s. Two examples of matrices in reduced row echelon form are

$$\left[\begin{array}{cc|c} 1 & 0 & 3 \\ 0 & 1 & 4 \end{array}\right] \quad \text{and} \quad \left[\begin{array}{ccc|c} 1 & 0 & 0 & 5 \\ 0 & 1 & 0 & 6 \\ 0 & 0 & 1 & 7 \end{array}\right].$$

Relation Any set of ordered pairs.

Remainder The amount left after the final subtraction when working out a division problem. In the problem

$$\begin{array}{r} 2x - 3 \\ x - 2\,\overline{)\,2x^2 - 7x + 9} \\ \underline{2x^2 - 4x} \\ -3x + 9 \\ \underline{-3x + 6} \\ 3 \end{array} \quad \leftarrow \text{the remainder is 3.}$$

Repeating decimal A number that in decimal form has one or more digits that continue to repeat. The numbers 0.33333 ... and 0.128128128 ... are repeating decimals.

Reversing an inequality When multiplying or dividing both sides of an inequality by a negative number, the greater than symbol changes to a less than symbol or the less than symbol changes to a greater than symbol. For example, to solve $-3x < 9$, we divide each side by -3. $\frac{-3x}{-3} > \frac{9}{-3}$, so $x > -3$. The $<$ symbol was reversed to the $>$ symbol.

Rhombus A parallelogram with four equal sides and no right angle.

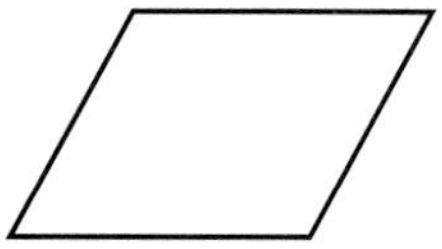

Right circular cylinder A three-dimensional object shaped like a tin can.

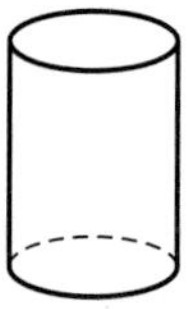

Right triangle A triangle that contains one right angle (an angle that measures exactly 90 degrees). It is indicated by a small rectangle at the corner of the angle.

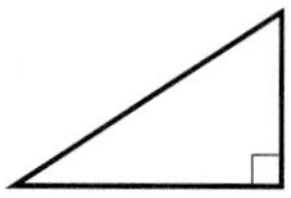

Root of an equation A number that when substituted into a given equation, yields a true mathematical statement. The root of an equation is also called the *solution of an equation.*

Scientific notation A positive number written in the form $a \times 10^n$, where $1 \le a < 10$ and n is an integer.

Set A collection of objects.

Signed numbers Numbers that are either positive, negative, or zero. Positive signed numbers such as 5, 9, or 124 are usually written without a plus sign. Negative signed numbers such as -5, -3.3, or -178 are always written with a minus sign.

Similar radicals Two radicals that are simplified and have the same radicand and the same index. $2\sqrt[3]{7xy^2}$ and $-5\sqrt[3]{7xy^2}$ are similar radicals. Usually similar radicals are referred to as *like radicals.*

Similar triangles Two triangles whose corresponding sides are proportional. For example, the following two triangles are similar.

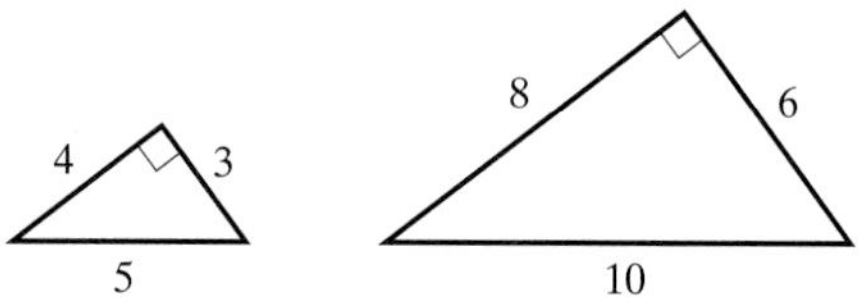

Simplifying a radical To simplify a radical when the root cannot be found exactly, we use the product rule for radicals, $\sqrt[n]{ab} = \sqrt[n]{a}\sqrt[n]{b}$ for $a \ge 0$ and $b \ge 0$. To simplify $\sqrt{20}$, we have $= \sqrt{4}\sqrt{5} = 2\sqrt{5}$. To simplify $\sqrt[3]{16x^4}$, we have $= \sqrt[3]{8x^3}\sqrt[3]{2x} = 2x\sqrt[3]{2x}$.

Simplifying imaginary numbers Using the property that states for all positive real numbers a, $\sqrt{-a} = \sqrt{-1}\sqrt{a} = i\sqrt{a}$. Thus, simplifying $\sqrt{-7}$, we have $\sqrt{-7} = \sqrt{-1}\sqrt{7} = i\sqrt{7}$.

Slope–intercept form of the equation of a straight line $y = mx + b$, where m is the slope and *(0, b)* is the y-intercept.

Slope of a straight line (3.2) A straight line that passes through the points (x_1, y_1) and (x_2, y_2) has

$$\text{slope} = m = \frac{y_2 - y_1}{x_2 - x_1}, \qquad \text{where } x_1 \ne x_2.$$

Solution of an equation A number that when substituted into the equation, yields a true mathematical statement. The solution of an equation is also called the *root of an equation.*

Sphere A perfectly round three-dimensional object shaped like a ball.

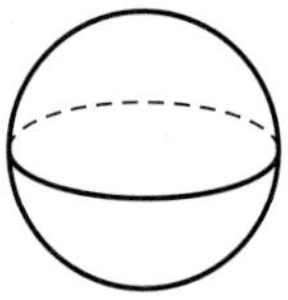

Square root If x is a real number and a is positive real number such that $a = x^2$, then x is a square root of a. One square root of 16 is 4 since $4^2 = 16$. Another square root of 16 is -4 since $(-4)^2 = 16$.

Standard form of the equation of a circle For a circle with center at (h, k) and a radius of r,

$$(x - h)^2 + (y - k)^2 = r^2.$$

Standard form of the equation of an ellipse For an ellipse with center at the origin,

$$\frac{x^2}{a^2} + \frac{y^2}{b^2} = 1, \quad \text{where } a \text{ and } b > 0.$$

This ellipse has intercepts at $(a, 0)$, $(-a, 0)$, $(0, b)$, and $(0, -b)$.

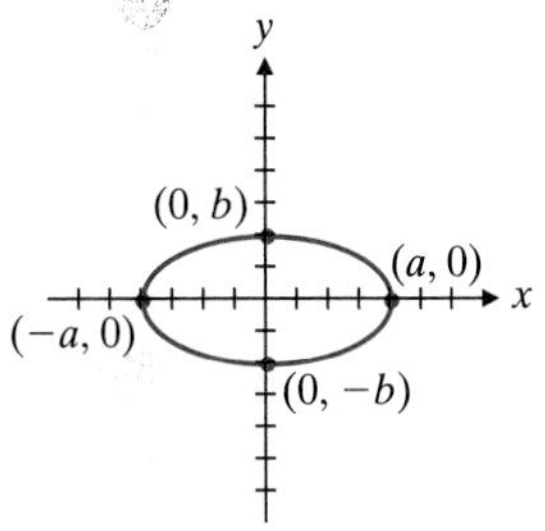

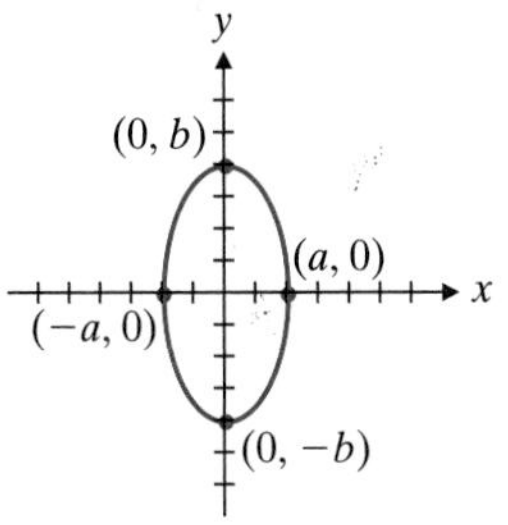

For an ellipse with center at (h, k),

$$\frac{(x - h)^2}{a^2} + \frac{(y - k)^2}{b^2} = 1, \quad \text{where } a \text{ and } b > 0.$$

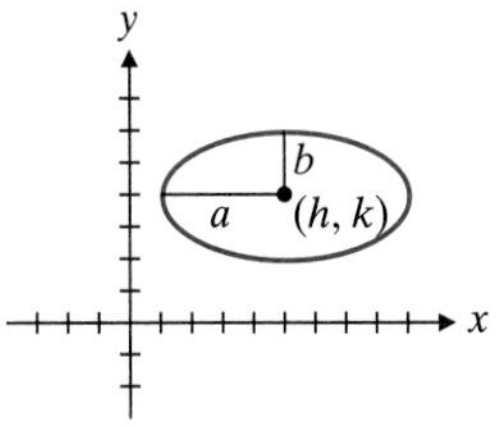

Standard form of the equation of a hyperbola with center at the origin For a horizontal hyperbola with center at the origin,

$$\frac{x^2}{a^2} - \frac{y^2}{b^2} = 1, \quad \text{where } a \text{ and } b > 0.$$

The vertices are at $(-a, 0)$ and $(a, 0)$.

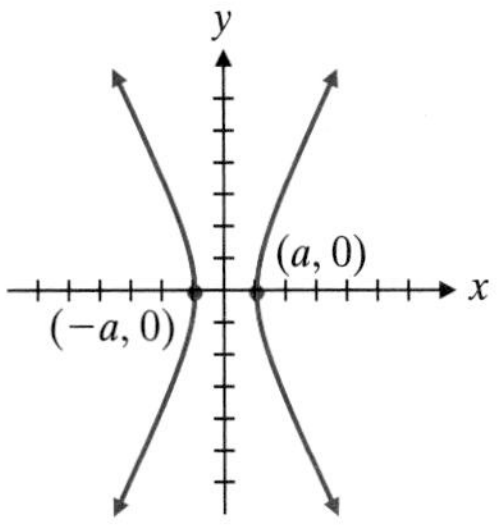

For a vertical hyperbola with center at the origin,

$$\frac{y^2}{b^2} - \frac{x^2}{a^2} = 1, \quad \text{where } a \text{ and } b > 0.$$

The vertices are at $(0, b)$ and $(0, -b)$.

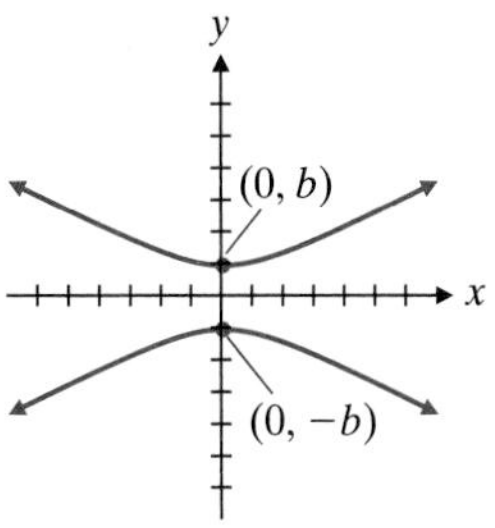

Standard form of the equation of a hyperbola with center at point (h, k) For a horizontal hyperbola with center at (h, k),

$$\frac{(x - h)^2}{a^2} - \frac{(y - k)^2}{b^2} = 1, \quad \text{where } a \text{ and } b > 0.$$

The vertices are $(h - a, k)$ and $(h + a, k)$.

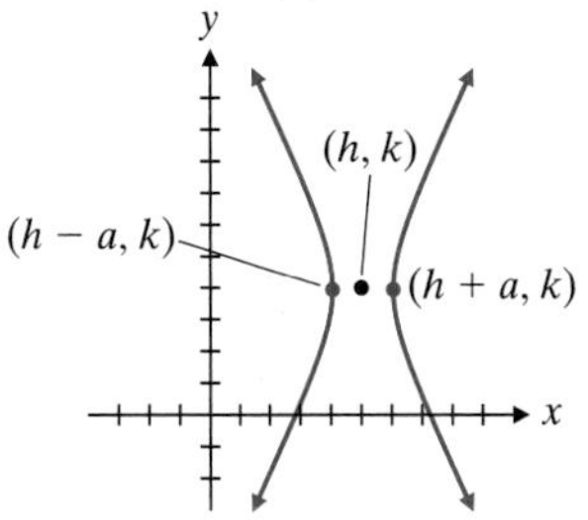

For a vertical hyperbola with center at (h, k),

$$\frac{(y - k)^2}{b^2} - \frac{(x - h)^2}{a^2} = 1, \quad \text{where } a \text{ and } b > 0.$$

The vertices are at $(h, k + b)$ and $(h, k - b)$.

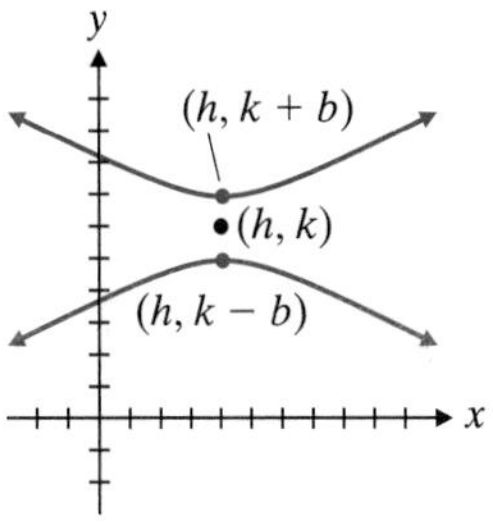

Standard form of the equation of a parabola For a vertical parabola with vertex at (h, k),

$$y = a(x - h)^2 + k, \quad \text{where } a \neq 0.$$

For a horizontal parabola with vertex at (h, k),

$$x = a(y - k)^2 + h, \quad \text{where } a \neq 0.$$

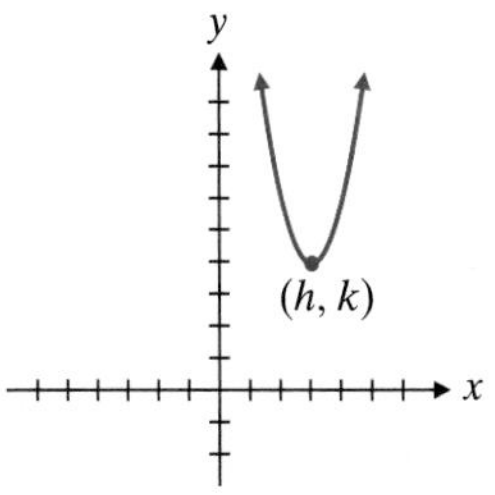

Vertical Parabola

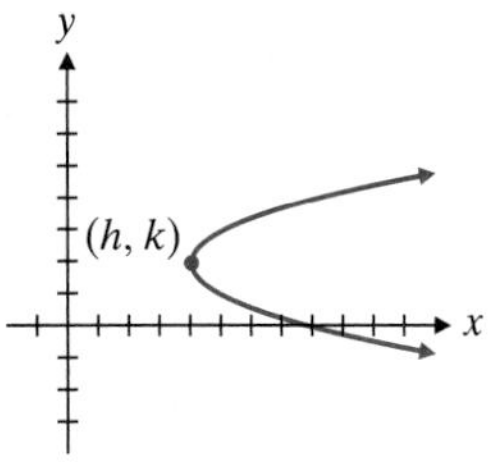

Horizontal Parabola

Standard form of the equation of a straight line $Ax + By = C$, where A, B, and C are real numbers.

Standard form of a quadratic equation $ax^2 + bx + c = 0$, where a, b, and c are real numbers and $a \neq 0$. A quadratic equation is classified as a second-degree equation.

Subset A set whose elements are members of another set. For example, the whole numbers are a subset of the integers.

System of dependent equations A system of n linear equations in n variables in which some equations are dependent. It does not have a unique solution but an infinite number of solutions.

System of equations A set of two or more equations that must be considered together. The solution is the value for each variable of the system that satisfies each equation.

$$x + 3y = -7$$
$$4x + 3y = -1$$

is a system of two equations in two unknowns. The solution is $(2, -3)$, or the values $x = 2$, $y = -3$.

System of inequalities Two or more inequalities in two variables that are considered at one time. The solution is the region that satisfies every inequality at one time. An example of a system of inequalities is

$$y > 2x + 1$$
$$y < \frac{1}{2}x + 2.$$

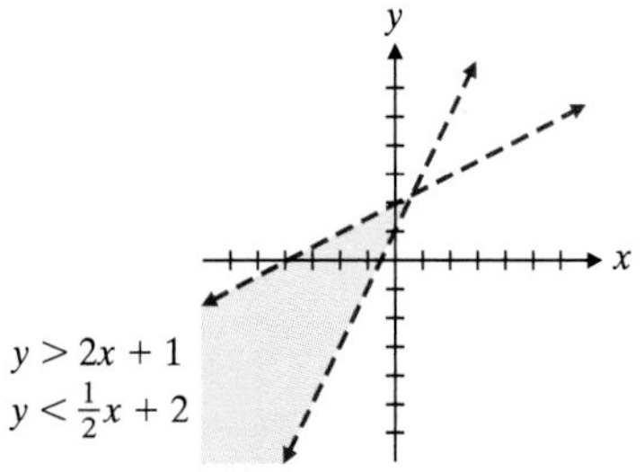

Term A real number, a variable, or a product or quotient of numbers and variables. The expression $5xyz$ is one term. The expression $7x + 5y + 6z$ has three terms.

Terminating decimal A number in decimal form such as 0.18 or 0.3462, where the number of nonzero digits is finite.

Trapezoid A four-sided geometric figure with two parallel sides. The parallel sides are called the *bases of the trapezoid.*

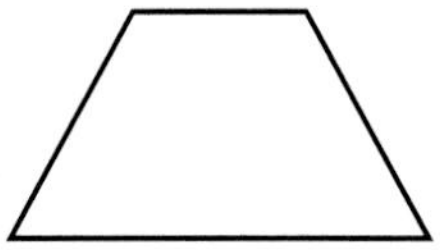

Triangle A three-sided geometric figure.

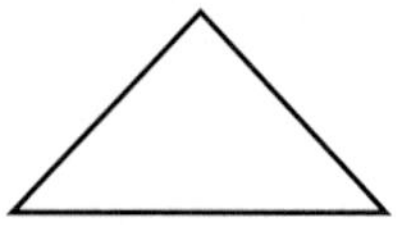

Trinomial A polynomial of three terms. For example, $2x^2 + 3x - 4$ is a trinomial.

Unknown A variable or constant whose value is not known.

Value of a second-order determinant For a second-order determinant $\begin{vmatrix} a & b \\ c & d \end{vmatrix}$, $ad - cb$.

Value of a third-order determinant For a third-order determinant $\begin{vmatrix} a_1 & b_1 & c_1 \\ a_2 & b_2 & c_2 \\ a_3 & b_3 & c_3 \end{vmatrix}$,

$a_1b_2c_3 + b_1c_2a_3 + c_1a_2b_3 - a_3b_2c_1 - b_3c_2a_1 - c_3a_2b_1$.

Variable A letter used to represent a number.

Vertex of a parabola In a vertical parabola, the lowest point on a parabola opening upward or the highest point on a parabola opening downward.

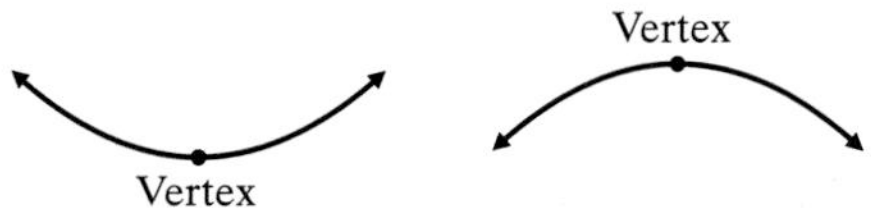

In a horizontal parabola, the leftmost point on a parabola opening to the right or the rightmost point on a parabola opening to the left.

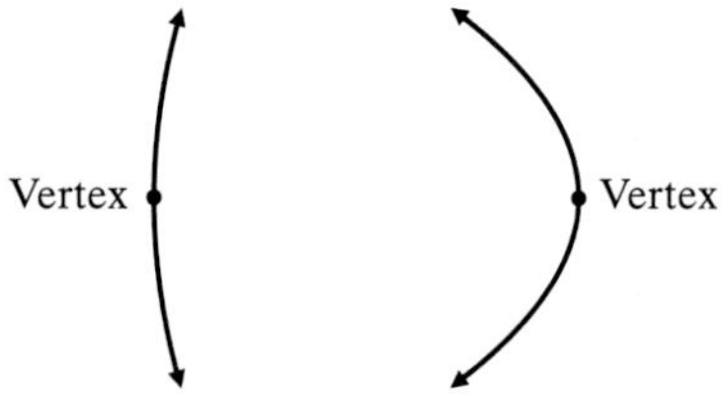

Vertical line A straight line that is parallel to the y-axis. The slope of a vertical line is undefined. Therefore, a vertical line has no slope. The equation of a vertical line can be written in the form $x = a$, where a is a constant. A sketch of a vertical line is shown.

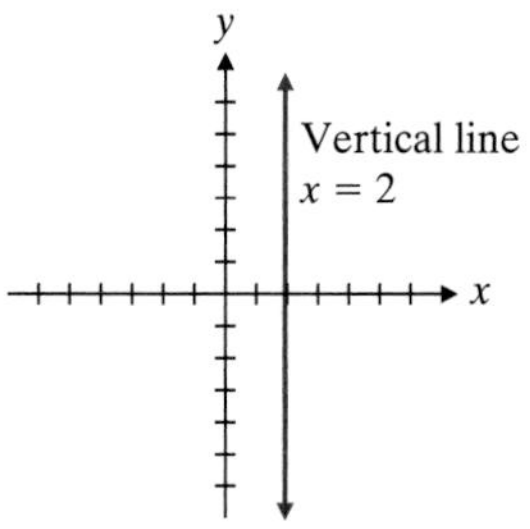

Vertical parabolas Parabolas that open upward or downward. The following graphs represent vertical parabolas.

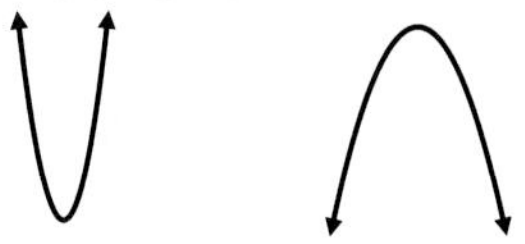

Whole numbers The set of numbers containing the natural numbers as well as the number 0. The whole numbers can be written as the infinite set

$$\{0, 1, 2, 3, 4, 5, 6, 7, \ldots\}.$$

***x*-intercept** The ordered pair $(a, 0)$ in the line that crosses the x-axis. The x-intercept of the following line is $(5, 0)$.

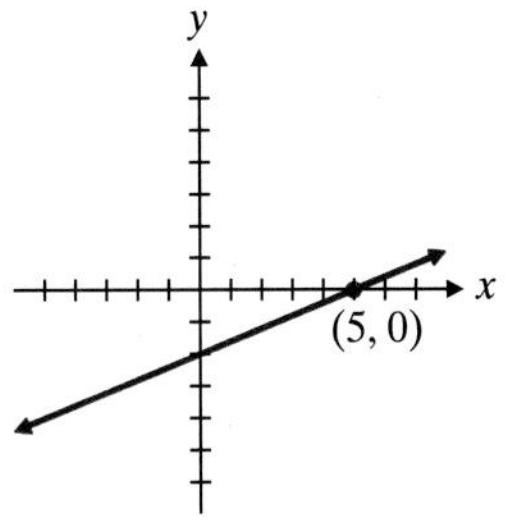

***y*-intercept** The ordered pair $(0, b)$ in the line that crosses the y-axis. The y-intercept of the following line is $(0, 4)$.

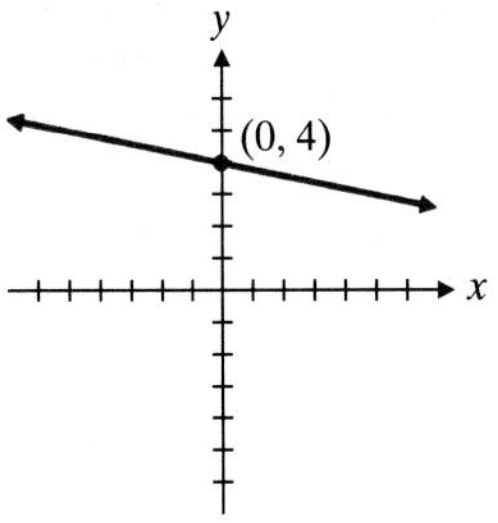

Index

Photo Credits

Table of Contents Martin Barraud/Getty Images, © Chip Simons/Taxi/Getty Images, Corbis Royalty Free, Stockbyte, RubberBall/SuperStock, Inc., © Royalty-Free/Corbis, Corbis Royalty Free, Randy Faris/Corbis/Bettmann, Bill Hatcher/Getty-National Geographic Society, SCOTTY Group Austria GmbH, Bill Bachmann/Creative Eye/MIRA.com, Jeff Lewis Photography

About the Author Robert F. Blitzer

CHAPTER P Martin Barraud/Getty Images **p2** Tim Davis/Lynn Images **p17** SuperStock Inc. **p31** William Sallaz/Duomo Photography Incorporated **p35** Photofest **p45** Corbis Royalty Free **p57** Gabe Palmer/Kane Studio **p68** Peter Arnold, Inc.

CHAPTER 1 © Chip Simons/Taxi/Getty Images **p84** Globe Photos, Inc. **p94** DreamWorks/Apatow Prod./Frank Masi/Picture Desk, Inc./Kobal Collection **p108** Michael Agliolo/Grant Heilman Photography, Inc. **p111** © 318/Gallo Images/CORBIS **p127** Stamp from the private collection of Professor C. M. Lang, photography by Gary J. Shulfer, University of Wisconsin, Stevens Point. "Germany: #5"; Scott Standard Postage Stamp Catalogue, Scott Pub. Co., Sidney, Ohio. **p129** Michael Keller/Corbis/Bettmann **p138** Corbis/Bettmann **p150** © Lester Lefkowitz/CORBIS **p164** Ron Kimball Photography

CHAPTER 2 Corbis Royalty Free **p186** Hans Neleman/Neleman Inc. **p202** Howard Grey/Getty Images Inc.—Stone Allstock **p216** David Schmidt/Masterfile Corporation **p217** Carol Simowitz/San Francisco Convention and Visitors Bureau **p231** (a) Spantrans/AGE Fotostock America, Inc. (b) LWA-Stephen/Corbis/Bettmann **p241** Douglas Kirkland/Corbis/Sygma **p246** SuperStock, Inc. **p256** Howard Koby Photography **p280** Skip Moody/Dembinsky Photo Associates

CHAPTER 3 Bill Hatcher/Getty-National Geographic Society **287** IPOL/Globe Photos, Inc. **301** David W. Hamilton/Getty Images Inc.—Image Bank **313** Steven Needham/Envision Stock Photography, Inc. **325** David Parker/Science Museum/Science Photo Library/PhotoResearchers,Inc.

CHAPTER 4 © Royalty-Free/Corbis **340** Olivier Laude/Getty Images, Inc.—Liaison **351** Pictor/ ImageState/International Stock Photography Ltd. **355** Royal Geographical Society/Alamy Images **366** Janet Foster/ Masterfile Corporation **p369** Hugh Sitton/Getty Images Inc.—Stone Allstock **370** Gary Kufner/Corbis Sharpshooters **383** (a) EPA/Mike Ivins/Landov LLC (b) Getty Images Inc–Rubberball Royalty Free (c) Robert Landau/Corbis/Bettmann (d) Rob Crandall/Stock Connection/IPNstock.com